THE IRVING STONE READER

By Irving Stone

BIOGRAPHICAL NOVELS

LUST FOR LIFE
(*Vincent Van Gogh*)

IMMORTAL WIFE
(*Jessie Benton Frémont*)

ADVERSARY IN THE HOUSE
(*Eugene V. Debs*)

THE AGONY AND THE ECSTASY
(*Michelangelo Buonarroti*)

THE PASSIONATE JOURNEY
(*John Noble*)

THE PRESIDENT'S LADY
(*Rachel Jackson*)

LOVE IS ETERNAL
(*Mary Todd Lincoln*)

BIOGRAPHIES

SAILOR ON HORSEBACK
(*Jack London*)

CLARENCE DARROW FOR THE DEFENSE

THEY ALSO RAN
(*Defeated Presidential Candidates*)

EARL WARREN

HISTORY

MEN TO MATCH MY MOUNTAINS

NOVELS

PAGEANT OF YOUTH

FALSE WITNESS

BELLES-LETTRES

WE SPEAK FOR OURSELVES
(*A Self-Portrait of America*)

I, MICHELANGELO, SCULPTOR—*and*—
DEAR THEO (*Vincent Van Gogh*)
(*Autobiographies, through letters, edited by Irving and Jean Stone*)

THE IRVING STONE READER

GARDEN CITY, N.Y.
Doubleday & Company, Inc.
1963

LIBRARY OF CONGRESS CATALOG CARD NUMBER 63-20500

PRINTED IN THE UNITED STATES OF AMERICA
FIRST EDITION

"Irving Stone" by Allan Nevins, reprinted from *The Book-of-the-Month Club News* for March 1961. Copyright © 1961 by Book-of-the-Month Club, Inc.

"The Biographical Novel," reprinted from *Three Views of the Novel* by Irving Stone, John O'Hara, and MacKinlay Kantor; Lectures Presented Under the Auspices of the Gertrude Clarke Whittall Poetry and Literature Fund. The Library of Congress. Washington, U.S. Government Printing Office, 1957.

"Arles" from *Lust For Life* by Irving Stone. Copyright 1934 by Irving Stone. Reprinted by permission of David McKay Company, Inc.

"Flaming Painter of Flaming Art" by Irving Stone. Copyright 1935 by The New York Times Company. Reprinted by permission.

"All At Sea" from *Sailor on Horseback* by Irving Stone. Copyright 1938 by Irving Stone.

"California" by Irving Stone. Appeared in the December 1954 issue of *Holiday* magazine. Reprinted by special permission from *Holiday*, copyright 1954 by The Curtis Publishing Company.

"This Is War" from *Clarence Darrow For The Defense* by Irving Stone Copyright 1941 by Irving Stone.

"Tilden and Greeley" from *They Also Ran* by Irving Stone. Copyright 1943 by Irving Stone.

"To Consecrate a Hearth" from *Immortal Wife* by Irving Stone. Copyright 1944 by Irving Stone.

"Desert Padre" by Irving Stone from the May 20, 1944, issue of *The Saturday Evening Post*. Copyright 1944 by The Curtis Publishing Company. Reprinted by permission of the author.

"Walls and Bars" from *Adversary in the House* by Irving Stone. Copyright 1947 by Irving Stone.

"The Case for Warren" by Irving Stone. Originally appeared in the May 10, 1948, issue of *Life* magazine. Copyright 1948 by Time Inc. Reprinted courtesy *Life* magazine.

"The Search" from *The Passionate Journey* by Irving Stone. Copyright 1949 by Irving Stone.

"Hometown Revisited" by Irving Stone. Reprinted from *Tomorrow* magazine, November 1950.

"The Aspirin Age: Calvin Coolidge" by Irving Stone, from *The Aspirin Age*, edited by Isabel Leighton. Copyright 1949 by Simon and Schuster, Inc. Reprinted by permission of the publisher.

"Adultery" from *The President's Lady* by Irving Stone. Copyright 1951 by Irving Stone.

"Beverly Hills" by Irving Stone. Appeared in the October 1952 issue of *Holiday* magazine. Copyright 1952 by The Curtis Publishing Company.

"My Heart and My Flesh" from *Love Is Eternal* by Irving Stone. Copyright 1954 by Irving Stone.

"The Trip Lincoln Promised Mary" by Irving Stone. Appeared in the February 1956 issue of *Good Housekeeping*. Reprinted by permission of *Good Housekeeping* © 1956, Hearst Corporation.

"Color in a Country" from *Men to Match My Mountains* by Irving Stone. Copyright © 1956 by Irving Stone.

"The City" from *The Agony and the Ecstasy* by Irving Stone. Copyright © 1961 by Doubleday & Company, Inc.

"Four Loves Had Davy Crockett" by Irving Stone. Published in *The American Weekly*, June 5, 12, 17, 1955. Copyright 1955 by Hearst Publishing Company.

"The Perfect Beauty" by Irving Stone. Appeared originally in the September 1958 issue of *Horizon* magazine. Copyright © 1958 by American Horizon, Inc.

For my wife

JEAN STONE

always the first reader

CONTENTS

THE IRVING STONE READER

INTRODUCTION

Irving Stone and the Biographical Novel

BY JOSEPH HENRY JACKSON

A WRITER is peculiarly fortunate when he discovers, reasonably early, both a principle and a pattern to which he may hew. Irving Stone made that happy discovery before he was thirty, which, as such things go, is early enough. Still better, by the time he found out in what direction his writing talents were best fulfilled he had developed two habits of mind that were to have the greatest bearing upon his success. He had become accustomed to the practice of a relentless, unflagging industry. And it was automatic with him never to be wholly satisfied with what he had done. Both attitudes persist in him to this day.

The book that gave direction to his career was his *Lust For Life,* an intimate and sympathetic study of the painter Vincent Van Gogh which celebrates its 20th anniversary this September in still another new edition. This was by no means his first published work; Stone was in one sense a professional writer when it appeared. But in that book he accomplished his first long reach toward the form he was to make uniquely his own in his time—that of the biographical novel. Both pattern and principle were explored in *Lust For Life,* though Stone has perfected the former and expanded the latter, as readers of his newest—and solidly his best—novel in that mold, his new *Love Is Eternal,* will discover for themselves. It is probably unnecessary to add that he is still not wholly satisfied, though he did take profound satisfaction in writing about Mary Todd Lincoln; his pleasure shows through this novel more clearly than in any other book he has written.

Stone was born in San Francisco. The date was July 14, 1903, an anniversary of France's Bastille Day. Stone likes to claim that this accident of birth has engendered in him a natural affection for anything French.

His mother and father were separated and there was never much money; at eight the boy was selling newspapers and he was seldom without a job after that—spare time during the school-year and full time in the summers. His mother was eager for her son to be a doctor, wherefore there was never any question of his missing school. Homework got done in the hours left over from jobs as delivery-boy, stock-boy in a leather goods store, and, as he grew bigger and stronger, clean-up man for a dairy, vegetable-wagon driver, and junior salesman for a sporting-goods firm. Summers he worked, as California country boys put it, "in the fruit"—picking apricots down near Hollister to the south of San Francisco, and then pears in the orchards up by Marysville. In his teens he found a better way to earn money. Saxophone players were relatively rare in the West then, and Stone saved his money, bought an instrument and learned to play. The saxophone pretty well paid his way for the next six years. It got him through college and he gave it away the day he graduated.

He entered the University of California at Berkeley in August of 1920 and found it made to order for a lad with his inquiring turn of mind. Though he had thought about law, he soon realized it was not for him and he began to prepare for teaching. With one part of his mind he took care to get good grades in economics, his major; with another he discovered books. The University's library has always been a good one, and Stone read everything he could get his hands on. In the process he encountered Shaw and Ibsen and a new enthusiasm was born. He would be a playwright. By now, however, he was old enough to be cautious; he had a living to make, after all. He took his A.B. in economics, then his Master's degree closer to home at the University of Southern California in Los Angeles. Then he returned to Berkeley to work for his Ph.D. Teaching would give him a financial base; he could write plays in his spare time. But one of his plays won a little theater prize. That was all that was needed. He had saved enough so that he might live on slim rations in Paris for a year, and to Paris he went.

This was in 1926, in the lovely boom period when everything seemed not merely possible but likely. Stone, his habit of hard work now ingrained, buckled down. Incredibly he wrote seventeen full-length plays in that Paris year. Nobody wanted them.

But something else happened to him in France. For the first time he saw the paintings of Vincent Van Gogh.

The painter opened a new world to him. His money had run out and he would have to go back to America and earn a living, but Van Gogh's hot color, his way of looking at life, new and fresh to the young man, would go with him.

The matter of living took care of itself when the young playwright discovered he had a knack for inventing rough-and-ready detective-story plots. He settled down to turning out the bread-and-butter yarns he knew he could sell to pulp magazines. Whenever he had a spare hour, however, he read everything he could find about the painter who had so fascinated him, especially the letters Van Gogh had written to his brother Theo. The fascination grew with his reading. Soon he was trying his hand at short scenes about Van Gogh's life, based on what he had read. When he was almost run down by a taxi because he was describing in his head the death of Van Gogh at Auvers sur Oise, he realized that the thing was approaching monomania.

At this point Stone came to a decision. He says, "Even though I was far too young, and felt I did not have sufficient technique to write a book about Vincent Van Gogh, I knew I had to try. If I didn't, I would never write anything else."

Somehow he managed to keep his subject at the back of his mind long enough to manufacture six pulp-magazine tales and to sell five of them. On the proceeds he went back to Europe for another six months. This time he had a definite plan—to follow the trail of the painter who had taken such a powerful hold on his imagination. How he absorbed so much in so short a time is another story, but he managed to cram into his head, and into a succession of notebooks, an enormous miscellany about the tragic life of Van Gogh, even sleeping in beds in which his hero had slept and visiting studios where he had painted. The market crashed—this was in 1929—but though Stone was aware of it as a fact in the news, it meant little to him in his obsessed state. Early in 1930 he was back in New York, ready to try to organize the mass of material he had got together but with very little idea of how to begin.

The first thing was to get time to work on the book. As he had done before, he put the idea temporarily from him and wrote two more detective stories. Again he had enough to keep him going for six months. Few young men can have worked harder at any job; in those six months Stone wrote *Lust For Life,* not once but four times before he felt he had the book in good enough shape to offer to a publisher.

This was when the great depression began to come home to him.

With their world fallen about their ears, would the American public want to buy, of all things, a story about a Dutch painter forty years dead? Obviously not. One after another, a round dozen book-publishers explained this to him with varying degrees of politeness. This went on for three years. Meantime he was courting a girl, Jean Factor, who read intelligently and possessed unusually good judgment when it came to books. When Stone asked her what she thought of his manuscript she told him. There were places where judicious pruning would help, and she pointed them out. He did the thinning and sent out the manuscript once more. That publisher accepted it, and Stone and his Jean went on their honeymoon. She still edits all his books, beginning with the third draft of the manuscript, and all of them (excepting *Lust For Life,* written for his mother) are dedicated to her.

Lust For Life has made publishing history in its twenty years of steady sales. But it meant much more than financial success to Stone. With that book he had found his special talent. With variations he has worked within the general pattern of that first book ever since. Indeed, *Lust For Life* has become, in Stone's unconscious, a kind of symbol, his rabbit's foot. Whenever possible his books are published on September 26, the day on which it appeared.

When it was evident that at last he had had a solid success, Stone did something that few writers have either the judgment or the courage to do. He took a good straight look at himself and his talent and came to some conclusions.

Working on detective stories he had learned a good deal—the necessity for careful plotting, the trick of keeping a narrative on the move, the techniques of construction. He had tried the "creative novel"—the term is his own—and learned that for several reasons it was not for him. But his attempts in the field had taught him something. Any fiction of quality depends largely upon people, upon character seen in the round and presented in the process of growth and development and change under stress. He knew this now, not as a textbook abstraction but from hard experience, and he also knew how to manage situations that illuminate character.

Lust For Life showed him one thing more—the kind of spark that would fire his imagination. That spark was character-ready-made, the story of someone who had lived, whose acts could be found in the record and whose motives might be traced by patient, careful, sympathetic investigation, with due balance and interpretation to follow. And, with Stone, what fanned this spark into flame was any suspicion that such a character had been misunderstood, perhaps even misrepresented through historical accident or through an early biographer's prejudice. Clearly the fiction form based on precise painstaking research (which he had learned how to conduct) was made to order for a man who found his greatest pleasure in saying "But look! It wasn't like that at all! *Here* is what happened, and why. *This* is what it was really all about!"

It is one thing to begin to see your proper direction and another to find exactly the right subject and the right frame for what you want to do. Stone had sensed the way he wanted to go, but for a time he wrote straight-out biography. His *Clarence Darrow For The Defense* was a full-length "life" in the accepted meaning of that term. *They Also Ran*, in which he brought together a group of "profiles" of defeated Presidential candidates, was biography crossbred with American politics. (This sortie into political undercurrents, by the way, was germinal; it has borne fruit in a dozen ways since, in his later work where his knowledge of the American political scene gave him indispensable background.) Both these books did very well indeed, but still he was not wholly satisfied. He was getting closer to what he wanted most to do, yet he had not quite found it.

Then Stone came upon the story of Jessie Benton Frémont, an exciting woman, intelligent and provocative, living in an age of extraordinary change, her career wrapped up with her country's Manifest Destiny. She had married a brilliant husband, moreover; her life seemed ideal for the biographer-novelist. Here Stone made the most significant imaginative leap of his career. For he saw something else in Jessie Frémont's story. Sufficiently in love with her husband to merge her brilliance with his, she thereby built a marriage that was a bigger thing-in-itself than either partner could have accomplished alone. Seeing this, Stone now perceived his road straight before him; it was this extra dimension—the third entity that was marriage—that he would make his theme. *Immortal Wife* was published in 1944, on September 26 of course. It was an immediate and tremendous success. More important, with that book Stone had released in himself fresh capabilities, a newly directed energy that now flowed smoothly and strongly in the channels he had found.

In *Adversary in the House* and then in *The President's Lady*, Stone examined two more marriages, that of Eugene Debs, which was a dark and sad mismating, and that of Rachel and Andrew Jackson. In the latter he made one more discovery about his own talent. He worked best when he wrote about a historical character who had been falsely represented as Rachel Robards had been. (If he had stuck to the law, plainly Stone would have made an admirable attorney for the defense.)

Sometimes a writer has the good luck to come upon the subject ideally suited to his gifts at the precise moment when he is ready for it, when he has served his apprenticeship, learned his trade and fully found his way. Earlier in his career, knowing less about his own abilities, still developing his techniques, Stone might have fumbled the theme that now suggested itself to him—the story of one of the least understood women in American history, Mary Todd Lincoln, who is the central figure in his new and by all odds his finest biographical novel, *Love Is Eternal.* As it fell out, he decided to write the story of her relationship with her husband—which is to say the story of a marriage—at the exact moment when everything he had done was a perfect preparation for the task.

The reader in America's past knows how Mary Todd Lincoln has been represented. Drawing on the memoirs of Lincoln's law-partner, Herndon (who was at cross-purposes with Mary Todd from the beginning), and upon other similarly biased sources often politically oriented, historians have painted a portrait of a violent-tempered, almost insanely jealous, arrogant woman, a cross her husband bore because of his high sense of duty. Lincoln never really loved her, so we have been told; the marriage came about from a confused notion of obligations due, an earlier collapsed romance, and whatnot else. Almost invariably the stories have followed this pattern of denigration. Part of it, no doubt, proceeded from good enough motives; by accepting the picture of Mary as a drag on his career one might emphasize the high nobility of Abraham Lincoln who could remain so gentle under provocation, give himself to his country so greatly even when his marriage was so unhappy a failure. This is where Mr. Stone applies the method he has taught himself so well. "Yes," he says, "but *was* it like that?" And he goes about finding out.

Stone's portrait of Mary Todd is that of a wholly different kind of woman—beautiful, clever, high-spirited, warmly loving and loved by many. She was a woman who knew what she wanted, moreover, and whose judgment of the man she married was uncannily accurate. From the beginning she saw the possibilities in the lanky, yarn-spinning lawyer whose uncontrollable spells of moodiness made life so difficult for him. Mary Todd, with her family background, understood politics as few women have; further, she saw as a sibyl sees that even the White House was not too high a goal for Abraham Lincoln. Her tragedy, and the tragedy of her "tumultuous marriage" as Stone speaks of it, was that attainment of the goal could mean only frustration in everything else a marriage stood for. In those fateful years Mary found herself a southern woman married to a northerner, a wife whose husband was not permitted by circumstances to be a husband any longer, only a sorely tried President. This, indeed, is the heart and core of the novel's universal appeal; the shining goal attained, the seeker who learns only then that it is not what it seemed.

Stone's evocation of an older, simpler, yet often more violent America—for the novel in his hands is that too—will reach the hearts of his widest audience in the story of Mary Todd Lincoln. For whatever else it is, it is the story of a great marriage, which is to say it is a great love story. Stone tells it beautifully, tenderly, with humor, tremendous narrative drive and a sure sense of drama, and with the warmth that always animates him when he is saying, as he does with more emotion than ever before, "But, look! It wasn't that way! *This* is how it was!"

There remains the question of historical accuracy, both in fact and in interpretation. The biographical novel, embraced by the public with *Lust For Life* in 1934, has become increasingly popular as Stone has published each consecutive successful book. Only gradually, however, has the biographical novel, based on sound research yet written with creative imagination, been accepted by historians as a legitimate way to present past events to the reader. Now the experts agree.

For example, William H. Townsend and J. Winston Coleman, Kentuckians both and authors of half a dozen Lincoln books between them, have seen advance copies of *Love Is Eternal.* Their praise is unstinted: "The book will be received by Lincolnians as the very best thing that has ever appeared about Abraham and Mary in novel form . . . a grand piece of research; it is Stone's best book yet." Roy Basler, Director of the Reference Department of the Library of Congress takes a similar view: "It is amazing to see how much historicity can be achieved within the framework of fiction."

And so Irving Stone rounds out twenty years of work at his own particular art form. He has both dignified and popularized the biographical novel. He has done it with scholarly research, passionate belief in his characters, and creative skill to bring them to life.

JOSEPH HENRY JACKSON
Literary Editor, San Francisco Chronicle

Irving Stone

BY ALLAN NEVINS

WHILE Irving Stone was busy some dozen years ago collecting material for *The President's Lady*, his romantic story of Andrew Jackson's union with his wife Rachel, a story not only appealing in itself but a source of illumination on the morals, manners and political intrigues of Tennessee and Washington, he spent months of investigation in State and National archives. One episode in Old Hickory's early career puzzled him. Irascible, fearless, ambitious, Jackson in his many quarrels—with John Sevier, Tom Benton, William H. Crawford—seemed never without what he considered just cause. Yet one affray appeared to point to an unprovoked explosion of anger. Walking the Nashville streets, he had encountered one Samuel Jackson (no relation) and without parley violently assaulted him. It was a drunken fit of rage, said his enemies. And previous biographers, like the industrious James Parton in three volumes and the scholarly John Spencer Bassett in two, had found no rational explanation of the attack.

Groping among the manuscripts of the Congressional Library, Irving Stone lighted upon a yellowed, neglected and almost undecipherable letter by Andrew Jackson which completely upset previous versions. It was to Samuel Jackson. It showed that he had circulated a foul libel on Andrew Jackson's niece, accusing her of bearing an illegitimate child; that Andrew had called on him to retract and apologize; and that he had refused. Thereupon Andrew, meeting the traducer, had soundly trounced him. An episode which had been widely used to show that General Jackson was passionately brutal was completely transformed; it proved instead that he was the sensitive guardian of his family, quick to vindicate its honor.

This story is akin to another pertaining to Irving Stone's researches into the life of Michelangelo. Working on the history of the Medici Palace in the Florentine archives, he became obsessed with the belief that somewhere he could find a complete inventory of the contents—furniture, pictures, sculptures, china, hangings—in Michelangelo's day.

He searched for months; an expert Italian researcher whom he employed also searched, without result. Go back and look some more, he kept telling her; there *must* be an inventory. "There doesn't have to be one just because *you* need it," she used to retort. And she seemed right.

Finally Irving had an inspiration. "You pay death taxes?" he asked the experts. "Yes," they replied. "You have paid them for centuries?" "Yes." "Then the Medici must have paid them, and must have submitted an inventory of property," he asserted. A new search was made in the records of estates—and the inventory came to light. Only then did Irving make a remarkable discovery. A century or more earlier an Englishman had found the inventory and deposited a copy in the British Museum; but it had never been used.

The central fact upon which all of us who know Irving Stone and his work well would insist is his professional integrity as a biographer and literary artist. As Marguerite Yourcenar says in a note appended to her *Hadrian's Memoirs,* history has its laws, and poetry or imaginative reconstruction also has its laws; "the two are not necessarily irreconcilable." Irving Stone believes that in the hands of a conscientious writer they are perfectly reconcilable. He has written both conventional biography and—like Miss Yourcenar, Robert Graves, Catherine Drinker Bowen—biography which admits imaginative detail. In books like those on Jack London, Clarence Darrow and the painter John Noble he scrupulously restricts himself to proved fact and direct inference. In books like *Lust For Life* (Van Gogh), *Immortal Wife* (Jessie Frémont) and *The President's Lady* he lets a controlled imagination fill some gaps, but is careful not to go beyond the reasonably conjectural, or to alter the spirit of historic truth.

These rules exact from Irving a research more laborious, and a composition more scrupulous, than any but his close friends are likely to realize. He spares no pains, and like Macaulay will travel hundreds of miles for a single precise fact. He believes some use of the imagination will make his characters more human, but he talked with fifty men to get an exact measure of Debs's pacifism when Debs was sentenced to ten years in Federal prison. He knows how to write description with color, but he goes through shelves of old newspapers to find how a street in Lexington, Kentucky, looked when Mary Todd walked along it in girlhood.

Thus he meets the historical canons which he learned under Herbert Eugene Bolton at the University of California, where he graduated in 1923. I have heard from Anna Strunsky, whom Jack London valued for her "flashing soul," of the pertinacity with which he drew from her all she could tell about London. I have heard elsewhere how when he prepared to write of the Lincolns in the White House he insisted on knowing the precise plans of their second-floor domestic menage. Nobody knew, not even William Adams Delano, expert on White House architecture. Partitions had been shifted, dimensions altered, new facilities installed. Yet Irving felt he had to know the size and aspect of the guest room in which Willie Lincoln had died, and of the hallway which Lincoln paced when bent under the burdens of the war. In the end, levying on memoirs, letters, newspapers and other sources, he drew a plan of the mansion which he could trust as accurate, and could therefore visualize without fear of error.

Irving Stone, vigorous and youthful-looking at fifty-seven, prides himself on being a man of letters, depending on his pen alone. As a man of letters, he puts system, assiduity, and vigilant care into his occupation. He is at work before 9 A.M. Whether inspiration comes or falters, he remains at his desk, for he knows that patient effort will bring it, and then, as he says, "I am *there.*" He keeps on until one, usually with his wife cutting manuscript in another part of the house—he dedicated his Jack London book, *Sailor on Horseback,* "to Jean, who collaborates." A light lunch, a walk or a swim, and he is back in his workroom until six. He writes all manuscript in pen and ink, and revises endlessly. But in the evening he relaxes, reading in a living room hung with carefully selected works of modern art both American and foreign, talking with friends, listening to music, or going to a lecture or play at the University of California Los Angeles, at whose parent institution in Berkeley he once taught.

Success came gradually; the Stones have reared their two children under as many difficulties as most families meet; and it was not until he settled himself to write his recent Western history, *Men to Match My Mountains,* that he was able to hire his first full-time research helper. In Italy, dealing with the mountainous accumulations of data on Michelangelo in Italian, French, German and Latin, he had to employ expert assistance on a larger scale. One aide in Rome was research worker, translator and cicerone in finding and explaining historic places, all in one. But Irving has been especially happy in seeing final success come in two forms. His *Lust For Life* (translated into a score of tongues) probably did more than any other single book to break down the barriers to appreciation of impressionist and postimpressionist painting. Artists and amateurs of art alike have offered many tokens of gratitude. Meanwhile, he has seen abundant evidence that his books on historic figures have given a lively impression of the past to hundreds of thousands of readers who could have been reached by no method less vivid and vigorous than his.

Allan Nevins, long Professor of American History at Columbia University.

PROLOGUE

The Biographical Novel

BY IRVING STONE

THE biographical novel is a true and documented story of one human being's journey across the face of the years, transmuted from the raw material of life into the delight and purity of an authentic art form.

The biographical novel is based on the conviction that the best of all plots lie in human character; and that human character is endlessly colorful and revealing. It starts with the assumption that those stories which have actually happened can be at least as interesting and true as those which have been imagined. Alexander Pope said that the proper study of mankind is man; the biographical novel accepts that challenge and sets out to document its truth, for character is plot; character development is action; and character fulfillment is resolution.

The biographical novel attempts to fuse not only its parent sources of biography and the novel, but that of its grandparent, history, as well. It must tell the story of its main character, not in the bulk of millionfold detail, but in essence; it must recreate the individual against the background of his times, with all of its authentic historical flavor; and it must live up to the exacting demands of the novel structure.

Let me joyfully proclaim that basically the biographical novelist is a yarn-spinner, and the biographical novel a vigorous medium that has been created in order to tell the fine stories that have been lived. The form is fortunate in its opportunity to utilize the single greatest virtue of the novel: growth of character. This growth may be into good or evil, into creativity or destruction; it cannot be static. There are few joys for the reader to surpass that of watching an interesting story unfold through growth of character; and in this field no form surpasses the biographical novel, which by the very definition of its nature is always about people rather than impersonal forces.

The biographical novelist has a greater freedom to interpret than has the biographer, and the reader has a greater chance of coming away with a more personal understanding of human motivation. If there is a tendency to oversimplify, it is in the same fashion that man's memory does as he looks back on his span of time, forgetting nine-tenths of the bulk, remembering only the distillation which has meaning. For the biographical novel is based not merely on fact, but on feeling, the legitimate emotion arising from indigenous drama. Facts can get lost with almost too great a facility, but an emotional experience, once lived, can never be forgotten. Nor can this emotion be artificially induced for the sake of raising the reader's temperature. While a biography can be written purely out of a life's worthiness, with details of important names, places and dates, the biographical novel must emerge naturally and organically from the conflicts of man against himself, man against man, or man against fate. Since an experience shared will remain with one forever, it is the aim of the biographical novel to bring the reader into the very heart of the emotion being engendered so that he will make that emotion his own. For the feelings have a memory and a wisdom of which the mind could well be covetous.

In the fields of straight biography and history, the reader stands on the sidelines. What is transpiring on the page is something that happened long ago, and to other people. When reading the biographical novel he is no longer a spectator, but a participant. He starts to live the story as though its first incident had its inception at the instant he opened the book. Perhaps the biographical novel has become so popular because the reader is allowed to participate intimately in history, to become one of its prime actors and motivators. Thus all history becomes contemporary, as in truth it is. The old joke about the man who thought he was Napoleon can come true.

In the biographical novel therefore, the reading and the doing, through identification, become synonymous; the reader can live a thousand different lives during a relatively brief span of years. Therein lies the genius of the form, therein lies its enchantment and its hope for a permanent place in the literary heavens.

With the exception of Merejkowsky's *Romance of Leonardo da Vinci* and Gertrude Atherton's novel of Alexander Hamilton, *The Conqueror,* the biographical novel was unknown and unaccepted in the United States thirty years ago. Yet today it can be found in the catalogue of every major publisher. Now that the biographical novel has come of age, a few ground rules can perhaps be laid down for its practitioners.

The first of these must surely be that history is not the servant of the biographical novelist, but his master. No biographical novel can be better than its research. If the research is deep and honest, the novel will be deep and honest; if the research is sleazy, shallow, evasive or sensation-seeking, the novel will be sleazy, shallow, evasive, sensation-mongering.

Not every life will fit into the form of the biographical novel. There are specific dramatic elements that must be present, recurrent themes of conflict and accomplishment woven through its entirety, an overall, perceivable pattern into which the parts can be fitted to make an organic whole. There are many lives, important and significant in their end results, which are nonetheless diffuse, their content and design antithetical to the nature of the novel; others seem to have been lived as though the subject himself were constantly aware that he was creating a dramatic structure.

While the biographical novelist is assuredly licensed to search out and select those lives which make good copy, the basic demonstrable truth cannot be pushed around to serve a plot purpose. The writer who must twist or pervert the historic truth to come out with what he thinks is an acceptable or saleable story is a tragically misplaced person in his field. The biographical novelist, on the other hand, who becomes moralistic or political, turns into a pamphleteer. We have had experiences of American biographical novelists twisting history out of shape and proportion in order to make it conform to a preconceived line. What has emerged has been neither legitimate biography nor authentic novel, but propaganda. Biography is rich in materials which can be used to serve a purpose; and the biographical novel, young as it is, has not been free from those who would use the form unscrupulously. But this is a danger incident to all of the arts, particularly in a time of war for man's mind; our nostrils must become aware of the rancid smell of such books. In the biographical novel, as in all art forms, personal and professional integrity lie at the base of lasting accomplishment.

An integrated, successful, first-rate biographical novel can emerge only from a union of the material chosen and the author of the choice; from a free, mutually respectful and frequently self-sacrificing partnership in which the story that has been lived and the author who is recreating that story in print, must be equal, and the final product remain more important than either of the contributing partners. If either one assumes an ascendancy the novel will lack for balance: the material will dominate the author, take directions in defiance of the structure; or the author will dominate the material, make it a creature of his own will and desiring. Few authors are qualified to write equally well or profoundly on all subjects. The wise author waits, or searches, for that meaningful story which he can understand, which moves him, and which he senses he can bring vividly to life. If the author chooses unwisely, perhaps because he does not know his material well enough before he starts, or does not know himself well enough, the result can only be false and fragmentary or at best a dismal regurgitation.

The author has a right to ask, as he looks at the outline of a human life, "Can this story serve my purposes?"—but only after he has demanded of himself, "Can I serve the purposes of this story?"

Because of the principle of selection, the biographical novel will inevitably end up as much a portrait of the author as of the subject, for the biographical novelist is a distiller, deriving his spirits not from rye, and we hope not from corn; but from the boiling-pot of human experience. It follows that the biographical novel, even though it leans so heavily on biography and history, can be no better than the mind of its author. If the author is dull, the novel will be dull, and neither biography nor history can save him. If the author is cold, the novel will be cold, no matter how flaming the material being handled. If the author is humorless, the novel will be humorless; if the author is narrow in his interests, his novel will be narrow in its interests, no matter how wide a slice of life it may be reflecting. And if the author is dishonest, what emerges from the pages must be a dishonest novel, regardless of the integrity of the character being portrayed.

How is a reader unacquainted with the field to distinguish between the honest and dishonest biographical novel, the complete and the fractional? How can the question, "How much of this is true?" be answered? Only by insisting that the biographical novel must be as complete in its documentation as the most scholarly history and biography, and as honest in its interpretation.

If it takes four years to train a schoolteacher or engineer, five years to train a pharmacist, six a dentist, seven a lawyer, and eight a doctor, is there any reason to believe that it can take less time to develop a qualified and professional biographical novelist?

He must become experienced in the writing of imaginative novels, wrestling with this form in order that he may come up against the challenging complexities of structure, mood, master scenes, dialogue, with its accompanying lyricism of language, the mounting involvement and suspense of the fictional tale. He would be well advised to write a half-dozen plays to absorb the superb economy of the form, and learn how to stage his tale under a proscenium instead of in the wings: for what the reader does not see with his eyes he never really knows.

He must be trained as a biographer, working at the assembling of materials about one man or group of men, mastering the technic of close-knit organization of these materials, the perceiving and the weaving back and forth of the life theme, evolving a style, personality, and manner of writing by means of which one man's story can be brought to life all over again by black hieroglyphs on white paper: the eternal miracle of literature: for each life has a distinctive face and figure; and this must be captured in order to differentiate this one special story from the hundreds of millions that have been lived.

The biographical novelist must become as scientific a researcher as was Dr. Jonas Salk in his medical laboratories. During the six years that I attended the University of California there were no courses in the fascinating science of research. I had to stumble my way toward a modus operandi. Today most colleges give courses in research which make the tools of this exciting trade as available and usable as those in accounting or electronics. The biographical novelist must be as dedicated to his digging as the archaeologist who uncovers ancient cities after years of pick and shovel work; and he must be grimly resolved that there is absolutely nothing in the historic record which cannot be found if one will search for it long enough, arduously enough and ardroitly enough. Fresh and daring ideas about where and how to look are as important to successful research as are the extracting of fresh and daring drawings by painters from their own minds. Parenthetically the biographical novelist must be as stout of heart as the most ardent lover, for important new materials are frequently buried deep, yielding their charms and protected virtues only to importunate courtship.

Though research is as fascinating as the resolution of a crossword puzzle or a murder mystery, it is also hard work, thoroughly exhausting and unending in its demands. The researcher sometimes gets lost in his forest of facts. To change the metaphor, the biographical novel must be built like an iceberg, about one-ninth of solid substance showing above the literary water line, and the other eight-ninths submerged, but giving a solid base to that which is permitted to appear. If the biographical novelist does not know nine times as much as he reveals, the substance of the print he spreads over the page will be painfully thin: for the eight-ninths which he does not reveal permeates the whole, giving to the pages a discernible bouquet, a subtle emanation which enables the reader to feel comfortable and secure.

For every printed page has a feel and a smell to it, just as surely as does a piece of fruit; it is the research which gives the page of the biographical novel its consistency, which enables the reader to feel that this particular piece of literary fruit is sound at its core, and will not soon decay if allowed to sit on the library table. In the biographical novel, research is the hard firm flesh under the surface skin of the printed page.

The biographical novelist must also be uncrushable in his faith that the truth will out, for when he finds three differing versions of the same happening, accompanied by three different sets of dates and circumstances, he must not become disheartened, but must believe that if he will continue to dig he will find a fourth, authentic version based on irrefutable documents. As Charles A. Beard, one of America's most brilliant historical researchers, told me in his library in New Canaan while helping me with an elusive problem, "Every day I find new source material which controverts something I have believed for thirty years."

To the biographical novelist history is not a mountain, but a river. Even when there are no new facts to be found, there are fresh insights, modern interpretations which can give an old story new focus and meaning; for the biographical novelist, like the archaeologist, is not just a pick and shovel man. The sweat on the forehead and the callouses on the palm are the merest preparation for the real work to come: interpretation of the uncovered materials which will throw light on a story long since lived.

The biographical novelist must also be a perennial skeptic and challenger of the printed word. My confrere, Robert Graves, recently told me in his workshop in Majorca that his biographical novel *I, Claudius* was born at the moment when, reading Tacitus, he cried out, "That's a lie!"

The number of lies and part-truths still resting comfortably and respectably in history is a constant source of astonishment to me; as I am equally amazed at the whole areas of history, even American history as late as the Civil War, or the turn of the twentieth century, that are inadequately researched, or simply not researched at all. It is here that the biographical novelist has his magnificent opportunity: for with vigor and enthusiasm, and a fresh point of view, he can change "That is a lie!" into "That is the truth!" just as he can throw beams of light into areas of history which have remained dark and damp through sheer neglect and want of a champion to rescue them from oblivion.

It also follows that the biographical novelist must be a fighter. Frequently the best stories, and the most meaningful, are those of the underdog, of the man or woman who has been vilified and traduced. From the body of my own work may I suggest as examples the stories of Eugene V. Debs, Rachel Jackson and Mary Todd Lincoln. All efforts to cut through the jungle of prejudiced print, to find the balanced, sympathetic yet judicious truth will be met not only with opposition but frequently with ridicule: for man is as unwilling to give up his vested interest in his prejudices as he is any other of his possessions.

Lastly, the biographical novelist must believe that first there came the Book; he must love books with an unflagging ardency, for he will spend the greater part of life with his nose inside one volume or another: and some of them will be mighty tough customers. He must be able to survive the eyestrain engendered by tiny type, the headaches brought on by handling crumbling yellow pages, the fading ink of aged diaries and letters; and worse, the bottomless depths of Dead Sea writing which would break the teeth of any man imprudent enough to read it aloud.

I would like to outline some specifics.

Having determined that he is going to write a biographical novel about the life of Leonardo da Vinci or Alexander Hamilton, the biographical novelist must put out of his mind for six months or a year any illusion that he is a writer, and become a library mole. He must read all the books and articles written by his subject, study the works created by him, be they art or engineering, read every findable word that has been written about the man or work. He must read all the letters that have passed between the hero and his contemporaries, as well as his private notes, journals and memoirs; or, in the case of a heroine, those wonderfully confiding diaries that are kept locked in the middle drawer of a desk. If the subject is of recent times, there will be a need to interview or correspond with everyone who has been involved in the drama, no matter how slightly.

Having grasped more fully the outlines of his story, the biographical novelist then takes to the road, seeing with his own eyes the places his hero has lived, the quality of the sunlight, the native earth beneath his feet, the personality of the cities and the feel of the countryside: for only then can he write with the intimacy and knowledgability of tactile experience.

This is the first and direct line of attack. The second is equally important: the biographical novelist must now begin the study of his hero's times, its fads and fancies, its majority and minority ideas as well as the prevailing conflicts in religion, philosophy, science, politics, economics and the arts; in short, the overall social, mental, spiritual, esthetic, scientific and international climate in which his characters lived and evolved their codes of conduct. He must read the source books of the period in order to absorb its background, the old newspapers, pamphlets, magazines, the novels, plays and poetry of the times, in order to learn the uncountable thousands of illuminating details which he must have at his fingertips in order to recreate the period: what people wear, the architecture of their houses as well as the fabric on their furniture, how they heat their homes, cook the foods they eat at the various hours of the day; what they are buying in the shops and why, how much it costs as well as how it tastes and smells and feels; what ailments they are suffering and how they are treating them; what colloquialisms they are using to enrich their conversation; what their preachers are preaching on Sunday morning and their teachers teaching on Monday morning.

If the biographical novelist has any feeling for his job he will eventually find emerging out of this seemingly vast and inchoate mass of material certain recurrent patterns, strains of character and action that provide a dominant motif and rhythm for the story he will tell, even as the dominant strains of a symphony are enunciated early. Above all, the biographical novelist is looking for those interwoven designs which are perceivable in every human life: for nearly every life works out its own tightly-woven plot structure. Any action forced upon the participants which does not arise indigenously, which arises instead from the author confusing motion with direction, tears the fabric of the story.

Yet by the same token the biographical novelist must be the master of his material; the craftsman who is not in control of his tools will have his story run away with him. For after his research labors, the biographical novelist must then expend as much time and energy as the writer of fiction to create a novel structure which will best project his material, and be unique to the particular story to be told.

And all this new knowledge must never come between the reader and the narration. In the biographical novel a basic tenet is that the author must stage his story as though it were happening right now; he may not emerge at intervals to inform the reader of what will happen two or twenty or two hundred years later. The reader may never be in possession of information which is not available to those who are acting out the day-by-day passion of their lives. The story must unfold for the reader even as the pageant of events unfolds for the participants. There are few soothsayers; the biographical novelist may not turn himself into an a posteriori prophet. Whatever the reader may divine about what lies ahead must arise from his own perception, and not from the biographical novelist fudging on time sequence. If there be wisdom in the author (and God grant that there may sometimes be!) it will emerge from the nature of the story he wants to tell, from his selection of materials within the framework of that particular story, from his understanding of what motivates his people, and from the skill with which he shapes the unassimilated raw action of human life.

Perhaps a glimpse of my own approaches and technics from *Lust For Life* through *Immortal Wife* and *Love Is Eternal* may shed further light on this still nascent form. I first stumbled across the paintings of Vincent Van Gogh when taken to an exhibition by insistent Parisian friends. Seeing a whole room of Vincent's blazing Arlesian canvases was an emotional experience that I can liken only to my first reading of *The Brothers Karamazov*. I left the exhibition hall determined to find out who this man was who could move me to such depths. I read all the fragments I could find about him in English, French and German; when I returned to New York and to the writing of my plays, I would spend my evenings at the public library at Forty-second Street and Fifth Avenue, reading the three volumes of Vincent's letters to his brother Theo. I had no intention of writing about Vincent; I was only trying to understand him. But slowly over the months the Van Gogh story took possession of me; I found myself waking at three in the morning, writing dialogue passages between Vincent and Theo, or describing Vincent's death scene at Auvers sur Oise. Vincent's ordeal became for me one of the world's most meaningful stories. At the end of a year, when I found myself unable to think of anything else, I decided that I would have to write Vincent's story if for no other reason than to clear it from my mind.

My background for writing such a story was inadequate, for I had grown up in San Francisco where art was a portrait of two dead rabbits hanging by their feet. My first task then, was to read all the books I could find about art and modern painters, and then to search out the canvases that were available. I returned to Europe with a rucksack on my back and followed the trail of Vincent, going down into the mines of the Borinage where he had descended, living in his bedroom at Madam Denis's bakery, writing notes in the parsonages where he had lived with his family in Holland, and going to the south of France to work in the Yellow House, to live in the asylum at St. Remy where he had been incarcerated, and finally to sleep in the same room and bed in the little hotel in Auvers on the fortieth anniversary of his death.

Since I did not know how much I did not know about the writing of a biographical novel, I sat down to my first morning's work with a little calling card in front of me on which I scribbled four strictures: 1. Dramatize. 2. Plenty of dialogue. 3. Bring all characters to life. 4. Use anecdotes and humor.

It is somewhat chastening to me, these many years later, when I write myself fifty pages of notes on precisely how the new book must be written and, collaterally, how it must not be written, to find that I emerge with a product which a lot of people feel is no better than *Lust For Life.* I sometimes wonder if I have spent the past twenty-five years enunciating intellectually the things I knew intuitively at the beginning.

It is also a source of considerable astonishment to me that I waited through three biographies to get back to the form in which I had achieved such a happy result; and that only a fortuitous accident pushed me back into the field.

Through my chapter on John C. Frémont in *They Also Ran,* the story of the men who were defeated for the presidency, I once again came across the woman with whom I had fallen in love in college, and in whose image I married: Jessie Benton Frémont. Jessie's story came to possess me, even as Vincent's had.

In the spring of 1943 I wrote myself a list of sixty-two specifics for *Immortal Wife.* I should like to read a few of them as samples of how one biographical novelist sets the boundaries and dimensions of his task.

I quote directly from my notes:

The story must flow swiftly, smoothly, lyrically. It is a story of people, not history. People come first, history follows. It must be at least half dialogue. Jessie's interior monologue and thinking must be quietly done, understated. Everything must be seen through her eyes. All characters must be brought sharply and vividly to life. Every scene, every word, must be contemporary. Every reader must identify himself with Jessie. Panorama of a changing world: 1840, 1900 through one woman's eyes. Nothing described for description's sake, only as seen by Jessie and as important in her life. No fact for fact's sake, everything human. Material constantly new, refreshing, yet fitting into life pattern. Humor as constant leaven. Patience in developing and revealing major themes. Must be primarily a love story. Constantly changing nature of their love, yet fundamentally same. Always the third dimension of failure, error, human failing. The fourth dimension of mysticism: faith in each other and the world, undying hope as wellspring of human life. Thorough and penetrating job on love and marriage. Keep language universal. Never the whole story; always the essence. No skimping of material; no overblown presentation. Vivid imagery of detail of times, rich contrast of changing scene: Washington, St. Louis, Mariposa. Use interest-

ing mechanisms for history, not just plumped down. Should embrace the whole of a life, one life, as symbolic of all.

Seven years later, when I came to the formulating of *The President's Lady,* I wrote myself advice under the heading of "What devices can be used to get inside Rachel?" some of which may prove germane at this point:

We must react to situations with her mind. We must see people through her eyes, our sense of values must be her sense of values. We must suffer from the things that disturb her, and want (at least for her) the things that she wants. We must share her love for Andrew, endure with her the long terrifying loneliness. The form of our anxieties must be identical with the form of her anxieties; we must evaluate all events through the focus of her needs. We must cling to, and love, the friends and relatives she does. We must want fame and greatness for Andrew, and yet fear them terribly too. We must turn religious, need and justify that religion when she does. She must be the stage upon which history is acted out. We must tremble, then rejoice in her few social triumphs, and die when she dies, acknowledging the lethal blow. We must like Rachel, care about her, understand, sympathize with her. We must enjoy her life from inside her mind and heart.

This can be achieved by warmth of approach; by the author liking her, himself. By a simple, honest directness of storytelling, by understatement, so that the reader builds up his own emotions. By keeping her clear; by moving her swiftly through events, almost too swiftly for her. By finding and portraying the illuminating detail about her. By finding in her the universal elements of suffering in love and marriage. By discerning the basic structure of her life, and sticking to that; by particularizing her, distinguishing her from all other women. By making her a tool and victim of fate; as we all are. Yet proving that her story has never been lived before; or since.

At the end of eighteen months of work, just before beginning the penultimate chapter, I also wrote a five-page note asking "What is the cement that holds this book together?", reviewing the whole meaning and purpose of the book to make sure that nothing that had been enunciated at the beginning had gotten lost in transit, and saying to myself, "This book doesn't have to prove anything but doesn't it have to illuminate a great deal?"

I had been interested in the Lincoln story for many years, and had read rather widely in the field, but had never been able to achieve a point of departure, for I had always said to myself, "Poor Abraham Lincoln, married to Mary Todd." After some ten years of incubation (most biographical novels come out well only if they have been incubating at least five years) while I was doing a magazine article about the Lincoln marriage, I came across some obscure source material which threw the marriage and its daily workings into high relief, particularly in relation to Mr. Lincoln in his role as a husband. I found myself exclaiming, "Poor Mary Todd, married to Abraham Lincoln." From that moment of understanding of the truly equal nature of the marriage I was able to begin work on the thesis which Abraham Lincoln inscribed inside the wedding ring he purchased in the square on the Sunday morning of his wedding, "Love Is Eternal." A little of the detail I sought before starting Chapter IV, just after the Lincoln marriage, may give an idea of the tens of thousands of questions a biographical novelist must ask: for his curiosity must be insatiable:

What changes have taken place in Mary, in Abraham Lincoln? How much time does Abraham spend with her? Where is Mary's room located in hotel? Front, back, side, corner? Does it get some sun? Is it warm or cold? Does she rearrange the room, or leave it as it was? (Rearrange to make it her own?) What are the dimensions? What does it look out over? Is it painted, or wallpapered? How much time does she spend in her room, in the parlors? Does she ask for special things, i. e., reading table; buy a few little things, i. e., lamps? How does she occupy her time in the mornings? Reading, sewing, writing letters? What kind of service is available? How does she arrange her money affairs? Does A give her money for incidentals: drugs, materials, etc.? Does she have any money of her own? Does she pay at stores, or do they have credit accounts? Since Abraham wants to live economically, does she spend, or follow his wishes? Does she have visitors at hotel? Family, friends to dinner and supper? Is it expensive? She is later accused of being stingy, but if so, does she learn economy from A? Where is dining-room of Globe? How big is it? How decorated? Does Lincoln suggest they eat with others at big tables, or do they have the same table for two? Who was next to, or across from the Lincolns? We know of Bledsoes—what kind of piano, and what pieces, would Mrs. Bledsoe be playing? Would she invite Mary to play?

As I was preparing the last two chapters, I wrote myself a long, stern directive, of which the following lines are typical:

Let's get simple, and stay simple. Do only symptomatic scenes; step up pacing and speed; in perspective distant scenes are always foreshortened. Don't fight the entire Civil War, only those elements that come into the White House. Avoid name-calling, side-taking, prejudice, bitterness. Awaken no hatred, only pity and compassion. Underwrite the grief, underplay the emotion. Don't stack cards, either for or against Mary. Keep the author out, let the story tell itself.

But beyond the specifications for any one particular book, I found the following obiter dicta to be essential to all biographical novels:

No use of names because they later become important elsewhere. No asides, or smart whisperings. No fixations, or prejudices carried over from past feelings or readings. No harpings, or preconceived "theories, into which all history and happenings must fit." No name-calling, let the reader call the proper names. No fiery passions, for or against; they cloud judgment. No assumptions as to the reader's tastes, opinions, ideas, education. No writing for any one class, age or geographic group. No condemnations of people or events; give them their rightful place in the story, and let God judge them. No seeking the sensational for its own sake; and no philosophizing. No concealing of important evidence, no lies, cheating or defrauding the reader. No dullness; throw out the slow, meaningless passages. No striving for effects, no manifest anger or hatred, no browbeating. Watch comparative materials and balance them; no disproportions about materials where I happen to know more. No inheriting of other people's prejudices, hatreds, blindness. No details that illuminate little but themselves. No posturing, no exhibitionism: "See what I know!" No striving for novelty for its own sake. No doctrinairism, or fitting material into one school or pattern. No destructivism, nor defeatism. No pugilism or blind spots. No lethargy. No weasel phrases; all space is needed for direct lines. No meandering down pleasant paths. No use of material that does not tie into focal core of book.

Because of the tender youth of the biographical novel there has as yet been little discussion of its particular character, of its strengths as well as its limitations. Is it a history, a biography, or a novel? Is it none of these? Or perhaps all three? If in this paper I presume to provide a beginning critique, standards of judgment against which the biographical novel may be viewed, it is done with the happy reassurance that all such strictures will be altered, expanded and materially improved by later practitioners of the craft.

Professor Carl Bode of the University of Maryland recently wrote in the magazine *College English,* in the first serious study of the biographical novel to be published, "In the last ten years several prominent people have been doing their best to make an honest woman of the biographical novel. Considerable progress has been made, but not quite enough. The biographical novel still goes its bosomy way, its flimsy clothing tattered and torn in exactly the wrong places." "Sometimes powerful and often picturesque, it deserves much more attention than it has received from the critics."

When Professor Bode speaks of the biographical novels going their bosomy way, their flimsy clothing tattered and torn in exactly the wrong places, I am afraid he is concerned with such books as *Forever Amber* or *Kitty,* whose writers took the license of combining sensational material from a hundred different sources, letting their fictional fancies run wild, a privilege not accorded to the biographical novelist, who must remain inside the confines of the life he is writing about. They are certainly not biographical novels, and I doubt very much that W. R. Guthrie or Robert Penn Warren would consider them historical novels.

If anything, the biographical novel has suffered from an excess of good taste and respectability, perhaps because the biographical novelist has been awed by the fact that his characters once actually lived, and hence were endowed with certain inalienable rights, not of concealment, but of privacy and decorum. Bedroom scenes of which critics complain in the lurid, so-called historical novels are not to be found in the biographical novel, a sometime limitation to the sale of the genre, but one which calls forth the subtlety of the biographical novelist if he is to convey to the reader the all-important love and sex life of his subject.

I am going to take the liberty of quoting Professor Bode's analysis of my own work because I believe he has drawn an architectural blueprint for me, and for other biographical novelists, to follow in the future. Speaking of my own five biographical novels that followed the story of Vincent Van Gogh, he writes:

Each volume showed the advances in novelistic technique. The scholarship deepened too, though less steadily. The peak for the present day biographical novel was approached with the publication of Stone's book on Mary Todd Lincoln and her marriage. The scholarship is just as sound, according to a leading Lincoln specialist, as it is in the recent and respectfully reviewed biography of Mrs. Lincoln by a trained historian. It deserves to be called meticulous. Many an example can be found of Stone's deep scholarly concern with the life he was writing. He painstakingly prepared a floor-plan of the White House of Lincoln's day—one has never been reconstructed before—as a piece of independent research, and he created most of his dialogue out of skilled paraphrases of historically accurate source material. Furthermore, the handling of the data is judicious. Mrs. Lincoln is always a controversial figure, and Stone could be excused if he slanted his information one way or the other. But he does not. Rising above his declared intention to vindicate her, he portrays her bedeviled neurotic character with fairness. She and Abe emerge as memorable human beings, one great and the other not, but human beings both. The minor characters are carefully differentiated, very seldom are they mere historical names. The scenes are well handled, with pace and suspense to some of them in spite of the fact that historians already know how they come out . . . The descriptions give rich color to the picture Stone creates . . .

The aim behind the best writing of this kind is a noble one. It is to see beneath the surface reality of facts and to reveal the true reality to others. It is to use historical data more daringly but more penetratingly than the professional historian can.

Samuel E. Morison, professor of history at Harvard University, writes in an essay called *History As A Literary Art*: "The historian can learn much from the novelist. The best writers of fiction are superior to all but the best historians in characterization and description. When John Citizen feels the urge to read history he goes to the novels of Kenneth Roberts or Margaret Mitchell, not to the histories of Professor this or Doctor that. Why? American historians have forgotten that there is an art of writing history. In this flight of history from literature the public got left behind. American history became a bore to the reader and a drug on the market."

It is to this mournful state of affairs that the biographical novel addresses itself.

It is important, too, to set down the discernible differences between the biographical novel, the fictional novel, the historical novel, and the straight biography.

A few years ago when I was visiting with Ernest Hemingway in Key West, we discussed the approaches to our two novels in progress. Hemingway said, "There is no such thing as fiction. Everything we write is based on the lives we have lived, and other lives we have observed." Yet the fictional novelist has the opportunity to regroup and rechannel experience, to combine portions of a dozen different lives, to imagine a better world, or a more evil one, if that suits his temperament, and of conjuring up varying resolutions to the human situations he has evoked.

The biographical novelist is a bondsman to the factual truth; yet he will succeed very little if he remains a mere reporter. As Robert Graves said to me, "The biographical novelist who does not have strong intuitions about his subject, and later finds from the documents that his intuition has been substantiated, is not likely to get far in understanding his subject."

Inside the skeletal outline imposed on him, the biographical novelist is free to soar to any heights which his own inner poetry and perception will allow him. There are few if any differences of structure between the two types of novel; with the biographical novel the reader asks, "Did this happen?" and with the fictional novel, "Could this happen?" Therein lies the major distinction between them. Credibility lies at the base of both. A chance reader, unacquainted with the material, setting and character of the two stories, should not be able to tell them apart; he should be able to think that the fictional novel actually happened somewhere, or that the biographical novel was invented by the author. I remember with considerable satisfaction the day in September 1934 when Mrs. Stone asked the telephone operator in her office how she had liked *Lust For Life,* and the girl replied, "Fine, but why did Irving have to kill off the poor man?"

The historical novel is the closest to the biographical novel in its nature and scope; again the difference is not of form but of approach. In the biographical novel all of the characters have lived; in the best historical novels, such as *War and Peace,* only the history has actually happened, while the characters are invented, or built up by accretion, and then set in the authentic framework of the period and the action being written about. The main characters of the historical novel become the apotheoses of their times; they are true in that such characters did live in this particular period, and this dramatic series of events did take place, but to other people, perhaps half a hundred of them, in modified form and sequence. Sometimes the historical novel will be so close to the biographical novel, such as with *All the King's Men,* the story of Huey Long, that little is changed except the names of the characters and a few incidental pieces of personal action. In H. G. Wells' *The World of William Clissold,* Clissold and his various loves were imaginary, but the protagonists were called by their right names, and once again put through their roles in history. In still another type, roughly half of the characters are real people who act out their own historicity, while the other half, more often than not the "heroes" of the tale, are invented.

I would like at this moment to interject, with less bitterness than puzzlement, I hope, the question of why the historical novel, with its accurate background but fictional characters, should have been more acceptable to the academicians than the biographical novel, which is accurate not only in background but in the people involved? The answer to this riddle has remained a mystery to me.

The differences between the straight biography and the biographical novel are considerable, not in substance, since both draw their nourishment from the same source, but in structure, manner, attitude, and relationship between the author and the reader.

The biography has traditionally been in indirect discourse, a chronicle told by a second party, the writer, to a third party, the reader. The biographer, for example, relates what his principals have said; the biographical novelist enables the reader to listen to the conversations as they develop. The biographical novelist, in order to recreate a character, must not only understand his every motivation, but must write of it from behind the eyes of his protagonist. Only then can the reader feel everything that he feels, know everything that he knows, suffer his defeats and enjoy his victories. The biography has been expected to be objective; too often it has been written in cool blood. The biographical novel must be written in hot blood.

Even so, the form of biography is changing, and perhaps the wide public acceptance of the biographical novel has had something to do with this change. The biographies I read in school contained as many footnotes as lines of text, while the quotations were indented in small type in the center of the page, presenting a pedagogical, dull and fatiguing sight to the eye as well as to the emotional interest of the reader. When in 1937 I wrote *Sailor on Horseback,* I put my quotations from Jack London on a continuing line with the main text, separated only by a comma and a quotation mark, so that there would be no break in the reading mood and the typographical page would remain unified and interesting. When I received the first half of the galleys from my then publisher in Boston, all the quotations had been centered in tiny typeknots in the middle of the page. In answer to my anguished telephone call, the proofreader said that he had set my manuscript according to the standard form, since I obviously had not known how to do so. At that point the editor broke into the conversation and ordered the manuscript reset as I had written it. By now the practice has become almost universal.

Up to recent times it was not permitted in biographies to stage dialogue sequences, even when such dialogue was completely documented, evidently on the grounds that recreated dialogue might be less true, or might lead the reader to think he was reading a novel instead of a biography, and hence not believe that what he was reading was factually accurate. This never appeared to me to be a tenable point of view, and, in 1940, when I wrote *Clarence Darrow For The Defense,* I staged, as though they were being acted under a proscenium, all of the conversations that seemed interesting and important; at the back of the book I listed my documentation for every spoken word. I feel sure they had considerably more emotional impact than if I had related at second hand what the conversations had been about.

When I was growing up, few except scholars read biographies. It is my opinion that the biographical novel arose, and has become popular, because of this failure of the biography to reach a reading public that was hungry for authentic human stories. It is also my opinion that the biography will continue to learn from the biographical novel, and lean on its technics. A book is written for purposes of communication; it does an author no service whatever to have his book unreadable and hence unread. It must also be said that the biographical novel will be eternally indebted to the straight biography, for it has learned from it the science of research and the organization of materials.

The biographical novel, like all living creatures, was born in pain. It was called a bastard form, the result of an unfortunate indiscretion on the part of its otherwise eminently respectable parents, biography and the novel.

What are the criticisms that have been and still are, in some unconvinced corners, levied against the biographical novel? It is said to debase the biography and the novel, discrediting both and adding to the stature of neither. Allegedly it mines biography without regard for the verities, strains history through the author's personality, reshapes that history to fit the novel form, oversimplifies, prevents the reader from separating fact from fiction, chooses only those subjects which allow for a lively sale, violates the privacy of people long dead, and makes character the victim of plot.

All of these criticisms have sometimes been true, and probably a good many more of which the critics happily have not yet thought. But to decide that any art form is untenable because of its weakest example or its potential for error is similar to saying that the human race should be obliterated because of the shortcomings of its least admirable percentage. I find that in the course of my twenty-three years in the field most major critics have become reconciled to the fact that the biographical novel is here to stay. The more courageous and perceptive of them now welcome it to the literary boards; by the same token they insist that each volume achieve standards of literary and historical excellence. Instead of categorically damning the form without bothering to read the book, they are judging each succeeding biographical novel on the basis of its writing, research, storytelling, perception.

One of the assets of the human race is said to be that it can learn from experience; history and biography constitute the greatest mine of lived experience; and it is the fond dream of the biographical novelist to bring the wisdom of that experience to the problems and complexities of the modern world.

My own biographical novels have had two motivations: I have hoped to feel deeply about simple things; and I have wanted to tell the story of man, against obstacles, for man.

VINCENT VAN GOGH came from a line of Dutch dominies, admiralty officers, and international art dealers. Uncertain of what he wanted to do with his life, he entered the service of the Goupil Galleries, owned by his uncles. While being trained in the London Gallery, Vincent fell in love with the daughter of his landlady. However, Ursula was secretly engaged and contemptuously rejected him. The rejection led him to inherit the disinherited of the earth. He became an evangelist in the poverty-stricken Borinage coal-mining region, gave away his food, clothing, earnings until he was reduced to living in a shack with straw on the floor. For this intemperance he was dismissed from the evangelical church, and fell ill. He was rescued by his love of drawing, at which he now began to work faithfully; and by the love of his brother, Theo, who recognized the power of Vincent's drawing and desire to become an artist. Theo pledged his friendship, and money from his wage as a dealer with Goupil Gallery in Paris. In 1880, when he was twenty-seven years old, Vincent returned to Etten, in Brabant, to live with his parents and to sketch and paint, finding his subjects and themes among the peasants of the countryside. But his manner alienated the staid people of the community, who considered painters to be idlers. In 1886, at Theo's invitation, Vincent moved to Paris, into his own maturity, as well as the revolutionary age of the Impressionists, and his new friends, Gaugin, Seurat, Cezanne, Henri Rousseau. After a year of absorbing the new theories of light and color, Vincent decided that he had to strike off alone, to find painting country he could make his own. He chose Arles, in the south of France, because Toulouse-Lautrec had told him, "It's a painter's paradise."

LUST FOR LIFE

Arles

I

THE Arlesian sun smote Vincent between the eyes, and broke him wide open. It was a whorling, liquid ball of lemon-yellow fire, shooting across a hard blue sky and filling the air with blinding light. The terrific heat and intense clarity of the air created a new and unfamiliar world.

He dropped out of the third-class carriage early in the morning and walked down the winding road that led from the station to the Place Lamartine, a market square bounded on one side by the embankment of the Rhône, on the other by cafés and wretched hotels. Arles lay straight ahead, pasted against the side of a hill with a neat mason's trowel, drowsing in the hot, tropical sun.

When it came to looking for a place to live, Vincent was indifferent. He walked into the first hotel he passed in the Place, the Hotel de la Gare, and rented a room. It contained a blatant brass bed, a cracked pitcher in a washbowl, and an odd chair. The proprietor brought in an unpainted table. There was no room to set up an easel, but Vincent meant to paint out of doors all day.

He threw his valise on the bed and dashed out to see the town. There were two approaches to the heart of Arles from the Place Lamartine. The circular road on the left was for wagons; it skirted the edge of the town and wound slowly to the top of the hill, passing the old Roman forum and amphitheatre on the way. Vincent took the more direct approach, which led through a labyrinth of narrow cobblestone streets. After a long climb he reached the sun-scorched Place de la Mairie. On the way up he passed cold stone courts and quadrangles which looked as though they had come down untouched from the early Roman days. In order to keep out the maddening sun, the alleys had been made so narrow that Vincent could touch both rows of houses with outstretched fingertips. To avoid the torturing mistral, the streets wound about in a hopeless maze on the side of the hill, never going straight for more than ten yards. There was refuse in the streets, dirty children in the doorways, and over everything a sinister, hunted aspect.

Vincent left the Place de la Mairie, walked through a short alley to the main marketing road at the back of the town, strolled through the little park, and then stumbled down the hill to the Roman arena. He leaped from tier to tier like a goat, finally reaching the top. He sat on a block of stone, dangled his legs over a sheer drop of hundreds of feet, lit his pipe, and surveyed the domain of which he had appointed himself lord and master.

The town below him flowed down abruptly to the Rhône like a kaleidoscopic waterfall. The roofs of the houses were fitted into each other in an intricate design. They had all been tiled in what was originally red clay, but the burning, incessant sun had baked them to a maze of every colour, from the lightest lemon and delicate shell pink to a biting lavender and earthy loam-brown.

The wide, rapidly flowing Rhône made a sharp curve at the bottom of the hill on which Arles was plastered, and shot downward to the Mediterranean. There were stone embankments on either side of the river. Trinquetaille glistened like a painted city on the other bank. Behind Vincent were the mountains, huge ranges sticking upward into the clear white light. Spread out before him was a panorama of tilled fields, of orchards in blossom, the rising mound of Montmajour, fertile valleys ploughed into thousands of deep furrows, all converging at some distant point in infinity.

But it was the colour of the countryside that made him run a hand over his bewildered eyes. The sky was so intensely blue, such a hard, relentless, profound blue that it was not blue at all; it was utterly colourless. The green of the fields stretched below him was the essence of the colour green, gone mad. The burning lemon-yellow of the sun, the blood-red of the soil, the crying whiteness of the lone cloud over Montmajour, the ever reborn rose of the orchards . . . such colourings were incredible. How could he paint them? How could he ever make anyone believe that they existed, even if he could transfer them to his palette? Lemon, blue, green, red, rose; nature run rampant in five torturing shades of expression.

Vincent took the wagon road to the Place Lamartine, grabbed up his easel, paints, and canvas and struck out along the Rhône. Almond trees were beginning to flower everywhere. The glistening white glare of the sun on the water sent stabs of pain into his eyes. He had left his hat in the hotel. The sun burned through the red of his hair, sucked out all the cold of Paris, all the fatigue, discouragement, and satiety with which city life had glutted his soul.

A kilometre down the river he found a drawbridge with a little cart going over it, outlined against a blue sky. The river was as blue as a well, the banks orange, coloured with green grass. A group of washerwomen in smocks and many-coloured caps were pounding dirty white clothes in the shade of a lone tree.

Vincent set up his easel, drew a long breath, and shut his eyes. No man could catch such colourings with his eyes open. There fell away from him Seurat's talk about scientific pointillism, Gauguin's harangues about primitive decorativeness, Cezanne's appearances beneath solid surfaces, Lautrec's lines of colour and lines of splenetic hatred. There remained only Vincent.

He returned to his hotel about dinner time. He sat down at a little table in the bar and ordered an absinthe. He was too excited, too utterly replete to think of food. A man sitting at a nearby table observed the paint splashed all over Vincent's hands, face, and clothing, and fell into conversation with him.

"I'm a Parisian journalist," he said. "I've been down here for three months gathering material for a book on the Provençal language."

"I just arrived from Paris this morning," said Vincent.

"So I noticed. Intend to stay long?"

"Yes, I imagine so."

"Well, take my advice and don't. Arles is the most violently insane spot on the globe."

"What makes you think that?"

"I don't think it. I know it. I've been watching these people for three months, and I tell you, they're all cracked. Just look at them. Watch their eyes. There's not a normal, rational person in this whole Tarascon vicinity!"

"That's a curious thing to say," observed Vincent.

"Within a week you'll be agreeing with me. The country around Arles is the most torn, desperately lashed section in Provence. You've been out in that sun. Can't you imagine what it must do to these people who are subject to its blinding light day after day? I tell you, it burns the brains right out of their heads. And the mistral. You haven't felt the mistral yet? Oh, dear, wait until you do. It whips this town into a frenzy two hundred days out of every year. If you try to walk the streets, it smashes you against the buildings. If you are out in the fields, it knocks you down and grinds you into the dirt. It twists your insides until you think you can't bear it another minute. I've seen that infernal wind tear out windows, pull up trees, knock down fences, lash the men and animals in the fields until I thought they would surely fly in pieces. I've been here only three months, and I'm going a little *fou* myself. I'm getting out tomorrow morning!"

"Surely you must be exaggerating?" asked Vincent. "The Arlesians looked all right to me, what little I saw of them today."

"What little you saw of them is right. Wait until you get to know them. Listen, do you know what my private opinion is?"

"No, what? Will you join me in an absinthe?"

"Thanks. In my private opinion, Arles is epileptic. It whips itself up to such an intense pitch of nervous excitement that you are positive it will burst into a violent fit and foam at the mouth."

"And does it?"

"No. That's the curious part. This country is forever reaching a climax, and never having one. I've been waiting for three months to see a revolution, or a volcano erupt from the Place de la Mairie. A dozen times I thought the inhabitants would all suddenly go mad and cut each other's throats! But just when they get to a point where an explosion is imminent, the mistral dies down for a couple of days and the sun goes behind the clouds."

"Well," laughed Vincent, "if Arles never reached a climax, you can't very well call it epileptic, now can you?"

"No," replied the journalist, "but I can call it epileptoidal."

"What the devil is that?"

"I'm doing an article on the subject for my paper in Paris. It was this German article that gave me my idea."

He pulled a magazine out of his pocket and shoved it across the table to Vincent.

"These doctors have made a study of the cases of several hundred men who suffered from nervous maladies which looked like epilepsy, but which never resulted in fits. You'll see by these charts how they have mapped the rising curve of nervousness and excitement; what the doctors call volatile tension. Well, in every last one of these cases the subjects have gone along with increasing fever until they reached the age of thirty-five to thirty-eight. At the average age of thirty-six they burst into a violent epileptic fit. After that it's a case of a half dozen more spasms and, within a year or two, good-bye."

"That's much too young to die," said Vincent. "A man is only beginning to get command of himself by that time."

The journalist put the magazine back in his pocket.

"Are you going to stop at this hotel for some time?" he asked. "My article is almost finished; I'll mail you a copy as soon as it's published. My point is this: Arles is an epileptoidal city. Its pulse has been mounting for centuries. It's approaching its first crisis. It's bound to happen. And soon. When it does, we're going to witness a frightful catastrophe. Murder, arson, rape, wholesale destruction! This country can't go on forever in a whipped, tortured state. Something must and will happen. I'm getting out before the people start foaming at the mouth! I advise you to come along!"

"Thanks," said Vincent, "I like it here. I think I'll turn in now. Will I see you in the morning? No? Then good luck to you. And don't forget to send me a copy of the article."

2

Every morning Vincent arose before dawn, dressed, and tramped several kilometres down the river or into the country to find a spot that stirred him. Every night he returned with a finished canvas, finished because there was nothing more he could do with it. Directly after supper he went to sleep.

He became a blind painting machine, dashing off one sizzling canvas after another without even knowing what he did. The orchards of the country were in bloom. He developed a wild passion to paint them all. He no longer thought about his painting. He just painted. All his eight years of intense labour were at last expressing themselves in a great burst of triumphal energy. Sometimes, when he began working at the first crack of dawn, the canvas would be completed by noon. He would tramp back to town, drink a cup of coffee and trudge out again in another direction with a new canvas.

He did not know whether his painting was good or bad. He did not care. He was drunk with colour.

No one spoke to him. He spoke to no one. What little strength he had left from his painting, he spent in fighting the mistral. Three days out of every week he had to fasten his easel to pegs driven into the ground. The easel waved back and forth in the wind like a sheet on a clothesline. By night he felt as buffeted and bruised as though he had been given a severe beating.

He never wore a hat. The fierce sun was slowly burning the hair off the top of his head. When he lay on his brass bed in the little hotel at night he felt as though his head were encased in a ball of fire. The sun struck him completely blind. He could not tell the green of the fields from the blue of the sky. But when he returned to his hotel he found that the canvas was somehow a glowing, brilliant transcription of nature.

One day he worked in an orchard of lilac ploughland with a red fence and two rose-coloured peach trees against a sky of glorious blue and white.

"It is probably the best landscape I have ever done," he murmured to himself.

When he reached his hotel he found a letter telling him that Anton Mauve had died in The Hague. Under his peach trees he wrote, "Souvenir de Mauve. Vincent and Theo," and sent it off immediately to the house on the Uileboomen.

The following morning he found an orchard of plum trees in blossom. While he was at work, a vicious wind sprang up, returning at intervals like waves of the sea. In between, the sun shone, and all the white flowers sparkled on the trees. At the risk every minute of seeing the whole show on the ground, Vincent went on painting. It reminded him of the Scheveningen days when he used to paint in the rain, in sandstorms, and with the storm-spray of the ocean dashing over him and his easel. His canvas had a white effect with a good deal of yellow in it, and blue and lilac. When he finished he saw something in his picture that he had not meant to put there, the mistral.

"People will think I was drunk when I painted this," he laughed to himself.

A line from Theo's letter of the day before came back to him. Mijnheer Tersteeg, on a visit to Paris, had stood before a Sisley and murmured to Theo, "I cannot help thinking that the artist who painted this was a bit tipsy."

"If Tersteeg could see my Arlesian pictures," thought Vincent, "he would say it was delirium tremens in full career."

The people of Arles gave Vincent a wide berth. They saw him dashing out of town before sunrise, heavy easel loaded on his back, hatless, his chin stuck forward eagerly, a feverish excitement in his eyes. They saw him return with two fire holes in his face, the top of his head as red as raw meat, a wet canvas under his arm, gesticulating to himself. The town had a name for him. Everyone called him by it.

"Fou-rou!"

"Perhaps I am a red-headed crazy man," he said to himself, "but what can I do?"

The owner of the hotel swindled Vincent out of every franc he could. Vincent could not get anything to eat, for nearly everyone in

Arles ate at home. The restaurants were expensive. Vincent tried them all to find some strong soup, but there was none to be had.

"Is it hard to cook potatoes, Madame?" he asked in one place.

"Impossible, Monsieur."

"Then have you some rice?"

"That is tomorrow's dish."

"What about macaroni?"

"There was no room on the range for macaroni."

At length he had to give up all serious thoughts of food, and live on whatever came his way. The hot sun built up his vitality, even though his stomach was getting little attention. In place of sane food he put absinthe, tobacco, and Daudet's tales of Tartarin. His innumerable hours of concentration before the easel rubbed his nerves raw. He needed stimulants. The absinthe made him all the more excited for the following day, an excitement whipped by the mistral and baked into him by the sun.

As the summer advanced, everything became burnt up. He saw about him nothing but old gold, bronze and copper, covered by a greenish azure sky of blanched heat. There was sulphur yellow on everything the sunlight hit. His canvases were masses of bright burning yellow. He knew that yellow had not been used in European painting since the Renaissance, but that did not deter him. The yellow pigment oozed out of the tubes onto the canvas, and there it stayed. His pictures were sun steeped, sun burnt, tanned with the burning sun and swept with air.

He was convinced that it was no more easy to make a good picture than it was to find a diamond or a pearl. He was dissatisfied with himself and what he was doing, but he had just a glimmer of hope that it was going to be better in the end. Sometimes even that hope seemed a Fata Morgana. Yet the only time he felt alive was when he was slogging at his work. Of personal life, he had none. He was just a mechanism, a blind painting automaton that had food, liquid, and paint poured into it each morning, and by nightfall turned out a finished canvas.

And for what purpose? For sale? Certainly not! He knew that nobody wanted to buy his pictures. Then what was the hurry? Why did he drive and spur himself to paint dozens and dozens of canvases when the space under his miserable brass bed was already piled nearly solid with paintings?

The desire to succeed had left Vincent. He worked because he had to, because it kept him from suffering too much mentally, because it distracted his mind. He could do without a wife, a home, and children; he could do without love and friendship and health; he could do without security, comfort, and food; he could even do without God. But he could not do without something which was greater than himself, which was his life—the power and ability to create.

3

He tried to hire models, but the people of Arles would not sit for him. They thought they were being done badly. They were afraid their friends would laugh at the portraits. Vincent knew that if he painted prettily like Bouguereau, people would not be ashamed to let themselves be painted. He had to give up the idea of models, and work always on the soil.

As the summer ripened, a glorious strong heat came on and the wind died. The light in which he worked ranged from pale sulphur-yellow to pale golden yellow. He thought often of Renoir and that pure clear line of his. That was the way everything looked in the clear air of Provence, just as it looked in the Japanese prints.

Early one morning he saw a girl with a coffee-tinted skin, ash-blond hair, grey eyes, and a print bodice of pale rose under which he could see the breasts, shapely, firm and small. She was a woman as simple as the fields, every line of her virgin. Her mother was an amazing figure in dirty yellow and faded blue, thrown up in strong sunlight against a square of brilliant flowers, snow-white and lemon-yellow. They posed for him for several hours in return for a small sum.

When he returned to his hotel that evening, Vincent found himself thinking of the girl with the coffee-tinted skin. Sleep would not come. He knew that there were houses in Arles, but they were mostly five-franc places patronized by the Zouaves, negroes brought to Arles to be trained for the French army.

It was months since Vincent had spoken to a woman, except to ask for a cup of coffee or a bag of tobacco. He remembered Margot's loving words, the wandering fingers over his face that she followed with a trail of loving kisses.

He jumped up, hurried across the Place Lamartine and struck into the black maze of stone houses. After a few moments of climbing he heard a great hubbub ahead. He broke into a run and reached the front door of a brothel in the Rue des Ricolettes just as the gendarmes were carting away two Zouaves who had been killed by drunken

Italians. The red fezzes of the soldiers were lying in pools of blood on the rough cobblestone street. A squad of gendarmes hustled the Italians to jail, while the infuriated mob stormed after them, shouting,

"Hang them! Hang them!"

Vincent took advantage of the excitement to slip into the Maison de Tolérance, Numero I, in the Rue des Ricolettes. Louis, the proprietor, welcomed him and led him into a little room on the left of the hall, where a few couples sat drinking.

"I have a young girl by the name of Rachel who is very nice," said Louis. "Would Monsieur care to try her? If you do not like the looks of her, you can choose from all the others."

"May I see her?"

Vincent sat down at a table and lit his pipe. There was laughter from the outside hall, and a girl danced in. She slid into the chair opposite Vincent and smiled at him.

"I'm Rachel," she said.

"Why," exclaimed Vincent, "you're nothing but a baby!"

"I'm sixteen," said Rachel proudly.

"How long have you been here?"

"At Louis's? A year."

"Let me look at you."

The yellow gas lamp was at her back; her face had been in the shadows. She put her head against the wall and tilted her chin up towards the light so that Vincent could see her.

He saw a round, plump face, wide, vacant blue eyes, a fleshy chin and neck. Her black hair was coiled on top of her head, giving the face an even more ball-like appearance. She had on only a light printed dress and a pair of sandals. The nipples of her round breasts pointed straight out at him like accusing fingers.

"You're pretty, Rachel," he said.

A bright, childlike smile came into her empty eyes. She whirled about and took his hand in hers.

"I'm glad you like me," she said. "I like the men to like me. That makes it nicer, don't you think?"

"Yes. Do you like me?"

"I think you're a funny man, *fou-rou.*"

"*Fou-rou!* Then you know me?"

"I've seen you in the Place Lamartine. Why are you always rushing places with that big bundle on your back? And why don't you wear a hat? Doesn't the sun burn you? Your eyes are all red. Don't they hurt?"

Vincent laughed at the naiveté of the child.

"You're very sweet, Rachel. Will you call me by my real name if I tell it to you?"

"What is it?"

"Vincent."

"No, I like *fou-rou* better. Do you mind if I call you *fou-rou*? And can I have something to drink? Old Louis is watching me from the hall."

She ran her fingers across her throat; Vincent watched them sink into the soft flesh. She smiled with her empty blue eyes, and he saw that she was smiling to be happy, so that he might be happy, too. Her teeth were regular but dark; her large underlip drooped down almost to meet the sharp horizontal crevice just above her thick chin.

"Order a bottle of wine," said Vincent, "but not an expensive one, for I haven't much money."

When the wine came, Rachel said, "Would you like to drink it in my room? It's more homey there."

"I would like that very much."

They walked up a flight of stone steps and entered Rachel's cell. There was a narrow cot, a bureau, a chair, and several coloured Julien medallions on the white walls. Two torn and battered dolls sat on top of the bureau.

"I brought these from home with me," she said. "Here, *fou-rou*, take them. This is Jacques and this is Catherine. I used to play house with them. Oh, *fou-rou*, don't you look droll!"

Vincent stood there grinning foolishly with a doll in each arm until Rachel finished laughing. She took Catherine and Jacques from him, tossed them on the bureau, kicked her sandals into a corner and slipped out of her dress.

"Sit down, *fou-rou*," she said, "and we'll play house. You'll be papa and I'll be mama. Do you like to play house?"

She was a short, thickset girl with swelling, convex thighs, a deep declivity under the pointed breasts, and a plump, round belly which rolled down into the pelvic triangle.

"Rachel," said Vincent, "if you are going to call me *fou-rou*, I have a name for you, too."

Rachel clapped her hands and flung herself onto his lap.

"Oh, tell me, what is it? I like to be called new names!"

"I'm going to call you *Le Pigeon*."

Rachel's blue eyes went hurt and perplexed.

"Why am I a pigeon, papa?"

Vincent ran his hand lightly over her rotund, cupid's belly.

"Because you look like a pigeon, with your gentle eyes and fat little tummy."

"Is it nice to be a pigeon?"

"Oh, yes. Pigeons are very pretty and lovable . . . and so are you."

Rachel leaned over, kissed him on the ear, sprang up from the cot and brought two water tumblers for their wine.

"What funny little ears you have, *fou-rou,*" she said, between sips of the red wine. She drank it as a baby drinks, with her nose in the glass.

"Do you like them?" asked Vincent.

"Yes. They're so soft and round, just like a puppy's."

"Then you can have them."

Rachel laughed loudly. She raised her glass to her lips. The joke struck her as funny again, and she giggled. A trickle of red wine spilled down her left breast, wound its way over the pigeon belly and disappeared in the black triangle.

"You're nice, *fou-rou,*" she said. "Everyone speaks as though you were crazy. But you're not, are you?"

Vincent grimaced.

"Only a little," he said.

"And will you be my sweetheart?" Rachel demanded. "I haven't had one for over a month. Will you come to see me every night?"

"I'm afraid I can't come every night, Pigeon."

Rachel pouted. "Why not?"

"Well, among other things, I haven't the money."

Rachel tweaked his right ear, playfully.

"If you haven't five francs, *fou-rou,* will you cut off your ear and give it to me? I'd like to have it. I'd put it on my bureau and play with it every night."

"Will you let me redeem it if I get the five francs later?"

"Oh, *fou-rou,* you're so funny and nice. I wish more of the men who came here were like you."

"Don't you enjoy it here?"

"Oh, yes, I have a very nice time, and I like it all . . . except the Zouaves, that is."

Rachel put down her wine glass and threw her arms prettily about Vincent's neck. He felt her soft paunch against his waistcoat, and the points of her bud-like breasts burning into him. She buried her mouth on his. He found himself kissing the soft, velvety inner lining of her lower lip.

"You will come back to see me again, *fou-rou?* You won't forget me and go to see some other girl?"

"I'll come back, Pigeon."

"And shall we do it now? Shall we play house?"

When he left the place a half hour later, he was consumed by a thirst which could be quenched only by innumerable glasses of clear, cold water.

4

Vincent came to the conclusion that the more finely a colour was pounded, the more it became saturated with oil. Oil was only the carrying medium for colour; he did not care much for it, particularly since he did not object to his canvases having a rough look. Instead of buying colour that had been pounded on the stone for God knows how many hours in Paris, he decided to become his own colour man. Theo asked Père Tanguy to send Vincent the three chromes, the malachite, the vermilion, the orange lead, the cobalt, and the ultramarine. Vincent crushed them in his little hotel room. After that his colours not only cost less, but they were fresher and more lasting.

He next became dissatisfied with the absorbent canvas on which he painted. The thin coat of plaster with which they were covered did not suck up his rich colours. Theo sent him rolls of unprepared canvas; at night he mixed the plaster in a little bowl and spread it over the canvas he planned to paint the following day.

Georges Seurat had made him sensitive to the sort of frame his work was to rest in. When he sent his first Arlesian canvases to Theo, he explained just what sort of wood had to be used, and what colour it had to be painted. But he could not be happy until he saw his paintings in frames that he made himself. He bought plain strips of wood from his grocer, cut them down to the size he wanted, and then painted them to match the composition of the picture.

He made his colours, built his stretchers, plastered his canvas, painted his pictures, carpentered his frames, and painted them.

"Too bad I can't buy my own pictures," he murmured aloud. "Then I'd be completely self-sufficient."

The mistral came up again. All nature seemed in a rage. The skies were cloudless. The brilliant sunshine was accompanied by intense dryness and piercing cold. Vincent did a still life in his room; a coffee pot of blue enamel, a cup of royal blue and gold, a milk jug in squares of pale blue and white, a jug in majolica, blue with a pattern in reds, greens and browns, and lastly, two oranges and three lemons.

When the wind died down he went out again and did a view on the Rhône, the iron bridge at Trinquetaille, in which the sky and river were the colour of absinthe, the quays a shade of lilac, the figures leaning on their elbows on the parapet blackish, the iron bridge an intense blue with a note of vivid orange in the black background and a touch of intense malachite green. He was trying to get at something utterly heartbroken and therefore utterly heartbreaking.

Instead of trying to reproduce exactly what he had before his eyes, he used colour arbitrarily to express himself with greater force. He realized that what Pissarro had told him in Paris was true. "You must boldly exaggerate the effects, either in harmony or discord, which colours produce." In Maupassant's preface to "Pierre et Jean" he found a similar sentiment. "The artist has the liberty to exaggerate, to create in his novel a world more beautiful, more simple, more consoling than ours."

He did a day's hard, close work among the cornfields in full sun. The result was a ploughed field, a big field with clods of violet earth, climbing toward the horizon; a sower in blue and white; on the horizon a field of short, ripe corn; over all a yellow sky with a yellow sun.

Vincent knew that the Parisian critics would think he worked too fast. He did not agree. Was it not emotion, the sincerity of his feeling for nature, that impelled him? And if the emotions were sometimes so strong that he worked without knowing he worked, if sometimes the strokes came with a sequence and coherence like words in a speech, then too the time would come when there would again be heavy days, empty of inspiration. He had to strike while the iron was hot, put the forged bars on one side.

He strapped his easel to his back and took the road home which led past Montmajour. He walked so rapidly that he soon overtook a man and a boy who were dallying ahead of him. He recognized the man as old Roulin, the Arlesian *facteur des postes*. He had often sat near Roulin in the café, and had wanted to speak to him, but the occasion had never arisen.

"Good day, Monsieur Roulin," he said.

"Ah, it is you, the painter," said Roulin. "Good day. I have been taking my boy for a Sunday afternoon stroll."

"It has been a glorious day, hasn't it?"

"Ah, yes, it is lovely when that devil mistral does not blow. You have painted a picture today, Monsieur?"

"Yes."

"I am an ignorant man, Monsieur, and know nothing about art. But I would be honored if you would let me look."

"With pleasure."

The boy ran ahead, playing. Vincent and Roulin walked side by side. While Roulin looked at the canvas, Vincent studied him. Roulin was wearing his blue postman's cap. He had soft, inquiring eyes and a long, square, wavy beard which completely covered his neck and collar and came to rest on the dark blue postman's coat. Vincent felt the same soft, wistful quality about Roulin that had attracted him to Père Tanguy. He was homely in a pathetic sort of way, and his plain, peasant's face seemed out of place in the luxuriant Greek beard.

"I am an ignorant man, Monsieur," repeated Roulin, "and you will forgive me for speaking. But your cornfields are so very alive, as alive as the field we passed back there, for instance, where I saw you at work."

"Then you like it?"

"As for that, I cannot say. I only know that it makes me feel something, in here."

He ran his hand upward over his chest.

They paused for a moment at the base of Montmajour. The sun was setting red over the ancient abbey, its rays falling on the trunks and foliage of pines growing among a tumble of rocks, colouring the trunks and foliage with orange fire, while the other pines in the distance stood out in Prussian blue against a sky of tender, blue-green cerulean. The white sand and the layers of white rocks under the trees took on tints of blue.

"That is alive, too, is it not, Monsieur?" asked Roulin.

"It will still be alive when we are gone, Roulin."

They walked along, chatting in a quiet, friendly manner. There was nothing of the abrasive quality in Roulin's words. His mind was simple, his thoughts at once simple and profound. He supported himself, his wife, and four children on a hundred and thirty-five francs a month. He had been a postman twenty-five years without a promotion, and with only infinitesimal advances in salary.

"When I was young, Monsieur," he said, "I used to think a lot about God. But He seems to have grown thinner with the years. He is still in that cornfield you painted, and in the sunset by Montmajour, but when I think about men . . . and the world they have made . . ."

"I know, Roulin, but I feel more and more that we must not judge God by this world. It's just a study that didn't come off. What can you do in a study that has gone wrong, if you are fond of the artist? You do not find much to criticize; you hold your tongue. But you have a right to ask for something better."

"Yes, that's it," exclaimed Roulin, "something just a tiny bit better."

"We should have to see some other works by the same hand before we judge him. This world was evidently botched up in a hurry on one of his bad days, when the artist did not have his wits about him."

Dusk had fallen over the winding country road. The first chips of stars poked through the heavy cobalt blanket of night. Roulin's sweet innocent eyes searched Vincent's face.

"Then you think there are other worlds besides this, Monsieur?"

"I don't know, Roulin. I gave up thinking about that sort of thing when I became interested in my work. But this life seems so incomplete, doesn't it? Sometimes I think that just as trains and carriages are means of locomotion to get us from one place to another on this earth, so typhoid and consumption are means of locomotion to get us from one world to another."

"Ah, you think of things, you artists."

"Roulin, will you do me a favour? Let me paint your portrait. The people of Arles won't pose for me."

"I should be honoured, Monsieur. But why do you want to paint me? I am only an ugly man."

"If there were a God, Roulin, I think he would have a beard and eyes just like yours."

"You are making fun of me, Monsieur!"

"On the contrary, I am in earnest."

"Will you come and share supper with us tomorrow night? We have a very plain board, but we will be happy to have you."

Madame Roulin proved to be a peasant woman who reminded him a little of Madame Denis. There was a red and white checked cloth on the table, a little stew with potatoes, home-baked bread and a bottle of sour wine. After dinner Vincent sketched Madame Roulin, chatting with the postman as he worked.

"During the Revolution I was a republican," said Roulin, "but now I see that we have gained nothing. Whether our rulers be kings or ministers, we poor people have just as little as before. I thought when we were a republic everyone would share and share alike."

"Ah, no, Roulin."

"All my life I have tried to understand, Monsieur, why one man should have more than the next, why one man should work hard while his neighbour sits by in idleness. Perhaps I am too ignorant to understand. Do you think if I were educated, Monsieur, I would be able to understand that better?"

Vincent glanced up quickly to see if Roulin were being cynical. There was the same look of naive innocence on his face.

"Yes, my friend," he said, "most educated people seem to understand that state of affairs very well. But I am ignorant like you, and I shall never be able to understand or accept it."

5

He arose at four in the morning, walked three and four hours to reach the spot he wanted, and then painted until dark. It was not pleasant, this trudging ten or twelve kilometres home on a lonely road, but he liked the reassuring touch of the wet canvas under his arm.

He did seven large pictures in seven days. By the end of the week he was nearly dead with work. It had been a glorious summer, but now he was painted out. A violent mistral arose and raised clouds of dust which whitened the trees. Vincent was forced to remain quiet. He slept for sixteen hours at a stretch.

He had a very thin time of it, for his money ran out on Thursday, and Theo's letter with the fifty francs was not expected until Monday noon. It was not Theo's fault. He still sent fifty francs every ten days in addition to all the painting supplies. Vincent had been wild to see his new pictures in frames, and had ordered too many of them for his budget. During those four days he lived on twenty-three cups of coffee and a loaf of bread for which the baker trusted him.

An intense reaction set in against his work. He did not think his pictures worthy of the goodness he had had from Theo. He wanted to win back the money he had already spent in order to return it to his brother. He looked at his paintings one by one and reproached himself that they were not worth what they had cost. Even if a tolerable study did come out of it from time to time, he knew that it would have been cheaper to buy it from somebody else.

All during the summer ideas for his work had come to him in swarms. Although he had been solitary, he had not had time to think or feel. He had gone on like a steam-engine. But now his brain felt like stale porridge, and he did not even have a franc to amuse himself by eating or going to visit Rachel. He decided that everything he had painted that summer was very, very bad.

"Anyway," he said to himself, "a canvas that I have covered is worth more than a blank canvas. My pretensions go no further; that is my right to paint, my reason for painting."

He had the conviction that simply by staying in Arles he would set his individuality free. Life was short. It went fast. Well, being a painter, he still had to paint.

"These painter's fingers of mine grow supple," he thought, "even though the carcass is going to pieces."

He drew up a long list of colours to send to Theo. Suddenly he realized that not one colour on his list would be found on the Dutch palette, in Mauve, Maris, or Weissenbruch. Arles had made his break with the Dutch tradition complete.

When his money arrived on Monday, he found a place where he could get a good meal for a franc. It was a queer restaurant, altogether grey; the floor was of grey bitumen like a street pavement, there was grey paper on the walls, green blinds always drawn, and a big green curtain over the door to keep the dust out. A very narrow, very fierce ray of sunlight stabbed through a blind.

After he had been resting for over a week, he decided to do some night painting. He did the grey restaurant while the patrons were at their meal and the waitresses were scurrying back and forth. He painted the thick, warm cobalt sky of night, studded with thousands of bright Provençal stars, as seen from the Place Lamartine. He went out on the roads and did cypresses under the moonlight. He painted the Café de Nuit, which remained open all night so that prowlers could take refuge there when they had no money to pay for a lodging, or when they were too drunk to be taken to one.

He did the exterior of the café one night, and the interior the next. He tried to express the terrible passions of humanity by means of red and green. He did the interior in blood red and dark yellow with a green billiard table in the middle. He put in four lemon-yellow lamps with a glow of orange and green. Everywhere there was the clash and contrast of the most alien reds and greens in the figures of little sleeping hooligans. He was trying to express the idea that the café was a place where one could ruin oneself, run mad, or commit a crime.

The people of Arles were amused to find their *fou-rou* painting in the streets all night and sleeping in the daytime. Vincent's activities were always a treat for them.

When the first of the month came, the hotel owner not only raised the rent on the room, but decided to charge Vincent a daily storage fee for the closet in which he kept his canvases. Vincent loathed the hotel and was outraged by the voraciousness of the owner. The grey restaurant in which he ate was satisfactory, but he had sufficient money to eat there only two or three days out of every ten. Winter was coming, he had no studio in which to work, the hotel room was depressing and humiliating. The food he was forced to eat in the cheap restaurants was poisoning his stomach again.

He had to find a permanent home and studio of his own.

One evening, as he was crossing the Place Lamartine with old Roulin, he noticed a *For Rent* sign on a yellow house just a stone's throw from his hotel. The house had two wings with a court in the centre. It faced the Place and the town on the hill. Vincent stood looking at it wistfully.

"Too bad it's so large," he said to Roulin. "I'd like to have a house like that."

"It is not necessary to rent the whole house, Monsieur. You can rent just this right wing, for example."

"Really! How many rooms do you think it has? Would it be expensive?"

"I should say it had about three or four rooms. It will cost you very little, not half what the hotel costs. I will come and look at it with you tomorrow during my dinner time, if you like. Perhaps I can help you get a good price."

The following morning Vincent was so excited he could do nothing but pace up and down the Place Lamartine and survey the yellow house from all sides. It was built sturdily and got all the sun. On closer inspection Vincent found that there were two separate entrances to the house, and that the left wing was already occupied.

Roulin joined him after the midday meal. They entered the right wing of the house together. There was a hallway inside which led to a large room, with a smaller room opening off it. The walls were whitewashed. The hall and stairway leading to the second floor were paved with clean red brick. Upstairs there was another large room with a cabinet. The floors were of scrubbed red tile, and the whitewashed walls caught the clean, bright sun.

Roulin had written a note to the landlord, who was waiting for them in the upstairs room. He and Roulin conversed for some moments in a fast Provençal of which Vincent could understand very little. The postman turned to Vincent.

"He insists upon knowing how long you will keep the place."

"Tell him indefinitely."

"Will you agree to take it for at least six months?"

"Oh, yes! Yes!"

"Then he says he will give it to you for fifteen francs a month."

Fifteen francs! For a whole house! Only a third of what he paid at the hotel. Even less than he had paid for his studio in The Hague. A permanent home for fifteen francs a month. He drew the money out of his pocket, hurriedly.

"Here! Quick! Give it to him. The house is rented."

"He wants to know when you are going to move in," said Roulin.

"Today. Right now."

"But, Monsieur, you have no furniture. How can you move in?"

"I will buy a mattress and a chair. Roulin, you don't know what it means to spend your life in miserable hotel rooms. I must have this place immediately!"

"Just as you wish, Monsieur."

The landlord left. Roulin went back to work. Vincent walked from one room to another, up and down the stairs again, surveying over and over every inch of his domain. Theo's fifty francs had arrived just the day before; he still had some thirty francs in his pocket. He rushed out, bought a cheap mattress and a chair and carried them back to the yellow house. He decided that the room on the ground floor would be his bedroom, the top room his studio. He threw the mattress on the red tile floor, carried the chair up to his studio, and went back to his hotel for the last time.

The proprietor added forty francs to Vincent's bill on some thin pretext. He refused to let Vincent have his canvases until the money was handed over. Vincent had to go to the police court to get his paintings back, and even then had to pay half the fictitious charge.

Late that afternoon he found a merchant who was willing to give him a small gas stove, two pots, and a kerosene lamp on credit. Vincent had three francs left. He bought coffee, bread, potatoes and a little meat for soup. He left himself without a centime. At home he set up a kitchen in the cabinet on the ground floor.

When night closed over the Place Lamartine and the yellow house, Vincent cooked his soup and coffee on the little stove. He had no table, so he spread a paper over the mattress, put out his supper, and ate it sitting cross-legged on the floor. He had forgotten to buy a knife and fork. He used the handle of his brush to pick the pieces of meat and potato out of the pot. They tasted slightly of paint.

When he finished eating, he took the kerosene lamp and mounted the red brick stairs to the second floor. The room was barren and lonely, with only the stark easel standing against the moonlit window. In the background was the dark garden of the Place Lamartine.

He went to sleep on the mattress. When he awakened in the morning he opened the windows and saw the green of the garden, the rising sun, and the road winding up into the town. He looked at the clean red bricks of the floor, the spotlessly whitewashed walls, the spaciousness of the rooms. He boiled himself a cup of coffee and walked about drinking from the pot, planning how he would furnish his house, what pictures he would hang on the walls, how he would pass the happy hours in a real home of his own.

The next day he received a letter from his friend Paul Gauguin, who was imprisoned, ill and poverty stricken, in a wretched café in Pont-Aven, in Brittany. "I can't get out of this hole," wrote Gauguin, "because I can't pay my bill, and the owner has all my canvases under lock and key. In all the variety of distresses that afflict humanity, nothing maddens me more than the lack of money. Yet I feel myself doomed to perpetual beggary."

Vincent thought of the painters of the earth, harassed, ill, destitute, shunned and mocked by their fellow men, starved and tortured to their dying day. Why? What was their crime? What was their great offense that made them outcasts and pariahs? How could such persecuted souls do good work? The painter of the future—ah, he would be such a colourist and a man as had never yet existed. He would not live in miserable cafés, and go to the Zouave brothels.

And poor Gauguin. Rotting away in some filthy hole in Brittany, too sick to work, without a friend to help him or a franc in his pocket for wholesome food and a doctor. Vincent thought him a great painter and a great man. If Gauguin should die. If Gauguin should have to give up his work. What a tragedy for the painting world.

Vincent slipped the letter into his pocket, left the yellow house, and walked along the embankment of the Rhône. A barge loaded with coal was moored to the quay. Seen from above, it was all shining and wet from a shower. The water was of yellowish white, and clouded pearl grey. The sky was lilac, barred with orange to the west, the town violet. On the boat some labourers in dirty blue and white came and went, carrying the cargo on shore.

It was pure Hokusai. It carried Vincent back to Paris, to the Japanese prints in Père Tanguy's shop . . . and to Paul Gauguin who, of all his friends, he loved the most dearly.

He knew at once what he had to do. The yellow house was large enough for two men. Each of them could have his own bedroom and studio. If they cooked their meals, ground their colours, and guarded their money, they could live on his hundred and fifty francs a month.

The rent would be no more, the food very little. How marvellous it would be to have a friend again, a painter friend who talked one's language and understood one's craft. And what wonderful things Gauguin could teach him about painting.

He had not realized before how utterly lonely he had been. Even if they couldn't live on Vincent's hundred and fifty francs, perhaps Theo would send an extra fifty francs in return for a monthly canvas from Gauguin.

Yes! Yes! He must have Gauguin with him here in Arles. The hot Provence sun would burn all the illness out of him, just as it had out of Vincent. Soon they would have a working studio going full blaze. Theirs would be the very first studio in the South. They would carry on the tradition of Delacroix and Monticelli. They would drench painting in sunlight and colour, awaken the world to riotous nature.

Gauguin had to be saved!

Vincent turned, broke into a dog-trot and ran all the way back to the Place Lamartine. He let himself into the yellow house, dashed up the red brick stairs, and began excitedly planning the rooms.

"Paul and I will each have a bedroom up here. We'll use the rooms on the lower floor for studios. I'll buy beds and mattresses and bedclothes and chairs and tables, and we'll have a real home. I'll decorate the whole house with sunflowers and orchards in blossom."

"Oh, Paul, Paul, how good it will be to have you with me again!"

6

It was not so easy as he had expected. Theo was willing to add fifty francs a month to the allowance in return for a Gauguin canvas, but there was the matter of the railroad fare which neither Theo nor Gauguin could provide. Gauguin was too ill to move, too much in debt to get out of Pont-Aven, too sick at heart to enter into any schemes with enthusiasm. Letters flew thick and fast between Arles, Paris, and Pont-Aven.

Vincent was now desperately in love with his yellow house. He bought himself a table and a chest of drawers with Theo's allowance.

"At the end of a year," he wrote to Theo, "I shall be a different man. But don't think I'm going to leave here then. By no means. I'm going to spend the rest of my life in Arles. I'm going to become the painter of the South. And you must consider that you have a country house in Arles. I am keen to arrange it all so that you will come here always to spend your holidays."

He spent a minimum for the bare necessities of life, and sunk all the rest into the house. Each day he had to make a choice between himself and the yellow house. Should he have meat for dinner, or buy that majolica jug? Should he buy a new pair of shoes, or get that green quilt for Gauguin's bed? Should he order a pine frame for his new canvas, or buy those rush-bottom chairs?

Always the house came first.

The yellow house gave him a sense of tranquillity, because he was working to secure the future. He had drifted too much, knocked about without rhyme or reason. But now he was never going to move again. After he was gone, another painter would find a going concern. He was establishing a permanent studio which would be used by generation after generation of painters to interpret and portray the South. He became obsessed with the idea of painting such decorations for the house as would be worthy of the money spent on him during the years in which he had been unproductive.

He plunged into his work with renewed energy. He knew that looking at a thing a long time ripened him and gave him a deeper understanding. He went back fifty times to Montmajour to study the field at its base. The mistral made it hard for him to get his brush work connected and interwoven with feeling, with the easel waving violently before him in the wind. He worked from seven in the morning until six at night without stirring. A canvas a day!

"Tomorrow will be a scorcher," said Roulin one evening, very late in the fall. They were sitting over a bock in the Café Lamartine. "And after that, winter."

"What is winter like in Arles?" asked Vincent.

"It's mean. Lots of rain, a miserable wind, and a biting cold. But winter is very short here. Only a couple of months."

"So tomorrow will be our last nice day. Then I know the very spot I want to do. Imagine an autumn garden, Roulin, with two cypresses, bottle green, shaped like bottles, and three little chestnut trees with tobacco and orange coloured leaves. There is a little yew with pale lemon foliage and a violet trunk, and two little bushes, blood-red, and scarlet purple leaves. And some sand, some grass, and some blue sky."

"Ah, Monsieur, when you describe things, I see that all my life I have been blind."

The next morning Vincent arose with the sun. He was in high spirits. He trimmed his beard with a pair of scissors, combed down what little hair the Arlesian sun had not burned off his scalp, put on his only whole suit of clothes, and as a special fond gesture of farewell to the sun, wore his rabbit-fur bonnet from Paris.

Roulin's prediction had been right. The sun rose, a yellow ball of heat. The rabbit-fur bonnet had no peak, and the sun pried into his eyes. The autumn garden was a two hour walk from Arles, on the road to Tarascon. It nestled askew on the side of a hill. Vincent planted his easel in a furrowed cornfield, behind and to the side of the garden. He threw his bonnet to the ground, took off his good coat, and set the canvas to the easel. Although it was still early morning, the sun scorched the top of his head and threw before his eyes the veil of dancing fire to which he had become accustomed.

He studied the scene before him carefully, analysed the component colours, and etched the design on his mind. When he was confident that he understood the scene, he softened his brushes, took the caps off his tubes of pigments, and cleaned the knife with which he spread on his thick colour. He glanced once more at the garden, burnt the image on the blank canvas before him, mixed some colour on the palette, and raised his brush.

"Must you begin so soon, Vincent?" asked a voice behind him.

Vincent whirled about.

"It is early yet, my dear. And you have the whole long day to work."

Vincent gaped at the woman in utter bewilderment. She was young, but not a child. Her eyes were as blue as the cobalt sky of an Arlesian night, and her hair, which she wore in a great flowing mass down her back, was as lemon-yellow as the sun. Her features were even more delicate than those of Kay Vos, but they had about them the mellow maturity of the Southland. Her colouring was burnt gold, her teeth, between the smiling lips, as white as an oleander seen through a blood-red vine. She wore a long white gown which clung to the lines of her body and was fastened only by a square silver buckle at the side. She had a simple pair of sandals on her feet. Her figure was sturdy, robust, yet flowing downward with the eye in pure, voluptuous curves.

"I've stayed away so very long, Vincent," she said.

She placed herself between Vincent and the easel, leaning against the blank canvas and shutting out his view of the garden. The sun caught up the lemon-yellow hair and sent waves of flame down her back. She smiled at him so whole-heartedly, so fondly, that he ran a hand over his eyes to see if he had suddenly gone ill, or fallen asleep.

"You do not understand, my dear, dear boy," the woman said. "How could you, when I've stayed away so long?"

"Who are you?"

"I am your friend, Vincent. The best friend you have in the world."

"How do you know my name? I have never seen you before."

"Ah, no, but I have seen you, many, many times."

"What is your name?"

"Maya."

"Is that all? Just Maya?"

"For you, Vincent, that is all."

"Why have you followed me here to the fields?"

"For the same reason that I have followed you all over Europe . . . so that I might be near you."

"You mistake me for someone else. I can't possibly be the man you mean."

The woman put a cool white hand on the burnt red hair of his head and smoothed it back lightly. The coolness of her hand and the coolness of her soft, low voice was like the refreshing water from a deep green well.

"There is only one Vincent Van Gogh. I could never mistake him."

"How long do you think you have known me?"

"Eight years, Vincent."

"Why, eight years ago I was in . . ."

". . . Yes, dear, in the Borinage."

"You knew me then?"

"I saw you for the first time one late fall afternoon, when you were sitting on a rusty iron wheel in front of Marcasse . . ."

". . . Watching the miners go home!"

"Yes. When I first looked at you, you were sitting there, idly. I was about to pass by. Then you took an old envelope and a pencil from your pocket and began sketching. I looked over your shoulder to see what you had done. And when I saw . . . I fell in love."

"You fell in love? You fell in love with me?"

"Yes, Vincent, my dear, good Vincent, in love with you."

"Perhaps I was not so bad to look at, then."

"Not half so good as you are to look at now."

"Your voice . . . Maya . . . it sounds so queer. Only once before has a woman spoken to me in that voice . . ."

". . . Margot's voice. She loved you, Vincent, as well as I do."

"You knew Margot?"

"I stayed in the Brabant for two years. I followed you to the fields each day. I watched you work in the wrangle room behind the kitchen. And I was happy because Margot loved you."

"Then you did not love me any more?"

She caressed his eyes with the cool tips of her fingers.

"Ah, yes, I loved you. I have never ceased to love you since that very first day."

"And you weren't jealous of Margot?"

The woman smiled. Across her face went a flash of infinite sadness and compassion. Vincent thought of Mendes da Costa.

"No, I was not jealous of Margot. Her love was good for you. But your love for Kay I did not like. It injured you."

"Did you know me when I was in love with Ursula?"

"That was before my time."

"You would not have liked me then."

"No."

"I was a fool."

"Sometimes one has to be a fool in the beginning, to become wise in the end."

"But if you loved me when we were in the Brabant, why didn't you come to me?"

"You were not ready for me, Vincent."

"And now . . . I am ready?"

"Yes."

"You still love me? Even now . . . today . . . this moment?"

"Now . . . today . . . this moment . . . and for eternity."

"How can you love me? Look, my gums are diseased. Every tooth in my mouth is false. All the hair has been burnt off my head. My eyes are as red as a syphilitic's. My face is nothing but jagged bone. I am ugly. The ugliest of men! My nerves are shattered, my body gone sterile, my insides poisoned from tip to toe. How can you love such a wreck of a man?"

"Will you sit down, Vincent?"

Vincent sat on his stool. The woman sank to her knees in the soft loam of the field.

"Don't," cried Vincent. "You'll get your white gown all dirty. Let me put my coat under you."

The woman restrained him with the faintest touch of her hand.

"Many times I have soiled my gown in following you, Vincent, but always it has come clean again."

She cupped his chin in the palm of her strong white hand, and with her fingertips smoothed back the few charred hairs behind his ear.

"You are not ugly, Vincent. You are beautiful. You have tormented and tortured this poor body in which your soul is wrapped, but you cannot injure your soul. It is that I love. And when you have destroyed yourself by your passionate labours, that soul will go on . . . endlessly. And with it, my love for you."

The sun had risen another hour in the sky. It beat down in fierce heat upon Vincent and the woman.

"Let me take you where it is cool," said Vincent. "There are some cypress trees just below on the road. You will be more comfortable in the shade."

"I am happy here with you. I do not mind the sun. I have grown used to it."

"You have been in Arles long?"

"I came with you from Paris."

Vincent jumped up in anger and kicked over his stool.

"You are a fraud! You've been sent here on purpose to ridicule me. Someone told you of my past, and is paying you to make a fool of me. Go away. I'll not talk to you any more!"

The woman held his anger with the smile of her eyes.

"I am no fraud, my dear. I am the most real thing in your life. You can never kill my love for you."

"That's a lie! You don't love me. You're mocking me. I'll show your game up."

He seized her roughly in his arms. She swayed inward to him.

"I'm going to hurt you if you don't go away and stop torturing me!"

"Hurt me, Vincent. You've hurt me before. It's part of love to be hurt."

"Very well then, take your medicine!"

He pressed her body to him. He brought his mouth down on hers, hurting her with his teeth, crushing his kiss upon her.

She opened soft, warm lips to him and let him drink deeply of the sweetness of her mouth. Her whole body yearned upward to him, muscle to muscle, bone to bone, flesh to flesh, in complete and final surrender.

Vincent thrust her away from him and stumbled to his stool. The woman sank down on the ground beside him, put one arm on his leg, and rested her head against it. He stroked the long, rich mass of lemon-yellow hair.

"Are you convinced now?" she asked.

After many moments Vincent said, "You have been in Arles since I came. Did you know about *Le Pigeon?*"

"Rachel is a sweet child."

"And you don't object?"

"You are a man, Vincent, and need women. Since it was not yet time to come to you and give myself, you had to go where you could. But now . . ."

"Now?"

"You need to no longer. Ever again."

"You mean that you . . . ?"

"Of course, Vincent dear. I love you."

"Why should you love me? Women have always despised me."

"You were not meant for love. You had other work to do."

"Work? Bah! I've been a fool. Of what good are all these hundreds of paintings? Who wants to own them? Who will buy them? Who will give me one grudging word of praise, say that I have understood nature or portrayed its beauty?"

"The whole world will say it one day, Vincent."

"One day. What a dream. Like the dream of thinking that I will one day be a healthy man, with a home and a family and enough money from my painting to live on. I have been painting for eight long years. Not once in all that time has anyone wanted to buy a picture I've painted. I've been a fool."

"I know, but what a glorious fool. After you are gone, Vincent, the world will understand what you have tried to say. The canvases that today you cannot sell for a hundred francs will one day sell for a million. Ah, you smile, but I tell you it is true. Your pictures will hang in the museums of Amsterdam and The Hague, in Paris and Dresden, Munich and Berlin, Moscow and New York. Your pictures will be priceless, because there will be none for sale. Books will be written about your art, Vincent, novels and plays built around your life. Wherever two men come together who love painting, there the name of Vincent Van Gogh will be sacred."

"If I could not still taste your mouth on mine, I would say I was dreaming or going mad."

"Come sit beside me, Vincent. Put your hand in mine."

The sun was directly overhead. The hillside and valley were bathed in a mist of sulphur-yellow. Vincent lay in the furrow of the field beside the woman. For six long months he had had no one to talk to but Rachel and Roulin. Within him there was a great flood of words. The woman looked deep into his eyes, and he began to speak. He told her of Ursula and the days when he had been a Goupil clerk. He told her of his struggles and disappointments, of his love for Kay, and the life he had tried to build with Christine. He told her of his hopes in painting, of the names he had been called, and the blows he had received, of why he wanted his drawing to be crude, his work unfinished, his colour explosive; of all the things he wanted to accomplish for painting and painters, and how his body was wracked with exhaustion and disease.

The longer he talked, the more excited he became. Words flew out of his mouth like pigments from his tubes. His whole body sprang into action. He talked with his hands, gesticulated with his arms and shoulders, walked up and down before her with violent body contortions. His pulse was rising, his blood was rising, the burning sun sent him into a passion of feverish energy.

The woman listened quietly, never missing a word. From her eyes, he knew she understood. She drank in all he had to say, and still was there, eager and ready to hear more, to understand him, to be the recipient of everything he had to give and could not contain within himself.

He stopped abruptly. He trembled all over with excitement. His eyes and face were red, his limbs quivering. The woman pulled him down beside her.

"Kiss me, Vincent," she said.

He kissed her on the mouth. Her lips were no longer cool. They lay side by side in the rich, crumbly loam. The woman kissed his eyes, his ears, the nostrils of his nose, the declivity of his upper lip, bathed the inside of his mouth with her sweet, soft tongue, ran her fingers down the beard of his neck, down his shoulders and along the sensitive nerve-ends of his arm pit.

Her kisses aroused in him the most excruciating passion he had ever known. Every inch of him ached with the dull ache of the flesh that cannot be satisfied by flesh alone. Never before had a woman given herself to him with the kiss of love. He strained her body to him, feeling, beneath the soft white gown, the heat of her life flow.

"Wait," she said.

She unbuckled the silver clasp at her side and tossed the white gown away from her. Her body was the same burnished gold as her face. It was virgin, every beating pulse of it virgin. He had not known that the body of a woman could be so exquisitely wrought. He had not known that passion could be so pure, so fine, so searing.

"You're trembling, dear," she said. "Hold me to you. Do not tremble, my dear; my sweet, sweet dear. Hold me as you want me."

The sun was slipping down the other side of the heavens. The earth was hot from the beating rays of the day. It smelled of things that had been planted, of things that had grown, been cut away and died again.

It smelled of life, rich pungent smells of life ever being created and ever returning to the stuff of its creation.

Vincent's emotion rose higher and higher. Every fibre of him beat inward to some focal core of pain. The woman opened her arms to him, opened her warmth to him, took from him what was the man of him, took into herself all the volcanic turbulence, all the overwhelming passion that hour by hour wracked his nerves and burst his body, led him with gentle caressing undulations to the shattering, creative climax.

Exhausted, he fell asleep in her arms.

When he awoke, he was alone. The sun had gone down. There was a solid cake of mud on one cheek, where he had buried his perspiring face in the loam. The earth was coolish and smelled of buried, crawling things. He put on his coat and rabbit-fur bonnet, strapped the easel to his back, and took the canvas under his arm. He walked the dark road home.

When he reached the yellow house, he threw the easel and blank canvas on the mattress in his bedroom. He went out for a cup of coffee. He leaned his head in his hands on the cold stone-topped table and thought back over the day.

"Maya," he murmured to himself. "Maya. Haven't I heard that name somewhere before? It means . . . it means . . . I wonder what it means?"

He took a second cup of coffee. After an hour he crossed the Place Lamartine to the yellow house. A cold wind had come up. There was the smell of rain in the air.

He had not bothered to light the kerosene lamp when he had dropped his easel. Now he lit a match and set the lamp on the table. The yellow flare illumined the room. His eye was caught by a patch of colour on the mattress. Startled, he walked over and picked up the canvas that he had taken with him that morning.

There, in a magnificent blaze of light, he saw his autumn garden; the two bottle green, bottle shaped cypresses; the three little chestnut trees with tobacco and orange coloured leaves; the yew with pale lemon foliage and a violet trunk; the two blood-red bushes with scarlet purple leaves; in the foreground some sand and grass, and over all a blue, blue sky with a whorling ball of sulphur-lemon fire.

He stood gazing at the picture for several moments. He tacked it lightly on the wall. He went back to the mattress, sat on it cross-legged, looked at his painting and grinned.

"It is good," he said aloud. "It is well realized."

7

Winter came on. Vincent spent the days in his warm pleasant studio. Theo wrote that Gauguin, who had been in Paris for a day, was in vile frame of mind, and was resisting the Arlesian idea with all his strength. In Vincent's mind the yellow house was not to be simply a home for two men, but a permanent studio for all the artists of the South. He made elaborate plans for enlarging his quarters as soon as he and Gauguin put the place into working order. Any painter who wished to stay there would be welcome; in return for his hospitality he would be obliged to send Theo one canvas a month. As soon as Theo had enough Impressionist pictures on hand, he was to leave Goupils and open an Independent Gallery in Paris.

Vincent made it very clear in his letters that Gauguin was to be the director of the studio, master of all the painters who worked there. Vincent saved every franc he could in order to furnish his bedroom. He painted the walls a pale violet. The floor was of red tile. He bought very light, greenish lemon sheets and pillows, a scarlet covering, and painted the wooden bed and chairs the colour of fresh butter. The toilet table he painted orange, the basin blue, the door lilac. He hung a number of his pictures on the wall, threw away the window shutters, and then transferred the whole scene to canvas for Theo, so that his brother might see how restful his room was. He painted it in free flat washes, like the Japanese prints.

With Gauguin's room it was another matter. He was not willing to buy such cheap furniture for the master of the studio. Madame Roulin assured him that the walnut bed he wanted for Gauguin would come to three hundred and fifty francs, an impossible sum for him to muster. Nevertheless he began buying the smaller articles for the room, keeping himself in a constant state of financial exhaustion.

When he had no money for models, he stood before a mirror and did his own portrait over and over. Rachel came to pose for him; Madame Roulin came one afternoon a week and brought the children; Madame Ginoux, wife of the owner of the café where he took his drinks, sat for him in her Arlesienne costume. He slashed the figure onto the canvas in an hour. The background was pale lemon, the face grey, the clothes black, with raw Prussian blue. He posed her in a borrowed armchair of orange wood, her elbows leaning on a green table.

A Zouave lad with a small face, the neck of a bull, and the eye of a tiger agreed to sit for a small sum. Vincent did a half length of him in his blue uniform, the blue of enamelled saucepans, with braid of a faded reddish orange, and two pale lemon stars on his breast. There was a reddish cap on the bronzed, feline head, set against a green background. The result was a savage combination of incongruous tones, very harsh, common and even loud, but fitting the character of the subject.

He sat at his window for hours with pencil and drawing paper, trying to master the technique which would enable him with a few strokes to put down the figure of a man, a woman, a youngster, a horse, a dog, so that it would have a head, body, and legs all in keeping. He copied a good many of the paintings he had made that summer, for he thought that if he could turn out fifty studies at two hundred francs each within the year, he would not have been so very dishonest in having eaten and drunk as though he had a right to it.

He learned a good many things during the winter: that one must not do flesh in Prussian blue, for then it becomes as wood; that his colour was not as firm as it should have been; that the most important element in southland painting was the contrast of red and green, of orange and blue, of sulphur and lilac; that in a picture he wanted to say something comforting as music is comforting; that he wished to paint men and women with that something of the divine which the halo used to symbolize, and which he sought to give by the actual radiance and vibration of his colouring; and lastly, that for those who have a talent for poverty, poverty is eternal.

One of the Van Gogh uncles died and left Theo a small legacy. Since Vincent was so keen to have Gauguin with him, Theo decided to use half the money to furnish Gauguin's bedroom and send him to Arles. Vincent was delighted. He began planning the decorations for the yellow house. He wanted a dozen panels of glorious Arlesian sunflowers, a symphony of blue and yellow.

Even the news of the free railway fare did not seem to excite Gauguin. For some reason which remained obscure to Vincent, Gauguin preferred to dawdle in Pont-Aven. Vincent was eager to finish the decorations and have the studio ready when the master arrived.

Spring came. The row of oleander bushes in the back yard of the yellow house went raving mad, flowering so riotously that they might well have developed locomotor ataxia. They were loaded with fresh flowers, and heaps of faded flowers as well; their green was continually renewing itself in strong jets, apparently inexhaustible.

Vincent loaded the easel on his back once again and went into the countryside to find sunflowers for the twelve wall panels. The earth of the ploughed fields was as soft in colour as a pair of sabots, while the forget-me-not blue sky was flecked with white clouds. Some of the sunflowers he did on the stalk, at sunrise, and in a flash. Others he took home with him and painted in a green vase.

He gave the outside of his house a fresh coat of yellow, much to the amusement of the inhabitants of the Place Lamartine.

By the time he finished his work on the house, summer had come. With it came the broiling sun, the driving mistral, the growing excitement in the air, the tortured, tormented, driven aspect of the countryside and the stone city pasted against the hill.

And with it came Paul Gauguin.

He arrived in Arles before dawn and waited for the sun in a little all-night café. The proprietor looked at him and exclaimed, "You are the friend! I recognize you."

"What the devil are you talking about?"

"Monsieur Van Gogh showed me the portrait you sent him. It looks just like you, Monsieur."

Gauguin went to rouse Vincent. Their meeting was boisterous and hearty. Vincent showed Gauguin the house, helped him unpack his valise, demanded news of Paris. They talked animatedly for several hours.

"Are you planning to work today, Gauguin?"

"Do you think I am a Carolus-Duran, that I can get off the train, pick up my palette, and turn you off a sunlight effect at once?"

"I only asked."

"Then don't ask foolish questions."

"I'll take a holiday, too. Come along, I'll show you the town."

He led Gauguin up the hill, through the sun-baked Place de la Mairie, and along the market road at the back of the town. The Zouaves were drilling in the field just outside the barracks; their red fezzes burned in the sun. Vincent led the way through the little park in front of the Roman forum. The Arlesiennes were strolling for their morning air. Vincent had been raving to Gauguin about how beautiful they were.

"What do you think about the Arlesiennes, Gauguin?" he demanded.

"I can't get up a perspiration about them."

"Look at the tone of their flesh, man, not the shape. Look at what the sun has done to their colouring."

"How are the houses here, Vincent?"

"There's nothing but five-franc places for the Zouaves."

They returned to the yellow house to work out some sort of living arrangements. They nailed a box to the wall in the kitchen and put half their money into it—so much for tobacco, so much for incidental expenses, including rent. On the top of the box they put a scrap of paper and a pencil with which to write down every franc they took. In another box they put the rest of their money, divided into four parts, to pay for the food each week.

"You're a good cook, aren't you, Gauguin?"

"Excellent. I used to be a sailor."

"Then in the future you shall cook. But tonight I am going to make the soup in your honour."

When he served the soup that night, Gauguin could not eat it.

"How you mixed this mess, Vincent, I can't imagine. As you mix the colours in your pictures, I dare say."

"What is the matter with the colours in my pictures?"

"My dear fellow, you're still floundering in neo-impressionism. You'd better give up your present method. It doesn't correspond to your nature."

Vincent pushed his bowl of soup aside.

"You can tell that at first glance, eh? You're quite a critic."

"Well, look for yourself. You're not blind, are you? Those violent yellows, for example; they're completely disordered."

Vincent glanced up at the sunflower panels on the wall.

"Is that all you can find to say about my sunflowers?"

"No, my dear fellow, I can find a good many things to criticize."

"Among them?"

"Among them, your harmonies; they're monotonous and incomplete."

"That's a lie!"

"Oh, sit down, Vincent. Stop looking as though you wanted to murder me. I'm a good deal older than you, and more mature. You're still trying to find yourself. Just listen to me, and I'll give you some fruitful lessons."

"I'm sorry, Paul. I do want you to help me."

"Then the first thing you had better do is sweep all the garbage out of your mind. You've been raving all day about Meissonier and Monticelli. They're both worthless. As long as you admire that sort of painting, you'll never turn out a good canvas yourself."

"Monticelli was a great painter. He knew more about colour than any man of his time."

"He was a drunken idiot, that's what he was."

Vincent jumped to his feet and glared at Gauguin across the table. The bowl of soup fell to the red tile floor and smashed.

"Don't you call 'Fada' that! I love him almost as well as I do my own brother! All that talk about his being such a drinker, and off his head, is vicious gossip. No drunkard could have painted Monticelli's pictures. The mental labour of balancing the six essential colours, the sheer strain and calculation, with a hundred things to think of in a single half hour, demands a sane mind. And a sober one. When you repeat that gossip about 'Fada' you're being just as vicious as that beastly woman who started it."

"Turlututu, mon chapeau pointu!"

Vincent recoiled, as though a glass of cold water had been thrown in his face. His words and tense emotion strangled within him. He tried to put down his rage, but could not. He walked to his bedroom and slammed the door behind him.

8

The following morning the quarrel was forgotten. They had coffee together and then went their separate ways to find pictures. When Vincent returned that night, exhausted from what he had called the balancing of the six essential colours, he found Gauguin already preparing supper on the tiny gas stove. They talked quietly for a little while; then the conversation turned to painters and painting, the only subject in which they were passionately interested.

The battle was on.

The painters whom Gauguin admired, Vincent despised. Vincent's idols were anathema to Gauguin. They disagreed on every last approach to their craft. Any other subject they might have been able to discuss in a quiet and friendly manner, but painting was the meat and drink of life to them. They fought for their ideas to the last drop of nervous energy. Gauguin had twice Vincent's brute strength, but Vincent's lashing excitement left them evenly matched.

Even when they discussed things about which they agreed, their arguments were terribly electric. They came out of them with their heads as exhausted as a battery after it has been discharged.

"You'll never be an artist, Vincent," announced Gauguin, "until you can look at nature, come back to your studio and paint it in cold blood."

"I don't want to paint in cold blood, you idiot. I want to paint in hot blood! That's why I'm in Arles."

"All this work you've done is only slavish copying from nature. You must learn to work extempore."

"*Extempore!* Good God!"

"And another thing; you would have done well to listen to Seurat. Painting is abstract, my boy. It has no room for the stories you tell and the morals you point out."

"I point out morals? You're crazy."

"If you want to preach, Vincent, go back to the ministry. Painting is colour, line, and form; nothing more. The artist can reproduce the decorative in nature, but that's all."

"Decorative art," snorted Vincent. "If that's all you get out of nature, you ought to go back to the Stock Exchange."

"If I do, I'll come hear you preach on Sunday mornings. What do you get out of nature, Brigadier?"

"I get motion, Gauguin, and the rhythm of life."

"Well, we're off."

"When I paint a sun, I want to make people feel it revolving at a terrific rate of speed. Giving off light and heat waves of tremendous power. When I paint a cornfield I want people to feel the atoms within the corn pushing out to their final growth and bursting. When I paint an apple I want people to feel the juice of that apple pushing out against the skin, the seeds at the core striving outward to their own fruition!"

"Vincent, how many times have I told you that a painter must not have theories."

"Take this vineyard scene, Gauguin. Look out! Those grapes are going to burst and squirt right in your eye. Here, study this ravine. I want to make people feel all the millions of tons of water that have poured down its sides. When I paint the portrait of a man, I want them to feel the entire flow of that man's life, everything he has seen and done and suffered!"

"What the devil are you driving at?"

"At this, Gauguin. The fields that push up the corn, and the water that rushes down the ravine, the juice of the grape, and the life of a man as it flows past him, are all one and the same thing. The sole unity in life is the unity of rhythm. A rhythm to which we all dance; men, apples, ravines, ploughed fields, carts among the corn, houses, horses, and the sun. The stuff that is in you, Gauguin, will pound through a grape tomorrow, because you and a grape are one. When I paint a peasant labouring in the field, I want people to feel the peasant flowing down into the soil, just as the corn does, and the soil flowing up into the peasant. I want them to feel the sun pouring into the peasant, into the field, the corn, the plough, and the horses, just as they all pour back into the sun. When you begin to feel the universal rhythm in which everything on earth moves, you begin to understand life. That alone is God."

"Brigadier," said Gauguin, *"vous avez raison!"*

Vincent was at the height of his emotion, quivering with febrile excitement. Gauguin's words struck him like a slap in the face. He stood there gaping foolishly, his mouth hanging open.

"Now what in the world does that mean, 'Brigadier, you are right?' "

"It means I think it about time we adjourned to the café for an absinthe."

At the end of the second week Gauguin said, "Let's try that house of yours tonight. Maybe I can find a nice fat girl."

"Keep away from Rachel. She belongs to me."

They walked up the labyrinth of stone alleys and entered the Maison de Tolérance. When Rachel heard Vincent's voice, she skipped down the hallway and threw herself into his arms. Vincent introduced Gauguin to Louis.

"Monsieur Gauguin," said Louis, "you are an artist. Perhaps you would give me your opinion of the two new paintings I bought in Paris last year."

"I'd be glad to. Where did you buy them?"

"At Goupils, in the Place de l'Opéra. They are in this front parlour. Will you step in, Monsieur?"

Rachel led Vincent to the room on the left, pushed him into a chair near one of the tables, and sat on his lap.

"I've been coming here for six months," grumbled Vincent, "and Louis never asked my opinion about his pictures."

"He doesn't think you are an artist, *fou-rou.*"

"Maybe he's right."

"You don't love me any more," said Rachel, pouting.

"What makes you think that, Pigeon?"

"You haven't been to see me for weeks."

"That was because I was working hard to fix the house for my friend."

"Then you do love me, even if you stay away?"

"Even if I stay away."

She tweeked his small, circular ears, then kissed each of them in turn.

"Just to prove it, *fou-rou,* will you give me your funny little ears? You promised you would."

"If you can take them off, you can have them."

"Oh, *fou-rou,* as if they were sewed on, like my dolly's ears."

There was a shout from the room across the hall, and the noise of someone screaming, either in laughter or in pain. Vincent dumped Rachel off his lap, ran across the hall and into the parlour.

Gauguin was doubled up on the floor, convulsed, tears streaming down his face. Louis, lamp in hand, was gazing down at him, dumbfounded. Vincent crouched over Gauguin and shook him.

"Paul, Paul, what is it?"

Gauguin tried to speak, but could not. After a moment he gasped, "Vincent . . . at last . . . we're vindicated . . . look . . . look . . . up on the wall . . . the two pictures . . . that Louis bought from Goupils . . . for the parlour of his brothel. *They are both Bouguereaus!*"

He stumbled to his feet and made for the front door.

"Wait a minute," cried Vincent, running after him. "Where are you going?"

"To the telegraph office. I must wire this to the Club Batignolles at once."

Summer came on in all its terrific, glaring heat. The countryside burst into a riot of colour. The greens and blues and yellows and reds were so stark they were shocking to the eye. Whatever the sun touched, it burnt to the core. The valley of the Rhône vibrated with wave after wave of billowy heat. The sun battered the two painters, bruised them, beat them to a living pulp, sucked out all their resistance. The mistral came up and lashed their bodies, whipped their nerves, shook their heads on their necks until they thought they would burst or break off. Yet every morning they went out with the sun and laboured until the crying blue of night deepened the crying blue of day.

Between Vincent and Gauguin, the one a perfect volcano, the other boiling inwardly, a fierce struggle was preparing itself. At night, when they were too exhausted to sleep, too nervous to sit still, they spent all their energy on each other. Their money ran low. They had no way to amuse themselves. They found an outlet for their pent up passions in mutual exacerbation. Gauguin never tired of whipping Vincent into a rage and, when Vincent was at the height of his paroxysm, throwing into his face, *"Brigadier, vous avez raison!"*

"Vincent, no wonder you can't paint. Look at the disorder of this studio. Look at the mess in this colour box. My God, if your Dutch brain wasn't so fired with Daudet and Monticelli, maybe you could clean it out and get a little order into your life."

"That's nothing to you, Gauguin. This is my studio. You keep your studio any way you like."

"While we're on the subject, I may as well tell you that your mind is just as chaotic as your colour box. You admire every postage stamp painter in Europe, and yet you can't see that Degas . . ."

"Degas! What has he ever painted that can be held up alongside of a Millet?"

"Millet! That sentimentalist! That . . . !"

Vincent worked himself into a frenzy at this slur at Millet, whom he considered his master and spiritual father. He stormed after Gauguin from room to room. Gauguin fled. The house was small. Vincent shouted at him, harangued him, waved his fists in Gauguin's powerful face. Far into the tropical, oppressive night they kept up their bruising, battering conflict.

They both worked like fiends to catch themselves and nature at the point of fructification. Day after day they battled with their flaming palettes, night after night with each other's strident egos. When they were not quarreling viciously, their friendly arguments were so explosive that it was impossible to summon sleep. Money came from Theo. They spent it immediately for tobacco and absinthe. It was too hot to eat. They thought absinthe would quiet their nerves. It only excited them the more.

A nasty, lashing mistral came up. It confined the men to the house. Gauguin could not work. He spent his time scourging Vincent into a continuous ebullition. He had never seen anyone grow so violent over mere ideas.

Vincent was the only sport Gauguin had. He made the most of it.

"Better quiet down, Vincent," he said after the fifth day of the mistral. He had baited his friend until the storm within the yellow house had made the howling mistral seem like a mild and gentle breeze.

"What about yourself, Gauguin?"

"It so happens, Vincent, that several men who have been a good deal in my company, and in the habit of discussing things with me, have gone mad."

"Are you threatening me?"

"No, I'm warning you."

"Then keep your warnings to yourself."

"All right, but don't blame me if anything happens."

"Oh, Paul, Paul, let's stop this eternal quarreling. I know that you're a better painter than I am. I know that you can teach me a great deal. But I won't have you despising me, do you hear. I've slaved nine long years, and by Christ, I have something to say with this beastly paint! Now admit it, haven't I? Speak up, Gauguin."

"Brigadier, vous avez raison!"

The mistral died down. The Arlesians dared go out in the streets again. The blistering sun came back. An uncontainable fever settled over Arles. The police had to cope with crimes of violence. People walked about with a smouldering excitement in their eyes. No one ever laughed. No one talked. The stone roofs broiled under the sun. There were fights and knife flashes in the Place Lamartine. There was the smell of catastrophe in the air. Arles was too engorged to stand the strain any longer. The valley of the Rhône was about to burst into a million fragments.

Vincent thought of the Parisian journalist.

"Which will it be?" he asked himself. "An earthquake or a revolution."

In spite of it all, he still painted in the fields without a hat. He needed the white, blinding heat to make fluid within him the terrific passions he felt. His brain was a burning crucible, turning out red-hot canvas after canvas.

With each succeeding canvas he felt more keenly that all his nine years of labour were converging in these few surcharged weeks to make him, for one brief instant, the complete and perfect artist. He was by far surpassing his last summer's work. Never again would he produce paintings that so utterly expressed the essence of nature and the essence of himself.

He painted from four in the morning until night stole the scene from him. He created two, and sometimes even three complete pictures a day. He was spilling out a year of his life blood with every convulsive painting that he tore from his vitals. It was not the length of his stay on earth that mattered to him; it was what he did with the days of his life. For him time would have to be measured by the paintings he poured out, not by the fluttering leaves of a calendar.

He sensed that his art had reached a climax; that this was the high spot of his life, the moment toward which he had been striving all these years. He did not know how long it would last. He knew only that he had to paint pictures, and more pictures . . . and still more and more pictures. This climax of his life, this tiny point of infinity, had to be held, sustained, pushed out until he had created all those pictures that were gestating in his soul.

Painting all day, fighting all night, sleeping not at all, eating very little, glutting themselves with sun and colour, excitement, tobacco and absinthe, lacerated by the elements and their own drive of creation, lacerating each other with their rages and violence, their gorges mounted higher and higher.

The sun beat them. The mistral whipped them. The colour stabbed their eyes out. The absinthe swelled their empty bowels with turgescent fever. The yellow house rocked and throbbed with the tempest in the tropical, plethoric nights.

Gauguin did a portrait of Vincent while the latter was painting a still life of some ploughs. Vincent stared at the portrait. For the first time he understood clearly just what Gauguin thought of him.

"It is certainly I," he said. "But it is I gone mad!"

That evening they went to the café. Vincent ordered a light absinthe. Suddenly he flung the glass and the contents at Gauguin's head. Gauguin dodged. He picked Vincent up bodily in his arms. He carried him across the Place Lamartine. Vincent found himself in bed. He fell asleep instantly.

"My dear Gauguin," he said very calmly the next morning, "I have a vague memory that I offended you last evening."

"I forgive you gladly and with all my heart," said Gauguin, "but yesterday's scene might occur again. If I were struck I might lose control of myself and give you a choking. So permit me to write to your brother and tell him that I am coming back."

"No! No! Paul, you can't do that. Leave the yellow house? Everything in it I made for you."

During all the hours of the day the storm raged. Vincent fought desperately to keep Gauguin by his side. Gauguin resisted every plea. Vincent begged, cajoled, cursed, threatened, even wept. In this battle he proved to be the stronger. He felt that his whole life depended upon keeping his friend in the yellow house. By nightfall Gauguin was exhausted. He gave in just to get a little rest.

Every room in the yellow house was charged and vibrating with electrical tension. Gauguin could not sleep. Toward dawn he dozed off.

A queer sensation awakened him. He saw Vincent standing over his bed, glaring at him in the dark.

"What's the matter with you, Vincent?" he asked sternly.

Vincent walked out of the room, returned to his bed, and fell into a heavy sleep.

The following night Gauguin was jerked out of his sleep by the same strange sensation. Vincent was standing over his bed, staring at him in the dark.

"Vincent! Go to bed!"

Vincent turned away.

At supper the next day they fell into a fierce quarrel over the soup.

"You poured some paint into it, Vincent, while I wasn't looking!" shouted Gauguin.

Vincent laughed. He walked to the wall and wrote in chalk,

Je suis Saint Esprit
Je suis sain d'esprit

He was very quiet for several days. He looked moody and depressed. He hardly spoke a word to Gauguin. He did not even pick up a paint brush. He did not read. He sat in a chair and gazed ahead of him into space.

On the afternoon of the fourth day, when there was a vicious mistral, he asked Gauguin to take a walk with him.

"Let's go up to the park," he said. "I have something to tell you."

"Can't you tell me here, where we're comfortable?"

"No, I can't talk sitting down. I must walk."

"Very well, if you must."

They took the wagon road which wound up the left side of the town. To make progress they had to plunge through the mistral as though it were a thick, leathery substance. The cypresses in the park were being swayed almost to the ground.

"What is it you want to tell me?" demanded Gauguin.

He had to shout into Vincent's ear. The wind snatched away his words almost before Vincent could catch them.

"Paul, I've been thinking for the past few days. I've hit upon a wonderful idea."

"Forgive me if I'm a little leery of your wonderful ideas."

"We've all failed as painters. Do you know why?"

"What? I can't hear a word. Shout it in my ear."

"DO YOU KNOW WHY WE'VE ALL FAILED AS PAINTERS?"

"No. Why?"

"Because we paint alone!"

"What the devil?"

"Some things we paint well, some things we paint badly. We throw them all together in a single canvas."

"Brigadier, I'm hanging on your words."

"Do you remember the Both brothers? Dutch painters. One was good at landscape. The other was good at figures. They painted a picture together. One put in the landscape. The other put in the figures. They were successful."

"Well, to bring an interminable story to its obscure point?"

"What? I can't hear you. Come closer."

"I SAID, GO ON!"

"Paul. That's what we must do. You and I. Seurat. Cezanne. Lautrec. Rousseau. We must all work together on the same canvas. That would be a true painter's communism. We would each put in what we did best. Seurat the air. You the landscape. Cezanne the surfaces. Lautrec the figures. I the sun and moon and stars. Together we could be one great artist. What do you say?"

"Turlututu, mon chapeau pointu!"

He burst into raucous, savage laughter. The wind splashed his ridicule into Vincent's face like the spray of the sea.

"Brigadier," he cried, when he could catch his breath, "if that's not the world's greatest idea, I'll eat it. Pardon me while I howl."

He stumbled down the path, holding his stomach, doubled over with delight.

Vincent stood perfectly still.

A rush of blackbirds came out of the sky. Thousands of cawing, beating blackbirds. They swooped down on Vincent, struck him, engulfed him, flew through his hair, into his nose, into his mouth, into his ears, into his eyes, buried him in a thick, black, airless cloud of flapping wings.

Gauguin returned.

"Come on, Vincent, let's go down to Louis's. I feel the need of a celebration after that priceless idea of yours."

Vincent followed him to the Rue des Ricolettes in silence.

Gauguin went upstairs with one of the girls.

Rachel sat on Vincent's lap in the café room.

"Aren't you coming up with me, *fou-rou?*" she asked.

"No."

"Why not?"

"I haven't the five francs."

"Then will you give me your ear instead?"

"Yes."

After a very few moments, Gauguin returned. The two men walked down the hill to the yellow house. Gauguin bolted his supper. He walked out the front door without speaking. He had almost crossed the Place Lamartine when he heard behind him a well known step; short, quick, irregular.

He whirled about.

Vincent rushed upon him, an open razor in his hand.

Gauguin stood rigid and looked at Vincent.

Vincent stopped just two feet away. He glared at Gauguin in the dark. He lowered his head, turned, ran towards home.

Gauguin went to a hotel. He engaged a room, locked the door and went to bed.

Vincent entered the yellow house. He walked up the red brick stairs to his bedroom. He picked up the mirror in which he had painted his own portrait so many times. He set it on the toilet table against the wall.

He looked at his red-shot eyes in the mirror.

The end had come. His life was over. He read that in his face.

He had better make the clean break.

He lifted the razor. He felt the keen steel against the goose-flesh of his throat.

Voices were whispering strange tales to him.

The Arlesian sun threw a wall of blinding fire between his eyes and the glass.

He slashed off his right ear.

He left only a tiny portion of the lobe.

He dropped the razor. He bound his head in towels. The blood dripped onto the floor.

He picked up his ear from the basin. He washed it. He wrapped it in several pieces of drawing paper. He tied the bundle in newspaper.

He pulled a Basque beret down over the thick bandage. He walked down the stairs to the front door. He crossed the Place Lamartine, climbed the hill, rang the bell of the Maison de Tolérance, Numero I.

A maid answered the door.

"Send Rachel to me."

Rachel came in a moment.

"Oh, it's you, *fou-rou*. What do you want?"

"I have brought you something."

"For me? A present?"

"Yes."

"How nice you are, *fou-rou*."

"Guard it carefully. It is a souvenir of me."

"What is it?"

"Open, and you will see."

Rachel unwrapped the papers. She stared in horror at the ear. She fell in a dead faint on the flagstones.

Vincent turned away. He walked down the hill. He crossed the Place Lamartine. He closed the door of the yellow house behind him and went to bed.

When Gauguin returned at seven-thirty the following morning, he found a crowd gathered in front. Roulin was wringing his hands in despair.

"What have you done to your comrade, Monsieur?" asked a man in a melon shaped hat. His tone was abrupt and severe.

"I don't know."

"Oh, yes . . . you know very well . . . he is dead."

It took Gauguin a long time to gather his wits together. The stares of the crowd seemed to tear his person to pieces, suffocating him.

"Let us go upstairs, Monsieur," he said stammeringly. "We can explain ourselves there."

Wet towels lay on the floor of the two lower rooms. The blood had stained the stairway that led up to Vincent's bedroom.

In the bed lay Vincent, rolled in the sheets, humped up like a guncock. He seemed lifeless. Gently, very gently, Gauguin touched the body. It was warm. For Gauguin, it seemed as if he had suddenly got back all his energy, all his spirit.

"Be kind enough, Monsieur," he said in a low voice to the police superintendent, "to awaken this man with great care. If he asks for me, tell him I have left for Paris. The sight of me might prove fatal to him."

The police superintendent sent for a doctor and a cab. They took Vincent to the hospital. Roulin ran alongside of the carriage, panting.

9

Doctor Felix Rey, young interne of the hospital of Arles, was a short, thickset man with an octagonal head and a weed of black hair shooting up from the top of the octagon. He treated Vincent's wound, then put him to bed in a cell-like room from which everything had been removed. He locked the door behind him when he went out.

At sundown, when he was taking his patient's pulse, Vincent awoke. He stared at the ceiling, then the whitewashed wall, then out of the window at the patch of darkening blue sky. His eyes wandered slowly to Doctor Rey's face.

"Hello," he said, softly.

"Hello," replied Doctor Rey.

"Where am I?"

"You're in the hospital of Arles."

"Oh."

A flash of pain went across his face. He lifted his hand to where his right ear had once been. Doctor Rey stopped him.

"You mustn't touch," he said.

". . . Yes . . . I remember . . . now."

"It's a nice, clean wound, old fellow. I'll have you on your feet within a few days."

"Where is my friend?"

"He has returned to Paris."

". . . I see . . . May I have my pipe?"

"Not just yet, old fellow."

Doctor Rey bathed and bandaged the wound.

"It's an accident of very little importance," he said. "After all, a man doesn't hear with those cabbages he has stuck on the outside of his head. You won't miss it."

"You are very kind, Doctor. Why is this room . . . so bare?"

"I had everything taken out to protect you."

"Against whom?"

"Against yourself."

". . . Yes . . . I see . . ."

"Well, I must go now. I'll send the attendant in with your supper. Try to lie perfectly still. The loss of blood has made you weak."

When Vincent awoke in the morning, Theo was sitting by his bedside. Theo's face was pale and drawn, his eyes bloodshot.

"Theo," said Vincent.

Theo slipped off the chair, went on his knees beside the bed, and took Vincent's hand. He wept without shame or restraint.

"Theo . . . always . . . when I wake up . . . and need you . . . you're by my side."

Theo could not speak.

"It was cruel to make you come all the way down here. How did you know?"

"Gauguin telegraphed yesterday. I caught the night train."

"That was wrong of Gauguin to put you to all that expense. You sat up all night, Theo."

"Yes, Vincent."

They were silent for some time.

"I've spoken to Doctor Rey, Vincent. He says it was a sunstroke. You've been working in the sun without a hat, haven't you?"

"Yes."

"Well, you see, old boy, you mustn't. In the future you must wear your hat. Lots of people here in Arles get sunstroke."

Vincent squeezed his hand gently. Theo tried to swallow the lump in his throat.

"I have some news for you, Vincent, but I think it had better wait a few days."

"Is it nice news, Theo?"

"I think you'll like it."

Doctor Rey walked in.

"Well, how's the patient this morning?"

"Doctor, may my brother tell me some good news?"

"I should say so. Here, wait a minute. Let me look at this. Yes, that's fine, that's fine. It'll be healing fast, now."

When the Doctor left the room, Vincent begged for his news.

"Vincent," said Theo, "I've . . . well, I . . . I've met a girl."

"Why, Theo."

"Yes. She's a Dutch girl. Johanna Bunger. She's a lot like mother, I think."

"Do you love her, Theo?"

"Yes. I've been so desperately lonely without you in Paris, Vincent. It wasn't so bad before you came, but after we had lived together for a year . . ."

"I was hard to live with, Theo. I'm afraid I showed you a bad time."

"Oh, Vincent, if you only knew how many times I wished I could walk into the apartment on the Rue Lepic and find your shoes on the sideboard, and your wet canvases all over my bed. But we mustn't talk any more. You must rest. We'll just stay here with each other."

Theo remained in Arles two days. He left only when Doctor Rey assured him that Vincent would make a rapid recovery, and that he would take care of his brother, not only as a patient but as a friend.

Roulin came every evening and brought flowers. During the nights Vincent suffered from hallucinations. Doctor Rey put camphor on Vincent's pillow and mattress to overcome his insomnia.

At the end of the fourth day, when the Doctor saw that Vincent was completely rational, he unlocked the door of the room and had the furniture put back.

"May I get up and dress, Doctor?" asked Vincent.

"If you feel strong enough. Come to my office after you have had a little air."

The hospital of Arles was of two stories, built in a quadrangle, with a patio in the center, full of riotously coloured flowers, ferns, and gravel walks. Vincent strolled about slowly for a few minutes, then went to Doctor Rey's office on the ground floor.

"How does it feel to be on your feet?" asked the Doctor.

"Very good."

"Tell me, Vincent, why did you do it?"

Vincent was silent for a long time.

"I don't know," he said.

"What were you thinking of when you did it?"

". . . I . . . wasn't . . . thinking, Doctor."

Vincent spent the next few days recovering his strength. One morning, while he was chatting with Doctor Rey in the latter's room, he picked up a razor off the washstand and opened it.

"You need a shave, Doctor Rey," he said. "Would you like me to give you one?"

Doctor Rey backed into a corner, the palm of his hand out before his face.

"No! No! Put that down!"

"But I'm really a good barber, Doctor. I could give you a nice shave."

"Vincent! Put that razor down!"

Vincent laughed, closed the razor, and put it back on the washstand. "Don't be afraid, my friend. That's all over now."

At the end of the second week Doctor Rey gave Vincent permission to paint. An attendant was sent down to the yellow house to get the easel and canvas. Doctor Rey posed for Vincent just to humour him. Vincent worked slowly, a tiny bit each day. When the portrait was finished he presented it to the Doctor.

"I want you to keep this as a souvenir of me, Doctor. It is the only way I have of showing my gratitude for your kindness."

"That is very nice of you, Vincent. I am honoured."

The doctor took the portrait home and used it to cover a crack in the wall.

Vincent stayed at the hospital two weeks longer. He painted the patio, baking in the sun. He wore a wide straw hat while he worked. The flower garden took him the full two weeks to paint.

"You must drop in to see me every day," said Doctor Rey, shaking hands with Vincent at the front gate of the hospital. "And remember, no absinthe, no excitement, and no working in the sun without that hat."

"I promise, Doctor. And thank you for everything."

"I shall write your brother that you are now completely well."

Vincent found that the landlord had made a contract to turn him out and give the yellow house to a tobacconist. Vincent was deeply attached to the yellow house. It was his sole root in the soil of Provence.

He had painted every inch of it, inside and out. He had made it habitable. In spite of the accident, he still considered it his permanent home, and he was determined to fight the landlord to the bitter end.

At first he was afraid to sleep alone in the house because of his insomnia, which not even the camphor could overcome. Doctor Rey had given him bromide of potassium to rout the unbearable hallucinations that had been frightening him. At length the voices that had been whispering queer tales in his ears went away, to come back only in nightmares.

He was still far too weak to go out and work. The serenity returned but slowly to his brain. His blood revived from day to day and his appetite increased. He had a gay dinner with Roulin at the restaurant, quite cheerful and with no dread of renewed suffering. He began working gingerly on a portrait of Roulin's wife, which had been unfinished at the time of the accident. He liked the way he had ranged the reds from rose to orange, rising through the yellows to lemon, with light and sombre greens.

His health and his work picked up slowly. He had known before that one could fracture one's legs and arms, and after that recover, but he was rather astonished that one could fracture the brain in one's head and recover after that, too.

One afternoon he went to ask after Rachel's health.

"Pigeon," he said, "I'm sorry for all the trouble I caused you."

"It's all right, *fou-rou*. You mustn't worry about it. In this town things like that are not out of the way."

His friends came in and assured him that in Provence everyone suffered either from fever, hallucinations or madness.

"It's nothing unusual, Vincent," said Roulin. "Down here in Tartarin's country we are all a trifle cracked."

"Well, well," said Vincent, "we understand each other like members of the same family."

A few more weeks passed. Vincent was now able to work all day in the studio. Thoughts of madness and death left his mind. He began to feel almost normal.

Finally he ventured out of doors to paint. The sun was burning up the magnificent yellow of the cornfields. But Vincent could not capture it. He had been eating regularly, sleeping regularly, avoiding excitement and intense enthusiasm.

He was feeling so normal he could not paint.

"You are a *grand nerveux*, Vincent," Doctor Rey had told him. "You never have been normal. But then, no artist is normal; if he were, he wouldn't be an artist. Normal men don't create works of art. They eat, sleep, hold down routine jobs, and die. You are hypersensitive to life and nature; that's why you are able to interpret for the rest of us. But if you are not careful, that very hypersensitiveness will lead you to your destruction. The strain of it breaks every artist in time."

Vincent knew that to attain the high yellow note which dominated his Arlesian canvases he had to be on edge, strung up, throbbingly excited, passionately sensitive, his nerves rasped raw.

If he allowed himself to get into that state, he could paint again as brilliantly as he had before. But the road led to destruction.

"An artist is a man with his work to do," he murmured to himself. "How stupid for me to remain alive if I can't paint the way I want to paint."

He walked in the fields without his hat, absorbing the power of the sun. He drank in the mad colours of the sky, the yellow ball of fire, the green fields and bursting flowers. He let the mistral lash him, the thick night sky throttle him, the sunflowers whip his imagination to a bursting point. As his excitement rose, he lost his appetite for food. He began to live on coffee, absinthe, and tobacco. He lay awake nights with the deep colours of the countryside rushing past his bloodshot eyes. And at last he loaded his easel on his back and went into the fields.

His powers came back; his sense of the universal rhythm of nature, his ability to smash off a large canvas in a few hours and flood it with glaring, brilliant sunshine. Each day saw a new picture created; each day saw a rise in his emotional gauge. He painted thirty-seven canvases without a pause.

One morning he awoke feeling lethargic. He could not work. He sat on a chair. He stared at a wall. He hardly moved all through the day. The voices came back to his ears and told him queer, queer tales. When night fell he walked to the grey restaurant and sat down at a little table. He ordered soup. The waitress brought it to him. A voice rang sharply in his ear, warning him.

He swept the plate of soup to the floor. The dish smashed in fragments.

"You're trying to poison me!" he screamed. "You put poison in that soup!"

He jumped to his feet and kicked over the table. Some of the customers ran out the door. Others stared at him agape.

"You're all trying to poison me!" he shouted. "You want to murder me! I saw you put poison in that soup!"

Two gendarmes came in and carried him bodily up the hill to the hospital.

After twenty-four hours he became quite calm and discussed the affair with Doctor Rey. He worked a little each day, took walks in the country, returned to the hospital for his supper and sleep. Sometimes he had moods of indescribable mental anguish, sometimes moments when the veil of time and of inevitable circumstance seemed for the twinkling of an eye to be parted.

Doctor Rey allowed him to paint again. Vincent did an orchard of peach trees beside a road, with the Alps in the background; an olive grove with leaves of old silver, silver turning to green against the blue, and with orange-coloured ploughed earth.

After three weeks, Vincent returned to the yellow house. By now the town, and especially the Place Lamartine, was incensed against him. The severed ear and the poisoned soup were more than they could accept with equanimity. The Arlesians were firmly convinced that painting drove men mad. When Vincent passed they stared at him, made remarks out loud, sometimes even crossed the street so as to avoid passing him.

Not a restaurant in the city would allow him to enter the front door.

The children of Arles gathered before the yellow house and made up games to torment him.

"*Fou-rou! Fou-rou!*" they cried out. "Cut off your other ear."

Vincent locked his windows. The shouts and laughter of the children drifted through.

"*Fou-rou! Fou-rou!*"

"Crazy man! Crazy man!"

They made up a little song which they sang beneath his window.

Fou-rou was a crazy man
Who cut off his right ear.
Now no matter how you shout,
The crazy man can't hear.

Vincent tried going out to escape them. They followed him through the streets, into the fields, a jolly crowd of singing and laughing urchins.

Day after day their number increased as they gathered before the yellow house. Vincent stuffed his ears with cotton. He worked at his easel, making duplicates of his pictures. The words of the children came through the cracks and the walls. They seared into his brain.

The young boys became more bold. They clambered up the drain pipes like little monkeys, sat on the window sills, peered into the room and shouted at Vincent's back.

"*Fou-rou,* cut off your other ear. We want your other ear!"

The tumult in the Place Lamartine increased. The boys put up boarding on which they could climb to the second floor. They broke the windows, poked their heads in, threw things at Vincent. The crowd below encouraged them, echoed their songs and shouts.

"Get us the other ear. We want the other ear!"

"*Fou-rou!* Want some candy? Look out, it's poisoned!"

"*Fou-rou!* Want some soup? Look out, it's poisoned!"

> *Fou-rou* was a crazy man
> Who cut off his right ear.
> Now no matter how you shout,
> The crazy man can't hear.

The boys perched on the window sill led the crowd below in a chant. Together, they sang with an ever rising crescendo.

"*Fou-rou, fou-rou,* throw us your ear, throw us your ear!"

"*FOU-ROU, FOU-ROU,* THROW US YOUR EAR, THROW US YOUR EAR!"

Vincent lurched up from his easel. There were three urchins sitting on his window sill, chanting. He lashed out at them. They scampered down the boarding. The crowd below roared. Vincent stood at the window, looking down at them.

A rush of blackbirds came out of the sky, thousands of cawing, beating blackbirds. They darkened the Place Lamartine, swooped down on Vincent, struck him, filled the room, engulfed him, flew through his hair, into his nose and mouth and eyes, buried him in a thick, black, airless cloud of flapping wings.

Vincent jumped onto the window sill.

"Go way!" he screamed. "You fiends, go way! For God's sake, leave me in peace!"

"*FOU-ROU, FOU-ROU,* THROW US YOUR EAR, THROW US YOUR EAR!"

"Go way! Let me alone! Do you hear, let me alone!"

He picked up the wash basin from the table and flung it down at them. It smashed on the cobblestones below. He ran about in a rage picking up everything he could lay his hands on and flinging them down into the Place Lamartine to be hopelessly smashed. His chairs, his easel, his mirror, his table, his bedclothing, his sunflower canvases from the walls, all rained down on the urchins of Provence. And with each article there went a flashing panorama of his days in the yellow house, of the sacrifices he had made to buy, one by one, these simple articles with which he was to furnish the house of his life.

When he had laid the room bare, he stood by the window, every nerve quivering. He fell across the sill. His head hung down toward the cobblestone Place.

10

A petition was immediately circulated in the Place Lamartine. Ninety men and women signed it.

To Mayor Tardieu:

We, the undersigned citizens of Arles, are firmly convinced that Vincent Van Gogh, resident at Place Lamartine, 2, is a dangerous lunatic, not fit to be left at large.

We hereby call upon you as our Mayor to have this madman locked up.

It was very close to election time in Arles. Mayor Tardieu did not wish to displease so many voters. He ordered the superintendent of police to arrest Vincent.

The *gendarmes* found him lying on the floor below the window sill. They carried him off to jail. He was put in a cell, under lock and key. A keeper was stationed outside his door.

When Vincent returned to consciousness, he asked to see Doctor Rey. He was refused permission. He asked for pencil and paper to write Theo. It was refused.

At length Doctor Rey gained entrance to the jail.

"Try to restrain your indignation, Vincent," he said, "otherwise they will convict you of being a dangerous lunatic, and that will be the end of you. Besides, strong emotion can only aggravate your case. I will write to your brother, and between us we will get you out of here."

"I beg you, Doctor, don't let Theo come down here. He's just going to be married. It will spoil everything for him."

"I'll tell him not to come. I think I have a good plan for you."

Two days later Doctor Rey came back. The keeper was still stationed in front of the cell.

"Listen, Vincent," he said, "I just watched them move you out of your yellow house. The landlord stored your furniture in the basement of one of the cafés, and he has your paintings under lock and key. He says he won't give them up until you pay the back rent."

Vincent was silent.

"Since you can't go back there, I think you had better try to work out my plan. There is no telling how often these epileptic fits will come back on you. If you have peace and quiet and pleasant surroundings, and don't excite yourself, you may have seen the last of them. On the other hand, they may recur every month or two. So to protect yourself, and others about you . . . I think it would be advisable . . . to go into . . ."

". . . A *maison de santé*?"

"Yes."

"Then you think I am . . . ?"

"No, my dear Vincent, you are not. You can see for yourself that you are as sane as I. But these epileptic fits are like any other kind of fever. They make a man go out of his head. And when a nervous crisis comes on, you naturally do irrational things. That's why you ought to be in a hospital, where you can be looked after."

"I see."

"There is a good place in St. Remy, just twenty-five kilometres from here. It's called St. Paul de Mausole. They take first, second, and third-class patients. The third class is a hundred francs a month. You could manage that. The place was formerly a monastery, right up against the base of the hills. It is beautiful, Vincent, and quiet, oh, so quiet. You will have a doctor to advise you, and sisters to take care of you. The food will be plain and good. You will be able to recover your health."

"Would I be allowed to paint?"

"Why, of course, old fellow. You'll be allowed to do whatever you wish . . . providing it doesn't injure you. It will be just like being in a hospital with enormous grounds. If you live quietly that way for a year, you may be completely cured."

"But how will I get out of this hole?"

"I have spoken to the superintendent of police. He agrees to let you go to St. Paul de Mausole, providing I take you there."

"And you say it is really a nice place?"

"Oh, charming, Vincent. You'll find loads of things to paint."

"How nice. A hundred francs a month isn't so much. Perhaps that's just what I need for a year, to quiet me down."

"Of course it is. I have already written to your brother, telling him about it. I suggested that in your present state of health it would be inadvisable to move you very far; certainly not to Paris. I told him that in my opinion St. Paul would be the very best thing for you."

"Well, if Theo agrees . . . Anything, just so long as I don't cause him more trouble . . ."

"I expect an answer any hour. I'll come back when I get it."

Theo had no alternative. He acquiesced. He sent money to pay his brother's bills. Doctor Rey took Vincent in a carriage to the station where they boarded the train for Tarascon. At Tarascon they took a little branch line that wound up a green, fertile valley to St. Remy.

It was two kilometres up a steep hill, through the sleeping town, to St. Paul de Mausole. Vincent and Doctor Rey hired a carriage. The road led straight to a ridge of black, barren mountains. From a short way off Vincent saw, nestled at their base, the sod-brown walls of the monastery.

The carriage stopped. Vincent and Doctor Rey got out. On the right of the road there was a cleared, circular space with a Temple of Vesta and a Triumphal Arch.

"How in the world did these get here?" demanded Vincent.

"This used to be an important Roman settlement. The river, which you see down there, once filled this whole valley. It came right up to where you're standing. As the river receded, the town crawled lower and lower down the hill. Now nothing is left here except these dead monuments, and the monastery."

"Interesting."

"Come, Vincent, Doctor Peyron is expecting us."

They left the road and walked through a patch of pines to the gate of the monastery. Doctor Rey pulled an iron knob which sounded a loud bell. After a few moments the gate opened and Doctor Peyron appeared.

"How do you do, Doctor Peyron?" said Doctor Rey. "I have brought you my friend, Vincent Van Gogh, as we arranged by mail. I know that you will take good care of him."

"Yes, Doctor Rey, we will take care of him."

"You will forgive me if I run, Doctor? I just have time to catch that train back to Tarascon."

"Of course, Doctor Rey. I understand."

"Good-bye, Vincent," said Doctor Rey. "Be happy, and you will get well. I will come to see you as often as I can. By the end of a year I expect to find you a completely well man."

"Thank you, Doctor. You are very kind. Good-bye."

"Good-bye, Vincent."

He turned and walked away through the pines.

"Will you come in, Vincent?" asked Doctor Peyron, stepping aside.

Vincent walked past Doctor Peyron.

The gate of the insane asylum locked behind him.

IN late September of 1935, a year after the publication of *Lust For Life,* I received a telephone call from the director of the Museum of Modern Art in New York. He asked if I would come to discuss a matter connected with Van Gogh's paintings. When I reached his office on the top of an old brownstone on Fifty-third Street, which had been converted into a museum, he told me that the museum had been planning to put on a one-man exhibition of Van Gogh's paintings in 1940, to celebrate the fiftieth anniversary of Vincent's death. However, since *Lust For Life* had awakened considerable interest in Vincent's work, the board had decided to stage this first comprehensive American exhibition at that very time. The exhibition, which was being brought from Europe, had been underwritten by the museums of four other cities, Boston, Philadelphia, Chicago, and San Francisco, but it had proved to be very expensive to bring to the United States, and the director was now worried that there would not be sufficient interest in New York and the country to attract a wide enough audience to cover the costs.

When I asked how I might help, he told me that he had asked the editor of the New York *Times Magazine* if he would run an article about the forthcoming exhibition. The editor had replied that he would do so if I wrote the piece.

I got in touch with the editor to determine how long my article might be. The next morning I began work. My major problem was one of selection. I had lived in Europe on the trail of Van Gogh, and worked on the materials of his life for over two years, and had written a novel of a quarter of a million words. How was I going to crowd into the space of 2500 words sufficient excitement to draw people who might not otherwise have considered going to an art gallery, perhaps had never been in one before?

The manuscript took more days to cut than to write. I then left for a month's lecture tour of the Midwest and missed the formal opening of the exhibition. When I returned I walked down Fifth Avenue toward Fifty-third Street and saw a large crowd massed up ahead. To my astonishment, it proved to be a line of people, four abreast. I turned the corner and saw that the line continued in a solid phalanx all the way to the front stairs of the Museum of Modern Art.

I had an appointment with the director, but it took a considerable time before I was able to gain admission. Inside, the rooms were so jam-packed that it was almost impossible to move. En route to the stairs, I saw that a considerable portion of the viewers had copies of *Lust For Life* in their hands; many were reading the sections that described the particular painting they were in front of.

Heady wine, for a young writer.

FLAMING PAINTER OF FLAMING ART

NO artist ever loved his work more passionately or received less material reward for it than Vincent Van Gogh, the first comprehensive American exhibition of whose paintings and drawings will open at the Museum of Modern Art on November 6.

Though he painted for only ten years, from the age of twenty-seven until his death at thirty-seven, Van Gogh produced the astounding sum of 829 drawings and 741 oils. Their total value today would possibly exceed $10,000,000; yet during his lifetime Van Gogh was able to sell only one canvas, to the sister of a fellow Dutch artist, for $80.

From Arles he sent a group of sunflowers to his brother Theo in Paris, writing hopefully, "This study ought to be worth at least $100." Even at this humble price there were no buyers. A canvas of the same subject, when it was being shipped last month to the Museum of Modern Art, was valued at approximately $50,000!

To all appearances Van Gogh died a defeated man—one who had wasted his life at a craft for which, as everyone insistently told him, he had no semblance of talent. How can we explain then, the high price of canvases which a junk peddler, hawking a cartload of them through the Brabant, was unable to sell for one franc the piece? How is it possible that a man's work, which from his death in 1890 until 1905 was scorned and ridiculed by the public, became sought after in every country in Europe?

Vincent Van Gogh was a pioneer, a precursor of a new age. He anticipated the movements of the early twentieth century. The advance guard of young painters, such as Matisse and Derain, were just catching up to him in 1905. These men, casting about for inspiration and sanction for what they were trying to do, found it in the work of Van Gogh.

Art dealers follow the judgment, first of painters, second of critics, and lastly of collectors. When the important painters of the time burst Van Gogh's fame upon the world, dealers began scouring the countryside where he had worked, searching for his canvases. Soon the collectors of Holland, Russia, and Germany started to buy, but it was not until after the war, when America entered the market, that the prices soared to their present height.

The attributes for which Van Gogh was abused and neglected during his lifetime—his thick, rough brushwork, his amazing richness of color, his freshness and spontaneity, his boldness, his crude authenticity of drawing—all these are now the very qualities which have endeared his work to the public. Van Gogh's creative genius was like a blast of fresh air from the new century blown into the lungs of a dying culture.

The people of his day were accustomed to dull and sober pictures, for the most part bathed in the brown gravy of the Academy, or the misty tonalities of the Impressionists. How could they suspect that this fiery, dramatic painter's work would head the movements of two decades and lead to a re-evaluation of much of the art of the past? How could they know that similar changes were about to take place in all the arts, in the whole tone and manner of living?

Van Gogh was born in the provinces of Holland in 1853. There was little in his childhood to suggest that here was developing a painter in the sublime line of Rembrandt, El Greco and Frans Hals. He was a good-looking chap, strong, heavily built, awkward, reticent, stubborn; not easily given to friendships. His youth was marked by the same excess of intensity and passionate clumsiness which later made his love-life so unfortunate, but which proved to be the dominating force in his painting.

He did a little sketching as a boy, but no more than most school children do. At the age of sixteen he seemed happy to go to his Uncle Vincent Van Gogh's Goupil Gallery in The Hague, and to work there for five years as an art clerk. Oddly enough, it was an episode the like of which may occur in the experience of any young man, which changed the entire course of his life and set him adrift, a wanderer, despised, starved and wretched, searching for his place in the world, feeling always that there was some good in him, some contribution he could make, if only he could learn what it was.

When Van Gogh turned twenty-one, his uncle promoted him to the Goupil Gallery in London. Uncle Vincent was childless; it was an open secret that young Vincent had been named heir to the Van Gogh half of the Goupil Galleries. In his clumsy and incoherent fashion, he fell in love with Ursula Loyer, daughter of the house in which he boarded. Ursula gave him every encouragement; yet when he declared himself, she seemed to find pleasure in telling him that she had been engaged all the while, and was soon to be married.

This was the first time he had come in contact with pain and through it he inherited the disinherited of the earth. At the Goupil Gallery he refused to sell any pictures except those in which the artist had expressed human suffering. This commodity was the last thing in the world the English people wanted to hang upon their walls. At the end of a few months he had done so much damage to the London trade that the manager of the gallery asked Uncle Vincent to remove him.

Van Gogh was convinced that in the end he could persuade Ursula to love him. He refused to leave England; worked as a teacher in a boys' school and as an assistant to a Methodist minister in Isleworth. It was part of his job to go to the slums of Whitechapel and collect the fees of the students. Here he first witnessed human misery in the mass, and he knew at once what his calling must be. He would become an evangelist and do God's practical work among the poor.

Shortly thereafter Ursula married, releasing Van Gogh from his bondage. He returned home to Holland. His father was a dominie, and there had been a dominie in the family for many generations back. The family was pleased to learn that young Vincent planned to enter the church, but they would not hear of his becoming anything so undignified as an evangelist. They sent him to Amsterdam to prepare for a six-year course at the university.

However, it was too late for Van Gogh to pore over mathematics and Greek. He burned with a zealot's passion to serve God and the afflicted. After a year of textbooks and torture, he fled Amsterdam for the coal-mining regions of Belgium. His Uncle Vincent had already "washed his hands of him," and now the rest of the wealthy Van Gogh uncles, who were paying for his education, gave him up in despair.

When he reached the Borinage, he found the miners shivering in wind-swept huts, stricken with black fever, unable to earn enough money to buy warm clothes or keep their families in food. Van Gogh worked as a nurse among the sick and dying. He gave his clothing to the children. He spent the fifty francs a month his father sent him for medicine for the stricken ones. He gave up his warm, comfortable room above the bakery to live in one of the most miserable shacks in the region. He became known among the Borains as a Christman.

At the end of a year, when the evangelical committee came out from Brussels to determine whether or not Van Gogh deserved a paying appointment, they found him lying upon a sack of straw in his shack, covered only by a rough piece of burlap, holding services for the forty miners who had been killed in an explosion the day before. The committee was so horrified by his "return to barbarism" that they expelled him from the church.

Van Gogh was now twenty-six, fever-ridden, abandoned, without a purpose or meaning in his life. To ease the ache of his failure and aloneness, he began sketching the miners as they came out of the shaft and the miners' wives bending over their stoves. He had no other thought in mind than to fill the long hours with forgetfulness; but soon his interest quickened. He wrote to Theo in Paris, and Tersteeg of the Goupil Gallery in The Hague, asking them to send him art books from which he might copy.

At this fateful moment Theo was sent to the Borinage by the Van Gogh family to shame his brother into returning to a respectable job. Theo was astounded not only at the number of drawings Van Gogh had made, but even more so at their crude but passionate authenticity. When Theo perceived that his brother's real work was drawing, that it was his job in life to become an artist, Van Gogh's illness and despair disappeared as though by magic.

With Theo's money and confidence to back him, Van Gogh returned to Holland, where he attacked his craft with tremendous vigor, sketching the peasants and weavers as they worked in the fields and over their looms. His cousin, Anton Mauve, who was the leading painter of the Dutch school, agreed to become his master, so Van Gogh moved to The Hague, where he worked from five o'clock in the morning until midnight drawing diggers, scrubwomen, fishermen, working people of all kinds.

"To stroll on wharves, in alleys and markets and even saloons, that is not a pleasant pastime, except for an artist!" Van Gogh mused. "As such, one would rather be in the dirtiest place where there is something to draw, than at a tea party with charming ladies."

At the end of a few months the most terrible of all blows fell: Mauve told him that he did not know how to draw, that he was clumsy and amateurish, and that he could waste no more time on a man who showed so little aptitude for the work.

Tersteeg of the Goupil Gallery, who was the outstanding critic of Holland, was eager to buy Van Gogh's paintings both because he and Van Gogh were old friends and because the gallery was owned by the Van Gogh family. But within a year he, too, felt constrained to tell Van Gogh that he was no artist, and that he had better give up before it was too late to salvage his life.

It was at The Hague that Van Gogh met Christine, a prostitute with five illegitimate children. The woman was carrying a sixth child, and was critically ill. Demanding of the world, "How does it happen that there is upon this earth even one desperate woman?" he befriended Christine, paid for her delivery, and announced his intention of marrying her "as soon as he could earn the necessary amount of money at his craft."

In spite of the opposition of Mauve, Tersteeg, and the Van Gogh family, he kept Christine in his home for two years. Theo sent all he could from his modest salary as an art clerk, but there was not enough to go around. Starvation and sloth overtook the household. Van Gogh often went a week without a morsel of solid food. In the end Theo had to come and rescue him once again from destruction.

After another long period in the Brabant, during which Van Gogh aspired to become the Dutch Millet and paint "that which does not pass in that which passes," Theo finally summoned him to Paris. Here Van Gogh lived under Theo's protective wing and became friends with the young iconoclasts of the day, Georges Seurat, Henri Rousseau, Paul Gauguin, Emile Zola, Toulouse-Lautrec. From these men he learned to lighten his palette, to paint living, luminous air and pictures riotously mad with the sun.

Realizing that he could never fully express himself until he cut loose from the ateliers of Paris, Van Gogh went south to Arles, where the heat is dry, the color magnificent and the sun a whirling liquid ball of lemon-yellow fire. Here he became a blind painting machine, dashing off one sizzling canvas after another.

He saw about him nothing but gold, bronze, and copper, covered by a greenish azure sky of blanched heat. His canvases were masses of bright burning yellow. He knew that yellow had not been used in European painting since the Renaissance, but that did not deter him.

It was at Arles that he painted the sunflowers, plowed fields, night cafes, orchards in bloom, cornfields, and the two hundred other glowing canvases upon which his fame now rests. It was here that he painted the panels for the ill-fated Yellow House, which he hoped to leave as a permanent studio for the painters of the Southland. And it was to this Yellow House that he invited his friend Paul Gauguin, who played his insensitive part in Van Gogh's destruction.

Van Gogh was an epileptoid. When his first attack overcame him at the age of thirty-five, he cut off his ear and presented it to one of the girls in a brothel. During two subsequent attacks he overturned a table in a restaurant, crying out that his soup had been poisoned. He threw all the furniture of the Yellow House down at the children in the street who were tormenting him to cut off his other ear.

Cast into the Arlesian jail because of these attacks, Van Gogh was informed by a doctor friend that he could get out of jail either by summoning Theo from Paris or entering a nearby asylum. Van Gogh went voluntarily to the insane asylum because the doctor assured him that it was a quiet place, very much like a hospital, where he could paint and grow strong.

Instead, he was incarcerated in a third-class ward with a dozen raving maniacs. He continued to paint, but with an ever decreasing force. Four epileptic attacks followed in quick succession. Between the attacks he was completely rational. After a year he returned to Paris, visited Theo and his new wife and baby, and then went to Auvers sur Oise.

Fearing that his next seizure would render him a hopeless idiot, and that he would thus become a further burden on Theo, Van Gogh shot himself. He died two days later in Theo's arms.

Van Gogh's paintings are not as technically perfect as those of, say, Paul Cezanne, for they were painted in hot blood. What marks his canvases is his conscientious study of character, his continuous search for the quintessence of each object, his deep and almost childlike love of nature and truth.

He was the tempestuous, passionate lover of nature, and nature never repulsed him. During the early stages of his drawing he remarked to his father: "At bottom nature and the true artist agree."

Van Gogh rarely painted a still life because there was no still life within him, and he saw nothing still in nature. For him everything lived and breathed and moved in its own universal rhythm.

He once declared that he wanted to paint "Humanity, humanity, and more humanity." His portraits of poor people, the only ones who would pose for him, show a profound love and compassion for his fellow beings.

Because of the extreme hardships of his life, and his self-destruction at thirty-seven, Van Gogh's life is often considered a tragic one. Nothing could be further from the truth. His life was magnificently fulfilled. He painted everything he wanted to paint, and said everything he wanted to say.

What more can be vouchsafed to any lone mortal?

JACK LONDON, born in Oakland, California, in 1876, was the illegitimate son of a brilliantly erratic Irish astrologist, Professor W. H. Chaney, and Flora Wellman, black sheep of a pioneer family of Massillon, Ohio. Jack learned of his illegitimacy at an early age. The knowledge had a great deal to do with the shaping of his character. When Jack was seven his mother married John London, a gentle creature who gave Jack warmth and affection, as did Eliza, London's daughter by an earlier marriage. John London was able to make a good living, but Flora's spiritualism and bad judgment kept the family in poverty. Jack had little formal education; he helped to feed the London family by a series of backbreaking jobs. He fell in love with the Oakland waterfront at fifteen, became an oyster pirate on San Francisco Bay, by his daring, garnered enough cash to buy the *Razzle Dazzle*, acquiring with it Mamie, queen of the oyster pirates. At the same time he discovered the Oakland Public Library, and encouraged by Ina Coolbrith, its poet-librarian, began reading: Kipling's *The Light That Failed*, Melville's *Typee*, Zola's *Germinal*. It was the beginning of a vigorous course in self-education; although he continued on the sea, as a member of the Fish Patrol, as a sailor on the *Sophie Sutherland*, hunting for seal; though he rode the rails throughout America, and went to the Klondike during the Gold Rush, he never stopped studying the exciting minds of his age: Darwin, Spencer, Marx, Haeckel, Nietzsche. From his experiences as sailor, hobo, gold seeker, he began to write short stories and articles, working prodigiously, and at last beginning to sell to the magazines.

SAILOR ON HORSEBACK

All At Sea

FOR me the New Year begins full of worries, harassments, and disappointments.' He was three thousand dollars in debt, one of his greatest liabilities being that people liked and trusted him and consequently gave him too much credit; he was unable to earn enough to support his growing list of dependents; he was dissatisfied both with the rate of progress he was making in his work and with the speed at which he was becoming known. Yet the greater part of his distress was caused by his recurrent bouts of despondency, the cyclical nature of which had manifested itself early in his youth. 'I dined yesterday on canvasback and terrapin, with champagne and all manner of wonderful drinks I had never tasted before warming my heart and brain, and I remembered the sordid orgies of my youth. [In more vigorous moods he recalled these orgies as romantic adventures.] We were ill-clad, ill-mannered beasts, and the drink was cheap and poor and nauseating. And then I dreamed dreams, and pulled myself up out of the slime to canvasback and terrapin and champagne, and learned that it was solely a difference of degree which art introduced into the fermenting.'

Disillusioned words, sick words, but only momentarily meant, the relapse-mood of the rampant individualist who spends most of his energy conquering the world. Caught in the grip of his dejection he wrote, 'What is this chemical ferment called life all about? Small wonder that small men down the ages have conjured gods in answer. A little god is a snug little possession and explains it all. But how about you and me who have no God? There's damned little satisfaction in being a materialistic monist.'

From a professional viewpoint he had little cause to feel despondent, for on the twenty-seventh of December, George P. Brett, president of the Macmillan Company, one of the most vigorous publishing houses in America, had written to tell him that his stories represented the very best work of the kind that had been done in the country, and expressed a keen desire to publish him in America and England. In reply Jack had sent Brett a group of Alaskan-Indian stories under the title of *Children of the Frost.* Only five days after he had penned his melancholy sentences about this chemical ferment called life, Macmillan accepted *Children of the Frost,* and agreed to his request to advance him two hundred dollars. His weariness disappeared as he wrote to Brett, 'I don't know whether *Children of the Frost* is an advance over previous work, but I do know that there are big books in me, and that when I find myself they will come out.'

In February began Jack's migration to the hills. He found a house in Piedmont on five acres of ground, in a clump of magnificent pines, half the ground in bearing orchard, the other half in golden poppies. There were a large living-room and a dining-room finished in redwood, and in the pines a small cottage for Flora and Johnny Miller. 'We have a most famous porch, broad and long and cool, and our view commands all of San Francisco Bay for a sweep of thirty or forty miles, and all the opposing shores such as Marin County and Mount Tamalpais, to say nothing of the Golden Gate and the Pacific Ocean . . . and all for $35 a month!'

The house was always full of people; rarely were the spare beds unoccupied. Writers on a visit from the East were promptly brought to Jack's house, socialists on lecture tours, actors, musicians, intelligent friends of other friends. Since everyone was welcome and made to feel wanted, Jack's circle grew apace . . . as did his entertainment bills. The *Examiner* continued to give him special assignments such as interviewing Governor Taft when he returned from the Philippines, but Jack groused to Cloudesley Johns: 'Lord, what stacks of hack I'm turning out. I wonder if I'll ever get clear of debt?' When an Oakland grocer wrote him asking for a hundred and thirty-five dollars due, he answered in a fit of temper with a scorching letter in which he upbraided the tradesman for annoying and insulting him, told him to be courteous and wait his turn and he would be paid, that if he attempted to blacklist him or make trouble, he would forfeit his turn among the creditors. The grocer turned the letter over to the newspapers for its advertising value, and the papers played it up with great glee, the picture of a debtor putting a creditor in his place being too delicious to resist. The article was syndicated all over the country, and should have taught Jack not to write tempestuous letters . . . a lesson he was never able to learn.

He was invited to speak before the Women's Press Association of San Francisco, and told them he would lecture on Kipling, who was still thought of by a considerable portion of the American public as a crude and vulgar barbarian. The subject was widely advertised, the combination of Jack London and Rudyard Kipling drawing a large and distinguished audience. When Jack mounted the platform he announced that unfortunately he found he had sent his article on Kipling to an English magazine in the hope of selling it, and since he could not speak without his material, he would give them instead his lecture on 'The Tramp.' The cold waves generated by the rigidly circumspect group of San Francisco women would have frozen anyone less impervious to his audience. However, the women did not remain frigid at the end of the lecture, in which Jack justified the tramp, and blamed his position on society; they attacked him with such vehemence that the chairlady had to bang on the table with her gavel and adjourn the meeting to prevent a free-for-all.—Of course the papers ran the story.

Already known as an odd and colorful character around the Bay, his reputation for eccentricity now became national in scope. A reporter sent to interview him from *The Reader* magazine writes, 'Jack London is one of the most approachable of men, unconventional, responsive, and genuine, with a warmth of hospitality which places the visitor on an immediate footing of a friend. He is boyish, noble, lovable; primitive, free, and unhackneyed.' Jack is reported as saying, 'any style I have has been acquired by sweat. Light out after it with a club, and if you don't get it you'll get something that looks remarkably like it.' The San Francisco *Chronicle,* which first had begun to publicize him when he was but a month in his mother's womb, gave a full-page spread to the Piedmont Literary Colony, with pictures of Jack and his home in the pines acknowledged to be its center.

In addition to the numerous hack articles he was writing a novel for juveniles called *Cruise of the Dazzler,* a group of adventure stories for *Youth's Companion* under the title of *Tales of the Fish Patrol,* serious Alaskan stories, and *The Kempton-Wace Letters* with Anna Strunsky. *The Kempton-Wace Letters,* a brilliant philosophical analysis of the realist versus the romantic attitudes, continued to be a curious defense by both of their position in their love for each other. Jack, who had married Bessie on what he liked to call the basis of reason, wrote: 'Considered biologically, marriage is an institution necessary for the perpetuation of the species. Romantic love is an artifice, blunderingly and unwittingly introduced by man into the natural order. Without an erotic literature, a history of great loves and lovers, a garland of love songs and ballads, a sheaf of spoken love tales and adventures—without all this man could not possibly love in the way he does.' Anna Strunsky, the poet, insisted that 'the flush of roselight in the heavens, the touch of a hand, the color and shape of fruit, the tears that come for unnamed sorrows are more significant than all the building and inventing done since the first social compact. You cannot explain the bloom, the charm, the smile of life, that which rains sunshine into our hearts, which tells us we are wise to hope.'

By March they had fifty thousand words written, and Jack was convinced the book would go. In order that their work might be expedited he invited Anna to come and stay in his home. Two years later she was to tell inquiring newspaper reporters: 'I received a letter from Mr. London asking me to come to his house in Piedmont to revise the manuscript. His wife and mother added their requests. During the first days of my stay there Mrs. London was cordial and manifested great interest in our work, but after a stay of five days I became convinced that she had begun to dislike me. [In 1937 Bessie London confided that she had come upon Miss Strunsky sitting on Jack's knee in his study, their heads glued together over the manuscript; no great breach, but upsetting to a woman of Mrs. London's strict sense of the proprieties.]

'She did nothing of any importance to make me feel out of place, but judging from several little occurrences I decided it was best for me to leave. I left very much against Mr. and Mrs. London's will. The farewell between Mrs. London and myself was that of two acquaintances between whom existed a mutual liking. Mr. London and I treated each other as friends, no more. Besides, Mr. London is hardly the man to make love to another woman in his own house. His behavior was most circumspect to me, and always has been. My observation at the time served to convince me that he was blindly in love with his wife.'

That Miss Strunsky, a woman of the highest integrity, was telling the simple truth is confirmed by Jack, who wrote about her, 'It was her intellect that fascinated me, not her womanhood. Primarily she was intellect and genius. I love to seek and delve in human souls, and she was an exhaustless mine to me. Protean, I called her. My term for her of intimacy and endearment was what? a term that was intellectual, that described her mind.'

McClure still owned the rights to *A Daughter of the Snows*. Though he did not like the manuscript well enough to publish it himself, he made every effort to sell it to another house for book publication. At length he was successful, Lippincott's accepting it and paying an advance against royalties of seven hundred and fifty dollars. After Mc-

Clure deducted what was still owed him, there remained a hundred and sixty-five dollars in cash for Jack. Jack wanted to withdraw the manuscript, but he was powerless to do so; besides, though it was a small sum of money, it enabled him to meet the demands of his more pressing creditors. When galley proof began to arrive for correction he was heart-broken; each batch seemed the worst, until the next batch came, and finally he commented that it was futile to try to doctor a sick thing.

On July 21 he received a telegraphic offer from the American Press to go to South Africa to report the Boer War. He was still three thousand dollars in debt; Bessie was pregnant again, and that would mean more expense; and it was the call of Adventure. He accepted by telegraph within the hour, packed his bag that night, and the following morning kissed Bessie and his daughter good-bye at the Oakland mole—where eight years before, when pursuing Kelly's Industrial Army, he had crawled into an empty freight car. On the train bound for Chicago he encountered a woman whose accidental presence served to accelerate the developments of his own life plot. 'Let me tell you a little affair which will indicate the ease with which I let loose the sexual man. You remember when I started for South Africa. In my car was traveling a woman with a maid and a child. We came together on the jump, at the very start, and had each other clear to Chicago. It was sexual passion, clear and simple. Beyond being a sweet woman, she had no charm for me. There was no glamour of the mind, not even an overwhelming intoxication of the senses. Nothing remained when our three days and nights were over.'

Nothing but the memory of pleasure; for he had always enjoyed women for their entertainment value. He had no horoscope to which he might point and cry, 'Alas! It is my fate,' as had Professor Chaney, even though he had inherited in full measure his father's predatory instincts. 'The flesh, in my cosmos, is a little thing. It is the soul that is everything. I love the flesh as the Greeks loved it, and yet it is a form of love that is almost, if not quite, artistic in nature.' A little later his men friends were to call him, with pride, the Stallion.

Despite the fact that he writes, 'I easily went the limit in those days,' this affair on the train seems to have been the first time he let himself go in the two years of his marriage. Nor was it until he returned from England that his 'little affair which will indicate the ease with which I let loose the sexual man' developed its full psychological consequences.

Once again he arrived in New York in the full heat of summer. This time he did not 'batter the main stem for light pieces' with which to buy glasses of iced milk and imperfect copies of new books to read while lolling on the grass of City Hall Park; instead he went straight to the Macmillan Company, where for the first time he was able to clasp hands with a publisher. George P. Brett was an astute editor, a liberal and honest man with a deep love for literature; he was in addition a staunch friend who was to be Jack's guardian angel through many stormy years, and a lifelong Jack London admirer. Jack had a boat to catch and there was little time for negotiating, but the two men agreed that when Jack returned from South Africa they would enter into a permanent relationship under which Macmillan would publish all the books Jack wrote. Jack told Brett about *The Kempton-Wace Letters,* which he accepted at once for publication.

When he reached England, where he was supposed to interview British generals for their views on the future in the Transvaal before sailing for South Africa, Jack found a cable canceling the engagement. His round-trip transportation had been paid, and a small amount of advance money which he had already spent. Here he was in London, seven thousand miles from home, without resources, and without a job to do.

Always a man of swift adaptability, he decided to go into the East End of London, which his extensive reading in sociology had taught him was one of the worst hell holes for humanity in the western world, and investigate conditions. It did not occur to him that this was a daring and difficult task, that it took almost foolhardy courage for an utter stranger, an American who had been on English soil only forty-eight hours, to attempt to understand, analyze, and then confound a nation with one of its major economic problems. His first volume of short stories had already been released in England, and had received, from a usually conservative press, surprisingly good notices. His publishers were friendly; he could have spent an amusing few weeks among the English literati, enjoyed a vacation. Instead he found a second-hand store on Petticoat Lane, bought a pair of well-worn trousers, a frayed jacket with one remaining button, a pair of brogans which plainly had seen service where coal was shoveled, a thin leather belt, and a very dirty cloth cap, and plunged into the heart of the East End. He rented a room in the most congested district of the slums, then ventured forth to become acquainted. His publishers had been horrified, had told him that it was impossible, that he would be murdered in his sleep. Jack was a son of the people; he laughed at their fears.

He was taken for an American sailor who had been ditched at port. Once again he became Sailor Jack, slipping into the rôle as easily as though he had never left it. He was no outsider, no research man looking down from academic heights; he was one of them, a seafaring man down on his luck. The people of the East End accepted him, trusted him, and talked to him. What he learned about this human shambles he put into a book called *The People of the Abyss,* which is fresh and vigorous and true today, one of the world's classics about the underprivileged.

'I took with me certain simple criteria with which to measure. That which made for more life, for physical and spiritual health, was good; that which made for less life, which hurt, dwarfed, and distorted life, was bad.' From the basis of these 'simple criteria' he found that life in the Abyss, where lives one tenth of London's population, was a prolonged, chronic starvation, families of father, mother, and children working long hours and every day, and earning enough to afford only one room in which the entire family had to cook, eat, sleep, and discharge all the duties of intimate living. He found disease, despair, and death the inseparable companions of the People of the Abyss, saw homeless men and women, guilty of no crime but ill health and poverty, pushed about and maltreated as though they were loathsome animals. That some of these people were congenital loafers and wastrels, he soon found out, but just as from his experiences on The Road in America, he discovered that ninety per cent of the East-Enders had been conscientious workingmen until old age, sickness, or business slack had thrown them out of their jobs. Now, unemployed, or at best making sweat-shop products in their rooms, they and their families were left by the City of London to rot away until providential death cleaned them off the streets.

'The London Abyss is a vast shambles; no more dreary spectacle can be found. The color of life is gray and drab, everything is hopeless, unrelieved, and dirty. Bathtubs are a thing totally unknown; any attempts at cleanliness become howling farce. Strange, vagrant odors come drifting along the greasy wind; the Abyss exudes a stupefying atmosphere of torpor which wraps about the people and deadens them. Year by year rural England pours in a flood of vigorous young life that perishes by the third generation. At all times four hundred and fifty thousand human creatures are dying miserably at the bottom of the social pit called London.'

On the coronation day of Edward VII Jack walked up to Trafalgar Square to watch the majestic medieval pageant. For company on his walk he had a carter, a carpenter, and a sailor, old now and out of work. He saw that from the slimy sidewalk they were picking up bits of orange peel, apple skin, and grape stems and eating them; stray crumbs of bread the size of peas, apple cores black and dirty, these things the men took into their mouths and chewed and swallowed. 'It has been urged that the criticism I have passed on things as they are in England is too pessimistic. I must say in extenuation that of optimists I am the most optimistic. I measure manhood less by political aggregations than by individuals. For the English I see a broad and smiling future, but for a great deal of the political machinery, which at present mismanages them, I see nothing less than the scrap heap.'

He rented a room in the home of a London detective which he could use as a place of refuge to bathe, change his clothes, do his reading, and write his book without becoming suspect. In the course of three months he studied hundreds of pamphlets, books, and government reports on poverty in London, interviewed countless men and women, took pictures, tramped miles of streets, lived in workhouses, paupers' homes, stood in bread lines, slept in the streets and parks with his newly made friends, and in addition wrote a complete book—a triumph of energy, organization, and burning passion for his subject.

He arrived in New York in November with the manuscript of *The People of the Abyss* in his suitcase. He hoped that Macmillan would publish it, but he well knew that he could not make money from his sociology. The man who had told Anna Strunsky he was going to extract every last dollar from his writing, who had written to Cloudesley Johns that the magazines could buy him body and soul if they paid the price, here gave the lie to himself. He was a writer first, a socialist second; the man who wanted to earn money ran a very poor third.

A friend who met him at the dock writes, 'He wore a wrinkled sack coat, the pockets of which bulged with papers and letters. His trousers bagged at the knees. He was minus a vest, and his outing shirt was far from immaculate. A leather belt around his waist took the place of suspenders. On his head he wore a dinky little cap.' George P. Brett, however, had eyes only for Jack's manuscript. He thought *The People of the Abyss* a penetrating job, made some trenchant sociological criticisms, and accepted it at once. Jack told him, 'I want to get away from the Klondike. I have served my apprenticeship at writing in that field, and I feel that I am better fitted now to attempt a larger and more generally interesting field. I have half a dozen books, fiction all, that I want to write. I have done a great deal of thinking and studying in the last two years, since I wrote my first novel, and I am confident that I can today write something worth while.'

Brett was equally confident, and acceded to Jack's plea that Macmillan pay him a hundred and fifty dollars a month for two years. In return they were to publish all the books he wrote during that period. In parting Brett gave him what was perhaps the best single piece of advice he was ever to receive. 'I hope that your work from this time on will show the marks of advancement which I found so strong in your earlier books, but which is not so marked in the last volume or so, these showing signs of haste. There is no real place in the world of literature for anything but the best a man can do.' To which Jack replied, 'My hope, once I am on my feet, is not to write prolifically, but to turn out one book, a good book a year. Even as it is, I am not a prolific writer. I write very slowly. The reason I have turned out so much is that I have worked constantly, day in and day out, without taking a rest. Once I am in a position where I do not have to depend upon each day's work to keep the pot boiling for the next day, where I do not have to dissipate my energy on all kinds of hack, where I can slowly and deliberately ponder and shape the best that is in me, then, at that time, I am confident that I shall do big work.'

On the train headed west Jack spread opposite him on the Pullman seat his three books that had been published in October, just a few weeks before he returned to New York: *A Daughter of the Snows, The Cruise of the Dazzler,* and *Children of the Frost.* He realized that the publication of three books by one man in a single month was not only a record, but also a foolhardy piece of business, the one for which Brett had chided him. He resolved that now that he had 'settled down with one publishing house' he would manage his affairs better. Along with the books, he spread out clippings from the newspapers to see how his work had fared. About *A Daughter of the Snows,* which had been put out by Lippincott, the press made many incisive criticisms, accused him of making Frona Welse unbelievable, and of not handling his construction problems; but for the rest the critics were tolerant, spoke enthusiastically of his strong, graphic style, and predicted that he would do better with his second novel. Jack, who had anticipated a lashing, blew a sigh of relief. *The Cruise of the Dazzler,* which was released by the Century Company, received only the mild reception that he could expect from a novel for juveniles. The most important of his three books, *Children of the Frost,* the Alaskan-Indian stories that were Macmillan's first publication, established him as the dominant figure in the American short story.

Sitting back in his seat pleasedly musing over the past few crowded years as the landscape flashed by unseen, he mingled his memories of his determination to recreate the American short story with the lines of praise the critics had lavished on *Children of the Frost:* '. . . has few superiors as a story-teller . . . a domain which is his by right of conquest . . . marvelous literary development, will last . . . will win fame both wide and permanent.' Though he was happy and proud of himself he realized that he had gained merely the bottom rung of the ladder, that the fight had only begun. Mulling over his ideas and plans, he vowed to do for the American novel what he had already done for the short story. Since Herman Melville there had been no great sea novels in American literature; he would write great sea novels. There were as yet no great proletarian novels in American literature; he would not only write great proletarian novels and make the critics and public like them, but he would also hasten the socialist revolution. He had his work cut out for him; it would take a full twenty years to accomplish everything he had in mind. He determined to fulfill every demand of his program before his time on earth was up.

When Jack reached Piedmont he found that Eliza had been living with Bessie for some six weeks, keeping peace and quiet between Bessie and Flora. His reunion with his family was a joyous one; on November 21, 1902, in writing to Brett a brief survey of his life, Jack said: 'Finding myself anchored with a household, I resolved to have the compensations of a household, so I married and increased the weight of my anchor. But I have never regretted it. I have been well compensated.'

More than ever he found that he had become a busy literator, for not only had he his new work to write, but proofs to read on *The Kempton-Wace Letters,* and corrections and additions to make to the manuscript of *The People of the Abyss.* He so relished being immersed in the welter of books and stories and publications that he went back to his schedule of nineteen hours a day of work, with five hours of sleep. The only time spent in relaxation was during his Wednesday open house, when his old friends gathered and new friends came into the fold, when he played poker and practical jokes, and initiated his cronies into the intricacies of the English puzzles he had packed into his lone suitcase.

When Bessie came out of her travail she found that she had once again presented her husband with a daughter. Jack's hand was not cut this time; what was cut was the lifeline of hope that he would have a son to whom he could hand down not only his name but his literary tradition. He made himself miserable and ill with frustration; his disappointment made Bessie ill, too.

After wandering about disconsolate for a number of days, a fresh idea shook him out of his lethargy. It was a dog story, which he intended to do in four thousand words, a companion-piece to another dog story he had written the year before. At the end of four days he had written his four thousand words and discovered to his surprise that he had barely begun, that the story was taking on motivation and scope of which he had never dreamed. He decided that he would name it *The Call of the Wild*, and let it grow however it willed, for the story was master now and he the servant writing it; it had taken hold of his imagination and fired him as no other yarn he had ever tackled. For thirty glorious, labor-laden days he wrote with his thick pencil on the rough scratch paper, made his few word corrections, and transferred the material to the typewriter. He neglected everything else—friends, family, debts, the new baby, galley proof arriving in daily batches from Macmillan; living only with his dog Buck, half Saint Bernard and half Scotch shepherd, who had been a country gentleman on a ranch in the Santa Clara Valley until he was kidnapped and shipped into the primitive wilds of the Klondike.

Then at a Wednesday open house Jack made good his neglect of his friends. He settled himself in the comfortable lounging chair by the fire while his guests placed themselves in the window seats and on cushions on the floor. With a grave look in his gray-blue eyes, one hand combing fondly through his hair, he read to them the story of the great dog Buck, who remained faithful to his love of man until the call of the forest and the recollection of wild wolves drew him back to primitive life. There were no card games that night, no wild laughter or practical jokes. Jack read until one in the morning, the silence growing ever deeper about him. When he had finished, his usually loquacious friends could say little, but he saw their thoughts in their shining eyes. His three years of writing Alaskan tales had been at last justified; he had expressed himself in an art form so flawlessly and completely that for these few hours his listeners shared with him the ecstasy he had known in its creation.

The following morning he put the manuscript into an envelope, stamped it, enclosed another stamped envelope to bring it back to him, and sent his story to the *Saturday Evening Post*, the most popular and highest paying magazine in the world. He knew no one on the staff; they had never been hospitable to his work, and he had little expectation of selling them the story. But the 'cunning arrangement of cogs that changed a manuscript from one envelope to another,' against which he had inveighed so strongly four years before when he had been a novice, failed to function. The *Saturday Evening Post* did not use the stamped return envelope with which he had provided them. Instead they sent him a flat, oblong one, in which he found a glowing letter of acceptance, and a check for two thousand dollars.

Two thousand dollars for a month's work! He had always said that serious literature could pay dividends. He had always said he would write his own way, and make the editors like it. Two thousand dollars . . . enough to pay the doctor bills for his second daughter, Bess, the accumulated doctor bills for Flora and for the mother of Johnny Miller, to pay his hundreds of dollars in debts to insurance companies, department stores, grocers, butchers, druggists, clothing, typewriter, and stationery stores, to help all his friends who needed assistance . . . enough to buy those new glass bookcases he wanted, and to order that list of forty books from the East. Not since he had sold *An Odyssey of the North* had he known such an overflowing measure of exultation. Had he not justified everything he stood for? Had he not, within sixty days of his heroic resolution on the train from New York, begun his revitalization of the American novel? When those friends who had listened to the reading of *The Call of the Wild* thronged back into the house to congratulate him, to wring his hand and slap him on the back, had he not to send down for another gallon of sour Italian wine and get tipsy dreaming more roseate dreams for the future?

Now that things were better for him he engaged a second servant to help Bessie, who was having a difficult time recovering her strength, and entertained more widely. Into his house came many attractive women; after his successful siege of work Jack began to avail himself of them. There perhaps had been an insufficient sexual compulsion in his marriage, but even if that were not so, there was the burden of Bessie having been pregnant for eighteen and recovering from her deliveries for at least another six of the thirty-two months of their marriage. A man of vigorous appetites, accustomed to sexual satisfaction since the days of Mamie on the *Razzle Dazzle*, this had worked a hardship on him; his three days and nights with the woman on the train to Chicago remained strong in his memory. Less than three years after he had written, 'My heart is large, and I shall be a cleaner, wholesomer man because of a restraint being laid upon me in place of being free to drift wheresoever I listed,' he renounced all obligations to abstinence.

'You know my sexual code,' he later wrote, 'you know the circumstances of the period, you know I had no compunction of dallying along the primrose path.' Dally he did, to the fullest extent of his opportunities, yet for him, outside of his marriage, there was no emotion tied up with the sexual act; it was a purely sensory experience, giving pleasure to both parties and hence, since he was a hedonist, a deed of virtue in direct proportion to the harmless pleasure incurred. 'Though I have roved and ranged and looted, I have never looted under false pretense. Never once have I said, "I love you" for the gain it might often have brought me. I have been fair, and fastidiously so, in my dealings with women, demanding no more than I was willing to give. I bought, or took in fair exchange, and I never lied to get the best of a bargain or to get the bargain that was otherwise beyond me.' And, in an effort to justify himself: 'Man can pursue his lusts, without love, simply because he is so made. Mother Nature cries compellingly through him for progeny, and so man obeys her urging, not because he is a wilful sinner, but because he is a creature of law.'

Jack had not mentioned *The Call of the Wild* in the list of books he outlined to Macmillan because he had not known he was going to write it. He sent the manuscript to Brett, who replied on March 5, saying that he did not like the title. 'I like the story very well indeed, although I am afraid it is too true to nature and too good work to be really popular with the sentimentalist public which swallows Seton-Thompson with delight.' Brett then made him an offer of two thousand dollars for immediate publication on an outright sale basis, instead of contracting for it on a royalty basis and postponing publication for a year or two. 'I would like to try an experiment in relation to this book, putting it out in a very attractive typographic form and spending a very large sum of money in endeavoring to give it a wide circulation and thus assist the sale of not only your already published books, but of those still to come. But don't let me overpersuade you in the matter. The decision is entirely in your hands and if you decide not to accept the cash offer we will publish the book in due course under the terms of our agreement.'

He had already spent the two thousand dollars from the *Saturday Evening Post;* the Macmillan hundred and fifty dollars a month was inadequate to support his family of six, two servants, and Mammy Jenny. No book of his had ever earned one thousand dollars in royalties, let alone two thousand dollars, and there was no reason to believe this one would be an exception. Even if the book were to earn two thousand dollars, he would have to wait at least two years for his royalties, and then the money might well have been absorbed by his advance hundred and fifty dollars a month. This was two thousand dollars clear, right now, and money in the hand was money that could be spent . . . particularly for that trim little boat called the *Spray* he had his eye on.

He accepted Brett's proposition and sold out all interest in *The Call of the Wild.*

The *Spray* was a sailing sloop with a good-sized cabin in which he could cook and sleep two persons. He bought her not only because he longed once again to live upon the water, but because he had been contemplating a sea novel, and he wanted the feel of a ship under him before he began writing. It was nine years since he had come off the *Sophie Sutherland;* his gear had gone rusty. 'It will be almost literally a narrative of things that happened on a seven months' voyage I once made as a sailor. The oftener I have thought upon the things that happened during that trip, the more remarkable they appear to me.' Brett replied, 'I feel very great hopes for your sea story. So few sea stories are appearing, and none of these good for anything, that a really good sea story at the present time would without question achieve a very remarkable success.'

With Brett's encouraging words ringing in his ears, he provisioned the *Spray* with food and blankets and went for a week's sail on the Bay, retracing the trips he had made up the sloughs and straits when he had been a daring oyster pirate and member of the Fish Patrol. At the end of a week, with the sea salt in his nostrils and the feel of sail-ropes in his calloused hands, he returned home, sat down at his desk and wrote *The Sea Wolf,* Chapter One. Whenever the interruptions proved too great, the friends about him too many, he put food on board the *Spray* and pushed off by himself, writing his fifteen hundred words each morning as he sat on the hatch and let the early spring sun warm his body to the pitch that his thoughts about *The Sea Wolf* were warming his brain. Later in the day he went sailing, shot ducks on the Sacramento River, fished for his supper. On Saturday afternoons and Sundays he sometimes took Bessie and his two daughters, Eliza and her son, and a crowd of his friends for a sail.

It was a busy and exhilarated period. *Wilshire's,* a socialist magazine, published *The People of the Abyss* serially, which put him in the front rank of American socialists; he wrote 'How I Became a Socialist' for *The Comrade,* and a series of critical articles for the *International Socialist Review. Wilshire's* paid him a modest sum for *The People of the Abyss,* but for the socialist newspapers he wrote always without pay. He also composed two new lectures to give to the socialist locals about the Bay, 'The Class Struggle' and 'The Scab,' both of which were published in the socialist press. Fellow socialists began to write to him from all parts of the country; invariably they began their letter, 'Dear Comrade' and ended it 'Yours for the Revolution.' Jack answered every letter himself, beginning 'Dear Comrade' and ending 'Yours for the Revolution.'

With the spread of his name and fame, Jack's home in Piedmont became an intellectual center of the Bay area. No less than a hundred people a week walked through his front door, enjoyed his hospitality. Even with two servants, and Mammy Jenny to care for the children, there was a great deal of work to be done. Bessie was not always in the mood for more and more company and more and more work; for one Wednesday night open house she is reported as purposely preparing less food than would be necessary to feed the horde of people that would be coming in. Nor was she too pleased at the way the women were flocking about her Jack—Jack of the warm, golden smile and booming laugh—flinging themselves at his head. She grew jealous. Jack wanted Bessie to buy beautiful clothes for the many formal affairs to which he was now invited; Bessie declined to buy them. Eliza shopped with her and showed her how stunning she looked in a long velvet gown and a velvet hat with a plume, but she insisted upon wearing blouses, sailor skirts, and sailor hats, even to such affairs as the dinner at the swank Bohemian Club in San Francisco at which Jack was the guest of honor. Jack felt badly about this; he admired Bessie's figure and wanted to show her off to her best advantage. That she was far from well, and had little desire to be out at all, is part of the explanation; the other part is that Fred Jacobs had probably admired her in blouses and sailor skirts.

In spite of these minor frictions, Jack and Bessie got along well together. The one complaint he voiced to her was that he wished she would read more, so they could discuss the new books. Bessie replied that there was nothing she would like better to do, but that she was awakened at six by the baby, and from that moment until ten at night it was an unending round of routine tasks. Jack patted her hand sympathetically, said yes, he knew, and that when the children grew a little older she would have more time for her reading. Though people attest, thirty-five years later, that they appeared an incongruous couple—Bessie seemed middle-aged and matronly, Jack a vivacious young boy—everyone agrees that they lived together harmoniously. Eliza London Shepard, who saw a great deal of them at the time, often staying in their house, attests to this most strongly. Apparently the only criticism Jack made against his wife in his own mind—as reflected by the notes he kept at the time—is that Bessie was literal-minded, that 'she had a narrow band around her forehead.' In all fairness to his wife he also acknowledged that he had always known this, that the emotional stability it gave her was something he sorely needed, and had attracted him to her in the first place. It is at this very time, March, 1903, that Jack wrote to Cloudesley Johns, who at Jack's wedding had said, 'I will withhold my congratulations until your tenth anniversary': 'By the way, I think your long deferred congratulations upon my marriage are about due. I have been married nearly three years, have a couple of kids, and think it's great. So fire away. Or, come and take a look at us, and at the kids, and then congratulate.'

He swung along vigorously on *The Sea Wolf*, the creating of which was bringing him far greater joy than had even *The Call of the Wild*. In his spare hours he wrote such excellent Alaskan tales as *The One Thousand Dozen, Gold Hunters of the North*, and a dozen others. In addition to the *Spray* he bought a horse and rig to cart his family and friends around the countryside, for warm weather was coming on and he liked to take a crowd into the hills to picnic and play games, swim in the reservoir, and broil steaks over wood fires. Late in April he was thrown from the buggy and had the tip of one of his thumbs cut off. 'It feels as though it had a heart beating at the end of it,' he complained, but the accident did not prevent him from writing his thousand words a day on *The Sea Wolf*, the main character of which was based on Captain Alex McClean, of whose amazing exploits he had heard while he was on the *Sophie Sutherland*. He continued to sail the *Spray* for relaxation and privacy, once having his sails cut to ribbons in a surprise storm, and finding it difficult to make the Estuary.

In June *The Kempton-Wace Letters* was published anonymously, receiving a good press. 'Unusual . . . thoughtful, frank . . . sure to have a wide reading . . . has much of the enquiring spirit of today . . . good meat for the mind . . . a new departure in novel writing . . . piquant, clever, original philosophy.' The San Francisco *Argonaut* recognized one of the authors by the 'evolutionary deductions,' and the news spread so rapidly that when Macmillan was printing its second edition it asked Jack's permission to acknowledge the authorship. *The Kempton-Wace Letters* sold only moderately well, having too little action, plot, and swiftness for the general public, but Jack and Anna Strunsky exchanged letters between Piedmont and New York, where she was now living, congratulating each other on an important job well done.

Late in June, desiring to take her two children to the country for the summer, Bessie rented a cabin in a grove of cabins which had been put up by Mrs. Ninetta Eames as a summer resort at Glen Ellen, in Sonoma County in the Valley of the Moon. Jack wanted to continue to sail the *Spray* and concentrate on *The Sea Wolf*, so he remained in Piedmont.

One night toward the end of the month when he was crossing the hills in his buggy with George Sterling and some other men friends, the buggy ran off the road and plunged into a ravine. Jack's leg was badly hurt. Charmian Kittredge came frequently to nurse him. At the beginning of July, as soon as he was able to walk, Jack left for Glen Ellen to join his family. Charmian Kittredge also went to Glen Ellen, to join her aunt.

The *Overland Monthly* having folded up, Roscoe Eames and Edward Payne were now out of work. Edward Payne and Mrs. Eames had built a large rambling house called Wake Robin on the banks of a stream opposite which Payne, who was a renegade preacher without a pulpit, had put together picnic tables and log seats to hold revival meetings and philosophical discussions. In order to make money out of the project, Mrs. Eames had built the cabins and put up tents, which she rented out to families.

When Jack reached Glen Ellen he found his family comfortably entrenched in a cabin with a canvas top, located in a grove of wine-colored manzanita and madrone. The campers lived as a communal group; everyone cooked their meals in a common kitchen by the river bank, and ate on long picnic tables. Jack spent a few dollars to dam the clear, cool stream where it flowed along the sandy beach, and the entire camp collected to swim and sun itself. Here Jack spent his afternoons playing with the youngsters, teaching them to swim. In the mornings he went to a shaded and secluded spot on the bank of the stream where, on the sawed-off trunk of an oak tree, he scrawled his thousand words a day. And one night toward the end of July the entire camp assembled, even the small children, snugly wrapped in blankets, to hear him read the first half of *The Sea Wolf*. He read the manuscript as it rested on the tree trunk on which he had written it, flanked on either side by candles, the campers and neighbors spread out on the ground at his feet. Dawn was beginning to mottle the sky over Sonoma Mountain when he turned the last page. The people alive today who heard Jack London read *The Sea Wolf* by the bank of that stream in Glen Ellen, in late July, 1903, still remember it as one of the most beautiful and moving experiences of their lives.

And then, within a few hours, came the explosion that shattered the existence of the London family. It would perhaps be best to have Bessie tell the story in her own words.

'One day toward the end of July, after lunch, Jack and I stayed down by the stream and talked. He wanted to get away from Oakland for a time, because there were too many interruptions to his work. He said that he had been thinking about buying a ranch on the Southern California Desert, and asked if I would mind going down there to live. I told him, not at all, as long as there would be modern conveniences for the children. [Bessie was mother first, wife second.] Jack promised, and we made plans to leave in the fall.

'At about two o'clock I took my two babies back to the cabin to put them to sleep. Miss Kittredge had been waiting around, and I saw them walk over to a big hammock at the side of Mrs. Eames's house and begin to talk. I thought nothing of it. I put the two children to sleep and worked around the cabin straightening up. Miss Kittredge and Jack sat in that hammock for four solid hours and talked.

'At six o'clock Jack walked up to the cabin and said, "Bessie, I am leaving you." Not understanding what he was talking about, I asked, "You mean you're going back to Piedmont?" "No," replied Jack, "I'm leaving you . . . separating. . . ." Stunned, I sank to the edge of a cot and stared at him for a long time before I could stammer, "Why, Daddy, what do you mean . . . you've just been talking about Southern California. . . ." Jack kept repeating doggedly that he was separating from me, and I kept crying, "But I don't understand . . . what has happened to you?" He refused to tell me another word.'

No one, least of all Bessie, knew that Charmian Kittredge had happened to Jack. Of all the women of whom she might have been jealous, it had never entered her mind to be jealous of Miss Kittredge, who was between five and six years older than Jack, not attractive-looking, the subject of a good deal of biting talk and comment among the Piedmont crowd who knew her well. She had been around Jack a good deal, but Bessie was accustomed to that from the house in Piedmont. Jack apparently had not been seeing more of her than of anyone else at the camp. Besides, he had said a number of uncomplimentary things about her to his wife; Bessie knew that he did not care much for her.

In June, 1903, a month before the separation, Miss Kittredge was writing to Jack, 'Oh, you are wonderful—most wonderful of all. I saw your face grow younger under my touch. What is the matter with the world, and where do I belong? I think nowhere, if a man's heart be nowhere.' In the same month Jack writes to her: 'My arms are about you. I kiss you on the lips, the free frank lips I know and love. Had you been coy and fluttering, giving the lie to what you had already appeared to be by manifesting the slightest prudery or false fastidiousness, I really think I should have been utterly disgusted. "Dear man, dear love!" I lie awake repeating those phrases over and over.'

On July 7 Charmian Kittredge writes to Jack: 'I am growing frightened about one thing. I am afraid that you and I will never be able to express what we are to each other. The whole thing is so tremendous and all human modes of expression too inadequate.' A few days later she typewrites from her business office in San Francisco: 'You are a poet and you are beautiful. Believe me, oh my dear, my dear, that I never was so GLAD, so genuinely, satisfyingly GLAD over anything in my life. To feel that the man who is the greatest of all to me, has not found me wanting.'

In the canvas-covered cabin at Glen Ellen, with his two children sleeping peacefully, Jack spent what was probably the most wretched and confused night of his life. He was above all a gentle, kindly person. Sensitive himself, knowing the nature of pain, he had shrunk from hurting others. It had always been his great joy to help people, to share with them everything he had. Yet he was caught in the grip of such a shattering compulsion that he was walking out on his wife and babies just as he had walked out on Flora and John London when he was younger and emotionally unstable. A tender human being, a socialist who had compassion for all of humanity, who was willing to give the best in him, without hope of reward, to better the lot of the masses, his social and moral consciousness was shoved aside by the conflicting Nietzschean ideal, the strange but constant bedfellow of his socialism, which told him that he was the superman who could wrest from life whatever he wished, that he had no need to concern himself with slave morality, or the feelings of the slave-mass, of which Bessie was an unfortunate member.

In the morning Jack returned to Piedmont, moved his possessions out of the house he had written about so proudly to his friends, and rented a room from the family of Frank Atherton. Within a few days the newspapers had the story of the separation splashed over the front page. Since Jack refused to talk to the reporters, they blamed his separation on *The Kempton-Wace Letters*, for in it Jack had written, 'The emotion of love is not based on reason.' This sentiment was alleged to have hurt Bessie so deeply that it had caused a break-up of their marriage.

JACK's relationship with Charmian Kittredge started on a high plane of avowal and mounted ever higher. On September 1 she writes to him: 'You are my very OWN, and I adore you, just as blindly and madly and passionately and unreasonably as ever girl loved before.' The next day she continues: 'Ah, my love, you ARE such a man. And I love you, every bit of you, as I have never loved, and shall never love again!' Two days later: 'Oh, you are my dear Love my Own Man, my very, actual, true Heart Husband, and I love you so!' In her next letter she says: 'Think of me tenderly and lovingly and madly; think of me as your dear dear friend, your Sweetheart, your Wife. You are all the world to me, and I shall live on the thought of your face, your voice, your mouth, your masterful and tender arms—all the whole, sweet Man—until we meet again. Oh, Jack, Jack! You're so booful!'

Not to be outstripped in protestation or literary expression, Jack replies, 'You cannot know how much you mean to me. As you say, it is inexpressible. The moments when first I meet you, and see you, and touch you, are unspeakably thrilling moments. When I receive your letters you are with me, in the flesh before me, and I am looking into your golden eyes. Ah, dear heart, my love for woman did begin with you and will end with you.'

For fear of the scandal that would descend upon them when the cause of his separation became known, the lovers met secretly once or twice a week. During the days when they could not be together they released a torrent of letters to each other. From her business office in San Francisco Miss Kittredge wrote daily letters ranging from one thousand to five thousand words; the many hundreds of pages she composed and typed to Jack during the ensuing two years would be the equivalent of half a dozen normal-sized novels. Her letters are artful and coquettish, fluttery and flowery, but beneath the façade of verbiage can be detected the hand of a shrewd and clever woman. Pictured through her letters their love becomes the greatest love of all times. She tells him that she always knew she was intended for some extraordinary destiny. 'Oh, Jack, dear, dear Love, you are my idol, and you cannot know how I love you,' until he comes to believe that he is loved as no man since the beginning of time has ever been loved, and he answers, convinced, 'I doubt if I can ever love you enough, so greatly do you love me.' The way in which he takes her cues, letter by letter, is almost automatic; since he is the literary one of the relationship, can he write any the less gallantly, avowedly, passionately?

'Nay, nay, dear Love,' he writes, 'not in my eyes is this love of ours a small and impotent thing. That I should be willing to live for you or die for you is proof in itself that it means more to me than life or death. That you should be the one woman to me of all women; that my hunger for you should be greater than any hunger for food I have ever felt; that my desire for you should bite harder than any desire I have ever felt for fame and fortune—all, all goes to show how big is this, our love.'

Under the spell of Miss Kittredge's thousands of words beating daily against his eyes, he begins to sound like a fifth-rate Marie Corelli. Mesmerized by her literary style, he replies in her own florid-purple nineteenth-century effusion, a manner against which he had asserted his revolt since the days of his earliest writing; a style of effervescing about love from which he was never to recover, and which was to mar so many of his books. Jack, who in *The Kempton-Wace Letters* had been the antagonist of sentimental and poetic love, the advocate of the theory that love is just a biological urge, suddenly becomes 'God's own mad lover, dying on a kiss.' If Anna Strunsky could have read over his shoulder and seen how completely he had reversed his position, she might have enjoyed an ironic laugh while confronting him with his own line, 'Without an erotic literature man could not possibly love in the way he does.'

Writing from Stockton on November 10, 1903, he reaches the heights of his profusion. 'Know, sweet love, that I never knew how greatly you loved me until there came the free and utter abandonment, the consent of you and your love and of every fibre of you. When you sealed with your dear body all that your soul had told me, then I knew! I knew!—knew that the last of you and all of you were mine. Had you loved me as you do, and yet withheld, you would not have been quite so great a woman to me. My love and worship of you would not have attained the sheer pitch that they have. If you will go over my letters I am sure you will find that I was never utterly *mad* until after you gave greatly. It was *after* you gave greatly that I became your "slave," expressed willingness to die for you, and all the rest of the delicious hyperbole of love. But it is not hyperbole, dear, not the hyperbole of the silly sentimentalist. When I say I am your slave, I say it as a *reasonable* man—which goes to show how really and completely mad I am.'

In 1890, when she was nineteen years old, Charmian Kittredge was, in her own words, 'a rosy-cheeked girl whom many people call pretty, generally in good spirits except when jealous.' By 1903, at thirty-two, she was not considered pretty; she had thin lips, narrow eyes, and drooping lids, but she carried herself with an air of exciting bravado. In many ways she resembled Frona Welse, whom Jack had created to stand as a model for the twentieth-century woman. Forced by the death of her parents to earn her own living in the days when it was not considered genteel for a girl to work, she had made herself into a competent secretary 'earning the small and insufficient salary of thirty dollars a month.' She was well read, unconventional in thought; when Jack first met her, in 1900, she had already begun to collect a library of the more modern and daring novels the Oakland Public Library was banning. She had a genuine love for music, sang pleasingly, and even while working six days a week had had the force and discipline to train herself to become an accomplished pianist.

She had a sexually rich and stimulating voice with a wide tone range, laughed a great deal, even though the point of humor might be obscure, and was an indefatigable talker, being known to speak from four to seven hours without interrupting herself. She could carry on an intelligent and logical discussion, for she had a varied flow of words and phrases. A woman of great physical courage, she was the first to ride astride a horse into the hills when few women were riding at all, and those who dared were riding English side-saddle on the Golden Gate Park bridle paths. She had a deep love of horses. Ambitious, both socially and intellectually, she worked hard to advance herself, had saved her money with which to take a trip through Europe, did a little painting on China dishes, tried hard to make progress each year over the last.

However, as reflected by her frothy language and frilly lace caps, by her fluttering manner, in anything relating to love and sex she was a perfect blooming of the nineteenth-century woman, the exact opposite of Frona Welse. Many facets of her complex nature are revealed in her diary: her saccharine, sentimentalist approach to romance; every man she meets, no matter how casually, instantly becomes in her mind the source of a great romance. Every man looks at her either admiringly or passionately, and cannot tear his eyes from her. She has little use for her own sex; every woman is jealous of her and she is jealous of every woman. When there were men about she dramatized herself with verve, with gusto, making a conscious bid for the focus of attention. People who knew her disclose that she was no respecter of private property as far as men were concerned. Because of her preoccupation with the snaring of a husband, young women who were keeping company or were married were suspicious and afraid of her.

There is a continuous string of men who come into her life and are soon gone. One is hard-pressed to understand why so attractive a young woman was not able to achieve marriage. Miss Kittredge, too, is stumped. Auntie, who demands immediately if each new man's intention is marriage, is getting nervous as the years pass by and all the other girls marry but her niece somehow always misses out.

Miss Kittredge had been a frequent visitor at the London house in Piedmont on her return from Europe, and in his vagrant mood Jack went on the make. 'I confess what you already know, what you knew from the very first moment. When I first broke silence it was with the intention of making you my mistress. You were so frank, so honest, and not least so unafraid. Had you been less so, in one touch, one pressure, one action, one speech, I think I should have attempted to beat down your will to mine. . . . I remember when we rode side by side on a back seat, and I suggested "Haywards" and you looked me in the eyes, smiling, not mocking, with no offended fastidiousness in your face, no shock, no fear, no surprise, nothing but good nature and sweet frankness—when you looked me thus in the eyes and said simply, "Not tonight."'

Two months after his separation from Bessie, Jack writes, 'Sometimes I wonder why I love you, and I am compelled to confess that it is not for your beautiful body or mind that I love you, but for the flash of spirit that runs through all of you, that makes you carry your clothes, that makes you game, that makes you sensitive; that makes you proud, proud in yourself, proud of your body, and that makes your body in itself and apart from you, proud.'

There can be little doubt but that he had become entangled with Miss Kittredge during the month of June, when he was alone in the house in Piedmont, and that his suggestion to Bessie that they move to Southern California, leaving behind the San Francisco Bay he loved so dearly, was an attempt to escape from the situation in which he found himself. It apparently took Miss Kittredge four hours of solid talk to change his mind.

'If either of his two daughters had been a son,' observed one of Jack's closest friends, 'no force on earth could have torn him away from his family.'

Charmian Kittredge was genuinely convinced that Jack was mismated; she believed she could be the kind of wife he needed, one who would roam and adventure and dare with him, and not be tied down to a home and routine. Abetted by her Aunt Netta, who harbored the lovers from the very beginning, she appears to have been the motivating force behind the break-up in the London family, yet the fact that Jack was vulnerable is evidenced by the completeness with which he gave his mind's love to Anna Strunsky, and his body's love to the woman on the train to Chicago. It is likely that if not for the advent of Miss Kittredge with her particular background, Jack would have remained married to Bessie, using his home for headquarters while he traveled and adventured by himself. There is always the possibility, however, that if Miss Kittredge had not been successful in capturing him, the next woman, or the tenth from the next, might have. . . . As Jack had written so often in his stories, this was a world of dog eat dog, with the wolves devouring those who fell behind; if Bessie were too weak to hold her husband, that was no concern of Miss Kittredge; she had the right to fight for what she wanted and to take all she could get. Where Jack would be hurting three of the people he loved most, two of whom he had caused to be brought into the world, she would be hurting no one she loved.

In order to allay suspicion, Miss Kittredge went frequently to Bessie's house and accepted Bessie's confidences about her marital difficulties. On September 12, 1903, she writes to Jack, 'Last night I went to see Bessie. She was lovely to me—so lovely it made me sick. She begged me to come and stay all night with her, any time. She was so sweet and hospitable that it seemed as if all the trouble and tearing apart might be a dream. Sometimes I have to fight off a feeling of actual WICKEDNESS, when I think of it all, but my reason enters and helps me out; but oh!!!' Five days later she continues: 'I have about given up thinking Bessie really suspects me, though I would not be surprised at ANYTHING she did! She is deep, and I do not understand deceitful people.' Miss Kittredge played her part so adroitly that on October 2 Jack was able to write to her, 'All goes well with Bessie, so far as you and I are concerned. She told me last night she wouldn't know what she would do if it weren't for you. In fact you were exalted above all people.'

Though Bessie was stricken, she was too proud to fight, to cause scenes. Completely in the dark as to her husband's motives, she sat quietly and wondered why the man who had insisted that she marry him, who had insisted that she bear him children, who had accepted her financial help during the first year of their marriage and her assistance on manuscripts, notes, and the assembling of material, who had lived with her in peaceful comradeship for three years, should suddenly, without warning, discard her.

In her troubles she found one friend: Flora London. For three years Bessie and Flora had quarreled, driving Jack to distraction, but Flora had learned the meaning of motherhood through her love for little Johnny Miller; she now turned against her son for abandoning his family. Bitter at what he termed his mother's treachery, Jack's mind fell into chaos. He developed a persecution mania, charging that everyone was against him, that the world was conspiring to keep him from his 'love-woman.' On September 22 from the *Spray* he writes to Miss Kittredge, 'By every human right I should not have ridden off into the dark. You were mine, mine, and the world had no right to drive me away. And yet I was driven, ignobly driven, from the woman I love dearer than life.'

His thoughts became so confused that in spite of the magnificent critical reception of *The Call of the Wild*, which the press agreed was a 'classic enriching American literature,' he could not do a stroke of work. He decided that the only way he would ever finish *The Sea Wolf* was to escape the churning currents about him by slipping his cables. He had the *Spray* overhauled, then sent transportation money to Cloudesley Johns, who lived in Southern California and knew little of his troubles. The two men headed for the mouth of the Sacramento River; in the mornings they worked at their books, in the afternoons they swam, shot ducks, fished. After his woman-complicated world—though he himself had made the complications—he found the companionship of a man salutary. 'The more I see of Cloudesley, the more I like him. He is honest and loyal, young and fresh, understands the discipline of a boat, and is a good cook, to say nothing of being a good-natured and genial companion.'

Man fashion, he shoved his troubles out of his mind and wrote his thousand words on *The Sea Wolf* every morning. The only trouble he could not successfully ignore was that by September 14 he was again without funds. He wrote to Miss Kittredge, 'Bessie makes out to you that I am almost destitute. I feel pretty close to it, when all I have between me and pauperism is a bare $100, and an unexpected doctor bill comes in for $115.' He put aside *The Sea Wolf* to write a story for *Youth's Companion*, plotting a whole month of hack work in order that he might get a little ahead.

Every few days he called in at a small town, Stockton, Antioch, Vallejo, for his mail. One day he received a letter from Bessie telling him that Joan was down with typhoid. He raced back to his daughter and was at her bedside constantly, in anguish lest the child die. When the doctor reported that she was sinking, Jack felt it was retribution being visited upon him. He vowed that if only the child would get well he would give up his great love and return to his home. The newspapers reported that the Londons had been reconciled at the bedside of their daughter. However, when Joan began to recover, Jack was like the shipwrecked man who fell on his knees on the raft and prayed, 'Dear God, if you will only send me a ship I promise to be good for the rest of my life . . . never mind, God, I see a sail.' When Joan was up and about again, he went back to the *Spray*.

Though the present might be muddled he had done good work in the past and that good work brought its reward. *The Call of the Wild* caught the popular favor, and because of its universal theme was selling to all classes and ages of people. By November it was number three on the best-seller lists, topped only by *The Bar Sinister* and *The Little Shepherd of Kingdom Come,* and leading such favorites as *Mrs. Wiggs of the Cabbage Patch, Rebecca of Sunnybrook Farm,* and *Pigs in Clover.* In November *The People of the Abyss* was released to very nearly solid praise, the critics claiming that as a sociological document the book stood unequalled, that if he had never written anything besides *The People of the Abyss,* Jack London would deserve to be famous, and that it would make a smugly complacent civilization sit up and wonder if it had been making the best use of its opportunities. The English press, which might have been expected to consider him an unqualified intruder, accused him of exaggeration and of tackling his subject with an axe, but also admitted that no one had succeeded as he had in getting close to the heart of the London slums.

Jack had sent Brett the first half of *The Sea Wolf.* Brett was so excited by the tale that he sent it to the editor of *Century* magazine with a glowing recommendation. When he heard what Brett had done Jack shook his head in perplexity, for he knew the *Century* to be a staid and conservative family organ. It was unthinkable that it should run the vigorous and bitterly real *Sea Wolf.* The editor of *Century* was thrilled with the manuscript, agreeing that if he were given the right to blue-pencil the latter half, on which Jack was still working, if the man and woman when left alone on the island would do nothing to offend his subscribers, he would pay four thousand dollars for the serial rights.

Four thousand dollars! For the magazine rights alone! As much money as he had received for the total rights to *The Call of the Wild.* He spread full canvas and sailed at top speed down the Bay and through the Estuary to his dock. Immediately on landing he telegraphed the editor of *Century* that he could blue-pencil to his heart's content, that he 'was absolutely confident the American prude would not be shocked by the second half of the book.' The deal was closed and Jack dug in with renewed vitality and concentration, completing the book in thirty feverish days of writing. The *Century* magazine was already blazoning his name to the four winds in advertisements astounding in size and vigor as they told the whole world that Mr. Jack London, author of the popular *The Call of the Wild,* would have his new book, *The Sea Wolf,* published in the pages of *Century.*

Within a few months he was to be the possessor of four thousand dollars in cash. In the meanwhile, just one week before Christmas, he found himself practically penniless. He had exactly \$20.02 in the bank, and no Christmas presents bought. 'I wonder if on the strength of the sale of *The Call of the Wild* Brett is going to give me an honorarium for a Christmas present? It would come in handy.' *The Call of the Wild* was having what the publishers term a runaway sale, but Brett did not send him the honorarium. This does not appear to have been stinginess on his part, for he was liberal with his star author over a period of exacting years. Brett felt that Jack had made a bargain and that if he sent him an honorarium he would be breaking the agreement and setting a precedent. If Jack had kept his rights to *The Call of the Wild* the royalties during the next few years would have earned him close to a hundred thousand dollars—assuming that Brett would have invested as much money in promotion under the changed conditions. Jack never regretted his bargain; Brett had spent a fortune in advertising his name, and he knew the worth of advertising to his future career.

By New Year's Day of 1904 it appeared certain that Russia and Japan would go to war. Jack did not want this to happen; as a socialist he was against all war because he knew that in war the working people of the world were shot down to further or protect the moneyed interests. However, if war did begin he wanted to be on the spot to see it. He had studied military tactics and equipment for destruction, was interested to observe what modern warfare could do to destroy civilization. He also had a lot of theories about the Yellow Peril to investigate. In addition he felt that if he made his reputation as a war correspondent he would always be able to earn money. It was Adventure Road once again, offering an escape from his marital and love complications.

Magazines and newspapers began sending their correspondents to Japan. Jack received offers from five syndicates, and accepted the one that bid the most money, the Hearst chain. In the first week of January he went to the offices of the *Examiner* and had his picture taken on the roof of the building. Wearing a workingman's dark suit and high shoes and needing a haircut, he looked as though he had just come off a shift at the Belmont Steam Laundry. The pictures reveal the stress and anxiety of the six months since he had separated from Bessie in their cabin at Glen Ellen; the look of boyishness has been dissipated, he appears troubled and harassed.

He ordered Macmillan to send his monthly check to Bessie, asked Eliza to give Miss Kittredge anything she might need, the first intimation Eliza had had of what was going on, then commissioned George Sterling to edit *The Sea Wolf* before Macmillan sent it to press. On the seventh of January, 1904, five days before his twenty-eighth birthday, he crossed on the ferry to the Embarcadero and sailed on the S.S. *Siberia* for Yokohama.

On board the *Siberia* was a jolly group of newspapermen, which promptly named itself the Vultures. On the first day out from Honolulu, while playing jumping games on deck, Jack landed on a round stick and sprained his left ankle. His right ankle being weak from a spill off an express train when a Tramp Royal, this accident crippled him. 'For sixty-five sweaty hours I lay on my back. Yesterday I was carried on deck on the back of an English correspondent.' He had little time to brood over his ill fate, for the Vultures thronged his cabin, regaling him with yarns of other wars and other assignments.

When he docked at Yokohama he had a drink at each of the bars where as a boy of seventeen he had drunk shoulder to shoulder with Big Victor and Axel when they had been the Three Sports of the *Sophie Sutherland*. Then he took the train for Tokio, where he found correspondents assembled from all over the world, awaiting permission from the Japanese Government to go into the field. Because war had not been formally declared the Japanese officials were evading the requests, providing the correspondents instead with sightseeing trips, sumptuous banquets, diverting entertainment.

Jack had not come to Japan to attend banquets. After two days of encountering exquisitely polite evasions he did a little sagacious interviewing and learned what the other correspondents did not yet suspect, that the Japanese Government had no intention of allowing the newspapermen anywhere near the firing line. He realized that if he wanted to report the war he would simply have to go out and find it. Without breathing a word to any of the Vultures he slipped out of Tokio on a train for Kobe and Nagasaki, where he hoped to catch a boat for Chemulpo in Korea, where the Japanese forces were being rushed to the front.

After a few days of hunting up and down the coast he found a vessel going to Chemulpo on February 1. He bought his ticket, thinking of how he would be with the Army in Korea while the other correspondents were still being fed sumptuous dinners in Tokio. To fill his spare hours he went into the streets to take photographs of coolies loading coal and bales of cotton. Within a few moments he saw the inside of the first of a string of jails and Japanese military prisons that must have made him long for the comparative security of the hall man's job at the Erie County Penitentiary: for the Japanese officials had arrested him as a Russian spy! He was put through eight hours of grilling, moved the next day to a larger jail for more questioning, and finally released . . . too late to catch his boat.

Learning that soldiers were being called from their homes in the middle of the night, he frantically searched the coastline for another ship bound for Chemulpo. Finally on the eighth of February he secured passage on the *Kieogo Maru,* but the Government confiscated the vessel just before it was to sail. Outraged at the thought that he might not be at the front to report the first battle, he made a wild dash in a steam launch for a small steamer going to Fusan, a port en route to Chemulpo, catching it amid such confusion that one of his trunks was lost overboard. It was a native ship, with not a bite of white man's food aboard; in spite of the fact that it was alternately snowing and sleeting, he had to sleep on the open deck, reminding him of the nights he had lain shivering in the railroad jungles without a blanket.

At Fusan he made connections with a second boat, but when they reached Mokpo the Government seized the vessel and unceremoniously dumped passengers and baggage ashore. The speed with which the Japanese were shipping soldiers to Korea convinced him that war was about to be declared, yet here he was, several hundred miles from Chemulpo, and no ship to be had. He was being paid to write up the war, and by God! he was going to write it. But how was he going to get to it? The voice of Marshall Wellman, his maternal grandfather who had built a raft at Put-In Bay and floated it back to Cleveland, told him in clear and unmistakable terms. Charter an open native junk and sail it across the Yellow Sea, then along the Korean coast until he reached Chemulpo!

The thermometer read fourteen degrees below zero, but he had endured sixty below in the Klondike; the wind was howling over the Yellow Sea, but not any worse than it had howled over Lake Linderman; it was a magnificently courageous, foolhardy thing for him to try, but no more foolhardy or courageous than for the twelve-year-old lad to have sailed a leaky catboat across treacherous San Francisco Bay in a lashing southwester. That his journey would be as difficult and dangerous as that made by the Vikings who crossed the Atlantic in an open boat only made it the more appealing. He purchased what he considered a seaworthy junk, engaged three intrepid Koreans to help him man it, and set sail for Chemulpo.

'The wildest and most gorgeous thing ever! If you could see me just now, a captain of a junk with a crew of three Koreans who speak no English. Made Kun San at nightfall, after having carried away a mast and smashed the rudder. We arrived in the driving rain, with the wind cutting like a knife. You should have seen me being made comfortable —five Japanese maidens helping me undress, take a bath, and get into bed, passing remarks about my beautiful white skin.'

For the next six days and nights he was out in freezing weather, the tiny boat tossed by a fierce gale, in danger every moment of going under. There was no heat except from a charcoal burner, the fumes of which poisoned him even worse than the cold native food upon which he had to subsist. Both ankles being weak, he sailed the junk in a crippled state. His condition when he reached Chemulpo is described by an English photographer who had arrived there on the last boat to clear.

'When London arrived at Chemulpo I did not recognize him. He was a physical wreck. His ears were frozen, his fingers were frozen, his feet were frozen. He said he didn't mind his condition so long as he got to the front. I want to say that Jack London is one of the grittiest men it has ever been my good fortune to meet. He is just as heroic as any of the characters in his novels.'

Jack bought several horses, learned to ride, engaged servants and a *mapu,* or horse-boy, and started north across Korea in the direction of the Russian troops. The roads were covered with mud and ice, and by nightfall each day they had to beat the Japanese soldiers to the next village in order to find a place to sleep.

After several weeks of forced march during which he endured incredible hardship, he finally got to Ping Yang, the farthest point north to be reached by any war correspondent. Here he was held in jail for a week on a complaint lodged with the Japanese Government by the correspondents who were still being entertained in Tokio, and whose papers were sending sizzling cables demanding to know why Jack London could send dispatches out of Korea when they couldn't. Ordered back to Seoul, two hundred miles behind the front, he was thrown into a military prison on orders from Tokio because he had no permit to accompany the Army.

The Japanese Government then decided to make a friendly gesture to the other nations. 'Fourteen of us correspondents, who had refused to remain pickled in Tokio, were allowed to travel with the Army, but it was like a party of Cook's tourists with the supervising officers as guides. We saw what we were permitted to see, and the chief duty of the officers looking after us was to keep us from seeing anything. We did see part of the battle of the Yalu from the walls of Wiju, but when one Japanese company was annihilated, we were ordered back to camp.'

With the arrival of spring weather the correspondents were permitted to cross the Yalu River; in a grove beside a temple the Army built each of them a magnificent little camp. Jack swam, played bridge and other games, but his movements were limited to a radius of a mile and a half . . . while the Japanese were out bombarding the Russian entrenchments.

It was difficult to work when held captive forty miles behind the line of action, yet he did his best. He made a careful estimate of the Japanese Army: 'The Japanese soldiery and equipment command universal admiration.' He wrote analyses of the military tactics and maneuvers of both armies. He took photographs, utilizing the training Bessie had given him with a camera, of the Army on the march, digging trenches, making camp, caring for its wounded, the first war pictures to reach America. Though he sent out nineteen dispatches and hundreds of photographs, he had to wait until he got back to San Francisco to learn if the *Examiner* had received them. 'I am disgusted!' he cried. 'I'll never go to a war between Orientals again. The vexation and delay are too great. Never were correspondents treated in any war as they have been in this.' By June he was ready to go home, for he knew that he was wasting his time. 'I am profoundly irritated by the futility of my position in this Army and sheer inability to do any decent work. The only compensation for these months of irritation is a better comprehension of Asiatic geography and character.'

A threat of court martial gave impetus to his desire to leave. One day his *mapu,* reporting to Army headquarters for feed for his master's horses, was prevented from getting his full share by a Korean whom Jack had long suspected of robbing him. When Jack accused the Korean of this, the man made a threatening gesture with his knife. Jack knocked him down with a blow of his fist. He was promptly commanded to report to General Fuji, who threatened drastic punishment. When news reached Richard Harding Davis, splendidly marooned in Tokio, that Jack London was in danger of being executed, he burned the cables to President Roosevelt, who in turn sent angry protestations to Japan. General Fuji was ordered to release him. Jack packed his kit and made his way back to Tokio, where he found the correspondents he had left behind four months before, still awaiting official permission to join the Army. Davis rode with him to Yokohama to see him off, swearing that as soon as he heard a shot fired he was returning home, but after having waited all these months he couldn't leave without hearing that one shot!

'Only in another war, with a white man's army,' mourned Jack, 'may I hope to redeem myself.' He need not have felt badly; he had gotten out more dispatches than any other correspondent, had given his paper several scoops, especially with the war photographs, and they were well enough pleased with his work. Not the least important aspect of his Oriental junket was that the newspaper chain had given his stories flaming headlines. What with the success of *The Call of the Wild,* and the spectacular advertising *Century* had given *The Sea Wolf,* by the time he reached San Francisco the name of Jack London was becoming more widely known than that of any other American writer.

He confidently expected that when his ship tied up at the Embarcadero he would be greeted by Miss Kittredge's outstretched arms; instead he was greeted by the outstretched hand of a process server with a copy of Bessie's divorce complaint. Bessie had put an attachment on the earnings still due him as war correspondent for the *Examiner.* He flinched under the blow, but what stunned and made him heartsick as he read further in the complaint was that Bessie had named Anna Strunsky as the cause of her marital troubles!

Jack had been eager for Bessie to begin her divorce proceedings, but to involve Anna in a scandal, Anna whom he had not seen for two years . . . ! When he was able to blink the mist out of his eyes he saw to his relief that Bessie had not accused Anna of wrongdoing; she had merely charged that their collaboration over *The Kempton-Wace Letters* had caused her husband to become cold and indifferent to her.

There was no sign of Miss Kittredge anywhere on the dock. When Eliza, who had come down to greet him, handed him his mail, he found a letter from Newton, Iowa, where she was staying with an aunt. He read, 'I fear you will be disappointed that I am not in California. The terror of all my dear ones, the scandal, makes me sicker every time I think of the possible happenings during the next few months. I am not writing coldly, dear; indeed there never was a moment since we loved each other that I was madder for you than right now, but I am forced for the sake of others, as well as my own, to be level-headed.'

Jack was hurt, angry, disgusted. When he went up to Piedmont to greet Bessie and to hold his two daughters in his arms, the thought came to him, 'If I was brave enough to sail the Yellow Sea in a sub-zero gale, in an open junk, then why am I not brave enough to stand by my wife and obligations even though I have fallen in love with another woman?'

The next morning the news flashed across the continent that Jack London's wife was divorcing him, and naming Anna Strunsky. The San Francisco papers announced it in bold streamers; from that moment forward Jack found that he would live the smallest and most intimate details of his life on the front page of the newspapers. Cornered by reporters he cried, 'The only feature of the case that stirs me up is that Miss Strunksy's name should be mentioned, for she is an extremely sensitive person.' Miss Strunsky told the newspapermen: 'I am astonished. I have seen Mr. London only twice in the past two years, for I have been in New York and Europe. My visit to the London house occurred two years ago, and at that time there was not a breath of rumor to the effect that their married life was not a happy one.' Asked in 1937 why she had named Miss Strunsky, Bessie said that she regretted her mistake. 'I knew that Jack would never have left me except for another woman, and I couldn't think who it might be, except Anna Strunsky.'

It took Jack but a short time to convince Bessie that Anna Strunsky had nothing to do with their separation; once convinced, she withdrew Anna's name from the case. He then pointed out that if she stuck to her lawyer's advice to keep an attachment on his earnings, the lawyers would get most of the money and there would be little left for the children. Quite gray now, saddened, bitterly wounded, Bessie asked if he would build her a house in Piedmont so that she would always have a secure roof over her children's head. When he agreed, she withdrew the attachment, amended the suit to simple desertion. Jack wrote to Miss Kittredge, 'It has taken all the resolution I could summon to prevent my going back, for the children's sake. I have been sadly shaken during the last forty-eight hours—so shaken that it almost seemed easier to sacrifice myself for the little ones.'

Instead he told Bessie that Charmian Kittredge was the other woman. Bessie received the news in stony silence, her only comment being that she never cared to see Miss Kittredge again.

In July he went up to Glen Ellen, rented a cottage from Ninetta Eames, and waited for Miss Kittredge to come back to him. When she wrote that she needed money for transportation he sent her a check for eighty dollars. Still she kept writing that she was afraid to come home for fear of the scandal. At length Jack burst out: 'Am hugely disgusted. Somebody is not playing fair. I talked it over with Netta and Edward and both were satisfied that there was nothing to apprehend from Bessie. I wrote a check, which Edward cashed and mailed to you . . .' after which follows ten tumultuous pages of how 'hugely disgusted' he was with Ninetta Eames and Edward Payne, the first of a long series of disgusts that were to extract their toll on his psyche.

The only pleasure he derived from the hot summer weeks was taking the *Spray* for long sails. The boys along the banks of the creeks recognized him and cried out, 'Hello, Jack, how's every little thing in Korea?' When Manyoungi, the loyal and devoted Korean boy who had served him so well, and to whom he had given transportation money, arrived, Jack rented a roomy flat on the corner of Sixteenth Street and Broadway, where he installed Flora as his chaperon. Happy to have her son to herself once again, Flora forgot about her quarrels with Jack when he had left Bessie, and settled down to become a charming hostess, with Manyoungi keeping the house clean and cooking for 'Master.'

Jack entered one of the most unhappy and unproductive periods of his life. He was unhappy about losing his two children; he was unhappy about hurting Bessie and Anna; he was unhappy about Charmian not standing by; he was unhappy about having squandered his time and health in Korea and producing no good work; he was unhappy because his thoughts were dry and brittle, because no big ideas came to him, no internal force to conceive and execute big projects. At the bottom of his despair he wrote to Anna Strunsky, 'I wander through life delivering hurts to all that know me. And I am changed. Though I was a materialist when first I met you, I had the saving grace of enthusiasm. That enthusiasm is the thing that is spoiled.'

The Faith of Men, his fourth collection of short stories, which had been released by Macmillan in April, was selling so well that it had to be reprinted in June, and now again in August, but even this did not hearten him. He agreed with the critic of *The Nation* who regretted that a man with his powers should spend all his time in the frozen North. Both his body and mind went soggy and stale. He came down with the grippe; when he recovered he developed a nervous skin itch that put him through torture. He could not exercise, his weight fell off, he became thin, soft, jumpy. Because of his physical affliction and the low state of his mind he lived as a recluse.

In August he paid sixteen hundred dollars for a lot in Piedmont, called in an architect, let Bessie say what kind of house she wanted, and watched the work begin. When he had returned from Korea he had four thousand dollars in the bank from the *Century* and the *Examiner;* every dollar of it, plus a good-sized mortgage, went into the building of the house, leaving him once again without funds. Determined not to let his melancholia disrupt his discipline, he plunged into work. He read the dozens of books he had missed while in Korea; wrote articles, such as 'The Yellow Peril,' for magazines and newspapers; began a short prize-fight novel called *The Game;* lectured to every socialist organization in the vicinity; spoke free of charge to clubs and churches in order to make converts to socialism and thus hasten the revolution. He began work on his first play, *The Scorn of Women,* based on one of his Alaskan tales, gave readings on *The People of the Abyss* and *The Class Struggle.* His skin ailment receding, he again entertained his friends on Wednesday nights, went on swimming parties at the Piedmont Baths and on picnics in the hills. He worked hard and played hard because he did not want to have time to realize how wretched he felt. Yet he did not fool himself about the quality of the work he was doing. 'Still plugging away at *The Game.* Believe it is a failure, but the work is good for me. *The Scorn of Women* is not a big effort, I wouldn't dare a big effort.'

His one sustaining force was Brett of Macmillan. On the strength of the advance sale of *The Sea Wolf,* which reached twenty thousand by the beginning of October, Brett increased the monthly allowance to two hundred and fifty dollars. He assured Jack that it was a truly great book, and finally, at the beginning of November, communicated the magnificent news that *The Sea Wolf,* Jack's tenth publication in less than four years, had sold forty thousand copies to the bookstores before its release. In December he sent Jack a check for three thousand dollars, which Jack had figured he would need to get him out from under his load of insurance, mortgage, and personal debts.

The Sea Wolf shot onto the market like a thunderbolt, became the rage overnight, was on everybody's lips to be praised or cursed. Many readers were insulted and offended by its attitudes; others valiantly took up the cudgels in its defense. Part of the press called it cruel, brutal, and revolting, but the greater part agreed that it was 'rare and original genius . . . raises the quality of modern imaginative literature.' It marked another milestone in American literature, not only because of its realism and vigor, the wealth of characters and situations unknown to American literature, but also because it heightened the intellectual tone of the modern novel. Where before had Americans encountered such dread suspense, such authentic death-appeal as found in the conflict of the spiritual versus the materialistic as took place on board the *Ghost* between Wolf Larsen and Peter Van Weyden? Where before had they been presented with mature philosophy, had they found it made exciting, something to fight about? Jack had taken the scholar's revolution of the nineteenth century, dramatized it, popularized it, made it thrilling and intelligible to the great mass of people who had never even heard of evolution, biology, or scientific materialism. Darwin, Spencer, Nietzsche stalk through the book, its unseen protagonists. In dramatizing the teachings of his beloved masters he made the battles of the mind as exciting as the Irish bricklayers' free-for-all in Weasel Park in his later novel, *The Valley of the Moon,* no mean accomplishment.

Toward the end of the book Jack introduces its only woman character and thereby marred what was, and is still, a nearly perfect example of the novelist's art. When the literary critics declared that the woman was unbelievable, Jack cried, 'I was in love with a woman, and I wrote her into my book, and the critics tell me that the woman I love is unbelievable.' He had not only written Miss Kittredge into the book but also the poetic-hysteric manner of writing about her which he had absorbed while answering her letters. In everything pertaining to the woman and the love between her and Peter Van Weyden, *The Sea Wolf* shows the worst of the rococo nineteenth century; on all other counts it is a forerunner of the best in twentieth-century literature.

A few weeks after its release it ran fourth to such raspberry-syruped sawdust as *The Masqueraders* by K. C. Thurston, *Prodigal Son* by Hall Caine, *Whosoever Shall Offend* by F. Marion Crawford, and *Beverly of Graustark* by George Barr McCutcheon. Three weeks later it was leading the best-seller lists, far out in front, and the twentieth century at last had thrown off the shackles of its predecessor. *The Sea Wolf* is as thrilling today, as profound a reading experience, as it was in November, 1904. It dates very little. Many critics consider it London's most powerful work; readers who pick it up again are enthralled by it.

Miss Kittredge returned from Iowa; they had several rapturous though fugitive engagements in Oakland and San Francisco, then she left for Glen Ellen to live with Ninetta Eames. There followed an occasional impassioned meeting, Jack penned a few rhapsodic messages, but for the most part his letters became newsy and casual. He is no longer God's own mad lover dying on a kiss. Once again his fancy roamed. Miss Kittredge tells of the development. 'I know that your thoughts and interests for the past few weeks have been taken up by another woman. You're only a boy, after all, dear Man, and transparent enough. But the shock you gave me the night of your "Scab" lecture in the city, made me very thoughtful. I saw you watch for her in the audience when you were through speaking; I saw you wave to her; I saw her backing and filling and fluttering after her manner. I saw you come together in the light of your cigarette, and I knew that you had been together the evening before. It isn't the mere fact of your unfaithfulness—you haven't that kind of integrity, very few men have, and I have faced the probability of your infidelity for a long time, and accepted it in a way. You have been very happy of late, and I knew I was not responsible for your light-heartedness. Somebody was, of course, and so . . .'

The year 1905 was one of headlines for Jack; everything he did excited the press. He began the year peacefully enough with a trip to Los Angeles, where he had been invited to address the local socialists. Julian Hawthorne wrote of him in the Los Angeles *Examiner*: 'It is pleasant to look upon Mr. London. He is as simple and straightforward as a grizzly bear. Upon his big, hearty, healthy nature is based a brain of unusual clearness and insight. His heart is warm, his sympathies wide, his opinions are his own—independent, courageously expounded.' He had no sooner returned to Oakland than he was invited by the liberal-minded president of the University of California to address the student body, an honor for a man who had been forced to leave the University only seven years before to work in a steam laundry. Jack harangued the young people with one of the most fiery speeches he had ever made, telling them that the greatest revolution the world had known was in the making before their very eyes, that if they did not wake up it would descend upon them in their sleep. After the lecture, when he complained to a professor of English that the students were given literary pap to feed upon, the professor replied, 'I wouldn't say that, Mr. London. A chapter of *The Call of the Wild* is included in our new reference book.' The circle of faculty members laughed, Jack flushed, murmured something about being canonized, and subsided. The following day the president of the University was attacked for permitting Jack London to preach revolution. He replied calmly, 'It is the man we invite, not the subject. London has earned his right to appear before us.'

It was at Stockton, where Jack accepted his first invitation to speak to a club of businessmen, that he got into his initial embroilment of the year by an act comparable in its foolhardiness and courage with crossing the Yellow Sea in a howling gale, or descending into the slums of London to write *The People of the Abyss*. The report of the Stockton paper, though a little biased, is a vivid one: 'He lectured the club of businessmen as though they were unruly schoolchildren; he demanded to know what each of them knew about the subject of socialism; he informed them that they had read little and seen less; he pounded the table and puffed out volumes of cigarette smoke—all of which so alarmed and befogged his auditors that they subsided into embarrassed silence.'

They did not remain silent long; at the close of his talk Jack horrified the businessmen of Stockton by telling them that the socialists in Russia who had participated in the 1905 uprising and killed several of the Czarist officials were his brothers! The audience jumped to its feet, storming at him. The next morning headlines screeched across the country: 'JACK LONDON CALLS RUSSIAN ASSASSINS HIS BROTHERS.' A furor arose, retractions were demanded, editorials flamed out against him, one of the papers cried, 'He is a fire-brand and red-flag anarchist, and should be arrested and prosecuted for treason.' Jack stood his ground. The Russian revolutionists were his brothers, and no one could make him repudiate them.

Society had persistently tried to lionize him as California's one literary genius, saying, 'Socialism is his hobby. A little extreme, but he's so young and original. His socialistic theories are only a fad, he'll get over them.' Now the gates were locked against him as tightly as though he were still a tramp on The Road. No longer was he invited to what he called pink teas, or to formal dinners where he wore his soft white shirt and flowing tie in a sea of starched linen; for society at last concluded that he had been serious when he had so charmingly told them over their dinner tables that as a class they were a parasitic fungus growth.

The scandal had no sooner died down than Jack gave another lecture in which he mentioned that William Lloyd Garrison had said, 'To hell with the Constitution!' when he was condemning slavery in 1856, and that General Sherman Bell had said it more lately in putting down strikers. The next morning he was once again the man of the hour, with hundreds of newspapers from California to New York shouting: 'JACK LONDON SAYS TO HELL WITH THE CONSTITUTION.' He did his best to explain that he was not the author of the phrase, but newspapers are rarely interested in the aftermath of a flash story.

If the freedom of the press allowed bigots to tear a man to shreds, it also permitted wiser men to speak their piece. In the San Francisco *Bulletin,* by no means a radical paper, he read, 'The hot sincerity and hatred of wrong that burns in the revolutionary heart of young Jack London is the same spirit that characterized the tea-overboard party in Boston Harbor. It is the spirit that will ultimately reserve for the Republic all that is best, for it is the opposite of the dull spirit of slavish respect for the Established, which slavishness is composed of abasement of mind, and selfishness of character.'

A few days later he was invited to speak by the debating society of his own Oakland High School. When the principal learned about it he refused them the use of the school building. Once again the papers played up the story, and every man and woman in the state discussed the merits of the case. The San Francisco *Post* remarked caustically, 'Socialism may be all that is urged against it, but the best way to propagate its doctrines is to forbid their propagation.'

Jack was delighted at the nationwide publicity that socialism was earning through his efforts. Besides, the free advertising, which would have cost him thousands of dollars if he had had to buy it, was booming his work. *The Call of the Wild, The Sea Wolf, The People of the Abyss* were being widely bought, and even more widely read and discussed. People might disagree with his ideas for an economic democracy; they might quarrel with the manner in which he was revolutionizing American literature; but it was no longer possible to gainsay the fact that he was the leading young writer in America. And his enemies had helped him arrive!

In the midst of the furor over his socialism, Macmillan released his *War of the Classes.* The book aroused so much interest that it had to be reprinted in June, October, and November, an astounding accomplishment for a collection of revolutionary essays in a country which denied vehemently that there was such a thing as a war between the classes, where socialism was ridiculed and despised, accused of being a hydra-headed monster that devoured its young. His was a voice crying in the wilderness, but more and more people were coming to hear that voice, particularly the generation just growing up, just throwing off the shackles of a restricted pioneer mentality, and beginning to count the human costs of large-scale industrialism. Jack London was a great name to this generation; it went to his books with burning faith. All over America one still meets people who relate with pride that Jack London turned them into socialists; the fact that their socialism did not always stick is perhaps not Jack's fault.

In March he once again agreed to run for Mayor of Oakland on the Socialist ticket, receiving 981 votes, exactly four times as many as he had received in 1901. In April he and Manyoungi went to Glen Ellen, where he paid Ninetta Eames six dollars a week for a cabin at Wake Robin. Mrs. Eames gave out the report that 'Jack had come home to Mother because of troubles in Oakland.' The trusting farmers of the neighborhood suspected nothing.

Spring in Sonoma County was beautiful. He regained his good spirits and full working force; the melancholia of the winter was forgotten. Having sold a story to *The Black Cat,* he spent two hundred and fifty dollars of the three-hundred-dollar check for a saddle-horse which the indefatigable Miss Kittredge rode all the way from Berkeley to Glen Ellen, a distance of thirty miles. They rode horseback among the groves of redwood and pine on Sonoma Mountain, over the trails through the wine-colored manzanita and madrone. The air was clear, fragrant, and intoxicating, and when the full moon rose the valley was filled with a luminous white mist. 'Now I know why the Indians named this place the Valley of the Moon,' commented Jack.

His creative force in full flower again, he wrote *White Fang,* a sequel to *The Call of the Wild,* the story of how White Fang, instead of going from civilization back to the call of the primitive, comes out of the wilds to live with mankind. Although the book does not rise to the heights of *The Call of the Wild,* it is a beautiful and moving dog story, carrying with it the thrill of first-rate literature. Each week he did a full-page book criticism for the Hearst chain, outlining the existing struggle between labor unions and employers when he reviewed *The Walking Delegate,* giving the sweat-shop system a blasting when he praised *The Long Day,* which told of the privations of a factory girl in New York. The Intercollegiate Socialist Society was organized in the East by Upton Sinclair and J. G. Phelps-Stokes, and Jack was elected president at the first meeting of the executive committee. When Macmillan published his fight story, *The Game,* and the critics condemned it as trivial and unbelievable, he sent them news clippings to prove that a fighter could smash in the back of his skull when falling to the mat from a hard blow.

The heat of summer coming on, he again spent a few dollars to have the creek dammed. Here his neighbors collected to swim. He worked in the mornings, swam in the afternoons, and enjoyed himself . . . except that he missed his two children. Then one hot afternoon, when he was riding across the mountains inhaling the sage scents that beat upward from the slope, he stumbled onto the Hill Ranch, one hundred and thirty acres of majestic land leading up from the floor of the valley to Sonoma Mountain. 'There are great redwoods on it, some of them ten thousand years old. There are hundreds of firs, tan-bark and live-oaks, madrone and manzanita galore. There are deep canyons, streams of water, springs. It is one hundred and thirty acres of the most beautiful, primitive lands to be found anywhere in America.'

He went wild about the place and decided at once that he must own it, a sentiment in which Miss Kittredge heartily encouraged him; only by getting him away from the city and from contact with other women would she avoid the danger of losing him, as she had almost lost him a few months before. Jack rode into the small village of Glen Ellen where he learned that the land was for sale and that the price had been set at seven thousand dollars. That afternoon at five he was at the home of the Hills, excited as a schoolboy, ready to buy. 'I hear you set the price of the land for Chauvet at seven thousand dollars,' he said to Mr. Hill. 'Yes,' replied Hill, 'that was the price I set him ten years ago.' 'I'll buy it!' cried Jack. 'Not so fast,' said Hill, 'you'd better go home and think it over for a few days.'

After Jack left, Mr. Hill told his wife that he had asked seven thousand dollars of Chauvet because Chauvet had wanted to utilize the water rights, but since Jack expected to farm the piece, five thousand dollars was all he could ask. The next day Jack dashed in more excited than ever; he had been unable to sleep for the planning of his beautiful ranch. 'Now I want to talk to you about the price . . .' began Hill. Jack leapt out of his chair, his face reddened, and he shouted in a burst of anger, 'You can't do that to me! I won't stand for it! You can't raise the price! Everybody around here is trying to do me. Seven thousand is the price you agreed to and that's the price I'm going to pay!' Unable to break into the torrent, Hill waited until he had subsided, then said quietly, 'All right, Mr. London, take it at your price.'

Years later, when Jack and the Hills had become close friends, Mr. Hill told him how he had done himself out of two thousand dollars. Jack laughed heartily, said that it ought to teach him to control his temper.

That night he and Miss Kittredge laid their plans. There was a ramshackle barn on the Hill Ranch that could be remodeled to house their horses and hired man. While Jack was away that fall on a lecture tour of the country, the hired man could clear a number of the acres, plant hay and corn, build pigsties and chicken houses, and get the ranch in working order against the day when Bessie's divorce would be granted and they could marry.

Jack wrote to Brett for the seven thousand dollars with which to buy the Hill Ranch. Brett replied, 'I am doubtful as to the advisability of any man who has a part to play in the world tying himself down to the purchase of real estate in any part of the country, no matter how beautiful and productive.' Jack wrote back, 'I was careful to buy a piece out of which no profit could be made. I'll never be bothered with a profit or loss account, but in twenty years it will be worth one hundred and twenty thousand dollars. I am anchoring good and solid, and anchoring for keeps.' Resignedly, Brett sent him the seven thousand dollars against the *Sea Wolf* royalties, and Jack exultantly became owner of the Hill Ranch. He then hired a farm hand, bought several horses, a colt, a cow, a calf, a plow, a barrow, a wagon, a buggy, harnesses, chickens, turkeys, and pigs.

When he finally came out of the wild buying spree he found that he did not have a dollar left, and that no money would be due from Macmillan for a long time. 'All this buying was unexpected, and has left me flat broke. Also I am expecting to receive, and dreading to receive, a notice from Bessie that she wants several hundred dollars with which to buy a horse and surrey. I've taken all the money I could get from Macmillan to pay for the land, and haven't enough left to build a barn with, much less a house. Am writing some short stories in order to get hold of some immediate cash.'

By October 4 he had overdrawn so heavily from Macmillan that they asked him to pay interest on the new advances. His bank book showed $207.83 to his credit, while among the immediately necessary outlays were $75 to Bessie, $55 to his mother, $57.60 for ranch tools, $24 for rent at Glen Ellen, $50 for store bills. 'I must pay my way and Manyoungi's way to Chicago; Charmian follows in twenty-four hours, and there are her expenses. My mother wants me to increase her monthly allowance. So does Bessie. I have just paid hospital bills of over $100 for Johnny Miller's mother. I have promised $30 to pay for printing of appeal of Joe King, a poor devil who had a fifty-year sentence hanging over him and who is being railroaded. There is a bill for over $45 for the hay press, and in November I must meet between $700 and $800 in insurance. So you see I am not only sailing close into the wind but that I am dead into it and my sails flapping.'

During his lifetime, in the course of which he earned well over a million dollars from his writing, he was almost never the owner of his money when it reached him. He always spent first, then split his head trying to figure where the necessary money was to come from. As Emil Jensen had said in the Klondike, he was never one to count the cost. It apparently never occurred to him that if he didn't spend his money until he had earned it he would not only keep out of debt, but out of trouble as well. 'The habit of spending money, ah God! I shall always be its victim!'

In October he started on his lecture tour attended by Manyoungi. Miss Kittredge returned to her aunt in Newton, Iowa, so that she could be closer to him. The tour, which included most of the large cities of the Mid-West and the East, was carried out in a blaze of publicity, for he was rapidly becoming one of the most romantic figures of the period. In addition to being the voice of socialism, the voice of scientific evolution, the voice of a new and robust realism in American literature, he also represented the youth and courage of the world. The women's clubs liked his virile figure, his smoke-puffing masculinity, his passionate sincerity on questions of social reform, his golden smile and infectious laughter. He made several hundred dollars a day, found amusing and intelligent company in each town, and was treated with friendliness by the newspapers. 'Jack London is a personality of unusual magnetic attraction. If it had been possible to spoil him he would have been spoiled by the regiment of adorers who beset him. He has been subjected to the same experiences as the matinée idol. However, he is without personal vanity.'

Then, on Saturday, November 18, he received a telegram in Chicago that Bessie's final divorce decree had been granted. He wired Miss Kittredge to come on at once from Newton to be married. She reached Chicago Sunday afternoon at five, but Jack had no marriage license. The bureau of course was closed, so he engaged a carriage and drove at top speed through the Chicago streets to enlist the aid of influential friends. The first two visits proving fruitless, a third friend was taken from his dinner table because he knew a city official. After another long drive they reached the home of the official, who said that he would be glad to do anything to help Jack London, but what was his blistering hurry, anyway? Why couldn't he wait until morning when the license bureau would be open and he could do everything in apple-pie order? Jack refused to wait, brought all his considerable force of argument to bear, ended by persuading the official to get into the carriage and drive with them to the south side of town, where the marriage-license clerk was routed out of bed. The clerk was dumbfounded, but under Jack's determined will he dressed and accompanied the party to the City Hall, opened his office, and made out the license. After several vain attempts they located a justice of the peace, Mr. Grant, who married Jack to Charmian Kittredge in the library of his home.

The following morning, November 20, 1905, the press of the nation was shocked by what they termed the 'indecent haste' of his marriage. Up to this time people had assumed that his separation from Bessie was caused by internal differences which made it mutually desirable. By his terrific sweat to remarry Jack showed that he had broken up his home for another woman . . . and that put an unpleasant face on affairs. Friendly as the press had been up to Saturday, on Monday it turned against him, not only its anger and indignation, but its ridicule as well. On Tuesday morning the nation was informed 'JACK LONDON'S MARRIAGE INVALID,' for the new divorce laws of Illinois, which were still in confusion, declared that no marriage could be valid unless it took place a year after the granting of the final decree. Cornered by reporters, Jack, once again feeling that he was being persecuted, cried out in impetuous ardor, 'If necessary I'll get married in every state in the Union, as fast as I can get from one to the other!' Many witty stories were written about the much-marrying Mr. London.

Had he waited until he returned to California, had he waited a few circumspect months he could have avoided the entire scandal. His marriage would have passed with brief notice. Instead he laid himself open to attack from every quarter. Sermons against him were preached from pulpits; the towns of Pittsburg and Derby banned his books from the public library, suggesting that other cities follow their lead; syndicated dispatches were released urging the women's clubs to cancel his lectures; many papers commented that it was strange that persons who were unable to regulate their own domestic affairs set themselves up as teachers of humanity at large. Articles were written questioning the mystery and haste of his second marriage. Miss Kittredge was attacked for breaking up his marriage to Bessie.

Because of the conduct of their leader, the socialists of America took severe punishment. The capitalist press utilized the weapons at hand: 'There's socialism for you! Deserts its wife and babies . . . sanctions immorality . . . would bring about chaos . . . socialism is anarchism, would destroy our civilization . . ." It was bootless for his comrades to protest, 'You cannot blame London's erratic conduct on socialism! Socialism disapproves of this sort of thing as vigorously as does capitalism!' Their leader had violated certain codes, and their Cause consequently had to suffer. Accused by his comrades of retarding the socialist revolution in America by at least five years, he smilingly replied, 'On the contrary, I believe I still have accelerated the revolution by at least five minutes.'

Just what motivated his theatrical rush to have that belated ceremony performed, to flaunt a new marriage in the face of the public? Part of it was a romantic gesture for Miss Kittredge. Part of it was rash, impetuous thoughtlessness, the act of a man who doesn't stop to question what the world will think. Part of it was sheer bravado, the act of a thick-skinned Irishman who doesn't care what it thinks. Lastly, the immediate taking of another wife was an appeasement to his conscience for the wrong he had done Bessie, and hence all wives.

The attacks against him in press and pulpit continued for several weeks. The seriousness of his work was injured in the minds of many readers, but in return the blazing publicity extended his public. It remained for the fashionable Averill Women's Club to administer the crowning blow, and close the discussion. At an open meeting the ladies passed a resolution approving free textbooks for public schools, and resolutions denouncing college football and Jack London.

In January of 1906 the lecture tour finally brought Jack to New York, where he was met by Doctor Alexander Irvine, handsome Irish idealist, minister of Pilgrim's Church in New Haven and head of the New Haven Socialist Local. Doctor Irvine had come to New York to persuade him to lecture at Yale University. Jack heartily concurred that the opportunity of launching a bolt of socialism at three thousand Yale students was too good to pass up. Doctor Irvine took the next train back to New Haven, where he then proposed to the Yale Debating Club that they sponsor the lecture. The members nervously agreed to present Jack London the following evening—on condition that he was not to say anything radical.

Elated, Doctor Irvine went that night to a socialist painter by the name of Delfant, who made ten posters on which were drawn a likeness of handsome Jack in his turtle-necked sweater, and under it a mass of red flames with the title of the lecture, 'Revolution.' Just before dawn Delfant and Doctor Irvine went about the campus tacking up the posters on trees. Yale was aghast when it awakened and saw the glaring announcements. A faculty member immediately summoned the chairman of the Debating Club and informed him that the meeting would have to be canceled, that if it were not, he would have permission to use Woolsey Hall revoked. There would be no revolution preached at Yale University! The club was about to obey when Doctor Irvine urged its members to go to the younger professors and see if they couldn't raise support against the reactionaries. The first professor to whom the chairman presented his problem was William Lyon Phelps, who asked, 'Is Yale a monastery?'

The rebuke was so adroitly yet gently put that it silenced the opposition. At eight o'clock that evening three thousand students and three hundred faculty members, nearly the entire university, jammed Woolsey Hall. Jack was given a warm reception as he walked onto the stage, and was listened to attentively as he told of seven million men in all countries of the world who 'are fighting with all their might for the conquest of the wealth of the world, and for the complete overthrow of existing society. They call themselves comrades, these men, as they stand shoulder to shoulder under the banner of revolt. Here is tremendous human force, here is power; the revolutionists are swayed by a great passion, they have much reverence for humanity but little reverence for the rule of the dead.' After an hour of dissecting the capitalist system with an economic scalpel he concluded with the challenge, 'The capitalist class has failed in its management, and its management is to be taken away from it. Seven million men of the working class say that they are going to get the rest of the working class to join with them, and take that management away. The revolution is here, now. Stop it who can!'

In spite of the fact that he 'shocked them out of their socks,' as Doctor Irvine put it, and that not twenty students in the audience agreed with a word he uttered, he received an ovation when he finished. Yale University sportingly refused to take any rent for the Hall, and the entire gate, at twenty-five cents a head, went into the treasury of the New Haven Socialist Local, a windfall.

After the lecture Jack, Doctor Irvine, and a hand-picked group of a dozen of the best debaters at the University went to Old Mory's for beer and solid talk. It was Jack against the field; from all reports of the rough-and-tumble discussion, in which he tried to prove that private property is based on either seizure or theft, Jack held his own even if he did not make any converts. When he and Doctor Irvine reached the latter's home at four o'clock in the morning they found a group of workingmen waiting to thank him for his lecture. At eight o'clock the next morning the doorbell was rung by a gangling, red-headed reporter from the Yale *News* who wanted a personal interview with Jack London because it would help his chances on the paper. The reporter's name was Sinclair Lewis.

By January 19 he was back again in New York after two weeks of lecturing to speak on 'The Coming Crisis' for the first open meeting of the Intercollegiate Socialist Society, of which he had been named president. Reports of how many people crowded into the Grand Central Palace vary from four to ten thousand, but every socialist on the Atlantic coast who could scrape up the fare to New York was present. In spite of the title of the organization, there were probably not a hundred college students scattered among the thousands of working people. On his way north from a lecture in Florida, Jack's train was late. Upton Sinclair, who was just having published a book about the Chicago stockyards titled *The Jungle*, and who was the organizing force and brains behind the Intercollegiate Socialist Society, kept the crowd interested by telling them that they could help bring economic democracy to America. At ten o'clock, when Jack appeared in a black cheviot suit, with a white flannel shirt and white tie, and well-worn patent leather pumps, his hair flying, the crowd thronged to its feet to give him the greatest reception of his life: Eugene V. Debs was their giant, but Jack London was their fighting young leader and prophet. Upton Sinclair says that the audience cheered and waved tiny red flags for fully five minutes before Jack had a chance to make himself heard. When he predicted the downfall of capitalist society by the year 2000, the crowd went delirious with delight even though not a soul among them would be present to witness that great Judgment Day.

He remained in New York for a week. New York always had a strange effect upon him; it excited him physically and depressed him nervously. He told Doctor Irvine that every time he found himself entering the city he wanted to cut his throat. The day following his lecture for the Intercollegiate Socialist Society he met Upton Sinclair at luncheon to discuss plans for the Society. Sinclair, who was an ardent prohibitionist, reports that Jack had been drinking before he arrived, that his eyes were excitedly bleary, that he continued to drink straight through the luncheon. Before reaching New York Jack had written a glowing review of *The Jungle* which now sent that muckraking classic and its author on their way to fame.

On February 3, when lecturing in St. Paul, he fell ill and his mouth became covered with cold sores. He canceled the balance of his lectures to return to Glen Ellen, where he rented part of Wake Robin from Ninetta Eames and Edward Payne, the joint owners. It was here he hatched his plans for an adventure which was to make all other adventures of his thrill-packed life seem pale by comparison.

The summer before, while sunning himself on the beach at the swimming hole at Glen Ellen, he had read to the group of vacationers from Captain Joshua Slocum's book *Sailing Alone Around the World*. Captain Slocum's boat had been thirty-seven feet long; Jack mentioned jokingly that he would not be afraid to sail around the world in a small boat, say forty feet long. Now, back at Wake Robin, having had his fill of crowds and cities and adulation, sensitive to the fact that he was being attacked from many corners and for many reasons, that the people of Glen Ellen were hostile because of the haste and circumstances of his second marriage, he once again began talking about the voyage around the world. He had long planned just such an expedition to the South Seas; it was one of the great dreams of his life, kindled by the romantic tales of Stevenson and Melville. Charmian, whose forte was adventure, encouraged him, as did Ninetta Eames and Edward Payne, who hoped Roscoe Eames would become captain of the ship.

'I had a house to build on the ranch, also an orchard, a vineyard, several hedges to plant, and a number of other things to do. We thought we would start in four or five years. Then the lure of adventure began to grip us. Why not start at once? Let the orchard, vineyard and hedges be growing while we were away. After all, I'd never be any younger.' Always impetuous, swift of decision, heedless of cost, he resolved that he too was going to circle the globe in a small boat.

Ten days after his return to Wake Robin he wrote to half a dozen of the leading Eastern magazine editors in an attempt to get them to underwrite his adventure with hard cash. 'The boat is to be forty-five feet long. It would have been a bit shorter had I not found it impossible to squeeze in a bathroom otherwise. I sail in October. Hawaii is the first port of call; from there we shall wander through the South Seas, Samoa, New Zealand, Australia, New Guinea, and up through the Philippines to Japan. Then Korea and China, and on down to India, the Red Sea, Mediterranean, Black Sea and Baltic, across the Atlantic to New York, and then around the Horn to San Francisco. I shall certainly put in a winter at St. Petersburg, and the chances are that I shall go up the Danube from the Black Sea to Vienna. I'll go up the Nile and the Seine; there is no reason at all why I shouldn't come up to Paris and moor alongside the Latin Quarter, with the bow line out to Notre Dame, and a stern line fast to the Morgue. I shall not be in a rush; I calculate that seven years at least will be taken up by the trip.'

Although there were several seaworthy boats on San Francisco Bay that could be bought for a reasonable price, Jack discarded this idea; he would sail no man's boat but his own. There were expert ship architects in San Francisco, but he would sail in no vessel but one that had been fashioned in his own mind. There were competent shipbuilders with yards on the Bay, but he would be master of no boat but the one he had built himself.

He decided to design a boat that would be a departure in sailing vessels, even as everything in his life design had to be a departure. He hit upon the idea for a 'ketch,' a compromise between a yawl and a schooner which would retain the virtues of both, but he frankly admitted that he had never seen a ketch, let alone sailed one, that the whole thing was a theory in his mind. He sunk himself in the details of boatbuilding, pondering such problems as whether a two-, three-, or four-cycle engine would be best; whether he should use a make-and-break or jump spark for ignition; what was the best kind of windlass; whether the rigging should be set up with lanyards or turn buckles. Always a swift and penetrating student, in a few weeks he taught himself a great deal about modern shipbuilding.

Roscoe Eames in his palmier days had sailed small boats around San Francisco Bay. On the basis of this experience Jack hired him at sixty dollars a month to take the plans down to San Francisco and supervise the building of the *Snark,* an arrangement which pleased everyone concerned and gave to the aging and cantankerous Roscoe the first wage he had earned in years. Jack decided to call his boat the *Snark* after an imaginary animal in *The Hunting of the Snark. Cosmopolitan* had suggested that he name it after their magazine; Jack agreed that if they would pay the cost of building the boat he would not only name it *Cosmopolitan Magazine,* but would also take subscriptions along the way. He calculated the *Snark* would cost seven thousand dollars to build and, so calculating, said to Roscoe, 'Spare no money. Let everything on the *Snark* be of the best. Never mind decoration; pine board is good enough for me. Put the money into construction. Let the *Snark* be as staunch and strong as any boat afloat. Never mind what it costs to make her staunch and strong; I'll go on writing and earning the money to pay for it.'

Having dispatched Roscoe with the boat plans and an open check book, Jack cast about for his next serious project. It was four months since he had done any creative work. Among the many books he had ordered from England by catalogue was Stanley Waterloo's *Story of Ab,* one of the first attempts to re-create in literature the life of man when he was still more animal than human. Waterloo had put in ten years of study and work on his book; the result was erudite but unexciting. Jack saw his opportunity: here was a mechanism with which he could bring to life Darwin's theory of evolution! That afternoon he formulated his outline, leaning heavily on Waterloo's book, and the next morning he began to write *Before Adam,* illustrative of his talent for conceiving titles. By using the simple device of a modern boy who dreams at night that he is growing up as a primitive child, he contrasts the two periods with telling effect. The writing is so warm and honest that the reader believes this is how man really lived after having taken his historic step forward from the ape. 'It is going to be the most primitive story ever written!' exulted Jack.

Conceived in the dark days when organized religion was fighting the theory of evolution as a diabolical concoction of sacrilegious souls, before the methods of scientific investigation had made much headway against the stone wall of ritualistic dogma, *Before Adam* was a brave attempt to popularize Darwin and Wallace, to bring the meaning of their work to the masses so they might better understand their antecedents. He was a superb story-teller, and this book about primitive people is as absorbing as any of his Alaskan tales. Though *Before Adam* misses being first-rate literature because of the tumultuous haste in which it was poured out, it makes delightful and illuminating reading, particularly for young people just beginning to sharpen the teeth of their mind.

Roscoe bought supplies, hired workmen, rented space in a shipbuilding dock, then informed Jack that the keel of the *Snark* would be laid on the morning of April 18, 1906. On the eve of the eighteenth Jack talked for hours about his trip, recalling that 'when I was a small boy I read a book of Melville's called *Typee,* and many long hours I dreamed over its pages. I resolved then and there, mightily, come what would, when I had gained strength and years I too would voyage to Typee.' In the very early morning, awakened by the floor shaking under his bed, he assumed that he had been dreaming of the valley of Typee and had tossed in his sleep in excitement. When dawn finally came he saddled Washoe Ban, rode to the top of Sonoma Mountain, and saw San Francisco in flames. He returned at top speed to Wake Robin, caught a train to Oakland, and then a ferry across to San Francisco, where he took photographs and dashed off a telegraphic story for *Collier's.*

Among the many major tragedies brought on by the San Francisco earthquake and fire, there was the minor tragedy that the keel of the *Snark* could not be laid. Supplies that had been paid for were burned; there were no workmen to be had; the ironworks had been razed, equipment ordered from New York could not be brought into the city. There could be no lick of work done on the *Snark* for many weeks. Jack left Roscoe behind to get construction under way again just as soon as possible, and returned to Glen Ellen to write some of his finest Klondike stories, among them 'Love of Life,' 'The White Man's Way,' 'The Story of Keesh,' 'The Unexpected,' 'Negore,' 'The Coward'; he had begun to suspect that the *Snark* might cost a little more than his original estimate of seven thousand dollars to build.

In June the keel of the *Snark* was at last laid. Jack also conceived the motif for the novel based on the economic life of the people, for which he had long been casting about in his mind. 'I am deep in the beginning of a socialistic novel! Am going to call it *The Iron Heel.* How is that for a title? The poor futile little capitalist! Gee, when the proletariat cleans house some day!' Again his vigorous imagination, which just two months before had invented a device to plunge a story backward in time some tens of thousands of years, now created a device to project *The Iron Heel* forward by seven hundred years: the finding of the manuscript of Ernest Everhard where it had been hidden just after the Second Revolt of the People had been bathed in blood by the Oligarch. Anatole France, who called Jack the American Karl Marx, wrote in an introduction to *The Iron Heel,* 'Jack London has that particular genius which perceives what is hidden from the common herd, and possesses a special knowledge enabling him to anticipate the future.'

A special knowledge inherited straight from Professor Chaney, one of whose greatest delights was predicting the future, nearly always accurately. In *The Iron Heel* Jack once again proved that ideas can be more exciting than action, and that they control the world; just as in *The Sea Wolf* and *Before Adam* he had paid his debt to his masters, Spencer, Darwin, and Huxley, he now paid his debt to his master, Karl Marx, popularizing his teachings, dramatizing socialism and the revolution, making it intelligible to the masses. Karl Marx would have been pleased with *The Iron Heel.*

In writing his book Jack went to the extensive files and catalogues he had studiously compiled over a period of years, drawing from them sufficient factual material to make it one of the most scathing indictments against capitalism ever conceived. Economics was not only considered dry and dull and boring by Americans, but any discussion of the principles underlying private property and distribution of wealth was as tabu as discussions of evolution. Industrialists and bankers ruled by what had been known before the republican revolution as the Divine Right of Kings; workmen were told to be grateful for the labor and bread provided them through the wisdom and goodness of their employers. The Church, as exemplified by Jack's contact with it in Chicago while on his lecture tour, when the only two allegedly liberal ministers in the city refused to speak at the funeral of former Governor John P. Altgeld because he had pardoned the men railroaded in the Haymarket Riot, was a pot-bellied handmaiden of industry, as was the so-called higher education in the colleges, which taught only what its paymasters permitted.

All this he documented and wrote into one of the most terrifying and beautiful books ever written; if *The Iron Heel* is not his greatest contribution to the realm of literature, it is certainly his greatest contribution to the economic revolution. In it he not only predicted the coming of the now current Fascism, but detailed the methods by means of which it would murder all opposition and wipe out existing culture. *The Iron Heel* reads as though it were written yesterday . . . or ten years from today. In all contemporary literature there is no chapter more exciting than the one in which Ernest Everhard faces the Philomath Club (note the resemblance of the club name to the one Chaney invented, the Philomatheans), whose members formed the wealthiest Oligarch on the Pacific coast. Nor was there ever a more prophetic paragraph than the one in which the leader of the Oligarchs answers Everhard, who has just laid bare the waste and rapine of the profit system, and predicted the taking over of industry by the working people. 'When you reach out your vaunted strong hands for our palaces and purple ease, we will show you what strength is. In the roar of shell and shrapnel and the whine of machine-guns will our answer be couched. We will grind your revolutionists down under our heel, and we shall walk upon your faces. The world is ours, we are its lords, and ours it shall remain. As for labor, it has been in the dirt since history began, and in the dirt it shall remain so long as I and mine have the power.'

In the extensive bibliography on communism, Bukharin lists only one book by an American author, *The Iron Heel.*

Compared in scope as an adventure of the mind to his seven-year plan of sailing a forty-five-foot boat around the world, *The Iron Heel* makes the contemplated *Snark* voyage seem like a ferry ride across San Francisco Bay. He wrote the book in full consciousness that it would make him bitter and powerful enemies; he wrote it in full knowledge that it would injure his career, that it might hurt his past books and kill any new ones he might write. He wrote it in full awareness that Macmillan's might be forced to refuse to publish it, that no magazine would dare serialize it, that there was no way to make enough money from it to pay for the food he consumed during the months of writing it.

All of which was even more courageous in view of what was happening to his bank account over the building of the *Snark.* Fulfilling his own command, 'Never mind what it costs to make her staunch and strong,' he ordered the most expensive Puget Sound planking for the deck so that there would be no butts to allow leakage; built four watertight compartments so that no matter how large a leak the *Snark* might spring, only one compartment could fill with water; sent to New York for a costly seventy-horse-power engine; bought a magnificent windlass and had castings specially made so that the engine could transmit power to the windlass to haul up the anchor. He built a dream of a bathroom, with schemes, devices, pumps, levers, and sea valves. He bought a rowboat, and then a small launch with a motor in it. He had a bow built on the *Snark* that cost a small fortune, but over which no sea could break, the most beautiful bow he had ever seen on a boat. Reporters sent to interview him wrote that he became 'all boy' when the subject of the cruise was mentioned, that it was a new toy and he was going to have a lot of fun playing with it.

By midsummer he found that he already had ten thousand dollars in the *Snark,* and that she was not half finished. The ten thousand dollars had taken from him every dollar he could command; royalties and advances from Macmillan and his English publishers, the four hundred dollars he got from McClure who had bought *Love of Life,* the money he had received from other stories he had written after completing *Before Adam.* In addition to building his boat, he supported Flora, Johnny Miller, and Mammy Jenny in the house he had bought for Flora; Bessie and his two daughters in the house he had built for Bessie; Charmian, Roscoe Eames, and in part, Ninetta Eames and Edward Payne in Wake Robin; and had a foreman and hired men on the Hill Ranch who were planting and clearing, buying equipment and materials.

The editors to whom he had sent his excited letters in February were turning a cool cheek to his plea for advances against articles about the voyage. The acquiring of enough money to support his list of fourteen relatives, dependents, and workmen, and in addition to pay wages to the workmen on the *Snark,* became known as London's monthly miracle. Common sense told him to abandon the *Snark,* for the present at least, as he could not foot the bills. Or, if he wanted to continue pouring money into the *Snark,* to give up writing on *The Iron Heel.* He was a poor one for compromise. He continued his impassioned thousand words a morning on *The Iron Heel,* and in the afternoons, Sundays, and holidays turned out stories, articles, essays, anything to earn the hundreds and hundreds the *Snark* was consuming. In addition to buying a series of articles about the days when he had been a tramp on The Road, *Cosmopolitan* at last sent him a thousand dollars against an article he was to write about the *Snark before* he sailed; apparently *Cosmopolitan* entertained serious doubts about the forty-five-foot boat ever reaching another port.

By October 1, the date on which he had planned to cast off, he had fifteen thousand dollars in the *Snark,* and it was only half finished. He had poured into it the two thousand dollars from *Everybody's* magazine for the serialization of *Before Adam,* the two thousand dollars from *Cosmopolitan,* the two thousand dollars from the *Woman's Home Companion* which it had agreed to advance him against articles on the domestic life of the aborigines, and at least another two thousand dollars earned by the batch of Alaskan tales, but he found that if he wanted to continue work on the boat he would have to borrow against the house he had bought for Flora. And at last he perceived that Roscoe Eames was a tragic error. Eames was quarrelsome and could get little work out of his men; he was inefficient, the workmen were duplicating their efforts; he was so garrulous and chaotic-minded that he was paying three prices for gear, buying materials for which he had no use, giving checks for equipment no one bothered to deliver. Uncompromising in his demands upon himself that he master any field of knowledge or endeavor before he wrote about it, Jack had not thought to make such demands of the people he employed, accepting them on their self-evaluation.

To complicate matters further, *Cosmopolitan,* which had had to be bludgeoned for a thousand-dollar advance, ran full-page advertisements that they were sending Jack London around the world in the *Snark* to write stories for them. 'Everywhere prices have been raised, and stuck into me, and broken off, all upon the understanding that I wasn't spending my own money, but the money of a rich magazine.'

In addition to this false advertising, which hurt Jack doubly because it put his voyage in a different light, making him look like an employee rather than an adventurer, *Cosmopolitan* also mutilated his first article about the *Snark.* Jack was never in better form than when he was writing angry letters to people whom he felt had taken advantage of him. 'You're treating me scurvily. This is the first squabble I've ever had with a magazine. I hope it will be my last, but I'll make it hum while it lasts. Either we're going to work together, or we're not. Frankly I'd like to call the whole thing off. If you can't find a fair and square basis for treating me, then on your head be it. I'll neither give nor take quarter. You want to know when my next article will be sent to you. There are a few things I want to know first or else you will never know when that second article will be sent to you. You'll think the Day of Judgment will be a whole lot quicker in coming than that second article. I weave my stuff; you can't cut out parts of it and leave mutilated parts behind. Who in the dickens are you, anyway, to think that you can better my work? Do you think that I'll write my heart, my skilled professional heart into my work to have you fellows slaughtering it to suit your journalistic tastes? I refuse flatly and definitely to collaborate with anyone in your office!'

What vexed him more than the wasteful expense were the prolonged delays. The *Snark* was promised for November 1, then November 15, then December 1. In desperation he moved to Oakland, sent Roscoe home to study navigation, and undertook supervising the completion of the boat himself. He hired fourteen men, paid them earthquake wages, and a dollar a day bonus for working fast. In order to do this he had to mortgage the Hill Ranch. By December 15 in spite of the tremendous outlay of cash, he saw that the *Snark* was as far from completion as it had been on October 1; once again he had to postpone his announced sailing date.

The newspapers began to publish satiric rhymes about the procrastinating Mr. London; the *Woman's Home Companion,* upset because *Cosmopolitan* beat them to publication with an article about the *Snark,* protested against his not sailing and demanded an article on the aborigines while he was still in San Francisco; his friends bet with him against his sailing date.

His foreman at the Hill Ranch collected the first bet on New Year's Day, 1907, and this amount was added to the twenty thousand dollars invested in the *Snark.* 'After that the bets came fast and furious. My friends surrounded me like a gang of harpies, making bets against every sailing date I set. I was rash, and I was stubborn. I bet and bet, and continued to bet, and paid them all.'

So well had the voyage of the *Snark* been publicized by the newspapers and magazines that he received thousands of letters from all over the country, the writers pleading to be taken along. Ninety per cent were willing to work in any capacity, and ninety-nine per cent were willing to work without pay. 'Physicians, surgeons and dentists in large numbers offered to come along without pay; there were reporters, valets, chefs, illustrators, secretaries, civil engineers, machinists, electricians, retired sea captains, schoolteachers, university students, ranchers, housewives, sailors, riggers.' Only one of them was Jack unable to resist, a seven-page letter from a young lad in Topeka, Kansas, by the name of Martin Johnson. Jack wired him, 'CAN YOU COOK?' and Martin Johnson telegraphed back 'JUST TRY ME,' then rushed out to get a job in the kitchen of a Greek restaurant in Topeka. By January the future African explorer was in Oakland, ready to sail on the *Snark,* but the *Snark* was not ready for him. Because Jack insisted upon paying a fair wage to everybody who worked for him, Martin Johnson's wage was added to the roster.

Despite the fact that he now knew Roscoe to be incompetent, Jack did not fire him and engage one of the many available accredited sea captains to command his ship, any one of whom he could have had for the same one hundred dollars a month he was to pay Roscoe after they sailed. Nor did he accept the offer of any of the able-bodied seamen who begged to come along, with or without pay. Instead he hired for his lone engineer and sailor a Stanford University student by the name of Herbert Stoltz, who was a husky and willing young man. That was to be his crew: Jack, Charmian, Roscoe Eames, Martin Johnson, Herbert Stoltz, and a Japanese cabin boy, not one of whom, aside from Jack, knew how to reef a sail or haul up an anchor.

Having completed *The Iron Heel* he read the first two chapters to the Ruskin Club. An Oakland newspaper commented that he always tried out his socialistic ideas on Oakland because he knew that if they went there, they would go anywhere. He then sent the manuscript to Brett, who predicted that the newspapers would ignore it, or come down on the head of the author and publisher, but claimed that it was good work and agreed to publish it regardless of the consequences, a brave decision. His only request was that Jack delete a footnote which Brett was sure would land them both in jail for contempt of court. Jack replied, 'If they find me guilty of contempt I'd be only too glad to do six months in jail, during which time I could write a couple of books and do no end of reading.'

He had good reason to yearn for the comparative peace and quiet of a jail, for the *Snark* had landed him in a veritable bedlam. In February, one year after he had written his enthusiastic letters to the editors, the *Snark* had been so long in the building that she was breaking down faster than she could be repaired. The boat became a farce, London's folly. The newspapers laughed openly. Nobody took her seriously, least of all the men who were working on her. 'Old sea dogs and master sailors by the score have made pilgrimages to the *Snark* and gone away shaking their heads and voicing misgivings of many sorts.' Sailors said the *Snark* was badly planned and badly rigged, and would founder at sea. Bets were laid against the *Snark* ever reaching Hawaii. Manyoungi, the Korean boy who had served 'Master' faithfully for three years, was so sure he would never reach Hawaii that he forced Jack to fire him by demanding, 'Does God wish his coffee now?' Day and night the boat was surrounded by a crowd of curious jeering spectators.

Realizing that 'the stage was set against him,' that he could never complete the boat in San Francisco, Jack decided to sail her to Honolulu as she was and finish her there. His decision was no sooner made than the *Snark* sprang a leak that took days to repair. When he finally was able to start her for the boatways, she was caught between two barges and severely crushed. The workmen moved her to the ways and started her for the water, but the ways parted and the *Snark* dropped stern-first into the mud. Twice a day for a week, at high tide, two steam tugs pulled and hauled at the *Snark*, trying to get her out of the mud. When Jack tried to help by using the windlass, the specially made castings shattered, the gears ground, and the windlass was put permanently out of commission. In despair he turned on the seventy-horse-power motor, but it shattered the cast-iron bedplate that had come all the way from New York, reared up in the air, smashed all connections and fastenings, and fell useless on its side.

By now Jack had twenty-five thousand dollars sunk in the sunken boat. His closest friends advised him that he was whipped, that he had better leave the *Snark* where she was and abandon the voyage. They assured him that to sail in her, if he could ever get her to sail, was courting suicide. Jack cried, 'I can't quit!' Day after day he spent in a rage against the incompetent workmen, the defective materials that had been sent him, the merchants dunning him with bills, the newspapers that were openly ridiculing him. If he admitted defeat now he would be the laughing-stock of the country; he would never be able to live down the shame and disgrace! He was a man of his word. He'd sail that boat to Hawaii if it was the last thing he did. Better to die a hero's death in the deep Pacific than be jeered at by the workingmen and merchants who had mulcted him, the newspapers that had satirized him, the crowds of onlookers who had laughed and called him crazy, that had raised the odds against his ever reaching Honolulu to twenty to one, with no takers!

'By main strength and sweat we dragged the *Snark* off the wrecked ways and laid her alongside the Oakland City Wharf. The drays brought the outfit from home, books, blankets, and personal luggage. Along with this, everything else came on board in a torrent of confusion—wood and coal, water and water tanks, vegetables, provisions, oil, the lifeboat and launch, all our friends and those who claimed to be their friends, to say nothing of some of the friends of the friends of the crew. Also there were reporters and photographers, and strangers, and cranks, and finally, over everything, clouds of coal dust from the wharf.'

But at last the long, heart-breaking travail was over; they were to sail on Saturday, April 20, 1907. On Saturday morning Jack went on board with a check book, fountain pen, and blotter, and nearly two thousand dollars in cash, all he had been able to collect in advances from Macmillan and the magazines, and waited for the balances due the hundred and fifteen firms whom he felt had delayed him so long. Instead of the merchants coming on board for their pay, a United

States marshal arrived and tacked a notice on the *Snark's* mast that she was libeled for debt by a man by the name of Sellers to whom he owed $232. The *Snark* was a prisoner and could not move; Jack thrashed about the town trying madly to find his creditors, the sheriff, the mayor, anything to get clear. Everyone was away for the week end.

On Monday morning he sat once again on the *Snark* pouring out greenbacks, gold, and checks to his creditors, so blinded with anger and frustration that he could not even itemize the bills, make sure he owed the money, or that he hadn't paid the bill before. When he added it all up he found that the *Snark*, whose seventy-horse-power engine was lashed down for ballast, whose power transmission was a wreck, whose lifeboat leaked and motor launch wouldn't run, whose one coat of paint had already worn off, had cost him thirty thousand dollars.

Robbed, ridiculed, cried over, given up for a hopelessly romantic idiot, Jack hoisted Jimmy Hopper's California football sweater to the top of the mast, and raised his anchor by hand. Then, with a navigator who couldn't navigate, an engineer who couldn't engineer, and a cook who couldn't cook, the *Snark* limped down the Estuary, crossed the Bay, and sailed out the Golden Gate Strait into the Pacific.

I HAD READ William Faulkner's glorious piece on Mississippi in *Holiday* magazine, when I received a phone call from the editor asking me if I would do a portrait of California for the series. I was elated at the opportunity to do a piece of work that might come even moderately close to the Faulkner portrait. But I would have accepted in any event, because California is dear to me; it has almost taken the place of family and background in giving me roots and tradition.

The California article was a labor of love. There were sentences, whole paragraphs, that I had been aching to write for years.

I got into my car and drove several thousand miles through valleys and narrow mountain passes I had remembered from my journeys on foot as a boy, and the years from the age of sixteen to twenty-three, when I had to earn the money for an education which led me as close to the groves of the Academe as Candidate for the Ph. D.

The article took considerably over a month to write. I could have done it in less time had I known less, or had I cared less about my subject.

CALIFORNIA

SO much has been written about California there is little left to be told: except the truth. In a state where the hyperboles are picked green and allowed to ripen en route to the Eastern market, an ounce of astringency is worth a pound of praise.

Northern California is a lean, hard-bitten mountain man, a Jedediah Smith or Joseph Walker fighting his way across the snow-clad Sierras with a hunter's gun slung on his back; male, rugged, disciplined, carrying the indestructible seed of a new civilization. Southern California is a lush, red-lipped, sensual female who came up from Acapulco in the cabin of a well-rigged Spanish ship, and now suns herself in a patio surrounded by bougainvillaea, her gown cut sufficiently low to intimate how abundantly the coming generations may be nourished.

This love affair and marriage have been passionate and prolific, but not always peaceful; there have been quarrels, bills of divorcement; yet the partners have remained in wedlock because of the magic and wealth of the family name.

Intemperate Californians have been heard to say (it's not enough to be on your guard against the natives, the converts are the worst exaggerators) that their state is another Valley of the Nile or Euphrates, cradle of a civilization richer than any the world has ever known; a land of milk and honey and ripe orange groves, green fields, shining streams, sun-drenched ocean beaches: the Promised Land.

Can there be even a smidgen of truth in such outlandish claims?

Everyone knows about the North and South Poles, those two charming geographical concepts. If Moscow is the East Pole, and certainly the Kremlin is calling the tunes for the Orient, then California is the West Pole, the heartland of the new and fresh democracy we feel is being fashioned in the Far West.

What are its components?

It is the life of the individual homeowner, who is not buffeted or mastered by the changes of the economic or political cycle, to whom democracy means neighborliness, getting along with the people next door. It means living with lack of tension, suspicion, hostility, in a largely informal and classless society: for there is food and space, mountains and sea, fertile valleys, cities and villages, sunshine for everyone. We are not a cramped people, in spite of the staggering onslaught of newcomers into the state; neither are we pushed, harried or harassed.

It is living with nature, yet without the constant conflict with the elements, of drought and flood, of ice and sleet. It is the joy of going to work in the daylight and returning in the daylight, with the chance to recoup one's energies in the sun, the surf, the pines, the streams, or just cultivating one's garden.

The big houses are being torn down, the grounds subdivided to make room for twenty modern homes. So too with antiquated social distinctions: few Californians try to keep up with the nabob Joneses; they try to uncomplicate their lives and keep their pretensions down with the democratic Smiths. When each man owns his own garden, his sacred little piece of the good earth, he is anybody's equal.

Be forewarned: when all the facts about California are piled on top of each other, they will constitute a volume thicker and more amazing than Baron Munchausen's book of travels. Along with the Texan, the Californian identifies himself so strongly with his state that he constitutes himself an individual chamber of commerce, sometimes permitting a soupçon of braggadocio to enter his otherwise cool and objective appraisal of his birthright.

The state is almost eight hundred miles long (longer than Italy), embracing within its boundaries staggering contrasts: the stark, barren, primordial rock mountains towering above the sand and creosote-bush wastes of the Mojave Desert in the south; in the north, the dense green forests of redwood and *Sequoia gigantea,* the largest trees in the world, the epitome of long life, of the power of growth and survival.

The Californian offers equally astonishing contrasts: he came during the gold rush in a flash flood of humanity representing almost every race on earth: the Italians in the Sonoma and Napa valleys, the Armenians around Fresno, the Chinese of San Francisco and the Sacramento Valley, the Mexicans of Los Angeles and the Imperial Valley, the Germans around Sunland, the Scandinavians in the lumber towns and around Twin Peaks, the Japanese wherever flowers and vegetables will grow, the Portuguese and Finns of the northern fishing villages, so like the rugged coast of Wales; as well as the thousands of New Englanders, New Yorkers, Pennsylvanians, Southerners. Each group brought its mores, its heritage, the flavor and tone of its state or national character, creating in the Far West a cosmopolitan culture; for the state has the same assimilative powers as the ocean that rolls in from the Sea of Okhotsk and the Tasman Sea.

It was not the billions in gold taken out of the state that enriched California, it was the wealth of humanity that poured in.

Californians see themselves in the large; in their own minds they are all Paul Bunyans who can swing allegorical axes and level forests. Aside from those born here, which requires only modest courage, most of the people who made the long journey to the state were hardy, adventuresome souls. Courage is at the base of California character: the lone coward I've met in all my journeying up and down the state is myself, during the years I had to cross the cemetery on my way home from a night job.

One measure of people is how much they dare, and Californians have dared greatly: Isadora Duncan revolutionized the dance; Frank Norris (we consider any man who has lived here for five years as a true Californian, though of course not with all of the privileges pertaining to the native) liberated the American novel from sentimentality to realism; Jack London blueprinted the coming world of authoritarianism; Gertrude Stein released the American language from its outmoded word-forms; Luther Burbank created edible cactus, plumcots, stoneless prunes; John Muir, the naturalist, saved Yosemite and some hundred million acres of forest reserves for the nation; Upton Sinclair, at sixty, began an eleven-volume historical novel.

On the pediment of the State Office Building in Sacramento is the line: *"Bring Me Men To Match My Mountains."* A tall order: for the Sierras go up to the greatest heights in North America.

How would you like to enter California? From what direction, in what area of time, by what means? By Spanish ship with Cabrillo in 1542, around the Horn in an English ship with Drake in 1579, on foot from Lower California in 1769 with Padre Junipero Serra, by foot and horseback with Captain Juan Bautista de Anza from Mexico in the spring of 1774; down from the Bering Strait in a Russian ship to found Fort Ross in 1812, to remain until 1841 and then sell out just before the discovery of gold; into the harbor of San Diego with Richard Henry Dana (*Two Years Before the Mast*) in 1834, or in the hundreds of ships that sailed through the Golden Gate Strait into San Francisco Bay, true womb of California, with the thousands of gold miners in 1850? Would you prefer to come down from the north, after crossing the Oregon Trail with Parkman, or from the south, across the blazing heat of Death Valley with the Jayhawkers, or over the Sierras with John Bidwell, in covered wagons down the Humboldt with the Chiles-Walker Party in 1843, or with what remained uneaten of the Donner Party in 1847? Would you prefer an automobile on Highway 66, crossing bleak California deserts until you're sure you've been had by the chamber of commerce, and then suddenly come to the top of a bluff and see spread below you a land of ripe orange groves, green meadows, and sparkling streams. Or perhaps you want the last word, the DC-8 that leaves New York at three in the afternoon and reaches California at eight that evening when, replete with Martinis and pheasant under glass, you will circle the phantasmagoria of lights that is San Francisco or Los Angeles, and be taken in a limousine to a swank hotel.

The name California, like so much else in the state, is the invention of a fiction writer, one Odronez de Montalvo, who wrote around 1510,

"At the right hand of the Indies there is an island called California, very near to the Terrestrial Paradise. This island is inhabited by robust dark women of great strength and great warm hearts; when children are born the females are preserved but the males are killed at once, saving only those required to guard against depopulation. . . ." Sounds a little like present-day Hollywood.

The first inhabitants of California found it anything but a terrestrial paradise; the thirty-odd tribes of Indians were the sorriest to stumble onto the North American continent: poverty-stricken, living largely on nuts and berries, without the skill to grow food or make tools or weapons. The only characteristic they shared with their smarter cousins to the east was that they managed to get their squaws to do the work. When the Spanish arrived, the Indians would gladly have closed out the whole state for the same twenty-four dollars that bought Manhattan. Instead, the Spanish put the braves to work building missions, whereupon most of them folded their wretched huts and vanished. The best-known Indians remaining in California today are those who get themselves shot by television cowboys or troops protecting covered-wagon trains.

Cabrillo, sailing around the Horn in 1542, claimed California for the Spanish and set a four-hundred-year tourist precedent by exclaiming when he saw the coast at Carmel:

"The mountains seem to reach the heavens!"

By 1769, Junipero Serra began to build the missions that became California's first permanent settlements: San Diego, San Juan Capistrano, San Fernando, Santa Barbara, San Luis Obispo, near Monterey, Mission Dolores in San Francisco, Sonoma, most of them now rebuilt. Aside from the missions, and the sparsely manned military presidios at San Diego, Santa Barbara, Monterey, and San Francisco, the Spanish thought little of California: it was too remote, too undeveloped, without any of the golden wealth they had drained out of Mexico and Peru.

The Mexicans were barely settled when *americanos* began filtering in from the northern mountains or the southern desert: Jedediah Smith, a trapper, in 1826, James Pattie, a fur trapper, in 1828, Ewing Young in 1829, Joseph Walker in 1833, John Frémont and Kit Carson and John Bidwell in 1841, then American sailors who jumped ship when their barks anchored in California ports, and those put ashore sick and left to die. They did not die; of all the multitudes sent to California by their family doctors back home, not one has been known (publicly) to succumb. Many of the Americans became *Californios:* and why not, with thousands of acres of fertile land for the taking, and beautiful black-eyed *señoritas* languishing for husbands?

The first revolt of Americans for independence from Mexico was started by the wrong social set; that's probably why we hear so little about it. Isaac Graham, their leader, was the owner of a distillery, described by Hubert Howe Bancroft, our fabulous source historian, as "a wild and unprincipled man." Graham and his followers wound up in a flea-infested jail in San Blas, Mexico.

But six years later there were some seven hundred Americans in California, owning a great deal of land, restive under Mexican rule. In 1846, Colonel John C. Frémont, son-in-law of Thomas Hart Benton of Missouri, the most rabid western expansionist in the Congress, having appeared from over the mountains with a band of well-armed explorers and cartographers, had a brush with General Castro, the military commander of California, and raised the American flag on Gabilan Peak for three days of defiance. Then, moving northward, he was overtaken by Marine Lieutenant Gillespie, who had confidential dispatches from Secretary of State Buchanan. Frémont turned south, united the *americanos,* and so began the story of modern California.

Very soon thereafter an excitable young wheelwright by the name of James Marshall, while building a sawmill at Coloma for his Swiss boss, John Sutter, glanced over at the tailrace he had built across a bend in the American River, and noticed a number of flecks of yellow where the water was sluicing through a sandbar. If the Flower of the Pacific was wrested from Mexico through rape, and its birth as an American state must be branded as illegitimate, there was no questioning the legitimacy of that gold; it started a rush that has never slackened, and will not abate until some fifty million people call themselves Californians.

Superlatives are indigestible; let's sample a few, and have done with them.

California is the fastest-growing state in the Union. We have the largest number of owner-occupied dwelling units of any state, the widest diversification of agricultural crops and livestock, bringing the highest cash farm income; the widest diversification of minerals, of recreational facilities, the largest number of automobiles, driven by the wackiest drivers; the largest bank, the highest and lowest land points, Mount Whitney and Death Valley; the tallest trees, the tallest storytellers, starting with Mark Twain and his *Jumping Frog of Calaveras County*. We spend more money than any other state for public services: education, public welfare, highways. California is the second largest state geographically (alas, we can never become first), embraces 158,693 square miles, bigger than New England with New York and Ohio thrown in for friendly measure; has the longest coastline, twelve hundred miles, on the biggest ocean in the world; has the second highest per-capita income of the major states. . . .

What do these facts and figures mean? What is their true significance? The Himalayas are big, but they have produced no Athens or Florence, while I have yet to meet an elephant who has written *The Brothers Karamazov* or a dinosaur who has painted Van Gogh's *Vegetable Gardens.* Size and wealth are meaningless unless translated into terms of the good life for a whole people.

The best way to know California is from within, by working its veins and arteries, as the original gold miners did, and as this writer did; drive a San Francisco grocery wagon and have the horse fall down in its harness when you attempt to take him down the perpendicular Haight Street hill; dig holes for electric poles across the hot Central Valley; oil dynamos at a Kern River power plant in the mountains above Bakersfield; whitewash the trunks of apricot trees in Hollister, pick peaches in Marysville in the farm belt, wrap meat in a Los Angeles packing plant and watch the hams and bacons dance on the rack when an earthquake rocks the building; or check vacationers in and out of a swank Lake Tahoe mountain resort as a desk clerk. Deliver suits for Pauson's and fling a package up a long dark flight of stairs on Grant Avenue in San Francisco's Chinatown, fleeing in terror because you've been brought up to believe the stories of Chinese opium dens and white-slave trade; some years later play "Smiles" and "Margie" for an Italian wedding in a Grant Avenue hall with your back against a lattice-work partition, on the other side of which a Chinese orchestra is playing Old Country music for one of their weddings; blow a saxophone at the Orange Show in the lush southern citrus land of the San Bernardino Valley for ten days and nights, or on the back of a truck helping to gather Central California crowds in Benicia, Vallejo, Napa, and Sacramento, so that political haranguers can tell the people why they should vote for John W. Davis for President; entertain with a traveling vaudeville troupe through the mining regions of Angels Camp and Chinese Camp, the mountain and lumber towns of Jamestown, Sonora, Tuolumne; work as a stock boy in one of San Francisco's oldest bookstores where you unpack hundreds of copies of Ibanez' *Four Horsemen of the Apocalypse,* the best seller of the day, and at every opportunity read a few pages in the storage stacks until the manager tells you to take a copy home and read it on your own time; be signaled out of an eight A.M. senior discussion group in economics at the University of California at Berkeley, unshaven, and be asked by the professor to take the rostrum and replace the Teaching Fellow whose appendix had been removed an hour before, thus stumbling into the noble profession of teaching.

California is actually five different states, with a variety of cultures: the sun worship of the vast southern desert; the semitropical life of Los Angeles with its hundred-mile aura of influence; the valley culture of the five-hundred-mile-long, rich agricultural land between the Coast Range and the Sierras; the fog culture; the mountain and big-timer culture of the north.

San Francisco is the capital of the fog culture, though its natives will tell you that is has no fog, or if they are confronted with the sight of it rolling in from the beach at fourteen miles an hour, that they find it exhilarating. You will be driving north from Los Angeles, with the top of your convertible down, baking in the hot sun; you reach the south end of the suction cup, perhaps five miles down the peninsula from San Francisco, and find yourself engulfed in raw penetrating cold. The fog will blanket the whole city as you drive over the Mission hills, past the ball park, across Market Street, by the Civic Center with the beautiful Opera House, and out automobile row. The waters of the strait will be milk gray, with only the tips of the vast steel girders of the Golden Gate Bridge visible, as though they were hung downward from the sky. Yet once across the bridge, and through the cut in the hills, a matter of a mile or two, and you are again in the hot clear sunshine.

Do not gather the impression that San Francisco is a cold city; actually it is one of the warmest communities in the world, with the old Spanish tradition of the latchstring always being on the outside still predominant. San Francisco is warm and hospitable to strangers, trusts newcomers and takes them at face value. When you have done raving about the tiny tart shrimp at Fisherman's Wharf, the cable cars clanging up Powell and California Streets, the view of the Golden Gate Strait from Pacific Heights with tramp steamers coming through the narrows, the Bay Bridge seen from Coit Tower or the Top of the Mark, the *soignée* San Francisco women, among the best groomed in the world, the breath-taking panorama of Market Street extending from the foot of Twin Peaks all the way down to the now obsolete Ferry Building; when all of this has been recounted, it still does not disclose the secret of why San Francisco is one of the world's most beloved cities: the incredible fact that after an hour you feel that you belong, that this city which embodies and projects a quality of delight could be your home forever.

A lot of folks came originally to find gold, but when they grew bored with digging, or the gold did not pan out, they resumed the trades they had practiced at home: carpentering, farming, doctoring, trading, bookkeeping, schoolteaching, the law.

When I told my mother, who had read from cover to cover but one book in her life, Mary Antin's *Promised Land,* that I was determined to become a writer, she wept with fear for her only son: for in one of my Aunt Julia's flats lived a writer with his wife and three daughters. They had no furniture except two beds, a kitchen table and chairs, no carpets on the floor. When the writer ran out of food money he would pick up a tray of toilet waters and peddle them to the wives of chicken farmers around Petaluma. To my mother's objection I replied:

"San Francisco is a good place for writers to be born." What more can any city give its children than the unshatterable faith that they can accomplish whatever they may set their minds and hearts to?

In 1923, when I was an economics instructor at the University of Southern California in Los Angeles, sharing an office with three other instructors, two handsomely dressed young men from the Janss Investment Corporation made us an offer: they would give each of us a large lot free, in something that was to be called Westwood Village, where a southern branch of the University of California was purportedly to be built, if we would contract to erect a $10,000 business building within three years. Though the four of us could not have collected ten thousand jelly beans, we piled into my Model T, drove through the miles of open plains on either side of Wilshire Boulevard, then trudged over the sand dunes wondering why these slick operators did not confine their confidence games to wildcat oil wells.

Today Westwood Village is one of the most sparklingly beautiful and prosperous communities in the state; you can't buy a lot there with money, let alone jelly beans, and the faculty complains that it is the only university town in America where the rentals are too high for the professors to live.

I, for one, should have known better: as a child I stood on a high sand dune in San Francisco overlooking the Pacific with my grandfather telling me how, in 1870, he had stood on this very dune waiting for sight of the ship, reported lost, coming from around the Horn with his wife and children. To my question of whether there ever would be houses on these miles and miles of lonely dunes, my grandfather replied:

"Never. There aren't enough people in the world to fill them up."

The only sand you can find today is on the beach south of the Cliff House.

Not long ago I drove through Los Angeles to the International Airport, out Sepulveda Boulevard past open fields and dunes where I had been horseback riding the day before. I flew to New York and remained long enough to send a book to press, three months at the most; when I returned I found the same countryside occupied by several thousand bungalows, with the streets in, trees planted, lawns and flowers already up, kids playing under the sprinklers.

Hard to believe? It happens every day. Two hundred thousand new residents will pour into the Los Angeles Metropolitan Area in 1954, a larger number than live in the entire state of Nevada.

Why do they come? Why are they willing to give up home, family, friends, jobs, clientele, roots? Why do so few become disappointed and return to the place of their birth?

The climate is one of the two commanding factors: in Southern California, the weather is a friend with whom you can have a delightful time the year around. People say, "If I'm going to have to work for a living I might as well do it where it is warm and pleasant all year." There are other reasons: most of the cities are new, clean and sun-drenched; the buildings rarely go over two to four stories and those coming from skyscraper cities can see their world horizontally instead of vertically, surrounded by a huge bowl of sky instead of cement walls. There is no snow to be shoveled, coal and oil to be burned, soot to be fought; men don't have to wear heavy overcoats and rubbers, women don't have to bundle up the children in wools and ear muffs. Folks live in their own homes, with flowers in front and a back yard where the kids can play in safety all year round. Many middle-cost builders are replacing the rumpus room or extra bedroom with a small swimming pool.

The second motivation is exemplified by my own family: my mother and stepfather moved down to Los Angeles from San Francisco in 1919 because Los Angeles, then a sleepy village, was just beginning to offer fresh business opportunities. With expanding aviation, automobile, steel, oil, motion-picture, real-estate and a hundred other industries there is work for all, and opportunity aplenty.

Fifteen years ago, when some friends moved to Los Angeles from New

York and I asked their sons what they were majoring in at school, they replied disdainfully, "Recess. Every time we turn around we have to go outside and play," to which their mother added, "Apparently you Southern Californians are trying to develop a race of seven-foot dopes." This is no longer true: in a leisurely two-hour drive from the beautiful UCLA campus in Westwood one can circle past Los Angeles City College, USC, and go east through the San Bernardino Valley past Occidental, California Institute of Technology, Whittier, Scripps, Pomona, Redlands and the liberal-arts branch of the University of California at Riverside, all fine educational institutions.

Los Angeles was once the capital of bad taste in America, with all manner of vulgar architecture, restaurants in the shape of hot dogs and tamales, with bastard Spanish or Moorish monstrosities for residences. In towns like Beverly Hills the original builders built thick-walled narrow-windowed Spanish houses, black dungeons which are being ripped out and converted to moderns to make way for the sun and light. The intellectual tone of the community, totally insular and isolationist, was dictated by senior citizens retired from the rigors of the Midwest farm states, who came because living was cheap.

Though Los Angeles still has to borrow San Francisco's opera company for two weeks out of the year, it now has its own symphony orchestra, growing art museums, many little theaters, vigorous bookstores, superb private collections of paintings and sculpture available for local showings. The motion-picture industry helped to make the change, bringing in creative artists from all over the world.

Even in California, the democratic West Pole of the world, we have our dissenters and defeatists and crackpots. In spite of the maturing of our arts and education, Los Angeles still remains one of the most powerful anti-intellectual centers in the country. In 1953 a group of Paleozoic patriots pushed resolutions through the City Council that UNESCO could never be mentioned in the public schools. A similar group picketed the annual art show of the Los Angeles County Museum because it showed nonobjective paintings which, the protesters maintained, were communist and subversive because they couldn't understand them.

Yet there is a vitality abroad that is building new schools, libraries, whole outlying communities: a vitality that says make way for life, the California life.

The country for one hundred twenty miles south of Los Angeles to the Mexican border, the first half dominated by the oil derricks of Culver City, Signal Hill, and Huntington Beach and the wells out in the ocean, is a narrow strip with houses hugging the mountains overlooking the sea. Behind this wall of mountain there are tremendous valleys where only a few cattle graze. In South Laguna you can have your own private beach and catch fish from the rocks, or skin dive for abalone and put out lobster traps. San Diego is a big town now, straining toward a half million; it has beautiful views of the ocean and bay wherever you turn and the most exciting zoo in the world.

The most beautiful and cultivated trio of towns in the Los Angeles area are Santa Barbara, Pasadena, and La Jolla, generically alike and formerly known as the "Three R's": rich, Republican, and reactionary. This canard can no longer be charged; the cities are extremely prosperous, but many of the great Eastern and Midwest fortunes that founded them have gone to their rewards: the Treasury Department. Pasadena's big estates are being broken up for handsome two-story modern apartment houses, while whole suburbs of precision-instrument workers are moving in to man the new plants. La Jolla is being settled by the overflow of middle-class families from San Diego, while Santa Barbara is becoming an important college center with its new University of California campus.

A hundred miles of magnificent beaches are a half-hour's drive from anywhere in the Los Angeles area; so are the mountains with good fishing in summer and skiing in winter. Except for Old Los Angeles, Southern California is sparkling new, with the gleaming whiteness of house and market and street, a constant joy to the newcomer.

The word "slum" has dropped out of the language; even the rundown sections have a bit of lawn, shrubs, a few flowers in front of the houses.

Southern California families live as much outdoors as they do in; modern architecture includes the out-of-doors as part of the interior decoration. This willingness to experiment, to try the new and different has helped to lessen the tightness and tensions of a more rigid world.

California has always been a romantic area and concept, from the beginning romance of its name, through the discovery of romantically free gold, the romance of its semitropical flowers and brilliant sunshine, its golden oranges and golden poppies, its Mediterranean date crop around Indio in the Coachella Valley, and finally that great romance breeder which has made the name of Hollywood famous in the remotest villages of Afghanistan.

The proper way to describe Hollywood is in terms of the motion-picture industry: the various companies are only ostensibly in competition. Actors, producers, directors, writers shift from M-G-M to Fox to Warners to Paramount to Columbia to Universal-International and back to M-G-M without changing a picture on their desks or knowing that they have actually moved. The steady and secure core of the industry are the technicians, the engineers, sound men, electricians, property men, all well but not exorbitantly paid, and enjoying almost full security. These are the gentle folk, the soft-spoken, the totally decent and reliable.

Do the movie big shots have a more amoral set of values than the leaders of other industries? If you were playing poker with twenty dollars in the pot and saw an opportunity to cut a corner in order to win, you probably would not be tempted to take advantage; but if there were two hundred thousand dollars in the pot, and you saw a chance to cheat. . . . Only in Hollywood can a man who is earning five thousand dollars a week be unemployed the following Monday, the man who is broke and cannot meet the payment on his home suddenly get a contract or sell a property to the movies and have a hundred and fifty thousand dollars in the bank.

Only in the motion-picture industry are millions spent each year on promoting individual personalities, until actors and actresses believe their own press notices and come to regard themselves as kings and queens with the divine right of royalty. Imagine what this does to the integrity of human beings; imagine what these men and women will not do to remain at the heart of the greatest romance creator of our age, and to reap its fabulous harvest—even though in their hearts they know they really earn but the smallest portion.

What is the effect of living in Southern California, through whose communities are spread the thousands of people engaged in the motion-picture industry? It is a pleasant one: the man going past you on the Freeway in an open convertible is Robert Taylor; the little fellow sitting next to you at the Coliseum, watching the Rams football game in a weird sweater and snow cap, is Mickey Rooney; the attractive woman with the bold streak of gray, putting her child on the train in Glendale for summer camp, is Joan Crawford; the girl at the next table at Wil Wright's having an ice cream soda is Marilyn Monroe; at the sneak preview at your nearby movie house you will see the entire cast of big pictures as well as the director, producer, and cameraman of the film which will be splashed across the newspapers three months hence. Not even the gala international world *premières,* with the lights and the stars and the special stands, can make any shattering change in your life; but all these things are fun, they are gay, they lend color and character to Southern California.

Picture to yourself two high walls of mountains, the Coast Range and the Sierra Nevada, going up over fourteen thousand feet at Mount

Whitney; and between the two a mammoth valley some five hundred miles long and forty wide—roughly half the size of England.

Two thirds of the state's agricultural lands are here, irrigated by the Central Valley Water Project, which stores water high on the Sacramento and San Joaquin rivers and carries it five hundred miles south to the once desert lands around Bakersfield. Every species of temperate-zone and subtropical fruit, vegetable or field crop is produced: pears, asparagus, celery, beans, onions, rice, lettuce, grapes, prunes, peaches, apricots, plums, olives, cotton (more cotton than any state in the South, except Texas), oranges, lemons, pomegranates, figs, avocados, loquats, guavas, almonds, walnuts, dates, artichokes, cherries, honeydew melons, cantaloupes, tomatoes, cauliflower, spinach, dry beans, garlic, alfalfa, apples, sugar beets, grapefruit, barley.

In this earthly paradise have grown prosperous modern communities whose millions of people live free of insecurity and want. The three most important towns of the Central Valley are Sacramento, about a hundred miles northeast of San Francisco, which grew up around Sutter's Fort, with orange and magnolia trees shading the streets, architecturally half old, half new, with hundreds of suburban ranch-style houses; Stockton, an inland port, important as a trading post long before the gold rush; and Fresno, center of the billion-dollars-a-year trade of the San Joaquin Valley, halfway between San Francisco and Los Angeles, a young, vigorous, almost completely new city.

In towns like San Jose, forty miles south of San Francisco, a center of canning, dried fruits, and wineries, three quarters of the families own their own homes, as they do in Sacramento and such prosperous southern towns as Pomona, with its colleges, Redlands, Riverside, and San Bernardino. Nine million Californians want no part of the life in the world-known cities of San Francisco and Los Angeles; they like the intimacy and camaraderie of the coastal towns or the hot, small communities of the Central Valley: Marysville, Lodi, Stockton, Modesto, Merced, Fresno, Visalia, Salinas, San Luis Obispo, and a hundred others, many of them with a single shopping center and conventional neon signs which are slowly draining their individuality. In towns like these you can know nearly everyone of your own generation; you need never live among strangers. You can, and do, marry young, frequently out of high school. Friendship is strong because it underlies almost every social activity. There is a homogeneity, not merely of ideas and values, but of income levels as well. No one need get lost. The weekly poker game you start during the last year of high school will still be going twenty years later with the same fellows, and probably the same gags. You won't enjoy much privacy; the other women will know exactly how much your wife spends on clothes and when you and she last quarreled. And you will also know everything about them.

Without this Central Valley, this modern-day Valley of the Nile, California would be a magnificent front, able to support less than half its population, hollow at its economic core.

The newest culture in the state, and perhaps the most exciting, is the life of the desert. The desert can be cruel; to many newcomers it appears hostile, fruitless. But the desert is also intensely alive, mysterious, masterful. Palm Springs is the center of the vacation area; no hospital or sanitarium, industrial plant or farm is permitted in this particular mountain-enclosed valley. Palm Springs is attracting more devotees each year by what they like to call its optimum climate: the greatest amount of beneficent clear sunlight and the least humidity in the United States; but what is not generally known is that thousands of families are exchanging the business-suit-and-necktie life of formal cities for the open-sport-shirt-and-sandal life of the Coachella Valley, which includes Indio, heart of the date palm.

You drive through the eye-burning smog of Los Angeles, then climb up the San Gorgonio Pass, through Beaumont and Banning into the desert itself, with its towering wall of sheer brown rock; and suddenly you can breathe deeper, suddenly you are in a world of brilliant sunlight and color, the openness of vast areas where no person or object can fence in your body or your thinking. No matter how tired or ill you may be, or possessed by *Weltschmerz,* your troubles and complaints fall away: for there is little tension on the desert, pressures dissolve in the hot sun, as do the nervous confusions of a competitive world.

The recuperative power of the desert, its ability to bring one closer to the eternalities of nature, the ever-shifting forms of the sand, and the shadows on the mountains, with the sun on your back during the day, the warm silk-soft air of the night on your face, have caused thousands of people to move into the area around Palm Springs and make it their permanent home. There will be hundreds of thousands more in the balance of the Coachella and Imperial Valleys, now that they are watered from the Colorado River through the new All-American Canal.

The desert is one vast *Kaffeeklatsch;* everyone is friendly and helpful because everyone is himself a new arrival, remembering how it felt to be lonely. When you live with the vastness of sky and sun and mountain, with the magnificent panorama of changing pastel colors, vivid purple sunsets, skies so thick with stars you can reach up and pick them like bunches of grapes, you stop worrying about Molotov, Chou En-lai, hydrogen bombs, income taxes; you become, instead, in your own simple way, a philosopher. The products of philosophy, alas, cannot be boxed and shipped like the superb Coachella grapefruit and dates or the Imperial Valley melons; but by breeding an anxiety-free man, the desert is adding a new dimension and a new health-drenched culture to the complex geographical and mystical entity of California.

Northern California, the third of the state that lies north of San Francisco, is as different from Southern California as New Hampshire is from Florida. The mountains and stands of pine, redwood, Douglas fir, incense cedar, western yew, mountain birch, and white oak are majestic, the towns and people few. There is privacy and solitude, great hunting, fishing, camping for a hardy stock that can take thirty-five below zero in winter, ninety-eight above in summer, and will not hesitate to brave the worst of these extremes to bag a fine mule buck or catch a large brown trout, or be averse to taking a wee drop now and then. The people living in the far north conceive of themselves as still living in an almost-frontier country; they enjoy the romantic conception of the hardy, robust, difficult life.

Northern Californians, too, live close to nature; it is an outdoor interest that explains the presence of most of the residents, particularly among the professional classes, yet the rugged four-season life is the exact opposite of that led by the new desert dwellers. They are never more than a few minutes away from upland meadows, mountain torrents, rock gorges through which the Kings and Kern rivers have cut their beds, high Sierra peaks and passes often snow-laden, nearly impenetrable forests carpeted with fern, huckleberries, buckthorn, elderberry, teeming with bear, antelope, mountain sheep and mountain lions, fox, beaver and muskrat.

The towns of Northern California are old and so inbred that if you have an argument with a merchant or city clerk in Alturas you find that you have offended half the families of Modoc County. The people here are harder, sterner, more ruggedly set than the soft, easygoing, fast-changing but slower-moving and slower-talking Southern Californians.

The social life is exhausting: bridge parties, community concerts, baseball, bowling and rifle-shoot competitions, an endless round of luncheons, cocktail parties, dinners, dances, and picnic suppers. In a town like Ukiah, a hundred miles north of San Francisco, the community life of the churches, PTA, fraternal, scouting, political organizations, and volunteer government committees is so highly organized that there is almost never a free hour; while the most often repeated line in Alturas is, "I got a meeting tonight." There are few book or music shops in these northern towns; however, the book clubs do a flourishing business and many middle-class families maintain credit accounts at San Francisco and Oakland bookstores.

The people of Northern California are a little like their redwoods: lean in temperament, resentful of intruders though exhaustingly hospitable to friends; opposed to change, to the new or different, disdaining the Southern California backyard-barbecue and swimming-pool set. To the Southern Californian, anything that is not built tomorrow is old-fashioned; to North Californians, that which smells of paint, the most cherished of all perfumes in the south, is parvenu.

Around Lake Tahoe, where California and Nevada make an elbow bend, the rings on the *Sequoia gigantea* add up to four thousand years, probably the oldest inhabitants of the state; the northern people have somewhat the same solidity of tradition, priding themselves on being an "old" culture. This is true all the way down to Fresno, about midway in the state, after which the pride comes in being spanking-new.

California is not utopia, yet it is a land to dream on; seventeen co-operative colonies, from the religious Fountain Grove near Santa Rosa in Northern California to Madame Modjeska's agricultural colony near Anaheim in Southern California, have been essayed in the past hundred years. When you drive through the gold-rush regions, pass abandoned mines and the high piles of rock displaced by hydraulic mining, and the river beds where millions in golden dust were taken out, it's all you can do to restrain yourself from jumping out of the car, grabbing a shovel, and commencing to dig.

The state is changing: subdividers are ripping out walnut orchards and orange groves in the south for residential tracts, prune orchards and vineyards in the north for drive-in theaters or hardboard factories. The old-timers in Mendocino County don't want to be industrialized any more than the original settlers of San Diego want their two-lane roads expanded to superhighways.

Sentiment in the East used to be, "You can live cheaply in California, but you can't earn a living there." Today there is work for all, but the cost of living is high.

When I grew up in San Francisco a human being was a precious commodity, there were so few of them on Market Street or Powell. When I moved to New York in 1926 I was stunned by the hordes of humanity jammed on Fifth Avenue or Forty-second Street during the day and on Broadway at night. If there are so many people in the world, I thought, can any one of them be truly valuable?

A Californian moving to New York today would not be so stunned by the difference: for we are fast acquiring people. By the year 2000 we should have a population of 50,000,000, outnumbering most of the countries of Europe.

To this writer, who has spent his summers in the north since he was six, the Sonoma and Napa valleys, and Jack London's Valley of the Moon, are the most beautiful parts of California, surpassed only by the view of the Umbrian plain from the top of Assisi. The immigrating Italians, back in the seventies and eighties, searching all over America for their native Italy, found it in these valleys, cleared the mountainsides of first-stand redwood and pine, manzanita and madrona, planted their vineyards and made some of the world's finest wines, enriching the country with the best of their native character, particularly gastronomically. But the third generation no longer wants to plow the fields or cultivate the grapes; they've become Americanized and prefer to work in factories. The superb little wineries, with some exceptions, have been sold to the larger distilleries.

What is the character of the state today?

Californians are by nature a gentle people somehow given to violence, doubtless a vestige of the pioneer days when folks had to take care of their own hangings. If you feel the urge to blow up your parents on their yacht, or poison the milk of your best friend because you're in love with his wife, California is far and away your best bet: true-blooded Californians are too close to the pioneer days to convict anyone for a crime of passion.

Politically, it is clean; it would be after fifteen years of Earl Warren as attorney general and governor; yet we are not too aseptic to elect an occasional hack politician to high office, and have him celebrate his victory on election night by getting falling-down drunk in one of the swankier night clubs.

In the early part of the century, California was so predominantly Republican that we hardly knew there was a two-party system. I was first introduced at the age of nine to the Democrats by a gang of Mission District boys who grabbed me and shouted, "Who are you for?" I was for Teddy Roosevelt, but since it appeared obvious that they would not have grabbed me had I been for the right candidate I answered, "Taft!" Their leader bulked his fist in front of my face and cried, "You be for Woodrow Wilson, or I'll punch your nose in." I had never heard of Mr. Wilson, but I quickly changed my registration.

Like my entry into active politics, I was first rudely introduced to the California labor problem by being showered with broken glass from a rock thrown through a Masonic Avenue streetcar by striking motormen. San Francisco has always been known as a tough labor town; over the years there has been violence on the waterfront, swinging fists and swinging clubs, and the biggest general strike ever conducted in the United States. After persuading my wife, who was born in decorous Minnesota, that we should live in California because it was a peace-loving state, we spent our first day driving over a roadbed of crushed lettuce leaves, having bumped spang into an agricultural workers' strike in the Salinas Valley lettuce bowl.

Today neither management nor union is going to the wars quite as frequently as it used to: they are rather like the married couple that sits in the living room all night and holds hands, each afraid to let go for fear the other will haul off.

Los Angeles, by direct contrast, was kept an open-shop town for decades; to attract industry, the city advertised nationally that there were no unions there. As late as 1936 Los Angeles had one of the most docile and underpaid labor forces in America; grocery clerks, for example, earned eighteen dollars for a seventy-two hour week. Today, Southern California is organized, wages are high; the unions have achieved solidity without bloodshed or too agonized cries from management. Doubtless the influence of the benign climate.

Probably the most recognizable connecting links between the towns of string-bean-long California are the 540 or so Bank of America buildings, which stretch from Yreka, just south of the Oregon border, to National City, just north of the Mexican border. Though it has spread-eagled the state, it has managed to escape the charge of "octopus" both by keeping out of politics and by fulfilling A. P. Giannini's dictum that his bank must be for the little fellow: in truth, it is the common man's bank.

Started in 1904 by A. P. Giannini as the Bank of Italy in a modest building in the North Beach Italian section of San Francisco, it has since become the largest bank in the world, having revolutionized the whole concept of banking by creating branch banking, thus giving it statewide billions to finance vineyards, irrigation districts, and a thousand businesses. In 1944 when I had used up all my available cash in completing *Immortal Wife*, my own happily mortal wife informed me that we were overdrawn a hundred or so dollars. We drove from our home in San Fernando Valley to Hollywood to see the manager, a Mr.

Grille, who presided over the tiny branch in what had formerly been a corner grocery store. We told Mr. Grille that we were overdrawn. He replied: "Why don't you go home and finish your book, and let me worry about the banking business?"

A few weeks later he loaned us fifteen hundred dollars to take our completed manuscript to New York, the money enabling us to live and work there until publication: probably the first time in history that a bank midwived a successful biographical novel.

This illustrates another difference in California life: the neighborhood bank, branch department store, and supermarket as against the impersonal, coldly formal, monolithic downtown bank or shop.

Nor, in our economic prosperity, are we trying to live by bread alone. Bookstores were opened in the Sacramento Valley during the very height of the gold rush by men who thought it more important to sell and disseminate literature than to dig a fortune out of the ground. Probably no state, with the possible exception of Indiana, has bred more creative writers. The great University of California, which literally teems with creativity in the humanities and sciences, and has eight campuses stretching throughout the state, accessible free of charge to all of California's youngsters, was started a full century ago, also while gold was available for the digging.

We have art colonies at Carmel in the north, Laguna Beach in the south, Idyllwild high in the mountains, the music academy of the West in a beautiful Santa Barbara garden. Open-air art exhibits in the neighborhood parks of Los Angeles have attracted thousands of paintings and sculptures; granted little of it has anything more than therapeutic value for its creators, but even the most modest practice of an art is the first step toward its understanding.

The Californian today is assuredly not what he was during the gold-rush days, nor during the sleepy sun-baked 1880s when Los Angeles was an adobe village, nor yet what he was during the rambunctious days of San Francisco after the turn of the century with its Barbary Coast. The Californian today has been widely crossbred; in many parts of the state, prior to the Second World War, it was almost impossible to find anyone except a native son; today in Southern California, for example, almost 90 per cent of the adult population is from out of the state.

Our faith in the absorptive powers of the state is strong. With our magnificent dams and irrigation systems, with our new chemical marvels and improved farm machinery, we can raise enough food to sustain an empire. The Pacific Ocean is so vast that it is able to dissipate whatever poisons may be dumped onto its broad bosom; our mountains, deserts, valleys, hundred bustling little towns have the same powers of assimilation.

If Frank Lloyd Wright was correct in saying that only the Far West is vital because it is still growing, then perhaps out here in California we can evolve a breed of human being who is healthy in his mind as well as in his body; who can live a vigorous outdoor life, close to the beauties and mysteries of the desert, the mountains, the redwoods, the fertile valleys and the sea, and at the same time work prodigiously in the creative arts and intellects. Perhaps we can sire a breed of *homo sapiens* who does not want to fight and destroy but to construct and live at peace with his neighbor, be he next door in Santa Ana or Eureka, in Athens, Bangkok or Tokyo.

This is why we have the temerity to suggest that California is the West Pole. With half the world shutting down on freedom, California is offering ever increasing freedoms to all its people, those here and those on the way.

So much has been written about California there is little left to be told: except the truth. But would you look for truth in the eyes of a man in love?

CLARENCE DARROW, born on April 18, 1857, was the son of a Midwest iconoclast, Amirus Darrow, who had served as the Kinsman, Ohio, link of the Underground Railroad, a furniture and coffinmaker whose floors were covered with hundreds of annotated books. His mother too loved learning and ideas, but the Darrows were always in the minority. Amirus Darrow enjoyed his role as the oppositon, a passion and talent inherited by his son. Clarence went briefly to Allegheny College, read law, taught school, debated on Saturday nights, and at twenty-one passed the simple oral examination given by his fellow lawyers in Youngstown. He married, practiced county law in Andover and Ashtabula, was elected city solicitor. In 1888 at the age of thirty-one he decided to make the big move to Chicago, where he joined the Sunset Club, the Henry George Club, became skilled at public speaking. He also became a legal Lochinvar, dashing out to break a lance for every good social—and preferably minority—cause. He had a golden personality, became counsel for the Chicago & North Western Railway. When the Pullman Company workers went on strike, and Eugene V. Debs was imprisoned for taking out the railroad union, Darrow resigned, defended Debs, became known as a defender of labor. He spent two tortured years in Idaho defending Moyer, Haywood, and Pettibone, officers of the Western Federation of Miners, on charges of murdering ex-Governor Frank Stuenenberg. He returned to Chicago in 1907, broke, ill, without a practice.

CLARENCE DARROW FOR THE DEFENSE

This Is War!

SEEKING a quiet neighborhood where her husband might recover his strength and serenity of mind, Ruby searched along the South Shore until she found a top flat of a six-story building called The Hunter, on the Midway, which overlooked the University of Chicago, Jackson Park, with its Japanese bridge and pagoda, and Lake Michigan. "It was built by a man who forgot that neither he nor his building would be everlasting," says Ruby, "so every inch of the inside was solid oak. The nine rooms were exceedingly large, with high ceilings and high and wide windows; even the kitchen was wide enough for a small banquet hall, a very great inconvenience. There were five windows across the front, every one affording beautiful views of lake, park, trees, lawn and unbroken distances." Clarence was delighted with its spaciousness and the sense of being above the tumult of Chicago life, but he declined to sign a lease.

"We'll have to take it on a month-to-month basis, Rube, because I'm not sure enough about my income. We're between ten and fifteen thousand dollars in debt."

Ruby took their furniture out of its two-year storage vault, recovered some of the pieces, then spent four days and nights in fitting the front room with the red carpet from the Sheridan Road apartment. She put flatirons on the gas stove and with them burned red dye into the carpet to brighten it. She then ransacked the furniture marts until she found an oversized brass bed in which big-boned Clarence could roam comfortably, placing it in "the large bow windows across the south end, looking out over five beautiful maple trees and miles beyond, over other people's yards, lawns and trees. What breezes, what sunlight, what space and privacy and quiet there was." There were also windows facing east and west, so he could watch the sun rise or set from his big brass bed.

"There were seven pillows of many sizes," adds Ruby, "downy and refreshing, to bank back of himself as he pleased and back of me, too, when reading aloud together."

For a year and a half she cooked, scrubbed the nine-room flat, washed the household and personal linen, never spending a cent on anything but food. At the end of that time the Darrows had paid all debts. Only then did Ruby yield and hire a maid. Only then did Clarence sign a lease, a lease which was to run for thirty years, which was to see the rent rise from seventy-five to two hundred and fifty dollars a month as the district became popular and fashionable, drop slowly again to seventy-five dollars as the neighborhood ran its life circle and disintegrated; a lease which was to leave Darrow undisturbed while styles in housing changed and the big flats beneath him were remodeled into six apartments each; a lease which was to terminate only when he died in his roomy brass bed in the bow window at the age of eighty.

What he liked most about his new home was its proximity to the University of Chicago, where so many of the professors were old friends who liked to drop in for an evening of hearty talk over pipefuls of tobacco. He knocked out the walls connecting the front bedroom, living room and dining room to make one big ell-shaped library, thirty-three feet by twenty-five feet across the front, overlooking the Midway, and an additional twenty feet deep into the ell. The available walls were lined solidly with shelves to house his thousands of heterogeneous volumes. The room now being large enough to hold a considerable group comfortably, he took into his home the Evolution Club, of which he had been the guiding light and which had been meeting around town at various halls. The meetings were held once a week; young and enthusiastic instructors from the university gave courses in biology, archaeology, anthropology, paleontology, sociology, comparative religion. Sitting in one of Darrow's favorite wicker rockers in front of the fireplace, they lectured for an hour, then defended their science for another three hours while Darrow, rocking in the opposite wicker chair, guided the discussion with a deft hand, and the members munched on Ruby's sandwiches and wet their whistles with sour Italian wine.

When a young astronomy instructor arrived to open his course Darrow drew a chuckle by musing sardonically, "Now, Professor, don't try to tell us anything about what's happening down here on this earth; we know all about that; just tell us what's happening up in those stars."

These evenings became the most pleasant of his lifetime: visiting professors and philosophers, European writers and scientists, when they learned that the Midway library was the most exciting intellectual workshop in Chicago, came to dine with the Darrows and address the club. The instructors taught, and the members, who now numbered a hundred of the most vigorous minds in Chicago, learned, because the subjects were vital and important, because it was good to be alive in a world where knowledge was going forward, making constant encroachments against the darkness of ignorance and prejudice.

"When I think of Clarence Darrow," says Robert M. Hutchins, president of the University of Chicago, "I see a tall, majestic man debating with our faculty members, opposing their views, defending their rights, holding long, quizzical, deliberate conversations with them in the dark red library of his apartment on East Sixtieth Street, plumbing and challenging them, taking their measure."

"Cruelty is the child of ignorance," wrote Darrow to a friend during this period, "and someday men will stop judging and condemning each other. I am really more interested in this than anything else; I wish I could make the world kinder and more humane than it is."

It was this abstention from judgment, this refusal to condemn on the standard codes of good and evil, that made him a fire to which chilled human beings came to warm their hands and hearts. To the men and women who were struggling against a fear psychosis in a confused and competitive world, living in constant dread of a slip or a mistake, an accident or a failure, of somehow breaking down, not making the grade, of being judged and found wanting, he seemed a tiny spark of the godhead that saw everything, understood and never condemned. When the day's work was done his office would become crowded with young lawyers who wanted to talk to him, to get the feel of him, to grasp what it was that made this sprawling, drawling, inelegant, plain-faced and plain-mannered fellow a whole man in a sea of fractional human beings. They did not come to him because he was an omniscient casebook or crafty technician, for they knew by now that "he practiced law by ear"; they came because they felt what George Jean Nathan so well described in one word: he had "size."

Hundreds of the near great from every walk of life filed through his office, seeking advice or just a friendly word: Elbert Hubbard, Jane Addams, Senator Pettigrew, William Jennings Bryan, Herbert Bigelow, Harold Ickes, Hamlin Garland, Kenneth Harris, Joseph Medill Patterson, John M. Holmes, William Allen White, Sam Jones, socialist mayor of Toledo, Mayor Tom Johnson, who inaugurated municipal railway service in Cleveland. Youngsters from all over the Midwest pushed open his door to ask his opinion of the law, whether it was a good profession, one they should enter. He discouraged them mildly and, when they were on their way out, handed them a copy of one of his lawbooks, such as Chitty on *Common Law Pleading*.

It became increasingly difficult for him to make any progress when walking on the streets of Chicago; so many friends, acquaintances and strangers alike wanted to stop him for a little chat. Once when he was late for court and an associate chided him for letting himself be waylaid by an unknown admirer, he replied, "Oh, but he was such a nice fellow." T. V. Smith reports, sometime later, that when he escorted Darrow to a meeting of the Democratic convention it took them two hours to cover the few blocks between the Illinois Central Station and the convention hall. "It wasn't a walk," says Smith, "it was a reception." People stood about in clusters to share a few words, to be enveloped, if for only an instant, in that healing smile. It was not so much that he had become a celebrity as that he had become a public property.

An amusing picture of Darrow as his fellow Chicagoans saw him walking their streets in 1907 was published in the St Louis *Mirror:* "A man of more than average height, with well-rounded limbs and body, a deep chest which droops into a general bearing of relaxation while the whole frame ambles along carelessly with the toes kicked up in the process of walking: movements that range from the slowness of contemplation to the mercurial quickness of sudden recollection of something forgotten, now necessary to be done at once; on the broad shoulders a round head, delicate at the back, but marked in front by an oppressively full brow which overarches the face like a crag; underneath the brow, eyes of gooseberry size and color, which roam restlessly or else assume a fixed expression as though looking through a stonc wall or into the secrets of fate: a sallow, leatherlike complexion hanging loosely over the cheeks and jaws and shot through with heavy lines; lips that seem purple in contrast with the sallowness of the face; a varying expression, at times lowering into saturnine sorrowfulness while the wrinkles in the crag forehead rush together like sentinels and the gooseberry eyes sink deeper into the cavernous sockets; at others, mirroring the man's nature as his face melts into smiles and is wreathed in irresistible charm."

People hearing him lecture found it an exhilarating experience. "There was first his unerring judgment in selecting a great and vital theme, something that had vexed and puzzled the great thinkers of all times," recalls one of them. "Following this was the capacity of intellectual penetration which enabled him to grasp and then reveal the inner soul of his subject. While most men lost themselves in a labyrinth of preliminaries and technicalities, Darrow entered by the great gateway and walked calmly down the center aisle." It was this ability to walk calmly down the center aisle which enabled him, in the courtroom as well as the lecture hall, to achieve perspective for his listeners: slowly the walls of the room grew indistinct; the outer walls of the building began to fade; boundaries of state and nation, race and creed, fell away; prejudices and passions dissolved until the listeners were out in the wide world, seeing whole and timelessly as historian or internationalist.

The odd part of his heartening effect upon people was that he rarely had anything heartening to say about the world's conduct. He was no optimist who encouraged folks by telling them that everything would come out all right; the best he could convey was that the mess was not their fault. "How will things come out? I guess they just won't come out. Men have been hating each other, robbing and oppressing and killing each other for countless centuries; I see little on the horizon to indicate that they won't continue to do so for centuries to come." In a letter to a reporter for a labor paper he wrote:

"There are a lot of myths which make the human race cruel and barbarous and unkind. Good and Evil, Sin and Crime, Free Will and the like delusions made to excuse God for damning men and to excuse men for crucifying each other. Sunday I am to debate on the subject 'Is Civilization a Failure?' It ought to be easy to show. How anyone can think anything else I cannot conceive. I don't know why I do these things. I never convert anyone and don't want to. I am getting more and more convinced that if anyone has any 'dope' they ought to keep it. Chicago is now on a mad hunt for criminals; the big ones are after the little ones. People are getting more cruel all the time, more insistent that they shall have their way. I wish I was either younger or older. If I was younger I should go to the South Seas; if I was older I shouldn't care so much."

Hamlin Garland comments on this schizophrenic split between his Tolstoyan spirituality and Voltarian cynicism. "Darrow and his young wife were living in a new flat over near Jackson Park, and there we dined with them in 1907. I found him quite as grave and even more bitter than his writing indicated. He talks with much of the same acrid humor. He read to us some short stories called *The Law's Delay*, which were intolerably gloomy and savage but powerful. He impressed me as a man of enormous reserve powers, but his mind is uncultivated and undisciplined. As an advocate he weakens his cause by extreme expression. His uncompromising honesty of purpose and his aggressive cynicism make him repellent to many; hence he is to me a lonely figure.

In all that he writes, in all that he says, he insists relentlessly on the folly and injustice of human society. His writing is too bitter in quality, too pessimistic in outlook, to succeed, but it has in it a protest which it is well to consider."

Darrow's indirect answer to Garland was not given until twenty years later, when he wrote an introduction for a new edition of Voltaire called *The Best of All Possible Worlds.* "Voltaire's works abound in cynical statements. He seemed to approach the world with a sneer, but often it is a protective covering against the pain and anguish suffered by the man who feels the sorrows of the world. Of course he joked and laughed and sneered in his deepest miseries. When haunted by the profoundest tragedies that move the sensitive man he wore his mocking grin and cynic's smile, but his tireless brain, his constant energy, even his mocking grin, have done much to rid the world of the cruelty and intolerance that has blasted the lives and destroyed the hopes of millions of human beings since man came upon the earth."

Lieutenant Commander L. H. C. Johnson observes, "While Darrow's keen sense of humor and knowledge of world affairs made him very popular with the men, he was a riot with the women. I took him to a birthday party, and when it came time for us to go I couldn't find the chief. I finally found him on the porch, sitting in a low chair, surrounded by at least twenty women of all ages. I almost had to insult the females to get him home." Now that he had passed fifty his interest in women had subsided a bit, but he never lost his connoisseur's eye; when he was returning home from a lecture the porter informed him that Miss Cissie Patterson, of the publishing family, had her private car attached to the train and had asked him to breakfast with her. When Darrow rejoined his wife in Chicago "he mischievously asked me why in the world I didn't wear slinky, satiny, thin, clinging bright green pajamas and pink velvet and things a fellow could see through and get a thrill from—and, oh yes, the kind of slippers that have no heels or toes and have continuously to be pushed back on the feet."

The lawyers who thronged to his office tried to get him to talk about his past cases and triumphs, but he could never be persuaded to discuss them. When someone asked him whether Big Bill Haywood had been innocent or guilty he replied, "By Jove, I forgot to ask him." George Leisure relates, "Clarence Darrow was the most modest man I have ever known. You scarcely ever heard him use the pronoun I. I never heard him tell anything he personally did in a courtroom, although he delighted in telling of occurrences in which other lawyers had been able to do brilliant work and distinguish themselves." A number of years later, when a group of friends tendered him a birthday banquet and celebrities from every walk of American life made eulogizing speeches about him, "the religionists trying to prove him to be deeply religious, the scientists claiming him to be a scientist, the judges and lawyers pulling for their ranks, Darrow got up slowly and said in the oh-so-deceptive drawl:

"'I'm the one all this talk's been about. I always thought I was a hell of a fellow, but now I'm sure of it.'"

2

The firm of Darrow, Masters and Wilson was doing only fair to middling, for Darrow's two-year absence had cost them many of their profitable accounts, and the depression of 1907 had slowed down all business. Darrow, who had been their main business getter, found that his shattering illness and operation had taken their toll: he suffered recurrent spells of fatigue and general malaise that depleted his strength. The lines deepened in his face, making him look more than his fifty years. When the newspaper photographers laughingly offered to retouch the pictures he replied, "Don't wash out the lines, boys. I worked too hard to earn them." Partly because of this lessening of vigor, but also because he had seen so much bitterness and heartbreak in courtrooms, he began urging his clients to:

"Make a settlement. Give a little to get a little. Stay out of court. Court consumes your time, your money and your energy. Take less than you think you ought to have; you'll come out ahead that way."

He gave this advice to people who had damage claims against companies, to private individuals and business concerns that were hell-bent to sue each other, to unions that had claims against their employers and employers who had claims against their workers. "Make a settlement," he told them, and his clients followed his advice. He spent less of his time in courtrooms, earned less money; his clients never got quite as much as they thought they were entitled to, but they were spared the rigors of a trial. Both sides having compromised and shaken hands on their bargain, the ill will and passions that were generated by a public conflict were avoided. This was the way Tolstoy would have done his job had he been practicing law in an industrial city.

Though his partners did not complain they were not too pleased with this change in the chief. "Darrow was sometimes too anxious to make a settlement," says Francis Wilson. "This was in part due to his convalescence and his natural laziness, though of course it was also partly due to his long experience with litigation."

His growing reluctance to squander hours in the courtroom sometimes embarrassed his office. Once when he failed to show up at the Ashland Block in time to make a ten o'clock trial William Carlin was driven to tell the court that Mr Darrow was ill.

"That's strange," observed the court; "we rode down with him this morning on the Illinois Central train."

Another time, when he was in Indianapolis debating "Is There a Hereafter?" an associate "was forced into trial in Darrow's place. It was a personal-injury suit, and the question was one of assumed risk. The condition of the premises was important for the purpose of showing whether the plaintiff knew of the hazard. In the afternoon Darrow came into town and continued the trial. During the morning session his associate had described to the court the premises and put on a witness for the purpose of proving the condition. Darrow had evidently forgotten the facts while contemplating the hereafter, for the rest of the afternoon was spent by the court and the jurors in correcting him. Everybody seemed interested in steering him along the right course; the jurors and the court were helpful rather than antagonistic."

Within another year he had built up one of the most diversified practices in Chicago. William Randolph Hearst brought back the accounts of the *American* and *Examiner*; the International Harvester Company consulted him on their taxation problems; he was adviser to the Teachers' Federation of Labor; the Shuberts came to him with their theatrical complications, and in their wake came the actors Richard Carle and Grant Mitchell, who were involved in a dispute with George M. Cohan and Sam Harris. Mayor Dunne offered him the post of corporation counsel and, when he passed it on to his friend, James Hamilton Lewis, appointed him special counsel for the city in traction matters at ten thousand dollars a year. The firemen's union and switchmen's union retained him to present their case before a Federal board; the employees of the Kellogg Switchboard Company employed him to appeal all the way to the Supreme Court the conviction of certain of their members for picketing the plant in the face of an injunction that had been issued by a trial court; Bernarr MacFadden engaged him to represent his physical-culture school. The most famous case of the period that he turned down was that of Cassie Chadwick, who claimed to be the illegitimate daughter of Andrew Carnegie. Darrow made one trip to Cleveland to investigate "a certain lockbox which was purported to contain a will or trust involving many millions of dollars" to which Miss

Chadwick claimed she was entitled, but in the end, though the lady spent two weeks in Chicago importuning him, he refused to become involved in the litigation.

By 1908 there began a rush of labor cases in which Clarence was pleased to find himself acting not so much as lawyer as arbitrator. Since he was one of the few men in Chicago whom both labor and employers would trust, he was selected by both sides to settle disputes between the National Brick Company and their brickmakers, the newspaper owners and the typographical union, the brewers and their bottlers, the clothing manufacturers and their cutters. He sat at the head of big conference tables, never permitting the employers to range themselves on one side of the table and the employees on the other, as though they were separate entities and conflicting interests, but persuading them to sit next to each other, to rub elbows, tell a little joke, smoke each other's cigarettes, to come to know each other and perhaps even like each other. Then from his position at the head of the table he brought to bear his gentleness and humor, his warmth and understanding, until the antagonistic slabs of ice in the hearts of the contestants were melted, and he shamed them into being just a little kinder, just a little more generous and sympathetic human beings than they could ordinarily achieve. In each instance a strike was averted; the loss of profits and wages was averted; both sides accepted a compromise solution and lived up to the terms of the agreement for the period of time agreed upon.

As business picked up Ruby began spending money to disprove the canard that Darrow slept in his clothes. She had his black satin ties made to order by Marshall Field, his hats custom made by Knox, a degree wider in the brim and a degree higher in the crown than the largest hat in stock, his silk shirts cut to order so "there would be no yawning effect down the buttonhole pleats in front," his handkerchiefs cut oversized and initialed, his suits designed by the best tailors in Chicago from materials she picked out herself. For the opening of one important trial she gave him a manicure and pedicure the night before, then sent him to court with every stitch on him brand new, looking as though he had just stepped out of a Bond Street window. When the afternoon papers reached the Midway she was flabbergasted to read a report that Darrow had been dressed in his usual rumpled gray suit and soiled cotton shirt. Her housekeeper was so outraged she ran to the laundry bin and began flinging out silk shirts, crying:

"There, that ought to show them! He doesn't have a cotton shirt to his name. He wears nothing but silk shirts!"

With the money coming in once again, he decided to invest his savings so that he might within a few years be able to retire and achieve his one remaining personal ambition: to write a long novel. The most promising idea on the market at the moment was a new machine which was expected to produce gas cheaper than the regular coal-gas or water-gas plants. Darrow and a group of his friends bought the patent rights from a bond-selling organization for ten thousand dollars, which included an option on the gas plants of Ottawa, Illinois and Greeley, Colorado.

"The gas-making machine was impractical," relates Paul, "and no money was left to handle the plants. It was up to me to look over the two option deals and guess which one could be handled with the money that could be put up and whether it looked as if anything could be paid back. Ottawa had recently lost some of its industries, so I guessed on Greeley, which was in the center of irrigated farming country. The town was growing, so it meant building a new gas plant and putting in an average of a mile of new mains every year for twenty years. It took most of the money I could get from Father and his friends for ten years and a lesser amount for the balance of the time."

Paul's management of the Greeley gasworks made it a valuable property. When the plant was sold in 1928 Darrow found himself for the first time in his life a rich man. Though Paul had not been able to work up any interest in his father's law business, that had not prevented him from keeping his eyes open while walking through the offices. When he left for Greeley he robbed the firm of Darrow, Masters and Wilson of a lovely dark-haired, fair-skinned, blue-eyed girl by the name of Lillian Anderson. Once again Paul's judgment proved sound; he enjoyed a fine married life, and Lillian Darrow presented her father-in-law with three granddaughters who were to bring him a good deal of joy, in particular the youngest, Mary.

And so the weeks and months passed, and the first decade of the new century. The time he earned by staying out of court he employed to write short stories and articles, the most widely known of which was his deep-cutting and brilliant essay, "The Open Shop," which was circulated in the big cities where unions were trying to bring workingmen into their organization. Twenty thousand copies had been distributed among the workers of Los Angeles during the industrial warfare that preceded the explosion of the Los Angeles Times Building; it was his authorship of this pamphlet which proved to be the determining factor in his defending of the McNamara brothers, a decision which was to wreck his career and drastically alter the external pattern of his life.

3

To the flat on the Midway came Samuel Gompers, president and founder of the American Federation of Labor. He was in a state of agitation, for he was about to break a pledge made to Darrow by the executive board after the Boise trials: that they would never again ask him to defend a labor-murder case. Gompers paced the library so distractedly that sometimes he disappeared into the ell, and only his voice could be heard. Darrow knew that he had reason to be upset, for one of the most crushing blows in the history of the American Federation of Labor had befallen him. John J. McNamara, secretary of the International Bridge and Structural Iron Workers, and his brother, James B., had just been arrested for the dynamiting of the Los Angeles *Times* and for the murder of the twenty men who had been killed in the resulting fire. Nor was that all: the McNamaras and their union were charged with committing more than a hundred dynamitings between 1906 and 1911, of blowing up bridges, aqueducts, powerhouses, theaters, steel buildings, in every major city in America. The Los Angeles *Times* swore it would hang the McNamaras on the scaffold of San Quentin and that no force on earth could stop it.

"No force except you, Clarence," said Gompers, stopping before the fireplace where Darrow was crouched disconsolately in his wicker chair.

At first glance it looked amazingly like a replica of the Moyer, Haywood and Pettibone affair. There had been a state of war between the National Erectors' Association and the Structural Iron Workers' Union since 1906, when all concerns using steel in their structures had combined and pledged themselves to maintain the open shop. The William J. Burns Detective Agency had been employed by the erectors to trail union men and garner evidence against them; in April of 1911 James B. McNamara and Ortie McManigal were arrested in Detroit on charges of safeblowing, were moved without warrants to Chicago, where they were held captive in a police sergeant's house until extradition papers could arrive from Los Angeles.

After four days of being held incommunicado McManigal had confessed to numerous dynamitings. In the pamphlet containing the story, called *Ortie McManigal's Own Story of the National Dynamite Plot*, the frontispiece was not a picture of Ortie, the hapless author, but of William J. Burns. In it the uneducated McManigal purportedly had written, "Hindsight is a splendid quality, but how fine it would be if we could reverse its action. I did not realize then that unionism is a serious menace, not only to the existing government, with its glorious and patriotic traditions, but as a menace to all government and all liberty of the individual or even of the masses."

It would have required an even greater miracle than the regeneration of Harry Orchard for Ortie McManigal to have formulated those pontifical sentences. Since one finds the precise phrases and hundreds of their counterparts in Burns's autobiography, *The Masked War*, there can be little doubt of their authorship. Once again some member of the prosecution had been so confident of success that he had not even bothered to save face; once again it seemed clear that the opposition was not merely out to get McNamara and McManigal or to destroy an individual union. This time the war would be waged on a national front.

James B. McNamara had been handcuffed and bundled onto a train for California without an opportunity to fight his extradition in Illinois. Since McManigal had named as the brains and boss of the dynamitings John J. McNamara, he, too, was arrested, in his office in Indianapolis, and shipped out to Los Angeles by such a fraudulent conspiracy that both William J. Burns and Joseph Ford, assistant district attorney of Los Angeles, were subsequently indicted by the Indianapolis grand jury.

"History repeats itself," mused Darrow; "that's one of the things that's wrong with history."

The war over steel had begun many years before. When the industry was in its infancy Andrew Carnegie had kept a personal contact with his men, paid them fair wages, recognized their union and compromised his differences. In 1891 the Amalgamated Iron and Steel Workers' Union had been one of the strongest in the country, yet Carnegie's company had earned a net profit of almost two million dollars. Then in 1892 there came a gigantic merger of coal-and-iron lands and steel ovens. Darrow had learned in the Pennsylvania coal fields that mergers, cartels and trusts unfailingly acted as combinations against labor; the larger and more powerful the merger, the wider and more powerful the opposition to labor. Since it was in the natural and inescapable law of industry to combine for purposes of efficiency and economy, to control supply, processing and marketing, so was it equally inevitable that labor wars would extend to ever-widening fronts.

Yet so great had been the influence of one man, that this need not have been immediately true of the steel combine if Carnegie had seen fit to remain at its head. Instead he retired to his estate in Scotland, leaving the industry in charge of H. C. Frick who, like Pullman, was a mechanical and production genius without humanitarian ethics. More as a token of his power and policy than as a money saver, for steel investments were returning handsome dividends, Frick reduced wages during his first meeting with the union. When after a series of conferences he refused to come up to what the men considered a living scale, they struck.

Frick hired strikebreakers, ordered three hundred armed Pinkertons to come to Homestead and guard his new workers. When the strikers heard of the move they armed themselves, organized on a military basis, with companies and commanders and prepared to resist what they considered an invasion. They fired on the Pinkertons; the Pinkertons fired back; several men were killed on both sides—and the state militia was ordered to Homestead to protect the mills and the strikebreakers who were working them. By winter the union funds had run out; the families were growing hungry and cold and threadbare. The mills were running at full blast; the strikers saw that they had been crushed. Dispirited, broken, the men deserted their organization and went back to work on the best terms they could get as non-union men.

For thirteen years there was quiet in the steel industry while labor put in its seventy-two-hour-per-week stint at reduced wages and Frick zoomed the profits to forty millions a year. The discovery of the Mesaba iron range in northern Minnesota had so reduced the cost of making steel that the face of America was being renovated: cities of skyscrapers were beginning to rise; steel rails were pushing railroads to new borders; gigantic bridges, aqueducts, industrial plants, were being built of this safe and durable and light material. And along with the skyscrapers and bridges a new class of workmen had come into existence, the structural-steel worker: a crack mechanic, as tough as the material he handled, tireless, fearless, undaunted by the most insuperable obstacles, a master craftsman rebuilding the architecture of the nation. They built a strong union, the International Association of Bridge and Structural Iron Workers, which worked at peace with their employers as long as the companies remained comparatively small and independent. But it was an era of mergers: in 1905 the American Bridge Company was formed of firms throughout the country with contracts to build bridges, dams, and the like. The following year this was expanded into the National Erectors' Association, which embraced nearly every firm building with steel. Those firms that formerly had been independent and friendly with the union were obliged to participate in the general policy of the association. The structural-steel workers and the structural-steel builders soon split on the rock that was to cause succeeding decades of wrangling and bloodshed and over which the ultimate battle would be fought: the open shop.

4

Clarence Darrow had spoken for the workingmen of America when he had written, "In reality the open shop only means the open door through which the union man goes out and the non-union man comes in to take his place. The open shop furnishes, and always has furnished, the best possible means of destroying the organization of the men. The closed shops are the only sure protection for the trade agreements and the defense of the individual. The master naturally discharges those who have been most active in the union, who interfere the most with his business, who are ever agitating for higher wages, better conditions and shorter hours. He naturally employs those who are most complaisant, those who cannot afford to lose their jobs, those whom he can bring to be dependent on his will. The open shop means uncertainties, anxieties; it is a constant menace to the union man's interest. He understands that his job is dependent upon his lack of interest in the union; men who belong to the unions and accept their responsibilities cannot be persuaded to pay dues and make sacrifices for the benefit of the non-union men who work by their sides and who are always the first to claim and receive the benefits of every struggle made by the union, benefits they receive without danger, without labor and without cost. To prevent trade unionism from being conquered in detail, to keep its members from being thrown out through the open door, to maintain the best conditions in shop and mill and factory and strive for others better still, to save the workman from long hours of toil, all these need the effort of every union man, and without the right to protect themselves in a closed shop by refusing to work with those whose weakness or stupidity make them unfaithful to their class, trade unionism cannot hold that which it has won, still less go forward to greater victories."

He was thus the most literate and powerful proponent of the closed shop in America; since the McNamaras had been working through the years for the closed shop and anything they might have done against the Erectors' Association was done in their struggle against the open shop, that made Clarence Darrow the inevitable champion of the arrested McNamaras.

So Gompers told him. But Darrow refused to take the case.

His reasons were many and valid. The two hate-laden, fever-fraught years of the Western Federation of Miners cases had almost killed him. He was still by no means well or strong. He was now fifty-four years old and a little tired; he was convinced that younger men should conduct the case, men who had their full strength and vigor. He knew something of Los Angeles, which the workingmen of the country called "the scabbiest town on earth." If the Boise cases had been bitter and venom-laden, they would seem like a Sunday-school picnic compared with the vitriol bath in which he would be immersed in Los Angeles. The McNamaras had twenty indictments against them, one for each of the men killed in the *Times* fire; it would take him at least a year to try the first case, and if he earned an acquittal on that he would have to try the other nineteen cases.

When he had returned from Boise he had promised Ruby that he would take on no more labor trials. Ruby had threatened that if he broke his promise she would refuse to accompany him; that would stop him, for Clarence had become dependent upon his wife and would not consent to being separated from her. He loved his home on the Midway; he was getting along well with his practice; he would be able to retire soon to write his long novel.

He said no, he would not take the case. But Sam Gompers refused to take no for an answer. The entire country, labor and capital alike, had assumed it would be "Clarence Darrow for the defense." Unions from every city in America wrote to tell him how happy they were that he was to defend, because he would show up the conspiracy and save the McNamaras; letters arrived from plumbers in Schenectady, brickmasons of Duluth, carpenters of New Orleans, needleworkers in New York, lumbermen of Seattle, coal miners of Scranton, streetcar conductors of San Francisco, each enclosing a dollar bill, assuring him they would stand behind him in his defense. A major labor case without Darrow; that was unthinkable!

He spent the next few days in an unhappy state of mind. Ruby made it clear that she thought it suicidal for him to take the case. Masters and Wilson opposed his going with every argument at their command, even vowing to dissolve the partnership. When the executive board of the American Federation of Labor begged him to attend a meeting in Washington he could not turn them down. They offered him a fifty-thousand-dollar fee; they offered a two-hundred-thousand-dollar defense fund, to spend as he saw fit, without an accounting; they offered him the complete loyalty and backing of their press, of their millions of members. Still he refused.

On the following Sunday afternoon Gompers came again to the flat on the Midway, accompanied by some of the strongest voices in American labor. For hours they were quartered in the library, while Ruby waited with sickening anxiety in their bedroom.

Ed Nockels said, "The whole world is expecting you to defend the boys; if you refuse you convict them before they come to trial."

Gompers said, "You will go down in history as a traitor to the great cause you have so faithfully championed and defended if now, in their greatest hour of need, you refuse to take charge of the McNamara case."

"After many hours Dee came to me in the back," relates Ruby, "wearily, sadly, taking my hand and conducting me to a seat beside him, to break to me the news that he was asking me to break my pledge. He did not seem exactly afraid that I would refuse to do as he asked; he had never asked me anything that I had even hesitated about; he explained that the men in the front room were saying that he would go down in history as a traitor to his cause. He asked me to lift my pledge and promise to go along to Los Angeles. I did not add to his dismay and dread of the situation; I offered no objections to having him do as he deemed necessary and best."

"I felt I had done my share of fighting," writes Darrow of this moment of decision. "It was not easy to combat the powerful forces of society in the courts, as I had been doing for so many years, and I was now weary of battling against public opinion. I had fought through so many conflicts that I felt the need of rest from such strenuous work. The very name of Los Angeles was associated with so much misery and suffering that the thought of going back to that place and its painful memories seemed like a foreboding that I could not quiet. Yet hard as it was to give them my yes, it would have been harder to say no."

Masters and Wilson dissolved their partnership. "It would be the international limelight again," said Wilson, "a lure he couldn't resist. And there was always the chance of winning that fifty thousand dollars quickly, in a few months, so that he could retire to write his novel."

Darrow formed a nonactive partnership with a junior in the office, Jacob L. Bailey, so that his name should not disappear from the Chicago legal register while he was away.

Ruby covered her furniture with sheets and towels, packed their bags. "It may be imagined with what dread and distress we went West," she relates. "Enough had been brought out by the prosecution fine-combing for facts and by the relentless newspapers to show what a web of dangers and disasters awaited us. No one had any inkling about the truth, just how the explosion had occurred, what the motive was, who was most, or least, responsible; nothing could be sifted and weighed until it could be investigated in Los Angeles. Mr Darrow had never even heard of the McNamaras, had no idea what sort they were, what personalities he would find, what mental make-up. He had not the first or faintest reason for judging whether they were guilty. The situation frightened and bewildered him as nothing ever had in my acquaintance with him, and he would have given almost anything to escape giving himself over to that job. But it was a matter of honor now; he could not have borne the cry against him as a traitor to the cause."

"It was with heavy hearts that Mrs Darrow and I drove to the Chicago and North Western station," writes Darrow, "and boarded the train for Los Angeles."

5

Darrow went straight from the station to the county jail to meet his clients. He was pleased to find the McNamara brothers clean cut, intelligent, with a quiet and gentle manner. James B., who was twenty-eight, was lean of face and figure, had an amused, bright gleam in his eye and a poetic, almost mystical strain. His brother John J., the secretary of the union, was a year younger; he was broader of face and figure, with a touch of Irish melancholy in his eyes; he had come up from the ranks of labor, had given himself a legal education, was quiet spoken but intense.

He did not ask the brothers whether they were innocent or guilty as charged. "I've heard Mr Darrow say that he placed little value on the statements of clients," tells Mrs Darrow, "that he could do better work if he was allowed to presume his clients innocent."

It was easy to assume the McNamaras innocent because of their straightforward and honest manner. Fletcher Bowron, a reporter for the *Record,* who later became reform mayor of Los Angeles, says, "I talked to the boys frequently in the jail. From their appearance and way of speaking it would have been difficult to think them guilty. I thought they were innocent." Nor did the McNamaras leave many in doubt. When Sam Gompers came to Los Angeles John J. took his hand and said, "I want to assure you that we are innocent of the crime with which we are charged."

That afternoon Darrow went with Job Harriman, who had had

charge of the case until Darrow's arrival, to the charred hull of the Times Building, standing on the exact spot in ink alley where the explosion had taken place. Here Harriman re-created the scene for his chief:

Early in the morning of October first, after the editorial staff had put the paper to bed and gone home for the night, there had been an explosion in the roofed-over alley in which barrels of ink were unloaded from the drays and stored until they were needed for the presses. This explosion was followed immediately by a second, which was either the gas main or leaking gas blowing up. One whole wall of the stone building was blown out. The ink in the barrels caught fire at once, and within four minutes the entire building was a sheet of flames, the fire eating up the wooden floors that had not collapsed under the weight of their machinery in the second explosion. There were in the building some twenty telegraph operators, linotype operators, printers, machinists, compositors, pressmen, but the intensity of the fire made rescue work impossible. Those who had not crashed to the basement with their heavy machinery had fought their way through the fierce flames to the windows and doors. Those who jumped to the pavement below were killed; the others were sucked back by the flames, their stricken faces vanishing into the red curtain behind them.

Los Angeles had been awakened by the force of the explosions and the clang of the fire wagons. Within an hour thousands of people were standing opposite the burning building, many of them in their night clothes, fighting with the police to break their lines, to try to help in some sort of rescue. But it was to no avail: twenty men were killed in one of the most gruesome tragedies in American civilian life.

By dawn, while the firemen were still plying their hoses on the flames, a one-sheet edition of the *Times* hit the streets, having been printed in an auxiliary pressroom. An eight-column streamer read: UNIONIST BOMB WRECKS THE TIMES. Harry Chandler, son-in-law of the owner, Harrison Gray Otis, and the managing editor, wrote, "The Times Building was destroyed this morning by the enemies of industrial freedom. The elements that conspired to perpetrate this horror must not be permitted to pursue their awful campaign of intimidation and terror." The men who had been killed were called "victims of the foulest plot of foul Union Labor Ruffians."

The next day Otis cried in his paper, "O you anarchic scum, you cowardly murderers, you leeches upon honest labor, you midnight assassins, you whose hands are dripping with the innocent blood of your victims, you against whom the wails of poor widows and the cries of fatherless children are ascending to the Great White Throne, go look at the ruins wherein are buried the calcined remains of those whom you murdered. . . ."

"But how could he make those charges?" demanded Darrow of Harriman, "when the firemen were still poking around in the ruins and no one could know what caused the explosion?"

"Ah," replied Job Harriman, "you don't know Harrison Gray Otis."

6

Few conflicts in American life are sudden or inexplicable: they have their roots deep in the past. This trial that brought Darrow to Los Angeles in 1911 had its beginnings in 1890, when the four local newspapers threatened a twenty-per-cent cut and the union typographers struck rather than take the reduction in wages. Within three days the *Tribune* and *Express* had settled their differences with the men; by the end of the third month the typographers were back at work on the *Herald*. This left only the *Times* men on strike; they were eager to compromise in order to go back to work. The decision rested in one man's hands, Harrison Gray Otis, a former union printer who had taken part in fifteen Civil War battles and had come out with a captain's commission in his pocket and a taste for warfare in his mouth. The pattern of life in southern California would be formulated by Captain Harrison Gray Otis's blunderbuss.

Between the Civil War and his purchase of an interest in the *Times* in 1882 Otis was a government hanger-on, constantly importuning for appointments. Failing to land the job of collector of the Port of San Diego, on which he had set his heart, he bought a fourth interest in the weekly *Times,* which was slowly dying of attrition in the mud-baked metropolis of eleven thousand souls. By the end of four years, when the first land boom descended upon southern California, Otis had bought out his associates for trifling sums; people poured in; money poured in; the *Times* became a daily; Otis began buying up tracts of land—and was on his way to becoming a multimillionaire and arbiter of American civilization.

"Otis was a large, aggressive man with a walrus mustache, a goatee and a warlike demeanor, resembling Buffalo Bill and General Custer," writes Morrow Mayo in his excellent book *Los Angeles.* "The military bee buzzed in his bonnet. He called his home in Los Angeles The

Bivouac, and when the boom was at its height he built a new plant for the *Times,* which resembled a medieval fortress, with battlements, sentry boxes, surmounted by a screaming eagle. He was a natural warrior and not a man to be crossed. He was a holy terror in his newspaper plant; his natural voice was that of a game warden roaring at seal poachers."

Reporters on the *Times* accused Otis of never getting past the third reader, but they underestimated his functional intelligence for getting a specific job done. No man in all American history, not even in the blackest days of the War between the States, could touch Otis for range, power and intensity of vituperation, while a *schimpflexikon* of the abuse that Otis and the *Times* heaped upon the heads of workers, unions, liberals, progressives and the co-operative movements from 1890 to 1940 would constitute a confounding document. President Theodore Roosevelt wrote about him in the *Outlook* magazine: "He is a consistent enemy of every movement for social and economic betterment, a consistent enemy of men in California who have dared to stand against corruption and in favor of honesty. The attitude of General Otis in his paper affords a curious instance of the anarchy of soul which comes to a man who in conscienceless fashion deifies property at the expense of human rights. The *Times* has again and again showed itself to be such an enemy of good citizenship, honest, decent government and every effective effort to secure fair play for the workingman and-woman as any anarchist could show itself."

Otis declared that no man who had gone on strike could ever work for the *Times* again, that no union member would ever be employed by him in any capacity. Having embarked upon this road, there was no turning back; every step he took plunged him deeper into strife, and the continued strife only convinced him further that he was right. When he imported non-union printers from Kansas City in 1890 he set the tone for the long contest by writing, "These men came to Los Angeles much as the first settlers of New England came from the old country to escape religious intolerance and to gain personal freedom to worship as they saw fit. Like their hardy, selected forebears, these liberty-loving Los Angeles immigrants were pioneers who laid the foundation for the future growth of their adopted land." In 1929, when summing up in a supplement called *The Forty Years' War,* Harry Chandler carried on his father-in-law's tradition by writing, "It has been war, war in which many lives have been lost, millions of dollars of property destroyed, other millions lost through suspension of production. The cost to the city has been great, yet its profits infinitely greater."

There were other costs which the *Times* did not see fit to mention. "Outside pressure was exerted upon the Los Angeles police," writes Jerome Hopkins in *Our Lawless Police*, "by a dominant financial group, fanatically antilabor, which utilized the police as an adjunct to its open-shop industrial policies. Very early the Los Angeles police ceased to distinguish between economic dissenters, strikers, pickets and the criminal. This line of activity, kept alive by hysterical propaganda, has passed through successive phases: assistance in strikebreaking, espionage upon labor-union organizations, suppression of free speech, unlawful beatings, false arrest, brutality with arrest, unlawful detention, incommunicado and the third degree."

To Otis all this was another Civil War; it was his bounden duty to crush the Rebels. Battle was breath in his nostril. When his Civil War II began his cohorts promoted him from captain to general, and he was known as General Otis to the end of his days.

"It is somehow absurd but nevertheless true," laments Mayo, "that for forty years the smiling, booming sunshine City of the Angels has been the bloodiest arena in the Western world!"

By the decision of this one man Los Angeles became immersed in a half century of bloodshed, violence, hatred, class war, oppression, injustice and a destruction of civil liberties which was to turn it into the low spot of American culture and democracy.

7

The incalculable tragedy behind the Otis decision was that its tentacles soon spread to make this war a national affair. While Darrow was fighting for the American Railway Union in 1894 the groundwork for his present battle in 1911 was being laid, for in the midst of the railroad fight Otis called a meeting of the town's bankers, manufacturers and merchants, to form an organization called the Merchants and Manufacturers. Those businessmen who fought against being drawn into such an organization found their credit cut off at the banks; their customers were kept out of their shops; they found it difficult to sell their products anywhere in the country!

The San Francisco *Bulletin* wrote, "The Merchants' and Manufacturers' Association has one confession of faith, one creed: 'We will employ no union man.' The M. and M. has also one command: 'You shall employ no union man.' The penalty for disobedience to this command is financial coercion, boycott and ruin. 'You hire union men and we'll put you out of business,' says the M. and M., and the businessman knows that the oracle speaks. 'You declare an eight-hour day and we'll stop your credit at the banks,' and the M. and M. does what it says. The M. and M. sandwich man does not walk up and down the streets. He walks boldly into the front door and puts his ultimatum on paper. The merchant who disobeys the M. and M. command runs into something which robs him of his business, hampers him in securing raw material for manufacture, holds up his payment for work when it is completed and frightens him out of speech to rebel."

The large flow of workingmen, attracted by the advertisements of all-year sunshine, flowers and beauty, found themselves at the mercy of the employers. The hours went as high as fourteen a day; wages fell to a new low. All workingmen had to pay dues to the M. and M. If anyone protested he was promptly fired, black-listed, put out of his house, run out of the country. This was Otis's "American Plan" for Industrial Freedom.

The unions were harried and weak, but they never gave up trying. While the *Times* called them cutthroats, assassins, robbers, thieves, rascals, lunatics, anarchists, sluggers, ruffians, swine, they kept plugging for shorter hours, better wages, striking whenever they could: teamsters, carpenters, plasterers, laundry workers, brewery workers, dozens of strikes, hundreds of strikes, bitter strikes filled with smashed heads. *Always the unions lost!* "This is war!" cried Otis from the *Times,* and the Merchants and Manufacturers gave no quarter.

For San Francisco, four hundred miles north, the strongest union city in America, and where wages were thirty per cent higher, the chaos of Los Angeles created a danger; the workers were afraid their wage would be pulled down to the Los Angeles level; the employers were afraid lest their low-wage competitors underbid them and take away their contracts. Realizing that Los Angeles constituted an infection area for the entire country, the American Federation of Labor in its 1910 convention voted to establish a unified labor council in Los Angeles and to fight the open-shop issue to a conclusion. Such powerful labor leaders in San Francisco as Tom Mooney, "Pinhead" McCarthy, O. A. Tveitmoe and Anton Johannsen were sent down to Los Angeles to serve as General Staff.

Since the ironworkers were the toughest fighters and had a strong national organization behind them, the San Francisco leaders used them as a spearhead of the attack. A new scale of wages was asked for; when it was refused fifteen hundred men walked out of such big plants as the Llewellyn and Baker Iron Works. Strikebreakers were hauled in from the Midwest; strong-arm squads were summomed from San Francisco to meet them. Deputies beat up the strikers; the strikers beat up the non-union workers; the police beat up the pickets. Blood flowed in a dozen different parts of the city.

General Otis mounted a small cannon on the running board of his car and dashed about the city to direct his police and special deputies. In his editorials he screamed, "It is full time to deal with these labor-union wolves in such prompt and drastic fashion as will induce them to transfer their lawlessness to some other locality. Their instincts are criminal, and they are ready for arson, riot, robbery and murder!" His hysteria rose to such heights in promising Angelenos that their city was about to be bombed off the face of the earth that a considerable portion of the citizens thought he ought to be clapped in a madhouse. At the peak of the insanity Senator Hiram Johnson hired the auditorium to cry out:

"In the city of San Francisco we have drunk to the very dregs of infamy; we have had vile officials; we have had rotten newspapers. But we have nothing so vile, nothing so low, nothing so debased, nothing so infamous, in San Francisco as Harrison Gray Otis. He sits there in senile dementia with gangrened heart and rotting brain, grimacing at every reform, chattering impotently at all things that are decent, frothing, fuming, violently gibbering, going down to his grave in snarling infamy. He is one thing that all California looks at when, in looking at southern California, they see anything that is disgraceful, depraved, corrupt, crooked and putrescent—that is Harrison Gray Otis."

This was the city, this was the opposition, this was the intrastate conflict, this the hysteria multiplied to infinity by the deaths of twenty innocent men, into which Clarence Darrow plunged when he stepped off his train in sunny southern California.

8

By the end of two weeks Darrow was settled in a comfortable flat on the high hill of Bonnie Brae and had assembled a brilliant legal staff. For his mastery of California law he chose Le Compte Davis, member of a Kentucky family who had come to California in the hopes of cheating death of another consumption victim. Davis had been assistant district attorney, had prosecuted labor for unruly conduct, was known to be a conservative and had an unimpeachable reputation. Next in line Darrow selected Joseph Scott, the leading Catholic attorney of the community, whose presence in the case would swing sentiment toward the Irish Catholic McNamaras. Another wise choice was that of Judge McNutt, former Supreme Court justice of Indiana, who was known to be favorable to labor.

Job Harriman was the fifth member and the expert on the California labor background. A little past forty, Harriman had been sent to California to die of tuberculosis but had lived instead to become the leading socialist of the district. He was a bright, eager man, a theorist and idealist who made a good educator but who had failed as an administrator in charge of a socialist-utopia community. Harriman was later accused by Edward Cantrell, a fellow socialist whom Harriman was instrumental in having expelled from the party for causing factional strife, of having known beforehand that the *Times* was to be bombed. After his expulsion Cantrell went unsolicited to the *Times*, the archenemy of his enemies in the party, and gave them an article in which he told of being in San Luis Obispo for a lecture the night the *Times* was blown up and of having Harriman appear at his hotel for no apparent reason. The next morning, when Harriman read of the twenty deaths, reports Cantrell, he became overwrought and almost hysterical. From these two deductions, that Harriman had joined him in San Luis Obispo merely to establish an alibi and that he had become overwrought when he read of the deaths, Cantrell went before the grand jury to accuse Harriman of complicity in the Los Angeles dynamiting conspiracy. Cantrell, a retired clergyman, was an honest man, but his unconscious motive was revenge against the men who had expelled and hence discredited him. No scrap of evidence ever implicated Harriman in foreknowledge of the explosion; Le Compte Davis, who was unsympathetic to both labor and socialism, voiced the opinion of everyone who knew Harriman when he said:

"Not all the angels in heaven or all the devils in hell could ever convince me that Job Harriman knew anything about the conniving and dynamiting. You had only to be with him for a few minutes to know that he was a good and honest and peaceable man."

Darrow rented the major portion of a floor of the Higgins Building on the corner of Second and Main streets, with offices adjoining those of Harriman. He then moved in desks, chairs, filing cabinets, typewriters, secretaries, a publicity man and a staff of investigators under the direction of John Harrington. Harrington had been for many years an investigator for the Chicago Surface Lines, until he lost his job through insubordination. Since Darrow had always thought him a good investigator and needed someone in Los Angeles whom he felt he could trust, he brought Harrington to Los Angeles to head his local detective staff. Darrow both liked Harrington and felt sorry for him; since he was without an acquaintance in Los Angeles, the Darrows took him and his little daughter into their home.

The first great obstacle was the Ortie McManigal confession. Before he had left Chicago Darrow had had Harrington bring to his home on the Midway Mrs McManigal and McManigal's uncle, George Behm. Having been successful in getting Lillard, Steve Adams's uncle, to persuade Adams to repudiate his confession, he saw no reason why he should not try to get Uncle George Behm to persuade McManigal to repudiate, particularly since he "promised to defend McManigal if they had forced him to make that confession." Mrs Ortie McManigal was convinced that her husband had made the confession under fear and threats.

"Mr Darrow asked me if I was a union man," related George Behm. "I told him I was. He asked me if I was in sympathy with the labor movement and the McNamara case, and I told him I was as far as I know about it."

" 'Are you willing to go out there and see what you can do with your nephew in regard to changing his testimony?'

" 'Well, I can't hardly leave home. I have to put in my crop.'

" 'All right, you lay off and go home and put in your crop. Get your help to carry on the farm while you are gone.' "

He had paid the expenses for the farm hand and given Behm, Mrs McManigal and her little boy enough money to get out to Los Angeles. But Behm was having no luck with his nephew. He told Darrow that "Ortie refuses to recall his confession. He says he is better off in jail than out on the streets where someone would be liable to blow his head off." Darrow sent Behm back to the jail again and again, but nothing could move McManigal, who finally cried in exasperation, "You will have to cut it out, Uncle George, for I won't talk about it at all. I have got my mind made up to tell the truth." And that was the last word he would speak about the McNamara case.

It looked to the defense as though the prosecution's case was to be based solely on the McManigal confession. If Darrow could prove that it had been written by William J. Burns, who had been holding Ortie captive at the time, he could free the McNamaras: For although McManigal had admitted placing charges of dynamite under bridges and aqueducts, always at the order of the union secretary, John J. McNamara, he had sworn that he had not been in Los Angeles or had anything to do with the *Times* explosion. Darrow employed almost a hundred investigators who combed the country to check up on McManigal, to see if he had been where he said he had been, to determine just what had caused the explosions in the various cities and whether McManigal could have had anything to do with them, to find people who knew McManigal and might contradict any part of the confession. He also sent out an investigating staff under Harrington to learn what had caused the *Times* explosion, to find the men who had complained of leaking gas in the plant the very night of the accident. He ordered a complete model of the Times Building made, with all interior fittings, which he planned to blow up in court to prove that only gas could have caused the tragedy; he engaged expert technicians to experiment with gas explosions and their results. He hadn't wanted to take the case, but now that he was in it he gave to his clients every last ounce of his energy and resourceful mind.

Once his investigation had started in earnest there began a campaign of espionage and counterespionage. When reports came in from his Eastern investigators Darrow found that the information was in the possession of the district attorney by the following day. He made connections with a deputy in the district attorney's office who informed him that one of his secretaries was a Burns detective and was making copies of everything that came into the office. Darrow put this deputy on his pay roll; he was daily to report back the information Darrow's secretary had passed on to the district attorney! Darrow, Tveitmoe and Johannsen, the two San Francisco labor leaders, concocted a secret code based on the pagination of Webster's dictionary; Joseph Ford, the assistant district attorney and private attorney for William J. Burns, selected Burns men to get themselves hired as investigators for Darrow and decipher the code. The manager of Burns's Los Angeles office came to Darrow in a secret conference and offered to sell him copies of all of Burns's reports, pay rolls and books. When Darrow learned that the district attorney's investigators were also scouring the East to get corroboration of the McManigal confession he hired several of the Burns men who were working for the district attorney to report back to him everything the district attorney's investigators had found in the East. Before long some of the private detectives were drawing three separate salaries, passing around their information in a daisy chain; Darrow, Fredericks, the prosecuting attorney, and Ford knew what each other had had for breakfast.

If the situation had musical-comedy aspects the trickery assumed dangerous proportions. Defense witnesses and relatives of the accused men were so hounded by night and day that they lost their jobs, their homes, were put out of their hotels and boardinghouses. Defense employees were shadowed, threatened, bribed, kidnaped. Anyone helpful to the defense was hauled before Fredericks' grand jury and threatened with indictment unless he retracted. Darrow's telegrams were stolen, his account books copied, his telephone conversations taken on hidden dictaphones. Once when his investigators unearthed a witness whom he considered valuable he moved him to a small hotel and told him to keep out of circulation. The following morning his spy in the district attorney's office informed him that the district attorney's spy in his office had learned of the man's value to the defense. The witness had then been kidnaped from his hotel and was being held prisoner in a barn in Culver City. Dr Atwater, a Los Angeles dentist, tells that "that night I drove Darrow in my buggy to Culver City. We left the buggy a safe distance from the designated barn, approached it quietly and saw two deputies stationed in front. We went around to the back, tunneled under the wall and found our witness lying on a pile of hay in a drugged or semiconscious condition. We pushed and dragged him under the wall, carried him to the buggy and got him away."

Dirty and stupid business for Clarence Darrow to be engaging in? War is dirty and stupid business.

9

The pressure of work left Clarence little time for social life, but once a week he and Ruby would go to a party given in their honor by Joseph Scott in Pasadena or by the Le Compte Davises for the cream of the Los Angeles intellectuals. He did not care greatly for big and formal parties; he preferred informal chin fests with cronies who loved books and thought that talking about literature was as important a pleasure as there was in life. His friend Fay Lewis came out from Rockford to stand by his side; Billy Cavenaugh, the stonecutter, who was working in Los Angeles as a policeman, gave him alcohol rubs several nights a week; an old pal from the Chicago *Inter-Ocean* by the name of James H. Griffes, who was publishing a little magazine in Los Angeles called the *Everyman*, ran a series of his articles on everything from Robert Burns's poetry to prison reform and acquainted him with southern California artists and writers.

Best of all he liked a little group of new acquaintances who never discussed the McNamaras nor law courts: Gerson, a young and sensitive physician; Reynold E. Blight, a young member of the Board of

Education with a penchant for books, and Edward M. Williams, who liked to discuss philosophy. Once a week the four couples met at one of their homes for dinner, and then Darrow would settle in an armchair and read for an hour, mostly from Israel Zangwill and Tolstoy. When he had read something particularly pleasurable he would shyly lift his eyes above the book and look at his friends with a sparkling smile. These evenings so rested him and took his mind off his affairs that Ruby gave frequent little supper parties for them. He delivered only one lecture, at the Philharmonic Auditorium, where Blight reports that "he held twenty-four hundred people in thralldom just telling stories about Tolstoy. There was no flamboyance or purple passages in his talk; it was the simplicity, directness and clarity of what he said that held his audience."

As the scorching summer heat came on Darrow slowly became depressed and then dejected: his investigators could find no evidence to controvert the Ortie McManigal confession, no evidence to show that the McNamaras had not been guilty of the violence charged. Worse yet, the district attorney's investigators were sending in mountainous piles of proof to sustain McManigal. When McManigal told how they had bought dynamite from a certain well digger that well digger was found and identified James B. McNamara as one of the men who had bought it. When McManigal told of registering at a certain hotel just before the setting of a blast, there was J. B.'s signature on the register and people to identify him from his picture. When McManigal told of renting a house to store the explosives there was the landlord to identify J. B. One day, when his spy in the district attorney's office brought him a copy of a particularly damaging piece of evidence against J. B., Darrow walked into his cell and cried:

"My God, you left a trail behind you a mile wide!"

McMamara did not answer.

That night Clarence spent some wretched hours, torn by the most basic of his inner conflicts. "I never believed in violence on either side; I don't believe in the violence of war; I don't believe in the violence that everywhere abounds on earth. I know who is responsible for this struggle: it is the men who have reached out their hands and taken possession of all the wealth in the world; it is that paralyzing hand of wealth which has reached out and destroyed all the opportunities of the poor. The acts of the poor are protests against their wrongs; yet I don't believe in the violence of the poor and the weak, who think they can obtain their rights by fighting the rich and the strong." Harry Orchard had accused Moyer, Haywood and Pettibone with a hundred crimes, most of which had been uncommitted; McManigal had accused the McNamaras of a hundred crimes, all of which had been committed, most of which the prosecution could prove! True, the McNamaras were not yet charged with these other and distant crimes; they were charged with the bombing of the Times Building, which did not appear to have been bombed at all and on which no implicity for the McNamaras had been found. But how quick people would be to assume that if they had committed a hundred other bombings and the *Times* had been their archenemy, therefore, they must also have bombed the *Times*. It would only be circumstantial evidence, and it was difficult to hang men on circumstantial evidence; but if he managed the miracle of an acquittal the brothers and the officers of the ironworkers' union would be indicted in every major city in America for the property bombings.

In the dark hours of the dark night he became ill with a despair which was rarely to leave him, night or day, for two years; a despair whose seeds had been sown in the days when he had come to understand that in defending Big Bill Hayward he was defending a philosophy of force. Part of his illness in Idaho had been due to this conflict of loyalties within himself, perhaps enough of it to turn an ordinary mastoid into the freak mastoid which had trebled his suffering. When he had returned to Chicago it had been not only his physical malaise that had converted him to the doctrine of settlement, for he had always believed in peaceful compromise—whenever he could find any peace. The Haywood case had brought him to grips with what he had always known, that in any conflict of force both sides were wrong and both sides must lose; in the unlikely event that either side should win a victory it could only mean that the war would have to start again. Every aspect of the McNamara case confirmed him in his judgment.

If he defended these practitioners of violence, would not the country be entitled to assume that since he defended sabotage, force, crimes against property, he must necessarily condone the use of dynamite and violence? That he defended labor leaders, guilty or innocent? Would not his defense of dynamiters eventually convict the labor groups and leaders he had previously defended? Would not his presence in future cases stigmatize his clients as having been guilty of using force? Would not all his years of pleading for the broader view, for tolerance and sympathy, for co-operation and understanding between apparently conflicting interests, be undone? By portraying the barbarities on both sides of the class war he had been able to establish a kind of justification for force, but he did not want to become an apostle of force, confirm other firebrands in their belief that they could solve their problems by any number of crimes and any amount of violence, that they could never be brought to bay. How could he who had militantly in book and lecture preached for peace earn an acquittal for the philosophy of force, enstrengthen it to continue until it brought the industrial world down in flames?

Every American was entitled to a defense and a defender, the very best he could hire, yet Clarence Darrow was heartsick at the thought of betraying his own instincts and teachings.

He could not abandon the McNamaras now, he knew. Nor did he pass judgment against them for what they had done. They had been childish and misguided to imagine that they could conquer a billion-dollar industry by random explosions; he thought they had been blind not to see over the years between 1906 and 1911 that they were getting nowhere with their violence; that they must eventually be caught and do infinite damage to the union movement. Yet he understood their motivations. They were guilty of standing up and fighting in a war which they believed had been forced upon them by the National Erectors' Association. They had worked and sacrificed for years to establish their union, and now their efforts would be wiped out; they would become puppets of the steel trust. The only property the union man owned was his skill with his hands. He said:

"All right, we'll keep this a war of property. If you blast our property we'll blast yours. So long as you don't slug or club our men we won't hurt your men. You want to make our membership in a union so costly to us that we'll abandon our union; all right, then we'll make your membership in the erectors' union so costly to you that you will abandon your union."

They had kept their word; in all the explosions no man had ever been injured. In one instance where a watchman would have been hurt because his sentry box was close to the scene of the explosion, they had gone to the trouble and danger of setting off a small charge a distance away so that the watchman would run to investigate and not be hurt by the major explosion. He knew the McNamaras would cry:

"They had all the money, all the power. What else was left open to us? What else could we do? We had no way to fight them in terms of peace. If we did nothing we were licked, destroyed. We had to use force; it was the only weapon left to us. We had to fight the devil with fire!"

What could he answer them? Should he quote Matthew, "Resist not evil, but whosoever shall smite thee on thy right cheek, turn to him the other, also"?

He suffered an agony of mind over the trap in which he was caught. He had a suspicion that if Le Compte Davis, Joseph Scott and Judge McNutt were to learn of the overwhelming guilt of the McNamaras in past dynamitings they would feel obliged to withdraw, an act which would convict his clients before they came to trial. Job Harriman, he felt, had known all along, but he did not discuss the piling evidence with him. What made his burden heavy was that labor throughout the country was still passionately convinced that the McNamaras were innocent of any dynamiting or other criminal acts; its press wrote flaming articles against the injustice in Los Angeles. May Day of 1911 was called McNamaras' Day; demonstrations were held in every major city of America at which tens of thousands voiced their protests against the frame-up. Twenty thousand men paraded in Los Angeles carrying banners which read, DOWN WITH OTIS! REGISTER YOUR PROTEST AGAINST THE MCNAMARA FRAME-UP! Every union in the country was contributing funds; thousands of letters poured into the office in the Higgins Building from workmen who wanted to assure him of their loyalty and contribute a further bit from their savings.

He felt like a man with a rumbling volcano in his pocket, trying to hold back the eruption with his naked hand.

10

Early in the summer a strong socialist movement had begun in Los Angeles to offset the *Times* and the Merchants' and Manufacturers' Association. Eugene Debs was circulating forty thousand copies of his *Appeal to Reason* each week, and the paper was being read avidly as an antidote to the *Times*. Job Harriman was nominated for mayor; a strong ticket was put into the field. Alexander Irvine, a clergyman who had been stripped of his pulpit in New Haven for preaching Christian socialism, was sent out by national headquarters to conduct the campaign. Socialism was on the upswing in America; many socialist congressmen and legislators had already been elected; several cities had socialist mayors, while others were going into the new campaign with excellent prospects. Considering the heat and hysteria of the moment, the socialist platform was moderate: though it demanded the ultimate replacement of the capitalist system it was willing to settle in the meanwhile for woman suffrage, more schools, social centers, public beaches and plunges, public hospitals and employment bureaus, civil service, an eight-hour law, municipal ownership of such utilities as city railways, telephone, icehouse, cement plant. If the socialists could win in Los Angeles it would assure a sympathetic trial for the McNamaras.

In addition to everything else that was being charged against him Darrow was now accused of starting the socialist campaign to take over the city, and of financing its campaign out of McNamara defense funds. He had not started the socialist campaign; there had always been a strong movement in southern California; neither had he contributed more than a few hundred dollars for its literature, but once it was under way he gave it every aid he could, lecturing on those nights when he could break away from his work. Big Bill Haywood came to exhort large gatherings on the blessings of socialism and to swear that the McNamaras had been framed just as he had been in Idaho. Educational pamphlets were distributed by the tens of thousands; Harriman, who was an intelligent man of about forty, with thick, well-ordered hair, honest eyes and strong features, went about lecturing to the effect that "the labor unions are the only organized expression of the wage-worker's interest within the present system of production, and they can no more be disbanded or crushed out of existence than can the wage-worker himself cease to work for wages."

Thus were the McNamara defense and the socialist campaign inextricably interwoven.

The primaries would be held in October, and from the intensity of socialist interest in the city it appeared that the vote would be close, for the Good Government League of the Merchants and Manufacturers had been exposed in a series of land frauds and manipulations. The election would come in December; Darrow asked Judge Bordwell to set the opening of the McNamara case over until December. Bordwell decreed instead that the case should open on the eleventh of October.

On the day before the trial was to begin Sam Gompers addressed fifteen thousand labor sympathizers in Philadelphia, who shouted in unison their belief of the McNamara innocence. Seventeen thousand people paraded the streets with banners which read: "Down, Down with Detective Burns, the Kidnaper!" The *Times* rebutted with "Socialism is not anarchy, but it is a halfway house on the road to anarchy. It would prove the inevitable precursor of a condition of lawlessness, of robbery, of riot and murder. Carry Los Angeles for socialism? Carry it for business stagnation, abandoned industries, smokeless chimneys, bankruptcy, ruined homes, chaos of civil government. Carry it for hell!"

This was the temper of the country; this was the temper of Los Angeles when Darrow walked into Judge Bordwell's court on October 11, 1911, to begin his defense. People the world over gazed lovingly at his picture in the newspapers, assured each other that he would get the boys off, that he would expose the frame-up, that he would win another great victory for labor and the common people.

But Clarence Darrow walked into the courtroom a beaten man. He had learned that the McNamaras were guilty as charged.

II

In the summer of 1910 three men had gone to the Hercules Powder Plant on San Francisco Bay, represented themselves as businessmen from Folsom, California, and ordered a quantity of eighty-per-cent nitrogelatin, a rarely used explosive, for the avowed purpose of blasting boulders and tree stumps. A few days later they had rented a motorboat called the Peerless, painted another name over the first, picked up their explosive, carried it across the bay to a wharf in San Francisco, where they had loaded it onto a wagon and carted it to an empty house rented for the purpose. The three men were David Caplan, a San Francisco labor leader, Matt Schmidt, a young and brilliant engineer who had been traveling with James B. McNamara, constructing time bombs for his explosions, and James B. McNamara. All three were identified by the Hercules Powder employees, by the owners of the Peerless, by the landlord of the empty house, by people who had seen the wagon pulled through the streets of San Francisco. The district attorney's office claimed that the day after the *Times* explosion two suitcases had been found, one near Otis's house, one near the house of the secretary of the M. and M., containing time mechanisms made by Schmidt and sticks of the eighty-per-cent nitrogelatin which Hercules men identified as the explosive purchased by J. B. McNamara, Caplan and Schmidt.

And Darrow realized that his journey along the downward trail, which had begun when he defended Big Bill Haywood, who was innocent as charged but guilty of crimes of violence against mine property, had at last brought him into the swamps of defending men who were guilty as charged. It was no good to tell himself that the McNamaras were guilty of dynamiting but not of murder; that they had not intended to kill anyone but only to frighten Otis; that they certainly would never hurt their fellow workingmen, and that if Otis had not indulged in the negligence of letting gas escape in his building no one would have been hurt. Men who dealt in violence must ultimately have caused disaster; he knew too well that the McNamaras were morally responsible for the deaths of the twenty *Times* employees.

This day was one of his blackest, yet even in his despair he did not condemn the McNamaras. They had done what they thought was right; they had been fighting for labor; they had worked for the cause and not for personal profit or aggrandizement. He himself had been instrumental in showing them that they must battle the open shop. They had fought with the only weapons at hand. He could not abandon them, not even in his mind, yet the knowledge of the indictment that would be brought against labor made him ill. What a field day Otis, the Merchants and Manufacturers, the National Erectors' Association, the Steel Trust would have! And what could he do to stop them?

To further harrow him he found that James B. McNamara and young men like Matt Schmidt, who had started as labor's martyrs, had grown flushed with success because they had operated for years without being caught. In the early days they had lived carefully, had worked cautiously, but their victories had made them contemptuous of both the law and their opponents. Without knowing it they had become enamored of the life itself, the excitement, the suspense, the danger of hiding out in swamps and bulrushes through the night, the fascination of the flight, the pursuit; all the nefarious thrills of the life of crime that ensnares the young and emotionally unstable.

Over and above the excitements there had been the pleasures of the irregular life: freedom from routine, from constant supervision, from responsibilities of the family and the home, the zest of the nomadic life, the constant travel with its changes of scenery, its new faces and cities and ways of life. The men had been paid two hundred dollars an explosion, in addition to certain expenses; they had lived irregularly; they had lived well, and slowly they had become unable to resist the subtle encroachments upon character that result from such an existence. They fell into the habit of acquiring new women in each successive town, of necessity posing as something they were not: concealing, dissembling, lying and finally of drinking, in their enforced idleness, in their excitement, in the letdown after the tension of placing the bomb and hearing it explode. They had started out as soldiers in a war and not as evildoers; nor were their deteriorations in character known to them; that was why they had grown bolder, defiant, careless. And that was why the McNamaras were now in jail after being responsible for the deaths of twenty innocent workmen. That was why their union would now be wrecked and every union man in the world injured.

J. B. McNamara says, "On the night of September 30, 1910, at 5.45 P.M., I placed in ink alley, a portion of the Times Building, a suitcase containing sixteen sticks of eighty-per-cent dynamite, set to explode at one o'clock in the morning. It was my intention to injure the building and scare the owners. I did not intend to take the life of anyone. I sincerely regret that these unfortunate men lost their lives; if the giving of my life would bring them back I would freely give it."

Slumped behind his desk in the Higgins Building, feeling confused and torn, Darrow asked himself two questions:

"How can I defend the McNamaras? How can they be defended?"

He shambled slowly over to the jail, had the guard admit him to the McNamara cell and sat on a bunk between his two clients. He had sat in many cells with many clients, but for him this was the most hopeless meeting of all. . . .

"Why did you do it?" he asked hoarsely of no one in particular.

There was a long silence, during which J. B.'s face looked long and thin and solemn. His feverish eyes gleamed.

"There was a labor parade," he answered in a hoarse, impersonal tone, as though talking to himself. "The police beat up some of the boys. The next morning the *Times* praised those cops for their heroic work. It was more than I could stand."

It was a reason. . . . But to Darrow it was little consolation; he knew with a terrible surety that these two men, warm live flesh that touched him on either side, both under thirty, would be convicted, would be walked up to the scaffold at San Quentin, the ropes adjusted about their necks, the traps sprung beneath their feet, their necks broken in the noose.

The passage of the years, the burden of suffering and of death he had seen, had not made him hard shelled, had not blunted his almost pathological empathy. And of all the brutalizing acts he had encountered, there was none he found more degrading or more injurious to the spiritual fabric of the people as a whole than the taking of a life by the state.

"That capital punishment is horrible and cruel is the reason for its existence," he wrote in *Crime, Its Causes and Treatment,* the book in which he paid his debt to John P. Altgeld and carried forward Altgeld's teachings. "That men should be taught not to take life is the purpose of judicial killings. But the spectacle of the state taking life must tend to cheapen it. Frequent executions dull the sensibilities toward the taking of life. This makes it easier for men to kill and increases murders, which in turn increase hangings, which in turn increase murders, and so on, around the vicious circle."

He believed passionately in the sanctity of human life; if the state could take human life for revenge or punishment, why could it not take it for a thousand other reasons? If every last iota of life was not made sacred, how could the preciousness of life, and hence the human race, be maintained?

Mrs Edgar Wilson, who was now living in Los Angeles, saw him riding home on the streetcar that night. He did not see her. Mrs Wilson says that he slumped down into a corner, looking haggard and mortally ill, only the shell of the man she had known in Boise. Fletcher Bowron, who went up to his office every morning to find if there was any news, saw at once that something crucial had happened to Darrow; his fire was gone; his confidence was gone; his concentration, singleness and clarity of purpose, his grip on the organization of his job, had disintegrated. He was confused, helpless, terror-stricken.

He didn't know where to turn or what to do.

12

It was during this period that certain questionable acts began to happen around defense headquarters. One of the most damaging witnesses against J. B. McNamara was Diekleman, a Los Angeles hotel clerk who had registered J. B. McNamara as J. B. Bryce a few days before the *Times* explosion. Diekleman had in the meanwhile joined the Harvey restaurant system and been transferred to Albuquerque, New Mexico. The prosecution knew at all times where he was because it kept Burns' operatives surrounding him. One day Burt Hamerstrom, Ruby's itinerant-journalist brother, turned up at Diekleman's restaurant in Albuquerque, introduced himself as Mr Higgins (name of the building in which Darrow had his defense offices) and said:

"We are trying our best to save that man. He is innocent. Don't you think it would be right for you to consider the least doubt there is and be on our side?"

"I don't think there is any doubt," replied Diekleman.

"Now you are a valuable witness to us, and whatever your price is we will give it to you. Do you know Rector's Restaurant in Chicago?"

"Yes."

"Well, I think Mr Darrow is interested in that. How would you like to be assistant manager there?"

Diekleman refused to leave Albuquerque. Hamerstrom came back several times, offering railroad fare to Chicago and thirty dollars a week for expense money until the trial was over and a round-trip ticket to Los Angeles. When Diekleman still refused Hamerstrom assumed that he didn't want to leave his girl friend behind and offered to pay her expenses too. Diekleman agreed, accepted a railroad ticket and left for Chicago on September 19, 1911. The morning he arrived in Chicago he had a meeting with Hamerstrom and Ed Nockels, then wired the district attorney's office in Los Angeles where he was and returned to Albuquerque on the afternoon train. It was a fiasco which was to cause Darrow a deal of trouble, as did the wild ride of Mrs Dave Caplan.

Mrs Caplan's husband was now a fugitive from justice, for he was one of the three men who had bought the nitrogelatin from the Hercules Powder Plant, and it was his wagon in which the explosive had been hauled from the Embarcadero to the empty house he had rented. When Mrs Caplan was served with a subpoena and told that she would remain under subpoena from October eleventh on, Tveitmoe and Johannsen hired a limousine and chauffeur, picked up Mrs Caplan and had her driven for two nights to Reno, Nevada. The next day Johannsen accompanied her on a train to Chicago.

With the passage of the weary and disheartening days, only one good thing happened for the defense: Job Harriman won the primary runoff by a whopping vote. It was clear to everyone that he would defeat Alexander in the final election. There would still be the same district attorneys, Fredericks and Ford, the same *Times* and Merchants' and Manufacturers' Association, the same Erectors' Association in the East, which was paying Otis to keep up his fight; but at least the city government would be in friendly hands. The election would be a protest vote againt the M. and M., a vote of confidence in liberalism, unionism—and, incidentally, in the McNamaras. The election of a socialist government in Los Angeles could not help but have an effect upon the jury.

For therein would lie the solution of this case: the jury.

When the first venire lists were drawn Darrow engaged a man by the name of Bert Franklin to set up an agency which would investigate all prospective jurors. For the five years previous Franklin had been a deputy investigator for the United States marshal's office in Los Angeles; before that he had been for four years in charge of the criminal investigations under Captain Fredericks, before that he had been a guard in the Los Angeles jail. He was recommended to Darrow by Job Harriman and Le Compte Davis. Franklin opened an office, engaged a crew of private detectives and set to work.

"Mr Darrow said he wanted to find out the apparent age, religion, nationality, of every prospective juror, what their feelings were toward union labor, their feelings and opinions regarding the *Times* explosion, their opinion as to whether the McNamaras were guilty or not guilty of the crime with which they were charged, their financial condition, their property, the bank at which they did business."

The prosecution had a similar investigating staff. As soon as the lists were drawn each side would make a copy of the names, and the investigators would dash out of the courtroom to get to the potential juryman first to investigate him and bring back a report. Each day as his investigators brought in their reports Franklin took them to the Higgins Building and placed them on Darrow's desk. As Darrow looked over each summary Franklin suggested, "Challenge him when he is called up; he is antagonistic to labor. Accept the next fellow; he is a liberal. Get rid of that next one fast; his brother is a member of the M. and M." When the trial opened on October eleventh Darrow would go into court with Franklin's reports and suggestions to use as a basis for questioning prospective jurors. The only difficulty was that everyone whom Darrow would consider acceptable would be thrown out by the prosecution, and everyone the prosecution wanted would be promptly dismissed by Darrow. So complete was their system of checks that over three hundred jurors would be examined before six men could be found who were acceptable to both sides.

On the sixth of October Franklin went to the home of Robert Bain, an elderly carpenter whom he had known for twenty years and who was about to be drawn for jury duty. Although a workman himself, Bain was known to the prosecution to be hostile to the unions and hence would be acceptable to them. When no one answered his ring at the Bain house Franklin went next door, left his card with the neighbor and asked her to please tell Bain to telephone him at his office. Later that day he went back and found Mrs Bain at home. Franklin relates his conversation with Mrs Bain:

"I told her that I would like to have Bob on the McNamara jury, that I was in a position to pay him five hundred dollars down and two thousand when he had voted for an acquittal for McNamara.

" 'Well,' she said, 'you know that Bob is a very honest man.'

" 'Yes, Mrs Bain, I realize that. I have always felt so.'

" 'But that sounds good to me. I would like to have Bob consider it.' "

That night Franklin returned to the Bain house. "I asked him what he thought about the matter, and he said he raised some objection when his wife spoke about it but that she had convinced him that it was to the interest of both of them to accept the proposition, as he was getting old and that it would only be a matter of two or three years until he would have to quit his labors. I asked him his financial condition. He told me he had but very little money and that he was paying for his place. I then asked him if he would accept five hundred in cash with the promise of two thousand more after he had voted for acquittal. He said that he would. I first asked that the curtains be drawn, then took four hundred dollars from my pocket and gave it to him. He asked me what assurance he would have of getting the balance of the money, and I told him that we would be compelled to pay the money; if we didn't he could report it. He agreed, and then I left."

Franklin handed his employer a satisfactory report on Robert Bain. Bain was called into court and accepted by both sides as a juryman, the first to be seated.

The days spun themselves out as Darrow thrashed in his mind to find a tenable means of defense. He asked Judge Bordwell for a postponement, but it was refused. He caused every conceivable delay, sometimes for good reason, sometimes for bad. Judge Bordwell seemed hostile; Darrow asked for a change of judge. Bordwell refused to eliminate himself. The people in the courtroom observed that he questioned for hours and days prospective jurors, even when it was obvious that he would dismiss them—killing time, earning the postponement the judge had refused him, waiting for the break or development that would enable him to prepare a telling defense. He continued to carry the burden alone: to the world the McNamaras were still proclaiming their innocence; Gompers and Debs were declaring them innocent; the great mass of workers were declaring them innocent. His defense associates might have gleaned that portions of the McManigal confession were true, but neither Davis, Scott nor Judge McNutt had access to his private files; they could not know that the McNamaras were guilty as charged. And he was afraid to tell them.

In the third week of October another juror was selected, in the fourth week two more, in the first week of November a fifth. It was on the fourth of November that Bert Franklin made another important trip, this time to the small ranch of George Lockwood, near Covina. Lockwood, who was past sixty, had spent most of his life working for the police and district attorney's office as policeman, deputy, investigator, guard in the jail with Bert Franklin under Captain White.

"George," said Franklin, "I want to talk to you confidentially. May I do so?"

"Yes, Bert."

"This is a matter of the strictest confidence, and it might lead to complications. I consider you are my friend, and I know that under no circumstances will you repeat anything that is said to you without my permission."

"Bert, under no circumstances will I do anything that will cast any reflections on you."

"Did you know I was working for the defense in the McNamara case?"

"No, but I am glad to hear you are employed."

"George, you and I are getting old, and both of us have worked very hard and accumulated very little, and I think the time has come when you and I should use our brains a little more and our feet and hands less."

"Yes, Bert, I agree with you."

"George, I have a proposition to make to you whereby you can make some money and be of material assistance to myself at the same time."

"All right, Bert, spit it out."

"Did you know that your name was on the prospective list of jurors that might be called at a future date?"

"No, I didn't."

"In the case that you are drawn, upon proper arrangements would you vote for a verdict of acquittal in the McNamara case?"

"Well, I don't know."

"Take your time and think it over, and if you see your way clear I can give you five hundred dollars in cash, and at the end of the case I will give you two thousand more."

"Bert, that is a matter I would want to think over."

While Lockwood was thinking over the deal offered to him by his former associate, before his name was drawn from the county lists, Lincoln Steffens, in his early years one of America's most penetrating muckrakers and fearless researchers into big business's corruption of government, arrived in Los Angeles and went to see his old friend, Clarence Darrow. Thereupon the McNamara case took on a new dimension.

13

In his popular magazine articles and in such books as *The Sham of the Cities, The Struggle for Self-Government,* Lincoln Steffens had been, along with Henry Demarest Lloyd, author of *Wealth against*

Commonwealth, among the first to demonstrate that a political democracy has difficulty surviving under an industrial oligarchy. During the months of Darrow's preparation for the McNamara trial Steffens had been abroad seeking material with which to muckrake England and Europe. Certain that the McNamaras were guilty and having been converted to the stand of Kier Hardie, the British labor leader, that "labor has done it, and capital and the world should learn why," he conceived the plan of selling New York newspaper editors on the idea of sending him to Los Angeles to show why labor was guilty and what lay behind their acts of violence. The editors were so astounded to find a labor sympathizer convicting his men before their trial, they gave him the assignment.

Steffens immediately asked Darrow for permission to see the McNamara brothers. Not knowing his mission, Darrow gave his approval. Though the brothers did not know Steffens they greeted him warmly as a friend of labor. He then told the boys that he wanted to write a series of articles called "Justifiable Dynamiting," in which he would reveal to the world why labor had been forced into violence. While the McNamaras sat in shocked silence Steffens continued:

"It's a doubtful experiment and a risk for you, but it's got to be done sometime. Why not now? Why not help me dig up on the side, while the legal case is going on, the case of Labor against Capital as a parallel, as a background to the case of California versus the McNamaras? I might be able to show why you turned to dynamite."

John J. McNamara asked sardonically, "Have you seen Darrow about this?" Steffens reports James as saying, "If you could do what you propose I'd be willing to hang," then continuing to his brother, "It's for this that we have been working, Joe, to force attention to the actual conditions of labor. He means to go and get the actual cases of blacklisting that have made it impossible for discharged men to ever get work. Why wouldn't I risk my life to get that told? It's what I've been risking my life for right along."

Elated, Steffens walked briskly back to Darrow's office to make the most extraordinary proposal ever made to a lawyer who had clients to defend against a murder charge. A cold sweat broke out on Darrow's brow. He told Steffens to forget it and dismissed him—but he himself was not able to forget it. If Steffens was so positive that the men were guilty, must not others be equally sure about it? If it was as plain as that to people who had no access to the mass of evidence accumulating in his file, what chance would he stand in a courtroom? If, as Ruby says, he was frightened and bewildered when coming out on the train, he was now plunged into a shattering hopelessness. Every avenue of escape was blocked. He could not withdraw from the case now; that would hamstring his clients. Though sufficiently ill to be admitted to any hospital, he could not sneak out that way.

At odd moments he would think he saw some hope, some chance, then he would realize that it was wishful thinking. His moods changed so swiftly that Steffens reported of him, "At three o'clock he is a hero for courage, nerve and calm judgment, but at three-fifteen he may be a coward for fear, collapse and panicky mentality. He is more of a poet than a fighting attorney; his power and his weakness is in the highly sensitive, emotional nature which sets his seeing mind in motion in that loafing body." When someone brought Darrow further bad news, Steffens says, "His face was ashen; he could hardly walk; he was scared weak and did not recover for an hour. He said, 'I can't stand it to have a man I am defending hanged. I can't stand it.' "

That Saturday, November nineteenth, E. W. Scripps invited Darrow and Steffens to spend the week end with him at his ranch, Miramar, near San Diego. Scripps, like Hearst, had founded a chain of newspapers and a great fortune upon liberalism and the cause of the American masses. An astute student and merciless thinker, his grounding in sociology had given him a genuine sympathy for the labor movement. He met Darrow and Steffens at the station but, because Darrow looked fagged and forlorn, steered the conversation away from the McNamara case. However, Darrow could think and talk of nothing else; that night as they sat in the patio after dinner he outlined to Scripps the strength of the evidence that had come in against the structural-iron workers. Scripps rose, went into his study and emerged with the manuscript of an article he had just written for his papers, an article in which he explained and justified labor's use of force and dynamite.

" 'We, the employers, have every other weapon,' " he read to Darrow; " 'we have the jobs to give or withhold; the capital to spend, or not spend, for production, for wages, for ourselves; we have the press to state our case and suppress theirs; we have the Bar and the Bench, the legislature, the governor, the police and the militia. Labor has nothing but violence and mob force.' "

Darrow remained silent, thinking, "That's all true, but how does it help me? My boys are charged with murder." Then Scripps made an observation which stopped the wheels from churning in Darrow's head. After three months he was to reach his first decision.

"Workingmen should have the same belligerent rights in labor controversies," observed Scripps, "that nations have in warfare. There has been war between the erectors and the ironworkers; all right, the war is over now; the defeated side should be granted the rights of a belligerent under international law."

Darrow looked beyond the flower-filled patio to the deep night sky. "I wish the people of Los Angeles could see it that way," he murmured. "I believe it would be to the best interests of the community and also right and just to get rid of this case without shedding any human blood. I wish we could make a settlement."

14

The next night Darrow and Steffens took the sleeper back to Los Angeles; while they breakfasted at the Van Nuys Hotel Steffens asked, "Did you mean it when you said you wanted to make a settlement?"

"Yes, but I don't believe it will be possible to bring such a thing about. The feeling is too bitter, and the people are not in a reasoning state of mind."

"I think I can convince the businessmen of Los Angeles," said Steffens, hardly able to contain his excitement, "that it would be better all around to avoid the passions of a trial and to accept a plea of guilty from James B. McNamara."

"I am perfectly willing you should do it, but if you see anybody you must make it very plain that it does not come from me or from our side, for if it should get out to the community that we are making overtures it will make it that much more difficult to defend the men and save their lives."

"I will take it up on my account, and if any proposition comes it will come to you, not from you."

"I must caution you to use great care. At all events there will be no use to try to get a settlement unless the *Times* people are in favor of it, as it was their building that was destroyed."

That night Steffens returned to Darrow to tell him that he had seen some of the local politicians and businessmen and "that they believed the matter could be put through to permit James B. McNamara to plead guilty, receive a life sentence and end all other prosecution in Los Angeles." Steffens was afire as he outlined to Darrow how he was going to bring love and brotherhood to Los Angeles, how everyone would forgive everyone else and become friends, and there would be no more labor troubles in Los Angeles. Darrow believed none of this nonsense; he knew his adversaries too well, yet he was eager for the settlement to be arranged.

"I told Steffens that if such a thing could be done it would take a great burden off me, and I thought it would be a good thing both for labor and capital, especially for the defendants and the city of Los Angeles. I did not have confidence enough to present it to any of my associates at the time or even to my clients, although I felt that I knew what they would think about it."

The next morning, November twenty-second, when Le Compte Davis walked into court he was met by District Attorney Fredericks, Otis's protégé who had been elected to his position by the *Times*.

"Why don't you get those boys to plead guilty and quit your horse-play?" demanded Fredericks.

Taken aback, Davis replied, "I was not hired for that purpose."

"You know you're going to do it; a committee has been consulted about it, and I have been approached."

When Darrow reached court and saw the expression on Davis's face he promptly explained the Steffens' mission and his reasons for wanting to make a settlement: the prosecution had a great mass of evidence to produce and every day was bringing people into court to look at James B. McNamara and identify him; the defense had no contradictory evidence to offer, nor could they let James B. testify on his own behalf; he wouldn't be able to stand up under cross-examination. The trial would be a rout.

"Is J. B. willing to plead guilty?" asked Davis.

"I haven't talked to him yet, but I think I can make him see the reasonableness of it. You are a good friend of Captain Fredericks; will you go to him and work out a settlement?"

"I don't think we have any right to do it without consulting organized labor," replied Davis. "The American Federation of Labor is my employer in this case, and I won't do anything until I have their approval."

"Well, Gompers and all the other boys are at the convention in Atlanta. I wired for them to send someone out here. They ought to be here very soon, but if they are not it is up to us to act when the time comes anyway."

"As far as I'm concerned, I don't believe it's right," insisted Davis. "The money to defend the men has been furnished by labor, and it will ruin you with labor if you do this without consulting them."

"The money was furnished by organized labor," answered Darrow, "but these two men are our clients, and nobody can possibly give us money that can in any way influence us in an action that is due our clients. As far as I am concerned, I have no right to consider myself; all I have to consider are these two men, and if they think it best and we think it best, we should act, whatever the consequences are."

That afternoon Darrow wired Fremont Older, crusading editor of the San Francisco *Call* and one of the most respected men on the Pacific coast, to come to Los Angeles for an important conference. Older arrived in Los Angeles the following morning, November twenty-third; over the luncheon table Darrow detailed the situation to his old friend and asked for approval of the plan. Older, who had thought the boys to be innocent as charged, or at least to have a fighting chance in court, was too stunned to answer. After a time he managed:

"Well, Clarence, you know best—if you think it's the thing to do. . . . It will be misunderstood by a large number of laboring men who never believed that dynamite was placed in the Times Building—but I'll do what I can to make them understand. I suppose you know what this will do to you with organized labor?"

"Yes, I know—but the lives of my clients come first. The McNamaras have a right to know that their case looks bad, that they will probably hang. I won't advise them to plead guilty; I will merely tell them their case looks hopeless. They have the right to choose, to save their own lives."

That same evening Ed Nockels arrived from Chicago, listened to Darrow's presentation of the case and agreed that a settlement was the best way out. Darrow sent Nockels to see Le Compte Davis.

"Are you empowered to speak for the American Federation of Labor?" demanded Davis.

"Yes."

"Very well, I'll undertake to settle with Captain Fredericks."

The next morning, November twenty-fourth, Davis went to see Captain Fredericks, and Darrow went to see his clients. They listened attentively while he showed them why they had no chance; that a plea of guilty on the part of James would be the best way out, not only for themselves but for their union and their friends. He assured them that he would work to have John J. freed entirely; that he would insist that James be allowed to plead without giving a detailed confession which would implicate other men; that he would secure from the state a promise not to pursue or bring to trial Dave Caplan or Matt Schmidt; in short, that they be granted an honorable surrender.

"John, who had done more of the consulting with us than the other," writes Darrow, "said without hesitation that it ought to be disposed of, and he believed organized labor would come to understand it if they didn't at once. He thought there was little chance to save James's life without it, which was the controlling interest with him, and that his own case was also very dangerous. James from the first was willing to plead guilty and take a life sentence but not willing for John to plead guilty at all."

In the meanwhile a Merchants' and Manufacturers' Association committee had received Steffens' proposal with interest. The mayoralty election was only a few weeks off; Job Harriman's plurality assured him of winning. They did not want to give up their trial, but they saw a way to kill socialism in southern California for at least a generation: they would let James B. McNamara plead guilty—provided he did it before Election Day! The confession of guilt would wreck Harriman's chances. Harry Chandler, Otis's son-in-law, thought this was a wise plan, but Otis was adamant: they had the evidence to destroy unionism, and he wasn't going to rest until every last shred of it was brought out in trial and publicized to the world.

Le Compte Davis went to see Otis on the morning of November twenty-fifth. "Take the bird while you've got it in your hand, General," he said. "By his plea of guilty McNamara will give you a complete victory and prove that everything you have been claiming is right. If you take a chance and force them into trial, lightning might strike; an accident might happen; they might get off."

Otis grumbled, barked, swore, "I want those sons of bitches to hang!" and finally agreed—but not until he showed Davis a telegram from the National Erectors' Association, which was helping to finance the prosecution, in which the erectors said that John J., the directing mind behind the dynamiting, was the one they really wanted and that they would accept no settlement unless he also pleaded guilty and received at least a ten-year sentence.

For Darrow the need to accept punishment for John J. and to plead the McNamaras guilty in time to wreck the socialist campaign was a heavy defeat. Since James B. had never been a structural-iron worker or a member of their union, his activities could somehow be interpreted as happening outside the sanction of the body of workers. But John J. was the directing secretary; when he pleaded guilty he thereupon pleaded his union guilty. Further, to sacrifice the Socialist party and their vigorous campaign on the eve of a stunning and nationally important victory was not only to deal his friends a deathblow, but to do it by means of a stab in the back: for Job Harriman, who had been too busy campaigning to take much part in the preparation of the Mc-

Namara defense, had not been informed of the plans to make a settlement; Darrow had not told him for fear he would refuse to sacrifice the Socialist party and the election for the McNamaras.

It was a nasty price to have to pay, but it was obvious to Darrow that he could have his settlement on no other terms. He consoled himself by thinking that if socialism were as truly a historical imperative as its adherents claimed it was, it did not need to ride into office and power on the coattails of guilty men.

15

On the afternoon of Saturday, November twenty-fifth, Darrow took Le Compte Davis, Judge McNutt and Lincoln Steffens with him to the jail to impart the bad news to the brothers. James refused to plead guilty if his brother had to plead with him, and no amount of reasoning on Darrow's part would change the older brother's mind. He sent Davis back to Captain Fredericks to see if the district attorney would reconsider and let John off. The following morning, Sunday, November twenty-sixth, the group reassembled in the jail. John J. had been thinking things over during the night.

"It's all right," he said; "I'll take ten years. Anything to save Jim's life."

"It's not all right," repeated James. "I won't let them send Joe to prison. Besides, his pleading guilty will have a bad effect on labor. It will have a pretty serious effect on you too, Mr Darrow."

"You needn't bother about that part of it," grunted Darrow. "Neither do I think that labor has any right to be consulted about a lawyer's duty. I don't think you should sacrifice your lives when something better can be done." But James would not be persuaded.

Darrow says, "I was anxious to have it closed up as soon as possible; if they did not plead before the election we could never get the district attorney to accept the plea; it was getting to be a great burden, and I did not want anything to happen that could prevent the settlement."

He took John J. aside and talked the matter over with him. John said that his brother's consent wasn't necessary; he would save James's life without it: he was not on trial at the moment, and as soon as Darrow pleaded James guilty, he, John, would come into court and accept some sentence, as light a one as possible, but ten years if that was the best he could do.

16

This same Sunday, November twenty-sixth, while Darrow was bringing the settlement to a head in the county jail, his chief investigator, Bert Franklin, was on his way out to the George Lockwood ranch.

"George, haven't you been served yet?" Franklin asked.

"No."

"Well, your name was drawn yesterday, and you will be served between now and tomorrow morning. There will be four thousand in it for you, and I want you to have that money."

"Bert, if I go into this I don't want no mistake about the money."

"There won't be any trouble at all. Captain White will be custodian of the money. We both know him, and he is straight; the money will be perfectly safe in his hands, and he will turn it over to you when the trial is over."

"When the trial is over," protested Lockwood; "why, there might be no one know anything about the balance of the money."

"I can't see any way out of it but Captain White."

That night Franklin went to see Captain White, former head of the Los Angeles jail under whom both he and Lockwood had served as guards but who was now running a jewelry store. Franklin told White of his plan to bribe Lockwood.

"My God, Franklin," exclaimed White, "I wouldn't trust Lockwood as far as I could throw a bull by the tail!"

"Captain," said Franklin, "I believe that George Lockwood is the kind of a man that if he gives his word he will do a certain thing, he will do it."

"If you are satisfied," the captain replied, "why, other people should be."

Franklin then offered to pay White a hundred dollars for his trouble if he would act as intermediary and hold the thirty-five hundred dollars' balance until Lockwood voted for an acquittal. Captain White agreed.

The following morning, Monday, Davis came to Darrow's office to report that he had had a final conference with District Attorney Fredericks and that the settlement would go through on the terms agreed upon in the jail the night before: a life sentence for James, with the possibility of commutation, and ten years for John, who could be freed at the end of seven years for good behavior. Darrow then asked Judge

McNutt, Davis and Steffens if they fully approved the plan. Everyone agreed that it was the best way out.

Darrow left for his flat on Bonnie Brae, and, like a fever-racked man who has passed his crisis, slept soundly for the first time in months.

17

While Darrow slept Bert Franklin was hard at work. That morning he had received a telephone call from Lockwood to come out to the ranch.

"Shall I bring the Big Fellow along?" asked Franklin.

"Yes."

When Franklin reached the Lockwood ranch that evening it was well covered by detectives from the district attorney's office. Lockwood led Franklin out to the barn, where a stenographer was planted to take down the conversation, and asked:

"Where is Darrow?"

"Why, George, did you think Darrow was coming?"

"Yes, that is what I understood."

"Well, you was mistaken; I intended to bring Captain White, but he didn't wish to come."

Lockwood expected to be paid his five hundred dollars that night, but Franklin didn't have the money on him. He said, "George, be at the corner of Third and Los Angeles streets tomorrow morning at nine, and I will see you there at that time." He then returned to Captain White's house, where he made arrangements for the captain to meet him at the corner of Third and Main streets the following morning at eight forty-five, where he would give him four thousand dollars in cash, five hundred of which White was to turn over to Lockwood.

The next morning Darrow rose early. Ruby gave him a manicure and cut some of the hair off the back of his head. Happy to see that he was looking better, she laid out a fresh linen suit and a clean white shirt and tie. After a light breakfast he strolled the two blocks to the car line; since there was no car in sight he walked through Echo Park as far as the aqueduct, the warm November sun lighting his face. At the aqueduct he boarded the car, rode to the terminal at Second and Hill streets and walked to his office. He arrived at his usual eight-thirty, sat down to his desk and dug into the work of clearing up his accounts.

In the meanwhile Bert Franklin was meeting Captain White on the corner of Third and Main streets.

"Good morning, Captain," said Franklin. "I have the money."

"This is a poor place to hand it to me," grumbled White. "We'd better go into this saloon."

They went into the saloon, had a drink at the bar, then Franklin handed Captain White a thousand-dollar bill and six five-hundred-dollar bills. The two men left the saloon together, but once on the sidewalk Franklin left White and walked ahead of him to the corner of Third and Los Angeles streets. Here he met Sam Browne, captain of the Los Angeles detectives, with Detective Campbell following him. Franklin exchanged greetings with Detective Browne, slipped down a side street, came back through an alley and entered a saloon on the corner of Third and Los Angeles, where he could watch White pass the money to Lockwood. While Franklin slipped down the alley Detectives Browne and Campbell went up to the second floor of a rooming house where they, too, could watch White pass the money to Lockwood.

A third detective by the name of Home, who had also been trailing Franklin, entered the saloon after him. He saw that Franklin was behind the red swinging doors of the toilet, the open doors making it possible for him to recognize Franklin from the knees down. When Franklin came out of the toilet Detective Home hid himself by turning his face toward the wall behind an icebox, which was some twelve feet away from the toilet. Franklin walked out of the saloon, looked around and came back in. This time a fourth detective, Dana Ong, followed him in, walked up to the bar beside Franklin and ordered a drink. After downing his drink Franklin walked to the swinging doors and looked over the top, as though searching for someone. He returned to the bar, had another drink, walked again to the swinging doors to peer out. Detective Ong followed him to the door to look over his shoulder. They both saw Lockwood come up Los Angeles Street and Captain White cross over to meet him. The two men shook hands.

"What is new?" asked Lockwood.

"Nothing, except a mutual friend of ours has entrusted me with some money to be paid to you on certain conditions. Are you ready to receive it?"

"How much money, and what are the conditions?"

"I am to hand you five hundred dollars and hold three thousand for you until such time as a verdict of not guilty is rendered or the jury hung in the McNamara case."

"It don't go. There was thirty-five hundred to be held, not three thousand. Where is Franklin?"

"He just went away from here."

"Well, it don't go at all, because there was to be four thousand."

"Possibly there is in this roll. I haven't had time to examine it."

"Well, go in that store and examine it."

"I ain't got no business in that store. I'll walk up the street a bit and look."

White walked up the block a ways, turned toward the store windows and counted the money. Then he returned, saying, "There is thirty-five hundred dollars in the roll aside from the five hundred I am to hand you."

"All right, I am ready."

White handed Lockwood a five-hundred-dollar bill, showing him the other bills as he did so.

"I think the passing of a five-hundred-dollar bill on a proposition of this kind is decidedly out of the way," complained Lockwood. "It ought to have been in twos or fives. It's all wrong in a case of this kind; how could a fellow go to work disposing of a five-hundred-dollar bill under these circumstances?"

Before White had a chance to reply a fifth detective, Detective Allison, came down the street on his motorcycle, stopping close to Lockwood and White. Just as he stopped Lockwood dropped his five-hundred-dollar bill to the sidewalk. As he stooped to pick it up Franklin, who was watching from behind the saloon doors, pushed his way out and joined Lockwood and White. After the exchange of a few sentences Franklin looked up, saw Detective Home watching him from behind the saloon doors, turned slightly and saw Detectives Browne and Campbell coming toward him.

"Don't look around," he said to Lockwood. "Let's get out of the way."

Franklin and Lockwood then walked down Third Street, away from the two detectives on foot, but in the direction from which the motorcycle detective had come a moment before. White trailed behind them.

When Franklin and Lockwood had walked half a block down Third Street they saw Clarence Darrow on the opposite side of the street. Darrow saw them and crossed the street. Just as he was about to put a foot up on the sidewalk Detective Browne stepped between Darrow and Franklin, pushed Franklin back sharply and said:

"Don't talk to this man, Mr Darrow. He's under arrest."

To Franklin he said, "Bert, I want you."

"What for?" asked Franklin.

"You've been a detective long enough to know what for. You know what you've been doing."

Darrow stood in silence, staring at the two men.

18

"The first thing that entered my mind," says Darrow, "was as to whether it would be possible to carry out the settlement, and if not, whether it would be possible to save these men's lives. I was shocked and broken up over it."

Steffens came into Darrow's office to ask, "Is this going to interfere with the settlement?"

"Not as far as I am concerned. What about your committee of businessmen?"

"I don't see why it should make any difference to them," replied Steffens. "Suppose they should think that you or any of the rest of the lawyers were connected with this: then what?"

"If that question is raised I want you to tell them that under no circumstances am I to be considered in this matter; if there is any man who thinks that I or any lawyer in this case had anything to do with the bribery, you tell them that there will be no bargaining on that case, that they can take care of that when the time comes. All we are proposing to settle is the McNamara case."

"This is quixotic. Why not get rid of them all at once?"

"No. I never in my life let my own affairs interfere with my clients, and I never will. You go and carry that message to the committee."

Wednesday morning and afternoon was spent in a series of conferences between the lawyers, the businessmen, the district attorney and Otis. By nightfall the district attorney's office had agreed to let the settlement go through, but the two McNamaras would have to plead guilty together. That would make it impossible for Joseph to plead after James had been sentenced. Darrow knew that it would be another difficult struggle with James. On Thursday morning, Thanksgiving, he again assembled his staff at the jail: Davis, Scott, McNutt—and Steffens, who brought the report that industrial warfare was over in Los Angeles: after the McNamaras were sentenced there would be a meeting between capital and labor at which the hatchet would be buried, all differences dissolved.

Darrow again reviewed the case for the McNamaras, showing them the hopelessness of their situation. James was unmoved: he would not permit his brother to go to prison. Each lawyer in turn presented his arguments in favor of the brothers pleading together; he fought them all. It was not until midafternoon, when they had all been defeated and it looked to Darrow as though they would have to go through with the trial, that Davis took a new tack.

"Jim," he said quietly, "I think you're right, and we've been wrong. It's best that you hang. It'll be better for labor."

J. B. stared at him without speaking.

"It's better that your brother hang too," continued Davis. "Then labor will have two martyrs instead of only one."

J. B. straightened suddenly, his body rigid, his face tense.

"Is that the way it looks to you?" he demanded. "That they'll hang Joe too?"

"That's the way it looks to me."

J. B. threw himself face down on his bunk and cried brokenly for a quarter of an hour. Darrow and the others sat huddled into themselves, trying not to see or hear or weep. Then J. B. raised himself on one elbow, pushed the tears off his eyes with the palm of his hand and said quietly:

"All right. I'm licked."

The next morning at the opening of court Darrow and Davis went into Judge Bordwell's chambers to tell him that the McNamaras had agreed to the terms; that they would plead guilty that morning.

"Ten years isn't enough for John J. McNamara," said Judge Bordwell. "He'll have to take fifteen."

Darrow had no authority to accept fifteen years for John; though he knew that the prosecution was laying it on now that they had the upper hand, he had no recourse but to hasten back to the jail and tell the brothers the additional bad news. Having resigned themselves to the idea of prison, the brothers had little spirit left. They agreed. Darrow rushed back to Judge Bordwell to tell him that John would take fifteen years. Judge Bordwell ordered the two men brought into court at two o'clock.

The arrangements had been so closely guarded that only those in the conference circle knew they had been going on. The city was overwrought because of the trial, the election and the torrents of abuse being unleashed on both sides. Thousands of people walked the streets wearing buttons that read: McNAMARAS NOT GUILTY! VOTE FOR HARRIMAN! The majority were passionately convinced that the McNamaras had been framed, that Darrow would excoriate the Otis-*Times*, Merchants and Manufacturers clique, that the trial would be a complete vindication not only for the McNamaras but for organized labor—and the people would be freed from their bondage.

That very morning, as he had every morning, Darrow found hundreds of letters on his desk, most of them containing money for the defense, all stoutly avowing their loyalty and faith in the McNamaras' innocence. All over America Thanksgiving meetings had been held to voice support of the McNamaras; the labor councils of nearly every major city: New York, Boston, Philadelphia, Chicago, Pittsburgh, Cleveland, San Francisco, were planning gigantic demonstrations "to protest against the dastardly frame-up, to force the capitalist class to release the McNamaras."

At two o'clock on the afternoon of December 1, 1911, Clarence Darrow had his two clients brought into the courtroom. The newspaper reporters, who had been sitting around bored during the questioning of prospective jurors, sat up in wonderment when they saw John J., for he was not on trial, and it was the first time he had been in court.

When the court opened District Attorney Fredericks rose and said in a low, undramatic tone, "Your honor, the defense wishes to address the court."

With that he sat down. Darrow nodded to Davis, whom he had decided was the closest to the court and the best man to speak. Davis rose and said without inflection, "May it please the court, our clients wish to change their plea from not guilty to guilty."

The announcement fell with a flat, sickening thud. Spectators turned to look at each other in befuddlement, wondering if they had heard aright. No one spoke.

Suddenly, as the import of the astounding twist in the case reached the consciousness of the people, "there was a psychic explosion" that was heard around the world. The reporters were the first to recover their power of action; they dashed, sprawling over each other, for their telephones. Some of the spectators wept; others stood shakily on their feet, their faces white and shrunken. A clamor went up; men rushed into the court from the corridors to learn if the news were true; fist fights started; the room filled with a bewildered, questioning, pushing, screaming, mauling crowd. Within a very few moments the extras were on the streets with the biggest headlines in their history: McNAMARAS PLEAD GUILTY, but the people of Los Angeles refused to believe: they had belonged to a cause; they had been fighting for a cause; they were strong, resolute; they had an army; they would fight unto the death. And now, suddenly, without warning, without explanation, their army, their strength, their cause, had collapsed.

Judge Bordwell instructed the McNamaras to be brought into court for sentencing on the morning of Election Day, then adjourned court.

For an hour the crowd milled about, constantly renewing itself, trying to find out if this heresy were true, to learn who was responsible for the debacle. The district attorney, the court officers, left; Darrow's defense attorneys left; slowly the crowd exhausted itself, dispersed and emptied the big room. Darkness fell. Darrow, who had been sitting slumped in his chair during the storm, his eyes closed wearily, tried to rise. He could not. He sat there in the gloom, aching, miserable, alone.

19

It was the most disastrous day for labor in American history, and Clarence Darrow was responsible for it.

Should he have pleaded the McNamaras guilty?

Two lives had been spared from almost certain hanging. He had obstructed the prosecution from exploiting the full force of its case, forestalled the putting into evidence of material which would have been used against union officials in San Francisco and Indianapolis. He had saved millions of peaceful workingmen from implicating themselves further in the fate of men who had betrayed the American Federation of Labor's pronouncement on peaceable methods; quieted a scandal which could reflect no possible credit on the ironworkers, the details of which would have revolted and alienated great sections of the American public. The country could now say, "The McNamaras are guilty; they have admitted their guilt and gone to prison; they are paying the penalty; let's forget about it and go back to work and our normal way of life." A year, two years, three years, would not be spent in whipping up passions, making accusations, spreading factionalism and warfare so wide and so deep that it might never be rooted out of American life. He had saved the union workers hundreds of thousands of dollars that would have been wasted in a futile defense; avoided a bitter and bloody class-war trial; prevented the horrifying precedent of having labor leaders hanged for their part in it; enabled the city to travel more quickly the road toward peace and co-operation.

He knew that if he had tried the case with all his force he might have brought in a hung jury. But could he have brought all his force to bear? No one knew better than he that his greatest effectiveness, not only before judge and jury, but before the country as a whole, had grown out of his burning honesty and conviction that his clients were innocent. Great and epochal phrases had poured from his lips, phrases that had helped to reshape the minds of men and the life of his country;

but how would they have sounded from the lips of a man who knew that he was being dishonest, who in his heart repudiated his own clients? He would be a mountebank and a hypocrite; his insincerity would show in every expression of his face, and he would convince no one.

He might have fought for a verdict of second-degree murder, exploded his miniature model of the Times Building, brought in experts to swear that the escaping gas had caused the huge explosion and the twenty deaths; yet he knew that it would be a feeble gesture at best, that with twenty men dead no jury would take into account the lack of intent to kill. Perhaps he could have appealed the convictions, used up years of time in the hope that passions would cool and his clients would be spared. But he knew, too, that the appeals could not save the lives of the men once they had been convicted in open court by a jury, and the constant appeals only would have continued to spread the details of their guilt and the ill will in the community.

Perhaps he could have let them hang and become labor martyrs. But he could not see the cause of labor building on false premises. If labor had to have martyrs, let them be innocent men. He could not have brought himself to making of the trial a campaign of education, when anything he might have said would have inflamed the hotheads in the movement to further violence, with everything in his nature crying out against the approval of violence. The National Erectors' Association had said, "This is war!" Otis had cried in the *Times*, "This is war!" War was cruel, destructive, brutal, senseless, and until it was banished from the face of the earth all barbarities would not only be condoned but approved, if they led to victory. He despaired of such methods, not only because they caused class war, destruction, bitterness and ineradicable ill will between men, but because they were shortsighted and futile, serving only one purpose: to perpetuate the struggle.

"I know I could have tried the McNamara case," said Darrow, "and that a large class of the working people of America would honestly have believed, if these men had been hanged, that they were not guilty. I could have done this and saved myself. I could have made money if I had done this—if I had wanted to get money in that way. But I know if they had hanged these men it would have settled in the hearts of a great mass of men a hatred so deep, so profound, that it would never die away."

He shook his hot and weary head as he recalled how John Mitchell had accused him of wanting to make a plea for socialism instead of better wages and hours for the miners; how Edmund Richardson had charged him, in Boise, with putting the interests of the Socialist party before those of Haywood, Moyer and Pettibone. Now the cycle had been completed: he would be charged by the socialists with sacrificing the party to save his clients.

Sitting alone in the darkness on the field of battle where he had surrendered his cause and his people to momentary defeat, he was completely convinced that he had done right. To the end of his days he never faltered in this belief. Yet after fighting for labor for twenty years, bringing them by his brilliance, devotion and fearlessness many miles along the saber-studded road to civilization, he had now been the indirect instrument of causing them great harm. Labor would never forget—he knew that—and would never forgive him. He had known that his career as a labor defender was finished the day he had learned that he was defending guilty men; labor would now put the seal upon his judgment.

Once again he tried to rise from his seat but could not. From out of the darkness came a friend to help him up. He walked slowly down the long aisle of the courtroom. When he reached the steps of the courthouse he looked down and saw a throng gathered there, waiting for him, standing in stark and sinister silence. In the flickering light of the gas lamps he could see the Harriman and McNamara badges littering the lawn and the gutters.

He shook off his helpful friend, straightened his shoulders and walked slowly down the stairs, his eyes straight ahead but unseeing. A murmur rose to greet him, a murmur which grew in intensity as he came closer. When he reached the sidewalk the crowd closed in: workers, union officials, socialists, liberals, intellectuals, men and women for whom he had spent his years fighting. From the outskirts someone called him a name: an evil name. Close by a man spat in his face. The crowd pushed in closer, surrounding him, pressed against him, heaping their frustration, their defeat, their humiliation, upon him in sordid imprecations. He was hemmed in so close now he could not move. Billy Cavenaugh pushed through the mob, caught Darrow by the sleeve and cried above the tumult:

"Come with me!"

Darrow gazed at the ring of dark faces about him.

"No, Billy, I shall go down the street with the crowd. I have walked with them to the courthouse when they cheered me, and I shall go back the way I came."

He took a step forward. A wall of sullen faces peered into his. He took another step—and the front line fell back. The crowd parted. He walked through it, cleanly, alone. As he went down the street, the crowd at his heels, one cry came out of the night:

"Traitor! Traitor!"

NINETEEN men enjoyed, or suffered, an identical fate: they were all defeated for the presidency of the United States. The truth can sometimes be seen more accurately at an oblique angle than head on: the lives of the Presidents too often have been sweetened to salve nationalistic pride; no one has thought it necessary to whitewash the defeated candidate. Their lives provide a high-powered lens with which to judge the standards of their times, the qualities of their victorious opponents and the political wisdom of the electorate. How often were the voters discerning, how often dumb? How frequently were they fooled, and how frequently did they go unerringly to the better man? How often did they elect the apparently superior candidate, only to find that the presidency was the one job he could not handle? How often did they choose the man who was more capable of solving the existing problems, only to have a radical change in the course of history render his particular qualities useless and make the defeated one the ideal executive to handle the new situation? What is the box score on democratic elections since 1800? Are the voters getting smarter, making fewer and fewer mistakes, or are they repeating the errors they made a hundred years ago?

THEY ALSO RAN

SAMUEL J. TILDEN

HE won the race by a head, but it was before the day of the photo finish, and the judges ruled him out. No American ever had a greater right to cry, "I was robbed!"

He wasn't built to be a hero: slight of figure, racked by illnesses—real and imaginary—cold by nature, battle-worn at sixty-two, without luster or fire. Yet he proved to be the outstanding hero among the Also Rans.

Samuel J. Tilden had it in his power to renew the Civil War, to plunge his country once again into bloodshed and disunion. Victim of a guerrilla uprising against the democratic form of government, no man would have said he was wrong to put down the revolt with force. No man, that is, except himself. All around him he saw people who loved their country with blind passion; he loved democracy with an icy and penetrating intellect. That intellect would not permit him to shatter the peace which was slowly emerging from a war already twelve years ended.

Rutherford Hayes is the man who Also Ran in 1876. But his is not half so interesting a story.

The Ice Myth with which Charles Evans Hughes was erroneously charged was true about Tilden: most of his life was spent inside his brainpan; aside from his parents he loved no one, and no one loved him. He had a big and powerful brain lodged on top of a weak and ineffectual body; his body was something he dragged grudgingly behind him all his days: his mind pulled him ahead of the field like a champion.

Tilden's life was compounded of ironies: though he became a millionaire through his work for the railroads, mines and manufacturers, he was interested in working people; though he loved the Democratic party above all things, he smashed it wide open in New York City when he prosecuted the Tweed Ring; though he had a cold, unapproachable personality, thousands revered him in every section of the land as the unconquerable warrior for reform; though he was a hypochondriac who was forever dosing himself with medicines and cures, he could work any group of healthy men into exhaustion; though he was a laboratory technician in the science of politics, he refused to utilize his skill to seat himself in the White House even after the people had given him a quarter of a million popular majority. He is the only man elected to the presidency who never got his foot inside the White House.

He was a rational man first and a human being second; that was why he never served as president.

The Tilden fiasco of 1876 provides the only major case in American history where the tradition that the majority must rule broke down. Frequently the elections have been corrupted by an unconscionable use of money; sometimes they have been befogged and muddled until everyone except the officeholders seemed to lose; sometimes the elections were lost to the nation in the convention halls, where the weakest men were selected; sometimes they were lost at the polls, where an efficient machine rolled up a majority for a useless man. But the election of Tilden was the first and only time that the majority, choosing the superior candidate, had their ballots flung back in their faces.

Tilden knew the nation could not endure many such breakdowns. They had to be avoided at all costs; and if one of the first costs was that of the presidency, Samuel J. Tilden was willing to pay it. Though he started with more handicaps than most of the Also Rans, he emerges through his self-abnegation as perhaps the greatest of the lot. Only Parker and Hughes would have endured the decapitation with the same legalistic phlegm.

He accepted the decision, but it came as close to killing him as the defeat did Greeley. He went into the campaign resolute, strong of will and purpose; when Hayes was finally inaugurated, to the hisses and groans of more than half the nation, Tilden was an old man, worn out.

Young Samuel had learned his politics at his father's knee; he took to it the way Greeley took to journalism, Scott to soldiering and Hughes to law; he became trained in the mechanics of political thinking the way other boys were being trained in the mechanics of carpentering or animal husbandry. In the home of his father, who was the leading political mind of the countryside, he listened to penetrating discussions of the issues of the day, of the manner in which elections best could be waged and won. In his father's home he met the political leaders not only of New York State, but of the nation. These men liked young Sammy for his eagerness and interest in politics; they discussed the complicated affairs of the nation with him seriously. What Sammy heard he absorbed.

Just as Greeley preferred to sit in a corner of the family cabin and read literature rather than go out of doors and play ball, young Tilden preferred to discuss the rechartering of the Bank of the United States to playing games with the neighboring children. While he was still a boy his father took him with him to visit William Cullen Bryant in the office of the New York *Evening Post;* all through the discussion the father solemnly would ask the son for an opinion on each of the national issues, and just as solemnly Samuel would reply. By the time he was eighteen he had published a paper in the Albany *Argus* outlining why the National Republicans and Antimasons should not combine against the Democrats, which the Albany *Journal* attributed to the hand of Martin Van Buren! This tract was symptomatic of Tilden's approach: written in cool, emotionless prose, the arguments were presented with such clarity and authenticity of research that there could be no answer.

When he was nineteen he wrote a paper on the tariff, defending President Jackson's stand. At twenty he wrote "Is the Treasury an Executive Department?" in which he defended Jackson's right to refuse Nicholas Biddle a recharter for his bank. By the time he was twenty-three he was publishing letters in the New York *Times* defending President Van Buren from attacks within the party.

In the meantime he was failing at everything else! He attended for scattered months at neighboring schools, mostly being unhappy and learning little. Sent to New York to further his development he wandered the city, read fitfully, was interested only in a course in elocution. He went to Yale for one semester, did barely average work, then dropped out. He attended New York University for a semester now and then, when he could find time to sandwich it in between elections and the writing of polemics. At twenty-four he apparently exhausted his course, finishing his work at the university without graduating.

He was a completely disorganized young man. He was still being supported by his father, who could ill afford the money; his health was precarious, his energy low, his determination and direction nonexistent. He had no interest in girls, no physical pleasures; he is the lone bachelor among the Also Rans. He was a brilliant and erratic young man with no discernible future except the vague feeling that he might like to be a lawyer since he enjoyed writing and debating. There was little reason to believe that he would make a better lawyer than he had a student or that he would have the health or determination to do anything but eke out a meager living. The bookies would have given heavy odds against him, with few tempted to play him as a long shot.

From this unpromising beginning he developed into one of the keenest legal minds of the country, became a bulwark of the Democratic party, carrying it to its first presidential majority in twenty years, since the election of Buchanan in 1856. Anyone who had put two dollars on his nose would have collected the equivalent of the daily double: for he became, momentarily, the great man of his day.

How could Samuel J. Tilden, legally elected to the presidency, allow an opponent to foul him on the home stretch and spill him ingloriously into the dust?

2

Samuel Jones Tilden was born at New Lebanon, New York, on February 9, 1814. As was almost universal with the Also Rans, both of his grandfathers as well as most of his granduncles fought in the Revolutionary War. Sam was a fighting man too, even though most of his battles were waged for such abstract causes as civil reform and efficient government.

Samuel's father, Elam, was a successful farmer as a young man, but being a social creature, interested in the problems of the day, he found the solitary life on a farm too lonely. He opened a general store at the crossroads of New Lebanon, where he became a sort of town-meeting moderator: with every keg of nails he sold to one of the hundred householders of the vicinity went a discussion of hard money versus soft, and with each pound of cheese an analysis of whether the state or Federal government should pay for internal improvements. Elam loved nothing better than political discussion, but he was no idle talker: he soon became the political sage of the community and for many years helped formulate the platforms and policies of the Democratic party.

Young Samuel grew up in an aura of respect and homage paid to the political sagacity of his father, a conditioning which gave the boy confidence in his own powers of analysis and deduction. From the time he was fourteen and Martin Van Buren came into control in New York State, the leaders of the Regency were in and out of the Tilden home. Consequently Sam followed the trade of politicking as surely as the blacksmith's boy grew up in the trade of the smithy.

In spite of his political activity and the debt of his party to him, Elam Tilden never wanted nor would accept any office other than that of local postmaster. His son followed him in this trait: though he was elected governor of New York and president of the United States, he did not want either office, preferring to earn his living at his profession. From his father Sam inherited his hypochondria, love of politics, power of analysis, interest in books: by the time he was fifteen he had bought out of his own spending money a copy of Adam Smith's *Wealth of Nations* and had read Thomas Jefferson's published letters many times over.

His mother was the adopted daughter of a physician, well educated for her day, a woman of unending love and loyalty for her family. Sam loved his mother; he looked a good deal like her, and from her he inherited his tendency to aloofness. The boy was as unsocial as his father was social; he had no young friends, played no games, never had a home or a wife or a woman he loved or a group of intimates whom he trusted. He would discuss political economy at the drop of a hat but cared little for other forms of social intercourse. Serious and literal-minded, with an occasional flash of dry humor but no laughter, he had been too delicate as a boy to learn the rough-and-tumble of comradery. Homely, sickly in body, awkward in manner, unable to speak freely or with pleasure except to his elders about politics, he became shy and then inhibited. He held himself apart from his contemporaries, and they in turn, though they easily might have liked him if he would have permitted it, kept away from him. Young Samuel steeled himself to do without people, closeting himself in a world of ideas. His shyness and discomfort in the presence of others was something he had to fight all his life; he preferred to stay out of public affairs, to be obliged to meet only those with whom he had business, whose relationship would be confined to law and industrial management.

It is one of the more diverting humors among the stories of the Also Rans that the man who least understood the human nature of people, and least wanted to associate with them, should have the greatest understanding of their political motivations and be forced into the most pitiless political spotlight in all American history. He was a lone wolf who, by the inexorable demand of the times, found himself at the head of a great pack.

In 1837 he became a law clerk in a New York office, entering at the same time the newly opened law school of New York University. During his three years' study of law and early American history he kept plowing as an artisan in the vineyards of the Democratic party. During the presidential campaign of 1840 he spent six full months working for the re-election of his friend Martin Van Buren, writing pamphlets and newspaper articles on political economy, resolutions for meetings of workingmen, addressing audiences on such subjects as "Prices, Currency and Wages," speaking at open meetings for Democratic causes. He anticipated by a full century the revolution which was to take place in American law when he announced that "institutions are founded not on property but upon humanity."

In addition to his other activities he was also preoccupied in his spare hours with such assorted ailments as rheumatism, chills and fever, neuralgia, swellings and lameness, to which afflictions he was applying poultices, mustard plasters, ice packs, being bled, taking mild narcotics and otherwise enjoying the adventure of bad health.

Tilden hated to make up his mind to anything which would project him into action; he was a congenital delayer, but once he reached a decision the movement that followed was irresistible. He was admitted to practice in 1841, was earning from fifteen to twenty dollars a week by the end of the first year, became a consultant for the leaders of the Democratic party as well as one of their most astute writers on controversial subjects, and soon enjoyed a flourishing law business which followed in the wake of his political activity. As his work and income increased, as he began to feel confident that he had found his place in the world, many of the illnesses began to fade.

The only office he ever ardently desired was that of corporation counsel of New York City, which was appointive. He held this post for a year before he was removed by a rival political faction; from it he received the experience he had wanted in matters of city business and procedure. In 1845, though he had no appetite for the job, he campaigned for the state legislature on the insistent demand of his friend Governor Wright, who was in sore need of him to command the Democratic forces. His outstanding achievement as state legislator was indicative of both his character and his future career: he investigated the long-standing land-tenure troubles in New York State, bringing in a report which gave justice to the tenants and yet won the approval of the landowners; when he had drafted the laws and helped push them through the legislature he found himself lauded throughout the state as a master of economic compromise, as a moderate and scientific reformer.

Due to the falling off of his practice, his activities as a legislator had cost him money, but he now was better acquainted with the inner workings of a state government, had overcome some of his shyness and inability to mix with people and had won the respect of the industrialists. When he returned to his office in New York City he found that railroads, banks, foundries, mills were knocking at his door, asking that he take over their reorganization, put their finances on a sound basis, handle their incorporations and mergers. He proved to have an almost uncanny ability to salvage, rearrange, combine and otherwise rescue sinking industries. From his reorganization of failing railroads he made large sums of money; this he began to invest in coal mines and new ironworks; and above all he had a nose for stocks.

By the time he was thirty-two the weak, sickly, irresolute boy who had been without any discernible prospect of success or fulfillment was a legal power in the inner sanctums of industry, an outstanding political power in his party, a polished man of the world who had become a patron of the opera and was assembling a magnificent library. He would give any amount of time and counsel to the needs of his party, but he was resolute in his determination to remain out of public office.

He appeared to be just another corporation counsel, a smart and capable lawyer who would become wealthy through his work, associate largely with the rich, dabble in politics, occasionally speak his piece for honest government and reform, and slowly disappear from public view. This was what he wanted. But just as was to happen to his lineal descendant, Charles Evans Hughes, in the same city and for the same causes thirty years later, the irresistible rush of events picked up his frail body and swept him to fame. Never again would he be able to retire to the simple pleasures of earning millions.

He had never been physically attractive; the older he grew the less handsome he became: he had sallow skin, a biggish nose, small, standoffish eyes, the thin, almost cynical mouth of the ascetic, a jutting, upturned chin which somehow gave his face an expression of contemptuousness. His thin graying hair he combed broadside to cover his growing baldness; his voice was hoarse and unpleasant from some obscure throat ailment. His figure had lost some of its awkwardness, but it was still unsightly, the shoulders thin and stooping; he looked as though the first strong gust of wind would surely blow him off the legal and political scene. He had none of the external appurtenances of a giant; the last thing in the world he wanted to become was a giant.

Shakespeare said, "Some are born great, some achieve greatness, and some have greatness thrust upon 'em." Greatness was never thrust upon more reluctant shoulders than the frail shoulders of Samuel J. Tilden.

3

For every political poison there is an antidote: the Tweed Ring was the poison, Tilden the antidote. Yet Tilden wanted to be a reformer as little as Tweed wanted to be reformed.

The Tweed Ring of New York City was not only the most corrupt of local governments in the history of American commonwealths, but it came to stand as a symbol for depravity and bold burglary in machine-dominated cities. Tweed had worked himself into control of the Democrats' Tammany Hall, but after a time he realized that he could not seize really empire loot unless he controlled not merely the machinery of the city but of the state. To this end he started to buy election officials, councilmen, legislators and judges. When he needed votes to win an election one of his judges solemnly would citizenize thirty-five thousand immigrants! His election officials would report the results in their districts without counting the votes; upon one occasion he put in his governor with more votes than there were voters.

Tilden was a Democrat; he had helped build New York City's Tammany Hall; as a practical politician he knew that the Democratic party needed the Tammany vote in order to help win state and national elections. If Tweed had confined his stealings to the modest scale of a few millions he would not have died in prison through Tilden's efforts, nor yet made a presidential candidate of Tilden.

By 1870 the Tweed Ring so completely controlled every facet of government within the state, including the force of public opinion, which they molded by the purchase of newspaper editors, that they grew careless and contemptuous of their victims. Safes whose value was three thousand dollars were charged against the city for half a million; a contractor of fire alarms who submitted a bid of sixty thousand dollars for a job was asked by Tweed if he would give the Ring half of the loot if he were paid four hundred and fifty thousand for the work. This overreaching ultimately outraged public opinion; all that was needed was a leader who would make their righteous wrath effective.

Tilden did not want to be the spokesman of the drive: he knew that the revelations would be injurious to his party; he knew the strength of the opposition that would be unleashed against him. But he was repelled by the use of the machine for brigandry. He became convinced that in order to preserve the strength of the Democratic party it must be the Democrats themselves who threw out the rascals, rather than the Republicans who would use the revelation as a club with which to beat the National Democratic party over the head. The Democrats turned to him to undertake the job not only because he was one of their most able and reputable men, but because they had confidence that he could destroy Tweed as an individual malefactor without seriously hurting their party.

Tilden tackled the problem, not by shooting off vocal firecrackers, hurling charges or demanding indictments, but by working patiently within the framework of political procedure. Instead of starting criminal prosecutions which he knew would be thrown out because the Ring controlled the courts, he started a drive to nominate honest judges to the Court of Appeals in the election just coming up, then campaigned arduously to put over the reform slate. When the state convention met he framed a platform of repudiation of the Tweed Ring and Tammany Hall, saw to it that anti-Tammany Democrats were selected to run for state officers and for the legislature, contributing a hundred thousand dollars out of his own pocket to have the polls policed. Some of his campaign speeches, in which he presented a scientific analysis of the evidence against the Tweed Ring, are among the best of his long career.

New York City and New York State rose in its electoral might, giving Tilden's reform candidates tremendous majorities. Tweed judges were swept off the Bench, his legislators out of Albany, his henchmen out of the city jobs. Tilden then began his impeachments of the remaining corrupt judges and his prosecutions of the Tweed Ring, spending a large portion of his time sending to prison all those who had not fled the country. He waged the four-year battle not only without compensation or hope of reward but at tremendous expense to his health and resources: for whenever there were no public funds to cover the costs of the investigations and prosecutions he would pay the money himself. At the beginning of his attack upon the Ring he was known in corporation circles as an able lawyer, in Democratic circles as an astute campaigner, to a small group of New Yorkers as a penetrating writer on political subjects; but to the nation at large he was unknown. At the termination of the prosecutions he had become a national hero, not only for the blows he had struck for honest government, but for the quiet skill and sagacity he had displayed as a commanding general of the citizen army.

For many years his name had been put forward by committees, clubs, newspapers and party groups as a proper man to hold office. He had rejected the suggestions. He had gone into the Tweed investigations as a private citizen and had had every intention of returning to private life when the job was done. But the deeper he got into the problem the deeper he saw he would have to go in order to be successful. Though the idea of holding office was still repugnant to him, he ran for the state legislature in order to complete the task he had undertaken, to secure the passage of laws to protect New York's cities from future gang raids.

In 1874, at the height of his Tweed purges, a movement as spontaneous as that to run Hughes for governor after his gas and insurance purges took form to elect Tilden the next governor of the state. He was so obviously the most capable man at the moment that outstanding Republicans and their journals joined in the boom. His unwillingness to hold public office was no longer tenable. He had been importuning the best men among the Democrats to train themselves and run for office. By what right could he now refuse to serve, when he was the best man available for that particular job at that particular moment and the people needed him?

Having decided, in his slow-moving, cautious, secretive way, that he must become the next governor, he threw all of his energies and experience into winning the battle. He waged a laboratory campaign, directing every slight move himself: collecting the funds, supervising every dollar spent, issuing a continual stream of articles and pamphlets from his own and the pens of the best writers he could find in the state, setting up an educative barrage the like of which had not been known before, speaking to thousands of voters in every section, speeches ringing with incontrovertible truth and zest for decent government. He knew more about the actual blueprint and mechanism of elections than anyone since his master, Martin Van Buren: he maintained an active list of fifty thousand Democrats, two in each school district, who supervised his campaign, while he estimated by a mathematical formula just how the vote was veering. He knew at every moment of his campaign exactly what his chances were. His winning majority of fifty thousand votes was precisely what he had estimated it would be.

He turned in an excellent record during his two years as governor, finishing off the Tweed Ring, smashing the upstate Canal Ring by a statistical investigation which revealed their plunderings beyond contradiction. From the moment he had been elected people talked jubilantly of moving him from Albany to Washington in 1876, and during his administration his candidacy grew apace. Nor was Governor Tilden any longer dilatory or reluctant: the die was cast, he was going to have to serve as a public officer; since the Grant Ring in the capital was the national counterpart of the Tweed Ring, it was merely a continuance of his job to be elected president, go to Washington, throw out the rascals and set up reforms which would protect the nation from further depredation.

How does a man secure the nomination for the presidency?

Bryan got his by setting the convention on fire with oratory; Parker got his because the conservative Democrats of the east saw in him an antidote to the silvery vocal Bryan. Greeley got his because his opponents accused him of wanting it, thus putting the idea in the nation's head. Clay got his by manipulating men, by keeping the party in line with magnetism and tongue-lashings. Cox got his by being an Ohio governor and editor chosen to oppose an Ohio editor and senator. Frémont got his because he had established a name as an explorer and pathfinder just when the infant Republican party needed a name and a man to blaze new political paths; McClellan got his because he publicly opposed Lincoln's Emancipation Proclamation, setting himself at the head of the northerners who wanted southern property protected, including the slaves; Hancock got his because, as a military governor in the south after the war, he manifested a desire for unity and brotherhood of the states, and no one could wave the bloody shirt in his face. Scott got his because he was the greatest general since Washington, because the only two of his fellow Whigs ever elected had both been generals. Hughes got his because the voting Republicans thought him the party's greatest asset, an idealist whose record equaled Wilson's.

The professional manipulators of the New York Democractic machine did not want Tilden any more than the Republican machine would want Hughes forty years later: he had made powerful enemies by his reform movements; he was what they called a "cold fish," not the kind of good egg with whom the boys could drink and play poker and hold smut sessions.

Some nominations are accidental, others are a result of wangle and wampum. Tilden's came out of a test tube. He waged a more detailed and meticulous campaign to win a unified nomination from his party than most candidates waged to win the election.

First he established a Newspaper Popularity Bureau which sent out paid advertisements to some twelve hundred rural newspapers and furnished the city papers with interesting and well-written articles about himself. A Literary Bureau, an extension of the idea he had used so successfully in his gubernatorial campaign, employed the best authors available to write articles, pamphlets, human-interest stories which were mailed out by the hundreds of thousands. Such an inventive manager was he that he selected the most attractive combinations of reds, blues and greens to be used in printing the circulars, an innovation in campaign literature. Nothing that modern thought had made available was neglected in his design to win the Democratic nomination. The material with which he blanketed the country was extremely high in caliber, for he believed wholeheartedly in a campaign of education. The articles and pamphlets included analyses of governmental expenditures, taxes, civil service, the eradication of patronage and graft, the structure of a businesslike administration.

He set up the equivalent of the modern Gallup and Fortune polls: reports poured into his office every day from the remotest sections of the land, surveying and estimating the sentiment of the people. His researchers took a census of college commencement exercises, found that a majority of them were about reform and Governor Tilden; the Fourth of July speeches also were tabulated, showing that the majority had made Tilden and Reform the heroes of the year. By such methods Tilden knew that reform was on the march, that it could sweep the country in an election; but even here he did not stop. He also kept an unsleeping eye on his enemies and opponents in order to gauge the direction and strength of their opposition.

Democrats in every state in the Union made it known through their newspapers, committees and rallies that they wanted Tilden nominated. Tilden, the technician, had left nothing to accident; when the doors of the convention hall swung open no one could be found to wager a dollar bill that he would not be nominated. Elam Tilden and Martin Van Buren would have been pleased with their protégé.

Five thousand people jammed the auditorium in St. Louis, for the sweet smell of victory was in the air, the first in twenty years for the Democrats. The platform, with its sharp cry for immediate and sweeping reforms, sent the delegates into an ecstasy of political fervor. The historical conjunction of Tilden, the country's greatest reformer, with the crying need for reform brought Tilden more than four hundred votes on the first ballot and the nomination by a landslide on the second.

It is claimed that his nomination was received by the voting Democrats with more enthusiasm than any leader since Jackson. However, the Democrats were a minority party. With the Republicans able to extract a fifteen-million-dollar campaign fund from their three hundred thousand officeholders alone, could Tilden gather a sufficiently large fund to cover the country with a hailstorm of educative literature? Could he entice enough Republicans into his camp, lure enough of the independent vote to secure a majority?

Could Samuel Tilden, a man without warmth or charm or attractiveness or personality, fire a nation for a great cause?

He was not a vote cadger, he was a vote manufacturer. He published a seven-hundred-page campaign bible exposing the Grant administration's frauds and mismanagement; his own principles of sound government were contrasted to the evil record. The Democratic campaign was rich in courage, energy and faith; it was poor in only one ingredient, cash, the national fund not being over half a million dollars, of which Tilden himself had contributed a hundred thousand.

Sam Tilden always had been a man of ideas: he waged the campaign of the Idea. It was successful. Then the Idea was blown to bits by surviving Civil War artillery.

4

The Republican nominee, Rutherford Hayes, had been three times governor of Ohio, had had an honorable if unspectacular career in Congress. He had pulled himself up by his bootstraps from a poor boyhood to considerable means, culture and comprehension of national affairs, including civil-service reform. However the majority of the public did not give him credit for wanting reform; they gave that credit to the man who already had proved that he could make reform effective.

The campaign started on a high plane, as directed by the two candidates, both of whom were high-minded men; then it sank lower and lower in both tone and manner as the fighting fell into lower and lower political hands. When it finally reached the hands of the ward politician, the county bigot, the frightened Republican officeholder, the job-smelling Democrat, the canvas conformed to pattern, the country suffering one of its recurrent ravages of filth, vituperation, chicanery, libel and slander. Tilden was accused of having been a Copperhead, of approving of slavery and secession; the Boys in Blue were fired to wage the war all over again, to vote as they had shot.

He was called the harlot of the railroad kings—all of whom had deserted when he cleaned out the Tweed and Canal rings; he was accused of being a millionaire aristocrat, an enemy of the working people and the common man; he was accused of wrecking industries in order to cheat the public out of their funds and pocket the profits, of evading his income tax; he was charged with being a crony of Tweed, of perpetrating election frauds; he was called a wirepuller and consummator of deals. Among the other accusations levied against him in print, in whispering campaigns, in speeches, was that he was "a drunkard, a liar, a cheat, a counterfeiter, a perjurer and a swindler," a defrauder, a sham reformer, a grafter. No tiny shred of his record or reputation was left untouched.

The same machine, spewing the same filth, had helped to kill Horace Greeley only four years before. Was it any wonder that Tilden had wanted to stay out of public life? That many men would not voluntarily endure this calumny?

Tilden was made of sterner stuff than Greeley; besides, he knew more about the inner workings of politics. The campaign of vilification neither caught him by surprise nor distressed him. In the great mass and crush of work he refused to become worried or excited. He spoke quietly, made momentous decisions with a barely discernible nod of the head. While working twenty hours a day and supervising every detail he kept himself detached and objective in relation to rising problems. The people around him thought him indifferent; he was merely the engineer refusing to land himself in the soup through emotion or hysteria.

Tilden answered the worst of the canards himself in letters and articles to the press. No one could tell whether the calumnies were traveling faster than the denials; one of the most encouraging signs was that a number of outstanding Liberal Republicans, men of the best families, artists and scholars such as James Russell Lowell, Lyman Trumbull, Charles Francis Adams, Professor William Sumner of Yale, Henry Cabot Lodge, came out for Tilden as the superior man.

The fever rose as election day came closer: there were huge bonfires, parades during the day with bands and marching men; at night crowds surged through the streets, singing campaign songs, wearing oilcloth over their hats and shoulders to catch the warm tallow that melted from the candle lamps. There were speeches and hecklings and fights and gnashed teeth and broken bones. But when election day dawned the patient had passed his crisis, the fever subsided, the nation cast its ballots quietly and in good order.

As post time drew near, Tilden was a five-to-two favorite. The bookies, with seven hundred thousand dollars to put on his ample nose, could find few takers. On the eve of election Tilden and his lieutenants pored over the mathematical formulas which Tilden had set up, and what they saw on the sheets convinced them that they had a clear victory on hand. The staff and workers of the Democratic committee were wild with joy, but Tilden sat by quietly, his left lid falling low over his eye, his thinning white hair combed neatly, parallel to his brow, his high stiff collar and black bow tie immaculate, his face a mask.

When it was learned on election day that New Jersey and Connecticut, both doubtful states, had gone for Tilden, there was every indication of a landslide. By nightfall Tilden also had captured New York State, and everyone knew that the election had been decided.

Rutherford Hayes went to bed that night saying that he had been defeated; Tilden, like Hughes, went to sleep believing himself to be president.

The following day the press in all parts of the country informed the people that Samuel J. Tilden was their nineteenth president. The New York *Herald* and the New York *Times,* though conceding that Tilden had a lead, refused to acknowledge his victory. Editor Reid of the *Times* had undergone great privations while held in a southern prison during the Civil War; his implacable hatred for everything connected with the south included the Democratic party and its candidate. His vituperation and ridicule of Tilden had been frenzied; it was Reid who now started the movement which put Rutherford Hayes in the White House.

The plot began at three forty-five in the morning of the second day after the election, while Reid and two of his assistants were sitting in the editorial rooms of the *Times.* At that moment they received a message from the chairman of the State Democratic Committee asking, "Please give your estimate of the electoral votes secured by Tilden. Answer at once." Reid exclaimed, "If they want to know the electoral vote, that means they are not certain they have won. If they are still in doubt, then we can go on from here and win the election!"

On November tenth the popular vote was 4,285,992 for Tilden against 4,033,768 for Hayes. The electoral vote stood: Tilden 184, Hayes 166, with the nineteen votes of South Carolina, Louisiana and Florida still doubtful. If the Republicans could establish a majority in all three states, Hayes would be elected by an electoral majority of one vote!

Going to the Republican National Headquarters at the Fifth Avenue Hotel, Reid awakened the Republican chairman and set before him his plan to capture the election. Securing the chairman's approval, Reid telegraphed south, "Hayes is elected if we have carried South Carolina, Florida and Louisiana. Can you hold your state? Answer immediately."

But how could the Republicans split up the south, solidly Democratic since Jefferson?

5

In South Carolina, Louisiana and Florida there were two separate factions, each with its own electoral board, still fighting the Civil War: the Republican carpetbaggers with their shepherded Negro vote, and the local white residents, all of whom were Democrats. Reid's telegram was asking whether the Republican Certifying Boards could set up a carpetbag-plus-Negro vote which would be larger than the resident white vote.

Rutherford Hayes wanted no part of these monkeyshines; he told a Cincinnati newspaper two days after the election, "I think we are defeated in spite of recent good news. I am of the opinion that the Democrats have carried the country and elected Tilden." Tilden, aware of the power of his adversaries, said, "The fiery zealots of the Republican party may attempt to count me out, but I don't think the better class of Republicans will permit it."

This was one of the few political errors of his long and sagacious career: for President Grant already was pouring Federal troops into the south to enforce the carpetbag count at the end of a bayonet. General Sherman, in charge of the Federal troops, later wrote, "The probabilities were that Tilden was elected." However that did not stop him from playing an important part in swinging the election.

There did not appear to be much doubt in anyone's mind that Tilden had won; the only issue was whether the Republican machine could force a majority in the three southern states.

In South Carolina the seven-man Certifying Board which was to determine whether Hayes or Tilden got the electoral votes was solidly Republican; in Louisiana the board of four also was solidly Republican; in Florida the board again was solidly Republican. Combined with the presence of Federal troops under Republican commanders, this potent fact, plus the promise of Federal patronage, plus the passage of certain large sums of money, plus the promise of southern amnesty and independence if its Democrats would throw in with the Republicans, made a formidable task force.

Letters, messages, telegrams poured in upon Tilden urging him to act, to take a stand, to make a strong statement, to choose his cabinet, to plan his inauguration, to denounce the plot and, with his usual mathematical genius, to expose what was already being termed a Mexican election, decided by bullets instead of ballots.

Samuel Tilden, pale-faced, sick at heart, his left lid drooping ever lower over his eye, could not be booted into action. He kept his finger on the minutest detail, pursuing a course of watchful waiting. If he had issued the kind of icily devastating blast of which he was capable, he might have chilled the plot and put an end to it. But he did not consider that this would be dignified conduct. He was first of all a lawyer, with an overpowering respect for the law and the Constitution; he would make no claims to the presidency even though his infallible charts proved that he had been elected. The people would have to decide this election within the framework of the existing legal machinery; he would do nothing to help.

He had conquered through ideas, but ideas were having a rough time surviving in the world of force.

The Democrats of the country wanted no part of Tilden's reserve: they staged victory parades, fired victory salutes, sang of their quarter-million majority. The more hotheaded ones among them began talking of fighting with their bullets if their ballots were powerless to win; this feeling was accentuated when in Louisiana, where Tilden had a seven-thousand-majority, the board threw out thirteen thousand of his votes; it burst into flame when in Florida, in spite of Tilden's conclusive majority, the board certified the Hayes electors.

When all of the electoral votes had been dispatched to the Senate it was found that Tilden still had one hundred and eighty-four votes. Hayes had one hundred and sixty-six. In dispute were nineteen votes of the three southern states where both parties claimed a majority. The Republicans, who had a majority in the Senate, claimed that that body not only had the right to count the electoral votes but to decide which ones were valid. The Democrats, who had a majority in the House, claimed that only the House could decide upon contested votes. The Constitution was vague on the subject.

Tilden was completely convinced that the House should decide between conflicting electoral returns; to prove his point he wrote and published a brilliant study under the title of *The Presidential Counts.* At times he seemed more interested in the case as a lawyer than as a prospective president, preparing long and detailed briefs because he believed that the election laws needed clarification so that this kind of impasse could not occur again. By distributing his material to the newspapers, by seeing that *The Presidential Counts* reached a large part of the influential public, he prevented the Senate from accepting the Republican votes of the southern states. Thus he put himself in the lead at the first turn, but it was to be a long race: for the Republicans were threatening war if the House tried to seat him.

The cooler Tilden remained in his legal fight, the closer the rest of the country approached the boiling point. The battle cry of "Tilden or Blood!" arose; Democrats began re-forming their old companies; officers demanded that he allow them to fight their way into Washington; thousands of men offered their services and their lives.

Another Civil War was in the making. It required only one word from Tilden, one barely perceptible nod.

He refused to say the word. He would countenance no force. He insisted on being installed in the White House through the existing legal machinery, by the decision of the House.

Since the Senate never would accept a decision of the House, nor the House a decision by the Senate, it became increasingly obvious that the affair could be settled only by arbitration. Numerous schemes sprang up in Congress, some of them involving the drawing of lots. Tilden killed these proposals by saying, "I do not care a snap of my fingers for the presidency, and will not consent to raffle for it."

He maintained that he would accept the arbitration of no extralegal body: according to his reading of the law the Constitution provided a means of settling electoral disputes and definitely did not provide for the setting up of arbitration commissions. However, inauguration day was drawing close, it was known that Grant wanted a third term, that he was hoping that Tilden and Hayes would stymie each other. Believing that justice would emerge out of the right on their side, the Democratic congressmen used all their persuasion to make Tilden accept an Arbitration Commission; he disapproved of the plan, but finally acceded to the wishes of his confreres.

Congress therewith passed a bill setting up a commission to be composed of five members of the Senate, five of the House and five from the Bench. Having declared the bill unconstitutional, Tilden and Hayes agreed to accept its decision. Of the fifteen men on the commission, seven were Democrats, seven were Republicans, and one, Judge Bradley, was to be neutral and objective. Some time before midnight of the last day one of Tilden's campaign managers read an opinion written by Judge Bradley in favor of Tilden's electors. He reported back to headquarters that Tilden would be selected. However he had left the judge's house a bit too early: a Republican senator and Republican cabinet officer spent the rest of the night with the judge.

The following day the commission declared Rutherford Hayes to be the legally elected president. Fourteen of the fifteen members of the commission were lawyers, yet they made their decision on straight party lines; the evidence played no part in their judgment.

When told of the result Sam Tilden smiled quietly and murmured, "It is what I expected."

But the nation was rent by cries of "Fraud! Dishonesty! Corruption!" Once again Grant sent Federal troops marching, while Tilden's supporters begged him to, "Lead us! We will put you in the White House, where you belong!"

Samuel J. Tilden relinquished all leadership. Bitterly disillusioned, exhausted, he reasoned that it was better to let Hayes and the Republicans have the election than to plunge the country once again into bloodshed and destruction. He permitted Hayes to be inaugurated under the heaviest burden ever carried by an American executive, to spend a miserable and execrated four years in the White House.

"I can retire to private life," said Tilden, "with the consciousness that I shall receive from posterity the credit of having been elected to the highest position in the gift of the people, without any of the cares and responsibilities of the office."

Though he lived for another ten years he was never in robust health; he remained as a counselor of his party, but refused the nomination in 1880.

It had been a photo finish, with history serving as the infallible camera. By the time the film could be developed the wrong people had collected their money and gone home, the stands were deserted, the track dark. Yet there remains the picture for all time, with Tilden out in front by a nose.

6

What kind of president would Tilden have made? Four million three hundred thousand American voters had rallied to his banners with the zeal of warriors. He had inflamed the nation as no man since Frémont or Lincoln. Such public enthusiasm is not always an indication of a man's ability to deliver, but in the case of Tilden, who had no personal charm or warmth to awaken interest, this zeal had to be based upon a record of past performances.

With Tilden as president there would have been no family life in the White House; an undemonstrative man with few friends, the White House might have been a chill place. He was methodical, secretive, cautious, wanting complete and perfect proof before making a decisive move. In certain upswing periods of American history these characteristics might have been a drag upon the country, but in 1877, when the greatest need of the day was to bring honesty, economy and prudence into the government, administrative conduct based upon fact and science rather than grab and revenge, they might have made Samuel J. Tilden one of America's most able presidents.

It is not necessary to minimize Hayes's solid competence to indicate that Tilden had the broader and deeper mind, the greater courage, the profounder conception of the structure of the nation. While he had been campaigning brilliantly on cogent issues, not even the most experienced newspaperman in the nation could get a syllable out of Hayes. "Seldom has a candidate more wholly ascended his party than did Tilden; seldom has a candidate been more completely submerged by his party than was Hayes."

As the legally constituted chief executive Tilden would have searched the country high and wide for the most able men to run the various services; he would have set on foot a movement to impeach corrupt officers, would have kept up a continuous education of the public on the work being done in reform. His activities as a legislator and governor had been precisely the kind needed in a president in 1876: he had helped put the state finances on a sound basis, abolished much graft, rescued

New York-owned enterprises from the hands of mulctors, helped draw up a new and modern constitution for the state. He would have striven to make his administration run as efficiently and cheaply as possible, setting up the Federal government as a model for lesser governments.

In relation to the south he would have made a complete and scientific study of conditions, then set up a progressive program to bring peace and prosperity to the ravaged states. Certainly he would have taken the corrupt carpetbagger off the neck of the south, helped it to function under its own government; this alone would have made him a great administrator.

Though Hayes's biographer admits that Tilden won the election, and "was one of the ablest men of the country, if not the ablest," he still believes that it was better for Hayes to have occupied the presidency because the Republican hatred of Tilden would have prevented him from accomplishing anything, either for the south or in the way of reform. This judgment leaves out of account two crucial factors: Tilden's adamant character, and the fact that he had a quarter-of-a-million majority of the votes. As an astute and scientific politician he would have known how to handle his die-hard opponents. He had handled them in New York with great success for the state. He would have made his reforms stick: in spite of his poor health and delicate condition he was a bulldog of tenacity whenever he was convinced that something had to be done.

Considering the handicaps under which Hayes took office he turned in a good record: he helped break up the unscrupulous Senate Ring of Roscoe Conkling and his followers, fought the corruption in the port collector's office, made attempts to reform the civil service—though he paid off for the electoral votes swung to him in the election. He made efforts to help the south, yet he remained at heart an insular governor of Ohio who knew little of the outside world.

Tilden's attitude would have kindled respect and enthusiasm for the democratic form of government, whereas Hayes, labeled with "Fraud!" across his forehead in several of the nation's papers on inauguration day, through no fault of his own created contempt for the system of popular elections.

Tilden was a better man than Hayes to start with; his defeat in an honest election would have been a blow to the nation. But to have him elected by a sizable majority, and then despoiled of his office by a corrupt machine, multiplied the tragedy of his loss by a mathematical formula which could have been worked out only by Sam Tilden himself.

HORACE GREELEY

"While there are doubts as to my fitness for president," observed Horace Greeley dryly, "nobody seems to deny that I would make a capital beaten candidate."

Until the advent of Abraham Lincoln, for whose nomination he was partly responsible in 1860, Greeley was the most widely known and heatedly discussed figure on the American landscape; from his pen poured a torrent of articles, essays and books, from his lips an almost equal torrent of words; for three decades, from 1840 to 1872, he exercised one of the strongest influences on the mind and motive of the nation.

"Having loved and devoured newspapers," he writes in his *Autobiography*, "I early resolved to be a printer if I could."

He could never have become anything else: he had printer's ink in his veins. By the age of twenty-one he was a known and respected printer in New York City, having set up a press and started his first paper; at twenty-three he had founded a literary weekly, and been invited by James Gordon Bennett to become a partner in the founding of the New York *Herald*; at twenty-seven he was commissioned by the political boss of New York State to publish a political paper, at twenty-nine began a second political paper, which dominated the Log Cabin and Hard Cider Campaign of 1840; at thirty he founded the New York *Tribune*, revolutionized the conception of a newspaper, its manner, form and content, and singlehanded created modern journalism.

"He chased rascals, not dollars."

He chased ideas even more ardently, and caught up with them—rascals, dollars, ideas, all three. The man who was too frightened to play baseball because of the speed with which the ball was thrown at him took his life in his hands to go bail for Confederate President Jefferson Davis after the Civil War, walking unafraid on the streets of New York with frenzied crowds around him singing:

"We'll hang Horace Greeley to a sour apple tree!"

He had the weirdest appearance in any professional circle, making Lincoln seem debonair: tall, skinny, angular, neither his head, torso nor limbs seemed to bear much relation to each other, as though all three had been sired by different parents and stuck together with mucilage. His head was as round as the baseball he feared, with a bulging forehead; his skin was a dead though not unhealthy white; his hair was colorless, his pale blue eyes almost expressionless. He wore his long hair around his face and under his chin until the advancing years had enabled him to achieve neck whiskers. He rarely went abroad without high boots, one trouser leg stuffed inside, the other hanging out. The rest of his getup consisted of a string necktie which generally hung over one shoulder, a white linen suit, a tall white hat and a bulging umbrella.

He appeared to be a mild, ugly, absent-minded and innocuous schoolmaster; actually the strange body, bulging head and fantastic garb housed one of the most powerful and penetrating spirits to which the United States had given birth.

As a child he had been all brain and little body; he could read at three, had finished the Bible by the age of five and devoured everything the countryside had to offer, from the *Arabian Nights* to the *Pilgrim's Progress.*

"His mind was a marvelous storehouse of facts, dates and events. He was a political encyclopedia, of the best revised edition, and entirely trustworthy."

He consumed such quantities of print that he became nearsighted; he read with his nose so constantly and so deep in a book that the book appeared to be a part of him, another organ of perception, such as an eye or an ear. He would sit in his little cubbyhole of an office at the *Tribune,* surrounded by a welter of newspapers, magazines, reports and scrawled copy, "his nose nearly touching the paper on which he was writing" furiously and uninterruptedly. His pen was an appendage without which he could not have lived: a third arm, an inky lung.

Next to Henry Ward Beecher he was also the most popular lecturer of his day. Few walked out on him; a listener might say after the first sentence of his unattractive voice, "Two minutes of this is all I shall be able to stand." Two hours later he still would be hanging on intently.

Horace Greeley had little to go on: no important family or connections, no charm, no physical attractiveness, no social graces, no money, no friends. All he had was a brain, integrity and passion.

They took him a long way.

2

"I am drifting into a fight with Grant," he said in 1872. "I hate it. I know how many friends I shall alienate by it, and how it will injure the *Tribune,* of which so little is my own property, that I dread to wreck it. Yet I should despise myself if I pretended to acquiesce in his re-election. I may yet have to support him, but I would rather quit editing newspapers forever."

He had a good reason to dislike the idea of fighting Grant. Greeley had been one of the founders of the Republican party in 1856, had waged a stout campaign for Frémont against Buchanan, had fought a superb journalistic battle for Lincoln in 1860. Though he had not been enthusiastic about General Grant he had supported him in 1868. Now he loathed the thought of doing injury to the party he had helped found, yet he knew that, just as Lincoln and the Republican party had contrived to win the war, Grant and the Republicans were contriving to lose the peace.

There was no thought in his mind when he said, "I am drifting into a fight with Grant," that Horace Greeley would be the candidate of the opposition. For thirty years he had been an office maker, not an office seeker. There had been a time, eighteen years before, when he would have liked to be governor of New York. He had reasoned that he could do a better job than most of the men whom he saw elected; in addition he had felt that the party which he served in election after election, without reward or compensation, owed him a gesture just once, a sort of loving cup bestowed publicly in token of his services. He had not wanted to be an officeholder for very long; he had never wanted to be anything but an editor; but he would have enjoyed successfully carrying an election, proving that he could be a first-rate public executive.

His ambition had been thwarted by politicians Weed and Seward, the men for whom he had founded his first political paper. In retaliation he had gone to Chicago in 1860, when it was certain that Seward would receive the nomination for the presidency, and by a shrewd campaign swung the nomination to Abraham Lincoln. Seward, in turn, prevented Greeley from being named for the United States Senate by the New York legislature.

Only once had he been elected to office—as a Whig congressman from New York City in 1848. A highly trained and astute political economist who believed that the well-being of a nation depended upon the humane and orderly functioning of its economic pattern, he had been for most of the right causes for the right reasons. He tried to limit the granting of public lands to actual homesteaders; he fought a congressional grab in the form of a proposed bonus; he killed a bill which would have raided the Treasury for the private printing of debates; he headed a movement to abolish flogging in the United States Navy.

His most colorful contribution, and one which brought down upon him the wrath of his confreres, was an exposure of the means by which congressmen were mulcting the public funds by drawing traveling expenses on the longest and most circuitious routes from their homes to Washington. He drew up charts showing how much each congressman could save by utilizing the newest and fastest routes of travel. The congressmen used them from that time on; he had left them no choice.

His record in the House had been as good as his position had been awkward; for he had felt obliged to use his job as editor of the *Tribune* to expose everything he found in his job as congressman. This infuriated the House, which promptly created the precedent that acting members of Congress might not use their inside information for the edification of their newspapers back home.

The year 1872 was not very old before Greeley realized that he would have to oppose the re-election of Grant in spite of the shattering injuries it might do to the Republican party and to the *Tribune.* He was not alone in his determination, for by now most of the outstanding editors of the land—Joseph Medill, Joseph Pulitzer, Carl Schurz, William Cullen Bryant and a host of others—had joined him in exposing the devastating list of crimes, corruptions, usurpations and incompetencies for which Grant had to be held responsible.

As soon as he announced in his *Tribune* that Grant must be defeated, his fellow Republicans assumed that he was waging his fight for selfish reasons, that his driving force was a desire to replace Grant in the White House. They set out to expose him to the country as a seeker of the presidency, doing such a good job that they sold the idea to Horace Greeley, the new Liberal Republican party, the Democrats and the country at large. He is the only one among the Also Rans who was in effect nominated by the opposition.

What kind of campaign would an editor be able to make? If he were elected would he set the precedent for a long line of newspapermen in the White House?

Eighteen years before, Greeley had said, "I am a beaten, broken-down, used-up politician and have the soreness of many defeats in my bones."

Nominated to the presidency at the age of sixty-one, he promptly forgot about the soreness in his bones, stumping the country in the most vigorous campaign since Henry Clay had tried to defeat Polk in 1844. From the first moment he was confident that he and the Liberal Republicans would win. For him to imagine that he could be defeated would have been a violation of the character of the boy who had been born on a rocky and mortgaged New Hampshire farm at the beginning of the century, February 3, 1811, and whose astonishing rise in the world formed a perfect model for the Horatio Alger stories which were to adorn the end of the century.

3

Young Horace was admitted to the public school in Bedford even though his parents did not pay taxes there, the board ruling that "No pupils shall be received from any other town, except Horace Greeley alone." In later years presidents, cabinet members, senators, all manner of public figures would amend this to read, "I wouldn't take that from anybody but Horace Greeley!"

He was such an outstanding student that a wealthy neighbor offered to send him to Phillips Exeter Academy and then through college. Horace's father, about to flee to Vermont to keep out of debtor's prison, refused on the grounds that a Greeley did not accept charity.

The Greeley family, which included four children besides Horace, went through years of rural poverty in New Hampshire and Vermont. At one time their total equipage consisted of two milk pans, the five children eating their mush out of one, the parents out of the other. Zaccheus Greeley was the third of that name, the first having arrived from England in 1640; he was a good man, cheerful and intelligent, but an unsuccessful farmer. Mary Woodburn Greeley was a woman of fine intellectual perceptions but a harum-scarum housekeeper; Horace's wife was to prove an even worse housekeeper than his mother. From his mother he acquired his love of poetry; she encouraged him to sit in a corner and read Byron and Shakespeare instead of going outside to play with other children.

The boy made his first attempt to become a printer at the age of eleven, walking to the neighboring town of Whitehall to apply for a job. The publisher took one look at the frail, white-faced youngster, another at the heavy hand presses, and sent the lad back home. At fifteen he tried again, this time successfully binding himself over to a printer at Poultney for his board, clothing and forty dollars a year.

He stayed four years at Poultney, working long hours in the print shop and loving it, reading widely in his spare time, learning the newspaper business. For another year he wandered on foot over Pennsylvania and upper New York State as an itinerant printer, ending in New York City in August of 1831 with ten dollars in his pocket, the clothes on his back, and not an acquaintance within a hundred miles.

Turned down by city newspapers because he looked like a country yokel, he set type for a Bible publisher, secured work on fly-by-night weeklies, became acquainted with other printers. He saved a few dollars, then formed a partnership with a friend and went into the printing business. Knowing that the best way to insure work for one's presses was to have a paper of one's own, Greeley started the *Bank Note Reporter*, which became successful as an organ of the lottery business. Other printing contracts came in; the firm began to make money.

When he was twenty-three he founded the *New Yorker*, a literary and political weekly which started with twelve subscribers and rose to seventy-five hundred. In the *New Yorker* Greeley cut his eyeteeth on editorial writing, encouraged such poets as Edgar Allan Poe, raised the tone of American journalism by imbuing the paper with a high quality of literary excellence. Within a year he had become known as one of the most competent editors in New York City. He married, set up a home, was well on his way to success, though a visitor to New York called him "the greenest specimen of an editor I ever looked at."

When the panic of 1837 hit New York, Greeley wrote an increasing number of the articles himself, set them in type, made up the pages. He found a sixteen- or eighteen-hour day in his office and print shop highly enjoyable. His rapidly whirling brain did not permit him to sleep much, perhaps five hours a night; when he grew tired during the day he would fall into a semicoma: he would hear everything that went on, but his body would be asleep.

At the invitation of Thurlow Weed, he set up the *Jeffersonian* to help the local Whig campaign in 1838, winning acclaim for his political articles. Two years later he introduced the *Log Cabin* to the country with an eighty thousand circulation and a new Whig campaign song with every weekly issue, starting a campaign-song custom that remained until the end of the century. Harrison defeated Van Buren, and Greeley became known nationally; however, the venture proved to be as costly to his purse as it was profitable to his reputation.

Being broke at thirty did not frighten him: he borrowed a thousand dollars from a friend, threw in the circulation of the *New Yorker* with what was left of the *Log Cabin* after the campaign, and started the New York *Tribune*. His timing was perfect: the *Tribune* was a success from the first issue that hit the streets.

4

"Newspapers are, or ought to be, printed for the information and entertainment of the whole community," announced Greeley in his revolutionary credo. "When they are mere advocates of petty or even of ponderous private interests, the advertisers of personal schemes, and puffers of men who have a large amount of axes to grind, they must lose all independence, manliness and substantial patronage."

His success as a publisher of the first modern newspaper came from the boldness of his mind and the daring of his imagination. There was little he could find to approve in the journalism of his day: he rejected the unreadability of the print, the unattractive appearance of the page, the illiteracy and grossness of the writing, the dullness of the content, the emphasis on crime news, the repetition of gossip instead of fresh and authentic news, the shallowness of the thinking and the partisanship of the opinions. He was not a man to be tied down by existing forms or bound by precedent: he invented a modern newspaper, whole, in much the same way that Edison invented the light bulb.

Above all it was Greeley's mind that dominated the paper and gave it flavor; his thinking was sharp, incisive, his writing utterly lucid, colorful, full of drama and dry humor, spiked with delicious phrases, writing that tickled or excited or soothed according to the need of the issue on hand.

"His paper bristled with important news, much of it as provocative as the editorials. The *Tribune* was a model of compactness and good editing, and extremely well printed. He possessed an equipment for the metropolitan newspaper field not duplicated in that day or this."

If he merely had been a good editor and journalistic innovator, his importance would have been limited; he was above all a great polemicist, a scientist at dissecting the economic and industrial forces at work behind society and government. He was a crusader and reformer because he burned to see mankind live in a just and orderly world, because mass suffering seemed to him to be not only brutal but suicidal. He spared no one and played no favorites; his was a powerful voice of liberalism trumpeting its calls in a social wilderness, always a half-century ahead of his times, sometimes a full century.

"For forty years Horace Greeley was the busiest and boldest editor in America. He pried under and tipped over with pitiless pertinacity. No rival journalist ever created an influence that penetrated so deeply. The

New York *Tribune* was Horace Greeley. Far and wide men and women followed his guidance in great causes. No matter of moment escaped him, no fears ever made him pause. He gave neither himself nor the nation rest."

He was a trust buster sixty years before Thodeore Roosevelt wielded his stick. "All combinations or bargains to raise prices," he wrote, "are exceptionable and contrary to law." He fought for the need of workmen to form trade unions only two decades after laborers were being arrested, convicted and imprisoned for attempting collective bargaining. "We believe that unregulated, unrestricted competition, the free-trade principle of every man for himself and buy where you can the cheapest, tends everywhere and necessarily to the depression of wages and the concentration of wealth. Capital can wait, labor cannot; it must earn or famish. Without organization, concert and mutual support among those who live by selling their labor, its price will get lower and lower as naturally as water runs downhill. We are in favor of trade unions or regular associations of workers for the establishment and maintenance of fair and just rates of wages."

He became the first president of the Printers' Union, bringing respectability and force to the movement. He worked for the distribution of public lands to the poor and needy, particularly those crowded into the slums of the cities. He was one of the first men in the United States to insist that, since the government was the agency of the whole people, it was up to that government to rescue its members in times of crisis, depression and poverty, not to allow whole segments of the population to decay. His program for the alleviation of the suffering caused by the depression of 1837 was similar in nature and detail to the program of the New Deal in the depression of 1937.

He was the first public figure of importance to sanction the cause of Fourierism, onto which his opponents tacked the label "Socialism," a new word designed to destroy the *Tribune* and Mr. Greeley with it. Greeley did not take flight; he devoted considerable space in his paper to educating the people on the principles of the new socialism.

"When I took up this cause," he said, "I knew that I went in the teeth of many of my patrons, in the teeth of the prejudices of the great mass, in the teeth of religious prejudice. But in the face of all this, I went on."

He gave money to certain of the experimental colonies, in particular five thousand dollars to Brook Farm; he was the vice-president of their association and the strongest voice in their behalf. But he was also their flagellating critic: "A serious obstacle to the success of any socialistic experiment . . . is the kind of person who is naturally attracted to it. Along with many noble and lofty souls who are willing to labor and suffer reproach for any cause that promises to benefit mankind, there throng the conceited, the crotchety, the selfish, the headstrong, the pugnacious, the unappreciated, the played out, the idle and the good for nothing generally who, finding themselves utterly out of place and at a discount in the world as it is, rashly conclude that they are exactly fitted for the world as it ought to be."

Tireless, incorruptible, sensitive, on the side of the angels, every day of the week he was a mighty force for good. Circulation of the *Tribune* soared until it reached three hundred thousand, the paper literally sweeping the country, for Greeley published a weekly edition which was mailed to every hamlet of the land.

People everywhere began to ask, "What does Horace Greeley think about this?" They saw him make mistakes, but they were positive of his integrity, certain that he would state the truth that was in him at all costs, that he followed principle rather than master, that he was hard to fool, that he had the gift of analysis and clear, forceful statement; above all, that he would use his gifts for the common people and not for the spoilers, political or economic.

He refused to make a fortune out of the *Tribune*. The best young writing talent of the nation beat its way to the door of the *Tribune*, and its editor spared himself no cost to make his paper the finest news collector and disseminator in the world. Yet Greeley could have become a wealthy man in a very few years, as had Bennett from the *Herald*. Instead, he took in a partner to handle the business end of the *Tribune*, and to this partner he consigned the tremendous profits. He paid himself a liberal wage, in consonance with the job he was doing, but would accept no profits as such, gradually selling off his shares at a modest figure. To preserve his integrity and full courage he must have only what his efforts earned; if he began thinking about how much profit he could make out of the *Tribune* he soon would be trimming his sails, placating, mollifying, hesitating to fight for fear of alienating subscribers or advertisers. A sure touch for every individual and every cause that held out a hand, he never would utter a sentence for the sole purpose of making money.

"The darkest day in any man's earthly career," he said, "is that in which he first fancies that there is some easier way of gaining a dollar than by squarely earning it. He has lost his way through the moral labyrinth and henceforth must wander as chance may dictate."

Horace Greeley was not a wandering man.

His fear of unearned money was his chief but by no means his lone peccadillo. So fiercely did he concentrate on a specific problem that he took no notice of what went on about him. When introduced to a roomful of people he would nod abruptly without interrupting the flow of his harangue. When at a buffet he would fasten onto some one plate, eat it clean, never thinking that somebody else might like a bit of cheese or a doughnut. Then he would touch nothing else. It was not safe to pass him a communal pitcher of milk or cream, for he would down it to the bottom. He was a vegetarian, did not drink or smoke, and crusaded against women's corsets as vehemently as against their equal rights or suffrage. Though he had many devoted friends among the women intellectuals, such as Margaret Fuller, Susan B. Anthony, Harriet Beecher Stowe, he had a low estimate of their capabilities, a state of mind encouraged by the growing misfortune of his marriage.

He met his first and only love at a boardinghouse conducted by Dr. Graham; though neither Dr. Graham's crackers nor his cracked diet did young Horace any appreciable harm, it brought him untold confusion in the form of a wife. Mary Cheney was a schoolteacher, "slight, exquisite, dressed in clouds of white muslin, cut low, her neck and shoulders covered by massive dark curls." Margaret Fuller called her "a typical Yankee schoolmistress, crazy for learning," while a long-suffering family friend described her as "a female crank, born so, who could not help doing as she did."

For the first five years the Greeleys were happy, entertaining in their home and mixing in the best literary circles. Mary Greeley idolized her first-born, a son, refusing to allow him to associate with other children, cooking him special, eccentric foods, working for hours every day over his complexion and his long silken hair, making him a hothouse flower of beauty and delicacy.

When the boy died of cholera at the age of five, his mother's mind was permanently affected. Though she bore six more children, four of whom lived, none was able to replace her idol. With the passage of the years she became increasingly psychotic, making Greeley's life a hell. At his home on Nineteenth Street, their farm at Chappaqua or their home in Turtle Bay he could find no comfort and no moment of peace. When she grew angry at his preoccupation she would seize the manuscript on which he was working and fling it into the fire. Nothing pleased her: she harped and criticized until the stricken husband would flee to a hotel for a few days to get his work done.

For the latter half of his life, as Greeley has said, he had no home.

He had taken a wife with the same name as his mother, and with the same housekeeping proclivities. His wife had a fixation on cleanliness, scrubbing everything in much the same manner as she had scrubbed her first-born, but this was her solitary domestic virtue. She cared nothing about her home, which was always a boar's nest of confusion and discomfort. She cared nothing about food, and it was impossible for him to bring friends home.

In spite of his burdens, Horace loved his Mary; he was unfailingly kind and sympathetic; he took no women in her place. Yet no man ever had greater need of a sensible wife, one who would have given him a comfortable home, seen that he had a balanced diet, stuck both trouser legs in his boots when he left for the office in the morning, laughed him out of his foibles and eccentricities. His effervescent mind needed a governor; and who better to provide it than a wife?

Thus he went his way, a tall, angular, absent-minded man in spectacles and a high white hat, carrying a whalebone umbrella; a Jeremiah of the inkpots, a faddist whose open mind would try any experiment to see if good might come of it; a pamphleteer in the tradition of Thomas Paine, a blood brother of Upton Sinclair, his twentieth-century counterpart.

5

As far back as his *New Yorker* days Greeley had been writing treatises to the effect that slavery was ruining the south economically, aside from the morals in the case. By the fifties he was taking a militant stand against further appeasement of the south, maintaining that it could keep its institution of slavery if it wanted, but that slavery must not be extended to one more free mile of American earth.

"It would be better to see the Union a thousand times shivered," he cried in the *Tribune,* "than to allow slavery to be planted on Free Soil."

He was no abolitionist, but he castigated the Fugitive Slave Law, waged a blistering campaign against Stephen Douglas for reopening, in his Kansas-Nebraska Bill, the possibility of extending slavery to the new territories. When a civil war in miniature broke out in Kansas, Greeley fought the slavers in such fulminating terms that twenty-two thousand dollars came by mail to the *Tribune* with which to buy rifles, jocularly referred to as Beecher Bibles, to be shipped into Kansas in shoe boxes. When John Brown raided Harpers Ferry, perhaps with some of the *Tribune's* Beecher Bibles, feeling throughout the country turned against Greeley as an incendiary.

Because of his telling blows, the anger and bitterness of the south concentrated on his paper. Any southerner daring to subscribe to the weekly *Tribune* would have been mobbed at his post office; the *Tribune's* reporters and agents had to travel under assumed names and conceal the nature of their business. Yet Horace Greeley was one of the strongest voices in the land for letting the southern states go, "providing they go peacefully," when they wanted to secede. Though he realized the dangerous possibility of an alliance between the south and England, or other European countries, of a Confederate-South American block aimed at the heart of the north, he was convinced on the basis of economic necessity that the south would sue for a return to the Union within a very few years.

"The cotton states are meditating a withdrawal from the Union because of Lincoln's election," he wrote in an editorial that went into three hundred thousand homes scattered through the farm belt, the northwest, and as far away as California. "We again avow our deliberate conviction that whenever six or eight contiguous states shall have formally seceded from the Union, and avowed the unanimous and earnest resolve of the people to stay out, it will not be found practicable to coerce them into subjugation; and we doubt if any Congress can be found to provide for such coercion."

But when the south fired on Fort Sumter, the *Tribune* fired a broadside at the south: "Fort Sumter is lost, but freedom is saved. There is no more thought of bribing or coaxing the traitors who have dared aim their cannon balls at the flag of the nation." In both attitudes the *Tribune* was voicing the sentiments of millions in the north.

War was no sooner declared than Greeley began to harass President Lincoln to strike immediately and in full force against the rebels. Lincoln listened not only because he knew that Greeley had helped to secure him the presidency, but because of the enormous weight and breadth of his influence.

When the battle of Bull Run was lost, and the north plunged into despair, contumely was poured upon Greeley for forcing the army into premature action. At each of the northern defeats Greeley suffered as only Lincoln must have suffered. Nevertheless he kept prodding and pushing for faster and greater action. He pounded at the president, lashed at the cabinet, hounded the Congress and flailed at the generals in a paroxysm of determination that the north fight, that it win, that it redeem its honor and preserve the Union. When the Draft Act was passed in 1863, mobs stormed the *Tribune,* threatening to burn down the building. Its editor sat unperturbed in his little wire cage, writing more incendiary editorials while the mob howled for his life. At the abyss of the northern defeats he suffered an attack of brain fever, in the course of which he asked if it might not be better to declare an armistice, to let the south go. He also participated in one mysterious peace conference.

Next to his determination that the north must throw its full resources into the war and win quickly, Greeley was most set upon an immediate emancipation of all slaves to assure the people that the ghost of slavery would never rise again. President Lincoln wrote to him frantically, "What I am trying to do is save the Union, not free the slaves!" When the Emancipation Proclamation finally came, at the earliest moment that Lincoln thought it safe for the war effort, Greeley was acknowledged to have been the spearhead of the drive.

Sometimes he had talked idealism without the men or guns to back up his words, but always he was a fighter who knew that there could be but one end to the conflict. If there is any truth in the charge that he was partly responsible for the war, then it is equally true that he was partly responsible for the victory.

6

He was an idealist and a humanist in the early New England tradition. Instantly upon the cessation of hostilities his mind turned to the binding up of all wounds. "We plead against the passions certain to be fierce and intolerant," he wrote only a few hours after Lee's surrender; "we plead for a restoration of the Union, against a policy which would afford a momentary gratification at the cost of years of perilous hate and bitterness."

Coupled with President Lincoln's determination that the south should not be bled or despoiled, the powerful voice of the *Tribune,* reaching families in every corner of the land, continued to carry Greeley's beautiful pleas for forgiveness, for brotherhood, for the restoration of the south to its full powers that endless misery and tragedy might be averted, generations of misunderstanding and hatred avoided, a unified nation made strong in a spirit of compassion.

But Abraham Lincoln was assassinated. The voice of Horace Greeley was drowned in the cry for blood. Convinced that the further incarceration of Jefferson Davis was a destructive act of vengeance which kept the south embittered, Greeley traveled to Richmond where, with Commodore Vanderbilt and several other northerners, he signed a hundred-thousand-dollar bond for the release of Davis.

He had spent a lifetime in the midst of frenzied battles, but all that had gone before was a gentle zephyr compared to the tornado that rocked him for this effort. The quarter of a million circulation of the *Tribune Weekly* fell off to fifty thousand, with post offices turning back the issues by the tens of thousands. The second volume of his history of the war, *The American Conflict*, after the first volume had been a tremendous success, was almost entirely canceled at the moment of its issue. He was hanged in effigy. He stood alone, his paper failing beneath his eyes, his name and character reviled. He became the most execrated man in the United States.

"At last a man has turned up who is more unpopular than Jefferson Davis, and that is Horace Greeley. I think if Greeley could be hung now, they would be content to let Davis go."

The Union League Club, which he had joined for patriotic reasons at the close of the war, decided to try him in Star Chamber for treason. Greeley wrote a two-column reply in the *Tribune* which should go down in history as one of the great cries of defense made by an authentic martyr. Only then did the feeling against him soften. He had few of the external appurtenances of a proper martyr, but then, martyrs so seldom look the part.

It was with misgivings that Greeley had supported General Ulysses S. Grant, the Republican nominee, against Horatio Seymour in 1868. He was grateful to Grant for bringing the war to a close, but he knew that the presidency, particularly in as difficult a period as the nation had ever faced, should not be handed out as a reward. He did not feel that a military man was the proper one to bring peace and harmony to a war-ravaged country; from what little he knew of Grant he felt pretty certain that the general could not handle the job.

It did not take him or the other penetrating minds of the country very long to see what Grant had let them in for: the incompetence and scandal stank to the high heavens. With other independent editors who held the interests of their country above the interests of their party, he rained criticism upon Grant, hoping to clear up some of the infected areas. President Grant turned from his critics with annoyance and distaste. After three years of intolerable conditions Greeley broke from the Republicans in power as dishonest perverters of the real aims of the party.

The recalcitrants called themselves Liberal Republicans. They assembled in convention at Cincinnati on May 1, 1872, drawing up a platform which contained a sizzling indictment of Grant and his followers that is almost word for word the indictment levied against Warren Harding half a century later. The strongest candidate of the convention was Charles Francis Adams, whose family already had provided two presidents for the United States. Greeley was the second choice, having been jockeyed into this position by the overzealous opposition. Adams started out strongly on the first ballot, but when it was realized that he would never be accepted by the Democrats of the south, with whom the Liberal Republicans were hoping to form an alliance, Greeley's strength increased. He was nominated on the sixth ballot.

In his *History of the Presidency* Stanwood comments, "The work of the convention was received by the Republicans throughout the country with a shout of derision. Greatly as Mr. Greeley was esteemed for his sincerity and respected for his ability, he had always been regarded as an erratic man, and there were few persons who credited him with the cool judgment and tact needed in a president."

When in 1868 honest, kindly, confused and politically unborn General Ulysses S. Grant had been asked if he wanted to become president, he had replied sagely, "No, I am a military man, not a statesman. I would just like to be mayor of Galena long enough to build a sidewalk from my house to the station." If he had stuck to that determination Grant might have saved the country from a holocaust as tragic in its social and economic implications as the war itself. Grant's conception of a statesman was one who could build a sidewalk from his home to the station; upon his induction he had loaded the government payrolls with so many relatives that Washington observed it had never seen anyone get in a family way so fast.

Grant's relatives proved to be the best of his appointments; his friends turned out to be the worst set of rascals the country had yet experienced, not to be equaled in viciousness until the advent of Warren Harding's inner circle in 1921. Seizing power in most states of the Union through the distribution of patronage, they not only kept the south prostrate and despoiled but outraged every function they could absorb in Washington, gouged the people of millions, perverted the machinery of government for their own purpose, weakening with every gesture the fabric of democratic civilization.

Even this graft and corruption did not accomplish as much fundamental damage as the fact that Grant had not the faintest conception of what a president should do, of what his duties or obligations were, of how much control he should exercise, of what the division of power should be between the three branches of the government. Like Harding, who, when faced with a complicated problem of national importance, would run a hand over his glazed eyes and murmur, "The hell with it, I can't make out what this is all about," Grant gazed with the mind of a child at the affairs of state, blinked uncomprehendingly, and turned them over to his friends to be kicked around.

The Republican press, while flailing Greeley, omitted any discussion of whether Ulysses S. Grant had displayed cool judgment, tact, or any one single quality that would have entitled him to be re-elected.

"I accept your nomination," said Greeley, "in the confident trust that the masses of our countrymen, north and south, are eager to clasp hands across the bloody chasm which has so long divided them, forgetting that they have been enemies in the joyous consciousness that they are, and must henceforth, remain brethren."

The Democratic party, but a shadow of its former strength, confirmed Greeley's nomination. Once again the Republicans hooted; they did not want to clasp hands with the south; they wanted to wave the bloody shirt of war, win elections and remain in power.

At the age of forty-three Greeley had complained, "I have the soreness of many defeats in my bones." At sixty-one those bones gathered up their strength for one final effort, giving as robust a performance as ever had been witnessed on the American landscape.

"I never saw a happier face than that of Greeley," said Colonel McClure of the Philadelphia *Times*. "He was entirely confident of his success, and in a facetious way reminded me that I had underestimated his strength with the people."

Greeley was not depending on any backlog of popularity or vague memories of his stands. He resigned as editor of the *Tribune* and jumped into the campaign with an energy and intentness that was worthy of two other Also Rans, William Jennings Bryan and Wendell Willkie. He opened his campaign in Portland, Maine, in the middle of August and fought hard every hour of the way, stumping the country and speaking in every important city. Tremendous crowds and great cheering greeted his appearance, with gigantic parades of men dressed in raincoats and hats to catch the dripping tallow from the candles held aloft in the night.

He was careful to document his speeches and think everything out beforehand so that, "I would not throw my chances away by any blunder." His attitude on the stump was marked by spirit and breadth of view; one Democrat from Indiana observed that, "for elevation of thought, for broad philanthropy and for Christian statesmanship, the speeches of Mr. Greeley have no parallel in American history."

President Grant said nothing.

The *Tribune* supported Greeley with great vigor, but the *Sun,* now edited by Dana, whom Greeley had trained on the *Tribune,* opposed him, as did his old friend Henry Ward Beecher, who abandoned him on the grounds that the Republican party must not be broken up, no matter how bad Grant was. The independent press, stroked by the brilliant pens of Schurz, Medill, Pulitzer and Bryant, did intelligent and constant campaigning for Greeley.

He enjoyed the canvass, except for the fact that his daughters sometimes had as many as four hundred to feed at Chappaqua of a Saturday afternoon; that the photographers were forcing him to assume ludicrous poses, in the manner of glacial Calvin Coolidge being photographed in an Indian hat and feathers. Through September and October he continued his fervid speeches, quoting figures, stripping bare the Grant malfeasance, uttering some of the profoundest sentiments for unity and peaceful reconstruction that the country had heard. He remained confident long after his supporters saw how the wind was blowing: that the soldier vote would be cast pretty solidly for its own general, and against the south; that vast sections of the country would be voting neither for Grant nor against Greeley, but for the Republican party which they had brought into existence; that there was no possibility of getting a fair comparison of Greeley and Grant before the electorate because the people were too tired and beaten to think; that the country was weary: weary of bloodshed, of wrangling, of accusation, of change.

"Grant may be kinda bad, like they say he is, but Greeley might be worse, who knows? Let's go along as we are for another spell."

Ballots were cast quietly and without tension, for there could be no doubt that Horace Greeley was beaten before he started. Grant received three quarters of a million more votes, the final score standing at 3,597,132 for Grant against 2,834,125 for Greeley.

7

What kind of president would Horace Greeley have made? How would he have stacked up against Ulysses S. Grant?

Many charges were made against Greeley during the campaign: he was a faddist; he was hotheaded; he was rash and tactless and flew into political rages; he was unpolished and had no manners; he was "a self-made man who worshipped his Creator"; he was dictatorial, refused to take orders, to work with the boys; he had failed as an experimental farmer; his attitudes were not always consistent; he had suffered from brain fever; he didn't look like a president; he was "unlike anybody else, including himself."

The charges fade into the background when one realizes the importance and the extent of his work for the nation, the depth and vigor of his brain, his grasp of political economy, his insight and understanding of the workings of government, his undisputed honesty and integrity and courage, the heroic and unflagging wars he had waged for the people, for efficient government, for liberal reform, for tolerance, for an economy based on justice and order. He was running against a man whose four years as president revealed him to be what he had been before the Civil War: a failure at everything he tried, unread, unthinking, with no understanding of the forces that were at play in the world, or any wish to understand them. "Grant's innocence of the nature of American government was as astounding as was his ineptitude. Blind to the great emergency confronting him, and incapable of dealing with it even if he could have seen it, Grant became little more than the political puppet of his flatterers, and consequently he stands today in our history as the most pathetic figure that ever occupied the office of the President of the United States."

In his one political office, that of congressman, Horace Greeley had done good work; as the founder and director of national newspapers he had a brilliant record not only of success, but of raising the tone of journalism and public thinking. He was already old and tired, he would have been better in the office fifteen years before, but deep fires still burned in his soul, fires to right the wrongs of Reconstruction, to bring the south back to health, to take government out of the hands of the incompetents and swindlers, to make the government an efficient agent for the whole people.

One of Grant's contemporaries said that Grant missed the greatest opportunity since the inauguration of George Washington. Horace Greeley would have done something with that opportunity. He would have made mistakes, he would have made enemies, he would have made blunders in proportion to the enormity of the task, but it would always have been on the side of trying to do too much for the nation and its people rather than too little. With the opportunity to accomplish great things, the training, the intelligence, the courage and the will to essay them, he might have been, in spite of his shortcomings, one of America's most valuable presidents.

"A fussy old man in a white hat and a linen duster," says one of Grant's biographers in describing Greeley; "it was hard to think of him as president."

It was true. But the fussy little man in the white hat who burned to serve humanity and help to release it from its chains of ignorance and poverty, whose head under that tall white hat was bloody and scarred from doing battle for liberty and truth, might have turned in a job of which Thomas Jefferson, Andrew Jackson and Abraham Lincoln would have been proud.

Mary Greeley died just five days before the election. It was a bitter blow to Horace, who watched over her and nursed her during her last hours. After his defeat, tired, discouraged, ill with weariness, he resumed the editorshop of the *Tribune,* only to learn that a strong movement was under way to oust him from the paper he had founded. Under this blow he became more ill, feeling himself now to have no place and no purpose. He spent feverish days and sleepless nights, and died only three weeks after the election.

"While there are doubts as to my fitness for president," he had said, "nobody seems to deny that I would make a capital beaten candidate."

They were wrong; the defeat killed him.

With his death all animosity and criticism stopped at once; his loss was more deeply felt than any since Lincoln's. Greeley would have enjoyed reading his obituary notices, though doubtless he would have done a little editing here and there, written a series of articles on the lessons of his life.

The "obits" came too late, too late for him to receive the loving cup across the chasm, too late to save the nation from another four years of corrupt and fratricidal government under Grant.

It was "thirty" for Horace Greeley, one of the most fantastic, lovable and valuable creatures ever produced on the soil of North America. All that would be remembered of him was that he once said, "Go west, young man!"

What he had meant by west was Erie County, Pennsylvania.

JESSIE BENTON, daughter of the powerful western expansionist Senator from Missouri, Thomas Hart Benton, fell in love with Lieutenant John Charles Frémont when she was only sixteen, and insisted upon marrying him. Senator Benton bitterly opposed the match, not only because of his daughter's youth, but because Lieutenant Frémont, of the United States Topographical Corps, was unknown, without family background. Jessie married Frémont secretly, Benton swallowed his chagrin and pushed an appropriation through Congress for an expedition to explore and map the country between Missouri and the Rockies. Lieutenant Frémont led the expedition. Jessie helped him write the report for Congress, which was approved and published, earning him the command of a second expedition, this time to Oregon. Senator Benton and Jessie went home to St. Louis, and here Jessie helped her husband secure a cannon from Colonel Stephen Watts Kearny, military commander of the area, and an old friend. When the War Department in Washington learned about the cannon, it recalled Lieutenant Frémont. Jessie suppressed the message, sent instructions to Frémont at Daw's Landing, to set forth at once. Colonel Kearny was chastised by the War Department. This altercation prepared the ground for their quarrel in California in 1846, when Frémont chose to obey Commodore Stockton rather than General Kearny. Kearny had Frémont brought back to Washington to stand court-martial. Frémont was judged guilty of mutiny. President Polk remitted the penalty of dismissal from the service. Jessie was grateful, but Frémont's pride had been shattered. He resigned. Senator Benton helped assemble funds for a private expedition, to locate a railroad pass through the Rockies. Jessie agreed to meet her husband in California, and establish a home there.

IMMORTAL WIFE

To Consecrate a Hearth

THE mid-March winds were icy and the wooden planks of the wharf slippery under foot when Jessie and Lily boarded the S.S. *Panama*. Tom Benton had insisted upon bringing them to New York, had filled their cabin with the newest books, fruit and flowers. They were determined to be lighthearted about the parting, hustling about the cabin unpacking valises and trying to make it seem a little like home. They spoke in quick rushes of how soon California could become a state, what John's chances were of being elected the first senator; of the possibility that there really was a large quantity of gold, and how quickly a genuine gold rush would settle the new territory. But at last there was no more time for impersonal talk, and father and daughter embraced, murmuring words of farewell.

She stood alongside of the rail while orders were shouted; there were the noises of the hauling up of the gangplank, of winches being turned. The ship pulled slowly into the bay. When she could no longer see the little wharf in the blackness, she turned and went down to her cabin. The two kerosene lamps were swinging from their hooks in the ceiling beams. Lily was in her berth, lying wide-eyed.

"Haven't you gone to sleep yet, child?" Jessie asked.

"No, Mother, I'm frightened. Won't you come in bed with me?"

"Yes, dear, I'll undress immediately."

It took only a moment to slip out of her clothes and don a warm flannel nightgown. Outside the two square portholes a gale was raging as the ship pitched its way forward. She got into the berth with Lily; they comforted each other in the darkness with talk about the future. Jessie tried to imbue the child with her own excitement and impatience to reach California.

The first three days were stormy. When she dressed and went out on deck on the fourth morning off the coast of Florida, she found the sun shining brightly and the ocean tranquil.

Captain Schenck of the S.S. *Panama* had assured Senator Benton that everything would be done to keep her comfortable. She sat on deck in a wicker lounge chair with the sun beating strong on her face, while Lily went forward to watch the sailors paint the gear. The sun had a soothing quality; so did the quiet and the blue skies, the flight of gulls out from the coast of Florida and the Bahamas. In the heat of the day she took long naps; at sunset, with the skies flaming cerise and indigo, she walked for an hour about the deck, storing up strength for the difficult days ahead when she must cross Panama.

Though she had planned to go around Cape Horn on the S.S. *Fredonia* which had left in January, her father had insisted that she have more rest before she made the journey, that John could not be in California before March, and that it would be better if he arrived there first and prepared a place for them. In addition he wanted her to wait a few months so that she could travel on the newly proposed line of government steamships. Rumors that gold had been discovered in California had reached Washington toward the beginning of 1848, but no one in the East had given them any serious credence; in December of 1848 a tea caddy filled with gold nuggets was delivered to President Polk. This first concrete evidence of gold had excited the easily inflammable and congenitally adventuresome, who prepared to get to California as fast as they could and by any means available. Though most people in the East did not consider one tea caddy of gold to be proof of a gold strike, the government used the additional inducement of gold on the west coast to establish regular steamship connections with California. The S.S. *California* left to go around the Horn and was to remain on the west coast plying between San Francisco and Panama City. The S.S. *Panama* left New York on March 13, 1849, for Chagres, the port of entry to Panama on the Atlantic coast. Jessie, Lily and the other passengers would cross the Isthmus, which had just been opened to travel, and catch the S.S. *California,* which would come down from San Francisco to pick them up.

In the evenings she read from the volumes on agriculture she had bought in Washington in order to prepare herself to be a farmer's wife. She did not think that John should become a farmer; he lacked not only the training, but the temperament as well; yet the important thing was to establish a permanent home in California. When Elizabeth Benton had heard of her daughter's plans to erect a log cabin in the Santa Cruz mountains outside of San Francisco, she had taken Jessie's hand and murmured, "Remember that you were born on land that had never been bought or sold, a crown grant for military services to my grandfather's father. Not only should your home be inherited, Jessie, but your servants and money as well. The gods are slow to consecrate a new hearth. You're not strong enough to endure the hardships of wild country like California. Let John complete his railroad expedition, return to Washington and find his life here. You would be a great deal happier."

On the ride to Cherry Grove eight years before, seventeen-year-old Jessie had shrugged off her mother's warnings as unimportant. But this was a chastened Jessie who had already endured much of the worst her mother had predicted.

"Someone has to build a hearth at the beginning, Mother," she had replied, "or the rest of us wouldn't be able to inherit it."

John would eventually find other activities more interesting to him than farming, but first their home place must be established. If her mother had been right in saying that "the gods are slow to consecrate a new hearth," then the more reason to begin at once.

At the end of two weeks of sailing, when she had her first sight of palm trees and the tropical growth of Chagres, it was another wrench to know that she would have to leave Captain Schenck, her last connection with home. She awakened while it was still dark, dressed herself by candlelight in the clothes she had laid out the night before. With Lily's hand clutched tightly in hers, she went on deck in time to watch the tropical sunrise, the sun bursting above the horizon as though it were shot out of a cannon, day breaking with the same roar with which the sea was breaking on the white beach of Chagres. It was her first view of the tropics; from a distance it looked friendly enough, with the palm trees fringing the sand bar and the heavy green growth along the river. When Captain Schenck came forward, Jessie turned a smiling face toward him.

"So the voyage is ended, Captain," she said. "You have made it pleasant for me and my little girl."

Captain Schenck did not return her smile. Anxiously he said, "Then let me perform one last service for Senator Benton and Colonel Frémont. Do not attempt to cross Panama. The country is rotten with Chagres fever. People are dying in the boats and on the trails. The food is abominable, the water is poisoned. That route should never have been opened."

The unexpected opposition to her continuing onward to meet John brought sharply to her mind the scene at the Delaware Indian Reservation where she had come so close to losing her love, her husband and everything that had meaning in her life. She valued it doubly now for having so nearly lost it. Any thought that she might fail in her efforts to join her husband in San Francisco brought back the intensity of those despair-fraught hours in Major Cummins' cabin.

"I am certain I will be able to stand the passage, Captain," she answered serenely.

The ship was rolling under them and she was anxious to get ashore. She returned to her cabin for her coat and purse. Having left her door ajar, she heard the heavy stomping of a man's boots. An unfamiliar voice cried:

"I ain't taking the responsibility for any Washington fine lady across Panama. She'll object to the Indians havin' no clothes on, she'll make trouble, she'll not be able to stand it."

She hadn't heard the phrase "fine lady" since the day she had left Miss English's Academy. She gave her hat a final touch, resolutely swished her long dark skirt out behind her, opened the door and faced the stranger. The man looked at her slender, ivory-tinted face, at her fragile figure, at the burning hazel eyes, and said stumblingly, "Why, you're not a fine lady at all; you're just a poor thin woman!"

She handed Lily to a sailor who carried her down the ship's rope ladder and placed her in the tender that was bobbing on the bay. Swinging from side to side Jesssie manipulated the ladder, edged herself into the tender. The little boat made its way to shore.

2

At the waterfront she was almost overcome by the stench of stale fish, tea and cinnamon; but she felt at home with the throngs of men who were jamming the beach ready to start their journey overland, for it sounded like St. Louis in the early days, soft Spanish intermingled with the French patois, Indians and Negroes talking their own dialects, the American and English swearing at everybody in their haste to arrange for transportation. She thought with a smile, if one were going to be a world traveler, St. Louis was an ideal training ground.

Jessie and Lily and their baggage were to be transported up the first eight miles of the Chagres River in one of the deep-water boats with a number of Americans who had been wise enough to arrange for passage. Within two hours after landing she was on her way. The banks of the river were low and covered with jungle growth to the water's edge, where white and scarlet flowers rose from the tangled green. By midafternoon the chugging motor had covered the eight miles and swerved into shore; they had had no food, no tarpaulin to protect them from the fierce heat, no water which she felt safe in drinking, though they were painfully parched, no way to take care of their personal needs. She disembarked and was informed by the native boatman, in sign language, that they would be transferred to the narrow dugouts which were tied to the thick overhanging branches. Each of the dugouts was manned by naked Negroes and Indians. Jessie felt Lily's hand clutching her own.

"Don't be frightened by their noise," she reassured her, "they're laughing and yelling out of excitement. It is only a three-day voyage up the shallows, and then we will be out on the trail."

A man in uniform appeared in the clearing. He came to her and said, "I'm Captain Tucker; I received a letter that you were coming. I have the company's boat ready for you and your daughter. I'm sorry I can't go along; you will be the only woman aboard, but the native crew is reliable, they frequently carry my wife to company headquarters."

"You mean we won't have to travel in those dugouts?" asked Jessie, realizing how far her heart had sunk at the sight of the savages.

Captain Tucker laughed. "I don't blame you for your consternation. But I think we can keep you comfortable. The company has tent camps at regular intervals up the river and my carriers have informed them that you are coming. Will you get into the boat now; there is no time to lose if you are to make the first camp by nightfall."

She thanked him heartily. The Jamaica Negroes pushed out against the heavy current, poling slowly upstream while they chanted in rhythm. Sometimes they traveled in midstream where the sun was so hot it burned the skin like a fire, but more often they stayed close to the shore, gliding lazily under the arching trees and canopies of flowering vines. When they could go no further because of growths of jungle creeper, Jessie and her daughter would have to go ashore and sit in the midst of the dank green foliage while the boatmen jumped into the water and with their long knives cut a trail along the riverbank. Then they would come back for Jessie, and half pull, half push the boat through the clearing while their wild singings joined in with the screeches of the tropical jungle birds.

They made their first landing while the sun was still bright. In a small clearing a company tent with a wooden floor had been set up. She wondered why they had stopped so early, but she soon knew the answer, for night came upon them with the swiftness of a falling star. The native boys made a small fire outside the tent flaps as a protection against the animals and the deadly dews, then brought her some cooked food, but she preferred not to eat it, feeding Lily and herself a few cookies and an apple which she had brought from the ship. After the child had fallen asleep, Jessie lay awake in her narrow iron cot listening to the discordant night noises of the tropics, to what seemed an unceasing rush of sound all around the tent.

There was no sleep in her, for she was possessed by the irony that she whose husband had marked and broken more trails across the continent than any other living American should be denied the right to travel on one of them and be plunged instead into this aboriginal nightmare. All the time she had worked on the three reports, watched John's maps grow, she had had the intensest personal interest in each mile of the terrain, for she had always thought that she would one day travel these routes. She had not only been prepared over a number of years, but had been anxious to encounter the hazards of the covered wagon, the plains, the snow-bound mountain passes, the hostile Indians, the moisture-parched deserts; all these images and the attendant hardships had been part of her thoughts since she had been a child. Yet here she was set down in the midst of country and hardship which she had never anticipated, and for which she was in no way prepared. Here she was on the first real voyage of her life, traveling without husband or friend by her side, in country so fantastic that not even the Spanish explorers had done it descriptive justice. This was land upon which no one she had ever known had laid eyes or foot; for perhaps the thousandth time she recalled Mary Algood, sitting by her blue-painted Delaware wagon, about to set off on the Oregon Trail. If only John's eyes had seen this country, John's drawing pencil sketched its character, she would have felt more at home.

The next morning they were off at the crack of dawn, being poled up the stiff current. She told Lily stories of how the first white men who had invaded Peru had carried their loot down this very river on their way to the Atlantic Ocean and back to Spain. The banks were brilliant with white and scarlet perch flowers; the native boys jumped into the river to cool off or cut food from the bank, but Jessie and Lily suffered agonies of heat, hunger, thirst and the other pressures to which the body is heir.

The nights were dank with mist; the cries of sudden death in the jungle gave the journey a mortal aspect. She was grateful for the floored tents and cots; without this barest of protection she doubted their chances of continuing. Though she had sympathized with her husband's privations on the trail, she now realized that her sympathy had been cerebral; her husband had suffered from the cold while she was suffering from the heat, he had been victim to the sparseness of vegetation while she was oppressed by its lushness, yet now that she was experiencing these momentary tortures with her own flesh she at last had an intimation of the agonies that must have racked the body of John Frémont.

On the morning of the fourth day they reached Gorgona, a little settlement where they transferred from the shallow Chagres to the trail over the mountains. Though it was only eight in the morning the sun was like a knife under the eyelids. The alcalde was down at the landing beach to invite her to his home for breakfast. His house was built on stilts with a thatched roof of palm fronds and wattled sides. They had no sooner seated themselves at the rattan table than native boys brought in two big baking dishes and popped off the covers. Jessie let out an exclamation of horror, for in the big casserole there was something that resembled a child.

"Special for the honored guests," said the alcalde, his eyes gleaming while he rubbed his hands in anticipation. "Baked ring-tailed monkey and boiled iguana lizard."

Her stomach slowly seemed to rise to her throat. One look at Lily's face told her that the child would not be able to eat the monkey. They needed strength for the arduous three-day trip over the mountains. She remembered how John had preferred the pangs and weakness of hunger to eating a portion of their pet dog. She decided that her husband was more fastidious than she. To her daughter she murmured:

"Remember what Sam Weller used to say: 'Weal pie ware a good thing when you knew it waren't made of kittens.' "

They both ate a little of the monkey, but the lizard was too much for them. Then the alcalde took them to the clearing which marked the beginning of the mule track to Panama. Part of Jessie's baggage was placed on a mule, the rest of it on a cow which was to head the procession. To the chief baggageman she said, "Will you please put my daughter on a mule immediately in front of mine, and make sure the animal is kept there?"

"He stay dere, lady," laughed the baggageman. "No place to go else."

There were fifty mules, a half-dozen cows and thirty men in the caravan. The native leader gave a fierce whoop which was echoed up and down the line, the mules began to move beneath them. The track followed the contour of the mountains, up to the top of a hill and down again into the valley on the twenty-one-mile pilgrimage to Panama City. The mule steps that had been cut by hand into the mountainside were rarely more than four feet wide, and at the edge one looked down a thousand feet into jungle growth. Mango trees and alders were packed solid along the trail, topped by towering palms and cocoanuts. In spite of the intense glare of the tropical sun, it was dark under the green roof; Jessie kept looking upward to find a ray of sunlight toward the top of the branches, then a few steps more and it would be dark green again, with a sudden burst of rain falling down through the matted foliage. There were no bridges across the narrow streams; the mules jumped them, and several of the travelers were dumped head first into the water. She was thankful that both she and Lily were experienced riders, and was proud, as she rode behind the slender form of her daughter, at the way the child was withstanding their travels, the constantly changing temperatures, the strange sights, steady hours of movement, the hardships of hunger, heat and personal discomfort.

The first night they slept in a tent with a wooden floor, but on the second night there was only a filthy Indian hut. Jessie took two blankets out of her boxes, rolled Lily in one and herself in the other and slept the sleep of exhaustion, impervious to the lizards, snakes and hundreds of insects which crawled across them in the course of the night. The sunrise was glorious: from the mountain top she looked down into a sea of blossoms, and beyond she saw as Balboa had seen from this very peak before her the Pacific Ocean at her feet. She ardently wished that Tom Benton could be sharing with her this first view of the Pacific.

Several hours before the sixth nightfall they reached Panama City. The trail came out of the mountains some distance from the walled city, with its ancient cathedral. Her first sight of the cathedral roof and spire of inlaid mother-of-pearl made her think that she had fallen victim of the Chagres fever, after all. At the trail's end there were Indian carriers, one of whom took her on his back, and another Lily, and carried them over the shallow water of the bay and across the sand reef to the entrance of Panama City. She walked on the ancient roadway through the railed gate, entered the walled town with its weather-stained old houses and wide balconies leaning out so far they almost closed over the narrow passages. In the streets were trotting donkeys carrying bundles of leaves and water jars, dusky Indian women wearing a single white garment.

Instead of finding a sleepy little Spanish town with a few natives wandering the streets, she found the place a bedlam of stranded Americans, several hundred of them camping on the hillside above the city, others hustling and jostling through the streets. While waiting for the Indian carriers to bring her baggage to the Cathedral Square, from which point she would seek a hotel, she inquired of the group of Americans who were wearing the western garb she knew so well from St. Louis:

"Why are so many of you men here?"

A lean, gray-haired man in a leather jacket and buckskin pants stepped forward and said, "Ain't you heard the news, ma'am, the ship ain't coming back to Panama."

Stupefied, having visions of Lily and herself camping endlessly on the hills above Panama, she could only gasp: "Ship not coming back? But why? What do you mean?"

A young man dressed in a black business suit much the worse for wear replied, "Don't you know what's happened in California, ma'am? All the ships' crews have deserted and gone into the gold fields. The *California* was due a month ago, but it never got here."

She looked from face to face anxiously, then asked, "Deserted their ships?"

There was a moment of silence while the men looked at each other. Then everyone began talking at once. "Yes, ma'am! All the rumors was true! Millions of dollars' worth of gold! People picking it up on the mountainside in sacks! Getting rich overnight! Here we're rottin' in Panama City, and millions of dollars of gold laying all over California just waiting to be picked up."

The verification that there was gold in California meant little to her except that she and Lily would be marooned in Panama City. She asked the first man who had spoken, the gray-haired one, if he knew anything about the hotels in Panama. He assured her that they were vermin-infested, that there were no rooms anyway. Night was drawing on when she saw coming toward her a Spanish woman with white hair under a black mantilla. Trailing her were several native boys. She came to Jessie and said:

"I am Madame Arce, cousin of the American minister from New Granada, General Herran. He wrote to me that you were coming and told me of the many happy hours he had spent in your home in Washington. It is now my privilege to return that hospitality. Will you come with me, Madame Frémont?"

She followed Madame Arce across the square to a great barrack of a house with twenty-foot ceilings, and windows as big as barn doors. When she was led to her bedroom she found it furnished with a lounge covered in a blue damask, two hammocks, and crystal chandeliers with wax lights. Madame Arce made available to her a velvet-footed girl with a soft laugh, named Candelarias. Jessie's relief at being rescued was so great that she murmured to Lily, "Now I know how your father must have felt when he found that pass across the Sierras."

Madame Arce's house was a tropical version of Tom Benton's home overlooking the Mississippi, built around an enclosed patio, with the floors red-tiled. She stepped out onto the wide gallery which surrounded the house and overlooked the cathedral. A few moments later there was a knock at her door and Candelarias asked if she would like to have a bath before dinner. Jessie called to Lily and they walked to an outside bathhouse much like her father's shower on C Street, for on a high ledge there were containers, ranging from small vases to four-foot-high jars filled with water from the well. The smaller jars were dumped on them by three grinning young girls, then the larger jars were overturned as they became accustomed to the coldness of the water.

The days passed, a week, two weeks, three weeks. Jessie spent many hours with Madame Arce in the coolness of the back garden speaking in the Spanish they both loved, walking along the ramparts of the old town at sunset and watching the twenty-foot tide crashing over the reefs. In the evening she strolled about the Cathedral Square talking to the men whom she knew from her own ship and those with whom she had become acquainted during her first hour in Panama. They were growing more desperate with each passing day. There was no food to be bought, they were living on the salted foods they had carried with them, and death from disease was an everyday occurrence in the camps that dotted the hillsides.

A month passed and still there was no ship and no news of any; the men were becoming frightened that they would all die here in Panama, that there would be no chance for them to escape.

Jessie was well cared for, yet she too was growing uneasy. There had been no word from John since he had left her side that early morning on the Delaware Indian Reservation. Some five months had passed since then; if all had gone well, her husband and his party should be safely in San Francisco. He would be waiting for her, scanning the sea for her arrival. He would be fearful lest she had encountered difficulties, or had been too delicate to withstand the rigors of Panama, where strong men were stricken and died within a few hours. She knew the heartbreak of worrying about a loved one; that had been her lot over the years; she did not want her husband to undergo this slow torture. And yet there was nothing she could do but sit and wait and let the days succeed each other as painlessly as possible.

3

The rainy season came down like a thunderclap, filling the streets of the little town as though they were shallow pools. Madame Arce's house was wet, the floors, ceilings wet; lanes of damp ooze trickled down the twenty-foot walls, while outside the rains filled the air with sickening inhalations. Jessie caught cold, and with it a racking cough. Madame Arce insisted that she remain in bed, while Candelarias kept a fire lighted in the room in a vain attempt to dry out the walls. She lay in the hammock, her dreams shattered by grotesque pictures of screaming, naked savages dancing around her, taunting her with being a fine lady, the hallucinations dissolving into pictures of the snow-locked Sierras where freezing men fell forward into the snow.

Another month passed, and then one night she was awakened by the booming of a cannon which told her, even as the noise tore her from her dream, that an American ship had arrived. She rushed out on the balcony to behold a wild scene. It was a bright moonlight night and every trail leading down from the hills was filled with singing and shouting Americans who were crying out with joy as they hurried toward the ramparts. The Indians too had been awakened, and they were singing and dancing in sympathy. On the balcony of every house were shrouded figures in their night clothes watching the scene. Even before she could return to her room to begin dressing and packing, there was another boom from a cannon; a second American ship had dropped anchor in the harbor.

Breathlessly she dressed Lily and herself, began throwing clothes into her suitcases, then went out on the balcony again to search for the ship as the light of day began to filter through. She saw a man in the uniform of the United States Navy stride across the square. She rushed down the patio stairs, across the red tile, and threw open the heavy door. With a glad cry she grasped the hand of Lieutenant Fitzhugh Beale, who had been a friend of Colonel Frémont's in California, fought with him in the conquest, testified for him at the court-martial and been their guest in the Benton home in Washington.

"Ah, Mrs. Frémont!" he cried. "I had surmised you were stranded here, waiting for the *California*. I've just come down on her, with naval dispatches and samples of gold dust."

"Have you heard news of Colonel Frémont?"

"No."

She led him to the back garden, then told him of her voyage while he sipped a warm drink. Lieutenant Beale was blue-eyed, blond, about thirty, with a long, horselike face. He loved danger and movement and an ever changing panorama: a congenital bachelor, he had been at sea since he was twelve; among his intimates he was known as "Beale of the steady hands and wandering feet." Jessie saw that he was uneasy, that he had something to tell her. He asked permission to light a cigar, gazing at the burnt match for a moment before speaking.

"I must hurry on to Chagres and deliver my papers to the next ship leaving for New York. Every possible facility has been given me to make the Panama crossing as quickly and easily as possible. Mrs. Frémont, you look ill; I don't think you should expose yourself to more hardship. I urge you to return to Chagres with me; there will be a fast ship for New York, and I will arrange for you to be taken care of."

Her thoughts colliding, she asked:

"But why should I return to New York now, when there is a ship to take me to San Francisco?"

"Mrs. Frémont, San Francisco has gone crazy wild. The original settlers have rushed off for the gold fields; the new arrivals are insane with excitement to get away and find their millions in gold. The hotels are dirty and cold and jammed, there is no help to be had except Indians and Chinese, and people will tell you that their time is worth fifty dollars a minute. San Francisco isn't a town, it isn't even a village, it's just a settlement of delirious maniacs living in shanties and knock-together cabins, waiting for the moment when they can get away to the gold fields. There is no water, no adequate food, no sanitary equipment. The streets are flowing mud streams impossible to cross. Why, I have seen men try to pave them with bales of cotton and bags of flour. There is no lumber available, no brick or stone, nothing with which you and the colonel could build a house. The shanty towns are full of fever and cholera, and the death rate is terrifying. Mrs. Frémont, I beg you not to risk arriving alone in the hysterical hamlet; there can't be more than two or three white women there."

She watched the young lieutenant puff animatedly on his cigar, feeling a familiar paralyzing fear clutch at her heart.

"Please tell me the news, Lieutenant Beale," she murmured. "You said that you had not heard from Colonel Frémont."

The lieutenant took the cigar out of his mouth. "It is true, I have not heard from him. But I have heard about him. There has been trouble, Mrs. Frémont. Your husband's expedition never got over the Rockies. The fur traders and the Indians warned them not to go in, told them that the snow and the cold had never been so intense, that it was impossible to cross the Rockies at that point. But Colonel Frémont insisted. He said there must be a pass on the thirty-eighth parallel . . . and he ran into the most impenetrable part of the Rockies, in the worst winter within the memory of anyone who knows that country."

Her body as cold as though she herself had plunged into the frozen Rockies, she asked, "My husband, is he safe?"

After a barely imperceptible pause, Lieutenant Beale replied, "We don't know. The colonel engaged Bill Williams to guide him. Williams wanted to take a southerly route, but your husband felt that would defeat the purpose of the expedition, that he had to find a central pass for the railroad. The colonel and Williams quarreled; they never found a pass. They pushed deeper and deeper into the snows until they could go no farther. Then they turned back . . . they lost their mules and supplies . . . The men began to die along the trail . . ."

"But my husband. What about Colonel Frémont?"

His head down, Lieutenant Beale repeated, "We don't know, Miss Jessie."

"Some of the party must have gotten out. Else how would you know?"

"The colonel sent out a relief party with Williams, Brackenridge, King and Creutzfeldt to get help in New Mexico and rush it back. King starved to death, but Williams, Brackenridge and Creutzfeldt got through. From them we learned about the disaster to the expedition."

Twisting her lace handkerchief between her taut fingers, Jessie cried, "If the relief party got out, then surely they must have sent back supplies. The rest of the men must be safe?"

Lieutenant Beale shook his head slowly. "The three men were almost dead before they reached a settlement. They did not have the strength to take back relief, and there was no one at the settlement who could go into the mountains. A runner carried the news to Kit Carson at Taos, but it would have taken too long for Carson to organize relief and get up into the Rockies. The rest of the expedition would have had to get out on its own resources."

"Then there is no word about Colonel Frémont?"

"None."

"He was still alive when the Williams party was sent out for relief?"

"It was the colonel who sent them."

"What was his condition then?"

"His leg was badly frozen."

"There has been no word from anybody left in the mountains?"

"None. Williams says they could not have lived more than a few days . . ."

She stalked agitatedly about the patio.

"My husband could not have perished in the snows! He faced greater hardships when he crossed the Sierras in '44. If Williams could get out with a relief party, then Colonel Frémont can get out with the rest of the expedition. Neither the snows nor the mountains could ever kill him. There is no man in the world better equipped to survive . . ."

Lieutenant Beale put his arm about her.

"The expedition is ended, Miss Jessie; the equipment was abandoned, no one got over the mountains and no one got through to California. Those who survived are returning east to St. Louis. If Colonel Frémont came out of the Rockies, he will be in St. Louis by now. I have made all arrangements to take you back across Panama. There are merchantmen in the harbor at Chagres; they will not be leaving before we reach there. Miss Jessie, I want you to pack your things and return with me. I will put you on a ship for New York."

Pale now, and coughing, she faced Lieutenant Beale determinedly. "You believe that my husband is dead?"

He did not answer.

"No, don't be afraid for me. I have gone through this before. Tell me if you think there is any chance that my husband is alive."

When Lieutenant Beale could not garner the courage to speak, she said, "Very well, you think he is dead."

He took her hand between his. "Please prepare to leave with me for Chagres. You will be in New York almost by the time your husband is in St. Louis. Within a few weeks you will be reunited."

Though he maintained that the reason he wanted her to leave was that her husband would have returned east, she knew that his real reason was that he believed she was going on to San Francisco to meet a man who was buried in the glacial snows of the highest Rockies.

"I thank you for your kindness, Lieutenant; I know how much you have my interest at heart; but you are mistaken. Colonel Frémont must be in San Francisco by now; he will be waiting; I promised I would meet him there."

He bowed. "Please think it over, Miss Jessie."

After he had left she sat rocking in a chair. So the fourth expedition had failed! For her own part she did not suffer too greatly over the failure: the men had met insuperable obstacles, that was all; they had done their best, but it had not been enough in the face of the unscalable Rockies. But how would John take it: the loss of the money that his admirers in St. Louis had invested, the loss of his opportunity to re-establish himself as an explorer and trail blazer? Would he not consider it a matter of personal inadequacy, count the failure his own, be stricken by it? Would he not fear the criticism and the disgrace of having some of the men perish under his leadership? Would this make it impossible for him ever to start out again?

And here again was the phantom of her husband's death. She could believe it this time no more than the last, but in the closeness of the warm spring morning she was gripped by the terrifying realization that John might have been seriously injured. Bill Williams had reported him suffering from a badly frozen leg. The mules had frozen to death or been killed for food; there was no way for him to come down the vastness of the Rockies except on his own feet, for his men would be too weak to carry him. What then if he could no longer drag that frozen leg? He was not stronger than the forces of nature: because he had forced the Sierras, there was no reason to believe he was an imperishable one.

Her mind would not allow her to conceive that her beloved was dead, yet there might be no way for him to get through to California. He would return to St. Louis or Washington to recoup his health. By what token should she go up to San Francisco, pestilential mudhole caught in the hysteria of the gold rush, where she had neither friend nor relative, where she would be alone with her daughter, with no place to go and nothing to do, and no husband to meet her?

She was so homesick that the tears coursed unrestrainedly down her cheeks. Would anyone blame her if she let herself be persuaded that there was no sense in going on to San Francisco? True, she had promised to meet her husband there; but if he had been unable to reach San Francisco, if he were even now on his way to St. Louis, what possible sense could there be in her going on? Why persist in this cruel voyage? They would have no way of communicating with each other, to tell whether she should once more take ship to Panama, or whether John would come overland in the summer to join her. The best that could happen would be confusion and heartbreak and more months of separation.

She got out of the chair and walked upstairs to the balcony. The cooler air refreshed her a little. The Cathedral Square was abandoned but the spire gleamed with oriental splendor. And standing there, feeling desperately alone, wanting her husband's arms about her as she had never wanted them before, not even in the darkest hours in St. Louis when everyone had thought he was dead, she knew that she could not return to New York. She had not said, "I'll meet you in San Francisco if circumstances permit," or "providing I'm sure you will be there to meet me," or "if I can make it." She had made a categorical promise, and promises were made to be kept, the hard ones as well as the easy ones. If she kept this promise, under these almost unendurable circumstances, then not only would John know that she always would keep her promises, but even more important, she herself would know that she could keep them.

4

She finished her packing. Madame Arce came to her bedroom to express her happiness that she would at last go on to her own country and her own people. Jessie embraced the older woman, murmuring softly, "If not for you I might have died here. How am I to repay your kindness?"

Madame Arce replied, smiling, "In the Spanish language we do not have the word repay."

They were still murmuring gracious words to each other when another clamor arose in the town. A new party of Americans had just come off the trail from Chagres. With them had arrived a carefully guarded United States mail sack, its destination San Francisco. A portion of the mail would surely be addressed to the Americans who had been detained in Panama City these several months.

The head baggageman turned the sack over to the American representative in Panama City, a Central American consul who had no authority to do otherwise than to deliver it to the first ship headed north for San Francisco. When the Americans learned that mail had come in they thronged the official's office demanding that he open the pouch. Jessie rushed through the courtyard to join the excited group in front of the consul's office. The consul kept repeating, "I decline to usurp functions. It is locked. It cannot be opened until it reaches San Francisco. Do you not see it is marked, 'Destination San Francisco'? I have no authority . . ."

The Americans had no intention of waiting several weeks for news of their families while the locked mail sack accompanied them to San Francisco. "We'll take the responsibility!" they shouted. "We'll sign a petition! Every last one of us will sign for his letter!"

If John had come down from the mountains alive there would be a letter from him in that sack. She was positive the letter was there, and she was determined to have it. She pushed her way through the crowd. The men cried, "Here's Mrs. Frémont! She wants news of the colonel. Open that blasted sack and give us our mail."

The consul took one last look at the men's faces, then gazed into Jessie's eyes and said quickly, "Very well, but I do not take responsibility. I do not cut open this sack! You must appoint a committee and the committee must take responsibility."

The pouch was torn open before the consul had his last words out. Someone cried, "For you, Mrs. Frémont!" With tears half blinding her, Jessie saw that she had a fat envelope from Taos addressed in her husband's handwriting, another from her father in Washington. She stumbled across the square, ran up the patio stairs, tore open John's envelope and read:

Taos, New Mexico
January 27, 1849

MY VERY DEAR WIFE:

I write to you from the house of our good friend Kit Carson. This morning a cup of chocolate was brought to me, while yet in bed. While in the enjoyment of this luxury, I pleased myself in imagining how gratified you would be in picturing me here in Kit's care, whom you will fancy constantly endeavoring to make me comfortable . . .

She could read no further, for tears were falling on the familiar and dearly beloved handwriting. He was safe! He had not perished in the snows! If she had yielded to her own weakness, if she had given in to the persuasiveness of Lieutenant Beale, she would have passed this mail sack on the trail to Gorgona, she would not have known that her husband was alive until she had reached New York.

She stretched out on the lounge and buried her face in the damask, unable to think or read, knowing only overwhelming relief at his safety. After some time she picked up the letter again. There were ten tightly packed pages of handwriting, for John had put them into journal form, making his letter to her serve as a record of the harrowing and tragic events of the fourth expedition. She paled as she read on: eleven men had perished out of the thirty-three, died of cold and hunger and insanity on the trail; those who had been saved had emerged as emaciated shadows, half out of their minds with grief and suffering. Everyone in the party was blaming, criticizing and hating everyone else; John blamed Williams for the tragedy; Williams blamed John for interference, for guiding the party into hopeless tracks. John was blamed for ordering the men to try to save the baggage instead of themselves, an act which had cost perhaps nine lives; Williams was accused of cannibalism while on his way out with the relief party. Both men were blamed for not having gone back to save the balance of the party after they had made their way out. John's own life had been saved only by meeting the son of an Indian chief with whom he had been friends years before. He had reached Kit Carson's home unable to drag his leg behind him, a scarecrow, sick in body and despairing of heart.

Yet in spite of his misfortunes, he ended the letter on a cheerful note, saying that he did not consider the expedition a failure, for he had learned much about that mountainous region, was convinced that a railroad pass could be found close by, and that he would one day find it under more favorable circumstances.

When I think of you, I feel a warm glow at my heart, which renovates it like a good medicine, and I forget painful feelings in strong hope for the future. We shall yet, dearest wife, enjoy quiet and happiness together—these are nearly one and the same to me now. I make frequently pleasant pictures of the happy home we are to have, and oftenest and among the pleasantest of all I see our library with its bright fire in the rainy stormy days, and the large windows looking out upon the sea in the bright weather. I have it all planned in my own mind.

She had been right, she thought exultantly. She had kept her pledge and they would meet in San Francisco!

But when? He had written this letter while in bed, unable to move about; there was no way for him to get to California except on foot or horseback, and he could not risk the hazardous journey until he was strong again. How long might that be? Perhaps months. Perhaps never! She had known frontiersmen whose legs had been frozen, and who had lost them. If John's leg did not heal he would need medical care; if it could not be provided in Taos, Kit Carson would have to take him back to St. Louis for hospitalization. Yes, she would meet her husband in San Francisco; but when?

She opened the letter from her father; in it he told her the bad news of the expedition, including an article he had written for the eastern papers. He told her how ill her husband was in Taos, how badly his leg and side had been affected. He was altogether certain there would be no way for John to make the crossing to California without seriously endangering his life. He told his daughter that he was sending dispatches to Taos urging John to return to St. Louis as fast as his health would permit; and he now urged his daughter with equal vehemence to return to New York, whence she could go to St. Louis to join her husband.

Jessie put aside the letter and stared at the high ceiling of Madame Arce's bedroom; yes, her father would urge John to return to St. Louis, just as Lieutenant Beale had urged her to return to New York. Sick as she was, she had refused to turn back; sick as he might be, John would refuse to turn back.

A sailor from the S.S. *Panama* knocked at Madame Arce's door to inform them that the captain wanted Mrs. Frémont and her daughter to come aboard. Two Indian boys carried her luggage to the waterfront. She was rowed in a small boat to the ship and then hauled up to the deck in a wooden tub suspended by ropes at the end of a boom. Captain Schenck welcomed her. The S.S. *Panama* had returned to New York after leaving Jessie at Chagres, and had now come around the Cape with another shipload of voyagers for California. As she gazed at the hundreds of Americans crowded into every spare inch, she asked, "Where will all of us stay?"

"I don't know, Madame Frémont," replied the captain, with a wistful smile. "But we dare not refuse anyone as long as there is standing room."

Within a few hours both the S.S. *Panama* and the S.S. *California* set sail for San Francisco. Jessie's ship, which had cabin accommodations for eighty passengers, carried four hundred men. There was no cabin available, but Captain Schenck put two iron cots under the spanker boom, covering the space with a large American flag. Everyone was so happy to be en route to San Francisco that no one complained, theatricals were performed on deck, Jessie and the passengers exchanged the few books in their possession, reading aloud in the clear sunshine off the coast of Mexico.

She was delighted to meet several companionable American women, chief among them Mrs. Matilda Gray, a youngish but matronly soul who was going out to San Francisco to join her husband; and Mrs. William Gwin, one of Louisiana's most famous hostesses. Her husband was William McK. Gwin, with a leonine head topping his superb six-foot-two figure, the voice of the professional orator, the carriage of the politician. Gwin's father had fought with Tom Benton in the War of 1812 and the families had been acquainted ever since; Gwin had no hesitancy in speaking frankly to Jessie. He had a great deal of political experience, having been a congressman from Mississippi.

"I left the most lucrative political job in the United States to migrate to California," he said. "Within a year I'll be back in Washington as the first senator from the new state."

Jessie felt a sense of amused shock, as though someone had read her thoughts aloud in public meeting.

"You seem quite certain of that, Mr. Gwin."

"I am not the only one," boomed Gwin. "Before I left Washington I told Stephen A. Douglas that by this time next year I would ask him to present my credentials to the Senate. Douglas exclaimed, 'God bless you, I believe you will.'"

To herself Jessie said, I can believe that, too; but there are only two senators from a state; how many men are headed for California with that identical ambition in mind?

When the ship reached San Diego she put Lily in the care of Mrs. Gray and locked herself in the other woman's cabin, fearful of the news that was coming, unwilling to be seen when she received it. Above the noise and shouts of the passengers who were disembarking at San Diego she heard the sound of running feet, then someone pounded on her door and a man cried, "Mrs. Frémont, the colonel's safe; he's riding up to San Francisco to meet you! He didn't lose his leg, only a bad frostbite."

Jessie unlocked the door and flung it open.

"Are you sure?" she cried.

"Yes, ma'am! He was here only a few days ago."

The last two days at sea passed swiftly in the anticipation of being reunited with her husband. On the morning of June 4 the S.S. *Panama* swung eastward toward shore. As she moved through the Golden Gate Strait into the bay, with the sandy beaches of San Francisco to the south and the rocky promontories and little islands to the north, Jessie had the impression that this channel in the curvilineal coast of California was not a strait at all, but rather a canal leading into the fertile womb of the bay, with the ship carrying the seeds of men, machinery, tools and ideas to give birth to a new civilization.

Anchored in the bay were a number of ships, their wooden masts standing up bare as winter orchards, several of them abandoned. She could see a small level square flying the flag of the California Republic, and around the sides a few wooden buildings. For the rest, there was little but unpainted shacks and cabins and miners' tents dotting the hills which rose immediately back of the square. The S.S. *Panama* fired a salvo of guns to inform San Francisco that she had arrived. A heavy anchor was dropped, and Jessie watched a number of small boats being rowed out to meet them. Once again she and Lily climbed down the side of a rope ladder and were rowed to shore. Since there was no place for the small boats to dock, the sailors had to carry them over the surf. There were hundreds of men on the beach, many of them shouting words of welcome. The cold and the fog set Jessie coughing again. She was glad this was the end of the voyage: she would need the comforts of her own home and the protection of her husband to nurse her back to vigor after the grueling months.

But as she stood uncertainly at the edge of the surf and then walked up among the red-shirted, bearded men, she caught no sight of John. Once again her heart sank. He had not yet arrived in San Francisco. She was here alone. Perhaps he had not reached California at all, and the reports in San Diego had been merely encouragement by kind-hearted men. As she stood on the edge of Portsmouth Square holding Lily by one hand, Mrs. Gray came to her side.

"Never you mind, dearie," she said, "the colonel's been delayed a day or two. This is my husband; Harry, meet Mrs. Frémont. Let us take you to the Parker House."

Appreciating the kindness, Jessie let Mr. and Mrs. Gray lead her to a hotel room at the Parker House and light a fire in the grate. The Grays took Lily for a walk to see the little mining village while Jessie slept soundly, awakening after dark to the clamor of men's voices. By looking out the window she saw that she was next door to the Eldorado gambling hall and that a brawl was apparently in process. She lay down on the bed again, but a few minutes later Mrs. Gray returned with Lily and a tray of food.

For five days she remained in bed, the cough she had contracted in Panama growing increasingly worse. From the conversation outside her window and from the information vouchsafed by her few visitors, she learned that San Francisco was almost deserted, that everyone had spent whatever money he had for supplies and miners' tools and rushed to the gold fields. Aside from the small amount of trade and the gambling casinos where the men spent the night in order to keep warm, there was no life in San Francisco. As a community it had hardly been born. She thought how greatly her father would have enjoyed this rawness, and was shamed that she could not be more wholeheartedly her father's daughter.

She had grown thin again, her King George's Mark throbbed unceasingly. There were several men in town who knew Colonel Frémont from Washington or his expeditions, and they made sure she had sufficient food and firewood for the grate. They kept assuring her that her husband would arrive any hour, but with the passage of the days she realized that although the trip from San Diego was a long and hard one by horseback, and the weather had been bad, if John had been there he would have had plenty of time to reach San Francisco by now.

There were days of heavy rains, converting the earthen surface of Portsmouth Square into a muddy bog. The nights were bitterly cold, for a penetrating wind came over the bay, seeping through the walls and the ill-fitted windows of the hastily constructed hotel. The brushwood fagots smoked, making her eyes smart, and she and Lily lay huddled in the narrow iron bed, comforting each other with hopeful words and bodily warmth. This cold, bare shacklike room was her first home and her first hearth in California. She wondered if her grandmother Benton had lived thus with her children when she had first reached Tennessee; she wondered if her grandmother had suffered the despair that was gnawing at her own heart. If only she could be sleeping on the hard cold ground of the Santa Cruz ranch, for that would be her own land and her home, and the open campfire would be a truer hearth than this acridly smoking grate which choked their lungs even while it warmed their flesh.

At dusk of the tenth day as she was sitting before the fire, her thin hands clasped in her lap, she heard men's voices outside her window. Someone cried, "Your wife's inside the house, Colonel." She moved out of the chair to open the door. Before she could do so, it was flung open and John had taken her in his arms and was crushing her against him.

Neither could speak. He led her back to her chair, threw some fresh fagots on the fire, then sat on the floor by her side holding her two hands in his, gazing up at her.

"You have been ill; you are ill now, my darling."

"No . . ."

The door opened and Lily entered. John embraced his daughter, then took her on his knee. Lily said, sober-faced:

"You didn't come. Mother almost died. A lady downstairs says she will die."

He rose before Jessie, put his arms about her waist and gazed into her face. His eyes were dark, self-accusing. She ran her fingers lightly through his long gray hair, then laid her cheek on his.

"In her innocence, Lily is partly right. Being away from you is a kind of a death. Only with you am I fully alive and well."

5

The next morning she propped a small mirror against a straightbacked chair and sat before it combing out her hair and massaging her face, interested in her appearance for the first time in months. John brought a breakfast of hot coffee and bread up to the room, then left for the office of the American consul to pick up the deed to the Santa Cruz ranch which had been deposited there by Consul Larkin of Monterey. Several hours passed before she heard his footsteps in the hall; her quick ear perceived that something was wrong: this was not the fast springy step of her husband who could not bear to move slowly; this was the plodding step of a man who had suffered a blow. She seized this last instant to tie a blue ribbon about her hair with a small bow on top and to cast a quick look at her blue quilted robe in the pocket mirror. She forced a smile to her face.

"John, what has happened?"

He did not answer for a moment, then said:

"Larkin didn't get our ranch."

She waited for him to continue, but when he did not, she demanded, "Didn't buy . . . ? But he's had a full year."

"He bought all right," John moaned, "but not the magnificent ranch with the beautiful vines and orchards that I told him to acquire; he used our three thousand dollars to buy a wild tract of land somewhere up in the mountains called the Mariposa." He took an official-looking document from his inside coat pocket and flung it angrily on the bed. "The Mariposa," he repeated, "several hundred miles from here, a hundred miles from the ocean or the nearest settlement, high up in the Sierras, impossible to farm, overrun with Indians, so we couldn't even set up a cattle ranch . . ."

She picked up the document from the bed, opened it and gazed unseeing at the title grant. "But what does it mean?" she asked. "You didn't tell Larkin to buy the Mariposa. You told him to buy the Santa Cruz ranch. Is it possible that he confused your orders?"

"No, no! When I handed him the three thousand dollars I gave him written instructions. He had been over the land with me. There was no possibility of an error." He jumped up from his chair, striding about the cramped little room. "I'll have to borrow a horse and ride down to Monterey."

"Is the Santa Cruz ranch still available?" asked Jessie. "Has no one else bought it?"

John's eyes fell. "Our consul thinks the land has been sold. He has heard . . . Jessie, it's just coming to me. Larkin must have bought that land for himself!"

"But if that's the case, John, we can sue him; we can recover, it's a fraudulent transaction."

"How? This is not the United States. This is still the Republic of California. They have no courts, no legal system, no judges, no police. It's the law of the frontier. Every man for himself . . ."

Shrewdly she asked, "Who was the previous owner of the Mariposa? Did Larkin own it, or did he buy it from someone else?"

John took the deed from her hand, glanced at it and replied, "According to this paper, Larkin bought the Mariposa from former governor Alvarado of California, who had been given it in a grant from Spain. It's a vast tract of mountains and valleys, freezing cold in winter; no one can live there. What good is a lot of land if it's valueless?"

She put her fingers lightly on his shoulder.

"I shall loathe being left here alone again, but there can be no doubt that you must see Larkin. We want either our land or our three thousand dollars!"

It had always been their intention that John should play a role in making California a state. But how could he do this if he suddenly were deprived of his property, if he were without a means of livelihood or position to buttress him? She did not want him to be known as a former explorer; that would be doubly unfortunate since the failure of his fourth expedition. In order to play a full-voiced part in the forming of the state, to be elected senator, he must be important in California while the state was being founded. But what was this job to be? Even now the delegates of the Constitutional Convention were being elected; William Gwin had thrown his hat into the ring while he was still wading ashore. John would have to move fast if he wanted to be sent to Monterey as a delegate.

She was awakened one night by a clangor in front of the hotel and saw that the sky outside her window was vividly red. The warehouse on the waterfront, where her trunks and heavy boxes were stored, was in flames. It burned all night; all night she sat by the window in her robe watching the last of her possessions go up in smoke: her clothing, her linens, blankets, books, silver, ornaments, beautiful and familiar things she had brought to make herself a home in California. First they had lost the Santa Cruz ranch, and now her only possessions were those in her small suitcases in the hotel room. Fortunately she had her money box with her; these gold coins were her last link to family and security. When they were gone, they would really be pioneers, starting from scratch like everyone around them.

John returned to the hotel after five days to tell her of his interview with Larkin.

"There's something strange about the entire transaction," he said with a baffled expression. "Thomas Larkin was always straightforward and honest, a shrewd Yankee trader, but one to be trusted. Now his answers are evasive . . ."

"But does he admit he took the three thousand dollars? Does he acknowledge that you instructed him to buy the Santa Cruz ranch?"

"Yes, he acknowledges all that, but he has a hundred strange reasons for what he did; reports came to him that the Santa Cruz soil wasn't good; he didn't think I wanted to be a farmer; he had a chance to buy the Mariposa from Alvarado and thought I would prefer to live in the mountains, since I loved them so much; he thought I would rather be a cattle rancher; he felt that he had the right to use his own judgment in my best interests."

"How much does he say he paid for the Mariposa?"

"The same three thousand dollars."

"Did you tell him we want either our land or our money?"

"Yes. He said it was impossible, that I had appointed him as my agent, with discretionary powers, and I had to accept the results of his judgment. He was sorry if I was disappointed, but . . ."

They sat in silence in the mean little room, the future staring them down. She knew that John was grieving mostly over the loss of the beautiful ranch and his opportunity to earn a living as a farmer. For her the blow was of a different and more subtle nature: she had been deprived of her opportunity to create a home. Perhaps the gods were not only slow to consecrate a new hearth, but actually reluctant to see one laid. If Consul Larkin had bought any piece of land other than the Mariposa, even though it might have been inferior to the Santa Cruz ranch, she would not have felt so bad, for they still would have had their chance to make a home place. But the Mariposa was wild and frozen mountainous country, overrun by hostile Indians; it would be impossible for them to settle there.

What were they to do next? John was not the kind to grasp a pick and basin and rush to the gold fields; nor was there any business he could enter into in San Francisco. Perhaps in time he might receive a government appointment, but that was months off. She had brought with her one thousand dollars in gold loaned to her by her father to buy lumber and farm equipment, but her husband had borrowed twice that sum in Taos in order to bring the remnants of his party through to California.

"What do you think we ought to do?" she asked, curled up crossways on the bed. He too curled himself across the bed, running his fingers gently over her sunken cheeks.

"I'm sorry you got the starved-cat wife again, John."

"I'll confess I was hoping to find the bumpy one."

"Be patient, my dear."

"You asked what we should do first," he cried. "We are going to cure that cold of yours and get some weight back on you. I'm going to show you the beauties of California: all you've seen so far is this mudhole, but down on the peninsula there are bright sunshine and rolling hills and lovely valleys. I'm going to take you where it's warm and the countryside is beautiful. When we have had a month's vacation, we will face the future."

She snuggled closer into his arms, murmured, "Thank you, darling. But shouldn't you spend that month campaigning? The elected delegates are to meet in Monterey in September to adopt a constitution."

He had a way of welding firmness with tenderness. "My first task is to nurse you back to health. You are more important to me than politics. Besides, I'm not . . . I'm not a campaigner. Most of the people in the state know me, or know of me. There's little I could say from a stump that they don't already know."

Her mind went back to the spring evening in the summerhouse on C Street when Tom Benton had perceived that his daughter was in love with Lieutenant Frémont. John had said, "I am not much interested in politics."

"But surely you want to participate in the Constitutional Convention?"

"Not as a delegate. As a friend and adviser of the delegates, as an influence behind the scenes. I think I can do more good that way."

She did not see how, but she thought it wiser not to press the point. Instead she closed her eyes to embrace the vision of a month of leisure in warmth and beauty, with her husband at her side.

Gregorio, an Indian boy who had stuck with John through the worst rigors of the cold and starvation and had accompanied him from Taos, joined them on their trip down the peninsula. Also old Knight, who had been with John on an earlier expedition and was one of the sharpest frontiersmen of the West.

The following morning John disappeared early, telling her to be in front of the Parker House in an hour. Jessie dressed in her black silk, with the silk bonnet that matched. She did not think it a proper costume in which to go camping, but it was the only one she had left. After an hour she and Lily went down to the entrance of the Parker House. Within a few moments her husband came driving across Portsmouth Square in a six-seated surrey, the first she had seen in California. John whoaed the horses, jumped out and helped his wife into the new and luxurious interior, with its upholstered cushions of Spanish leather, compartments for storage of suitcases and foodstuffs.

"Where ever did you find this in San Francisco?" she asked in awe, caressing the beautiful upholstery.

"I had it made for you in New Jersey before I left. It's been standing here in a storehouse for two months. It's guaranteed to ride as smooth as a boat, and look, it has reversible seats that make a bed. You can sleep in here as comfortably as you would at home. Lily will have plenty of space in this large boot to stretch out."

"Oh, darling," she murmured, "this is the first piece of good luck we've had in California."

"There's another piece of good luck waiting around the corner, afraid to come to you, but I have convinced him that all is forgiven."

Jessie saw Lieutenant Beale come striding toward her with a sheepish grin on his long face. He said, "Madame Frémont, I am a fool! I do not deserve your forgiveness! If you had followed my wretched advice you would now be in the East while your husband would be here. When I think how hard I tried to persuade you . . ."

"These are things that only women understand, Lieutenant," she replied gaily. "There's nothing to forgive; I was touched by your concern for me in Panama."

"Then may we take him along on our junket?" asked her husband. "He makes an excellent *pot-au-feu* when he doesn't throw too much pepper into it; and he's the one who begged, borrowed or stole these beautiful white horses."

They followed the trail down the peninsula, leaving behind the fog and cold of San Francisco, and within a couple of hours had emerged into warm clear sunlight, with the ripe fields of oats moving gently on the hillsides, and the wild cattle grazing under the trees. The countryside was like a park with mile after mile of beautiful grasses, wild flowers and magnificent trees. When the air grew a little cool, John threw his faded blue army cape over her shoulders.

They made camp in midafternoon by the side of a brook. While Jessie refreshed herself and Lily in the cold water the men rode off in search of a neighboring ranch house, returning with half a sheep and some fresh corn which they barbecued over live coals of the fire. The Morocco carriage cushions were piled in front of the fire for Jessie and Lily, who ate their meat from the ends of long twigs. John had brought along claret and tea and a box of French bonbons for Lily. Under the deepening cloudless sky the air was soft and warm. Supper was finished by dusk. Fresh logs were put on the fire, the men began telling stories of other camps on the frontiers of South America, the Orient, and this wide American continent. Gregorio told of his childhood with the Indian tribe. Beale told sea stories and little jokes to make Jessie laugh. Old Knight, tall and gnarled as a mountain pine, ageless, with a long white beard which seemed somehow transplanted from his bald and shiny head, spun yarns of the days when the frontier had been only a hundred miles west of Washington.

As the night skies deepened, the campfire lighted the trees and brook, then the stars came out and to Jessie it was a scene of great beauty. This is my first hearth, she said to herself, just the kind we should have in a new country. May all of my hearths be as serene.

By nine o'clock she and Lily were comfortably settled in the carriage. The men had tied their hammocks to the trees and fallen asleep. Jessie listened to the crackling of the logs on the fire, the mules munching their wild oats, the half-muted cry of a coyote who had not the courage to come in and steal her supper. At dawn John awakened her with a cup of hot tea, then made a dressing tent for her by the side of the brook from a pair of blankets. She took her tin basin, towels, French soap and cologne to the running water, scrubbed Lily and then gave herself a leisurely bath. A doctor might have told her that bathing in a cold stream at dawn was dangerous; they had told that to her father forty years before. By the time she had dressed and returned to the campfire the carriage was ready, with most of the gear packed. After a cup of tea and a couple of old Knight's hot muffins, she said to John:

"Now what is my share of the duties?"

"To eat with all the appetite you can gather, to be happy."

"That's all, no work?"

"No work," replied the men. "This is your holiday. Women are useless on the trail, anyway."

The sun was bright and warm when they started toward San José. There weren't any roads, but the sturdily built carriage could go anywhere that wheels could go, and so they drove through the dry fertile valleys, climbed up the hills to overlook the ocean, followed bridle paths among the pines ever southward into warmer country, the men holding back the carriage with their riatas on steep grades. Knight and Gregorio would walk ahead of the two packmules, which carried leather panniers loaded with clothing, cans and bottles of food, hammocks, pots and pans. John and Beale took turns driving the horses. At noon they stopped for luncheon and a siesta, throwing into the *pot-au-feu* large Spanish onions, sweet red peppers and whatever the men had shot that morning. They also scoured the countryside for eggs and fruits. When Jessie awakened from her nap they would drive on until time to make camp. For the first week her cough persisted; she began taking sun baths during the noon halt and by the end of the second week the pain in her chest was easing.

And so she moved through the balmy days, having no interest in time, regaining her joyousness with each passing hour. Sometimes in an inland valley behind the coast range the sun was burning hot, sometimes the air from the sea was soft and cool. When they put into a village they had their linens washed by the Indian women; sometimes they stopped at the ranches of the Californios where Jessie had proof that General Kearny's charges against her husband of maltreating the natives had been false. The Californios welcomed the party, staged fiestas in their honor, while Jessie and the women talked of clothes and babies. They had the good fortune to participate in a three-day wedding celebration, riding in the parade amidst the satin dresses and slippers of the women and the short velvet jackets and colorful velvet trousers of the men. Jessie's carriage was a matter of great interest to the Californios, who had nothing but solid wooden wheel carts pulled by oxen.

On the last night of July, while they were camped in the Santa Cruz mountains overlooking the sea, not far from the ranch which was supposed to have been their home, a sudden gust of rain swept across the ridge. John said, "I think your vacation is over, madame. We must decide now where we are going to settle down."

Jessie sighed reluctantly. "This has been a wonderful month. But I'm ready to set up our home. Where shall it be? How far are we from the Mariposa?"

"About two hundred miles, I should guess."

"Would it be difficult for us to see the land? I'm curious about it."

"It's a long journey on horseback across mountain trails and unbridged streams."

"What route would we take? Tell me how we get in."

His eyes lighted as he thought of the journey. "We'd go up the San Joaquin Valley, then straight into the Sierras."

"Would we pass the goldfields?"

"Yes, we'd go straight through the gold country."

They looked at each other, an expression of incredulity coming over their faces.

"By the Eternal, Jessie," whispered John, "I never thought of it before. We own the largest tract of mountain country in California. Men are washing out fortunes in gold dust only a hundred miles away . . ."

Her eyes wide with wonderment, she whispered too, "Darling, is it possible? Could there be gold on the Mariposa?"

He sprang to his feet. "It's the same mountain range; it would have the same rock formations, the same mineral deposits. It would have the same kind of rushing mountain streams to carry the gold dust down."

A slow, warm smile lighting her face, she said, "Could we start for San Francisco tomorrow morning? Could we buy picks and shovels and join the gold rush?"

"It's a risk, you know," said John. "Once we occupy the Mariposa, even to hunt gold on it, we will be making a legal acceptance of the land. We can never get our three thousand dollars from Larkin."

"We have no way of getting it back, anyway."

"How much cash do we have left out of your father's thousand dollars?"

"About five hundred."

"Then why don't we plunge the rest of our resources in a real gamble?"

"How do you mean?"

"While I was coming out from Taos I encountered a party of Sonorans from Mexico, en route to the gold fields. I rode with them for several days. When I was in Monterey I met them again; they were exhausted from the long march and planned to rest before starting into the mountains. I think I can make a deal with them: if I outfit them with food and tools and offer them half of all the gold they find on the Mariposa, they'll bring us down a fortune—if there is a fortune to be brought down. If there's no gold in the Mariposa, we will be broke."

"I'm not scared, John. Besides, I think it is futile to arrive in California at the height of the greatest gold strike the world has ever known and not take part in it. I'd like to wade up a mountain stream myself with a dishpan in my hands and see if I couldn't collect some gold dust . . ."

Exhilarated, he chuckled, "That's the mercenary streak in you, Jessie; let me be the luster after wealth in this family, it doesn't become you. I'll take the Sonorans up to the Mariposa. When we return you will be a rich man's lady."

"Just so long as I'm not a Washington fine lady," she retorted.

6

The next afternoon they reached the plateau above Monterey, with the little village nestling in the pines beneath them, and still farther down, the rocky shore of the crescent-curved bay. Jessie stood among the pines, watching the gulls flash white across the sun; she said to her husband, "Why couldn't we make our permanent camp here within sight and sound of all this beauty? It is warmer and quieter than San Francisco."

"Yes, I think you would be happy in Monterey. I will go into town to see if I can find us a house."

He was gone only an hour when she saw him swinging up the little trail from the village.

"There are no houses available," he announced, "but I've found two lovely rooms in the house of the wife of the Mexican general Castro, who was exiled to Mexico City after our conquest. She does not hold this against us. We will be comfortable there."

He helped her into the carriage and drove it down the winding path to the village. Madame Castro's house was the former Mexican governor's home: a huge ballroom fronted the bay, two adobe wings ran back from the water to meet a garden enclosed in soft-colored adobe walls; the roof was of rough red tile, the floors of smooth red tile, and there were hedges of pinks lining the garden walls and walks.

The ballroom was now rented as a warehouse for a flour merchant; Jessie was ushered into one of the wings which contained two rooms, high-ceilinged, the adobe walls whitewashed. They were innocent of furniture except for a wood stove in a small anteroom. Jessie presented her compliments to Madame Castro, who loaned them two cots and two chairs, several pots and pans, a few dishes and some flatware.

Leaving her to survey her new home, and to wonder how she was going to get it furnished, John went out to find his Sonorans, returning at lunchtime.

"The Mexicans have agreed to my proposition," he told her excitedly. "I must leave for San Francisco with them at once."

At her crestfallen expression, he added quickly, "I will be back in a couple of weeks, just as soon as there is news."

"Very well," said Jessie, "but since you are going up to San Francisco, you must use part of our funds to buy furniture and linens and dishes and silverware. This is the first time I shall be a housewife, and I am afraid I can't do very well with a few borrowed dishes. Let me give you a list; and you had better buy materials so that I can make some clothes for Lily and myself. Our two outfits are threadbare."

He left by midafternoon, assuring her that the first ship to reach Monterey would carry everything needed to make them happy at Madame Castro's. Jessie was delighted when Gregorio asked permission to remain behind as houseboy. She set about her duties as housewife, but the gold seekers had swept the country clean of every vestige of chicken, eggs, milk, meat, vegetables, fruits, canned goods and the wheat and grain staples. She could find little to buy but rice and beans, a little flour and sugar. She had never cooked anything more than a pot of coffee, and now she was thrust into the position of feeding herself, Lily and Gregorio on a few crude staples. Occasionally when she came back from a brisk walk in the hills with Lily she would find Gregorio squatting before the fire, a broad red sash around his waist and a red silk handkerchief tied around his jet-black hair, cooking a *guisado,* a compound of birds, squirrel, dried red peppers and rice stewed together.

Gregorio liked to picture himself in the role of houseboy, as he had been for the Mission Fathers, but he had preconceived notions of what a man might and might not do: he would light the fire in the open hearth in the living room, but a man did not chop wood, that was a squaw's work, so Jessie chopped her own firewood. Men shot food, but they did not cook over a stove, that was squaw's work, and so Jessie did the cooking.

"It's a good thing Gregorio is ornamental," she laughed to Lily, "with that red band around his straight Indian hair, because he really isn't useful. You and I do more cooking for him than he does for us."

"When he shoots a partridge or quail," answered Lily, "he cooks it over the open fire and brings it to us on a stick."

"Yes," agreed Jessie with a wry smile, "whether it's three in the afternoon or three in the morning! We have to eat it whether we're hungry or not, so that we won't offend him. I wonder if I'll ever be able to teach him the quaint American custom of cooking and serving food at mealtimes?"

"I don't think so," replied Lily, straight-faced. "You see, Mother, the Indians never had clocks and so they didn't know when it was mealtime. They ate when they got hungry, or they had shot something."

At the end of two weeks a ship arrived from San Francisco, and a number of sailors began bringing crates up to the Castro house. When everything had been assembled Jessie found that her husband had sent her two high, roomy New England bedsteads, plenty of sheets and blankets, woven East Indian wicker chairs, a beautiful inlaid teakwood table, enough Chinese matting to cover the tile floors, white lace material for curtains, Chinese satins and French damasks for draperies, two exquisitely shaped English pottery punch bowls to be used as wash-basins, colorful French and Chinese satin-cushioned bamboo couches and chairs; two big grizzly-bear skins to be thrown over the matted floor in front of the fireplace; tin candlesticks and tall white spermaceti candles under whose light she and her father had worked for so many hours in their library in Washington. Wrapped as though it were the prize of the shipment, she found a copy of Lane's translation of *The Arabian Nights,* the only book in her possession.

With help from Madame Castro, and with Gregorio doing the heavy work, Jessie tacked the lovely white curtains over the windows, spread the matting on the floor, set out the beds in the rear room and the teakwood table with the wicker chair in the living room. When the place began to look warm and homelike, she had Gregorio bring in the last big package and open it in front of the fire. For a moment she believed she was dreaming, for someone had sold to her husband as "very durable for a lady's winter clothes" harsh merinos, thick muslins and cotton-back satins in loud and garish patterns. After her first shock, she had to laugh.

"It serves me right," she said to Lily, "for letting a man buy cloth for women's clothes; but never mind, we'll make the best of it. Here we go for a winter wardrobe."

She carefully ripped up her one remaining set of cambric underclothes to use as a pattern, also the one faithful black silk dress which remained of her Washington wardrobe. She did the same for Lily, laying out the patterns on the living-room floor as a guide, attempting to copy their lines in these new and strangely intractable stuffs. She pinned, measured, and remeasured herself and Lily before daring to put scissors to cloth. She had grown so thin since the black silk dress had been made that the first fitting showed the need for drastic alterations. She told her daughter the story of the old lady in St. Louis who never shaped stockings, but knitted them straight to the heel, saying, "It's a mighty poor leg that can't shape its own stocking." She built Lily's wardrobe and her own on this plan, playing a game in which she became Mrs. Abbott of London, fashionable mantua maker, and Lily her wealthy and imperious client, having elegant gowns built for Washington society. The game had added piquancy, for John had taken nearly all their money to San Francisco to outfit the Sonorans, and Jessie was getting down to her last few dollars for food. Their furnishings, she surmised with a crooked smile as she gazed about her, had been bought on credit.

With her husband away, Lily became her companion. She took her daughter for long walks among the pine-covered hills overlooking the bay, spent several hours each day teaching her arithmetic, geography and history, gave the seven-year-old a feeling of participation in their communal life by letting her do her share of the housework. Although these separations from her husband gave her the opportunity to devote herself to her daughter, they also brought Jessie closest to Lily during those periods when the light was gone from her eye and the sparkle from her brain and spirit. Lily was an observant child, she commented on what a different person her mother was when Father was present, how much more gay she was then, her step and her words fast and strong. Jessie felt conscience-stricken and redoubled her efforts to make Lily feel her love, but the light, the inner warmth and glow went out when John left, and all that was available for her daughter was the shell of a woman, wishing away her days until her husband would return.

She was perplexed by Lily's unfolding nature; by some strange twist of fate she found her daughter unimaginative in everything except this suffering of her mother's while her father was away. While she knew that the child must resent her father's dominating her mother's love and interest, yet when loneliness overcame her, it was Lily who served as comforter, stroking her hair the way John did, speaking her father's words of endearment exactly in her father's tone. She could discover no way in which Lily was like herself or John. She was a great deal like her aunt Eliza: biggish and awkward in figure, with plain features, literal-minded, practical in a way that neither Jessie nor John could ever be. Jessie had once remarked to her husband that Lily was a demon for the unvarnished truth; the daughter frequently punctured the romantic imaginings of her parents. There were occasions when Jessie was grateful, for the Frémont family had no more room for romantics, and a practical nature at the family board could be a blessing.

Late one afternoon, about a month after John had left for San Francisco, while she was sewing before the hearth in the living room, with Gregorio and Lily squatting on their haunches before the fire toasting quail, the door was thrown open and John burst into the room, his face and clothing soiled from the long ride, but a fiery glow in his eyes. He was at her side before she could rise, had laid a heavy sack at her feet. She did not open it but only gazed up at him. He quickly untied the thongs about the neck of the sack, scooped his right hand into it and with his left hand grasping her wrist tightly, poured a slow, bright stream of powder into her palm.

"Gold!" she cried.

"Yes, my darling, gold. Do you know how much gold is in this sack? One hundred pounds! Worth almost twenty-five thousand dollars!" He left her side and ran to the door, crying over his shoulder, "Wait there, don't move." In a moment he returned with another heavy sack in each hand, the weight far more than he could ordinarily have borne. He dropped the two sacks in front of her on the hearth, untied the thongs and spilled out a handful of gold from each.

"Every creek is lined with gold. The Sonorans washed out seventy-five thousand dollars' worth in three weeks!"

This turn of events was more than Jessie could comprehend. She had been reduced to her last few dollars for provisions, and now suddenly she had hundred-pound sacks of gold dust dumped at her feet. When she at last found her tongue, all she could stutter, unbelievingly, was: "It's . . . all . . . ours?"

"No, only half is ours; you remember, I promised the Sonorans half the gold they found. But there are millions of dollars' worth of gold in there. It's richer than anything yet found in California. But that's not the most important part: I think the Mother Lode runs through our Mariposa!"

"Mother Lode?" she repeated meaninglessly, still too stunned to think.

"Yes. While crossing our land I saw geological formations that I thought gave promise of containing precious minerals. Then I found a large piece of gold-bearing quartz. Do you know what that means, Jessie? All the gold that we wash out of the rivers comes originally from the gold-quartz rock formations. A thousand men swarming over the streams of the Mariposa could wash out all the gold that the water has carried down for centuries; that supply can be exhausted within a few months. But if we have the original source, the deep layers of gold quartz that might run across a whole mountain range, then literally there are millions of dollars in the Mariposa!"

She didn't know whether to laugh or cry; there certainly was no disputing these three heavy sacks of gold, or the piece of quartz with the strong gold streak through it.

Money had never been important in her life, but that was because she had never wanted for it. Having arrived in a strange country, only to find themselves dispossessed of their ranch, several thousand dollars in debt, and with no means of earning a livelihood, she felt this discovery to be providential. This gold through which she ran her fingers in the open mouths of the sacks was to her more a symbol of happiness than of wealth, for she knew how much it could mean to her husband: in success, in accomplishment, while at the height of his powers and in the midst of overwhelming praise, John was modest, reserved, unassuming, warm-hearted, generous, lovable. He was built to withstand success; the greater the success, the finer John Frémont shone forth. But he was not equipped to withstand failure or defeat; these brought out the very worst in him. They made him suspicious, vindictive, intolerant, mean-spirited and small-souled. That was why she had been so stricken in Panama at the news of the collapse and destruction of the fourth expedition; that was why the loss of the Santa Cruz ranch, even though she had never thought that he should be a farmer, had been such a serious blow: she had feared it might turn her husband bitter, start him thinking in terms of conspiracy and persecution.

But now he would be rich. This was a kind of success everyone could understand and no one could dispute. Even more important than being rich, he would have become the darling of the gods: for he had discovered gold on his own land, not merely the gold that had been washed down by the streams, but the very source of that gold. She knew that when word of this discovery reached the East it would wipe out the criticism of his failure to find a new railroad pass, his failure to keep his party alive and return them all to safety. The news that John Frémont had discovered part of the Mother Lode on his Mariposa estate would sweep the East with as wild an excitement as had any of the reports of his first three expeditions—and it would do as much to intensify the ever growing migration to California! She uttered thanks to God, grateful that her man had once again been set on his feet.

7

By the following morning, when he had dashed off for the mines, it all seemed like a fantastic dream; every once in a while she would have to return to the sacks and run her fingers through the shining dust to reassure herself that she had not been dreaming. Yet the presence of the gold in the house brought little material change, for there was no additional food available, and there were no men left in Monterey to perform any kind of service; everyone had rushed to the gold fields, and the Indian women would do no work. One day a strapping Texan knocked at her door with a healthy young mulatto girl in tow.

"I hear you are in need of a servant, Mrs. Frémont," he said. "I come to sell you this slave girl. I'm going into the gold fields and I don't need her no more. I'll make a reasonable bargain."

"Would you allow her to work for me for wages?"

"No, ma'am," replied the Texan, "I want to sell her and get rid of her for good."

"I don't want to buy her," replied Jessie firmly.

"But why not, ma'am? I'm not even naming the price. I can collect from the colonel any time."

"I thank you for your kindness, sir," she replied, "but you don't understand. I don't believe in buying and selling persons."

"Why should you keep yourself from living in comfort?" asked the Texan. "Everybody buys and sells niggers."

"Colonel Frémont and I do not. We don't believe in slavery. We have always had colored people in our home, but they have been freemen, free to go when they wished."

And so she continued to scrub her own floors, pushing aside the gold sacks under the bed so that she could wash where they had been standing.

In addition to the gracious Spanish women with whom she could spend a neighborly hour now and then, she found that the United States Army officers were moving their headquarters to Monterey because living in San Francisco had grown too expensive. Generals James Benton Riley and P. T. Smith were there with their wives, and young William T. Sherman, with a consumptive cough but an inexhaustible supply of good stories. During August, Monterey became excited and busy, for it was to be the first state capital and within a few weeks the delegates would assemble to organize their government and draw up a constitution. Colton Hall, which the Reverend Samuel Wiley had been using as a school, was turned into a convention hall; a hotel had been started for the delegates, but since the mechanics had departed for the mines, there were few carpenters to work on it.

By the first of September the delegates began to ride into Monterey. For the most part they were a rough-hewn group of frontiersmen, all of whom carried weapons; some of them Jessie knew from Washington and St. Louis, with most of the others John was acquainted from his former stays in California. Six-foot-six Robert Semple, who had been important in forming the Bear Flag Republic, was chosen chairman; William G. Marcy, son of the secretary of war, was appointed secretary; J. Ross Browne, a traveling journalist, was made shorthand reporter; W. E. P. Hartnell, an Englishman, was engaged as interpreter for the Californios.

There were early settlers, professional politicians, Englishmen, Irishmen, Frenchmen, Spaniards: America in microcosm.

Two days before the convention opened the hotel owner abandoned all hopes of getting his building completed, announcing, "The weather will hold good; the delegates can roll up in their serapes and sleep under the pine trees." However, there was not a restaurant in town; some of the men brought their own food in packs, but others came totally unprepared. Hospitality was for Jessie as natural as breathing, and she held open house every afternoon. While she could serve no varied menus, she had become good at making rice puddings, and the delegates were expert with their guns and fishing lines. Few came to dinner without a bird or a fish in hand.

She and Gregorio set up a long wooden table in the big garden. Here every afternoon ten or fifteen delegates would gather to talk politics and discuss the coming convention. Of the thirty-six American delegates, twenty-two came from the north and only fourteen from the south; nevertheless, the contest over slavery was sure to be hotly waged. There were three other American women in Monterey, Mrs. Larkin, Mrs. Riley and Mrs. Smith, all pleasant and hospitable women who did their share in entertaining the delegates; however, because Jessie and John had already been friends with some thirty out of the thirty-six delegates, their home became the informal star chamber of the convention, and here many of the issues were rehearsed. Long experience in the clash of political theories had taught Jessie how to sustain an atmosphere in which these ideas could be fought to their logical conclusions. Her two rooms were small; the furnishings were bizarre and ill-fitted; the outdoor table was of rough wooden planks; but her warmth, her delight in participating in the creation of the new state kept the glow on her cheeks, her eyes sparkling, her tongue witty and welcoming.

As she looked about the rough board table with its covering of unbleached muslin brier-stitched with red thread, the oddly assorted silverware and unmatched Chinese and Mexican dishware; as she looked at the unshaven, roughly garbed frontiersmen eating the fish which they had caught themselves in Monterey Bay, and she had baked over the outdoor fire, with big bowls of rice pudding in the center of the table to finish off the repast, her mind went back to the highly polished mahogany table in the Benton dining room in Washington, with its shining damask cloths, gleaming silver and cut-glass bowls of fruits and candies, with Joshaam and Josheem padding about silently, passing the sides of rare roast beef, the terrapin, the roast duck and turkey, the beef and kidney pies.

Incongruous as were the furnished two rooms at Madame Castro's house, she developed a genuine love for them. Visited by men who spent most of the year sleeping on the ground or living in improvised shacks, tents or wretched boardinghouses, Jessie's rooms seemed like a breath of home. One Sunday evening when the weather suddenly turned cold, and they were eating indoors, William Gwin, John Sutter, Robert Semple, and Henry W. Halleck made an inspection of the rooms, and then Semple said: "Mrs. Fremont, we were saying among ourselves how surprising it was that you could achieve such comfort in a queer place like Monterey."

Jessie looked about her critically, trying to see the rooms with the eyes of a stranger. On the floor were the two grizzly-bear skins, their glass eyes lighted by the fire; the windows were draped with elegant Chinese brocade, the adobe walls were crudely whitewashed, and on the Chinese rattan furniture were cushions covered with exquisite French silks. The only wall decoration was a colored print of St. Francis, while on the Chinese teakwood table was the representative of another great religion, a bronze Buddha; alongside were a two-year-old copy of the London *Punch* and her Martha Washington sewing basket, the same one in which she had concealed the letter from Colonel Abert. She took the stance of a professional lecturer, raised one arm in the air for silence, and announced in her father's sometime pontifical tone:

"Gentlemen, at first glance you might think this room incongruous, but having made close study of it, I find it true to the period, Pioneer Forty-nine, worthy elements from all over the world, guarded by a California grizzly."

Her one disappointment was that her husband was not at home to join in the hospitality, the discussions, and the formulation of policy. She felt that John should have been a member of this convention, that even now he should be having serious talks with every delegate, helping to set official state policy. But word of the tremendous findings on the Mariposa had spread over central California and already several thousand prospectors were placer mining on the Frémont land. Their land grant did not give them exclusive mineral rights; anyone was entitled to wash out and pick up the gold lying in the Mariposa streams. John had felt that at that particular moment he should be with the Sonorans, helping them find the best streams in which to work, taking out their gold nuggets and gold dust before another several thousand prospectors flooded over the land. Jessie had not thought it so necessary to get out the last possible bag of gold dust; they had not come to California to be gold miners or to become rich; they had come to enter into the local politics; why then allow the accidental discovery of gold on the Mariposa to upset their plans and to keep John away from the California Constitutional Convention?

She had suggested all this to her husband, but he had declared that as long as he was not a delegate there was no proper place for him; that most of the delegates knew his stand and his politics from years of contact; that no one could blame him for making gold while the sun shone. Later, when they opened their regular quartz mines, their property would be safe and he would not have to be on the ground. It was unfortunate that the convention and the Mariposa gold rush were taking place at the same moment, but he felt he owed it to all of them to get out as much gold as he could and let Jessie be his representative in Monterey as she had been in Washington.

One evening Delegate Lippincott of Philadelphia brought fifteen delegates in to dinner. They watched Jessie standing over the stove cooking the food; they watched her cover the rough planks with the strips of unbleached muslin brier-stitched together; they watched her serve, with Gregorio's help, twenty-four guests; they saw her sit at the head of the table and with high spirits guide the political discussions so that they included everyone about the table; they saw her gather up the soiled plates, then wash the dishes and silver while William Sherman, the Reverend Wiley and Robert Semple stood about drying them, everyone keeping up a rapid-fire repartee. When the work was done and they had assembled in the living room, several of the lanky frontiersmen sprawling on the floor in front of the fire, one of the delegation said:

"Mrs. Frémont, we heard in town that you were offered a young slave girl to do your work and you refused to buy her. Is that true?"

"Quite true," replied Jessie. "Neither Mr. Frémont nor I believe in buying and selling human beings. I would never consent to use or own a slave."

"Not even if it meant you would have to scrub your own floors and wash your own dishes for the rest of your life?"

"Not even," said Jessie with a quiet smile.

"The women in San Francisco are crying for suv-vents, but if you, a Washington fine lady, can get along without, they shan't have them. We'll keep clear of slave labor."

Hallelujah! thought Jessie. At last that title "fine lady" may accomplish some good. Aloud she said:

"Colonel Frémont has called California the Italy of America. Isn't it an ideal place for small homes and well-tended acreage? If we keep slave labor out, we will have the wealthy and comfortable middle class, but no poor."

"That's a fine sentiment," replied William Steuart, head of the pro-slavery leaders, "but the aristocracy will always have slaves."

"How about you joining the aristocracy of emancipators, Mr. Steuart?" she shot back. "My father freed all his slaves in St. Louis before he went to Washington twenty-five years ago."

"But who's going to do all the hard and dirty labor?"

"You are," flashed Jessie, "and I am! I am raising a child in California, and before long you men will be bringing your wives out here or marrying and raising families. It isn't a pretty sight in a free country for a child to see and hear chain gangs clanking through the streets or to watch officers chasing a fugitive slave and putting him in irons. Is that what we're founding a new state for? If so, it would be better if we all returned east and left this beautiful country alone."

On the day before the convention was to open, John rode in from the Mariposa, unable to stay away. There was a gala party in the Frémont rooms that night, with every American in Monterey assembled, even Consul Larkin, looking sheepish, but wanting to be friends again.

The next morning the convention opened. Jessie and John sat behind the rough wooden railing which had been stretched across the middle of the hall. Using the constitutions of New York and Iowa as models, the delegates pushed forward rapidly in a series of sharp discussions, debates which seemed to Jessie to be on a high plane of intelligence and integrity. She remembered the story her father told her of the Constitutional Convention of Missouri, which much of the California procedure now duplicated.

William Gwin dominated the convention with his magnificent figure, leonine head and orator's voice. He was a sincere man, honest according to his lights, an able tactician in parliamentary procedure. Jessie saw that the delegates not only admired him but had faith in his judgment. As the days passed and Gwin directed more and more of the discussion, she became convinced that his boast in Washington would be carried out, that he would be returned by the legislature as one of the first two California senators. That left only one berth open. To whom would it go? To her husband, sitting quietly beside her, for some reason best known to himself never rising to his feet, never asking for permission to participate, content to exercise his influence at home over the dinner table in quiet and friendly chats?

After the convention had been in session for a week, and it was evident that California would become a free state, John could contain himself no longer. He rode south to buy several big cattle ranches which he had admired since he had first seen them during the conquest, then returned to San Francisco to invest some of his rapidly accumulating gold in tracts of land lying about a mile west of Portsmouth Square. He sent word not to expect him for a considerable time, as the Sonorans wanted to go home for Christmas and he thought he ought to stay on the Mariposa as long as possible. Gregorio went up to the mountains to be with him, leaving Jessie and Lily alone. With the last of the delegates gone, Monterey seemed quiet and lonely.

8

In October slashing rains were whipped against the windows by strong winds off the Pacific. The streets became the same kind of mudholes Jessie remembered from the early days of Washington, and there could be little visiting back and forth. One large window overlooked the bay, the deserted beach and the rocks beyond. She thought, With the sea one is never alone. Yet with the sea, as with everything else, its joys are enhanced a hundredfold when you have a loved one by your side to share in its rich variety. After supper Lily would get into her nightgown and then stretch out on the grizzly rug before the fire, where she would burn the resinous pine cones which crackled and made ever changing flame pictures.

The days and the nights were long, for she had too little to do, and her library consisted of exactly the one book which John had found in San Francisco while buying furniture. She read one story from *The Arabian Nights* to Lily each Sunday night, Lily calling it their Sunday dessert, for she wanted to make the book last as long as possible. Fortunately the flour merchant who had taken over the ballroom at the front of the house found five bound volumes of the London *Times* and a number of volumes of the *Merchant's Magazine,* which he gave to her. She had not much interest in commerce, but for want of something better to read she persisted and finally grew interested: for a lover of books is like a lover of women, he would rather have an interesting book than a dull one, but he would rather have a dull one than none at all. Then General Riley stumbled across a volume of Lord Byron's poems, and these brought her many hours of beauty as she sat before her fireplace while the winter surf boomed across the rocks and the night was filled with cold and rain.

Every week or two Gregorio or a trusted Sonoran would arrive with more sacks of gold dust, which she stored in trunks and boxes under the beds. One day in November, General Riley's wife was visiting when Gregorio came in with two of the heavy buckskin sacks. Mrs. Riley, who had been in the Army since she was nineteen, living on low-scale army pay, said:

"I really must congratulate you on your growing riches."

The well-meant remark, said without any apparent envy, threw Jessie's weeks of loneliness into focus. She did not enjoy being separated from her husband for the sake of making money; they had already been separated too much and too cruelly. Nor did she enjoy the thought of sitting in two rain-swept rooms with nothing to do but feed herself and her child, while the weeks and the months passed, and she had no part to play, no job to do. John would be obliged to spend a considerable portion of his time on the Mariposa; he thought it too remote and too dangerous for his wife to come there and make their home. What then was she to do? Sit here in Madame Castro's two rooms while they accumulated more and more wealth? To what end? She asked only a few simple things of life: the company and love of her husband; important work to do at his side; sons to bear his name. Turning to Mrs. Riley she murmured:

"Gold isn't much as an end, is it? It can't conjure comforts or an ounce of brain rations. I am simply famished for the taste of a good book. I'd give every last one of those buckskin sacks to have my husband here with me now."

As the long months of winter spun themselves out, and John managed to get home only for a day or two, Jessie realized that this was almost the same as his being out on another expedition. She counted back over the memories of her marriage, realizing that more than half the time she had been alone, prey to illness, anxiety and uncertainty over his welfare. She did not think that the quantity of money involved should have any influence on her feelings; she could not have felt more keenly a sense of life in abeyance if John had been earning single dollars instead of tens of thousands.

Toward the end of November she received in the mail a long envelope addressed to Colonel John C. Frémont, which proved to be a questionnaire relating to her husband's political beliefs. The committee that had written the letter wished to assure Colonel Frémont that if he would answer the questions satisfactorily, they would back him for the United States Senate.

She engaged an Indian to ride to the Mariposa and summon John, for an immediate answer was expected, and both letters would be published in the California newspapers. She made a copy of the letter to send with the messenger, so that he could be formulating his reply on the long ride home. He arrived at the end of the fourth day, tired and overwrought: there were now some three thousand prospectors pouring over the Mariposa; the Sonorans figured that they had enough money to last the rest of their lives in Mexico and would work no longer; there was no labor available at any price to take their place. Jessie saw that her husband was less than ever interested in politics. She boiled an iron tub of water over the outside fire in order that he might have a brisk scrub-up, then they had tea and biscuits.

"You see," she said, "I'm a better visionary than I am a cook: I predicted when you left on the second expedition five years ago that you would be one of the first senators from California."

He did not look as pleased at her outburst of confidence as she had hoped. His dark eyes could peer as fiercely inward as they could peer outward, and she saw that her husband had been undergoing several days of intense soul searching.

"If I am elected, Jessie," he said, "what do we do with the Mariposa and our mines? All the surface gold will be gone very shortly. We'll have to buy machinery, bring in a competent labor supply and follow the gold quartz into the sides of the mountains. If we don't start this work very soon, others will, and we will lose possession; under existing law we have no mineral rights even inside our land unless we set up permanent equipment to mine it. If I were to be elected and we left for Washington, how do we know when we would get back? Our dream of wealth will be gone; others will have pre-empted it."

She did not think this a serious problem; even after they had paid the Sonorans their half of the gold dust, there still would be about two hundred thousand dollars in gold for them. This was a great deal of money; it was a lifetime's money; why did they need millions, particularly if the cost of those millions was a seat in the United States Senate?

She knew it would not be wise to argue thus to her husband; it would seem that she was trying to force her peculiar values on him, as though she would oblige him to think that because in the Benton family a United States senator was the world's most important dignitary, John Charles Frémont, who had never shown any appetite for the Senate, should give up the opportunity to become one of the world's richest and most powerful men, an opportunity neither remote nor fanciful, but at his very finger tips.

"I don't want to influence you," she said—"that is, not too strongly. I've always dreamed of seeing you in the Senate, but there's no reason why you should shackle yourself with my ambitions. After all, it is you who will have to do the work, and so you should decide for yourself. If you want to go to the Senate, then we should write the strongest polemic on your political philosophy we can create; if you would prefer to stay here and start to mine on a big scale, then we will forget about Washington, and Lily and I will move up to the Mariposa with you and build our home there. You say you will need labor for the mines; the best way to attract it is to have a going community with comfortable cabins and a store and a school for the children."

"Yes, those are our alternatives."

"Then it's purely a case of values. Which means the more to you?"

He was silent for a long time, his chin resting on his chest, his eyes staring inward, not seeing the strained and hopeful expression on his wife's face.

"I should like to try to do both," he finally said; "I think we can work it out. I will stand for the election, and we will leave for Washington immediately if I am successful. When our ship arrives in New York, I will buy the mining equipment and send it out here. I will also try to hire mining engineers and have them accompany the equipment and install it. At the end of the congressional session we will come back to California for as long as we can, long enough to supervise the mines and set up a system."

He looked toward her hopefully. "Do you think we can do them both, Jessie, or am I being overly ambitious?"

"We can try, darling. Shall we begin work now on the answer to this letter?"

"No, I'm too tired. I need a night's sleep; besides, though it's difficult to keep track of time in the mountains, it seems to me that it has been a month since I embraced my wife."

"Only a month?" she murmured. "I would say it was a year."

They spent the next day drafting his free-state, Democratic stand, and his answer to the questions affecting California. The following day he returned to the mines, promising to be back for Christmas.

Once again Jessie was alone in her rooms overlooking the Pacific. Christmas approached slowly through a succession of dark and windswept days. Neither Jessie nor Lily could venture forth in such weather, and so Jessie would light a half-dozen candles in the tin holders John had sent down from San Francisco with the furnishings and go over the pictures in an illustrated London *Times*. Just two days before the holiday her door was wrenched open, rain swept into the room, then the door was slammed shut. She turned quickly from the fire to see John leaning against a now wet door, panting for breath, his sombrero, face and native jacket drenched, the water running off his high boots in rivulets onto the floor.

"Jessie, I couldn't wait, I have ridden from San José to greet the first senator's lady from California."

She cried from her chair, "John, you've been elected!"

"On the first ballot," he exulted. "I received twenty-four votes out of thirty-six. William Gwin was elected on the third ballot. We sail for New York on New Year's Day."

She sprang out of her chair, ran to him and flung her arms around him, kissing him joyfully.

"You'll get wet," he laughed. "I'd better not walk across the room, I'd make it a pool of water."

"Drop out of those clothes right where you stand, then come to the fire and get warm. I'll have dry clothes for you in a minute. You must be tired. It's a seventy-mile ride from San José."

After a gay supper of coffee, cold beef and bread, and a bottle of champagne to celebrate their victory, they sprawled out on the warm bear rugs facing the fire, their chins cupped in the palms of their hands, their fingers framing the ovals of their excited faces.

"Ah, my dear," she murmured, "it will be a happy day for me when I see you in the Senate. I will have that exact seat in the visitors' gallery where Father first put me to listen to him speak when I was only eight."

"It will be a happy day for me," rejoined her husband, "when I see Maylee serving you morning tea in bed."

Later, in the glow of the burned-down eucalyptus logs, they fell asleep on the rugs. At dawn, after a cup of hot coffee, Jessie embraced her husband and he left to ride the seventy miles back to San José.

In festive mood she had Gregorio cut them an evergreen from the hills above the bay and set it in a corner of her living room. Having no ornaments for the tree, she searched through her possessions until she found some old tin foil, rolled it into soft balls and stuck them on the ends of the branches. The tin candleholders she tied to the stronger branches, putting in red and yellow candles. Having opened a can of sardines for lunch, she had Gregorio cut up the tin into odd shapes and make little holes in them so they could be strung onto the tree, then sent him out to the hotel where she had seen pieces of sheet metal thrown down from the now finished roof. Gregorio cut this metal roughly into shapes of stars and crescents, which Jessie painted blue and red before hanging on the tree.

John returned on Christmas Eve with gifts for everyone, a beautiful doll just off the boat from China for his daughter, a soft red cashmere shawl for Jessie, and the first box of candy manufactured in California.

The week between Christmas and New Year's was crowded and exciting. John was busy making arrangements for agents to handle the mines. The Sonorans came down from the Mariposa and took their half of the gold. Jessie had a great deal of packing to do, the furniture had to be stored so that they could have it again when they returned to build a home on the Mariposa. She took a last sentimental walk through the empty rooms, remembering how uncertain their future had been when first they had moved in five months before.

The S.S. *Oregon* came into the harbor at Monterey on New Year's night, firing its guns to notify the passengers ashore. In the most torrential rain she had ever seen, and with the streets pouring rivers of mud down to the sea, they trudged to the waterfront followed by Gregorio and another Indian boy carrying their luggage. John lifted her into a rowboat, Gregorio carried Lily. They sat in the downpouring torrents while the two Indian boys rowed them out through the blackness of the night.

"Don't cry so hard, Gregorio," said Jessie, "you're waterlogging the boat. We promise to come back soon."

Once again she climbed up a ship's rope ladder, swaying from side to side as the wind-swept rain buffeted her. The S.S. *Oregon* stopped at Mazatlan to coal. Consul Parrott, who had fought with Colonel Frémont and the California Battalion, came aboard to invite them to his thick-walled Mexican house for dinner. The weather was warm off the coast of Mexico and Jessie had found her Monterey clothes too heavy for comfort. Searching through her bags she discovered a white, ruffled morning sacque to wear with her rough merino skirt.

By the time they returned to their ship the night air had turned cool. Jessie realized too late that she had made a serious error; her cough returned and she was confined to her bunk for the rest of the voyage to Panama. John too was stretched flat on his back, his left side and frostbitten leg gripped with rheumatism. Both were taken off the ship on stretchers, with Lily, white-faced with worry, watching over them. Again Madame Arce came to Jessie's rescue. She took the Frémonts to her home and installed them in the same bedroom Jessie had occupied eight months before. She and her servants devoted their full time to nursing the sick couple, concealing from them the fact that Lily was down with Chagres fever, as ill as her parents.

They had been scheduled to catch the ship which left Chagres five days after they had reached Panama City. Instead they lay in their hammocks in Madame Arce's house for a month. During the last week John was able to hobble around the room, and Jessie's fever went down. John L. Stephens, who was building the Panama Railroad, came in late each afternoon, murmuring, "I have come to take my chill with you."

When the last day arrived on which they could possibly catch the next steamer to New York, Jessie insisted that she was strong enough to travel. John limped out of the room and went aboard a United States man-of-war in the harbor. When he returned he said, "We can leave in the morning; I've borrowed a ship's hammock; we'll rig an awning over it to keep out the sun, and hire Indian bearers to carry you across Panama."

The next morning John Stephens brought four of his best Indian carriers. Jessie was taken out to her palanquin and lifted into it. Madame Arce settled a crimson silk, lace-trimmed pillow under her head and filled the flat canvas pockets with hankerchiefs and flasks of cologne. John and Lily each had a mule to ride. Lily was recovering, but all of her hair had been shaved off during the fever, and her face was pinched and white. Jessie had quite a start when she first saw her daughter, but the stolid Lily assured her that she was well again and perfectly able to ride the mule to Gorgona. As the Indian bearers moved through the streets of Panama, the natives came out from their houses to see the strange cortege.

After two days and nights on the trail, and two days in the boat going down the Chagres River, during which Jessie stoked herself regularly with quinine and coffee, she at last caught sight of the masts of the steamer. Once in their cabin, she sat on the edge of the berth, ran her hand over her husband's forehead, with her fingers combed the hair back from his brow. Then she lay down in the berth alongside of him, motioning Lily to come into her arms. She lay quietly, one arm about her husband, the other about her daughter; the bunk was crowded with the three of them in it, but Jessie did not care; she was happy to have them all together again.

From the docks in New York they drove direct to the Irving House. The manager told them they would have the suite just vacated by Jenny Lind. They walked into the sitting room and stood in the middle of the room in front of a long French mirror in which Jessie had an opportunity to survey her family. First came Lily; she had eaten steadily for two weeks aboard ship, was now plump and red-cheeked; her brown merino dress was too small for her and she seemed to be bursting out of it both fore and aft; it was also too short, revealing the unbleached muslin panties. She had on a pair of Indian buckskin shoes presented to her by Gregorio, and since her hat had blown overboard, her shaved head was wrapped in a black silk handkerchief, making her look like one of the immigrant children off the boats from Europe.

In the middle was her husband, dressed in knee-high miner's boots and his California outfit of miner's trousers, buckskin jacket, open-throated shirt and handkerchief tied around his neck, his gray-shot beard untrimmed, his hair as long as when he had come home from his expeditions. Then her eyes fell upon herself: emaciated, her pale skin made to look a jaundiced yellow by the rough-fitting, brown satin basque blouse. The dark skirt she had cut out of her riding outfit hung straight and shapeless to her ankles, and out of it peeped rusty black satin slippers, the only pair of shoes she had left; held on to her head with a China crepe scarf was a leghorn hat whose color clashed with the brown blouse and blue skirt.

To herself she murmured, The senator's lady from the Golden West! Miss English should see me now!

She had been away a year, six months of it spent in California, the rest in travel. She had made no home there, made no real indentation upon the country; she did not belong, yet she wanted to belong. In the back of her mind she knew that the reason she had failed had been that, in spite of her lifetime ambition to go west to the frontier, she had not set out for California with a wholehearted desire to settle there permanently and make it her life. She had gone with the idea that she and her husband would very soon return to Washington as Senator and Mrs. Frémont. In a sense she had been disloyal to the new land; perhaps that was why the gods had refused to consecrate her hearth. If she wanted a hearth in California, she would have to go there with the idea of remaining forever, loyal and devoted, and enduring of hardship. In spite of the battered apparition of the three of them in the glass, she knew that she did want to go back to California. Perhaps next time she could become part of the country, indigenous to its life.

9

They spent two days getting their land legs, buying clothes, preparing for the train trip to Washington. She had been able to send a telegram to her father announcing their safe arrival in New York, a telegram over the wires that Samuel Morse had begged Congress to build for the five lean years during which he had come so often to the Bentons' to show why the telegraph was practical.

Tom Benton met them at the station, looking old and harassed but happy at welcoming them home. It was the first time she had been away from the family, and it seemed to her that the year had made more than its proportion of changes: her sisters had grown into young ladies; Randolph had developed into a tall, pleasant lad with her mother's finely chiseled features and her father's slightly hoarse voice; her mother's face and body had grown frail; her father's battle-scarred features reflected his heavy burdens.

She walked about the house enjoying the smell of rose geraniums in the drawing room, looking with joy at the damask-covered dining table and silver service set out for dinner; she moved about the library touching the leather-bound books, the arms of comfortable chairs, her writing desk in front of the fireplace.

Their friends came in to welcome them and congratulate John on his election. James Buchanan gave a formal dinner in their honor. Jessie ordered a new gown of soft brocade with lace frills. As they sat down to the table flanked by friendly cabinet officers, congressmen, army and navy officers, ambassadors and a considerable portion of Washington society, Jessie and John exchanged a meaningful glance: they remembered how Washington had treated them when they left, with few people calling, the Army wanting no part of their indicted brother, the Cabinet officers remaining away for fear of embarrassing the administration, the congressmen unwilling to take sides. Now they were the darlings of Washington society, rich with their fabulous California gold, John the first senator from what would soon be the first state of the Far West. As Jessie gazed at her husband she saw that he wore his new dinner clothes with poise and dignity but that he looked thin, his gray hair and weather-beaten face making him seem far older than his thirty-seven years. When John looked at his wife he saw a young woman of twenty-six with flashing hazel eyes, brown hair a little thinner than when he had first known her but gleaming richly as it was combed over her ears and gathered low at the back of her neck; her skin as clear as a child's in spite of the rigors of Panama and California, her delicate sloping shoulders white and firm and warm to the eye above her Empire gown of deep blue brocade. Simultaneously they recalled that moment in the Irving House when they had first seen themselves in their crude, garish and ill-fitting clothes.

Jessie was delighted to be back in cultivated society. She laughed gaily, more intoxicated by the swift flow of conversation than by the many toasts she drank to California and its admission as a state. John too had a gleam in his eye while he told about the possibility of a railroad to California, of the wealth and beauty of the state; but mostly their eyes sought each other, for they could not believe that they were back in Washington, just as though nothing had happened to them.

James Buchanan leaned over and murmured to her, "Miss Jessie, I don't think you should engage in flirtation with your husband while sitting next to me."

"Flirtation?"

"I would describe it as such," he replied, "a mental wink, a flash of the eye, a fleeting smile . . . I am beginning to suspect that your husband loves you."

"An unwarranted hypothesis," laughed Jessie. "He is so stunned at seeing me in an evening gown, after my unbleached muslins and black merinos, that he can hardly believe his eyes."

There was a week of parties and dinners and fun, and then they settled down to work. Behind the closed door of the library, Thomas Hart Benton admitted to his young daughter that his position in the Senate was in danger. His long fight to prevent the extension of slavery had consolidated the slavery men of Missouri against him, and after thirty years of service it was growing apparent that they had a chance to defeat him in the coming election. The focal center of the slavery battle was now California: since its own legislature had declared California to be a free state, the slavery men in the Congress were determined that California must not be admitted to the Union.

Tom Benton thus faced a painful dilemma: for thirty years he had been working to bring the Pacific coast into the United States; he had always been opposed to the extension of slavery beyond the existing southern states; but if he fought for the admission of California as a free state, his waging of the battle would afford the last round of ammunition needed to put him out of the United States Senate.

John was a senator-elect from California, but California was not yet a state and so actually he had no job. Officially there was little he could do to hasten the admission, but unofficially the Frémonts served as goodwill ambassadors and an information service on the topography, climate and general future of that territory. Through the Benton home on C Street moved a large section of official Washington. Many of those who had been skeptical about the distant land left at the end of the evening having caught some of their enthusiasm. Neither Jessie nor John had anticipated a serious struggle over the admission of California: Why wage a war over a territory, pour thousands of settlers into its boundaries, and then refuse to incorporate it within the nation? Nevertheless the weeks and the months passed, the beautiful spring merged into the hot summer and the hot summer spent itself into an early fall while the slavery faction maneuvered to gain ever increased concessions as the price of admitting California.

John utilized some of his leisure to buy mining equipment which he shipped out to San Francisco. After the third of his buying junkets, during which he laid out a great deal of cash, he informed Jessie that he was going to have to capitalize the Mariposa, issue leases on certain of the mines, and sell stock in them. This would provide the capital to build dams, roads, and buy other expensive equipment so necessary for large-scale mining. She was disturbed at the idea, for it meant setting up in business; there would be stockholders, managers and boards, control would eventually be taken from John's hands, he would be responsible to a great many people. She asked her husband if he did not think it would be better to mine on a small scale and remain the master of his mines. He laughingly replied:

"Jessie, you sound as though you didn't want us to take too much gold out of the Mariposa. Don't you like money?"

"Yes, I love money," she exclaimed. "But like every other vice, it should be indulged in moderately. Besides, I think you're meant for more important things than just making money. Did I ever tell you what Nicollet said about money? He said that the accumulation of money was a period of affliction, like adolescence, which we had to pass through before we could reach maturity. I'd like to take just a modest amount of gold out of the Mariposa, John, enough to buy you the freedom and financing for whatever work may appeal to you: further expeditions, mapping a railroad route to California, building wagon roads to the West. I don't think the Mariposa gold should be an end, I think that it should be a means: a means of fulfilling your life and your work. Or do I sound like a moralistic schoolteacher?"

"You sound like a schoolteacher . . . and you sound right. However, one cannot fly in the teeth of fate; the gods dumped a Mother Lode into my lap; to do less than exploit it to its fullest, to refuse to extract the millions of gold from those quartz lodes would be like refusing to accept the gifts of the gods."

"Yes," she agreed thoughtfully, "I can see that point of view. But did it ever occur to you that the gods might also appreciate a bit of restraint? That it might be the better part of virtue not to gobble up their gifts? When the slavery men at Monterey told you that you could be the richest man in the world if you would use slave labor in your mines, you said that that was too high a price to pay for wealth. Then why isn't giving your own life to digging out gold too high a price to pay? I would rather have you a free workman than a bounden mine owner."

John did not agree, and so an English agent by the name of Hoffman was given the right to sell leases on the Ave Maria, West Mariposa and East Mariposa mines. The agreement signed, Hoffman took the next ship to England to set up stock companies, the proceeds of which were to be sent to John to turn the three mines into major producing units. A few weeks later she learned that her husband was dealing with a second agent by the name of Thomas Sargent, giving him the right to sell leases for half of the vast Mariposa tract. Sargent also planned to go to England to sell stock in the company. She had no wish to intrude upon her husband's business arrangements, and she was reassured by the fact that her father approved of Sargent and the granting of the additional leases.

On the morning of September 10, 1850, when John Charles Frémont was to be presented to the United States Senate, Jessie rose early, took a leisurely bath, creamed her face, dressed partially, then sat before her dressing table to brush her long brown hair and coil it low on her neck. When she tried to rise to put on her gown there swept over her the same wave of nausea that she had suffered while carrying her son. She laughed gaily to herself as she thought, California may be fertile country, but Washington is the better conceiving ground!

She rode with her husband and her father up to the Senate; they were as gay as children, laughing at silly jokes, yet there was an undertone of fatality about it, for Tom Benton knew that the South was rapidly losing its temper, growing angry and frightened, that this might well be his last session. He had always wanted to die in the seat behind his Senate desk, in the midst of a fiery debate; yet if he had to be dispossessed now, go down to defeat as one of the first casualties of the threatening conflict between the North and the South, it was a good feeling to know that his daughter's husband would take his place, that California from 1840 to 1870 would be the frontier of freedom and the capital of the West, just as Missouri had been during his thirty years from 1820 to 1850.

Jessie took her accustomed seat in the front row of the visitors' gallery across from the eagle poised on top of the canopy which covered the Speaker's chair. Below were seated the senators from thirty-one states, in their long, tight black trousers held down by straps under the heels of their boots, their long-tailed, square-cut black coats and the wide lapels which framed the bow tie and white shirt.

She believed that her husband was the youngest man on the floor. She also thought him the handsomest. She glowed with pride as she watched him being sworn in as a United States senator.

In the three weeks that remained of the session she worked hard as John's secretary. Her experiences as a traveler, housewife and mother enabled her to help her husband. Yet John needed little help: she had never seen his mind work with greater clarity or comprehensiveness. Although he was no lawyer, he dictated bills to extend the laws of the judicial system of the United States to California, bills to grant public lands for purposes of education and the building of universities, asylums for the deaf and dumb, the blind and the insane, bills to record land titles, settle land claims, to negotiate the working of mines, for a system of post roads and national roads to California. She saw that California was indeed being well represented. His eighteen bills to facilitate the migration of the people westward, and for the internal development of California, were all passed by the Senate. At the end of the session even those southerners who had so bitterly opposed the introduction of California, Barnwell, Davis, Calhoun, Clay, congratulated Senator Frémont on his legislative program.

Jessie carried the new child well, strong and happy and hopeful about the future. She indulged herself not at all, went for long walks, danced at the frequent balls. On the afternoon that the Senate adjourned, she asked, "When is Gwin going back to California to stand for re-election?"

After a moment of hesitation John replied, "He isn't going. At least, not yet . . ."

She blinked uncomprehendingly. "He isn't going to stand for re-election? But that's not like Gwin. He told me himself he's determined to remain a senator from California."

"Yes, that's true. But you know, Jessie, we have a long term and a short term."

"You were elected to the long term. You have another five years . . ."

John shook his head. "Neither of us was elected to the long term. I know you have been assuming all along, Jessie, that I had the long term, and you were so happy about it I just hated to put any doubts in your mind."

Her cheeks flamed.

"But why should I have had any doubts? You received an overwhelming majority of votes. That makes you the man they want in the Senate, that gives you the six-year term."

"The election laws don't say so. Gwin and I have to draw lots for it."

She lost her temper.

"It's too utterly preposterous, John, that you should agree to gamble over a seat in the Senate. What about fighting for your rights? I don't understand you, this is out of character; two thirds of the people in California meant for you to have the long term. Gwin has no real stake in California: he went out there as a political adventurer, determined to pull the prize plum out of the pie! What does he know about California? What part did he play in making California an American state, except trying to get it to go proslavery at the convention? Your expeditions and reports are responsible for half the families that are now living out there. You played a critical role in the conquest of the state; kept it from falling into British hands. You know every valley and mountain range. You know what the people are like and what their needs are, they trust you to do important things for them here in Washington . . ."

She slumped down into her chair, her anger burnt out.

"I'm sorry I shouted at you, dear, but it just seems so incongruous for the first citizen of California to gamble over a senatorial seat with a political adventurer. There is no rhyme or reason in it."

He sat beside her and brushed the tears from her eyes with a hard circular motion of his palm.

"There's nothing I can do, Jessie; what you suggest would cause a scandal. People would say that it was another of John Frémont's uprisings, a mutiny against established tradition. Don't you see, there's no law to sustain me; it has always been a gentlemen's agreement that two senators elected from a new state must draw lots for the long and short terms."

His reference to another John Frémont uprising quieted her.

"Your stand against slavery has earned you powerful enemies here in Washington," she pleaded; "at the end of a six-year term you will have made friends with them, you will have done so much good work for California that you will be re-elected again and again for thirty full years, the way Father has from Missouri. But if you go back now after only three weeks in the Senate, the slavery group will fight you tooth and nail."

John's black eyes peered at her unhappily.

"We have to take our chances; we have to draw lots. Wish me luck, dear. I'm going to draw the long term."

She smiled a little wistfully, kissed the niche in the corner of his mouth.

"Of course you will," she said.

There was no need for John to tell her the next day when he returned home, his face a polite but withdrawn mask, that he had drawn the short term. The thirty-year career in the Senate had evaporated to three short weeks! Another turn of the wheel of fortune: when they were down, the wheel spun, they found gold, they were elected, they returned to Washington triumphant. Then the wheel turned again, thousands of gold seekers flooded their lands; they had to incorporate and give away control over their property; the senatorial career was ended almost as it began.

10

She occasionally accompanied John to New York to buy the modern mining equipment with which to dig their tunnels into the sides of the Mariposa. He decided to spend the New Year holiday in Washington, then take the ship that left New York on January 2, 1851.

She had a long session with herself in which she weighed the comparatives of her problem: she was six months with child; though the roughness of the sea voyage was not too formidable a danger, the crossing of Panama might be. Having lost young Benton, this coming child meant twice as much to both of them; on the other hand she could not bear the thought of another long separation from her husband. She knew that with John to watch over her she would be well cared for on the trail across Panama; nor was there fear in her heart: this was the opportunity to demonstrate that she had the makings of the pioneer wife, that she meant to create a home and a hearth in California. This was her challenge, more serious and more important than her first lonely trip had been: to carry inside her the new generation of the frontier, to give birth to her baby in the almost unborn community.

"I won't be gone so very long, Jessie," he assured her, "just long enough to stand for re-election and to see that the mine machinery is installed. I will be back in Washington by July."

"You mean *we* will be back in Washington by July," she replied calmly. "I'm going with you."

A look of terror flashed into his eyes.

"But you can't . . . We can't risk the child. The rigors of crossing Panama . . ."

She stood resolutely before him, tossing her hair free from her head with a spirited gesture.

"We have nothing to fear," she said. "I never felt stronger, and I am positive that this is a healthy child I am carrying. If you are going to California, the children and I are going with you. Your son is going to be born in California."

"But Jessie," he protested, "the ocean is rough in winter. You have to go over the Gorgona trail by muleback . . ."

"No, no," she cried, "I will go over the trail in my palanquin. I had a comfortable ride last time. I've learned many things about Panama: I'm taking my own tea things, canned foods that are easy to prepare and digest. The passage will be swifter now, with so many thousands of Americans having made the crossing. Please, let's not discuss it. There's confidence in my heart, and that is the best protection our child could have."

They sailed on January 3 for Chagres. The first few days were rough, so Jessie stayed in her berth and slept through them. Lily kept her father company on deck. At Chagres a little wharf had been built, and she did not have to bob around in a tender. John had sent money and instructions ahead, so there was a boat to convey them up the Chagres to Gorgona. She got bumped around a little in her canopied hammock over the mountain trail, but she laughed at the hardship and felt not the slightest worry. They arrived in San Francisco early in April. When she landed at the broad wooden pier and caught her first glimpse of the town she was glad she had made her decision, for the city had grown miraculously, many homes had sprung up, hundreds of workmen were sawing and pounding, there were wooden sidewalks and Market Street was an imposing area of white-front hotels and business firms.

She did not want her child to be born in a hotel, she wanted him to be born at her own hearth, so they set out at once to buy a house. The only one they could find was an ugly wooden frame structure high up on Stockton Street overlooking the Portsmouth Square. There was no interior decoration, the walls were bare, but the rooms were large and the furnishings comfortable. They bought the house and moved in. On the morning of April 15 she gave birth to a son, whom they promptly named John Charles.

Gregorio had come running to join his family again. When the nurse announced that she would leave at the end of the first week, Gregorio said laughingly, "My mother had ten babies, I helped raise seven of them. I know everything to do. I take care of Charlie when the nurse go."

Jessie remained in bed while John went about San Francisco hiring mechanics for the mines, buying supplies, checking the homes and shops that had been built on the land he had bought before leaving for Washington. A committee of Australians who had established a colony on the Frémont holdings came to the house and presented to her a petition asking that they be allowed to buy their land so that they could feel permanently settled. She promised to urge their request on her husband. That evening she asked John to sell the Australians the property, pointing out that these people were as anxious for their own hearths as they were.

When the baby was fifteen days old, and she was rocking him in an improvised crib, she heard alarmed shouts below her. A few moments later she smelled smoke. Sending for Gregorio, she demanded to know what was happening.

"There's a fire on the south side of the square."

"Is it coming this way?"

Gregorio went to the bedroom window and called back, "I can't tell where the fire come, but the wind come this way."

At that moment John rushed in with extra blankets and a grass hammock.

"There's nothing to be alarmed about," he said reassuringly, "but we must be prepared. The houses below us on the hill are catching. If the fire rises much higher Gregorio and I will carry you and the baby to Russian Hill. The sand dunes will keep the fire from reaching there. I've already sent over our silverware and papers."

"I've ridden in hammocks before," she replied calmly; "just give me two minutes' notice to prepare Charlie."

By nightfall all of San Francisco was aglow, the air filled with smoke and flying ash. From her bed Jessie could watch the night sky grow redder and redder. Friends thronged up the hill to help John hang wet canvas and soaked carpet over the side of the house to prevent sparks from setting it aflame. Below her she could hear the shouts of the men fighting the fires; by the growing intensity and the heat she knew that the flames were coming ever higher on the hill. The sidewalks, made of wooden planks, carried the flames, and the crackling fires of the wooden houses mingled with the sounds of the fire bells and shouts of the men dashing through the streets trying to save their properties.

At midnight there was a sharp veering of the wind. The fire began racing south again across the square. Their home was saved.

The next morning, leaning on the arm of her husband, Jessie circled the house to survey the damage. Below her most of the city lay in ashes. The paint was blistered on her own home, but there was no other damage. It wasn't until she had gone back into the house and climbed into bed again that she realized her calm of the night before had been the same kind of protection with which she had insulated herself for the trip across Panama.

At the end of a month, when her strength had returned, and the machinery had arrived for the mines, John left for the Mariposa to begin the installation work. He was standing for re-election, yet he would do nothing to promote his candidacy. Jessie wondered why her husband declined to strive as mightily for the political office he wanted as he had striven to make himself a successful engineer. Electioneering demanded that a man get out on the stump, that he tour the state, speaking to every group that assembled, that he keep a steady stream of articles flowing to the press, that he treat politics as though it were a business or a profession and throw himself into it wholeheartedly if he expected to achieve the desired result. But John would not electioneer and would not campaign. As he had in Monterey, he said quietly to his wife:

"Everyone in this state knows me and knows whether or not he wants me to continue being senator. Shaking a few thousand hands won't change the results of the election; if the majority of the people in this state are in favor of slavery, then I'll be defeated; if the majority are in favor of freedom, then I'll be sent back to the Senate. No one is going to change the mind of a slavery man by making a speech at him; and besides I'm not a good speechmaker."

She respected his reticence, his refusal to fight for his seat in the Senate. Nevertheless she wished that there were some way to campaign for him. She would have been entirely willing to take her carriage and the team of horses and stump the state, speaking in every hamlet and village, debating with the slavery faction. But alas, there was nothing she could do; a wife could not campaign for her husband, and surely a wife could not urge that a man plunge himself into public conflict if it was against his temperament to do so.

And once again she was puzzled by the riddle of her husband's character. Why, under one set of circumstances, did he grasp more power and authority than he was entitled to, then in another field be modest, self-effacing, refuse to play the critical part which everyone expected of him? Was he behaving this way because the court-martial had declared him to be a usurper, a man seeking personal power and fame—and he wanted to live down the accusation? Or did this contradiction in his temperament arise from the various components within his mind: the components dealing with politics enclosing one set of attitudes; those dealing with war and the Army another and very different set? Only she knew how many dozens of separately locked compartments there were, and how divergent their contents.

She remembered how in the first days of her honeymoon she had dimly perceived that marriage might mean the spending of a lifetime trying to understand her mate, evolving the mysteries of character which even he didn't know were there. She had said to herself then, I would not want a man who would be obvious. It will be an exhilarating pursuit, trying to understand what will come next, fitting all the pieces together. And what a great hour it will be, ten years from now, fifty years from now, when I finally understand John. She had now been married for ten years, she understood many fragments of her husband's behavior, and yet she had to confess to herself that she was no closer to a solution of his character than she had been the day she married him.

San Francisco was growing at an amazing rate; she liked to walk down into the business district and shop for rare art objects or furnishings from the Orient, wines or sweets from Paris, woolens from England. On one of her trips she was delighted to find two sets of violet-colored muslin curtains, which she tied back with pink ribbons to brighten the parlor and dining room. There were a flourishing newspaper and theater; thousands of people were coming in from overland trails and by ship from Australia and the Orient. They were a conglomerate crew: along with the eastern farmers and settlers, the staid businessmen and the gold seekers, there was a large crowd of British criminals released from Botany Bay in Australia, as well as the irresponsible *Guarde Mobile* which had been shipped over from Paris for the greater safety of France; there were the wild ones, the professional adventurers and gamblers, the thieves, embezzlers, swindlers, murderers from all over America who had thronged to this fabulously rich and exciting frontier.

Despite the fact that Senator Frémont's bills for the setting up of courts and a legal structure had been passed in Washington, the machinery for these was not yet working in San Francisco. Violence flared everywhere; bands of armed thieves roamed the streets at night, plundering and shooting. Anyone who tried to protest had his house or business set on fire; women could not leave their homes after nightfall, and no man's property was safe from their depredations. The respectable merchants and settlers in San Francisco were organizing to put an end to the lawless element which, it was claimed, had started the fire. When the citizens' committee, who named themselves the Vigilantes, threatened to take the law into their own hands and punish the miscreants, civil war broke out in the town. One warm June afternoon as she was sitting in her back garden overlooking the bay, a handbill was thrown over the fence. She read:

If the people of San Francisco carry out their threatened intentions, we will fire the city. We will make your wives and families suffer for your acts.

She knew how fast fires could carry in the wind-swept city, and she was afraid that her own wooden structure would go up in flames before she could get the two children out to safety. From then on she did no more sleeping of nights, but read, wrote letters home and to her husband, kept a vigilant eye out of the windows which faced in three directions. In the morning, after Gregorio and his cousin, who had become Charlie's nursemaid, were awake, she would draw the blinds in her room and sleep until noon.

One Sunday morning after Gregorio and his cousin had gone to church, and just as the bells began to toll ten o'clock, the hour when the summer winds swept across San Francisco, she saw fire break out simultaneously in several parts of the residential district below her. She picked up little Charlie naked and wet from the bath and wrapped him in the skirt of her dressing gown. Lily came in with her two pet hens, asking, "Mother, could you find me ribbons to tie their legs?"

"Go up the hills to Mrs. Fourgeand's house on Clay Street and stay there until I come for you."

Lieutenant Beale came running, bareheaded, his face already black with soot, led her out of the house in her slippers and gown and up the several blocks of steep rough hill to Mrs. Fourgeand's. Here she found dozens of women and children gathered in this one spot of safety. Lily threw herself into her mother's arms, but Lieutenant Beale relieved the tension by exclaiming, "Look, the baby is still asleep on my shoulder."

Jessie went into the front room, which overlooked the burning city. A Frenchwoman was kneeling before the window, laughing hysterically as she watched her house go up in flames. After a few moments she turned to Jessie, recognized her and cried, "Madame Frémont! Your house goes next. Here, take my place. It is the best seat in the house, you can see your place burn up!"

Sympathetic women led the afflicted one away. Jessie stood by the window for a long time, while her heart cried out at the sight of her home, her baby's birthplace, catching like dry tinder, almost every part of it roaring into flames at once. At the end of an hour there was nothing left but the gaunt red brick chimney pointing up to the sky like an accusing finger. At dusk most of San Francisco had once again been burned to the ground. Lieutenant Beale returned to Mrs. Fourgeand's and said, "I have a place where you and the children can rest tonight; it is not very elegant, but at least we have food and blankets there. Come along, we'll pretend we're camping on the Monterey peninsula again."

That night she lay on a cot in a tent in the sand dunes, the baby sleeping in the crook of her arm, Lily and her two chickens with blue ribbons around their legs on a mattress on the floor. She spent the night alternately weeping and trembling over the loss of this first home of her own. Bitterly she remembered, "The gods are slow to consecrate a new hearth." Imaginary fire bells clanged in her ears; behind her feverish and tightly closed eyelids she once again watched the city burn, each succeeding house catching fire and going up in flames, until the whole world outside of her eyelids was blazing.

The next morning Lieutenant Beale came back to tell her that he and Gregorio had worked all night on a former army barrack several miles out in the dunes, scrubbing it and putting it in condition so that she could have a place to live until her new home could be built. Since there were no horses or carriages available, she trudged through the sand, her water-soaked slippers heavy with mud, her dressing gown trailing. When she reached the barrack she found that the men had assembled fresh clothing, some books, candles for lighting and boxes of foodstuffs. After the children fell asleep, she sat through the long night reading Donald Mitchell's *Reveries of a Bachelor* by candlelight. She was too nervous to go to bed; she had a feeling of despair at ever becoming settled in such a wild community. The baby woke at dawn, demanding its breakfast. The Indian girl announced, "Gregorio, he find a white goat with lots of milk . . ."

Jessie smiled and thanked her, but the girl did not move.

"Some people come see you," she exclaimed. "Please you talk to them?"

She washed her hands and face, combed her hair and slipped into a dress. She walked through the front room of the barrack and opened the door. Before her stood a middle-aged Australian and his wife; she recognized them as the spokesmen for the tenants who had asked for permission to buy their land. Looking over their shoulders she saw a long procession of people coming across the dunes, all of them carrying parcels and bundles and some of them pulling carts.

"What is it?" she asked, stupefied.

"It is like this, Mrs. Frémont," replied the Australian, "when the fire began on Sunday morning we decided the wind would carry it up to your house. All of us rushed up to your home to see if we couldn't save it. You and the little ones were already gone."

"We saw we couldn't save your house, Madame Frémont," broke in the wife, "so we did the next best thing: we saved everything inside your walls." She turned and indicated the trail of people. "We carried out all of your clothing, your furniture, mirrors, china, silverware and glasses, rugs, and your books. Madame Frémont, you lose the building, nothing else."

Jessie watched the tenants come up one by one to the front porch, deposit all of her valuables: her jewelry and personal effects, her dishes and perfume bottles, her dresses and lingerie, the children's clothing, and the toys they had brought from Washington, foods and cases of wine, even the violet curtains with the pink tie-backs. The Australians knocked the furniture together, set up two beds in the back room; moved the bookcase into the front room and arranged the books on its shelves; they put the curtains on the windows, hung her pictures on the walls, and on the floors laid her carpets and rugs. Within an hour the lonely barrack in the sand dunes had been transformed into the Frémont household. The leader then brought forth a heavy parcel tied in a red silk handkerchief.

"We knew the colonel was from home," he said, "and since there was a young baby in the house, we thought money might come in handy. We brought a quarter's rent in advance."

He untied the handkerchief and let fall onto a table a heap of coins. In her excitement Jessie could not control her tears. She shook hands with every last one, thanking them warmly.

Several days passed. Though she was comfortable, surrounded by her own possessions, she longed ardently to have her husband by her side. There was no regular mail service to the Mariposa and she was unwilling to send a courier after him. She would simply have to wait until he learned of the new fire that had swept the city.

It was almost a week later when, sitting on the front porch in the warm June sunshine, she saw his familiar figure trudging over the dunes. She jumped up and ran across the sand hillocks to meet him. When she could tear herself from his embrace she asked: "But how did you know where to find us?"

"I came by the night boat from Stockton," he replied. "I practically ran up the hill from the square, but when I got to our house there was nothing left but the chimney with the sun shining on it. I asked a passer-by if he knew where you were, and he replied, 'Near Grace Church.' From the front porch of the church I surveyed the landscape, and I saw this little house with violet curtains fluttering out the windows. When I saw the pink ribbons, I was sure it was you."

That afternoon Jessie sent for the Australian tenants. John had been writing busily at his desk. When they arrived he thanked them heartily, then picked up a stack of papers.

"These are your deeds of sale. You now own your land."

There was a moment of silence, during which the men looked over the deeds. Their spokesman murmured:

"Colonel Frémont, it is better than we expected. We could pay a little more."

"You have already paid that little more," he replied. "Good luck to you, and God bless you."

When each had clasped his hand and thanked him in turn, and they had left, Jessie kissed her husband sedately and said:

"Thank you, dear. That was a special gift to me."

That evening as they walked the hills above the burned city that was already again rebuilding on its ashes, John told her of his many difficulties on the Mariposa: serious quarrels had arisen with mining groups who claimed that they had located their mines before he arrived, that he had purposely staked out his boundaries to include their holdings. They had refused to abandon their mines and were threatening warfare if anybody tried to put them off. The machinery he had bought in New York was proving costly and inefficient; only a bare portion of the available gold was being secured. The mining engineers he had hired, and whose expenses he had paid to California, had left him and were staking out their own claims. In order to operate the mines he needed dams, roads, mills, but no money had arrived from England, and trouble had arisen in London over the stock companies based on the Mariposa leases. Hoffman, his first choice, had proved to be an honest and conscientious worker, but Sargent had placed fraudulent advertisements in the London newspapers, soliciting the sale of stock, and his manipulations had cut the ground out from under Hoffman's feet; banks and investors originally interested in Mariposa leases had withdrawn their subscriptions, while Sargent was collecting funds on a basis which could dispossess the Frémonts of the entire holdings.

Nor was that all. The Indians, who had not quarreled with the whites up to this time, were on the warpath because the miners had deprived them of their hunting grounds, killed and eaten their wild cattle, and driven them so deep into the mountains that the tribes could not secure enough food. They had met in common council, decided to kill and eat the white men's cattle, and then drive the white men out of the region. There had been shootings and killings; the mining on the Mariposa would have to be stopped unless the Indians could be placated. The United States commissioners had been treating with the Indians, attempting to move them out of the gold country and on to other hunting grounds; the Indians had agreed to move on, providing they would be furnished with beef during the time it would take to move their tribes and set up on the new lands. The small quantities of cattle available were being held for extortionate rates, and the commission had been unable to secure enough to guarantee the treaty. The Indians were preparing to wage open warfare in order to drive the white men out of the gold country.

"What about your cattle, John? Have you enough to take care of their needs?"

"Yes. But the commission has no funds with which to buy—hold on now! I'm perfectly willing to let them have the cattle on credit, but you know that I don't come off very well when I spend money for the government. My notes for a half-million dollars' worth of provisions taken during the conquest have never been paid . . ."

"But if you make a bona fide offer to the commission," said Jessie, "and they make a written acceptance . . . ?"

"Then when do we get our money? The commission doesn't return to Washington for a year. If the Department of the Interior refuses to believe that the Indians were in desperate straits and ready to pillage, they can disavow their own commission, just as they disavowed me. No one can sue the federal government, so I'll once again be in the awkward position of petitioning the Congress to get our money for the cattle. It isn't that I mind so much running the risk of never being repaid, or even of the trouble and weeks of work it will involve; what I don't like is being obliged to appear before the American people as someone trying to make money off the government."

"Then don't make money off them," she replied calmly. "Go down to the commission and give them an offer which will meet your costs. That will save the government money and avert warfare with the Indians. As long as you have the cattle available, can you do less?"

"No, Senator Benton, I can't do less. Confound it; it means I'll have to be away from the mines for a solid month, and then I'll probably never get my money back. But I can't do less."

The next morning he went to Commissioner Barbour and made him an offer. Barbour replied, "Your offer is the lowest and best yet made by a respectable man. I'll take it."

John reported to Jessie; she watched as he was once again in the saddle, off for Southern California to drive up the cattle himself.

11

September was a lovely month. The fogs disappeared, the sun came out bright and warm; each day Jessie roamed the hills and sand dunes with Lily and little Charlie, the baby carried papoose fashion by either Gregorio or his cousin. The bay and the strait sparkled in the early fall. The children thrived, grew strong and red-cheeked.

Jessie had talked to John about their home: whether they should buy one of the few remaining residences at no matter how extortionate a price, whether they should build their new house on their lot on Stockton Street, whether they should perhaps buy a farm near by on the peninsula where it would be warm. John had been uncertain. He had told her she could do anything she wanted, but had evidenced no enthusiasm for any of the alternatives. Nor had she been able to derive any idea of his plans for the future; he spoke of going back to Washington to try to push through some mining laws, returning to New York to design and build more modern ore-crushing equipment, going to London to straighten out the financial mess, of moving the entire family up to the Mariposa. As long as his mind was suspended she did not feel free to move in any direction, and so she remained in the little barrack in the dunes.

The winter before she had spent in Madame Castro's two rooms, watching the rain pour in from the sea; the November rain swept windwise across San Francisco, and once again she was isolated in two rooms. The senatorial election came and went without John uttering one word or making a single gesture toward succeeding himself. The organized groups beat the drums for their candidates; ever-growing slavery factions decried his political experience; his friends and supporters were scattered throughout the county, busy with their own affairs. There was nothing she could do with him away, apparently disinterested in the result, and so she had to sit back and watch her husband be beaten.

She had been well trained in the history and literature of exploration, but the work of exploring had worn out; she had read books on agriculture and done what she could to prepare herself to be a farmer's wife, but the farm had never materialized. She had hoped to be a senator's wife, had been equipped by both training and temperament to fill that job; now their seat in the Senate had vanished. There was no part she could play in gold mining, and she frankly had little interest in it.

Her mind went back as it so often did to her few moments of conversation with Mary Algood on the outskirts of St. Louis. Mary's lot was the hard one; she had had to cross the plains in her covered wagon, break ground in the Oregon wilds, live the life of unrelenting toil. Yet frequently Jessie found herself envying Mary: she had been free to go to Oregon in her covered wagon with her husband by her side; she had been free to stumble across stubble fields behind the plow to break the Algood acres; she had been free from public censure and the aggravations that follow the collapse of high ambition. Jessie knew that at each point the world would have said she was the more fortunate of the two: her husband was the famous explorer whose map the Algoods were using in their passage across the plains, yet being his wife meant that she had had to endure endless months of aloneness and agony over her husband's safety; she had a thousand times more money than Mary Algood would ever see after a lifetime of back-breaking toil, and yet that money only meant that she was separated from her husband for months at a time.

John seemed no longer to need her; the same accidental discovery of gold on the Mariposa which had removed him from any field of creative work had also removed her opportunity to collaborate with him. It seemed to her that before long she would be in her mother's position: mistress of a large home, children to raise, entertaining to be done, a background to be created for her husband—and nothing more. For the hundredth time she wished that Larkin had kept his Mariposa and left them in possession of the Santa Cruz ranch with its old vines and peaceful orchards and lovely view over the sea. She remembered what Nicollet had told her: "Any accident or scoundrel can take your money—and usually does—but no one can deprive you of the skill to turn out good work. The finest and most durable possession in all the world is good workmanship."

In proportion as they amassed gold, their marriage, that individual entity which was a third being created by their union, had deteriorated into routine. It was no longer something greater than the sum total of the two of them, but rather something less. She sat in the forlorn barrack on the sand dunes with her two children, prey to loneliness, while her husband remained away for months at a time extracting wealth from the earth. Their marriage could be a beautiful thing when they were apart for a purpose, such as an expedition; then it could glow with a sustaining light. Geographic separation did not detract from the stature or intensity of the marriage, but separation in ultimate desires, separation in one's conception of the good and valuable life could slash away at the stature of a marriage until this third being which was created by the meeting of two minds and two hearts had died, and there was little left but a husband and a wife.

This was the reverse of the shield of her despair on the Delaware Indian Reservation, but this could be the profounder tragedy of the two: either of the two mates might die, grow weary or calloused with the ideals of their relationship, become indifferent, disillusioned. Yet even when this happened, the other could maintain the marriage by tenderness, sympathy and patience, by hanging grimly on and fighting, by enduring difficult periods; the marriage would maintain its fundamental strength, would come back to robust life when the temporary derangement had passed. One had to refuse to think in terms of disruption or defeat or possible ending: one had to forgive transgressions, have an iron-willed, incorruptible faith in the permanence of the relationship: for a marriage, like a human life, must endure all manner of vicissitude; the weak mortal, the weak relationship went down to destruction at the first ill wind; the stalwart marriage survived all gales, even though sometimes it had to plunge blindly through black and mounting seas.

But if the marriage were dead! If it had slowly crumbled into meaninglessness, then everything was gone.

She knew that her plight was no one's fault, but rather a piling up of accidental circumstance. Yet accidental circumstance must not be allowed to be the master, or their lives would be buffeted by every changing wind. She did not want these gold mines, she did not want wealth; the gold had come into their hands only by an ironic twist of fate. Was John right in saying that if fate dumped a fortune down into your lap you were a fool not to take it? Perhaps they were the more fools in the taking!

She knew she could not impose this reasoning on John, for that would be obliging him to accept her standards. He had to reach that conclusion by himself, come to the point where he realized that the mines were costing him more in companionship and love and accomplishment than they were producing in other precious metals. She did not doubt that he would one day come to this conclusion; but how long and how far away? How many weary miles would they have to retrace their steps to find again that partnership which had characterized their earlier years?

Once again she was confronted by the unsolvable character of her husband: how could a man who was so indifferent to money and its trappings, who had worked for years in a field in which he could hope to earn nothing but the most modest army salary, suddenly devote his life to making money? How did one ever come to understand the enigma of another man's soul?

Her one joy during these long and troubled days was her love for little Charlie, which was multiplied in intensity because in it there was included the love for her lost son, Benton, and her profoundest gratitude for demonstrating that she could again bear healthy children. She insisted upon bathing the boy herself, in feeding him his morning and evening meal, so that they would grow close together, know and love each other's every move. Charlie was full of laughter, and Jessie whiled away many an hour playing games to make her son giggle.

The day before Christmas she roamed the hills with Lily looking for a Christmas tree. She rolled tin foil and made spur-of-the-moment ornaments. Friends came during the afternoon to bring gifts and extend the holiday greetings: some of the delegates to the Monterey convention who had known the warmth of her fireside and the hospitality of her table; army officers and their wives to whom she had brought memories of their homes in the East; the Australians, whose property they had made available on generous terms; their old friends Beale and Knight, to whom she and her children were like family; old acquaintances from St. Louis and Washington who had come straight from the wharf to the home on Stockton Street for a welcome to California; miners whom they had grubstaked, merchants from whom they had bought even though the wares were not yet satisfactory; the son of an Indian chief whose tribe had been rescued with John's cattle; the Saunders family, Negroes who had been saved from slavery because John had taken the man up to the Mariposa with him and helped him wash out seventeen hundred dollars in gold, enough to buy his freedom.

But by dark they had all gone, gone to join their families and friends for Christmas dinner. Jessie was left alone with her two children, for Gregorio and his cousin had ridden south for the holidays. After she fed Lily and Charlie and put them to sleep, she sat in a rocker by the Christmas tree, longing for her husband, for a roaring fire, for her parents and Eliza, for her young sisters and brother and the friends and relatives who gathered in the warm and brightly lighted rooms in their home on C Street. She fell to musing about the years that had passed and the years that were to come. There was no fireplace in this little two-room barrack, no hearthstone, yet in the mellowness of spirit engendered by Christmas she perceived that a hearth is not merely a fireplace: a hearth can also be a fire kindled in the hearts of other people, a kindness done here, a service done there, a man or woman given happiness on a frontier thousands of miles from home. It was a year and a half since they had first come to California; she had been almost the first white woman to cross Panama, hers had been one of the first American homes in Monterey; by her refusal to buy or use slaves she had played a small but significant role in keeping California free; by their discovery of gold on the Mariposa and their importing of machinery to set up permanent mines, they had quickened the migration of easterners to California, increased the buying power abroad of the new state; by John's willingness to provide beef for the Indians they had kept peace in the mining regions; by his comprehensive program in the Senate they were slowly bringing the United States to California; by their own return to California, by their steadfastness in remaining in San Francisco after the fires and violence and destruction, they had helped create a sense that this frontier would survive and be permanent; by making the long, hazardous trip by sea, by crossing Panama while heavy with child and by giving birth to her son in the primitive conditions of San Francisco, she had created a home of flesh and blood rather than wood and glass.

It was not much to have done, she knew, and not at all what she had planned. Yet some sixty years had passed since Grandmother Benton had set out for the frontier of Tennessee; times had changed, this new frontier was unlike any other the country had known; each one played his part according to the contour of the times and the nature of the need. If she could not duplicate Grandmother Benton's performance, it was perhaps not altogether her fault; she had done the best she could, had gone through much for her efforts. She was only twenty-seven, yet at moments like these she felt as though she had lived as long as Grandmother Benton or Grandmother McDowell.

She glanced at the clock and saw that it was an hour from midnight. She decided that she would remain awake long enough to see the Christmas Day in and would then go to her cold and lonely bed.

But the wish was stronger than the will, and in a few moments she fell asleep, her head on her chest, her breathing quiet in the still house. She dreamed that she heard the swift beat of a horse coming over the dunes, of a man springing from its back and rushing across the wooden porch. The image went back to that moment on the Delaware Indian Reservation when John had returned in just this fashion to offer his sacrifice, to bring her new courage and new life. She dreamed that the door was flung open, that heavy sacks were dropped on the rough wooden floor, that she was swooped up in her husband's arms, her face covered with kisses, that she was seated again in the same chair, but this time on John's lap with his arms about her and her head on his shoulder and her lips on his lips: and at last she knew it was no dream.

"My dear," she murmured, "you did come home for Christmas."

"Could you doubt it? Are you all right? Are the children well?"

He listened quietly, his dark eyes scanning her face, while she told him of the commonplaces of her routine, led him to the bedroom to show him how well his son and daughter looked. Then he brought the two sacks into the candlelight and began showing her the gifts he had managed to purchase in his hasty flight for home.

"They aren't much," he said, "most of the stores were closed. But how would you like a trip to Paris as a Christmas gift?"

"Splendid," she replied tartly; "let's also give Charlie a peep at the man in the moon."

He chuckled, took a wallet from his back trousers pocket, opened a brightly colored envelope and dangled two long steamship tickets before her unbelieving eyes, his index finger underscoring the lines.

"Read them, Miss Jessie. We're going to have a full year in Europe."

In a whisper she read, "San Francisco to Chagres. Chagres direct to Liverpool. Folkstone to Boulogne, France."

As the tears began to roll down her cheeks, he caught them in his palm and brushed them away. Her thoughts went back ten full years to the rainy afternoon when they had sat before the fire in Hassler's workroom, with Grandmother McDowell at the front window watching the funeral procession of President Harrison, and the ardent, dark-eyed young man sitting across the tea table from her had said, "I will always love you, Jessie, of that you can be sure. I may make mistakes, I may fail you in other ways, I won't come up to your expectations, but I will always love you."

How true it was that marriage required patience rather than logic, that it must not be disrupted at every unforeseen twist of fortune, but allowed time to work out its fundamental and organic pattern.

"Can you leave the mines?" she asked.

"The mines have already separated us too long. Let's spend our time and money together while we still have them, before I prove that Nicollet was right about a fool and his funds. It will be your first real vacation in ten years. The first since you spoke those fateful words, 'Whither thou goest I will go.' Do you remember, Jessie?"

I FIRST heard the story about the desert padre at my home in Encino, in the San Fernando Valley of Southern California, from a group of Father John J. Crowley's former friends and associates. Regeneration is a challenging theme to the writer, perhaps the most challenging of all; and in this particular case, where the regeneration of a whole people and land were tied up with the return of a human soul to a state of grace, the challenge became even greater. At this time, in 1943, I was planning to write a book to be called *The Male American*, which would include some twenty chapters about men whose lives, inside the context of American society, I had found challenging and rewarding. The history of Father John J. Crowley seemed to me to fit superbly into my design for the book. I promptly went up to Owens Valley to learn about the land, and speak with the people who had known Father Crowley. I returned home with a mass of documents, interviews and background material, and wrote the story at considerable length.

Since the *Saturday Evening Post* had serialized my biography of Jack London a few years before, I reasoned that they might want to publish *Desert Padre*. I was disappointed when they returned the manuscript. How could I have been so deeply moved by a story, only to find that the first editors to read it were disinterested?

By this time I had begun work on a novel about Jessie Benton Frémont. I put the story of Father Crowley in the manuscript file. A few months later, after finishing a long chapter of my new book, and wanting a change of pace, I took out the manuscript. I quickly saw what might have gone wrong: the manuscript seemed overblown, the pacing slow. I had told too much about Father Crowley, the dull as well as the exciting, the purposeless as well as the meaningful.

I threw out not only the repetitive material, but also that which was least illuminating. After several days of hard cutting, of peeling away everything that obstructed the main line of interest, I found that my manuscript was down almost to half.

Now the *Saturday Evening Post* accepted the story. It was reproduced in the *Catholic Digest*, was dramatized in a national radio broadcast, bought for a motion picture and published in an anthology, *The People's Reader*. I had had to learn all over again that a tightly organic, architectural form is as important in the writing of a story as is characterization, mood, and dialogue.

DESERT PADRE

IN the late fall of 1934 an automobile drew up before a church in Lone Pine, California, with three men in it. Two of them lifted the third from the car and carried him half stumbling into the church, where he lay down in one of the pews. Another man riding along the main street of Lone Pine had watched the scene and had thought he recognized the afflicted one as an old friend from Fresno. He parked his car and entered the simple wooden church.

"Hello, Father Crowley. What are you doing here?"

The stricken man looked up. "They told me I was going to die, so I asked for permission to die in Owens Valley. I hear they say you're going to die, too?"

"I don't pay any attention to it anymore."

The Very Reverend Monsignor John J. Crowley lifted himself to one elbow, then smiled slowly. He had a nice face, strong, plain, perhaps even a trifle homely, with large ears, a high and broad forehead topped by a thick shock of black hair shot through with gray, and based by a stubborn Irish chin. His eyes were beautiful: light blue, with a piercing quality, yet kind, the kindest eyes, people said, they had ever known.

"I have an idea, Ralph," he said softly. "Let us both get well. We'll find some good fight. We'll forget the past."

The condemned men shook hands gingerly on their bargain. Three days later the friend saw Father Crowley again. He was able to walk a few steps unaided; there was a faint touch of color in his cheeks.

"You must have found a good one!"

"The best," replied Father Crowley with a quiet chuckle. "We are going to work for the rehabilitation of Owens Valley. With God's help, we're going to persuade the city of Los Angeles to let us buy back our property, and use our water on it, and own our valley once again."

He was not underestimating the enormity of the task, for he was no stranger to this ten thousand square miles of desert that lay east of the Sierra Nevada Mountains; it had been his first parish. He knew Owens Valley to be more fatally ill than he, that this once abundant land, with its thousands of farms, ranches and homes, famous throughout the country as the producer of California's first-prize apples, grain and corn would require a miracle to keep from reverting irretrievably to the rock, the sage and the sand of the desert.

By the end of the month he had gained sufficient strength to be driven slowly through the parish to which he had first come as a young man in 1919. Where before there had been alfalfa fields waving like a green canopy to the very base of the Sierras, now there were barren wastes which could support little but chaparral, tarantulas and snakes. The home of the farmer who had grown this alfalfa was now abandoned, the glass broken out of the windows, the doors groaning on one hinge in the wind. Half of what had once been lovingly tended apple orchards were now uprooted, the other half stood bonily dead in the sun. The schoolhouse that had burned down had never been rebuilt. The roads that had led him to outlying farms had reverted to nature. The railroad tracks that had carried the cars of Owens Valley produce to Los Angeles were rusty threads in a wilderness. The yellow corn fields were gone, the silos caving in, the mills hollow enclosures where lizards scampered between the rocks. The Owens River, once a robust stream deep with the snow waters of the Sierras, was but a trickle in a dry streambed, the cottonwoods dead along its bank.

Water, mused the priest, water was one of God's greatest gifts. With it the pioneers had turned this strip of land between two gigantic ranges into a garden. Deprived of water, the valley and its people with it, were perishing.

No people less deserved such a cruel fate, Father Crowley knew, than these pioneers who had trudged their resolute way across the plains and settled the valley in the same year that the Civil War had begun in the east. The men, their wives and children put their shoulders behind mountain-born boulders and shoved them inch by inch to the river's edge; they plowed up the thick-crusted desert yard by yard; in the relentless sun they dug irrigation ditches with their crude hand tools. During the first year the Indians attacked with arrows; nearly everything died: the fruit trees, the grain, the livestock. But they were indomitable. They shivered and starved through the winter, and when spring came they plowed and planted again. More families came;

schools were built; little towns sprang up along the road through the center of the valley; board houses replaced log cabins. The cattle multiplied; the children grew up and married and multiplied; Owens Valley grew in population and riches and strength.

Then the promoters of Los Angeles had decided that the Owens Valley watershed could supply enough water to make their sun-baked little town a great world metropolis. Soon the melting snows of the Sierras were being diverted from Owens Valley to the desert of San Fernando Valley and Los Angeles, two hundred and twenty miles away. Owens Valley had been abandoned to its fate by the national and state governments, by the more tractable and fainthearted of its residents who sold out and abandoned the farms and homes they had created with their own hands.

Father Crowley too had abandoned the country a decade before, believing it to be doomed. He too had moved on to more fertile fields, leaving his first land and people to succumb to attrition. He had simply been doing his duty when, recognized for his work in building three churches in a section that had been attended only by visiting pastors, he had answered the call to become Chancellor of the new Monterey-Fresno diocese. But lying on his back in a hospital bed ten years later, he realized that he had been interested in his own people and not all the people of Owens Valley; that he had thrown his tremendous energies into building churches and not communities; that he had carved out of the desert a career for himself rather than a career for Owens Valley which might have rendered it indestructible. He had traveled day and night in rough stagecoaches, without sleep or food or the simple refinements of life, in an Herculean effort to administer each week to every part of his seventeen thousand square miles of parish. He had lived an irreproachable life of austerity and devotion. Judged in the midst of his youth he had thought he was doing well. Seen from the vantage point of a decade, and of a world collapsed, Father Crowley believed that he had done only half enough. As chancellor of a new diocese, he had helped build, at an amazing rate of speed, churches, a cathedral, hospitals, schools. He had been enormously successful. Then had come the stock-market crash in 1929, the impoverishment of his community, the inability to meet bank loans, his stepping down from the chancellorship, his intimacy with death. He was no longer a businessman desiring to create an empire in terms of wood and stone and steel. Now he wanted to build in terms of the spirit, of the happiness of human souls.

When the Bishop had come to him in the hospital in Bakersfield and asked, "My son, what one last favor can the Church grant you?" he had replied, "Let me go back to Owens Valley to die." But in his heart was the determination not to die until he had first enjoyed a reprieve sufficiently long to enable him to expiate his sins of omission. He intended to die in Owens Valley, but not quite yet.

He determined, standing again on the parched earth, with the grandeur of Mount Whitney towering to fourteen thousand five-hundred feet above him, that the water must be returned to Owens Valley, its land must be made green again, its people called home. He did not know how; yet the resolution made him strong. By the end of the second month he felt well enough to pitch into his work. Each day brought added strength, and Father Crowley had no more thought of dying.

He became a familiar sight on the streets of Lone Pine, Independence and Bishop, and on the dirt roads of Inyo and Mono counties, in his Army shirt with khaki riding pants and puttees; a medium tall, huskily built man, a little bandy-legged, with his right arm held out from the body because it had been broken at the elbow in a horse, rock and doc game when he was a child, and never properly set. He became an indigenous part of the desert and the sand-colored mountains of the Panamint. The only way one could tell he was not a prospector was by the clerical collar which he wore even in the bitterest heat.

First he was a man of the cloth, and his first efforts belonged to the church. He said Mass at six o'clock on Sunday morning in the majesty of Death Valley, his vestments over his khakis. At seven, when his duties were finished, he rolled up the cassock neatly, jumped into his sand-colored flivver and began the hundred-mile drive out of Death Valley, where he was below sea level, over the staggeringly bare Panamint Range on which he had to climb up to five thousand feet, down again to sea level in the Panamint Sink, then up once again to four thousand feet to get over the pass of the Inyo Mountain Range, before dropping into Lone Pine to say Mass at nine o'clock. He had exactly two hours between Masses to make the trip, one of the most awesome, difficult and nerve-racking rides in all the mountainous West.

He was never in such a hurry that he wouldn't stop along the way to rescue anyone who had been stranded between the gigantic ranges. Two easterners whose car had broken down needed a lift. He loaded them into the back seat of his car along with his blankets, briefcase, dog, cooking utensils, and shot away in a cloud of Panamint alkali dust. Father Crowley hit eighty on the straightaways, pouring out at the same time a comprehensive lecture on the plant life of the desert, the geological stratas of the mountains, the peoples who inhabited the region.

When the car finally pulled up before the Santa Rosa church in Lone Pine, Father Crowley jumped out, crying, "End of the line, folks. I've got a date with the Lord in three minutes!"

The services over at ten o'clock, he would once again slip out of his robe, tuck it under his arm, jump into the car and dynamite the sixty miles to Bishop, to hold his eleven o'clock Mass. His rattling car, which he always wore out before he could complete the payments, became the most important part of his equipage. There was no limit to the number of miles he would drive through his vast parish to get his work done. One evening he learned that Steve Esteves, a Portuguese stone mason, was dying in a hospital in Monrovia. He drove all night to reach Esteves, sorely distressed because the man, who had been living with an Indian squaw in Death Valley for many years, and had had several children by her, had never troubled to have the marriage ceremony performed.

"Steve," he said. "You ought to be married before you die, or you'll never get into heaven."

"She never make that long trip just to marry," replied Steve.

Father Crowley sat silently for a moment. Then he asked, "Steve, has Mary ever seen a streetcar?"

"Why no, Father, she never been in town."

"Do you think if I offered to show her a streetcar, she might come?"

"By God, Father, that might work!"

Father Crowley sped the two hundred difficult miles back to Death Valley, found Steve's Mary, then drove back at once. He quickly performed the marriage ceremony. That night Steve died. The next morning Father Crowley showed Mrs. Esteves a streetcar. By the time he reached his quarters in Lone Pine he had been forty-eight hours without sleep. His only comment was:

"Steve is now where he belongs—by God!"

Owens Valley could be saved only by some heroic effort on its own part. Yet how was that effort to be achieved when many of its best men had moved away in despair, when the conflicting groups in Inyo and Mono counties were at each other's throats in trying to distribute the blame for their plight?

As he sped across the star-studded desert in the deep night silence, he tried to evolve a strategy which would have its antecedents in the long struggle. Shortly after the turn of the century, the farmers of Owens Valley had seen that the excess flood waters which were wasted during the melting season ought to be preserved to furnish irrigation during the long dry autumn. They came to the conclusion that a dam built at the end of Long Valley, just above Owens Valley, could store their surplus water. However Los Angeles set out to buy all the land along the Owens River, all the land along the creeks which fed into the river, all the canal systems the Owens Valley people had built. Los Angeles set out to absorb every acre of tillable land in Owens Valley.

The city's agents, with $11,000,000 in their pockets, offered generous prices for the land. The more opportunistic had sold; those who had mortgages outstanding against their farms had difficulty in renewing their loans; others had their loans called in. Those farmers along a canal system who could neither be tempted by cash nor forced out by the bank, found Los Angeles refusing to keep clear the canals along the property they had bought. The farmers who could not spare the time nor the money to do the extra work were deprived of water for their crops. The little towns of Lone Pine, Independence, and Bishop still had enough drinking water to keep alive, but not enough to sustain their gardens or lawns.

At last Los Angeles owned the sixty thousand acres of tillable land in the valley. Ever thirsty for more water the city now sank wells between Lone Pine and Bishop to draw off the underground water. The people of the towns saw that they would soon have no water to drink. Los Angeles now bought up every piece of business property in the valley, and ninety per cent of the homes. Los Angeles alone determined who could rent property, and for how long. Any occupant could be forced out of his home or business in thirty days. Los Angeles was careful never to take pecuniary advantage of the Owens Valley folk. The prices paid were consistently generous; but the settlers stubbornly maintained that a man's home could mean more to him than a profitable sales price.

There had settled over the people of Owens Valley the pall of bitterness and hatred which Father Crowley now found lodged deep in every last inhabitant. The friendly, hospitable settlers had become morose, hostile, hopeless.

As he rode on horseback through Long Valley and the mountains above it, as he studied the waterflow charts, he saw that if the Long Valley dam had been built exactly where the settlers had judged that it should have been built thirty years before, Los Angeles could have had enough water to take care of a population of five millions, and Owens Valley could have grown until it would have been a beautiful and prosperous community. Several times it had seemed as though the plans were coming to fruition, but always something intervened: politics, land manipulation, seasons of short water. In the end, Owens Valley had been unable to convince the Los Angeles engineers that even with the Long Valley dam there would always be sufficient water for both Owens Valley and the expanding metropolis below.

Wiping the ever-present rim of perspiration from his spectacles, Father Crowley took a deep breath. He knew that the Long Valley dam must be built. But he perceived that the people had to wage the fight themselves, to regain their strength, to forget their bitterness. It was not the country alone that needed rebirth, it was the people as well.

He assigned to himself the task of becoming the friend of every last man, woman and child in his vast parish. He drove to their remote mines in Death Valley, their cattle ranches high in the Sierras, their shacks and huts in the far reaches of the desert. He shared their simple food, slept in their beds, talked to them of their common needs. When they asked why he now talked more about economics than he did about heaven, he replied, thinking of the Biblical story of the loaves and fishes, "No church can be successful preaching to a people who are hungry."

That he did not readily gain their confidence, he realized, was largely his own fault. When he had come to the valley in 1919 he had been a stiff-necked, literal cleric. He had talked little but religion, had caused untold anguish to a Death Valley couple by telling them that, since the wife was a Catholic and the husband a Protestant, they had not been married all these years. The letter of the law had been more important than the spirit.

The people of Owens Valley found him to be a changed man. Where he had been righteous and stern, now he was kind, understanding, easy to meet, warm in manner, plain. His eyes which had always been a little severe now twinkled as he made little jokes at every opportunity, for he believed that if he could start these people laughing they might laugh the hate-virus out of their blood.

He worked constantly for religious tolerance, and slowly his work became successful. Protestants forgave him for being a Catholic, and the Catholics forgave him for having so many Protestant friends. Somewhere along the line, the padre became The Padre, an understanding father to whom the weary, the frightened and confused could come for comfort and help. Always he worked to forge indissoluble links of friendship and common interest.

He rarely had a dollar in his pocket. When he was near friends, he could eat at their table, but many times when he was out alone he went without food because he had no coin with which to buy it. When he was not sleeping in his car or alongside the road in his blanket roll, he slept on a little cot under the eaves of his church in Lone Pine. His worldly possessions were a few extra garments hanging on nails in the rafters.

He had been well brought up for this lean life of the desert. In Ireland, where Father Crowley was born on December 8, 1891, his father had been a teacher of the lower grades, while his mother had taught bookkeeping. They had come to Worcester, Massachusetts, with their six children in 1903. The father found work as a bookkeeper, sired two more children and then died, leaving his wife with eight youngsters to support. The mother took in boarders. As the oldest child, now fourteen, John J. shared with her the responsibility of raising the other children. He did odd jobs after school, worked as a bus boy at resorts during the summers. Every cent he made went into the family pot. He was a serious lad, studious, determined to get what he wanted out of life, and equally determined that his seven sisters and brothers should have an education. He studied journalism for a year at Clark College, thinking he might become a newspaper reporter, but by the end of the summer vacation had decided to spend his life in the church.

He entered Holy Cross College, helped support his family, was an able student, contributed poems, short stories and articles to the Holy Cross literary magazine, of which he became editor in his senior year.

He had a rich Irish imagination and the lyrical flow of language of a visionary. He had a strong will, tried to find something funny even in sadness and had a tremendous physical energy, with no amount of work daunting him. He was always up to something, always had an answer to everything, kept his troubles to himself and lived in the utmost austerity. These were the main characteristics of his youth; this was the boy implicit in the man.

When John was graduated from Holy Cross the Bishop of Los Angeles called for volunteers for the west. Young John promptly raised his hand. In Los Angeles he had once again volunteered, to pioneer the deserts of Inyo and Mono. Here he had learned the validity of the old Piute saying:

"No man should attempt the country east of the Sierras until he has learned to sleep in the shade of his arrows."

Father Crowley was lean, his personal wants had been few, he had found himself able to sleep in the shade of his arrows. But he had not been content for his church to do so.

In 1924, when the first blows had already fallen upon his Owens

Valley parish, he had been called away to become Chancellor of the Monterey-Fresno diocese.

He was wise enough to know that before he could attempt to show Owens Valley how it might become prosperous again, he would have to put his own house in order. His parish being poverty stricken, there seemed no way to raise money for his church work. The average collection on Sunday morning was hardly enough to pay for his gasoline. The responsibility was his to keep three churches going, to carry on his educational work among the children and social work among the needy, to hold services for the C.C.C. boys who lived nine thousand feet up in the snow, and for the nomadic sourdoughs who lived below sea level in Death Valley.

To put his church on a solvent basis, he staged a street carnival, with booths for eating hot dogs and drinking soda pop and gambling a few nickels into the till. This netted him two hundred dollars. He cast *The Drunkard* from among the valley people; folks came for hundreds of miles around to see the show and help out the padre. When a Mexican woman deeded the church a lot he sold it, and with the money renovated the Lone Pine church property so that he was able to rent out the basement to an undertaker, offices on the ground floor to a doctor and a dentist, two living apartments for families upstairs, and the corner to a gasoline company. He found that he would have $120 a month with which to carry out his duties.

He had been back for more than a year when he called together the representatives of every tiny outpost. Thirty men assembled: the editors of the local newspapers, the superintendent of Death Valley National Monument, the resort owners, the leading miners, merchants, cattle and sheep men from the surrounding mountains. They agreed that all work must be accomplished through communal cooperation. The men would contribute of their time, their determination, but not one copper cent. Thus the Inyo Associates were formed one evening in the little sitting room of a pioneer home.

By the following morning opposition had already arisen. The Inyo county supervisors came out against the Associates because they feared it was designed to take away their political power. They would not believe that any such simple motives as securing the right to buy back one's home or shop, securing land, and water with which to irrigate it, and the attracting of tourists, could be genuine. Trained on intrigue, the people feared the organization. Certain of Father Crowley's own parishioners criticized him on the grounds that he ought not meddle in economics and politics. A few members of the powerful Masonic lodge objected to having a priest lead them, while other Protestants claimed he was doing all this to strengthen the influence of the Catholic Church.

Father Crowley was not disheartened by the obstacles. For sixteen hours a day he was in his jalopy, explaining to the people the aims of the association, trying to quiet their fears and suspicions, putting his shoulder against the dead weight of their torpor, their defeatism.

This was as magnificent a country as could be found anywhere in the world, with the most breathtaking contrasts; the trout fishing, hunting, skiing were superb. The country could have been a tourists' paradise, yet when the people of Los Angeles had tried to come up for vacations, they had met with biting hatred.

"Look, you good people," the padre now cried to his neighbors, "it's true that you've had a dirty deal. It's true that Los Angeles made you sell out. But all that is in the past. We have to set our faces to the future, to make a new life for ourselves.

And so the Inyo Associates inched their way into the confidence of the community.

He had always been a strictist in his ritual. Some of his parishioners had been heard to lament that Father Crowley would permit nothing but Gregorian music to be sung or played in his church, and would not permit the altar boys to set foot on the altar until they had learned every last word of their Latin. But once his church work was attended to, his energies were canalized into the problems of reconstructing the valley. He began to write a column for the Catholic press, which was reproduced in other papers, called *Sage and Tumbleweed,* using the by-line *Inyokel,* one of his little jokes combining the name of Inyo county with the implication that the author was a yokel, in which he brought to life for the outside world the beauty and drama of his region. He lectured in Los Angeles to make people feel that they were wanted in Owens Valley. He said Mass at the top of Mount Whitney, the highest point in the United States on which Mass had ever been said, and took along photographers. The newspapers snapped up the pictures, largely because of their scenic beauty. People in Schenectady, in St. Paul, in Kansas City began to ask, "Say, where is this Mount Whitney?"

One evening he sat in a meeting in Bishop. The following day was May first, the opening of the fishing season. He leaned over to Bob Brown, who was writing publicity for the Associates, and murmured: "Do you think you can get a photographer to get up at three in the morning?"

"I guess so," replied Brown.

"I have an idea. We ought to be able to crack a national wire with it." Addressing the group, he said, "I feel sorry for the Catholics on a day like tomorrow. The rest of you can get out on the streams at four and five in the morning, while my people have to wait to go to church at eight. But never let it be said that the Catholics are going to be beaten as fishermen. I'm going to hold a special fisherman's Mass tomorrow at three, and I want you all to come: Catholics, Protestants, Jews, pagans, everybody. It may do you some good; anyway, it can't do you any harm. Bring your worms. I'll bless 'em. We want to get some good pictures, so be sure to bring your waders and rods and baskets."

By three o'clock the little wooden church was full of people, the aisles stacked with fishing rods and reels and baskets and boxes of bait. The flashlights went off while the photographers took pictures. Then, when the excitement had died down, Father Crowley preached a three-minute sermon on Jesus the Fisherman.

Walking into a restaurant in Bishop one day for a cup of coffee, he fell to chatting with an elderly gentleman. "You're the fellow they call the desert priest," the man exclaimed, and invited him to drive with him to New York, all expenses paid, in return for relief at the wheel. The padre saw an opportunity for securing some sorely needed publicizing in the east, and promptly assented.

When he reached New York, he visited his brother, who was Dean of Education at Fordham University.

"See if you can get some of the boys from the city desks over here. Tell 'em your little brother, who is a priest from Death Valley, is here to see the big city . . ."

When the reporters were on their way, the padre took off his tight black coat, then his collar, and began to mop his brow.

"At least put on your collar," begged the younger Crowley.

"I know what I'm doing," replied the padre. "Just let 'em in."

"Your New York heat," he panted to the reporters as he continued to mop his brow, his face, his neck.

"You're hot!" exclaimed one of them. "You come from the hottest spot north of Hades, and you're hot in New York!"

"Why, Death Valley is a cool breeze compared with this town," groaned the padre with an irrepressible twinkle in his eye. "I want to get back home where the climate is agreeable."

It was a good show. The reporters laughed heartily. The padre proceeded to talk about the volcanic wonders of Death Valley, the majestic serenity of the Sierras, spiced with whoppers about the size of the trout in the mountain streams. The next morning his picture and some of the finest unpaid publicity about the far west appeared on the front page of the New York papers. From then on, everywhere he went, Boston, Philadelphia, Washington, Chicago, reporters thronged to his room for interviews. Great numbers of people heard for the first time of a new "Range of Recreation" and the joys of hunting, fishing and lake camping ten thousand feet up in the summer snows.

Thousands of tourists poured into the region, leaving behind them an average of five dollars a day per person. Trade picked up in the stores. New hotels and auto courts were built, using Owens Valley labor and materials. The cattle of the valley were bought at rising prices to feed the vacationists. National grocery and oil companies opened branches. The people of the valley were able to buy new clothes and tools. Every dollar left behind by a tourist passed through ten Inyo hands.

Even with this tangible success, the going was rough for the padre. Antagonisms and rivalries had grown up among the Associates. Indefatigably he worked to convince them that united they would stand and divided they would fall. He ironed out their difficulties, their squabbles. When he felt discouraged or ill, he revitalized himself with the thought that his methods were not only getting the necessary work done, but extending the character and ability of the people.

At last the small successes of the Associates began to dissipate the gloom and hopelessness of the valley. Folks said, "Maybe they can accomplish something. They've succeeded a little already; maybe they'll even be able to make a dent in Los Angeles. Maybe we ought to work with them."

He would never ask anyone to do anything he was not willing to do himself, that is, with one exception. He constantly warned the people, "Drive slow, and watch out for cattle." He himself was the fastest driver in the parish because he had thousands of miles to cover each week to get his work done.

He was sought after as a master of ceremonies, staged shows, rallies and stunts. He filled in, whenever he was asked for an impromptu talk, with the kind of simple, earthy and yet caustic humor that made Will Rogers so beloved.

"Laughter," said the padre, "is as important as food and drink and the shirt on your back. A people that can laugh can never be held down."

He loved the theatre and he loved to act. When the state-wide tourist organization decided to tax the Inyo-Mono Association a thousand dollars, which they didn't have, the padre listened, then rose and said meekly, "I'm just a hick priest from the sticks, and of course I don't know anything about this complicated publicity business, but it seems to me . . ." and launched into a penetrating analysis of how the group was failing to perform its job for themselves as well as for the Inyo-Mono Association. When he sat down there was a dead silence. The organization was reorganized. The thousand-dollar fee was forgotten.

During the second year the padre's Associates attracted to their district a hundred thousand tourists who left behind them half a million dollars. They proved to the state and Federal agencies that they were not a moribund community, and appropriations were passed to extend their agricultural experimentation stations, their fish hatcheries, their roads. They secured an appropriation for a road to connect Mount Whitney with Bad Waters in Death Valley, a project which the padre reasoned would attract millions of Americans because it connected the highest point in the United States with the lowest. To celebrate the opening of the road he staged a show, *The Wedding of the Waters.*

Two Indian runners, in breechcloths and moccasins, dipped a gourd into the icy lake just beneath the peak of Mount Whitney, the highest lake in the United States, and ran down the steep mountain trail with it. Four miles below they delivered the gourd to the pony express. While the crowds cheered and the newsreels ground, it was carried on a prospector's burro, in a covered wagon, a twenty-mule Borax team wagon, a narrow-gauge railroad, a streamlined automobile, and lastly an airplane, which flew below sea level and sprinkled the water into Bad Water, joining the highest water in the country with the lowest.

The big show had cost $6800. The padre was now in debt to the merchants for $800. He never counted costs, he never kept books; when he thought an object was desirable he went ahead and did it.

The padre's *Wedding of the Waters* brought immediate results. By 1940 a million tourists a year were coming into the valley, leaving behind them five million dollars. Old-timers began drifting back; children and grandchildren of the original settlers returned. Young men, attracted by the prospect of growing up with a community rich in promise, brought fresh capital, fresh ideas.

But Father Crowley's greatest ambition was yet to be achieved. He was determined that thirty thousand acres of Owens Valley should become green and productive again; that the Long Valley dam must be built.

In 1937, a hearing was secured with the Los Angeles commissioners. The chairman brought his fist down on the conference table, exclaiming: "Father Crowley, we own Owens Valley. We propose to have no interference. There are no issues for discussion."

The padre laid his fist down on the table alongside of the chairman's and said, "You may own the land of Owens Valley, but you do not own the valley. Human rights are the most precious rights in the world. We grant you ownership of the land and the water rights. I'm here to fight for human rights. If you won't let me fight for those rights in this room, I'll take my fight to the street corners."

After a distinct pause the chairman asked in a small voice, "What is it you want, Father Crowley?"

"The human equities of the people of Owens Valley have not been recognized. Their right to live with all the freedom of American citizens is not satisfied by the conditions created by Los Angeles as a landlord. When you gave us dollars for our lands and our homes, you did not leave us security. We cannot live without security."

It was an opening wedge, but it was not until 1938, when the Angelenos recalled their mayor and his ring, that a new era began for Owens Valley. The new mayor, Fletcher Bowron, agreed to visit Owens Valley with his commissioners.

One of the commissioners persisted, "Why is it so important that people own their own homes? When I look up at these majestic pines and the lofty imminence of Mount Whitney, when I look up at this great sky above us, with its myriads of gorgeous stars, I find myself forced to ask, 'What is the matter with this roof?'"

Just then a light sprinkle of rain began to fall.

"It leaks," replied the padre.

The laugh that went up dealt a deathblow to politics. Within a month the city offered to sell back the homes, businesses and property in the towns, to restore the water rights. Within two months appraisals were under way.

But another year went by, during which the padre was unsuccessful in getting Los Angeles to build the dam at Long Valley, even though the city had voted the money for it, and the plans were drawn. Then one evening, H. C. Van Norman, Los Angeles's chief water engineer, had to attend a meeting in Owens Valley at which the padre and his Associates were also present. When they brought up the subject of the Long Valley dam, Van Norman excused himself. The padre motioned to a man at the back of the room, and with a lean smile, said, "Close the door and lock it, Bill, will you? We can't let Mr. Van Norman miss this interesting discussion."

When Van Norman had heard about all he could stand, he jumped up and exclaimed, "If we build this damn dam, will that finally satisfy you people?"

"Yes!" went up a mighty shout.

"All right then; we'll build it!"

"When?" asked the padre, sweetly.

Van Norman set the date.

"And when will it be completed?" persisted the padre.

Van Norman set that date, too.

The ensuing months were happy ones for the padre. He drew up plans for an All Souls Chapel which would be a house of worship for all races and creeds, began planning what he thought would be the world's most beautiful stations of the cross, starting at Bad Waters and ending at Mount Whitney Portals, the pilgrim thus symbolically going from hell to heaven. He began building a house at Whitney Portals which would be the last station of the cross for the weary pilgrim. It would also serve as a retreat, and provide a few days of peace for clergymen and businessmen.

And so he went his way, a man of God, a short, stocky, bandy-legged fellow with a curious waddle as he walked, his crooked arm held out from his side, a beading of perspiration on his upper lip, his lips dry and cracked from the sun, his hair turning ever grayer.

One day in the middle of March, 1940, he was informed that his great and good friend Sister Anna had died in the convent in San Francisco. It was a sad blow.

After the funeral the Mother Superior called him into the office. "Father Crowley, you are one of Sister Anna's beneficiaries. She left you $25,000."

At dusk, the padre began his drive home. When he reached his own country it was two in the morning, the valley dark and utterly quiet. A good hour for reflection and reverie. He planned to spend the $25,000 as Sister Anna would have wanted: he would clean up his debts, start work on the All Souls Chapel, finish his retreat . . .

He had accomplished everything he had come back from that hospital bed in Bakersfield to accomplish. He did not know what his next task would be, but he was confident that, when the time came, God would provide.

As the tempo of his thoughts accelerated, his foot pressed harder on the gas pedal. A calf suddenly ran across the road. The padre tried to swerve out of the way. Just at that moment a loaded lumber truck was speeding down the road toward him. The padre's car hit the calf, was hurtled into the side of the truck.

The reprieve was over.

The funeral was the largest ever known on the desert. A truckload of flowers arrived with a note which read, "These flowers were not bought from a florist. We picked them ourselves at our homes because it was Inyo water that made them grow."

Of the eight pallbearers, seven were Protestants. Three of these were Masons.

The desert folk were grief-stricken. Everyone in the parish seemed different for having known the padre, a little kinder, a little more co-operative, a little more able. At one stormy meeting of the packers, when they were about to tear their organization to shreds, a cowboy-guide said, "I can't talk much, but if the padre was here, he'd tell you boys what to do. He'd tell you all to work together."

When the dam at Long Valley was completed, on the day the engineer had promised the padre it would be, Van Norman said, "You know, we ought to name this new lake after that little priest. He forced my hand in the neatest manner I've ever known."

Crowley Lake is filling with water now, water which will be used to make Owens Valley fertile again. There will be plenty of loaves and plenty of fishes. The padre would have been mightily pleased with the new lake, but he would have been mad as a hornet about missing the formal dedication. He would have put on a big show for that affair; not merely a rodeo or carnival or pageant, but something unique in the history of promotion. People who heard about it would exclaim, "Say, that sounds like a great spot for our next vacation."

And, who knows, he might once again have cracked a national wire.

EUGENE V. DEBS was born in Terre Haute, Indiana, on November 5, 1855, the son of Alsatian parents who raised six children by running the neighborhood grocery. Gene had a modest education before going to work at fifteen as a fireman for the Vandalia Railroad. He was offered the job of head of the Terre Haute local of the Brotherhood of Locomotive firemen . . . without pay. He worked nights, Sundays, holidays, studying reports and charts, started writing for the union paper, became editor of the *Locomotive Firemen's Magazine,* was elected city clerk of Terre Haute, and slowly built his union. When the national organization was on the verge of collapse, he became secretary-treasurer, moving its offices to Terre Haute. With courage, brains, energy, faith, he won the confidence of the workers and managers. When he was thirty, he married an attractive girl who was solidly bourgeois in her thinking, and opposed his entire way of life.

ADVERSARY IN THE HOUSE

Walls and Bars

WHEN his plans were well formulated, Gene walked into Theodore's office, gazed around him musingly and said, "Mighty nice office you've got here, Theo."

"Glad you like it. Drop in sometime and I'll show you how it works."

"Kind of attached to the place, aren't you?"

"I love it better than my own mother. Why?"

"It just occurred to me this is the first place you ever worked, outside of that little storeroom at the back of the grocery. It would be kind of a wrench to move away, wouldn't it?"

"My dear old pard," drawled Theodore, "stop bushing around the beat. You're never more obvious than when you're trying to be subtle."

"I wasn't trying to be subtle, Theo. I was just wondering if I couldn't get you the job of secretary-treasurer of the Locomotive Firemen."

"What do you mean, get me the job? I've been filling that job for five years while you've been gallivanting around the country looking at all the pretty scenery."

"I'm serious, Theo. There's no one could handle the work better than you."

"Always except you."

"That's what I'm trying to tell you, boy. I'm quitting."

Theodore jumped up from his seat as though someone had ignited the wood beneath him.

"You're what?"

"I'm no more good to the firemen. I've known it for at least two years now. Look, Theo, I want to ask you a question. You have a good job here with the Brotherhood. You can stay with them the rest of your life, you'll have security, it's the kind of work you like . . ."

"You're not asking a question, you're making a speech."

"All right then. Do you want to come along with me . . ."

"Of course," interrupted Theodore.

"Now wait a minute, you idiot. I haven't told you where I'm going."

"I don't care where you're going."

Gene leaned over the desk and clapped Theodore on the shoulder. "I have to leave for the Chicago convention now. I'll tell you about our new venture when I get back."

Theodore let him get as far as the door, then laughed. "Don't rush back on my account. I know about your plans."

"You do?"

"My boy, you couldn't hide anything inside of that head of yours if you covered it with a tarpaulin."

After a moment Gene replied quietly, "There won't be any money for wages."

"True."

"The whole idea may collapse, and we'd both be out of jobs."

"True, true."

"Theo, here I am endangering your job, your very livelihood and all you can say is . . ."

"True."

Gene laughed, picked up a magazine from the shelf near the door, flung it at his brother's head, and was gone.

It was two full weeks before he returned, exhausted from his struggle to resign from the group of men he loved best in the world.

As he turned the corner and came up Eighth Street, he saw Kate's figure behind the lace curtains of the dining room where she crocheted away her hours, keeping vigil for him. She saw him immediately, waved, and was at the front door before he could reach the bottom of the steps. She waited with her arms half outstretched and a warm smile on her face.

"This trip seemed so long, Eugene. I though you'd never get home."

"It seemed long to me, too, Kate," he replied wearily. "I've never been gladder to be back."

"Thank you, dear. We can have a little time together now, can't we? You don't have to rush off somewhere."

"No, I can stay home awhile now. And I'll have more leisure to spend with you, that is, right at first."

"You look tired, dear. I have a pot of coffee on the stove. I'll turn the light on."

She prepared breakfast for him. He ate ravenously, remembering that for several days he had hardly touched any food. He thought how nice it would be to spend a day or a week just lounging about the house and working in the garden, passing quiet hours with Kate in a kind of holiday mood. There was an empty lot next to the dining-room porch where he intermittently planted flowers and vegetables. That afternoon he pulled weeds, but even as he yanked on the unruly stubble he knew that he had made a decision which would have inevitable consequences for his wife, and that she was entitled to know about it right away. After an hour he put down his spade, wiped his hands on his old khaki trousers, and joined his wife on the porch, leaning down by the side of her chair.

"Kate, I have something important to tell you."

She looked up quickly, half frightened, for she never knew where Gene's unpredictableness would lead next.

"I have resigned from the Brotherhood of Locomotive Firemen."

A flash of joy went across her face. She put her arms around his neck.

"Oh, darling, I'm so happy and so relieved. I knew one day you'd give up that dreadful job; I knew one day you'd see that it was a blind alley."

"Wait, Kate, you haven't heard . . ."

"I kept telling my brothers it was just a temporary thing, that you'd grow out of it. And now at last you have. Eugene, you've made me so happy; it's as though I were in a prison and you unbolted the door and let me out into the sunshine. Now I don't have to be frightened every hour you're away that you've gotten into some kind of trouble. Do you know what you're going to do next? I have a little money saved up; you can open a business here in Terre Haute: a drugstore or a florist; one of my brothers said you'd do well in the wholesale grocery business."

Kate was so rarely ebullient; the flash of joy sent a warm pink glow flooding over her lovely marblelike complexion; it transfigured her, showed him all too well how little happiness he had brought his wife, and how much anxiety and dread. Poor Kate, he thought, she got a bad bargain in me. I'm the last man in Terre Haute she should have married.

Aloud he said, "But, Kate, I'm not looking for a new job. I have one."

"You have one? It's here in Terre Haute, isn't it? We won't have to move away?"

There was real terror in her voice now at the thought of giving up her house: her haven, sanctuary, testimonial.

"No, Kate, we won't have to leave our home. I can work out of Terre Haute just as I always have."

"Oh, you're going on the road again. Why can't you settle down here like every other businessman, go to work at eight in the morning, and come home at six?"

"Don't you want to know what I'm going to do, Kate?"

Her eyes glazed with anxiety. "Eugene, tell me: what are your plans?"

"I'm starting a new union, Kate."

She dropped back into her rocker and began sobbing.

"Oh no, not another union! What good does it do to transfer from one to another?"

He took her two hands in his and held them tightly. He had dreaded the moment when he would have to tell Kate that he was changing positions. He knew that she hated unions, and this jump from a small specialized trade union into a nationwide organization could only intensify her fear and dislike of his work. But without his knowing it an edge of excitement contoured his voice.

"This is a new kind of union, Kate. Something never tried before in the history of the world. It's going to be big and strong and important."

The sound of the adjectives lifted her from her gloom.

"Why is it going to be all these things? And what will it mean to you?"

"Take the railroad industry: there must be twenty different crafts or working groups. Every union is separate and distinct and cares not a tinker's damn for any other union. If the engineers demand higher wages, selfish firemen move up and take their places; if firemen ask for an increase, yardmen are glad to fill in for the extra money. It's dog eat dog. We're going to put an end to that, Kate. We're going to have a union in which every man works and fights for his neighbor, just as his neighbor works and fights for him."

"A union comprising all the men who work for the railroad, that could mean several hundred thousand members, couldn't it?"

"If our idea is sound, we should have no trouble getting several hundred thousand members."

"It will make you a powerful group, won't it?"

"That's what we're hoping for, enough strength inside the indus . . ."

"And rich!"

His heart sank.

"No, Kate, we'll never be rich, because there'll be no compulsory dues. A railroader, or a local for that matter, can join without putting out one penny."

"But, Eugene, that's ridiculous. Why should you let them in without dues? No business does that; if they're going to get the benefit . . ."

"Membership will be a dollar a year for those who want to pay it. There'll be no pressure brought on those who don't want to."

"How do you think you can run an organization with nobody paying dues?"

"The members will pay," he said stubbornly. "They will want to pay."

Cagily she asked, "How many of them can you count on?"

"About half."

"Then very soon you will be taking in from fifty to a hundred thousand dollars a year! And the very lack of compulsion will bring the others in."

"Yes, I think so."

"You're really very shrewd, Eugene, when it comes to understanding those men. You laughed at me when I said that you would be earning ten thousand, yes, and twenty thousand dollars a year. Now it will all come true!"

"Perhaps," he murmured tiredly, "but it's going to be a long way up to ten thousand a year from seventy-five a month."

The excitement died out of her face.

"Seventy-five dollars a month? What are you talking about?"

"About me. About Howard and Keliher. That's all the salary we're going to take for the first year, until we have a solid reserve in the treasury."

She settled weakly into her chair.

"You mean you are deliberately giving up four thousand dollars a year and going back to less than a thousand?"

"You yourself said only a few moments ago that this was a good idea."

"Because I thought it would be good for you! But if it's going to be bad for you . . . !"

He pulled a chair halfway across the porch, ignoring her automatic gesture of disapproval, and drew it up in front of her.

"Listen to me, Kate. This is the most important task I've ever tackled. It's given me new hope because I see a way of bringing security into the lives of thousands of people who have never had it before. Think what it will mean . . . Kate, you haven't been listening."

"But how can I run the house on seventy-five dollars a month? How can I continue to build up our savings?"

"You won't! You'll dip into the money we've saved to finance this new venture. That's what savings are for."

"Never!" broke in Kate. "I'll never spend a dollar of it. Savings are to earn money. Do you think I'd sell any of my stocks, when some of them are earning as much as twelve per cent?"

He laughed. "That's the first good reason I've ever heard for money earning more money without the owner working for it. Your twelve per cent interest is going to support us, Kate, while we build an organization that will oblige you to take six per cent for your savings and share the other six per cent with the men and women who create that wealth for you."

She could not control her tears, nor did she put her hands to her face in an effort to conceal them. He put her head on his shoulder, comforted her by stroking her hair and her cheek, while to himself he said, Kate, what bad luck you have! Every time I turn around I hurt you worse! Oh, Kate, how much of this pain can you stand?

2

The ensuing months passed in a joyous frenzy for him. Seven hundred railroad men attended his opening meeting in Hirzel's Hall in Terre Haute, some two hundred joining before the evening was over. He was ever on the move, speaking a dozen times a day, starting with two switchmen over a boardinghouse breakfast, and ending before a mass meeting under gaslight. Everywhere he planted the idea of equality of labor to replace aristocracy of labor; in the depression year of 1893, where employment was falling off, and money scarce, he took in locals with their full membership, unaccompanied by one dollar of dues.

By April he, Howard and Keliher had organized a hundred and eighty lodges in twenty-five states. Their efforts were confined mostly to the Midwest. Two Montana men came in as officers and began lining up the West: Martin Elliott, a squat, redheaded proletarian out of the copper mines of Butte, and Jim Hogan, who saw the humorous side of everything, using laughter and satire to bring in the men who could not be moved by serious argument. The roster of officers was completed with William E. Burns, a slender, handsome chap who was a good fighter in an argument, and Roy Goodwin, a prodigious reader. Working together with Gene, Theodore and Lou Rogers, editor of the *Railway Times,* they made an excellent organizing team.

The Brotherhoods could not openly oppose him: he had done too much for them, over too many years. He was the father of the brakemen's union, and they came in by the hundreds; so did his friends among the firemen. On certain lines the switchmen's locals joined en masse, but on others, management kept them out. Among the hundreds of thousands working for the railroads, very few had not heard the name of Gene Debs, read his magazine, been in some way benefited by his work. He had given the railroad employees eighteen years of devotion; tales of his selflessness had been notaried wherever trains were hauled over rails. They said he was the only man in any industry in America who had earned the confidence and friendship needed to create one big union.

And so the American Railway Union grew, two thousand members, ten thousand, twenty, thirty, forty, the idea sweeping across railroad flats like fire across a prairie. Theodore managed the office, Gene stayed on the road as teacher, preacher, organizer. On his occasional stay in Terre Haute for rest and recapitulation, he and Theodore would pore over the charts which showed how many members they had in each craft and in each state; then they would go over the lists of reasons why the engineers or conductors had refused to join, and together write articles for the *Railway Times* to answer these objections.

"We're doing fine, Theo, they're coming in faster than I dared hope. If only we have sufficient time, before anything happens . . ."

But there is never sufficient time: James J. Hill's Great Northern Railway cut the wages of its trackmen from a dollar and a quarter a day to one dollar and the men walked out. Since they belonged to no union except the American Railway Union their leaders went to George Howard, who was in St. Paul, demanding that he call a strike on the Great Northern. Howard had no choice; he sent out a strike order and a telegraphic appeal for help.

Gene and Theodore reached Minneapolis in a torrential downpour. They changed their sopping-wet socks, then sat around the hotel room in their stockinged feet because they had not brought extra shoes. George Howard came in, his black beard and face darker than the rain sheets pouring against the window. No one bothered to shake hands.

"What state are we in?" demanded Gene.

"State of confusion," replied Howard.

"Did you try to arbitrate with Hill?"

"He laughed at me."

Gene pulled a Morris chair up to the window, his bony knees digging into the wainscoting, the dark rain curtain providing a vivid reflector for his thoughts:

You don't make unions out of thin air; they have to be conceived and carried and given full form before emerging from the secure womb of darkness into a rain-swept world. Nor did you expose them to the bitterest of the elements before they had grown strong. He had always believed that strikes were bad medicine, that the path of labor was strewn with the corpses of unions that were doing well until they went out on strike. This was a premature, almost impossible test for the American Railway Union; but wasn't every test of brotherhood difficult and premature?

He turned back to Theodore and Howard, who had been talking in undertones behind him.

"I'll try to arbitrate with Hill. If that fails, we'll have to crowd every railway man in the Twin Cities into big halls and swing them along with us."

George Howard's opinion of these two possibilities was eloquently expressed by his bleak silence.

"We'd better prepare now for the second eventuality, George. Get to the newspapermen in this town as fast as you can and tell them that we are holding up your strike order on the Great Northern until we can hold a conference of the railroad men."

"Now wait a minute, Gene; if you start canceling my orders, you'll undermine my position."

Gene put his thin arm around Howard's shoulder and held him firmly with his long, lean fingers.

"George, trust me, we're in trouble. If we fail to take the Brotherhoods out with us, neither of us will have any position left to undermine." He turned to Theodore. "How much money did we bring with us? George, what have you in your wallet?"

The three men shelled their silver and greenbacks onto the middle of the bed. Gene counted quickly and pushed it over to Theodore. "Theo, hire us the biggest hall you can find in St. Paul for tomorrow night. Then find a printer and have handbills run off right away announcing our meetings. I'm going up to see James J. Hill."

He was ushered wordlessly and soundlessly into Hill's sanctum; even his feet as they went across the soft carpet made no sound. Hill received him with a probing flash of the eyes in which Gene found his welcome, his instruction to sit down in the big leather chair and to state his business quickly. Hill had a powerful head with a massive brow and massive eyebrows, a big, bony nose and a large, warm mouth and chin partly covered by a soft beard. Gene was glad to see that he was not angry or prepared to quarrel. Sitting there in silence with nothing moving but his big eyes, he radiated so much energy that the room fairly crackled with it. Only after he had grown accustomed to the pulsation did Gene perceive that the eye which seemed sunk behind the other was of glass. When Hill spoke, Gene found his voice chesty, chained.

"Mr. Debs, I am a quick reader of character; you are not like the usual labor agitator. Would you mind telling me briefly of your background?"

Gene sketched his childhood, his going to work at fourteen, scraping paint off railroad cars, his four years as a fireman, and then the advent of Joshua Leach and unionism into his life.

"I'm in this room as a horse trader, Mr. Hill; now I think you owe me a brief résumé of what brought you to the opposite side of this conflict."

"Fair exchange," murmured Hill. He turned in his swivel chair to the precise angle at which his bad eye disappeared from Gene's vision. "My beginnings are like yours, Mr. Debs. My father died when I was fourteen, and I worked for four years as a clerk in the village store at Rockwood. Like you, I waited almost in pain for the end of the day so I could get home to my studies. My imagination had been fired by my readings about the Orient, and I tried to get to the Pacific coast to find a ship. I landed in St. Paul just a few days too late to join a group of trappers, and so I went to work for a company running steamboats on the Mississippi. I was only a clerk, but I spent most of my time finding new commodities for the ships to carry, and new sources of fuel to keep them running. In 1875, the year you started your local, I formed my Northwestern Fuel Company. I ran steamboats, and began taking over bankrupt railroads. My friends told me I was insane, but I pushed a new line to the Canadian border, and built a system westward, until last year it reached the Pacific coast. So you see, Mr. Debs, our lives up to this moment are quite similar: I built railroads and you built unions."

For the first time a stern, almost ominous note crept into his voice. "Now we have a little issue to decide between us: which is more important, the railroad or the men who work for it."

The fact that Mr. Hill was now a multimillionaire seemed to Gene fair compensation for his accomplishment. But in the face of the man's fortune and talent it was inconceivable that he could persist in any effort to push a workingman's wage below a subsistence level. Surely a man who had taken over two bankrupt streaks of rust in a wilderness, and converted them into an empire, would know that it was bad business to pay men less than they could live on?

"They are equally important, Mr. Hill. I've been fighting strikes and discouraging them for eighteen years now. The last thing in the world I want to do is let these men go out. I'd like to arbitrate our differences in a friendly spirit."

"But, my dear sir, we have no differences to arbitrate. It's my task to run a railroad and get as much money as I can for the stockholders. It's your task to run a union and get as much money as you can for your members. Why don't we each of us do our own job according to our lights?"

"Because at this moment your lights and mine are colliding. We have convinced our men that management will arbitrate and compromise. If you make a liar out of us, Mr. Hill . . ."

"You will strike! What are you going to use to take men out?"

"Words: unity, brotherhood . . ."

"Words! You can't make a fire under them, or fry them in butter."

"True, but we can do something better: we can remake the world."

Hill laughed heartily, as though someone had set out to entertain him with a funny joke.

"Mr. Debs, that's naïve; no one can remake the world."

"Mr. Hill, you brought railroads and people to the wilderness, converted it into prosperous communities. You're not the right one to decry man's power to remake his world."

Hill glanced at the many papers on his desk, rose and extended his hand.

"It's been a most interesting discussion, Mr. Debs. Come see me again next time you're in St. Paul."

3

He sat in the Morris chair all night gazing sightlessly into the blackness. Theodore tossed and turned behind him, awakening every few moments and urging him to come to bed, to get some rest. But Gene was undergoing the severest inner conflict of his life: how was he to repudiate the rock upon which his eighteen years of work was founded? How did he tell men to strike, when he had been the country's most ardent opponent of strikes? If strikes destroyed unions, would it not be suicide to permit the American Railway Union to destroy itself? And if the strike were successful, was he certain he could hold it in control? Daniel had warned him long ago, "Unions mean strikes, and strikes mean violence." He had spilled out millions of words, in print and in person, against all violence, even in thinking, as the workingman's worst enemy. What did he do now, divest himself of his profoundest convictions and his beliefs as though they were a pair of old shoes whose soles had come loose and were flapping in the rain?

An ash-colored dawn sifted into the street below him. What did a man do when he came up against a stone wall? Did he turn and walk away, defeated? Or did he adjust himself to the realities of that wall? He had talked of alternatives to George Howard and James J. Hill. Now it was time to face them himself: either he refused to support his striking trackmen, in which event the American Railway Union would dissolve into the ash-gray mist, or he changed his beliefs to fit a changing industrial world.

He found it easier to abandon his convictions than his men. Chilled, exhausted, miserable in heart and mind, he resolved to call a strike on the Great Northern. The decision made, he crawled in beside Theodore and was asleep at once.

When they reached the hall that evening, they found it well filled. Theodore and Howard took seats in the last row. Gene walked up the side aisle alone. All faces turned in his direction; and as they turned, Gene realized how difficult his task would be: there was no fear or hatred in this audience, but neither was there any interest or sympathy.

It was absurd to think that the Brotherhoods would give up their contracts and security for a handful of unskilled laborers. Some of them knew Gene as a friend who had helped in their own early organization; the others were simply curious as to what he would say.

He mounted the little side stairs, passed the straight-backed chair sitting in the emptiness, and walked out to the rim of the slightly curved stage. A dozen of his friends applauded, the rest sat in tepid silence. After a moment Gene took a deep breath and began talking: he reviewed the history of the various Brotherhoods, showing how far they had come not only in wages but in security and status in the few years since their inception; he described the painful and slow descending curve of unionization from the top level of the engineer down through what had been an irresponsible and drifting class of trackwalkers; he proved what they already knew, that where the Brotherhoods stood together they gained their common ends, but when they failed each other everything was lost. He turned their attention to James J. Hill, outlining his vast railroad empire, giving figures on the amount of dividends that had been distributed to stockholders. He then reported Hill's categorical refusal to arbitrate.

It had been a good presentation of the facts. Nothing was left out that was important, nothing was included that was rhetorical or tangential. It should have convinced his listeners that he was right. Yet his orderly array of facts had left the men unmoved. He realized this in the very midst of a sentence; he stopped short, stood gazing for a moment at the composite mass of human faces before him, then turned and walked to the lone chair. He sat down, rested his bony elbows on his bony knees and buried his long, lean face in his long, lean fingers, shutting out all sight and sound. Under his chair he could feel the trains traversing the land; clackety-clack, clackety-clack, click-clack, click-clack.

Dear God, I have failed, he told himself. There's something wrong, they don't believe me, they're not interested, their minds are one solid cold shoulder thrust upward at me. It must be my fault, it can't be theirs: I know these men too well. I know that they yield to appeals for help. There's no callousness in them. Not a man out there but has suffered hunger and unemployment. Then why aren't they listening to me? Why do they sit there, immovable, as though these trackmen are some breed of animal who don't suffer when they are hungry and cold, and have no place in the world? If only I could pray, I would pray now, for I need help. I need something that's not in my mind or my voice or my presence here tonight. I mustn't fail. If we leave the trackmen in the lurch, no group will ever go down the line for any other group; labor will be the same kind of jungle as capital, with everyone indifferent to the fate of his neighbor, and the strong devouring the weak.

He made no movement of his body, but simply lifted his face out of the cup of his hands, and opened his eyes. For the first time he heard the silence in the hall, a deeper silence than he had had while speaking. Something had gone out over that hall; where before there had been some hundreds of men, each holding fast to his separate interest, grimly determined to retain the last ounce of his advantage, hundreds of unconnected islands in a vast sea of self-protection, now they were somehow merged, the sharp outlines of the separate heads and shoulders and torsos blurred. This was no longer a hall full of individuals. It was one man: mankind.

He rose, began speaking slowly.

". . . call them hands." He held his two hands in front of him, the fingers arched inwardly, his arms flexed. "They think it is a derogatory name, but I say it's good; for it is hands that have built this world, toil of millions of pairs of untiring hands. They are despised, these trackmen, because they have no strength, no power, just as we were despised a few years ago, because we were only hands. But now we're more than hands: we're brains and souls, we're people—and why? Because we knew that we all had to rise or fall together. We made sacrifices, we risked our jobs, our homes, our future, with every man standing shoulder to shoulder with his neighbor. This is the most beautiful thing in the world, not only because of the material gains we've earned, but because we've won something without which we are animals and our span on earth is meaningless. We fought for brotherhood. We earned our brotherhood. This is what makes us men. For every fellow creature we abandon, we cut away from our own stature. If you walk out of this hall tonight, leaving those unfortunate men and their families at the mercy of their employers, you will be closing and freezing your hearts against your companions who need you in their bitter hour. If we destroy brotherhood, what have we left? The food we put in our mouth? The clothes on our back?

"I know you men well. I've shared your food and your bunks in the icy caboose hurtling through the night; I've walked with you through sleet-filled yards when there was no work and your children were hungry. Then you were humble, you were at the mercy of powerful forces with which you could not cope. The trackmen of the West are in that same position tonight; their eyes are turned to you men sitting in this hall, for to them you are all-powerful. If they could pray, they would pray to you, pray that your hearts could be filled with love instead of indifference, with the brotherhood that makes us whole men."

He stopped. His eyes were blurred and he could see nothing of the faces before him.

There were several long moments of silence. No one moved. Then a man got up in the front row. Two more at the opposite side of the hall rose to their feet. Men rose from all over the hall now, singly, then in groups. Soon every last man in the hall was on his feet. They were shouting or cheering or crying, Gene could not tell which.

All men are brothers. If only they knew it.

For eighteen days the Great Northern stood still. From his hotel room in St. Paul Gene operated an office for the American Railway Union. In his office a few blocks away Mr. Hill tried to run his railroad. He offered inducements to the Brotherhoods to go back to work. Promises of preferential promotion, increased wages, a new and better contract. No man returned to work. Mr. Hill tried to secure troops to run his railroad, but no one would give him troops; he sought to enforce an injunction handed down by a local judge which declared it a criminal act for "men to combine to desist from work." But there was no one to enforce the injunction. The Minneapolis Chamber of Commerce, whose members were suffering sharp losses because their merchandise was neither coming in nor going out of the Twin Cities, asked Gene to state his side of the case to a full meeting of its members. Gene did not talk brotherhood with the Chamber; he merely explained that when wages are forced below a subsistence level workingmen cannot buy sufficient to keep either their mouths or the stores open long enough to sustain either of them.

The Chamber thanked him for his courtesy, and then Charles Pillsbury, the millionaire flour miller, took a committee with him to see Mr. Hill. Late that afternoon Gene received a message asking him to come to Mr. Hill's office. Hill was alone, but the room was filled with leftover cigar smoke and the remains of unsettled arguments. The two men did not greet each other. Gene dropped into the same chair he had occupied on his first visit, and waited for Hill to speak. Hill was apparently girding his industrial loins, for it took him several moments to open the conversation.

"Mr. Debs, I have decided to grant your request for arbitration."

"Mr. Hill, you're exactly eighteen days too late for arbitration. The last time I was in here I pleaded with you to compromise this problem;

if you had met us halfway, we would have met you halfway. I begged you not to force the men out on strike. You not only dared us to go out, but you spent most of the intervening time trying to divide our organization and make trouble between the American Railway Union and the Brotherhoods." He took a piece of hotel stationery out of his inside coat pocket, unfolded it, and laid it on Hill's desk. "These are the terms upon which we will go back to work."

"Less than three weeks ago you were crying for arbitration; now that I have the generosity to agree . . ."

"Mr. Hill, the men are convinced that their demands are just. If Mr. Charles Pillsbury and his committee will listen to both sides of this case, we will accept their judgment in the matter."

That evening Gene, Theodore and Howard met in Hill's office with Pillsbury and a committee of Twin Cities businessmen. Flanking Mr. Hill were a half-dozen members of his board of directors. It took seven hours for every man to speak his piece. Mr. Pillsbury then adjourned with his committee to a room down the hall. In an astonishingly few moments they were back with their decision: ninety-seven and one half per cent of the workers' demands had been granted! Theodore leaned over to Gene and whispered:

"They gave Hill that lonely two and one half per cent so that he could save face."

Hill was no bitter-ender; when the room cleared, he shook hands with Gene.

"You've got a raise for everybody else on the Great Northern," he said, "where do I go to get a raise?"

"Why, you join the American Railway Union. We'll start a new order known as the Brotherhood of Railroad Presidents."

Hill laughed. "If you don't mind my asking a personal question, Mr. Debs, just how much do you make out of this victory?"

"A fortune, Mr. Hill: one hundred and fifty thousand dollars a month for the men."

Utterly depleted now that the battle was over, Gene walked down to the station and threw himself onto one of the bunks in a caboose. He could feel the wheels beneath him, but they were barely turning.

"Theo, why are we moving so slowly?"

"I'll go see."

After a moment Theodore stuck his head in from the rear platform and said, "Gene, come here."

He rose wearily, went out on the platform. Lining the tracks on either side, some in their work clothes, others in off-duty dress, stood the railroad men of Minneapolis and St. Paul: the mechanics from the roundhouse, the brakemen and conductors off the freights, the inspectors and operators, the trackmen and truckmen. Word had been sent to the engineer to pull slowly out of the yards, for the boys wanted to say good-by. They were not shouting, they were not cheering, they were not even smiling; but as the train crept slowly down the rails the men took off their hats and stood with their eyes riveted on the two men standing on the rear platform.

As the train neared the end of the yards and the end of the bareheaded workmen, Gene realized that he was crying. To Theodore he murmured, "I guess I'll never get cured of being a sentimental Frenchman."

"Don't be silly," replied Theodore. "You got the same cinders in your eyes that I got in mine."

It was a beautiful early May morning when they pulled into Terre Haute. The station and the street beyond were packed with people. Someone caught sight of him and yelled, "There's Gene Debs!" A shout went up. Several firemen grasped Gene and Theodore and led them to the front of the station, where they had a band and carriage all decked out in colorful streamers. A banner along the side said: WELCOME HOME GENE DEBS. In his confusion Gene thought, Somebody forgot to provide the horse.

The band took its position in front of the wagon. A hundred eager hands grabbed the brothers. "Up you get, Gene and Theo," someone cried; "we're carrying you home in state."

Gene laughed. "I'm not dead yet, boys. I don't need a carriage. Come on, Theo, let's help pull this wagon."

There was a cheer, the band struck up and the little parade moved through the streets of Terre Haute. When they reached his house, Gene mounted the front steps to the porch, thanked his friends for their kindness and grasped the knob of his front door. It was locked. He took out his key and turned it, but the door was bolted from within. He pounded on the wood frame with his fist, calling out:

"Kate, Kate, it's Eugene. Come down and open the door."

Several minutes passed. He heard no sound from within the house. He walked around to the back, unlocked the kitchen door and went quickly through the lower floor. He found Kate upstairs, in their bedroom, sitting before her dressing table with her head buried on her arms.

"Kate, what's wrong, what's happened?"

Her eyes were terror-stricken.

"Eugene, that mob! I heard them coming down Eighth Street. I thought they were coming after you."

He was flabbergasted, then burst into laughter.

"Kate, for heaven's sake, that was my reception committee. They met me at the station with a band."

"Eugene, there's been so much talk against you in the papers. You would have been better off if you'd lost that strike. I thought they hated you before, but when James J. Hill conceded defeat! Oh, Eugene, if you could know the names they've been calling you."

He sat on her dressing chair, then held out his arms to her, pressed her to him to dissipate her terror.

"Didn't you hear the band music? Why didn't you come out on the porch? Of course I have enemies, but I also have friends."

She held her trembling frame tightly against him.

He talked to her quietly, patiently, showing her that there had been no violence and no hurt feelings; that the outburst she had read in the Chicago newspaper was not from responsible sources but from the hysterics.

"We came out on top, Kate. We got practically everything we asked for. There was no trouble, we've just been victorious."

She jumped up, began pacing the room agitatedly.

"You think you've been victorious; but sooner or later they will be the ones who come out on top, for they have the money and the power. And when they're on top, Eugene, they'll crush you, just as though you were . . . a . . . an empty grocery box lying in the way of a giant locomotive. Just you wait, Eugene, and you'll see that I'm right."

He did not have long to wait.

4

He was resting in his upstairs workroom, glancing over the evening papers, when he heard voices and what he thought was an altercation at the front door. He ran down the winding steps, but from the middle step he saw Kate on her way back to the kitchen.

"Kate, didn't I hear voices? Who was here?"

She flung over her shoulder, "Oh, just some strange men, wanting to disturb you. I told them you were asleep."

He went quickly to the front door and across the porch to the sidewalk. Three men were walking dejectedly up Eighth Street. He called out, "Hello there! Why are you rushing off mad?"

When the men turned around he saw that they were three union officials from the Pullman shops. They came back to him.

"Your wife told us you were asleep. She said you couldn't be disturbed."

He shook hands with each of the men, clapped them on the back and took them into his library. "I was just resting. Mrs. Debs thinks I'm a fragile creature. She treats me like an only child."

The men laughed. Kate appeared in the room saying, "Gene, you know you complained of a headache this morning. You shouldn't be working. But since you insist, surely you'll get this meeting over as quickly as possible?"

Her manner was curt, with so little regard for the men present that he considered it the better part of wisdom not to introduce them. He said, "Just give us one hour, Kate dear."

She left the room without signifying whether this compromise pleased or displeased her; when he heard her go upstairs he closed the door of the library, opened the windows wide, for it was a warm spring evening, and said:

"Now, boys, what's on your mind?"

There was plenty on their mind. Work at the Pullman shops had become scarce and George Pullman had taken a repair contract at such a low figure that it would mean a loss to the company of fifty thousand dollars. Despite the fact that the Pullman Company had made a net profit of five and one half million dollars the year before, and six and one half million dollars the year before that, George Pullman was determined that every penny of the fifty-thousand-dollar operating loss must be absorbed by his employees. He had reduced wages to the point where his workers' weekly income exactly matched their rent for the company houses.

The three men stopped talking as simultaneously as they had begun. While they waited tensely, Gene asked himself how it could be possible that so magnificently courageous and resourceful an industrialist as George Pullman could resort to the inhuman device known in the company coal towns as "mining the miners instead of the coal." George Pullman was one of the mechanical geniuses of his age; why then, he asked himself, wasn't this genius extended to the human beings who worked for him, as well as to the sleeping cars that worked for him?

When Pullman had been only twenty, working in his brother's cabinetmaking shop in upstate New York, he had taken his first overnight ride in a sleeping car. He was given a wooden bunk at one side of a converted coach, where he stretched out fully dressed on a rough mattress and covered himself with his overcoat. From this one trip he saw the need for a comfortable sleeping car on wheels.

He persuaded the Chicago and Alton Railroad to let him experiment on two of their old coaches. He hinged the backs of seats so they could be folded down to make a bed, hung the upper berths on pulleys so they could be closed during the daytime and would hold the bedding. The cars were upholstered in plush and lighted by oil lamps, with a washroom at each end.

Young George Pullman knew that remodeling old coaches was a makeshift, that he would have to build his sleeping cars from the tracks up. He spent four years drawing blueprints for the first complete Pullman car. The astounding part of this new car was not only its beauty and mechanical ingenuity, but the fact that Pullman had built his car too high to pass under existing bridges and too wide to be used at station platforms. Pullman, in his strength and daring, had said, "This is what a sleeping car must have; the entire railroad system of America will be changed to fit its needs."

"The men want to go out on strike, Gene," concluded the most forceful of the three visitors. "We want the American Railway Union to refuse to haul Pullman cars."

"Now, boys, wait just a moment. None of these Pullman workers is a railway man. What you're talking about is a sympathy strike. It's never been done in this country."

"No, and neither has there ever been an industrial union. But that didn't stop you from forming the American Railway Union!"

"We have one hundred and forty thousand members throughout the country, Ed," Gene replied, "but one hundred thousand of them have never paid a penny of dues. We don't know how strong their allegiance is to us. We have got to get some kind of gauge on their loyalty before we attempt anything as difficult as a nationwide sympathy strike."

Ed's face turned a dull red. "In other words, Gene, before you can help us you want ideal conditions! When does labor ever get ideal conditions? We have to strike when we have to strike! You should have learned that up in St. Paul."

"Sit down, Ed, and stop talking at me. We're going to give you all the help we can, but first I want your word that you'll go back to Chicago and do your utmost to arbitrate your differences."

The second of the two men rose and spoke quietly.

"We'll try anything, but in return we've got a request to make of you: come up to Chicago and go through the town of Pullman with us."

Ten days later he arrived at the American Railway Union headquarters in Chicago. He had sent word for the three Pullman delegates to meet him at the office.

Ed greeted him with a growl. "Mr. Pullman told us there is nothing to arbitrate, that he could not restore our wage scales because he had taken contracts for new work at a loss."

"Ed told Mr. Pullman that if he wouldn't restore wages, he could reduce the rents on our houses. Mr. Pullman replied that it was impossible to reduce rents, for the capital invested in these houses had to have its just return. The next day the three of us were laid off."

The third member, the quiet one, said, "We fulfilled our promise to you, Gene, now you've got to come out to the town of Pullman with us."

Riding south on the train, Ed handed Gene a pamphlet called *The Story of Pullman*. "Here, read this page, Gene." He read:

"Imagine a perfectly equipped town of twelve thousand inhabitants, built out from one central thought to a beautiful and harmonious whole, where all that is ugly and discordant and demoralizing is eliminated and all that inspires to self-respect, to thrift and to cleanliness of person and of thought is generously provided."

The four men left the train, and in a few moments arrived at the village that George Pullman had created from five hundred acres of unused prairie land. The main street had bright red flower beds in the center and houses of red brick with trim lawns in front. But when the men left the center square and walked one short block, they came into another world. The unpainted wooden houses were of the cheapest construction, the rooms inside were small and dark and airless, each house was provided with one faucet, in the basement.

"We can't get a job in the Pullman shops, Gene, until we rent one of these houses. If any repairs are needed before we move in, the Pullman Company advances the money and we pay it out of our wages."

Gene felt himself getting sick at his stomach. Ed and Charlie each took him by an arm and walked him to the back part of town. Here he found lawnless tenements with four and five families crowded into each railroad flat, all the families using one toilet. Behind the tenements were slums, wooden shanties that had cost only one hundred dollars to erect, occupied by marginal families who had eight dollars a month taken out of their wages, a return to the Pullman Company of almost 100 per cent on its investment. The residents were constantly spied upon, living under a reign of terror, afraid to trust their neighbors or friends.

Riding the train back to Chicago, Gene suffered a wave of revulsion against man's inhumanity to man. Ed had informed him that a meeting of the Pullman workers was scheduled for that night and that the workers would surely go out on strike. Bitterly as he hated strikes, Gene had learned that there were depths of hunger and degradation beneath which human beings could not be submerged. His mind went back to the enigmatic case of George Pullman, owner of a fifty-million-dollar corporation, and earner of several million dollars every year for his own purse and pocket. He thought, What a pity that there is no relation between the power of the brain to create and the ability of the spirit to love! Men who care enough about machines to invent new ones are not able to care enough about humanity to be concerned over its welfare. Men who care a great deal about the fate of humanity are not able to understand machines well enough to invent new ones.

If the world were full of sentimental godunks like me, he thought, there would be no poverty, but neither would there be progress. People would still be living in caves and using stone axes. If the world were full of mechanical geniuses like Pullman and Hill, there would be fantastic progress, with no people to use it because they all would have been mangled in a machine, run over by a railroad, or suffocated in a bank vault.

He stood on the stubby platform of Uhlich Hall facing four hundred American Railway Union delegates from the Midwest locals who had climbed aboard the cabs and cabooses and come into Chicago. The Pullman strike was now several weeks old, the town of Pullman as quiet as death itself. Funds for the strikers were coming in not only from such sympathetic unions as the typographers, painters and carpenters, but from the people of small towns, police and fire departments, singing societies, circus entertainers, ticket brokers, department stores, and Republican Clubs. If the American Railway Union was going to strike in sympathy with the Pullman workers, this was the hour to do so; but Gene did not want to strike. It was one thing to call his men out in the clean-cut issue of the workers of the Great Northern against James J. Hill's slash in wages. But if the American Railway Union refused to haul Pullmans they would close down the railroads of the nation, tackle the General Managers' Association and its interlocking billions of wealth. The American Railway Union was a lusty infant, but one which could grow to magnificent manhood only if nurtured carefully.

All this he told the delegates, who listened to him respectfully, some agreeing, some disagreeing, some thinking with their logic and some with their emotions. The Pullman strikers had asked permission for the Rev. William H. Carwardine, who had been a pastor in Pullman for many years, to address the convention. Gene introduced him to the delegates. The Rev. Mr. Carwardine was bald on top of his head but the rest of his face was framed in luxuriant and square whiskers, the sideburns coming down bushily to meet the ends of his mustache. The plight of the Pullman workers had aroused him, and he was speaking with a tongue and a temper he had never before known.

"No man craves Mr. Pullman's position before the American people today. The very qualities that made him successful in life have, untempered with nobler elements, placed him in his present predicament before the American public. Determination and resolution have turned into arrogance and obstinacy. My sympathies have gone out to the striking employees. Never did men have a cause more just, never did a corporation with equal pretenses grind men more unmercifully. He who denies the right of the clergy to discuss these matters of great public concern has either been brought up under a government totally foreign to the free atmosphere of American institutions, or else he has failed utterly to comprehend the spirit of the age in which he lives."

Gene was relieved to see that, magnificent as had been the Rev. Mr. Carwardine's philippic against injustice, he had failed to rouse the delegates to a point of white heat. Then he saw a movement toward the back of the hall and a number of men came down the aisle with a young woman in their midst. One of them called out:

"This here is Jennie Curtiss. She's worked in the Pullman sewing rooms for five years. We ask that she be heard."

"Any man or woman who wishes to address this convention will be heard."

He went to the little side steps, descended several of them, held out a hand to the young woman and helped her up to the platform.

Jennie Curtiss went to the edge of the platform near the stairs and stood staring out at the delegates. She was slight, black-haired, black-eyed, with pale skin and almost bloodless lips.

"My name's Jennie Curtiss. My father worked in the Pullman shops for ten years. The company charged us so much rent and repairs that when he died, after he was sick three months, we owed the Pullman Company sixty dollars. I worked in the repair shop sewing room five years. The company told me I have to pay my father's back rent. I been getting nine, sometimes ten dollars, for two weeks' work. But they wouldn't let me keep my wages. After I paid all I owed for my board, the company took the rest against the rent. I been paying for months and months and still I owe them fifteen dollars. When I go to the company bank to get my pay check, and there ain't enough left over to take something against the rent, the clerks insult me and call me dirty names."

Jennie Curtiss had been speaking in an emotionless voice that pierced the quiet of the room. No one moved. Gene knew that this was the critical moment, that anything could happen if Jennie remained on the platform. If he shut her off now he could control the convention. She had told her story, there could be nothing wrong with his stepping forward, thanking her, helping her down the stairs. Yet he could not get off his chair, for Jennie Curtiss was still standing there, her toes turned in toward each other, swaying slightly at the knees, her shoulders hunched from years over a sewing machine, her fingers clenched and held hard up against her belly: for Jennie Curtiss had one thing more to say . . . and Eugene Debs was not the man to stop her.

"We workers out at Pullman are on strike, on a strike for our lives. We ask you to help us. Not with your money, and not with your sympathy, but with the risk of your jobs. We ask you to come out with us, because nonc of us is fightin' just for ourselves. We're fightin' for freedom for workingmen all over the country. We ask you to stand by us and come out with us. Will you come?"

Men began climbing to their feet all over the hall. Some introduced motions, others resolutions, but most of them just cried out, "We won't haul Pullmans. We've got to stand by the Pullman workers."

Gene's eyes swept over the faces below him; there was not a man in that convention hall but was determined to go out. He had no way to stop them; their constitution gave them the right to declare a strike. He knew what a desperate struggle would ensue, what forces would be unleashed against them. He was their leader, he had given birth to this organization, built it to its present strength; yet if the delegates wanted to go out on a strike he must lead them, for what good is a leader if he will not implement the wishes of his people? He had preached brotherhood, and they had been converted all too well. There was no way to turn brotherhood on or off as if it were water in a spigot.

5

Any fear he might have had concerning the allegiance of the ranks was dispelled almost too fast: the Great Northern men, grateful for their recent victory over James J. Hill, abandoned their Pullmans at the first water tank. Gene had to send out a series of telegrams to get them back on their trains, to deliver the hapless passengers to their destinations.

By the third day forty thousand members of the American Railway Union were refusing to handle Pullman cars. All lines operating west of Chicago were at a standstill. By the end of a week some one hundred twenty-five thousand men were out. Telegrams, letters, money, promises of assistance in the fight against George Pullman came in from the thousands of local unions all over America. The Chicago Labor Council, with a larger membership than the American Railway Union, offered to participate in a general strike. Samuel Gompers rode in from New York to give Debs a sizable check. He and Theodore worked twenty hours a day in the office, keeping in touch with all major stations along the twenty lines that had been closed down. As in the Great Northern strike, the men went home and stayed home.

"If we can keep this up," said Gene, "we're going to win this strike."

Theodore had always been less emotional and more skeptical than Gene.

"I don't want to worry you," he said, "but have you had time to look at the newspapers today?"

He spread out sample front pages of the main Illinois papers, as well as those from Pennsylvania and New York. The headlines screamed:

NATION PARALYZED BY DEBS STRIKE

"These stories are too similar to have been made up by the local city editors. The General Managers' Association is sending handouts to the papers, portraying you to the country as a desperate revolutionist who is using this strike to seize control of the country. Governor Altgeld is getting hundreds of telegrams demanding that he send out the state militia to take over."

"Take over what?" replied Gene. "The state militia can only be sent at the request of local sheriffs and mayors when there are riot conditions they can't control. Have you forgotten, Theo, my boy, we're peaceable! We're not even blowing our nose in public for fear somebody will become alarmed at the noise."

Gene was right, but not quite right enough. The General Managers' Association went over the governor's head. Their representative in President Grover Cleveland's Cabinet was a lawyer by the name of Olney, who had spent many years as counsel for the Erie Railway, and gone straight from the railway offices into the Cabinet. Attorney General Olney waited until the newspaper attack on Debs had been solidly built, then took the papers in to President Cleveland to prove that Chicago was in a state of insurrection, that life and property were in grave danger, and that if he did not send in federal troops immediately, blood would flow down Michigan Boulevard.

President Cleveland was the first Democrat elected since the Civil War; he was friendly to labor, he did not want to believe these reports. He told the attorney general that his fellow Democrat, Governor Altgeld, had sufficient state militia to keep the situation in control. Olney accused Governor Altgeld of being an anarchist, for had he not pardoned the remaining three men convicted of the Haymarket Riot?

The next morning Gene was wakened by the tramp of heavy boots outside his hotel window on Jackson Street. Theodore murmured sleepily from the other half of the big bed, "They're getting started awful early for their Fourth of July celebration."

Gene pushed aside the curtain and studied the soldiers for some time. He turned slowly back to his brother.

"Theo, those are federal troops!"

Attorney General Olney arrived in Chicago and appointed Edwin Walker, a lawyer for the General Managers' Association, as special assistant attorney general in Chicago, with full federal powers to act. Edwin Walker acted swiftly: he appealed to two federal judges, William A. Woods and Peter S. Grosscup, to issue him an injunction which would forbid Gene and his brother officers of the American Railway Union from "interfering with, obstructing, or stopping any of the business of the twenty railroads now under strike conditions." Judges Woods and Grosscup issued the injunction. Gene and his fellow officers were subject to arrest.

He was surprised to have Clarence Darrow drop into a chair at the American Railway Union headquarters: for the past two years Darrow had been working as legal counsel for the Chicago and Northwestern Railroad.

"I was in Springfield last night," said Darrow, "and bring you a message from Governor Altgeld. The governor said, 'By remaining peaceful, by merely refusing to move trains carrying Pullmans, the strikers are on their way to victory; their demands are just, and the public is with them. The only thing that can defeat the strike now is violence.' "

Gene nodded his head in vigorous agreement.

"I'm in telegraphic touch with every junction on the lines. I've ordered the men to stay home, to stay sober, and to keep their hands off railroad property. But, Clarence, they're swearing in thousands of federal deputies, giving them guns. Who are these men? Are they responsible citizens?"

Darrow drawled, "Let's go find out for ourselves."

They took a streetcar into South Chicago, alighting at the point where the Illinois Central and the Rock Island paralleled each other. The outside line of both sets of tracks was guarded almost solidly by armed men. Gene and Darrow walked along the tracks, passing out cigarettes, striking up conversations. After two hours they returned to the streetcar and rode back to the hotel. They were both depressed.

"You wanted to know who has been sworn in as deputy marshals," commented Darrow; "rich men aren't going to risk getting hurt; professional men have too much work piled up; men with jobs can't give them up, and unemployed workers aren't going to carry guns against strikers. Who's left? You saw for yourself: the dregs of the Chicago tenderloin: gangsters, hoodlums, petty criminals, sharpers, loafers, alcoholics. Those armed men have nothing to lose: they would burn and destroy a city for the sheer pleasure and the pillage involved."

"What superb irony!" cried Gene. "These irresponsible ones are now officers of the United States Government; they're going to defend society against workers in revolt."

"You've got to find a way to keep your men from clashing with those deputies."

Gene thanked Darrow for his assistance, excused himself and went into the office of the American Railway Union. At least fifty railroaders were crowded into the little room.

"Drop whatever you're doing, men, and get out to the yards. Tell your boys to go home and stay home. Tell them not to tangle with the railroad deputies; tell them to keep their hands off railroad property. Come along, I'm going out there too."

Once again he rode the streetcar south. When he reached the stockyards he found his men standing in the yards glowering: for on the cowcatcher of an engine were half a dozen United States soldiers with their guns outstretched, and up in the cab were more soldiers at the throttle and the boilers. Along the track beside the engine walked solidly flanked troops, bayonets fixed.

For Gene, this was the worst blow of the contest: his workmen could fight the organization of railroads on an even basis, but how could they fight the Managers' Association and federal government combined? He was seized with such a passionate anger that he began trembling all over. One of the officials who had been in the office with him only an hour before came running up to him.

"What do you say now, Gene? Do we run home and hide under our beds? Or do we prevent these troops from breaking our strike?"

This was the moment of decision. The happenings of the past twenty hours had invalidated almost twenty years of his thinking and working for the peaceable solution. This world was not a vacuum, there were no ideal situations, and other things never remained equal. Everything that he and the railroaders had worked and suffered and sacrificed to achieve for two long decades was in process of being obliterated. Must he step down from his command, retire to the closed and airless room of theorizing?

He looked at the men about him. They knew him almost as well as he knew himself. They felt the conflict tearing at his innards; they knew how much he would have to repudiate. He searched their faces one by one. A voice inside him spoke, a voice compounded of Colonel Robert G. Ingersoll and Susan B. Anthony; of Wendell Phillips and Major O. J. Smith, of all the thinking and all the manhood of the fighters he had known.

"Federal troops must not move these trains. Spike the switches, but be careful not to harm railroad property."

Word went swiftly through the railroaders. They thronged onto the tracks, leaving him alone on a slight rise. The troops were able to move the cattle train only one block, then several hours passed while they repaired the switch. Once again the train began to crawl down the yard; this time there was no convenient switch to be spiked. Gene watched his men overturn freight cars in the path of the oncoming train. His heart sank, for he knew this was the beginning of a new and uncontrollable phase of the conflict. His men had deliberately disobeyed his orders. Or had they? He had told them that the car must not move; when an officer gives the command to fire, can he repudiate his men because someone has been hit?

A riot call was sent out. Swarms of deputies and soldiers moved onto the tracks, righting the freight cars, pushing them ahead of the cattle train. For many hours the contest continued. By nightfall the troops had been able to move the train exactly six blocks. The railroaders were jubilant; the overturned freight cars had not been injured, yet they had stopped the strikebreakers. But Gene lay awake all night tossing on his bed, talking fitfully to Theodore.

"The men think we've won, but this was only the first skirmish. The Managers' Association is going to bring a Pullman train into Chicago over the Rock Island in the morning; that will be harder to stop. Oh, we'll stop it all right, but what methods will we have to use?"

At dawn he and Theodore and some twenty of the union officers caught the first streetcar out to Fifty-first Street. A through Pullman train from the West was creeping down the track, its cowcatcher, cab and every platform bristling with federal troops and Gatling guns. The strikers and an enormous crowd of their families and sympathizers poured over the tracks like floodwaters over a valley road. The train stopped. An officer in the cab bellowed:

"Fix bayonets! Charge!"

The human floodwater evaporated from the tracks; the soldiers climbed back onto the train accompanied by jeers and curses and stones. The train began to move again, slowly. The strikers ran ahead to Fortieth Street and overturned freight cars in its path.

Gene stood in the hot July sun, moving along slowly with the Pullman, which managed to cover thirty blocks by the end of the day. This was a sharp defeat for the General Managers' Association. Gene told his men they had victory in their hands: if no trains could be moved, George Pullman would sooner or later be forced to arbitrate.

His optimism was short-lived: that night the railroad yards burst into flame, and with it the strike.

Freight cars were burned, roundhouses went up in smoke. Governor Altgeld sent in state militia, which took up their position between the strikers and the deputies. The crowds grew larger, milling about, calling names. Fist fights began. Excitement mounted. At three-thirty in the afternoon the mob broke loose. They charged into the militiamen who were trying to push them out of the yards. The militiamen fired. Three men fell dead. The railroad deputies broke loose with their pistols and clubs.

Watching all this, heartbroken, unable to control it, Gene realized that violence is not a form but a fluid content: it will pour into any available receptacle. And he also learned what he had known as a younger man: that you cannot deviate the slightest fraction from non-violence and still remain at peace.

He picked up a bleeding child and carried her to the nearby stock-yard hospital. The dead were brought in and laid on the floor beside him. He knelt down, took the burlap covering off their faces. The first was apparently a stockyard worker; the second was a railroad man, though one he did not know; the third was Pete Hararchy, a fireman on the Rock Island, an old friend and union member.

With tears in his eyes, he asked himself, Did I kill them? I started out as a man of peace. What a long road it has been . . . to violence and death!

6

He was resting in his room at the Leland Hotel when there was a knock on the door. He opened it.

"Is this Mr. Debs?"

Gene bowed his assent. The man continued:

"I am Marshal Arnold of Judge Grosscup's court. I have a warrant for your arrest. You must come with me immediately."

Theodore came in through the hall. They gazed at each other. Theodore took Gene's coat off the back of a chair and held it out for his brother. As they walked out of the hotel room two deputy marshals fell in behind them. There were two more armed deputies posted at the elevator. In a few moments they were in the Federal Building. Similar little parades kept entering the courtroom, with the American Railway Union officers surrounded by knots of deputies: George Howard's enraged face was as black as his beard; Keliher looked serene; Rogers was excited by the drama in which he was participating. Martin Elliott was cursing in his copper-mine patois, much to the amusement of his fellow Montanan, laughter-loving Jim Hogan. William Burns and Roy Goodwin were silent and serious. Gene was talking quietly to his associates when he saw Captain Stewart, a post office inspector, enter the room with a big bundle of books and papers. Gene looked at them with only half an eye as they passed, but even so they seemed familiar. A few moments later Lou Benedict ran into the courtroom, his collar and tie awry. He made straight for Gene.

"Mr. Debs, Mr. Debs, they've raided our offices and taken our records! Our bankbooks and money and files. Mr. Debs, they even grabbed up your unopened mail!"

Gene had been calm up to this moment, now he went white with anger. Marshal Arnold came to his side.

"Mr. Debs, the judge says I'll have to lock you up."

He was locked in cell 31, on the first tier. The floor was cold, of dirt-streaked cement. There was a short, splintered wooden bench on one side and an iron frame cot fastened to the wall on the other. Over everything was the stale and humid odor of refuse that had not been washed out; of food that had not been removed; of unwashed bodies inside thick airless walls; the stagnant air of men incarcerated, men momentarily dead. The only sounds were the heavy boots of the guards and the occasional hoarse cry or raucous laughter from one of the tiers above. A gaslight hissed at the intersection of the tier blocks, but it shed no light in his cell. Under him he felt the fast movement of a freight hurtling through the night.

He had been locked up too late to receive any supper; for this lack of interruption he was grateful. He sat on the hard bench with his face in his hands. He thought, Poor Kate, now all of her nightmares will come true. She will reproach herself for her failure to convert me, to make me desist from what she called my headstrong folly, my useless sacrifice. How can I explain to her that all this is a necessary and unavoidable part of the struggle? That my imprisonment and everything that may flow from it is part of the job, just as it is sometimes the part of a soldier's job to be captured by the enemy. What can I do to soften the blow for her, keep her from suffering a thousandfold for whatever may happen to me?

Idly he reached into his back pocket and took out his penknife, began slapping it roughly from one hand to the other, enjoying the physical pain and the comforting touch of an old friend. The knife slipped out of his hand and fell to the cement floor, the bone handle on one side smashed. He made no effort to retrieve the pieces, but sat numb with misery, thinking:

Everything has gone to smash, my knife, my organization, my beliefs.

Something whisked past him on the hard bench. His flesh crawled. Then he heard the almost noiseless scraping of claws on the cement.

At that moment he heard voices and heavy footsteps coming down the iron corridor. The guard and a visitor pulled up in front of his cell. The guard unlocked the door, the visitor entered and the door was clanged shut behind him.

"It's me, Gene, Clarence Darrow. I just got word of your arrest."

The two men shook hands in the darkness, barely able to see each other's face. The guard stood twirling his big key and gazing into the cell.

"How did you get in, Clarence? They told me no visitors were allowed after dark."

Darrow chuckled. "They think I am still the attorney for the Chicago and Northwestern Railway."

"They think . . . but aren't you?"

"Not since five o'clock this afternoon, I'm not. I told our president that when the United States Government and the General Managers' Association conspire to enjoin workers from striking, that's too much of a conspiracy for my weak stomach. I said, 'I'm giving up my job here, Mr. Hughitt, to defend Eugene Debs and the American Railway Union.'"

Gene's sadness was gone, replaced by an exaltation.

"What did the president answer?"

"He said, 'They haven't a chance, Clarence; this injunction is a Gatling gun on paper. Why give up a good position for a hopeless cause? Don Quixote only tilted at windmills; you're going to run into a high-powered locomotive under full steam.'"

The guard shoved his squarish, bony face against the bars and muttered, "You gotta talk plain English in there, Mr. Darrow, or I can't lecha stay."

Gene and Clarence smiled at each other in the darkness. At that instant Gene felt the rush across his legs once more. Darrow took out a block of matches from his coat pocket. He split off half a dozen and made a light. Two black sewer rats as large as cats were surprised in their antics under the iron cot and fled through the bars between the jailer's legs.

"We're very considerate in Cook County," drawled Darrow. "We don't let you get lonely in our jails."

The guard, who had a dim feeling that his institution was being insulted, said with a leering half-smile, "We'll take care of you the same way we did them anarchists. This is the same cell block where I guarded Parsons, Spies, Fischer and Engel. We hanged them for what they done."

Feeling slightly sick at his stomach, Gene asked Darrow, "Is it true, are these the same cells the Haymarket anarchists were in?"

"These, or the next ones."

"You're no better than them," cried the guard. "If you can make a rebellion, we can hang you too!"

"Rebellion?" Gene turned to Darrow inquiringly.

"He's seen the evening paper, Gene. The newsboys are crying, 'Read All about the Debs Rebellion.'" There was a harsh note to Darrow's voice when he spoke again. "You're in rebellion against the existing form of government, and are out to burn civilization to the ground."

"I broke into railroading as a fireman. I'm used to handling the stormy end of a scoop."

"But what you don't know," said Darrow, "is that a schoolteacher in New York City had her class debate this morning on 'Why Eugene Debs is the most dangerous man in America.'"

"Just think of it," murmured Gene, aghast. "Poisoning the minds of little children."

"We don't use poison in Cook County," said the guard; "we use the end of a rope, like on them Haymarket murderers."

The needling began to get under Gene's skin.

"Why the devil does he keep comparing me to the Haymarket anarchists? I never killed anybody."

"Neither did they."

Something inside Gene crashed. He remembered his father at the time of the Haymarket explosion saying, "They didn't do it, Gene. They had no reason." To Darrow he whispered, "But they had a public trial."

"So will you have."

"The jury convicted them, the judge was convinced of their guilt."

"So will yours be."

There was a long moment of stunned silence for Gene, then he murmured, "Clarence, is it true? Were they innocent?"

"To this very day no one knows who threw that bomb. There was not the slightest shred of evidence connecting any one of the anarchists with it. Every supposition of logic and reason tells us that they could not have been connected with it, for they had nothing to gain: they were conducting a peaceable meeting; the mayor of Chicago stayed through half of it and then left, telling his police captain that everything was peaceable. The anarchists were tried for conspiring to throw the bomb; actually the state never named anyone as the thrower of the bomb. Believe me, Gene, the only guilty men in that courtroom were the men doing the convicting."

The guard inserted his iron key into the door. "Your time is up; come on, Mr. Darrow."

The two men rose from the hard bench. Gene put his arm around Darrow's shoulder to comfort him.

"I feel much better since you've come. Now I know that I deserve to be in this cell."

"Deserve?"

"Because I believed those anarchists were guilty. I never gave them the benefit of doubt, I never examined the evidence. I entered into the mass hysteria you're talking about, Clarence; I wrote flaming articles against them in the *Locomotive Firemen's Magazine.* I should have known better, because my father told me they were innocent, and my father should have known, for he was an anarchist. But I became part of the mob. I helped kill those men."

Darrow left. Gene sat quietly on the hard bench, leaning the back of his head against the cold cement wall. From out the small cell window he saw a reddish glow: freight cars were burning in their yards, railroad property was going up in flames. Locked in his dark cell, the sewer rats scurrying past his feet, he felt the world and his heart on fire too.

7

The strike was quickly broken. The railroad lines began moving their trains. Within a few days service was back to normal. With the strikers black-listed, the American Railway Union discredited and declared illegal, its funds and papers seized, the General Managers' Association decided that it would be safe for the federal court to allow the imprisoned men out on bail. They so informed Attorney General Olney, who notified his representative, Edwin Walker, who passed on the instruction to Judge Grosscup. Gene and his fellow officers were released on ten thousand dollars bail each.

Gene went home to Terre Haute: to sit with Theodore amidst the ashes of their organization, while Clarence Darrow prepared the legal case in Chicago; to tell Daniel how terribly, bitterly wrong he had been about the anarchists who had been hanged; to assure Daisy that no jury would ever send him to prison.

Once again he found his own difficulties paralleled by the Rev. Mr. Hanford's. The All Faith Church had occupied the former vegetable store for a number of years now, but the Rev. Peter Hanford had been indiscreet; he had preached a fiery sermon praising Eugene V. Debs and the American Railway Union, and had then secured publication of his sermon in the *Gazette.* One noon the preacher reached the All

Faith Church to find his desk, box of Bibles, and oddly assorted string of benches out on the sidewalk. Gene asked his Terre Haute local if their meeting room could become the All Faith Church on Sundays: and so the All Faith Church and the Terre Haute Local of the Brotherhood of Locomotive Firemen merged.

At home no mention of the strike or the impending trial was ever made. Kate went stolidly about her household tasks, and in the evening when they sat together in the library they talked of other things. He was proud of the way she was bearing up under the strain.

At last the day came for his return to Chicago to stand before the bar of justice. When his bag was packed he went into his wife's room to see if she were ready. He found her standing in the middle of the floor, gazing downward at nothing. He saw no suitcase, nor had any wearing apparel been removed from her bureau.

"Kate, you must hurry. We'll miss our train."

Without raising her head or looking at him, she said:

"I'm not going."

"You're not going? But the trial may take weeks, even months. Don't you want to be with me?"

She looked up swiftly.

"I just can't make myself go."

Gently he whispered, "You don't have to, Kate. I thought you would want to be by my side."

"I couldn't stand the torture. Every time they acused you of something new, it would be like sticking a knife into me."

"Then put on your heavy suit of armor."

"Armor? What are you talking about? This is no time to make jokes."

"Don't you remember, Kate, what we used to say when we were children? 'Sticks and stones will break my bones'? There's no reason for you to be hurt by their charges or their name calling."

"My dear, when they accuse you of those horrible things before the whole world, who will there be to believe you? That's what hurts me so dreadfully, Eugene, the things their name calling will convict you of in the eyes of all the good people, and the right people."

She suffers so terribly, he thought. He took her in his arms, ran his fingers tenderly over her cheek.

"Kate, come with me to Chicago. You will see that we are not alone, that we are not defenseless. It isn't I who will be convicted in that courtroom, but George Pullman and the General Managers' Association."

She pulled away from him, shaking her head in despair.

"How can you be so childish as to think you can convict the greatest men in the country?"

"Kate, we have only fifteen minutes to train time. Let me help you pack your bag."

"No, Eugene. It's in your best interests if I stay home. Oh, don't you see? I've always been against your work, and this dreadful tragedy proves I was right. Haven't I predicted this would happen? If I sat in that courtroom, where the judge and the jurors and newspapermen could see my face, they'd know how I felt, Eugene. . . ."

"You mean they'd know you were against your own husband?"

Impetuously she threw her arms around his neck.

"Oh no, Eugene. I am for you. I have always been for you. That's why I've tried so hard to get you to go into a respectable business, into a safe and secure position where no one could ever harm you."

"No one is going to harm me, Kate."

She held her cheek against his, and he could feel the wet, salty tears against the corner of his mouth.

"Darling, they're going to convict you. Everybody knows that. They're going to send you to prison. And that will kill you. It will kill your spirit. Oh, Eugene, I've pleaded with you, I've offered you opportunities . . ."

Sternly he said, "I've done nothing wrong. I've broken no laws, and you can only send a man to prison in this country when he breaks laws. But even supposing the worst happens, suppose I am convicted, I shall be a political prisoner, Kate, not a criminal prisoner. If we are to be happy together for the rest of our lives, you must come to understand this difference."

She broke away and stared at him with wide-eyed terror.

"I knew it! You've realized all along they would send you to jail. You've tried to hide it from me. But now you gave it away." She dropped onto a chair. "Oh, Eugene, how could you have done this to us? You had so much promise. Your future looked so brilliant, and how do you end up? Hated and reviled by the whole country, convicted of starting a bloody revolution, sent to prison for your crimes, crimes you never intended, I know that, but crimes that had to come when you insisted on taking your own headstrong course, fighting the government and the powerful men of the country."

There had been a light but insistent knocking on the front door. Georgie and Aggie stood there owl-eyed.

"Mr. Debs, we've brought our penny banks for you. I have eleven dollars and Aggie here has three."

"We want you to give them the money, Mr. Debs," chirped Aggie, "So they won't make you go to jail."

Gene felt hot tears behind his eyelids. He crouched down, one coin-jiggling container in each hand, and hugged the children.

"Thank you, Aggie and Georgie. When I come back from Chicago, I'll bring you the most beautiful toys ever seen in Terre Haute."

He returned to the bedroom to find that Kate had not moved. Her face was pale. She took a few steps toward him, then stopped, began to speak in an almost inaudible whisper.

"If you go to prison, I will go to prison too. This house will be my prison. I will lock the windows, lower the blinds, bolt the doors. I will eat only the severest food, just enough to keep me alive. I will see no one, I will talk to no one. I will allow myself no moment of pleasure or happiness. I will never set foot out of this house until the day you return. So you see, Eugene, you will not be alone; I will be with you; I will be with you in spirit every moment of the night and day; I'll be in prison with you, suffering just as you suffer."

He wanted to answer, Kate, all this is useless. I have no intention of suffering. Only men who have done wrong suffer. But he could not say this to his wife, for she would not understand, and it would not lessen her anguish. Her burden would be a hundredfold greater than his, for he would be sustained by the belief that what he had done had to be done; she could have no such solace, for she had known all along that he was wrong and that his conduct would bring them to grief.

His heart ached for her. He wished that there were some comforting thought, some word of wisdom he could give as a parting gift.

"I am sorry to leave you all alone, Kate. If we had had children . . ."

Her eyes flamed; she cried out, "I'm glad we have no children! I hope we never have children! Then I won't have to fear for them, fear that every moment of their lives other children on the street will taunt them."

"Taunt them with what, Kate?"

"That their father is a . . . a . . ."

She could not finish the sentence. Stricken, Gene finished it for her, ". . . a jailbird?"

She did not answer, but he saw her nod to herself.

"Kate, you mustn't say things like that, you mustn't even think them. We're going to have children, lots of children. You know I'm not superstitious, but those words, they might put a curse . . . Kate, we don't want a childless home, an empty house."

He heard the long low whistle of the train coming across the prairie. He went out the front door without looking back.

8

The snow was being driven by a hard wind when Gene and Clarence Darrow entered the courthouse. They took off their heavy overcoats, still white and wet, and started down the center aisle, focus for every pair of eyes on the jammed rows of benches. A railing in front of the judge's dais enclosed the jury box and broad mahogany tables for the prosecution and defense. The press table directly across the enclosure from the jury box was occupied by some thirty newsmen, including representatives of the British and European newspapers. Gene murmured:

"This is going to be the greatest opportunity labor has had to educate the American people."

"Haven't taught school since I was a youngster," said Darrow, his big shoulders hunched over. "Had a great time then, boarded around with the parents of my pupils; they fed me pie three times a day."

"Nobody's going to feed you pie for defending me."

"Couldn't eat it if they did: spoiled my digestive system lawyering for the railroads."

Gene walked over to the front row of spectators to kiss Daisy and Daniel, who had come up to Chicago the evening before, Theodore remaining behind in Terre Haute to take care of the grocery store. Then he pushed open the little railing gate and joined his brother officials at the defense table.

He was about to seat himself when his glance encountered the battery for the prosecution. His heart pounded: for leaning over the portfolios, handsomely garbed in a gray suit, stood Ned Harkness, his full black hair combed back to fit the fine contour of his head, his face freshly shaved and powdered, looking more handsome and successful than Gene had remembered him from their meetings in Terre Haute.

Harkness looked up from the sheaf of papers on his table, saw Gene, straightened to his full height, the documents pushed aside. Silent thoughts ran between them; their eyes held. Then the contact was broken. Gene sank weakly into his chair: for into the front row behind the prosecution table slipped Paul Weston, Mrs. Weston and Gloria. She sat between her parents, her hands buried in her lap beneath her mink cape, her face partially concealed by the brim of her fur hat.

She's more beautiful than ever, Gene thought. And so cosmopolitan. Only her eyes were unfamiliar; they were grave, not unhappy, perhaps, but brooding. His own eyes became glazed; his insides felt hurt and hollow.

Judge Grosscup entered from his chambers. The clerk cried, "Everybody rise!" but Gene could not get off his chair.

Why has she come? To see me accused, humiliated? To prove to herself that she was right in marrying Ned Harkness? It's seventeen years since she said she loved me; has time changed her so much, have wealth and social position so captured her that she believes me a miscreant, and takes her place behind the prosecution?

Or was she only demonstrating her loyalty to her husband? For he knew that if Gloria had been his wife she would have been sitting in the front row behind the defense table.

Judge Grosscup said, "If both sides are ready, we will proceed."

Darrow, who had been sitting slumped forward in his chair, rose quickly.

"Your Honor, the defense protests against the presence of one of the prosecution's attorneys."

To Gene's lips flashed the words, Oh, Clarence, don't do that, Gloria will think . . . He tugged at Darrow's coattail.

"I have no objections to Mr. Harkness."

Darrow had not heard his client, nor would he have paid any attention to him if he had.

"Mr. Harkness at this very moment is legal counsel for the Chicago, Milwaukee and St. Paul Railroad. When a railroad counselor becomes at the same time prosecutor for the federal government, then the railroads and the federal government become one and the same agency."

Gene watched Gloria's face while Darrow made his charge, saw her lean forward intently, her face strained, her hands clasped tight in her lap.

"The Court sees no reason why Mr. Harkness should not assist in the trial. The government may open its case."

He watched her settle back on the bench, her face pale. Then he forced himself to study the selection of a jury, the eight farmers, the dealer in agricultural implements, the real estate agent, the insurance broker and the decorating contractor who had it in their power to convict him of "criminal conspiracy to obstruct the mails" and to send him and his friends to Atlanta penitentiary for as long as ten years.

9

At the end of the day the defendants were taken by deputy marshals to the jail. He found himself placed in a large cell with five other men, all accused of crimes but not yet tried. The three-bunk tier on either side so crowded the cell that half the men stretched out on their beds in order for the other half to sit around a table on the cement floor.

He quickly became acquainted with his cellmates. There was a winsome little pickpocket called Harry the Dip, a Negro by the name of Bass Huggard, accused of cheating his landlord out of two months' rent, a big square-jawed, flaxen-haired Norwegian arrested in a barroom brawl, an Italian accused of stealing sacks of cement from a warehouse, an old man, toothless, with white hair falling over his ears, picked up as a beggar.

At five o'clock armed guards came through the corridors to unlock the heavy doors, and the men were marched into the mess hall for supper. Here he had a chance to ask Keliher and Rogers how they were faring. He could not touch any of what the prisoners called slumgullion: boiled hogback with a few slivers of meat hanging to the bones.

After supper they were returned to their cells. He heard familiar footsteps ringing down the cement passage. While the guard stood rattling his keys, a voice cried out:

"Who's in this cell, a burglar or a poet?"

A laugh sprang to his lips as he replied, "A burglar."

"Good, then I must be the poet!"

The guard opened the door and James Whitcomb Riley entered the cell. He almost wrung Gene's hand off.

"I always figured some of my verses would land me in jail. But what is a big business executive like you doing in the clink? Have you absconded with the company's funds? Have you been cheating the public with short weights and measures? You should have been a versifier like me: then you could have been a guest at the White House, and had high society fawn over you!"

Gene examined his old friend: when last he had seen Jimmy Riley he had been an impecunious hall-bedroom lodger, eating when the opportunity presented itself, writing stanzas on such scraps of paper as might be available. Now he saw that Riley wore a good broadcloth suit with a gold watch chain strung across his vest.

"By all that's wonderful and miraculous," he exclaimed, "whatever happened to you? Did you marry the boss's daughter?"

"Even better!" replied Riley. "You know Bill Nye, the humorist? He was invited to perform before New York's famous authors at the National Arts Club. Took me along with him and introduced me as his encore. I gave them *Frost Is on the Punkin.* They ate it up, made me give six encores. Mrs. Grover Cleveland asked me if I wouldn't come to the White House and give my poems for the president."

"Well, what do you know!" murmured Gene.

"Remember how you had me to Terre Haute three times, and hardly took in enough to pay for my railroad ticket? Now I go to the theaters and find them hanging from the rafters by their tails."

"Well, what do you know!"

"So what do you care if the court fines you ten thousand dollars, Gene? I'll come get you out of hock."

"Time's up, Mr. Riley," said the guard.

Riley pulled on an expensive pair of kidskin gloves. "Here's a copy of the *Times;* you'll find something on page three that might interest you."

Gene opened the *Times.* In the center of page three was a poem called *Terry Hut.*

And there's Gene Debs—a man 'at stands
And jest holds out in his two hands
As warm a heart as ever beat
Betwixt here and the Jedgement Seat!

The guards turned out the lights, plunging the prison into inky blackness. Gene stretched out on his bunk. He was warmed by Riley's visit, miserable over Gloria's appearance at the trial, curious as to the sympathies of the jury after hearing Darrow's aside, "We are supposed to find twelve of your peers from among this group, but federal jury panels never include an employee!" Self-reproaches flooded his mind as he went back over the steps that had led him to this impasse. He should never have permitted the American Railway Union to go out; he had allowed his sentimentality to betray him. If a railroad manager needed to be hard as rock, then a union manager needed to be hard as granite. He should have fought the convention, used all manner of stratagems in turning down the Pullman workers: then his own organization would not have been destroyed.

His cellmates stirred restlessly, some asleep, some awake. During the daylight hours they could present a hard façade to the world, but now he heard them murmuring and groaning, all pretenses down, frightened children in the dark. From the adjoining wing came the soft weeping of the women prisoners, locked away from their families and their love, helpless ones imprisoned in steel and concrete for who knew what transgressions of the flesh or the purse? His own confused thoughts vanished, and in their place came heartbreak for imprisoned mankind, struggling upward through the darkness and the centuries, suffering untold torture at the hands of their fellow men: mendicants, like the white-haired old man in the bunk opposite, plodding their weary way up the road that leads from birth to death.

For six straight days he and his companions sat at the table directly below the witness stand, across which paraded newspaper reporters, railroad superintendents, police, businessmen, stockyard executives, nearby residents. Ned Harkness adroitly extracted from them the story of the strike, the stoppage of train service, the attempts to bring in cars over the Rock Island and the Illinois Central, the overturning of freights, the spiking of switches, the resistance of the strikers to federal troops, the ultimate clash, the burning of railroad property.

Halfway through the recital Gene leaned over to Darrow and asked, "Why are they going to such elaborate pains to establish what we do not contest?"

"That's their only case, Gene. They must prove that you conspired to obstruct the public highways."

"But we offered to run the mail through on special trains."

Darrow looked up sharply at the jury.

"I'm on your side; the ones you have to convince are those twelve jurymen."

As though from an inner need for collaboration, he turned his head the full half circle to where Gloria was sitting. She was bending a little forward, tautly, listening to her husband's every sharp sentence. How strange, he thought, for himself and Gloria to be sitting in the same room these several days and never once to have spoken, to have let their eyes meet in the avowal of friendship.

The nights would have been long had he not been allowed one visitor each day after court closed. Daisy and Daniel left this visiting hour free for his friends. Susan B. Anthony came one evening, her hair white at seventy-five, but her eyes as spirited and determined as the day he had protected her from the rowdies at Terre Haute. Samuel Gompers arrived to explain that the American Federation of Labor had had to repudiate Gene's industrial union in order not to hurt their growing membership.

Terence Powderly came back to the cell block to remind him of his prediction in Scranton that trade-unionism was little more than a soporific. Robert Ingersoll entered the cell with a fatherly smile on his face, twitting Gene for having supported the reactionary Democratic party, advising him to embrace the truly liberal Republican party. Major O. J. Smith visited several times, once with galleys on a laudatory story about the American Railway Union, a second time with a signed check made out to Gene, the amount left blank.

When he awoke on Sunday morning he felt that the prison was smothered under a brooding sense of loneliness and dejection. Weekdays were workdays, men handled themselves in the cold, rat-ridden prison as professionally as they could; but Sunday was family day. No one smoked or talked or told stories; the men lay dispiritedly on their bunks with their eyes closed, trying to shut out the immediate world of cement. He missed Kate terribly; missed the crisp white apron over her go-to-meeting dress, missed her glow of satisfaction at the beautifully shining silver on the Sunday dinner table, the warmth of his own study, and the convenience of Kate's marble bath.

His depression grew acute as the dinner hour approached, the moment when Daisy and Daniel gathered their clan about the dinner table: Theodore with his Gertrude, Mary and her three children, Jenny and Louise each with her child, Daniel presiding happily and proudly at the head of the table; Daniel, whose beard had grown white, who followed his son's expression and the testimony with intense interest. Gene had forced himself to go to the prisoners' mess for some watery mush and black coffee that morning, but he knew that he would not leave his cell for dinner, even though Harry the Dip had told him, with the first spark of life among the prisoners, that they had roast pork for Sunday dinner.

A few moments before the guards came to lock-step them to dinner, a voice called from down the corridor. Gene sprang to the bars.

"Theo!" he exclaimed. "I'm so happy to see you, that homely old phiz of yours looks absolutely beautiful."

Theodore was carrying an enormous wicker basket. While the guard unlocked the cell door, he replied, "I've always been beautiful, Gene; the only reason you haven't thought so is that I look too much like you."

The brothers embraced. Their happiness was a vast hole cut in the wall, a summer sun pouring down its light and warmth to dissipate the heartbreak of the cell.

"Boys, I want you all to meet my brother," Gene exclaimed radiantly. "Theo, this imp is called Harry the Dip; hold onto your hat while you shake hands with him. This Paul Bunyan out of the north woods is Sven Christofesen. This is my friend Bass Huggard, and I'll bet you that it's his landlord should be in this cell instead of him."

Theodore shook hands with each of the men. Then he put the wicker basket on the wooden table, unstrapped it, began taking out delicious-smelling foods.

"Since Daisy only got back to Terre Haute last night, Gertrude knew she wouldn't have time to prepare anything for you. Look, Gene, a roast turkey with walnut dressing, a ham baked with sliced oranges, and three pies, apple, mince and pumpkin."

Gene watched Theodore lay out the feast; his cellmates stood by, their eyes enormous.

"Fall to, everyone!" he cried.

10

Theodore came again at eight the next morning with a new shirt, collar and tie, saying, "As long as you are going to be the prima donna of the day, you might as well get all spruced up," then wrapped his brother in a blanket while he took his gray tweed suit to a tailor to be freshly pressed and his shoes to be shined.

The Sunday newspapers had announced that Eugene V. Debs would go on the stand early Monday morning. When Gene entered the courtroom through the rear door he saw Theodore and Louise in the front seats; and when he saw Gloria in the row opposite he realized how passionately he had been hoping she would be there to hear his side of the story. Even as he walked to his seat at the defense table he sensed that this group of spectators had a different feel from those of the week before: they seemed more sympathetically disposed. He mentioned this to Darrow, who scanned the audience, smiled and nodded several times before turning back to his client.

"You have attracted a distinguished audience, Gene; there are several professors out there from the University of Chicago, surrounded by their students, and at least half a dozen members of the Sunset Club. They'll provide good background for the story you're going to tell."

Gene was sworn in, then went to the witness box and stood in front of it for a moment, gazing out at the courtroom: tall, lean, angular, fair of complexion, his wide mouth raised slightly to one side, his eyes more gray than blue. A murmur went quickly over the spectators as he stood there, but Judge Grosscup banged his gavel, the courtroom quieted, and Gene sat down in the same box where fifty witnesses had sat in the prosecution's effort to portray him as a conspirator against the public peace.

Darrow began very quietly, leading Gene into the story of his life: that he had gone to work scraping paint off railroad cars at fourteen; that after a year of this work he had become a locomotive fireman, sharing the hard, dangerous life of the men who went down the rails for their living. Gene told of the depression year of 1873, when he had gone on to St. Louis to look for work, joined the thousands of unemployed who walked the streets cold and hungry, begging food for their children. He told of spending years as a clerk in Hulman's grocery store while in his mind he searched for his niche in life, for a job which would have meaning and purpose over and above the earning of necessities. To the jammed and hushed courtroom he explained how his imagination had been captured by the men who ran the trains; how he had suffered for them because they were being brutalized by a seventy-hour week, drinking themselves into insensibility for momentary escape, pushed about by a force they could neither understand nor control; maimed, crippled, killed on their job, often for no failure of their own, and then disinherited as no longer useful to their lines. He told of how Joshua Leach had come to Terre Haute to organize a local of the new Brotherhood of Locomotive Firemen, how the opportunity to work with the railroaders he loved, and the chance to help their poverty-ridden families, had brought him the joyful knowledge that here at last was a chance to serve.

Ned Harkness was on his feet constantly, protesting, "Your Honor, this material is irrelevant!"

But Darrow worked his way forward from Gene's first meeting with the firemen in the hall in Terre Haute, through the obstacles placed in their way by management, the indolence and ignorance of the railroaders themselves. He told how he had entered the labor movement for the simple purpose of providing benevolent insurance; of how he had progressed from this to the basic trade-union objectives of shorter working hours, higher wages, safer working conditions. Leaning forward eagerly in the chair, his rich warm voice sounding a clackety-clack, clackety-clack, click-clack, click-clack over the years, he addressed now the jury, now the judge, now the newspapermen at the press table, now the throng of spectators, now Louise and Theodore, who had their long, lean Debs faces turned up to him.

But mostly he was speaking to Gloria. Never by the slightest expression did he show that he knew she was there. She gazed at him intently, absorbing every word, revealing no emotion. In his heart he knew he was trying to justify himself to the love of his youth, and to that youth itself, wanting desperately for her not to condemn him, think him a misguided fool who had squandered his years and his patrimony, bringing little but trouble and confusion in his wake. He must convince her in order to convince himself, he must prove that what had been done could not have been left undone.

Ever since his arrest he had been portrayed in the big city newspapers as a dangerous and destructive character. Now for the first time as his own story poured forth, as his devotion became manifest to all people who ate their bread with the sweat still caked on their faces, millions of strangers came to know him as a man, as a cause, as a passion, as a voice crying in the wilderness, crying out for them, wherever they might be, in whatever dark or distant arena, in whatever plight or pain.

His repatriation was fleeting: Ned Harkness had a sharp legal mind and a driving will behind it. At last the two men faced each other; the silence in the crowded courtroom was tactile.

"Mr. Debs, you call yourself a railroader, do you not?"

"I work with railroad men."

"How long is it since you have done any actual labor?"

"Since your bosses put me in jail, Mr. Harkness."

"I am talking about the labor you do with your hands and your arms and your muscles, Mr. Debs. Actually it is twenty-two years since you turned in a full day of hard work, is it not?"

Gene suppressed a smile as he recalled Engles's similar accusation that he did his laboring safely behind a desk.

"It is that long since I shoveled coal into a boiler," he replied.

"And in the interim, Mr. Debs, you have been the manager of labor organizations, have you not?"

"I have been the secretary of several unions."

"Were you paid well for your efforts, Mr. Debs?"

"Yes."

"How much money were you earning at the time you declared your nationwide strike?"

"Three thousand dollars a year."

"I heard you tell the gentlemen of the jury that you started the American Railway Union at a wage of seventy-five dollars a month. That's a phenomenal rise in salary in one short year, is it not?"

"It is a good raise."

"Mr. Debs, who raised your wages from seventy-five a month to three thousand a year?"

"The officers of my union."

"You made no effort to refuse this enormous raise?"

"No."

"The various unions you have worked for, Mr. Debs, they give you an expense account, do they not?"

"I have had an expense account."

"Did anyone actually keep books on your expenditures?"

"None that I know of."

"Then you could have spent as many thousands of dollars on yourself, your traveling and your pleasures as you saw fit?"

"I never thought about it that way, Mr. Harkness."

"How much money was there in your treasury at the time you began your strike?"

"About forty thousand dollars."

"Who had control over this money?"

"The defendants you see at that table down there, Mr. Harkness."

"And also the defendant at whom I am gazing in the witness box, is that not so?"

"Yes."

"How much of that forty thousand dollars were you planning to spend on a higher salary for yourself and your expense account?"

"As much as I thought necessary to continue building our organization."

"In other words, Mr. Debs, there is very little control exerted over you, is that not so?"

"The General Managers' Association makes up for that, Mr. Harkness."

There was a quick laugh from the spectators. Ned Harkness did not like the sound of it, and turned to glare. Gloria sat with her head down, her face concealed.

"But actually, Mr. Debs, what is the essential difference between you and your distorted conception of a manager? You run your organization with autocratic methods; you spend as much of its money as you wish, without accounting for it; you raise your salary whenever it pleases you and to whatever extent you think safe at the moment."

Darrow was on his feet, exclaiming, "Your Honor, counsel is not cross-examining the defendant, he is making speeches to this court, and libelous speeches, in my opinion."

"Counsel will confine himself to cross-examination."

"Your Honor, every word I have elicited from the defendant is directly relative and material, for it is my thesis that this man sitting in the witness box is no leader of labor, but a vulture preying off them; a man who has not soiled his hands for twenty-two years, but like every demagogue has used labor's varying fortunes to cry havoc and fatten his own purse."

Ned Harkness leaned over the prosecution table, opening a sealed envelope. "Your Honor, I ask permission to offer this photograph in evidence. Mr. Debs, do you recognize this photograph?"

Gene saw it was a picture of his home in Terre Haute, standing in all its serene Queen Anne dignity, and looking very lovely.

"It is a picture of my home in Terre Haute."

"You built this home for yourself, Mr. Debs?"

"Yes."

"And you paid cash for it?"

"I did."

"And it has been completed for many years, has it not, Mr. Debs?"

"Mrs. Debs and I have lived in it for five years."

"Your Honor, I ask that this exhibit be passed among the jurymen."

Judge Grosscup nodded approval. The clerk handed the picture to the foreman, who looked at it quickly and passed it down the front row of the jury box. The spectators craned in the hopeless effort to see the picture; but they had no trouble in seeing that the jurymen were impressed by the Debs home.

"Mr. Debs, how much did it cost you to build that house?"

"I don't know."

"You don't know, Mr. Debs? Then who does?"

"My wife. I turn all my earnings over to her and she built the house."

"Did Mrs. Debs have a private source of income at the time this house was built?"

"My wife invested my earnings."

"Invested? In what, Mr. Debs?"

"Stocks and bonds, I suppose."

"Ah, I see. From your meager earnings as an employee of the Locomotive Firemen, your wife was able to build up an estate of first-rate stocks and bonds. What is the extent of your holdings today?"

"I don't know."

"You don't know?"

"Mrs. Debs handles all the business affairs of our family."

"I am glad you put it that way, Mr. Debs. For I want to make it doubly clear to this jury that you are a businessman, not a worker; that your stock in trade is the employees of the railroad; that you keep them at work or send them out on strikes as it suits the purpose of your business interests and your profits."

Once again Darrow was on his feet, but Gene waved him down.

"That is correct, Mr. Harkness, I am a businessman; the purpose of my business is to protect the employees of the railroads, to secure them a just and adequate wage, to build for them the security which every workingman and workingwoman deserves as the price of his labor."

Harkness turned to Darrow, saying sardonically, "Perhaps counsel for the defense would be so kind as to tell his client to come down off his soapbox and back into the federal court, where he is under indictment."

"My father made a living off of soapboxes in his grocery store for thirty years," interpolated Gene. "I have nothing against them."

Harkness left the defense table, walked between Gene and the jury box, took up a position alongside Gene, facing the courtroom.

"Mr. Debs, isn't it true that a strike is war, and that your primary purpose is to so intimidate the opposition over the potential loss of its equipment that they will surrender?"

"We simply refuse to work when conditions become intolerable."

"In this strike you were the leading general of your forces, Mr. Debs?"

"If the farfetched figure of speech pleases you, Mr. Harkness."

"It doesn't please me. It revolts me, revolts me to the very core of my nature, just as it revolts every right-thinking and right-minded American citizen. For it is now perfectly obvious, Mr. Debs, what you are after. You have built a union of one hundred forty thousand members, you have forty thousand dollars in your treasury, a three-thousand-dollar wage, and God alone knows how many more thousands for your private expenses. How many railroad employees did you hope to unionize?"

"The entire million men and women employed in every phase of railroading."

"And when you have your million members, how much money will you have in your treasury? A quarter million dollars? A half million?"

"Perhaps."

"And how much salary would you be taking for yourself, Mr. Debs? Twenty thousand dollars a year? Thirty? Forty thousand?"

This time Judge Grosscup sustained Darrow's objection to Harkness's harangue as being incompetent. Harkness drew himself to his full height, then turned to the jury box and smiled.

"The prosecution has no further questions to ask of Mr. Debs, for we are confident that we have portrayed him in his full light, a freebooter who has lived off the backs of labor for some twenty-two years, and has grown too big for his own bailiwick; who was waging a class war against American industry for the sole purpose of seizing control over the railroad empire and using it for his own selfish ends and personal advantage."

In the excitement-charged silence of the courtroom, Gloria Harkness suddenly rose and walked down the center aisle as quickly as she could. Gene bolted upright in the witness box; he watched Gloria's back until she had disappeared through the far door.

II

Clarence Darrow had subpoenaed George Pullman to the witness stand the following morning. Gene hardly slept that night, tossing and turning on his hard bunk with the anticipation of hearing Mr. Pullman explain the twenty-six million dollars of undistributed profits which lay in the company's treasury, and the three-million-dollar cash dividend which was distributed to the stockholders at the exact moment when the workers' wages were cut to match the sum owed by them for rent of company houses. Gene believed that the most important fact of the trial, and the one he most wanted to see spread across the front pages of the land, was that a mere hundred thousand dollars taken off the dividend and left in workingmen's wages would have avoided the starvation, desperation and industrial warfare. Just how would George Pullman justify his conduct before a civilized world?

He could have saved himself the sleeplessness: when Judge Grosscup convened court in the morning, with hundreds of spectators jammed into the side aisles and the press table occupied by some of America's best-known writers, George Pullman was eminently conspicuous by his absence. Deputy Marshal Jones, who had tried to serve the subpoena, testified that Mr. Pullman had fled from his office just as he had entered.

Gene thought it advantageous for the American public to have an opportunity to watch George Pullman flee from a subpoena.

"Send a marshal to cover his home as well as his office," he suggested to Darrow, "you'll have him in here tomorrow morning."

Gene had underestimated his adversary: the following morning Mr. Pullman's lawyer, Robert Todd Lincoln, announced to the court that his client had left on his private train for the East the night before.

"I insist that Mr. Lincoln tell this court," stormed Darrow, "whether his client did not know that there was a subpoena out for him?"

"Yes, Mr. Pullman heard about it, but he thought that a subpoena had no effect until it was served, and so he went ahead with his plans to vacation."

The son of Abraham Lincoln helping to keep the white workers of America in slavery!, thought Gene.

Darrow declared belligerently, "Your Honor, I ask that George Pullman be arrested for contempt of court, exactly as my client was! We hereby serve notice that we will subpoena every last member of the General Managers' Association to testify on this stand everything they know about their own sharp practices in conspiracy!"

The next morning, just as Gene was being brought in through the rear door of the court by the deputy marshal, George Pullman entered through the front door with Robert Todd Lincoln on his left, a second attorney on his right. The three men made their way to Judge Grosscup's room. Fifteen minutes later Mr. Pullman emerged from chambers, smiled to the courtroom and walked out. Judge Grosscup took his place upon the bench, declaring that Mr. Pullman had explained his absence satisfactorily and would not be required to testify at the trial.

Before Gene or Darrow could recover from their astonishment, Edwin Walker arose and announced that due to the illness of juror John Coe the prosecution asked that the case be adjourned and put on the calendar for retrial at a future date.

"Your Honor, I demand that court be recessed for a few days," said Darrow, "until John Coe can recover his health."

"I am afraid that would do no good," replied Judge Grosscup. "Prosecution has brought me a doctor's affidavit that Mr. Coe will be ill in bed for at least a month."

"Then the defense asks Your Honor to conclude this case with eleven jurors; we cannot be more than a couple of days away from completion."

Ned Harkness sprang to his feet.

"The prosecution cannot accept any such illegal proposal."

"Then I move that the defendants be discharged!"

"That will have to be denied," answered Judge Grosscup. "It is not agreeable to the government, and it is not practicable. I will set this trial for the first Monday in May." He rose, turned to the jury, and said, "Gentlemen, thank you for your close attention to this case. You are now dismissed."

Pandemonium broke loose as Judge Grosscup made his way quickly to his chambers. Gene went to Daisy and Daniel, who had come to Chicago to be by their son's side when the verdict was announced. When he turned back to the defense table to clasp hands with his comrades, he saw the jurors streaming out of their box. Before he knew what was happening, they had surrounded him with broad smiles on their faces, were shaking his hand, clapping him on the back. Everyone began speaking at once.

"You're not guilty of anything we could see. Too bad we didn't get Pullman up on the stand. You're all right, Mr. Debs. Nothing that Harkness lawyer could say would make us think different."

The foreman, who had waited for a moment of silence, spoke up. "Mr. Debs, when we were sworn in, several of us felt that five years in Atlanta penitentiary for you would have been about the right punishment. After listening to your story on that stand, every last one of us felt differently about you and your work. We would have acquitted you like a shot."

Clarence Darrow insisted upon taking the Debs family to a victory luncheon at the Bismarck Hotel. Everyone was jubilant. Darrow told them, "The prosecution is licked! They'll never haul us into court again: George Pullman and the General Managers' Association took too bad a mauling."

It was the first enjoyable meal Gene had had since the Sunday Theodore had arrived with Gertrude's basket. But he did not have an opportunity to finish his coffee: from the street outside they heard the cries of the newsboys, faint at first, then growing louder and clearer as they approached the hotel.

"EXTRY! EXTRY! Eugene Debs gets six months! Sentenced by Judge Woods for contempt of court! Read all about it, American Railway Officers go to prison!"

He turned white, then a bilious shade of green. At length he was able to whisper:

"Judge Woods? But how did he get jurisdiction: Judge Grosscup set our new jury trial for the first Monday in May. Clarence, can they turn around now and deny us a jury trial?"

The lawyer was even more stricken than his client. Judge Woods had co-signed the injunction which ordered Gene to put an end to the strike. If Judge Grosscup now saw fit to withdraw from the more serious case of conspiracy and hand jurisdiction over to Judge Woods on the lesser charge of contempt . . . Who was to stop Judge Woods from handing down a bench order, sending the seven men to jail for refusal to obey his injunction?

"You mean, can they do it legally? That all depends on whether you think the law was written for the protection of property or for the protection of people. The General Managers' Association was determined to send you to prison for conspiracy, and now they have conspired to get you there."

Daisy reached under the table for his hand and squeezed it. Daniel's eyes, fogged over with tears, found his son's and smiled reassuringly. Gene thought, Daisy and Daniel, they'll survive it. But poor Kate, what has she to sustain her? She knew all along I would go to jail. She understands her own people better than I do. How will she take the blow, all alone, with nothing to solace her?

12

He had twenty-four hours in which to surrender to Marshal Arnold for the trip to Woodstock. He and Theodore were discussing the plans to move the American Railway Union's headquarters to Terre Haute when the office door was thrown open and Ray Eppinghauser burst in. He was the fireman to whom Gene had given his new winter overcoat that freezing night in the Terre Haute yards. Ray had moved to Chicago a number of years before, married and taken over his father-in-law's prosperous coalyard.

"What you need, Gene," declared Ray, "is a drink, a good stiff drink."

Gene considered the idea soberly for a moment.

"You're right!" he replied with his eyes snapping. "When a man's been double-crossed by his own government . . ."

"Let's go down to Harvey's; we can get a booth and drink like gentlemen."

Harvey's was still quiet at this early hour, the waiters' aprons white and crisp, the snowy linen on the front tables gleaming as the three men walked to a secluded section at the rear. Eppinghauser exchanged greetings with the waiter, an older man with swooping handlebar mustaches.

"Oscar, these men are my friends. I want you to break out the best bourbon in the safe."

"Yes, Mr. Eppinghauser, and shall we make all three of them doubles, as usual?"

Oscar returned in a few moments with three tall glasses, clinking icily, the pure amber fluid just an inch from the top rim. The bourbon tasted acrid against Gene's palate, for he was not accustomed to anything so strong: he drank beer with the boys at their various meeting places, and very occasionally a single scotch and water, half of which he would leave in his glass. He took a long draught of the bourbon;

it didn't taste quite so unpleasant the second time. But his stomach seemed to have changed places with his mouth. Then his gorge slowly settled back down into the cavity in his chest, and as it got lower and lower, finally reaching its rightful place, a great sigh escaped him and he felt as though someone had snapped the taut cable which ran straight through his body, holding his feet and head rigidly on either end. He took another long swallow of the bourbon.

"Say, this is good stuff. The trouble with me is, I don't drink enough."

He threw his head back and emptied the remainder of the long drink.

"Take it easy, boy," said Theodore, "that's more liquor than you've had in the last year."

Gene heard only part of Theodore's remark.

It's funny, he thought, all your life they tell you you've got blood running faster'n hell up and down your veins, and the only time you ever believe it is when you cut yourself. But I can believe it now: I can fell that old blood tearing through me a mile a minute.

"I wish I could have felt this way in court, today, boys: I would have told 'em all what I thought of 'em." He turned to his brother, who was watching him with a tiny, indulgent smile. "Theo, you know what's the matter with the courts?"

"Yes," replied Theodore, "the judges."

Gene heard himself laugh an unnaturally loud laugh.

"What I'm talking about, in court you've got to watch your manners. A man like Harkness with greenbacks sticking out of his ears and calling you every vile name in the dictionary, can you tell him that he's contemptible? Oh dear no, you have to think of court etiquette. When Harkness calls you an extortionist, battening off helpless workers, all you can do is say 'Yes, sir' and 'No, sir'! Ah, Oscar, it's good to see you again. The trouble with me is, I'm too sober. Fill up my glass, double."

"I should have smuggled in a bottle of bourbon to your cell," said Ray, "then maybe you wouldn't have been so polite."

Gene raised his glass, closed his eyes, and swallowed half the liquid. He could no longer feel blood in his veins, now it was like ants, millions of little ants racing up and down on the outside of his arteries. He turned to Theodore.

"I propose a toast to King Pullman, monarch of that beautiful kingdom where all that is ugly and discordant is eliminated."

"You drink to him," said Theodore. "One of us is going to have to stay sober."

Oscar picked up the empty glasses. "Wouldn't you like to order now, Mr. Eppinghauser?"

"What do you want to eat, Gene?"

"Another bourbon."

"Oscar, bring Mr. Debs another bourbon, then bring us your special green cucumber salad, and thick steaks with french-fried onions."

Oscar brought the green cucumber salad with razor-thin slices of pumpernickel. But now the maggots had ceased to crawl up and down on the outside of Gene's veins, and his body had gone numb. Ideas raced brilliantly through his mind. Theodore fed him buttered slices of pumpernickel, while he devoured the cucumbers. Suddenly he leaned across the table to Ray.

"You think the American Railway Union is gone, don't you? You think it's dead and buried under Emperor Pullman's monument? That's what everybody thinks today, but they're wrong, do you hear me? The American Railway Union is alive, yes, and it's going to stay alive, it's going to grow stronger every day. In a month we'll have a quarter of a million members, in three months a half a million, by the time I get out of jail we'll have a million loyal members, every last person who works on the railroads."

"Here's your steak, Mr. Debs," said Oscar.

Gene tried to cut the meat, but the relation of the knife and the fork to the food on the plate was vague.

"Let me cut it for you," said Theodore.

Gene bolted the steak, the onions and several of the hard-shelled rolls. Oscar arrived with two more double bourbons. Gene took a liberal gulp.

"Easy, son, easy," cautioned Theodore. "I'll admit you're entitled to a good drunk . . ."

"You're right! I got a drunk coming. I'm sick of the whole mess. I'm tired of all this sentimental nonsense called service and usefulness and brotherhood. I say to hell with it all! You hear me, Theo, I'm satiated." He ran his right index finger in a sweeping gesture across the middle of his mouth. "Fed up, to the teeth."

"Right you are, Gene," agreed Ray. "You just become a grafting millionaire like that Harkness called you."

Gene's thoughts did a back flip. "And what's more," he exclaimed, "we're not going to stop when we have a million members in the American Railway Union: we're going out to organize every other great industry in America: steelworkers, miners, lumberjacks. You didn't know I had a great dream in the back of my head, did you, Ray? Well, I have, and it's even got a name. Society of Industrial Unions: twenty million workers and their families! It won't take us long, a few years at the most, and every man and woman who works for a living in America will be a member of one big union."

"My friend, you're drunk," announced Ray.

It was nine o'clock when they left Harvey's to go to Ray's house. Gene no sooner hit the fresh air than he felt as though someone had dropped his stomach down his gullet at the end of a string, and at any moment would pull it up. Theodore helped him into the hansom.

The three men were admitted to the brownstone house by Ray's wife, who took a quick look at her husband, murmured something about ". . . the town again," and then disappeared. Ray went to a cabinet, opened a new bottle of bourbon and announced, "Now we can get down to some serious drinking."

"Take it away," groaned Gene.

"The head of twenty million workers in the Society of Industrial Unions unable to handle his liquor! How do you expect to hold together a vast industrial union if you can't even hold four bourbons?"

Gene clutched the tall glass, swallowed. Mrs. Eppinghauser called in, "I fixed the bed in the spare bedroom, Ray, in case your friends can't get home under their own traction."

Ray sprang up. "My beautiful, wonderful Hannah: even when I am drunk she is indulgent. May you and yours prosper unto the seventh generation."

Mrs. Eppinghauser laughed. "If you don't stop spending our hard-earned money on hard liquor, we won't even prosper unto the second generation."

With tears in his eyes, Gene said, "How wonderful to have a good wife! I have a good wife, too, haven't I, Theo? But she has a bad husband, a jailbird. Poor Kate, all she wanted was to be respectable, and to keep in the right element. And what do I do to her? I break her heart, I ruin her social position, I use up all her savings. What does she get out of it? A prison sentence! Yes, Theo, Kate is going to prison, too . . . and what has she done to deserve it? Nothing but make me a good home and be a faithful wife."

He took several long gulps from his glass, then found himself in a rage.

"You know why Harkness did it, don't you? You think it was only to make himself look good to his bosses? Sure, he had to stage that attack so that they would raise his salary, but that wasn't what he was thinking about, he was just trying to make me look bad to his wife, that's all."

"Easy, Gene," cautioned Theodore.

". . . trying to prove to her that she made no mistake in marrying him. That it's all right to leech off big corporations, because everybody is leeching off everybody else. If I am living in a mansion I built off the backs of labor, that makes him look like a man instead of a lackey."

"You surely are drunk," announced Ray. "Here, let me fill your glass, it'll sober you."

Gene turned to Theodore, his face pale, his eyes big and hurt. "And she believed him, Theo. She didn't miss a word, an accusation. She never took her eyes off him for an instant, you saw that, didn't you, Theo?"

Suddenly he knew that he must have fresh air or he would suffocate. He went out into the back yard, then decided that he had to write to Kate, took out his pocket knife to sharpen a pencil, and promptly dropped them both into the fishpond. He murmured:

"Sleep now . . . sure wake me . . . four o'clock . . . train leaving for Woodstock at five."

"We'll just put Gene to bed," said Theodore. "I have to catch a train back to Terre Haute."

"Don't worry about a thing," said Ray. "I'll have him up by four."

Gene woke several times. When he tried to lift his head the pillow started going around as though it were on a circular motor. Ill and nauseous, he managed to get back to sleep. When at last he awakened, and was able to reach for his watch, he saw that it was seven o'clock; a quick look out the window told him that it was seven o'clock in the evening.

"I've missed the train," he groaned. "I gave Marshal Arnold my word I'd be back by four."

His eyes ached, his head throbbed, and his insides felt as though they were on fire, yet he managed to stumble into his clothes. Ray was seated at the table with his family, calmly eating dinner.

"Ray, for heaven's sake. You know I promised to be back by four!"

"You were so sound asleep, Gene, and I thought you needed the rest."

Gene collapsed onto a dining-room chair. "I have never felt so wretched."

"Get a good night's sleep for yourself, you'll be a new man in the morning."

Gene stumbled back to the bedroom, took off his clothes. All through the interminable hours of the night he tossed and rolled, sick to his stomach and sick to his head. The only comfort he could find was that Kate was not there to see him.

Ray came in at seven in the morning.

"Why, Gene, you still look under the weather. Whatever happened to you, laddie boy?"

"It must have been those green cucumbers I had at Harvey's. I never could eat cucumbers."

Ray shoved the morning paper under Gene's nose.

"The whole town's looking for you, including the sheriff's posse. We'd better get downtown before they smoke us out."

Shortly after eleven the two men rode up to the fifth floor of the Monadnock Building. Marshal Arnold's anteroom was crowded with newspapermen. Gene's entrance raised a hullabaloo and a barrage of questions.

"Where you been, Mr. Debs? Is that a mint you're chewing?"

"I've been sick, boys," said Gene lightly. "Friend Eppinghauser here took me to Harvey's where I had a green cucumber salad."

Marshal Arnold appeared in the doorway. "Will you two gentlemen kindly come into my office?"

Arnold closed the door behind him; he was white with anger.

"Mr. Debs, you have broken your promise and your word of honor. I came to respect you during the trial, and now you have forfeited that respect."

Gene blanched. The marshal was right. Stumblingly Ray explained about the cucumber salad and Gene's illness.

"Then why didn't you send a message that Mr. Debs was sick?"

Flabbergasted, Ray replied: "I am sorry. I didn't think it made any difference . . . whether Mr. Debs went to Woodstock yesterday or today."

In a towering rage, Marshal Arnold shouted, "Doesn't make any difference!"

Weak and sickish, Gene began to tremble. Deputy Logan came into the room. He was to take Gene to Woodstock; they had become friendly during the weeks of the trial.

"Marshal Arnold, Mr. Debs does look pretty bad. I know you don't want to send a sick man up to Woodstock. Sheriff Eckert might refuse to accept him. Why not let me set up a cot in the jury room? I'm sure that if Mr. Debs could have a few hours' sleep . . ."

Gene flashed him a look of gratitude. There was a pause, then Marshal Arnold said, "Well, all right, but be sure to lock the door on him."

It was cool and quiet in the jury room. Gene slept until three o'clock. He awakened feeling considerably better. In a few moments Logan looked in, then took him down to the dispatch cell to wait until train time.

He did not hear her enter, did not even know she was there until she sat beside him on the bench and turned her eyes full on his. In maturing she had fulfilled all the promise of the young girl: her eyes were deep, safe harbors for anyone's pain; her cheeks had slimmed, her bosom deepened, yet even after having borne two children, her figure was as slender and graceful as the seventeen-year-old who had leaned up high, very high, to get her hands locked about his neck while he held her supple body against him and kissed the sweet, loving lips. All so many, many years ago.

"Gloria," he whispered.

It was obvious that she did not know exactly why she had come, but had followed an impulse. They would have only five minutes together, five minutes out of a lifetime, and yet the seconds were ticking away while they sat in silence, knowing how surely and wondrously they had once been in love.

When she did speak, it was not about the memory pressing hard against their hearts: the day in the storeroom office behind the grocery when she had tried to say good-by, to give him fair warning that she was about to marry Ned Harkness. She talked about the friendly little practice her father had built up in Chicago, of his nostalgia for Terre Haute and the gay house on Tenth Street. Then, abruptly, her voice changed.

"Gene, you didn't mind my being in the courtroom?"

"No, Gloria. I was glad to see you sitting loyally behind your husband, even if it had to be against me."

Her voice was like Daisy's: soft, kind.

"No, I . . . I found out . . . you were alone, that your wife stayed in Terre Haute. Oh, Gene, I heard them planning what they would do to you . . . right in my own home, the railroad presidents and their lawyers! I had to let you know that you weren't alone, that someone was by your side . . . every moment in the court."

He held her hand in his.

"I sensed it then, Gloria, but now I know. Each day I brought the image of your face back with me into the rathole of a cell. You turned it into a cool green bank of the Wabash."

She sprang up with the quick, lithe movement he remembered. There was a radiance in her eyes.

"Some part of me will always love you, Gene, no matter how many years pass or what happens to us. There's nothing disloyal about it."

They were silent, each wondering how it was that human lives got so terribly, so meaninglessly scrambled. The guard knocked on the bars with his key.

"I'm sorry, Mrs. Harkness, but I can only give you another minute."

She stood facing him.

"Gene, I think you were right and they were wrong. They're fighting for dollars, you're fighting for human life. They are the ones who are in prison, Gene, the prison of their own insatiable greed. I've watched them, I know. The country thinks you lost and they won, but someday they'll find the decision has been reversed. Oh, Gene, there's no prison in the world that can have bars for you."

Then it was time to go, time to be parted again. For one blinding flash her lips were on his, her fingers locked tight behind his neck, and he held her to him, closely.

Then she was gone.

13

He was sitting by the window, Logan at his side and Curran opposite, when the train's fireman and engineer in their striped overalls and peaked caps came marching down from the head of the train. The engineer was Benny Balken, a former member of the Terre Haute Local; the fireman, Ed Ainsworth, had been a Great Northern switchman during the contest with James Hill.

"Hello, Benny and Ed. Nice to see you again," said Gene.

Benny growled. "Is this here the train that's taking you up to Woodstock?"

"The very same, Benny."

"Then they're going to have to get themselves another engineer."

"Yeah, and a fireman too. It ain't never gonna be said that Ed Ainsworth fired the engine that took Gene Debs to jail.

"It's all right, boys. It has to be this way."

"Not with us it ain't all right, Gene. Let them use a horse and buggy."

Already conscience-stricken at the trouble he had caused, Gene persuaded the deputies to walk him up to the engine. The four men climbed the steel rungs into the cab, Gene took off his coat, collar and tie, and rolled up his sleeves.

The train moved out at its scheduled time, with Gene handling the stormy end of a scoop. The shovel felt wonderful in his hands, and so did the heat of the boiler as he gradually worked the pressure up to 140. Soon his arms grew tired and his back began to ache, then blisters puffed up on his palms. At the end of a half hour he was in misery: Ned Harkness had been right in saying that he had grown soft. Yet he would not put down the shovel. This ordeal would be his retribution; he would sweat out the last of the alcohol. When he stepped down from the cab at the Woodstock station, exhausted, his face caked with sweat and coal dust, and every muscle aching, he felt whole and clean again.

Woodstock was a quiet village set in the midst of prosperous farmlands. They crossed the smooth green slopes of a park bordered by elm and maple trees. Some of the townspeople recognized him from the pictures in the newspapers, others knew by the appearance of the two deputies that this was the last of the American Railway Union prisoners. He felt their undisguised hostility: why did they have to have federal prisoners foisted upon them?

When they had crossed the public square with its bandstand and iron fountain, they came to the red brick jail. Sheriff Eckert, a brown-haired, brown-eyed man, was waiting, an unlighted cigar between his teeth. Deputy Logan handed over a batch of papers, saying, "Sheriff Eckert, this is Mr. Eugene V. Debs. If you will sign this delivery paper, I will leave him in your care."

Sheriff Eckert scrawled his name at the bottom of the receipt, then turned to Gene. He was courteous but cool.

"We play no favorites in this jail, Mr. Debs; neither do we discriminate against any of the prisoners. The rules are well established. We will expect you to abide by them."

"You will have no difficulty with me, Sheriff," replied Gene with a slow smile.

He turned to Deputy Logan and thanked him for his kindnesses. The sheriff unlocked a heavy iron door. Gene entered the prison quarters, which occupied the rear half of the jail building. There were twelve cells lining the wall which backed onto the sheriff's living quarters in the front half of the building. In front of the cages was a thirty-foot corridor, with a hanging kerosene lamp, and barred windows overlooking a quiet street; the bars across the windows were not unlike those across the front bedroom window of the house in which he had been born.

His seven colleagues set up a terrific din.

"Why, Gene, what do you mean by keeping the federal government waiting? Were those cucumbers aged in the wood? Why didn't you invite us on that party, President Debs?"

His pale face flushed with embarrassment as he walked down the row of cells, shaking hands with each of his associates.

"Don't squeeze the paw too hard, boys, I earned passage from Chicago shoveling coal."

Sheriff Eckert remained standing at the head of the cell block. Gene continued down the line, introducing himself to the four county prisoners occupying the remainder of the cells.

Then he was locked into his cell. It was clean and without malodor. By dint of spacing themselves systematically along the side bars, his comrades could see Gene and he could watch their faces as they exchanged the news of the past few hours.

At ten o'clock Sheriff Eckert returned to extinguish the hanging lamp; the rules forbade conversation after the light was out. Gene bade his fellows a quiet good night, got out of his street clothes, pulled down the narrow iron cot from the wall, covered himself with the rough-textured institutional blanket, and lay staring up at the ceiling. His comrades had been given three-month sentences, but this cell was to be his home for the next half year.

Sometime during the night it began to rain. At six in the morning when the sheriff opened the connecting steel door and banged on it to awaken the prisoners, the water was streaming in torrents against the corridor windows.

"Breakfast is at seven. The prisoners must clean themselves and their cells before food is brought in."

"Is there hot water available?" asked Gene.

"No, Mr. Debs, you will be obliged to wash and shave in cold water."

"I wasn't thinking of the shaving, Sheriff Eckert; if we had hot water and brushes, we could scrub the floors."

Eckert stared at Gene over a cocked shoulder, then replied, "Any two of you can come down into the basement and light a fire in the stove. Knock on this door when you are ready."

Elliott and Hogan insisted that only Montanans knew how to stoke a potbellied stove. They returned with two washtubs full of hot water, heavy brushes lying on the bottom. Each man took his turn scrubbing the cement floor, then Gene washed down the iron bars of his cell while the others laughed at him for being a spinster.

It was part of Mrs. Eckert's duties to cook for the prisoners; the breakfast was stone-cold by the time the sheriff got through his several round trips from the family kitchen to the end of the long cell block.

"I don't see why we have to eat off our knees on these bunks," growled George Howard from a middle cell. "Can't they just as well let us eat at that wooden table out in the corridor?"

Gene replied quickly, "I don't think we want to begin by asking favors, George; if those are the prison rules . . ."

Lou Rogers, in the cell next to Gene, whispered through the bars, "I don't know what's gotten into George; he has complained at everything in the jail, but I think his real grievance is against us."

Gene raised his eyebrows. Rogers answered, "Far as I can gather, he thinks we behaved stupidly and ruined ourselves for no gain whatsoever."

"George has been angry for a long time," said Gene, "but I thought it was at the authorities."

The rain-swept days that followed kept the cell block cold and damp. The central lamp did not shed enough light for good reading, and the inclement weather deprived the men of the exercise period in the yard. Gene had difficulty adjusting himself to life within a six-by-eight-foot world. He had brought along a number of books, but found himself unable to concentrate. He caught cold, his ear began to run, and the nerves of his eyes seemed to twist themselves into a cable in the center of his forehead. The dark brooding hours of the day merged into the dark pain-fraught hours of the night. The only activity he could force was the writing of a daily note to his wife in which he fabricated pleasant stories about his well-being. Through his mind pulsed her omnipresent stricture: "Eugene, be careful, be careful what you say; Eugene, be careful, be careful what you say."

Perhaps Kate had been right?

At the end of the first week his worst fears were being realized: they were disorganizedly urging the time to pass, sinking into long, meaningless reveries, more tinged with regret for the past than hope or plans for the future. Months spent in this kind of animosity, and they would come out confused and rudderless. They must get hold of themselves and organize their stay. But when? How?

Sheriff Eckert was a fair-minded man. He explained:

"Mr. Debs, we've had dozens of requests for interviews, people have been here from the newspapers and magazines. I hope you understand there's nothing personal in my not letting them in? It's just that the county rules prohibit visitors before two weeks." The sheriff champed the cigar across his mouth and back, then continued, "The whole country's watching this jail, Mr. Debs; if I should be too lenient . . ."

"I agree with your procedure, Sheriff," replied Gene. "I would do exactly the same in your place."

In his loneliness he reached into his back pocket for his penknife to sharpen a pencil, then realized that he had not seen it since he had come to Woodstock. Through his mind flashed an image of himself by the fishpond in the back yard of Ray's house in Chicago. He wrote to Eppinghauser, asking him to retrieve the knife and mail it to Woodstock.

14

The rain eventually lashed itself out. Two of the local prisoners completed their sentences, the third was released on parole. George Howard, after an acrimonious quarrel over religion with Hogan, requested his transfer to the county jail at Joliet, walking out on his comrades with the flat announcement that he was through with the labor movement forever. And on the morning of the seventeenth day the sun came out, warm and gloriously bright, filling the jail with light and hope.

At six o'clock, when Sheriff Eckert entered the cell block, he said, "Mr. Debs, I cannot treat you and your friends as though you were thieves."

"You haven't done so, Sheriff."

"No, but I've been severe with you. I see that you are a fine lot of men, in jail for doing your job for your union." He took a batch of keys out of his back pocket. "From now on there's no need for you to be locked in your cells. Just follow the rules: up at six, the cells cleaned by seven, lights out at ten. I know I can rely on you not to do anything to get me in trouble."

"We'll live up to your confidence, Sheriff."

"And from now on, you can take your meals in our dining room. The food will be better, and it'll be less work for Mrs. Eckert."

After breakfast the men took a brisk walk in the high walled yard behind the jail, arm in arm, glad to be alive again.

"Every time the sun comes out," said Gene, "a new world is born. Maybe it wasn't our fault, maybe the rain and the darkness caused it, but we have wasted seventeen precious days of our stay. I haven't been to school since I was fourteen; Keliher and Hogan never did get past the second grade. This may be the last opportunity in our lives to take a university course; we won't be able to say we graduated from Harvard or Yale, but we can always brag about our degree from the Woodstock jail, providing we use our time wisely."

"What do you plan, Gene?" asked Martin Elliott.

"I propose a rigid routine of study and discussion. I propose that we bring the *Railway Times* back to life. I propose that we write letters to our friends outside and ask them to send us every book they can find that has to do with American history and social conditions. Lou, you were a schoolteacher out in Iowa before you became a brakeman on the Quincy; if it is satisfactory with the rest of the boys, I name you professor and ask you to take charge of the study course."

"I accept the nomination."

"Martin Elliott, you've had experience running hotels, I suggest you become the inspector in charge of rules and quarters."

"Leave that to me, Gene." Elliott grinned. "If every man isn't up after I yell 'Six o'clock' he's subject to a fine of ten cents."

"Jim Hogan, you were in the army, I suggest you become the colonel in charge of morning and afternoon exercise periods."

Hogan grinned his pleasure.

"I will wield the birch rod during the debates. Lou, can you name a subject for tonight?"

"I can always name a subject: *Resolved, That the State Has a Stronger Claim on the Child Than the Parents.* I will take the affirmative. Keliher, how about you taking the negative?"

"I'm the best negative argufier ever turned out by the state of Montana," replied Keliher.

"Suppose we appoint Bill Burns general secretary to take care of the correspondence. Roy Goodwin is the right man to be treasurer in charge of fines and assessments."

The plan had a galvanizing effect; by the time they sat down to their one o'clock dinner William Burns had changed the name of Woodstock jail to Liberty jail, Gene had been elected president of what Roy Goodwin called their co-operative colony. Sylvester Keliher, who had been a carpenter, had secured some old wood from the sheriff and built bookcases on either side of the windows in the corridor to house the volumes that comprised their library: the poetry of Poe, Shelley and Burns, the novels of Victor Hugo and Nathaniel Hawthorne, and such social studies as *Criminology* by John P. Altgeld, *Christ Came to Chicago* by William T. Stead, Henry George's *Social Problems,* Laurence Gronlund's *An Essay in Ethics,* Carlyle's *French Revolution.*

The rules were tacked onto the wall above the bookcase, with a ten-cent fine charged against anyone speaking during the study period, a costly stipulation for Gene, who could not help exclaiming aloud every time he ran across something interesting in a book.

After the years of emotional turmoil it was not easy for the men to get down to disciplined study. For Gene Debs it was even more difficult; he was no longer content merely to look for information: what he wanted now was wisdom, a faith arising out of that wisdom which would enable him to reconstruct his life. Up to this point his thinking had been not only piecemeal but vulnerable: no matter how deep-grained his conviction, something always had happened to knock it into invalidation. He did not consider himself vacillating or weak, one who could be swept away by every new opinion let loose in the world; nevertheless, he had been obliged either to relinquish or to revise nearly every one of his working beliefs. What he wanted now was a fluid social philosophy within which he could think and work, modify and challenge, in much the same fashion that any good artisan plied his craft within the framework of its technique.

Having reached mid-passage sore and disabused, what was left for him to believe in? Money? Religion? He recalled yesterday's interview with the excitable Nellie Bly of the New York *World*, who had gained fame by circling the globe in eighty days. In her long string of questions, peripatetic Miss Bly had asked, "But have you no ambition to get rich?" and he had replied, "Money getting is a disease, as much as paresis, and as much to be pitied."

"But you must have some ambition in life, Mr. Debs?"

"If I had my choice of the gifts that come to men, Miss Bly, I would ask for the power to move people."

"You mean as an orator?"

"Yes, but as an orator with a vision by means of which men could achieve brotherhood."

Nellie Bly had drawn a bead. "Now we're getting somewhere, Mr. Debs. Exactly what is this vision? Surely it can't be religious? I've heard you called an infidel."

Gene had smiled gently. "There are few epithets I haven't been called. I am not an unbeliever; I simply don't subscribe to any creed. I wouldn't, if I could, disturb the religion of any human creature. But as for another world, I haven't time to think about it. I'm too intensely interested in this one."

Ah yes, he thought as he lay with his feet dangling several inches off the end of the iron cot, it is very simple. All I need is a faith. But what kind of faith?

His hunger was sharp and clear, and there was plenty of solid substance in the hundreds of books that kept pouring in from their friends. Yet all that he could find were negative answers: the United States Constitution had not been written to give all men political freedom and equality, but only those who possessed property; the precious ballot, which was to create a great and free culture, was even today, after the heroic efforts of Susan B. Anthony and her comrades, denied to the feminine half of the American population. The Supreme Court, which had been evolved as a check on the power of the Executive, from the very moment of its inception under the hand of John Marshall had set itself up as the champion of property over person. What was the philosophy that would resolve these ironies and bring actual freedom to a people who had achieved its external forms?

He found a detachment about being in prison which enabled him to think more sharply than he ever had on the outside; being in prison was like being on a high mountain peak: the exclusion of the little sounds and the little sights, the little anguishes and the little accomplishments lent one a penetrating objectivity. It was as though he had retired from the world and, wanting nothing further from it, was able to look at its civilization with the point of view of an anchorite scholar. There was one universality he could not escape: for the eight thousand years of recorded history mankind had been kept enchained by a ruling caste and a ruling dogma. Was it religion that had been in power? Then the peoples of the world were told that any attempt to challenge the Church constituted blasphemy and would result in their eternal damnation. Was it monarchy in power? Then the weapon held at the people's head was the divine right of kings, the military defense of the Fatherland. Was it property in power? Then once again there was a superstructure so elaborate, and by now so legalistic, that the ignorant masses had been led to believe they would perish without the sustenance provided by capital and private enterprise. The external formulas had changed; what had remained constant were the poverty and the helplessness of the people.

His testing hour was the quiet and blackness of the cell block after his comrades had gone to sleep, when he sorted out his impressions of the day, clarifying, reorienting, sometimes rejecting everything he had thought during the fourteen hours of study.

Ray Eppinghauser had written to say that he had recovered the penknife from the fishpond, but the hinges had become so rusted that the hardware man said they would have to be replaced. Wouldn't Gene rather spend the money for a new knife? Gene wrote back that the knife was precious to him because he had bought it on his way to his first union meeting with Joshua Leach, and to please have new hinges put in no matter what they cost.

When the knife finally reached him in Woodstock it was like the past come back. As he turned it over in his hands and opened the blades to inspect the new parts he realized that very little of the original knife was left: the big blade he had snapped trying to open the window of the meeting hall in Terre Haute after vandals had wrecked the room; one of the bone handles he had smashed on the floor of the cell in the Chicago jail on the night he watched the railroad yards go up in flames; the little blade which he used to sharpen his pencils now resembled a scimitar more closely than a straight-edged blade. In another year or two he would have to replace that small blade, and the other bone handle that was growing so brittle. Then it would be a completely new knife, and it would bear no relationship to the knife he bought the night Joshua Leach asked him to the meeting.

How like my own life that is, he mused. I started out as the organizer of a benevolent, self-help society; soon I had to throw away that blade and replace it with trade-unionism; trade-unionism rusted in the waters of changing times and had to be replaced by new hinges called industrial unionism. But industrial unionism was like the bone handle on my knife; I dropped it on the dirty cement floor of the Chicago jail and it smashed to a thousand pieces.

For that matter, what is there left of the original Eugene V. Debs? I married to have children and a warm, open house for my friends, but I am childless, in a cold house, its front door locked against new people and new ideas. I start out to resist not evil, and now I am in jail on charges of having used force and violence against the federal government. A few more changes and every part of the original Gene Debs will have been replaced; I will think I am still the same man; I will go about telling people that my name is Eugene V. Debs, son of Daisy and Daniel Debs of Terre Haute, but it will be a lie; I will be a different man, and there will be nothing left of that young fellow I remember who worked so surely and believed so surely and had such considerable faith.

The half hour after dinner and supper, while the men were still around the sheriff's table, was spent in making puns and laughter, with shop talk prohibited; as the warm spring days came on they played rough-and-tumble football on the back-yard lawn. The spirit of comradery and devotion was high; each man's problem became every man's problem; they helped each other through whatever dark hour or despondent mood may have seized them, when the brain and flesh ached with loneliness for a wife, for a child, for freedom.

AT THE beginning of 1948, an election year, *Life* magazine decided to run a series to be called, *Whom Should the Republicans Nominate?* There were five important contenders at this point, Vandenberg, Dewey, Stassen, Taft, and Warren. The *Life* editors spoke with Palmer Hoyt, editor-publisher of the *Denver Post,* who recommended that I do the Earl Warren article. When the *Life* editor called, I had just finished reading the first of their articles, on Taft.

At this time I was in the middle of a biographical novel about John Noble, a neglected American artist. I was reluctant to stop work, for I was moving along well. However, I was an ardent admirer of the work that Warren had done during his years of public service. I told the *Life* editor that I would not write the article to suit a political purpose, but would insist on doing an objective job. The editor replied, quite rightly miffed, that he had no intention of either dictating or censoring my material. I then said that I was hesitant to interrupt my novel for so long a time. The editor replied, "The newspaperman who wrote the Stassen article went home from his office about three o'clock on a Friday afternoon, and had the article completed that Sunday at midnight."

Reassured, I accepted the assignment; but I should have known better, for I have had no training as a journalist, and have never been able to work fast.

The next day Mrs. Stone and I drove up to Sacramento, spent a week working with the Governor and his family, as well as in the records in the Capitol, and then in Oakland and San Francisco, where Governor Warren had spent so many years as District Attorney and Attorney-General. The actual researching and writing took me between five and six weeks.

I thought the article had made an excellent case for the Governor, but the convention thought otherwise, and nominated Governor Thomas E. Dewey of New York. Governor Warren had assured me, before he left for the convention, that he would not take the nomination for the vice presidency. I was surprised, while listening to the radio broadcast, when he was nominated for the vice presidency, and when he accepted. At that point it appeared practically certain that President Truman would be defeated. However, the voters thought differently. A few years later Earl Warren went to Washington to become the Chief Justice of the United States Supreme Court.

THE CASE FOR WARREN

OUTSIDE the California Assembly Hall is a wooden railing with a sign which reads *Take Notice: No Lobbying in Assembly Chamber*. No such railing is needed in front of the Governor's permanently open door: few paid lobbyists have been rash enough to venture into Earl Warren's office in the six years of his governorship.

During the thirteen years that he was District Attorney of Alameda County, no case that Warren tried was reversed by a higher court, nor was any complaint ever lodged against his methods by the ever-vigilant American Civil Liberties Union. He prosecuted only when he had to, and when his evidence was complete. "I never heard a jury bring in a verdict of guilty," says Warren, "but that I felt sick at the pit of my stomach."

He is without rancor, tension or bitterness; even his political adversaries like and respect him. Democratic Governor Culbert Olson, whom Warren defeated in the heated campaign of 1942, says of him today, "Earl Warren has grown amazingly with the passage of the years." Robert W. Kenny, who was the Democratic Attorney-General during Warren's first term, and whom Warren defeated for the governorship in 1946, says, "He is delightful to work with, and his appointments are ninety-eight per cent excellent." Warren's good friend, Harold Stassen, says, "Earl Warren comes up on the right side of all human issues."

His personality and methods of work are bland; when he loses an issue he remains friends with the men who defeated him, though they know that he is a persistent fighter who will be back again next week or next year with the bill he feels is needed. When he took over the governorship, California was churned by feuds, strikes, social and political war. Warren has had a salutary effect on the state, binding its wounds, removing many sources of infection.

His outstanding characteristic is a distrust of power; he believes in government by law, and not by executive decree. He repudiates the concept of The Leader or The Superman as injurious to the well-being of a democracy. When he was re-elected by both parties in 1946, with the strongest mandate ever vouchsafed to a California governor, he might have considered himself justified in a seizure of all the power he could grab; yet he wanted, and took, no whit more of control than he had exercised during his first term. His satisfactions come from being of service; he has no omnivorous ego to feed.

He is the first since Hiram Johnson, in 1915, to be re-elected governor, and only the third to be re-elected in the century of the state's history. Yet he has no personal machine, and makes no effort to control the Republican structure. "No man can do his job as Governor," says Warren, "and run a political machine at the same time."

Perhaps for this reason he has the most completely nonpartisan record on the American scene. When he ran for Attorney-General in 1938, he filed on the Republican, Democratic and Progressive tickets; this cross-filing is legal in the state, and a practice followed by all candidates. Warren received the nomination from all three parties, and that was the end of the election! In 1946 he again was nominated by both parties in the primary, with almost as many Democrats voting for him as did Republicans. His nature is not partisan, prejudiced, one-sided; he can perceive many shades between black and white and he fears above all the closed minds of the extreme right and extreme left.

Earl Warren is a tall, broad-shouldered, open-faced man with a warm personality and a passionate dedication to logical and humane government. He likes people, and people find it as easy and natural to like him as they do to breathe. They seem to vote for him with the same facility.

Just a few weeks ago Governor Warren sent his annual budget to the legislature, asking for a near-billion dollars for state expenditures; by far the largest appropriation in the Union, and it was asked of a traditionally conservative legislature. The assembled legislators hardly blinked as Governor Warren read his message, calling for hundreds of millions for education, for public health, for child centers and hospitals, for roads, colleges, in what is probably the most vigorously progressive program in America today, and one of the most far-seeing in terms of the growth of the state and the future well-being of its citizens. The legislature will pass Governor Warren's budget because they know that it is scientifically constructed, without a dollar for the pork barrel.

What manner of young Lochinvar is this, come out of the West? What are the roots of his vision, and his courage? What goes into the making of a modern, freedom-loving and conscientious American?

Earl Warren is the son of Methias Warren, who was brought to the United States from Norway as a babe in arms. Neither Methias nor his older brother were strong physically, but they worked the harvests of Iowa and Minnesota. When Methias was nineteen and his brother twenty-one they landed in Chicago broke, and the older brother ill with tuberculosis. Methias Warren remained convinced to the end of his life that if they had had money for doctors and hospitals, his brother's life could have been saved. To young Earl he said over and over again: "Son, never let yourself be caught broke."

Methias met a young girl in Minneapolis. Her name was Crystal Herlund and her parents had brought her from Sweden as an infant. The couple was married. After the birth of their first child, a daughter, the family moved to Los Angeles for Methias's health. Here Earl was born on April 19, 1891. Methias got a start in the shops of the Southern Pacific Railroad and soon became a skilled car repairman.

In 1894, when Eugene V. Debs called the American Railway Union strike, Methias Warren went out with his union. The contest was lost and Methias was blacklisted by the railroad. He moved on to Bakersfield, was re-employed by the Southern Pacific, worked his way up to foreman of the repair shops and then to master car repairman for the entire division. Earl grew up on the wrong side of the railroad tracks, for out of his savings Methias built a five-room bungalow near the yards for his family. Over the years he bought other small pieces of land on which he erected cottages for rental to railroad employees.

Earl had a happy and healthy childhood, lived mostly out of doors. In the backyard he kept chickens, rabbits, dogs and a burro called Jack, who carried him over the mountain trails surrounding Bakersfield. He played in the outfield for the high school baseball team and was alternate center and end for the football team. Mrs. Warren and her two children had everything they needed, but the house was run under an austere economy.

When Earl was attending high school, and wanted to work in the railroad yards during the summer, his father extracted two promises from him: "Earl, you must give me your word of honor that you will put your earnings in a bank account, and that when the summer is over you will go back to school." From the earliest days the father planned to put his son through the university, and he did.

In the fall of 1908 young Earl went up to the University of California as a pre-legal student. At this point he was tall and skinny, 5′11″ in height, weighing only one hundred thirty pounds. He went to live at La Junta Club which shortly after became the Sigma Phi fraternity; and here he filled out his big frame. He had hurt his back in high school football and was unable to resume athletics, but he joined the Gun Club and participated in the weekly song fests at Pop Kessler's restaurant.

Every summer he returned home to Bakersfield to work in the railroad yards, and every summer his father made him repeat his vows. He took his A.B. in 1912, and his Doctor of Jurisprudence degree in 1914. Warren says, "I graduated at about the middle of my class, largely because I was rebellious, I guess. Toward the middle of my second year I began to tire of abstract legal theory and asked the professors if we couldn't have some practical courses which would prepare us for the actualities of the law. They refused on the grounds that students should stick to theory, and so in protest I took a job as law clerk in a Berkeley office, working several afternoons a week."

After graduation Warren spent two years clerking in a law office in San Francisco. He was drafted in 1917 and emerged after the Armistice as a lieutenant, but without having been overseas. At this point he made the critical decision of his life: he could return to the private practice of the law, or he could go into public service. The Assembly's Judiciary Committee, meeting in Sacramento, had a job open for clerk, and Lawyer Warren took it with alacrity.

He was well regarded by the state officials, and when Oakland needed an Assistant City Attorney, Warren was given the job. He moved back to Oakland, took an apartment with a former classmate from law college, and the following year became a Deputy District Attorney for Alameda County. By 1923 he was Chief Deputy, and two years later, when the District Attorney resigned to take an important state position, Earl Warren was appointed his successor.

Earl Warren now made the second important decision of his life: some two years before he had been introduced to a charming young widow with a four-year-old son. Like Earl's mother, Nina Palmquist had been brought to the United States from Sweden when only eight months old. Nina was a quiet, well-poised woman with a beautiful figure and a sympathetic manner. Earl Warren, now thirty-four, stood six foot one and weighed a hard, lean two hundred pounds. They were well matched, mentally and physically, and fell deeply in love. After deciding that six children would make an ideal family, "We wanted three girls for Earl and three boys for me," says Nina Warren, they celebrated his appointment to the District Attorney's office by being married.

A few months later Earl Warren ran for District Attorney. "I managed to win the election by meeting and talking to more voters than any candidate had ever talked to before," he says. Earl Warren was not only easy to like, but he inspired trust and confidence. His large blue eyes were clear and candid; he had a warm infectious laugh, a crystal-clear mind, and an abiding love for fair legal procedure.

Earl Warren was elected District Attorney of Alameda County three times. His office was a legal laboratory, not merely because he had to prosecute the murderers, bootleggers, gamblers and all the petty criminals who bob up in such rough seaport towns as Oakland and Alameda, but because he had a front-row seat from which to observe the workings of city and county government. What he saw shocked his rock-hewn Scandinavian honesty; city commissioners pocketing thousands of dollars from the 'patent paving' funds; sheriffs grafting on a vast scale from bootleggers, prostitutes and dope peddlers; bail bond brokers splitting their profits with police officers. He prosecuted these malefactors more determinedly than he did the ordinary run of law breaker: the burglar hurt one family, the grafting official was sticking a stiletto into the very heart of democracy. Not content with throwing the rascals out, Warren spent every spare hour lecturing to civic groups, showing them what happens to free, popular government when the voters grow careless and indifferent.

In the following ten years the Warrens fulfilled their complement of three daughters and two more sons. Their modest home had to be run economically, but this was neither a novelty nor a hardship to the Warrens. Nina Warren did much of her own housework. Governor Warren says, "I never brought the subject of crime or criminals into my home. Nor did I allow officials or businessmen to come there in the evening. If the matter were of sufficient importance, they could telephone me at any hour, and I would dress and go down to my office."

He had twenty lawyers working with him as deputies, men carefully selected for their skill and integrity. One of them says, "It was the closest thing to blood brotherhood we had ever known."

Serious accusations were made against him in only two of the hundreds of cases handled by him. When he first took office in 1925 he found that the Ku Klux Klan had elected a sheriff and a considerable part of the City Council of Oakland, that these men were in conspiracy with the large paving companies to defraud the city government. Warren indicted the ring on criminal charges. The indicted paving contractors resolved not to give one word of testimony to the grand jury. Warren said, "the people must be aroused!" and so he released to the reporters every day the evidence presented by defrauded citizens and minor officials who had decided to make their bed on the side of the law. The contractors alleged that Warren was releasing this grand jury testimony illegally, but Warren pointed to the statute which said that ". . . members of the grand jury may not disclose evidence," but not that the District Attorney couldn't do so. The conspirators were convicted and sent to the penitentiary.

The second case involved the murder of George Alberts, Chief Engineer on the *Point Lobos,* while the ship was tied to the dock in Alameda. The engineer's head had been bashed in with a bludgeon, his leg almost severed from the body by a knife. It took Warren six months to collect his evidence. When he indicted King, Ramsey, Connor, Wallace and the missing Sakowitz for the conspiracy to murder the engineer, the CIO set up a cry, claiming that Warren had indicted these officers of the Marine Firemen's, Oilers', Watertenders' and Wipers' Association in an effort to smash the Union. During the trial, Harry Bridges threw a thousand pickets around the courthouse, and in the later stages, some five thousand pickets. Yet Wallace confessed to acting as guard while Sakowitz murdered the engineer; and Connor confessed that he, King and Ramsey had sent Wallace and Sakowitz, both of whom had records of goon squad violence, to "tamp up" the engineer for his antiunion activities.

Since they had not committed the actual murder, Warren asked and secured a second-degree verdict rather than capital punishment. Former Governor Olson, whose Parole Board released Ramsey, King and Connor after they had served a number of years, says today, "I read the entire transcript of evidence when I first refused these men a pardon, and there was no doubt but that they had sent Wallace and Sakowitz to beat up the engineer." Former Attorney-General Kenny says today, "The union officials told Sakowitz to beat the engineer within an inch of his life, but he forgot to take a ruler."

The District Attorneys' Association of California elected Warren their president. All three California parties, Republican, Democratic and Progressive, combined in the primaries to send him to the state capital as their Attorney-General.

"I decided to behave like a new broom on my first day as Attorney-General," relates Warren, "and get to the office at nine o'clock sharp." Arriving there he found two telephone calls, both of which informed him that the retiring Governor Merriam's personal secretary had been selling pardons to San Quentin and Folsom prisoners on a cash basis, and had been appointed to the California bench by Merriam only the night before. By nine-fifteen Warren had the culprit in his office and was taking the deposition which not only kept the miscreant off the bench but led to his subsequent conviction.

For the first year and a half Attorney-General Warren and Democratic Governor-elect Culbert Olson worked together. With the fall of France both officials began to concentrate their energies on the potential defense of the state, Olson working through a civilian committee and Warren knitting more closely together the law enforcement agencies. Soon the two men came into conflict. Governor Olson, who wanted the right to rule by executive decree, felt that Attorney-General Warren was hindering him in his defense plans by challenging the legality of his activities. Warren held fast to his concept of government by law, and felt obligated to question this extension of executive power. Both men were sincerely convinced that they were right. Before long Olson began by-passing the Attorney-General's office.

This left Warren with little to do except the elimination of the gambling syndicates. When he took office he found the state law enforcement agencies at an all time low because, as he commented, ". . . no one is running a big gambling establishment without paying off public officials." First he cleaned out the officials who were taking bribes, then hauled the bookmakers and wire services into court. Tony Carnera, a big-time gambler opened a luxury ship called the *Rex* beyond the three-mile limit off Long Beach. Earl Warren's office spent months preparing its case. Then he put together a fleet of State Fish and Game Commission cutters, Fire Ships and fishing vessels manned by law enforcement officers who boarded the *Rex*, destroyed the gambling equipment and ended the ship's career.

By spring of 1941 the Attorney-General had worked himself out of a job. Governor Olson continued to ignore the office; the capitol had become a scene of bitterness and friction between the executive and legislative branches of the government.

One afternoon, after days of painful thumb-twiddling, Warren picked up his hat and walked home as fast as he could. To his wife he said, "Nina, I never thought of myself as governor, I don't want to be governor; I want to remain as Attorney-General. But I might just as well be out altogether as sit in the Attorney-General's office with no war job to do."

Earl Warren dug down into his savings, posted two hundred dollars as his filing fee on the Republican ticket and another two hundred as his filing fee on the Democratic ticket. Northern California organized a fund to pay for posters and campaign literature, but the Los Angeles Republican leaders decided that his cause was hopeless, and that they would concentrate instead on electing a solidly Republican legislature.

As he had done seventeen years before, Warren got into his car and traveled from one end of the state to the other, covering all the dirt roads and inland communities, meeting literally tens of thousands of Californians, telling them why he was running for governor and what his program would be. He defeated the incumbent Olson by almost 350,000 votes.

He became Governor of California while his country was at war. Some three million people began pouring into the state to man the factories and the fields. Millions more in the Armed services were stationed and trained in California, and embarked from its ports. The facilities for housing, education, public health and law enforcement were bulged past the breaking point. The tasks of a peacetime governor were multiplied a thousandfold, with Warren working night and day in conjunction with the Federal Government. Despite the pressures Earl Warren restored tranquillity between the executive and legislative branches. At the same time he streamlined the business structure of the state, closely integrating the many departments, eliminating duplication and waste. When he had a particularly difficult task, he called in the specialists and worked in conjunction with the legislative committee.

If the Governor couldn't get everything he wanted he compromised: "You cannot win all the time, and you cannot get everything you want; you have to be content with day-to-day progress and stay tenaciously with your major objectives." As Governor, he cut taxes, raised old-age pensions, instituted industrial safety measures, started thoroughgoing reforms in the prison system, set up a fine public health program; he expanded recreational facilities and child-care centers, increased appropriations for education. He was vigilant in blocking reactionary bills such as the one to abolish the eight-hour law; on the other hand, he amended the labor code so that the state could mediate if either party to a dispute wished it; this brought labor and management together, strikes fell off sharply. The rank-and-file of labor always backed him.

For six years the state capitol has operated in an aura of good will. A Republican himself, the Governor never lets anyone's political affiliation bar him from appointment; a Protestant himself, he never asks about a man's religion. The people who work with Governor Warren do so in an atmosphere of respect and confidence. They say, "The Governor builds us up. When we have a problem we go into his office, and in his calm, quiet way he indicates a course of action." He also backs his appointees to the hilt. A brilliant young administrator, whom Warren had been able to bring into the state government only by assurances of no political interference, stormed into the Governor's office crying, "I can get a competitive bid on the issue of those P.G.&E. bonds, but they say you'll make me give the rights to the San Francisco firm that supported your 1942 campaign." Warren replied gently: "In the future when anyone tells you what I will or won't do, invite him to my office to say those things in front of me."

The reporters who cover Warren, and there is no more cynical or politically disillusioned group in the world, are enthusiastic about him. Occasionally the newsmen accuse him of fence-sitting because he refuses to take sides on a specific issue; such a case was the hot cargo or secondary boycott act recently passed by the legislature, and which Warren refused either to sign or veto. Labor swung at him from the left and management from the right, but Warren said, "When I was Attorney-General I ruled that a similar bill was unconstitutional. I still think so, and I still think that an issue of this kind must be settled by the state Supreme Court." The California Supreme Court handed down the ruling that the hot cargo act was indeed unconstitutional.

For many years no governor's family had made Sacramento their home. Years ago the state bought a rococo Executive Mansion built in the 1870s. After Warren's election everyone pleaded with him to move into the house. When Mrs. Nina Warren stepped inside the front door her heart sank: the wallpaper was soiled and torn, the second story unused and dilapidated. The legislature gave her a modest appropriation to put the mansion back into shape. Mrs. Warren shopped throughout the state to get the best bargains in Saruk rugs, quiet but elegant wallpapers and rich upholstery fabrics. By the time the eight Warrens moved in, the house was warm, and beautiful.

Everyone agrees that Mrs. Nina Warren is the most delightful First Lady California has ever had. When a thousand girl scouts came to the mansion for tea, Mrs. Warren refused to serve them in paper cups because she wanted the children to find in the Governor's Mansion an exciting glamour. Her task has not been an easy one: with six children, four flights of stairs and some twenty-odd rooms, help has been hard to keep and there have been tragi-comic moments when the cook or serving maid walked out just as the wives of the legislators were coming to lunch or the Cabinet and Supreme Court arriving for dinner. She has been a leader in the cultural life of Sacramento, and is the chief fiction reader of the family, the Governor sticking to biography, history and world politics. On his shelves one finds volumes about George W. Norris, the Holmes family, George Washington Carver and books of a more general nature such as James F. Byrne's *Speaking Frankly, America and Palestine, Industrial and Labor Relations.* At the moment he is brushing up on his Californiana because of the centennial.

Earl Warren can get along with people, but he is also a powerful fighter when aroused. He says, "The American workingman can afford to die far better than he can afford a serious illness. Why can't the workingman pay out a cent or a cent and one-half of every dollar he earns, to be matched by a similar amount from the employer, so that when he becomes ill he can have doctors, hospitals, medicines and the best scientific equipment?"

The American Medical Association in California fought the bill bitterly, quadrupled its dues and sent to Sacramento a highly paid lobby. Defeated in his plan, Warren guided through the legislature a substitute bill giving workingmen the same twenty-five dollars a week for unemployment through sickness that they would get for unemployment through lack of jobs. In his Inaugural Address of January 1947 he returned to the fray, saying with gentle but ironic humor, "I am not unmindful of the discussions this will again provoke, because the memory of the controversy of two years ago is still fresh in my mind."

Warren's second major contest as Governor resulted from his proposal that two and one-half cents per gallon be added to California's very low tax on gasoline, the money to be used to build the new roads so sorely needed in their state-on-wheels, and to make safer the congested main arteries, on which thousands of Californians are killed every year. The oil companies fought him on the grounds that added taxes meant a lower sale of gasoline, while at the same time conspiring to raise their own gasoline price a uniform two and one-half cents a gallon. This was too much even for the conservative press: the weight of public opinion pushed Warren's bill through the legislature.

Lest anyone think that these were creampuff fights, let him consider that today the A.M.A. and the big oil companies are cold and unfriendly to the Governor, and will back him no further.

What kind of a President would Earl Warren make?

As has been his habit during his twenty-five years as an executive and an administrator, he would diligently search for the ablest men available in the country. There would be a refreshing absence of yes-men, poker cronies, and impoverished party hacks. He would work well with his appointees.

He has lived an impeccable public and private life. He hates corruption and waste in government. His administration would be rigorously honest. By the same token, he has a deep social conscience: he does not believe that he is his brother's keeper, but rather his brother's friend.

He has not traveled abroad, but he consumes the international news and has a thorough understanding of the particular phase of the world revolution in which we are so painfully caught. He is not a genius in the art of government, but rather a master-craftsman.

Though it may sound odd to say that the Governor who has asked for a near-billion dollars for state expenditures would conduct the Federal Government on an austere plane, it is nonetheless the fact: Warren has never asked his county or state to go into debt. Every dollar for which he asks is designated for a desperately needed service; it is already in the state treasury, or is due to come in during the year.

He has a high moral regard for the human race and wants it to prosper. His non-partisanship would project an era of tolerance, friendliness and good will, bring about a unity of the American people which we need urgently in the face of our international troubles.

Earl Warren has fulfilled each task on hand with energy and intelligence, and then moved on to a more important and more difficult job, growing in stature all the time. The transition from Governor of the rich, busy, complex, fast-growing state of California to the Chief Executive of the United States would be a natural one for him. The road from the Governor's Mansion to the White House is well traveled in American history; more of our Presidents have come out of state capitols than any other field, and logically so.

Yet he has made no effort to secure the Republican nomination, has allowed no one to build an organization for him or collect funds. He says, "I have made a distinction between a willingness to serve if called upon to serve, and a position of being an active candidate, which would take me away from my job as Governor and require me to solicit campaign funds and organizations throughout the country."

With the Warren family in the White House, the nation would see an example of the most loving family life, as well as the simplest; for the Warren children go to the public schools, ride the street cars and have been brought up to think of their father as a public servant whose tenure of office brings them responsibilities rather than privileges. Mrs. Nina Warren would be just as capable and charming as the First Lady of the Land as she has been as the First Lady of California.

Today Earl Warren is fifty-seven years old, just coming into the peak of his experience and mental power. During the winter he gets two or three pounds overweight because his only exercise is the walk from the Executive Mansion to the capitol and back; but during the summer the residents of Santa Monica see him swimming in the surf every day, and they know that the years have not decreased his stamina. He has a good speaking voice and projects well over the radio, as the nation-wide listeners to his *Meet the Press* program of a few weeks ago can testify.

He also has the disconcerting habit of believing that his party must fulfill the pledges of its platform; that is why he tried to put an FEPC bill through the California legislature: The Republican Party had promised to do so in its 1944 program.

Interviewers and political analysts leaving the state capitol murmur to themselves, "Can Earl Warren really be as good a man as he seems?"

He is.

BORN into a prosperous family in Wichita, Kansas, about 1875, John Noble was a maverick from the day he could walk, rejecting all conventional forms of schooling or values. His closest friend and confidant was his horse, Wichita Bill, on whom he roamed the plains and hills during the summer months, alone, or camping with Indian tribes. The elder John Noble was called "independent as a wild horse," and so was his son: big, tough, powerful of body, filled with contradictions; close-mouthed yet at times an exhibitionist; enjoying the wild life of drinking and gambling on the rough frontier, and at the same time reading Dante, Shakespeare, Blake, Poe, copying after the drawings of Michelangelo, Leonardo da Vinci, Rembrandt. He quit school at fifteen, refused to take a job, even declined a position as staff cartoonist for the Wichita *Eagle,* saying, "I want to keep my freedom." He worked hard at his art, searching for clues in Delacroix' *Journals,* Vasari's *Lives of the Artists.* He was terrorized by loneliness and the thought of death, a fear he tried to drown in alcohol. He was a mystic, a seeker after the White Buffalo of his Comanche friends, the God of his own people. He thought maybe He could be found in paint, in art. He wanted to go to Paris, to be among other painters. His family agreed to support him there.

THE PASSIONATE JOURNEY

The Search

HE emerged from the glass- and smoke-covered dimness of the Gare St. Lazare into the sparkling autumnal air of Paris, located a small hotel at the Place de la Trinité but did not bother to go up to the room with his bags, stepping out again into the brisk sunlight.

Paris was his first big city, for in New York he had walked from the railroad station, a heavy suitcase in each hand, through the dark streets to the pier, boarding his ship several hours early for fear he might miss the sailing. His first impression was the staggering contrast between Paris and Wichita, where everything was new, raw, sudden, hasty. As he walked half a dozen blocks south toward the dome of the Opera House, which served as a magnet, he realized for the first time that architecture too was a deeply moving art form, as emotionally gripping as painting or literature: the stone buildings, some of them obviously hundreds of years old, had solidity and structural grace. He circled the majestic block-square Opera House with wide-eyed admiration for its opulence, continued onward to the broad Boulevard des Capucines, with its expensive-looking shops and smartly groomed Frenchwomen going in and out, then stepped for a moment into the quiet darkness of the Madeleine church, which he felt must have been patterned after a Roman temple. As he stood by the fountains of the Place de la Concorde, gazing at the magnificent buildings which swept up the Champs Elysées, he understood that here in Paris, the art and cultural center of the occidental world, age signified all the heartening symmetries of tradition, of a word which he would not have dared to use in Wichita: sophistication. He felt warm and good and happy inside himself, happy because, a complete stranger in a foreign city, jostled by passing crowds of whose language he could not understand a single syllable, he nonetheless felt utterly at home.

He crossed the Seine at the Pont de la Concorde, and on a corner of the Boulevard St. Germain came upon a sidewalk café called Les Deux Magots. When the waiter appeared, John pointed to the table next to him where two young French students were drinking a purplish liquor, pouring water into it constantly, fading the color but keeping the quantity steady. He also raised his hand to his lips and went through the motion of chewing; the amused garçon brought him a dish of hard-boiled eggs. John ate three of them as he sipped his apéritif.

Refreshed, he rose and walked back to the river, sauntered slowly along the Quai d'Orsay, then recrossed the Seine and made his way down the slight grade of the Avenue du Bois de Boulogne to the deep green woods. Here he found a bench on a pathway frequented by crisp, gray-clad nursemaids pushing perambulators. Pleasantly fatigued, his mind went back lazily over all that had happened to him in the past week; the quick change in the railway station at Chicago, the few disjointed hours in New York until his ship sailed at midnight, the long smooth voyage on an ocean which made him feel that he was riding the open, endless prairies of Kansas.

The sun went down beyond the treetops. The air turned cool. He hailed the driver of an open carriage headed toward town. Back in the city the lamps were lighted. He passed a restaurant and told the driver to stop.

The main salon of the Brasserie Universelle was upstairs above the café. The maître d'hôtel seated him at a small table in the corner, then brought a blackboard mounted on an easel. He could read a little printed French but the chalk handscript baffled him completely. With a sweeping gesture he indicated everything on the blackboard. The waiter served him a chopped-herb omelet, a thin soup which he did not recognize, a filet mignon with hot butter sauce and small puffed-up potatoes. For dessert there was a deep glass of fruit and sherbet covered with champagne.

John sat back in his corner, sipping a brandy and watching the restaurant fill, enjoying the sight of the elegantly gowned women. He listened to the hum of French about him, and he knew that he would never speak nor learn this language no matter how many years he remained in France. Yet he felt no need to understand the words; as his eyes went from table to table he knew what these people were saying, knew as a draftsman knows: by the pitch of a shoulder, the gesture of a hand, the curve of a back, the fullness of the lips, the luster of the eyes.

He wandered around Paris for the rest of the night, walking along narrow quiet streets and sitting in obscure cafés, listening to a dozen different dialects, studying the faces of the men and women as they sat morosely over their drinks or engaged in sharp, spirited conversation. Shortly before dawn he found himself on a cobblestoned street with many carts and rough farm wagons loaded high with flowers, vegetables and fruits. His pace quickened, soon he entered the vast market place into which the choice produce of France was poured each night: huge piles of scrubbed carrots and green beans, bins of flowers in a riotous display of color. He took a pencil and paper from his pocket and began sketching a young boy unloading a family cart. The boy's father asked if he might keep the sketch. John suggested that the three of them have a drink together. The father led him to a hole in the wall where they ordered hot onion soup.

The sun was rising when he bade his companions adieu. While fumbling to put the change into his wallet he caught a glimpse of his railroad ticket with Gare St. Lazare stamped on it. He found a cabby, showed him the name on the ticket, and after a considerable journey came once again to the railroad station. He located the gate from which he had emerged the morning before, walked down the Place de la Trinité and at last was in his hotel.

Starved for the sight of good pictures, he slept for only a few hours, then dressed hurriedly and made his way to the Louvre, where were hung some three thousand of the world's most important paintings, representing every age, country and technique. Wanting to start chronologically, he sought out the Italian School, standing almost numb before Giotto's brilliantly colored and deeply spiritual *St. Francis Receiving the Stigmata from Christ*, and Fra Angelico's tender *Coronation of the Virgin*. He had never before been impressed by religious subjects, but Bellini's *The Saviour Blessing* and Leonardo da Vinci's *Annunciation* communicated a feeling of religious ecstasy through the sheer brilliance of craftsmanship alone.

The following morning he was back at the Louvre when the guards opened the heavy doors, going directly to the big room which housed the Spanish School. Here he saw Velasquez' paintings of the Infanta Margarita and Queen Maria Anna, so vividly and humanly alive they looked as though they could step down from their frames and go about their daily affairs. But as long as he had stood before Velasquez, he was even less able to tear himself away from the El Greco canvases: for here he heard a voice calling out to him, not only because of the long, lean, penetrating realism of the portraits, but because he felt that El Greco was an artist who was trying to say something beyond what could be read in the human face and human heart, no matter how eloquently they might be portrayed.

After the richness of the dark Spanish colorings and the overly bright flesh tones of the Flemish School, in particular Rubens, it was with excited amusement that he came into the Dutch School and found Jan Steen's tavern interiors, with ordinary workaday mortals considered worthy of being painted, even when they were ugly; and the full dozen Rembrandt canvases, with their dark, somber backgrounds, and the subjects lighted as fiercely as though the summer sun were upon them. The only major disappointment he suffered was in the French School where he found dull, lifeless academic canvases hanging alongside the volcanic and dramatic Delacroix.

Having had considerably more than he could absorb of some seven centuries of the best art, he now developed an eagerness to see where the newer French painters had lived and worked.

The manager at the hotel spoke a little English and was able to direct him to the forest of Fontainebleau where Daubigny, Rousseau, Corot, Millet, Dupré and Diaz had created the great landscape school. He also visited Auvers sur Oise where Vincent Van Gogh had painted his last powerful canvases, and Eragny, the little village where Camille Pissarro raised his family, fought bitterly for the few elusive francs with which to maintain his home and created what to John seemed the most lyrically beautiful of all the newer paintings.

He wandered the countryside in the shade of hundred-year-old trees, thinking back to the flat, treeless prairie of Wichita, recalling all the wonderful pictures he had studied since he left home. He had seen master technique, perspective, color, new approaches in sentiment, new attitudes toward light and shadow, form and subject. But in all of these pictures he knew that he had been looking for something above and beyond form, color, design. He had asked himself as he stood before each canvas:

Does this picture extend beyond its frame to the point of infinity? Does it glow and vibrate with a spirit and essence beyond its immediate detail?

2

He had talked to no one, far too excited to feel any need for company. Nor did he have any idea of the passage of time. He was surprised when the manager handed him a bill with his key one afternoon, remarking:

"It has now been a month since Monsieur has been with us. Doubtless he would like to pay his account."

"A month! You don't say. Have I really been here that long?"

"Oui, monsieur. And tonight at the Bal Bullier is the Quatz' Arts ball. Monsieur should go, since he too is a painter."

He paid his bill, went up to his room and stretched out full length on the bed, his hands under his head, staring at the ceiling. The element of time having been unwontedly thrust upon him, he began to review his situation in Paris.

During the past weeks he had seen men painting in the streets, in the Louvre, by the quais along the Seine, and in the forests at Fontainebleau. In the evenings he had passed sidewalk cafés where men in corduroy coats and flowing black ties bore all the outward signs of the painter. Yet he had not talked to them, for he would not have known what to say. Could he just go up to a man painting the Sacré-Coeur and ask:

"Look, pard, I'm an artist too. How's chances of running herd with you hombres?"

He could not bring himself to speak to these strangers, even if he could have made himself understood in their language. He did not know where the ateliers were located so that he could get good instruction. Unless he made some kind of conscious effort he might live in Paris for years without establishing himself in a painters' colony. More important, he must begin to paint, start to work again, give himself to the task with the whole creative and passionate vitality of his being.

He stopped thinking and lay still on the bed. The room was warm and silent. Loneliness overcame him like a suffocating quilt. He was no longer in Paris, but on some vast ocean, the only man on a small vessel with one white sail, wandering the face of the endless water, not knowing where the ship was going, having no wheel or map or compass and no knowledge of how to use them if they had been present. From the frayed look of the sail he saw that he had been on this ship a very long time, wandering directionless, seeing no other ship, no land, no human face, hearing no human voice.

He began to tremble. Then he stretched out his arm, locked the door, and flung the key blindly into a corner. Braced to endure whatever might come within the confines and privacy of this room, the pressure began to ease, his tense body relaxed.

He must not remain alone in Paris. He had come here to find friends and take his place among other painters, to plunge into the caldron of art.

He sprang off the bed, went to the big wooden wardrobe which stood against the red and yellow striped wallpaper, and flung open the two heavy doors. There were his cowboy chaps, his rattlesnake vest with the elk's-tooth buttons, the high boots and wide-brimmed Stetson and two six-shooters.

Because he could think of no one else to help him he went to the American Embassy where he was turned over to the Third Secretary, a pleasant and handsomely groomed young man from San Francisco.

"I need some help, Ambassador," said John. "I want to rent or buy the largest white horse in Paris. I also need a supply of rock salt and bacon rind. It would take me at least ten years to find these things by myself in Paris."

"Always happy to help a fellow Westerner," said the young Secretary;

"but would you mind telling me what you are going to do with a combination of a white horse, rock salt and bacon rind?"

"I intend you should know," replied John with a broad grin.

At dinnertime an enormous and ancient white horse was delivered to his hotel. The Third Secretary had bought him from the stockyards. John ran his hand over the animal's protruding bones.

"You're gonna have one last fling before you join your ancestors," he told the horse.

The Quatz' Arts ball was reaching its climax when he pulled up at the front door. The motif was the Pompeian era, and the walls of the huge wooden structure were hung with paper frescoes picturing the village of Pompeii at the moment the volcano erupted. The ceiling was covered with a painted cloth draped low and gathered in the center to represent the flaming volcano; streamers of hot lava simmered downward toward the dancers. The artists had created their own costumes from inexpensive sackcloth.

The costume prizes had just been awarded and the evening's first champagne served to the ring of tables around the sides of the hall when John kicked his heels into the old white horse; the horse leapt a dozen feet through the doors, landing on the dance floor. John caught a quick impression of the dimly lighted scene before he gave a bloodcurdling Indian war yell, pulled out his two pistols and fired the rock salt and bacon rind.

Women began to scream, men to shout as he galloped around the hall, shooting out each light as he passed it. The dancers ran wildly across the floor and the people at the tables rushed out the wide doors.

He circled the hall twice. Now there was only one light left burning which threw a macabre shadow over the houses, temples and volcano of Pompeii. He looked around the vast dark room. He was alone. He pulled in the horse at the bandstand, dismounted and found himself standing by a table with an unopened bottle of wine.

"Pull up a chair, Whitey," he said to the horse. "It looks like you and I are the only ones left at this party."

"Not quite the only ones," said a soft voice behind him.

A girl emerged from the shadows. She was tiny, surely no more than five feet, thought John. He could see her face well enough in the dim light to perceive that her features too were small, her skin luminously white, and the hair woven on top of her head, Pompeian style, a pale blond. Though her costume was scanty, it was quite ample compared to that of most of the girls he had seen running for the doors.

"It was an enchanting performance, monsieur. I could not tear myself away."

She spoke English with a piquant accent. John rose, took off his Stetson and gave her a sweeping bow.

"How nice to have company. Won't you sit down? Someone left this bottle of wine for us."

"My escort."

"Then it seems only fair that you should share it with me, mademoiselle. What might your name be?"

"Maud. What might yours be?"

"It might be Buffalo Bill, it might even be Charles Goodnight, and I frequently wish it were. But actually it is John Noble."

"Now that we have been formally introduced," she said, "perhaps you had better pour. The gendarmerie will not give you too much time to sip your wine."

He pulled the cork on the champagne bottle; it shot ceilingward with as much noise as the firing of his pistols.

"What shall we drink to, mademoiselle?"

"*A tous les deux?*"

"*Tous les deux?* That means both of us, doesn't it? A nice idea."

They leaned across the table to each other and clinked glasses. Inside Maud's low-cut blouse he saw nestled two white doves with shell-pink beaks; they fluttered softly as she raised her glass to her lips. John chuckled low in his throat.

"How does it happen that you were not frightened like the rest of them, Maud?" he asked.

"I was fascinated by your white horse," she replied, mocking him.

"It's too bad I upset the orchestra, or you and I could dance."

"I will sing."

He rose and held out his arms. She came close to him, running her fingers lightly over his powerful shoulders and chest, her eyes unabashedly speaking their admiration.

"Surely Monsieur did not develop these formidable muscles by holding a paintbrush?"

She slid into his arms. He whirled her about on the huge floor. Maud was finishing her song when they found themselves surrounded by a ring of gendarmes.

"We regret to disturb this charming *mise en scène,* monsieur," the one in charge said, "but it is my sad duty to inform you that you are under arrest."

"That is not altogether unexpected, Sheriff," replied John. "Will you join us in a drink before we go to the Bastille?"

3

He awakened to see a patch of sunlight moving across the lead-gray wall of the cell. He rose from the straw pallet, massaging the soreness out of his bones. In the chilly light of morning he appeared to himself as an utter fool. What had he gained from his ridiculous piece of buffoonery? He wouldn't have minded so much if he had caused a small riot while drunk; but to have put on this display while sober . . .

He heard footsteps coming down the stone corridor. He brushed the straw off his clothes and ran the open fingers of his hand combwise through his hair. The Third Secretary of the American Embassy looked as though he had been wakened too early, but he was dressed most impeccably. He stood for a moment gazing through the bars at John.

"Tell me, Mr. Noble, why do all the crazy Americans come to Paris and all the sane ones stay home?"

A guard unlocked the door. John stepped into the corridor. He picked up his two revolvers at the property desk. Outside the jail he fumbled in his pockets and brought forth a roll of bills, repaying the Secretary the amount of the fine. The streets were still deserted at this early hour, the metal shutters rolled down in front of the stores, the venetian blinds pulled tight in the houses.

"I know an American woman who runs a little restaurant in the Rue Jacob," said the Secretary. "It's the only place in Paris where you can get ham and eggs fried Western style. It's a good thing I'm a Californian and understand you Southwesterners; if the Third Secretary had been from New England, he would have let you cool your heels in that jail for a week."

It was one o'clock when he wandered back to the Bal Bullier to find the owner and pay for the damage. At the adjacent café the sidewalk tables were crowded with Parisians taking their midday apéritif. Since he had not gone to his hotel to change he was still wearing his cowboy outfit, the two guns in their holsters, the white Stetson set rakishly on his long blond hair. While a considerable distance from the café he heard the beginnings of a hubbub; by the time he reached the tables everyone was talking excitedly. A man rushed toward him, clutching him by the arm and shot a stream of highly voluble French at him.

"Don't get excited, partner," exclaimed John. "I'll leave. But first I want to pay for the lamps and whatever else I broke."

A tall thin chap stepped forward; he had close-cropped brown hair and wore silver-rimmed spectacles astride the hump of his long nose.

"He's not trying to chase you away, friend. He just wants you to work for him."

"Oh, you're an American," said John gratefully. "Lucky for me. Would you mind telling this chap I don't have to work for him, that I can pay off in cash."

The proprietor spoke now in soft but urgent tones. The American interpreted.

"He says he's never had such a crowd on a Sunday morning: that midnight ride has made you the talk of Paris. He's been saving this front table for you; you can have all you want to eat and drink, all you have to do is sit here in that Buffalo Bill costume."

John threw back his head and laughed, then sat down at the little table that had been reserved for him and placed his six-shooters on its marble top. Before long reporters began to arrive. John's new friend interpreted for him. When the newspapermen wanted to know who he was he told them tales of how he had driven herds of cattle from Texas to New Orleans during the Civil War to feed the Confederate Army; of how he had fought beside Custer against the Indians and been the only white man to escape; of how he had been a United States marshal rounding up desperadoes until he had grown weary of being on the side of the law, joined the Dalton gang and robbed railway express cars. Each reporter and each newspaper was provided with a different adventure. When the last of the men had disappeared, he had pretty well covered the history of the Southwest.

His new friend murmured, "Just who are you and what do you do?"

John shook his head sadly. "This is going to be something of a disappointment to you; I'm that most unsensational thing in all Paris: a painter."

"Well, welcome home!" exclaimed the American, putting out his hand. "I'm a painter too. Name is Gerald Addams. From Boston." He turned to four men sitting at an adjoining table, and introduced each of them formally:

"May I have the pleasure of presenting Marcel Charbert, who aspires to be another Gustave Courbet. Got a good chance, at that."

Charbert was a squat, powerfully built man of about forty, with an enormous, close-shaved head which seemed sunk into his huge shoulders; his smile was friendly and a little naïve. Angelo Verdinni from

Fiesole was a thin Italian boy whose blue-black beard and long blue-black hair contrasted strangely with the pallor of his skin. Angelo murmured his pleasure in the softest, most musical tongue John had ever heard. Anton van der Meetch from Leiden in Holland was a strawberry blond with deep blue eyes and strong yellow teeth; and Ichiro Kunogi, a young Japanese of not more than twenty, as tiny and graceful in his movements as a bright black kitten.

John shook hands with each of the men, said, "I am John Noble, out of Wichita, Kansas," and invited them to have a drink with him. A garçon pushed the two tables together and the six painters sat in a semicircle facing the street. His acquaintances all began talking at once.

"They're inviting you to come over to the Ruche to live," said Gerald. "It's a huge barn near the fortifications that was left over from the Paris World's Fair, and remodeled by Boucher, the French sculptor. He rents the rooms to artists for a few francs a year. There are almost a hundred painters living there. We call it the Beehive, though actually it's more like a Tower of Babel."

A deep, slow, involuntary sigh came out of John, carrying with it all his uncertainties. Only a few hours before he had cursed himself for an idiotic performance, for thinking that he could make a place for himself in the most civilized city in the world by shooting out lights with a revolver. Now he would live with painters, learn everything that was being painted in Paris, see hundreds of canvases with the paint still wet on them, participate in exhilarating discussions about new and exciting theories of light and color and composition, discover what motivated contemporary art.

"Count me in," he murmured gratefully.

4

The Ruche was a circular building at 2 Passage de Dantzig, built around an enclosed courtyard in which there were shade trees and a model's stand. On the main floor were lounging and dining rooms and work studios. The two upstairs floors, both of which had circular balconies overlooking the open court, consisted of about a hundred bedrooms each fitting into the circular pattern like spokes of a wheel, being wider at the outside street wall than the inside balcony wall. The bedrooms had originally been unfurnished but the tradition had grown of leaving behind whatever furniture each occupant brought, and so there was now an adequate though austerely simple supply of kerosene lamps, narrow cots, roughhewn tables, chairs, bureaus, washbasins and pitchers.

It was late afternoon and a number of the Ruche's bees were sunning themselves in the warm enclosed courtyard, some smoking and chatting, a few reading the papers, others sketching from the model up on the stand. Apparently most of them had been at the Bal Bullier the night before; they grinned broadly as they wrung his hand and told him in French, Russian, Norwegian, German, Dutch, Magyar, Italian and Spanish that he was welcome. He was introduced to Karl Leipsche, a fiery redhead from Heidelberg, a Slav by the name of Oscar Magozanovic, with huge black eyes and a diffident smile; a beautiful Piedmontese Italian called Giuseppe Donello who towered over the courtyard to some six feet four in height and had light blue eyes and corn-colored hair; to a Turk by the name of Nejat to whom nobody could talk because no one in the Beehive understood his language; to an American Negro by the name of Tanner, with eyes and manner as gentle as a lamb; an Englishman, George Turnhouse, in an incredibly wrinkled suit of once good tweeds; a Belgian from Brussels, a young Russian named Alexei, who could not have been more than twenty-one and yet had an enormous beard covering all of his face; and a dozen Frenchmen from practically every arrondissement: a sailor from Marseilles, a postal clerk from St. Brieuc, a former art teacher from Grenoble, an ex-monk from Reims.

The obvious leader of the Ruche was Charbert, whom he had met at the café. He ran the office of the Ruche, collecting funds, paying bills, trying to establish a sales gallery and an artists' supply shop, writing and setting into type a four-page weekly pamphlet for the members and scouring Paris to secure for the less fortunate of the Ruche a warm suit, a stout-soled pair of boots, medical care and medicines in exchange for canvases.

Gerald Addams led John to a third-floor cubicle.

"Here's a room for you. It was occupied by a wild-haired Bulgarian who upped and disappeared last week; the poor fellow lived on one egg a day, which he cooked by holding a lighted newspaper under it."

John dropped his suitcases onto the bare floor. The two men sat down on the bed, and John offered Addams a cigarette. They puffed for a moment in comradely silence. Then John turned to Gerald and said, "Tell me what's going on in Paris now, among the art groups, I mean. What kind of work are they doing? Who are the most impressive of the painters?"

Addams took a deep breath.

"Well, there's the American Art Association on the corner of the Notre Dame des Champs; it was set up by an American millionaire and has a good restaurant and comfortable rooms for students of painting, architecture and writing. They have some pretty good painters coming in and out: Alexander Harrison from Philadelphia, the French call him Le Grand Harrison because of his poise and beautiful white hair, is the leader; then there's George Luks, a former newspaper cartoonist from Williamsport, Pennsylvania, Charles Hawthorne, Fred Waugh from New Jersey, who is a fine seascape man. Then there's the group of young Frenchmen and Spaniards who live up on the winding streets of Montmartre. The best of them is Henri Matisse, who first studied under Bouguereau but revolted against the brown-gravy painting; Pablo Picasso, a vigorous and irrepressible young Spaniard; and a number of good young French painters like Georges Rouault, who does religious subjects, Raoul Dufy, who paints gay outdoor scenes of the race tracks and yachting harbors, and Georges Braque, who does still lifes, mostly homely objects thrown onto a kitchen table . . ."

Addams sprang off the bed, snapped his spectacles into a black oblong box which he then thrust into his trousers pocket. He walked about the small, triangular-shaped room agitatedly for a few seconds.

". . . the age of giants is gone," he exclaimed. "Toulouse-Lautrec is dying here in Paris, Cézanne is a hermit in Aix-en-Provence, Gauguin will never come back from Tahiti. All of us here in Paris are in a kind of vacuum; we don't know in what direction to go, or why. We don't want to imitate or repeat, and yet innovation for its own sake is the worst of all impasses. There will be years of seeking and experiment . . . for we somehow have to begin a new era, start a school of painting of our own, with a technique which belongs in the twentieth century. I don't mean to frighten you . . ."

"On the contrary," replied John. "I know that I have many years of groping ahead of me, and now I see that I won't be alone."

"Alone? Indeed not! Here in Paris we believe that all painters are brothers."

John gazed up at Gerald, his eyes shining like summer stars seen from the top of the Rockies.

"Could I throw a party tonight for the men? A sort of initiation?"

Gerald passed the word in French, then advised John, "Give whatever money you wish to spend to Jacques and Etienne. They know where to get the best food in Paris for the least cost."

That evening long planks were set up on wooden horses in the dining room. The dishware and cutlery consisted of what each man had brought to the feast. The bottles of cheap but strong red wine stood at attention down the long table like a company of soldiers, while at frequent intervals were big platters of beefsteak, french-fried potatoes, endive salad with tomatoes and cauliflower, and long, hard-crusted French breads. John found himself sitting at the head of the banquet table with some forty to fifty painters stretching below him on either side. Gazing down at the infinite variety of faces, he remarked to himself how resourceful an artist God was, to have so little raw material to work with; a few teeth, a pair of eyes, a nose, mouth and chin: and to be able to make each face so distinct and different. He thought back to Wichita where he had been only a few weeks before, to Wichita where he was the lone painter of the town, where painting was thought to bear no possible relation to life; yet here in one room were men who believed that painting was the most important thing in life, that nothing much else really mattered.

The last of the food had been dispatched, the last drops of the wine pounded from the bottles, the last echoes of the animated discussions about the application of paint, the strangle hold of prettiness and sentimentality on the Royal Academies and official salons, had drifted from the air. John saw that the painters of the Ruche took courage from the fact that everything which had constituted an advance in their art or involved change had been fought ferociously by the critics as something not only unworthy but indecent. Knowing about the vilification of the men who had gone before them, they were nonetheless determined to carry forward and extend their craft.

Now he felt a strong need to see their work; if their painting was as penetrating or wise as their analyses of other men's art . . . He asked Gerald if it would be possible.

"Don't be so hesitant," laughed Gerald; "there's nothing these men like more than to show their canvases."

He spent the night going from room to room. Not only was every nationality, religion and temperament represented in the Beehive, but every degree of intelligence and ability as well: the best talents were at the hub of the wheel, the lesser talents fanning out toward the rim until at last there were only those upon whom the wheel turned, a flat surface that took the bumps and the punishment. The test at the Beehive was not, "Can he paint?" but rather "Does he paint?" No judgment was passed on the quality of a man's work, only on the quality of his sincerity. Most of the men had been painting for years, but few of them yet knew what they wanted to say or how to articulate in paint the things they felt. They could not stand still, become little Cézannes or

Van Goghs. The road ahead would be uncharted for them as it had been for all the others who had spent a lifetime of unrelenting labor to find out how best they could express themselves.

It was dawn when he finally took off his clothes, threw himself down on the rough blanket spread over the cot and covered himself with his buffalo robe. He was filled with a sense of pleasant fatigue, exhilaration . . . and a kind of graspable despair: for although he had seen what he believed to be all degrees of talent and experience during his night's travel through the Beehive, he felt that no one of these men was as yet doing mature work.

What, then, were the chances for him? Through how many years and how many stages and how many dark labyrinths must he stumble and blindly grope before he could reach the fullness of expression, the excellence of technique which he saw nowhere around him in the Beehive, and yet for which his companions were working with what he perceived to be an almost fanatical devotion? Would any of these men whose paintings he had gazed at during the night become great painters? Would he, John Noble, ever achieve anything worth setting down on canvas? Was there even the slightest chance that he might find that which he was seeking, and the technical skill with which to create it?

Suddenly he understood that no man had the right to ask himself that question. The only question he could ask was: Can I persevere?

5

He dreamt that someone was boiling coffee and the aroma made him run his tongue over his wine-parched lips. He had not awakened to the smell of fresh coffee since he left Wichita; for a moment he almost believed he was home again.

Then his eyes shot open: this coffee was far too real to be cooking in his dreams. Across the narrow room he saw a woman leaning over a little stove. He sat up on his cot. The woman heard his movements, turned her head and smiled.

"Maud!" he exclaimed. "From Pompeii. How in the world did you find me?"

"It was not difficult," she replied, her eyes sparkling. "I asked a few questions at the Café Bullier . . . described your snakeskin vest . . ."

She picked up several of the Parisian newspapers which she had dropped on the wooden table.

"The papers say that among other things erupted by the Bal Bullier volcano was a wild Westerner by the name of Buffalo John. Would you like me to translate these stories for you?"

"No thanks," he grimaced, his blue eyes smoky. "I know what's in them. But if I could have a cup of that coffee, instead?"

She poured the coffee with quick, deft movements. It was black and strong, and he drank it gratefully.

He threw the buffalo robe aside and sat on the edge of the bed watching her as she set some breakfast buns onto a chipped plate. Though she was tiny her figure in the simple brown cotton dress seemed robust enough, and nicely proportioned. He took some American greenbacks out of his pocket.

"Here, you'd better take this money to pay for the stove and the food."

"The stove didn't cost anything . . . and the brioches were only a few centimes. Have you paid your rent yet?"

"No."

"Then suppose I take twenty-five dollars and give it to Charbert? That will pay you up for a year."

There was only one chair in the room. She pulled it up to the table for him. Then she poured another cup of coffee and seated herself on the edge of the table, facing him. He spread jam onto a brioche while he studied her face. No one of her features alone would have been good enough to be considered pretty: her nose was a little too short and too thin, her lower teeth were irregular and her skin a touch on the sallow side. Yet her eyes were good, well spaced and with a curious milk-gray color. He decided that she was pretty.

"How do you happen to speak English, Maud?"

She smiled fleetingly. "In your country you would call me a specialist. When I was fifteen I had a chance to pose for a young American who had just arrived in Paris. From him I learned a little English. Whenever an American or an Englishman wanted a model people would say, 'Get Maud; she can speak your language.' "

John wondered how many Americans had contributed to Maud's knowledge of the language; but that was hardly his affair. They chatted animatedly while they finished their coffee and smoked their cigarettes. There was neither accusation nor bitterness in her voice as she told how her father had abandoned her mother, how she had lived in various orphanages until she had been apprenticed at the age of eleven as a slavey to a dressmaker. After four years she had stumbled onto the American painter, who had taken her in with him.

"Would you like me to pose for you?" she asked.

"Not particularly."

"All the others have."

"I'm just not interested in figure drawing."

"*Tiens!* You don't like the nude female? A man who wears rattlesnakes on his chest and has killed whole tribes of Indians?"

"I'd much rather draw a nude horse."

Maud laughed delightedly.

"You make the strangest jokes." Then a hurt tone crept into her voice. "Is it that you don't like my shape? You do not think it would look beautiful on canvas?"

She quickly took off her dress, slipped out of her shoes and peeled the stockings off her slim white legs. She then stretched her arms upward and gracefully arched her back, bringing into relief the line of her breasts. Into his mind flashed the picture of the two white doves with their flesh-pink beaks as they had moved softly under her Pompeian gauze.

"Would you still prefer a naked horse?"

"Only for certain purposes."

He picked her up and laid her none too gently on the buffalo robe.

When she had slipped into her clothes again, he said, "Sometime you shall pose for me. I don't intend to paint undraped women, that's a lifetime job in itself. But didn't Vincent Van Gogh say that figure drawing is the basis of all good craftsmanship, even in landscapes? Why are you laughing?"

6

Each morning the Beehive emptied as though someone had rung a bell, the individual bees scurrying forth with canvas and easel and paints under their arms, their heads stuck out ahead of them with eager expectancy. He found that his companions at the Ruche were driven by a terrifying urgency: paint, and paint some more; never mind what the subject or how well you understand it, just get something down on canvas, for everything you get down gives you more experience, more grasp, more insight, more power. Some were painting street scenes, others going to the markets or railroad stations or the surrounding woods, still others specializing in houses, churches, open squares or passers-by who could be persuaded to stand still in return for a few centimes. He watched them painting avidly every scene, every detail, every idea they could lay eyes or mind or brush on.

"Come and paint with us today," each group urged him. "We can show you a view over the roofs of Paris . . . a little section where the streets and the houses merge into the horizon . . . a fish market where the shadows are the deepest of silver and blue . . ."

On the fifth morning Gerald Addams took him down to the shop of the color merchant, Lefèbre Foinet, where a large portion of the young painters traded and met to discuss the newest processes of grinding colors. John opened a charge account, bought a new palette, easel, brushes and supply of paints.

Each day he went out to paint with another of the men, for he too caught the fever of sheer activity, painting all day, every day, the pretty, the obvious, the banal, the obscure, the meaningless . . . as well as all of the wonderfully paintable vignettes which Paris offered so profusely. Like his comrades, he became a painting machine, dashing the oils against canvas on the quantitative theory that two paintings were twice as valuable as one. When the weather was too cold or rainy to work in the streets he accompanied Gerald Addams to the Louvre or the Luxembourg to copy old masterpieces. He never stopped to ask himself whether he was doing good work or bad, but indulged in an orgasm of expression for its own sake, painting dozens of canvases about subjects in which he had never been interested and for which he had no real emotion.

Late every afternoon he dressed in his cowboy outfit, strapped on his pistols and went to the Café Bullier. The same table was reserved for him at the apéritif hour, the café was always jammed with people who had come to see Buffalo John, the fabulous Indian fighter and two-gun desperado. Admiring crowds gathered around his table while he spun his yarns. Dave Leahy had taught him:

"Stories must be as big as the country and the people they are told about."

He always took a couple of the painters from the Beehive with him, the ones he thought were the most starved at the moment, ordering the biggest dinner the café could serve, then making his tale last as long as his companions needed to devour the food.

"When I was only a month old my family was massacred by the Unkpapas. The Indians named me Crazy Horse, and Sitting Bull trained me to become a great warrior. Sitting Bull and I moved into Little Big Horn Valley with twelve thousand tribesmen from the Minneconjous and Cheyennes. First we drove General Reno and his troops across the Little Big Horn and killed half their men. Then General Custer and his famous Seventh Cavalry attacked us from the other end of the valley, and we annihilated them. Yes, sir, with my lieutenants Dull Knife, Two Moons and Little Wolf we wiped out the entire United States Army."

There was a gasp of amazement from the spectators.

"More, tell us more . . ."

"The following year I entered West Point. I learned that I was a white man and that the Indians had massacred my family. So I pursued Sitting Bull and the Unkpapas all the way up to the black pines of Canada, where they could never fight again. When I finally conquered Geronimo and the Apaches, that was the end of the Indian wars in America."

During the cold evenings the men of the Ruche gathered in the downstairs studio around a blazing fire, with each of the models posing in turn. The crackling of the logs in the fireplace induced the men to talk nostalgically about their homes, their families and childhood and the strange, complicated paths which had led them to this hub of the art world.

The letters he started to his mother were never finished, for the things that were important to him he could not bring himself to write about. Whenever he had a drawing or sketch that he thought was well done, he mailed it to the family in Wichita. His mother answered these drawings as though they were long and detailed letters.

Sometimes when he walked the streets alone at night, moved by nostalgia for Wichita, he looked for the North Star but he never could find it. Apparently it was not a city star. Then he would pull his mother's silver star from inside his shirt and grip it firmly in his hand, the points cutting into his palm with pleasurable pain.

"Why don't you let me wash that string for you?" Maud asked in his room at the Ruche one night. "It's turning black."

"No, thank you."

"If you don't wash it soon, it will dissolve into thin air, no string, only dirt."

"It's never been off my neck. I'd be afraid I'd lose it."

His attachment to the ornament piqued her. When he asked her what she would like for Christmas, she replied: "How about the star you wear around your neck on that filthy string?"

"No, Maud."

"But you said I could have anything I wanted?"

"Why are you so anxious for that little star? It really has no value."

"Except that you protect it so strongly. It's funny about painters:

you always leave somebody behind that you can't forget. And you always go home to marry them."

"Not this time, Maud. It's my mother. She gave me this as a going-away present. A good-luck talisman . . . to watch over me . . . when I haven't enough sense to watch over myself. But I'll get you a necklace for Christmas."

He had grown fond of Maud, in a casual way; when he wanted feminine company, instead of taking the nearest girl at hand he would send word to Maud or set out to find her. She had an apartment in the Impasse du Maine, at the top of several flights of narrow wooden stairs, and when they attended a late party on her side of town, he stayed the night there.

There was a big wooden bed on the dark end of the one room, and a pair of comfortable chairs under the windows which gave a magnificent view of Paris. Off the room were two alcoves, one serving as a kitchen, which she rarely used for anything more than coffee, the other as a bedroom. There were no feminine touches, no gaily colored curtains on the windows or soft rugs on the floor, no decorations, no table of perfumes or personal treasures. Maud had lived here for five years; for all the impression she had made on the place, it could have been rented only the hour before. When on occasion he offered her money she replied, "I don't need any. I work at the dress shop, and I am doing their difficult beading now. They pay me well."

He had given little thought to her personal life, and so he was mildly surprised to learn that she was faithful to him.

"It's the only kind of monogamy permitted to me," she retorted, her milk-gray eyes deepening with anger. "One man at a time, and not much of that one man, either: little more than the dregs, really."

It was the first time he had seen her emotionally upset. He lowered his head, unable to meet her eyes, for he knew that she was right. Like the other painters in the Beehive he was functioning almost completely outside the realm of love. Each man had his model and girl, but these relationships were rudimentary. Painters, working in a group, were like cowboys or sailors: they went on long, hard-driven and abstemious voyages on canvas, leading monastic lives, taking their joy from the work's progress and the companionship of the painters about them. Then, when the voyage was terminated, the ship brought home safely, the herd delivered to the railhead, the group of paintings completed, they turned their backs on their work in satiation, bellowed loudly for their girls, took them to the cafés for food and drink, danced through the night and returned to their cells for the climax of their carousal.

But they fooled neither themselves nor their girls: no matter how much passionate abandon they might pour into these few hours or days of rebellion, they knew that very soon they would clumsily wash out their neglected brushes, select a fresh piece of canvas, begin the first stumbling steps of the new journey: a journey alone.

7

On the first of December he received an extra check from his father for the holidays. He turned it over to Charbert, for Christmas did not promise to be a hearty season at the Beehive. Charbert summoned the men to a meeting in the big dining room.

"We've got to sell some canvases, and sell them fast. That's why we're going to stage a new kind of exhibition. It should earn us a *succès fou.*"

The men blew smoke into the room and waited anxiously for him to continue.

"Each of us will hang what we consider to be our best canvas, and under it we will write the legend of what we were attempting to do and what we conceive to be our derivations: whether we think our landscapes derive from Breughel, our portraits of lined old faces from Rembrandt, our pointillism from Seurat."

The painters chewed on this for a moment.

"I don't like people coming here to view an idea," exclaimed Karl Leipsche, the red-haired German. "If they want a history of art let them go to the Sorbonne."

"What do you care what method is used to get the critics and buyers in here?" shouted Charbert. "Haven't we tried endless times to attract dealers? They say we are amateurs, beginners."

"It won't work," said Giuseppe Donello in his soft, placating voice. "Painting, like music, cannot be described in terms of words."

But Marcel Charbert was a stubborn man.

That night the Beehive was rocked by considerable soul searching. As John went from room to room he found the painters going over their stacks of canvases, their eyes serious and troubled.

"They're not good enough . . . I thought at least this one . . . up to now I had imagined that I had captured something. . . . How can I show this when I know it is not right, when I have come so far during the past weeks . . . ?"

Deep in the night he at last came to Charbert's room. Marcel was leaning over his table writing furiously, invitations, advance notices for the newspapers.

"Look, Marcel, I think this is a great idea, but you will just have to count me out. I am not good enough to exhibit . . . I'll disgrace you."

Charbert's powerful body set as though coiled to spring.

"You're not the best painter in La Ruche, nor are you the worst. We have seen only too well that the most mediocre painters of France get the highest honors, The Bougereaus, Delaroches and Greuzes. And who do you think were the members of the Salon des Refusés in 1863, the men not considered good enough by the official judges of the Salon even to have their canvases hung in the great state show? Shall I tell you their names? Fantin-Latour, Legros, Manet, Whistler, Jongkind, Laurens, Harpignies . . ."

"I know that, Marcel, but just at this moment everything I do is so confused, I'm like a composite picture worked on by thirty men. You can take any square inch at random and say who I copied it from."

Charbert picked up his drafting pencil and continued writing on one of his articles. "Then stop wasting your breath and go to work. You have a month." He looked up, and when he spoke it was with a whimsical smile. "There probably isn't a canvas in the Ruche tonight which will hang on the walls of the show."

He began work on a project which had been haunting him: a ship upon a sea, an endless sea which had no shores or harbors or piers; overhead on the right there would be a molten, fiery sun, while to the left there would be a single pure white cloud. He did not want to paint any particular ocean, nor was the ship to be any definitely recognizable one; nor yet was this lopsided sun nor even this rhythmically shaped cloud to be a sun or a cloud which one had seen on a specific day and remembered for its color or shape or form. No, these objects were to be rather the essence of the things they represented: a vast shoreless ocean which was all oceans, a ship which was the spirit and embodiment of all ships which plied all seas; a sun and a cloud which would convey the inner reality and significance of all suns and all clouds seen through a man's lifetime.

The month passed in a fever of concentrated work. He never went near the Café Bullier nor visited with Maud. All social activity was suspended and when the girls came in to the Beehive they came in as models, posing for long hard hours.

As he went about to the other workrooms he realized that every painting was a self-portrait even when it was a still life or a scene over the roofs of Paris; for no man ever pictured anything but himself, his core, the things that he was basically. With every brush stroke the artist was mercilessly exposed: he could conceal nothing, he could pretend to be another person, to believe in other values, but in the end he would fool no one. Only now, years after having read through the works of Shakespeare, Dickens, Scott, Poe, Balzac did he realize that even the most profilic writer created only one novel; throw away the individual bindings and the whole of each man's writing constituted one book: the true and complete portrait of himself. An artist had one thing to say, and one only; he might flail about, seek new techniques, forms, color combinations, subjects, but intrinsically he would always paint the same canvas, write the same book.

Yes, each of his painter friends here in the Ruche had his own White Buffalo: Angelo Verdinni painted over and over again a pale young girl's face which showed the line of her nose curved away from the light; the Pole from Bydgoszcz painted the suffering of his people, shown eating a hard crust of bread, or being whipped by overseers; Jacques, from Lyon, was trying to prove that the earth, rocks and trees beat with an inner pulsation of their own; Karl Leipsche sought the ultimate meaning of life in broad-bosomed, thick-buttocked nude women, never bothering to finish their heads or their feet; Pablo Anza scorned the idea that there could be any spiritual or literary content to a canvas, and attempted to capture pure emotion by the delights of color alone; Alexei, the Russian, went looking for the corrupt, the diseased, the sordid, revenging himself in canvas after canvas on someone who had crushed all goodness and beauty out of his youth; Kunogi, the young Japanese, believed that all of art could be expressed by the grace and charm of the delicate line; Marcel Charbert, who had painted over half of Europe, pictured only house-lined streets, forever seeking a home and never finding it; Anton van der Meetch painted only men at work, digging, hammering, cleaning fish, compensating his troubled conscience because he himself was not engaged in manual labor; the fisherman from Brittany painted wave after wave pounding against the rocks and throwing sheets of spray into the air; Tanner, the American Negro, painted only religious scenes, laid in a whimsical heaven; Gerald Addams only copied masterpieces in the museums, forever pursuing some mythical concept of perfection as attained by other men.

And what about himself?

The thing he loved most about the West was the vast, horizonless prairie. Did he not have to admit then that the prairie was synonymous with heaven in his mind, just as the sea was synonymous with the prairie; and the vast dome of the sky synonymous with the prairie and the sea? These were the three scenes which interested him most; in them he always painted the three symbols that were synonymous with God in his mind: the white buffalo on the prairie, the white ship on the sea, the white sun in the sky.

Some people were born with a hunger for power, some with an unquenchable thirst for adventure, for movement, for learning, for sexual passion. There was no man born without his hunger, even if it was only the hunger for a shell to crawl into or the hunger to be let alone, to have no hunger. Yet there could be no man without the hunger, for that was the driving force of life.

Some few, like himself, had a hunger to know God; and this hunger too became a relentless preoccupation which fed on itself, recreating its own needs.

He returned to his slice-of-pie-shaped cubbyhole and studied the painting on the easel. He perceived that his own desire to capture the ocean of oceans, the sun of suns, the ship of ships, was in reality his effort to paint a portrait of God. He took out the piece of scratch paper which would be tacked under his painting at the exhibition and wrote:

"All forms of art are a seeking after truth. Yet it is not the finding of this truth which determines the worth of the work, but rather the intensity and faithfulness of the search."

8

The painters were dressed in their Sunday best, scrubbed and pressed, and waiting with the terrible fear and expectancy of the creative artist whose efforts are to be exposed to the frequently rude and disinterested eyes of strangers.

John did not know the language well enough to understand the discussions that took place before each of the canvases, but when he stood in front of his own painting and watched the expressions of the passers-by he learned quickly that indifference sounds the same in any tongue.

When the last of the guests had gone the men gathered about the fire in the studio, anger banked deep in their eyes.

"Didn't we sell anything?" asked John.

"No one even came to Charbert at the desk to ask the price of a canvas," replied Gerald.

"But what hurts most," growled Charbert, "is that not one of the major critics bothered to come."

Not a single line, not even a bad or contemptuous notice, appeared in the Parisian press. The gloom at the Beehive could be cut with a dull palette knife.

John was working in his studio when he heard a tentative knock on the door and threw a mumbled *"Entrez"* over his shoulder. After a few moments he felt someone standing behind him. He turned, irritably, then gasped in astonishment.

"Marty! Marty Buckler!"

"It's me, all right. But for a minute there I wasn't sure it was you."

John sprang up, warmly pumping Marty's hand.

"Marty, let me look at you, you old cay-utte. Will you look at that brand-new suit, all fresh-pressed, and that beautiful shirt and tie."

"That's more than I can say for you, John! You still look like a bundle of soiled linen that's been dumped at Buckler's Laundry. But it's good to see that homely old phiz of yours, even if it is unshaved."

"Here, sit down, boy," urged John, running his hands quickly over the bed to flatten out a space. "How is Frances?"

"All right . . . I guess."

"What do you mean, you guess? Don't you know?"

"Can anyone ever know, with Frances? She keeps her thoughts and her feelings to herself."

Uneasy, not wanting to learn more, John asked about his family back home, and then about Marty's businesses. Marty's body had filled out considerably, but his face was just as bony as ever. His purple eyes, which had been troubled, now flashed happily.

"That's the big news, boy. We're going to open Buckler's National Bank in the spring. The builder broke ground just before I left Wichita."

"Marty, you're going to be a banker! Well, I'll be a ring-tailed Texas steer! Marty Buckler, Banker! And a National Banker, to boot. If only your mother could see you now, eh, Marty? Say, how about staying with me while you're in Paris? We'll move another cot in here."

Marty gazed at the disheveled cell, his mouth slightly awry.

"Thanks, John, but Cook's Tours booked me into the Crillon."

"The Crillon! Where all the visiting royalty stays! If you're not careful, you're going to be President of the United States! I can see the title on the cover of the book right now. *From Sod House to White House,* by Horatio Alger Buckler."

Marty squirmed, not unpleased.

"What do you say, Marty, we throw a barbecue for all the painters here at the Beehive? To celebrate your arrival and the Buckler National Bank."

"I was hoping you'd suggest that, John. I'd like to meet your friends, get to know Paris . . ."

"Great. We'll have plenty of food and drink . . ."

". . . and girls, John?"

Marty's lips had gone dry. He stood licking them, nervously.

"Girls? Why sure, Marty, if you want them. Why don't we hire some musicians, then we can clear away the tables afterwards and have dancing."

"That's swell, boy."

John measured his old friend with a glint in his eye.

"Got some money? I'll give it to the boys who stage these roundups."

"Sure." Marty took a clip of crisp French bank notes from his wallet. "Here, take what you need."

John lifted the entire packet.

"Might as well use it all, Marty. That's what money is for, to spend."

John spread word over the Latin Quarter that all painters and their models were welcome. Many of the girls came in the Pompeian costumes they had worn to the Bal Bullier, and by midnight Marty Buckler, of Wichita, Kansas, was having his own private Quatz' Arts ball.

The party was the most lavish the Beehive had seen since the day Boucher opened its doors. There were enormous tureens of *panade,* a bread soup; large quantities of *charcuterie,* assorted cold meats; salamis and cheeses; liver loaf on toasted French bread; platters of sardines and *saumon;* red caviar on buns; big brass bowls filled with raisins, apples, green almonds; hundreds of petits fours; buckets of Reims champagne.

The dining room grew hot with the dancing, smoking and drinking. Maud, noticing John search the room for Marty, explained:

"He went with Yvette . . . in the middle of the last dance."

Marty disappeared four times in all before daybreak, and on each occasion with a different girl. He had been drinking champagne steadily; just before dawn, with a half-finished glass in his hand, he suddenly slumped forward on the bench where he was talking to a scantily clad model by the name of Mercedes. John caught him before he hit the floor, carried him to his room, took off his suit, wrapped him in the buffalo robe and settled him on the floor. Maud put a pillow under his head.

Marty awoke at dusk. He had a cup of the coffee which Maud had brewed before she left, then washed and shaved in the cold water of the communal bathroom, and was eager for another celebration.

"All right, Marty, but you'd better stop off at that Cook's Tour of yours and get some more of those pretty bank notes."

John bought himself a new suit so that he wouldn't disgrace Marty, then suggested they have dinner at the Brasserie Universelle, where he had dined on his own first night in Paris. Afterward they went to the Moulin Rouge. Marty was fascinated by the show, but it was not until the entr'acte when they went out into the foyer to have a drink at the bar, surrounded by flashy women in low-cut evening gowns, that he really became excited.

"Say, these ladies are wonderful, John. Look at those hair styles . . . and those slit dresses. They've got more class than those little models last night, haven't they?"

"Oh, sure," replied John.

He didn't see any use in telling Marty that these were prostitutes, while the models who had been kind to him at the Beehive had done so out of a sense of gratitude and camaraderie, without thought of personal gain.

"There's a stunner, John, that tall brunette talking to the little guy in the black suit. Do you think I could meet her?"

"Oh, I imagine so, if we play our cards right."

He gave the brunette the eye. She came to the bar with a too bright smile, holding up the train of a slightly threadbare gown. John ordered a drink for her, then slipped a ten-franc note into her hand, murmuring in bad French:

"Make my friend think you are doing it for love."

"*Oui, monsieur, je comprends parfaitement.*"

"What's she saying, John?"

"She says she finds you very exciting."

"Swell. How about you getting one of these girls?"

"That was last night. I'll wait here at the bar."

Marty was back in less than an hour, but his eyes were dancing and he seemed highly pleased with himself.

"Where do we go next, John? It's just the shank of the evening. Let's find another café . . . and another girl."

The following weeks were a blurred kaleidoscope for John, trying to satisfy Marty's insatiable appetites for noise, music, excitement and, above all, women. Early one evening, pacing Marty's room at the

Crillon while Marty bathed and dressed, he noticed a little diary propped open on the desk against an inkwell. Glancing down idly, he saw that the page contained Marty's entries for the night before: the names and descriptions of the women he had had, and a brief comment on the anatomical character and performance of each. Intrigued, John slipped into the chair and began reading; to his amazement he found that Marty had each of the girls numbered, and the ones of the night before brought the total up in the seventies.

"What are you planning to do with these souvenirs of Paris, Marty? Take the little book home and save it for your grandchildren?"

Marty flushed, but only a little.

"You know I have a systematic mind, John. I promised myself when I left Wichita that if it was possible I would have me a hundred women."

"But, Marty, this bookkeeping system makes it sound as though these girls were units of something you wanted to accumulate . . . dollars, maybe. You remind me of a painter who thinks that when he's painted fifty canvases he'll be twice as good an artist as he was when he had painted twenty-five. Never mind the quality of the work, forget about its emotion, it's only quantity that counts. That's one of the things wrong with this world, Marty: the quantitative theory."

"Aw, cut out the morbid stuff, John. You know I don't understand all those hifalutin theories. Come on, let's paint the town."

But Marty's fun was spoiled. He ordered a bottle of whiskey to be put on the table, and then refused to touch it.

"John . . . was she . . . cold . . . to you?"

"Cold? Who?"

"You can be honest with me, boy. It doesn't matter any more . . . particularly since I've had all these girls in Paris." He leaned halfway across the table, his eyes holding John's. "Was Frances cold to you? I've got to know."

John gulped, and at the core of that gulp was a picture: Frances in his arms while they lay on the sofa in his darkened studio; so sweet of lips, so warm of embrace. He thought, There's no substitute for love. Aloud he said:

". . . we had only . . . childhood kisses . . ."

Marty brushed aside the evasion as though it were smoke blown at him from the next table.

"John, sometimes I think Frances despises me . . . sometimes I seem to catch an expression in her eyes . . ."

"You're imagining things, Marty. Frances loves you."

"As a . . . business partner. That's how I got her interested in me, by involving her more and more in my deals . . . my money-making schemes . . ."

He was silent for a moment, his face averted. John watched him wretchedly. Marty's food had grown cold; he pushed the plate aside in revulsion.

"John, you know I've always had an itch for the things that came to you so natural: books, ideas, painting. But I never had time when I was growing up, nor money either. And now that I got the time and money . . . I don't use 'em. I haven't read a book from cover to cover since you left Wichita. I'm lucky I can get through the paper at night, I'm so tired . . . on edge . . . with the day's figures spinning through my head. That's why Frances will never love me the way I want her to: I only got one string to my fiddle: business. She's bored with me, John, as bored as I am with myself."

John lighted a cigarette; he held the match aloft until it burnt his finger.

"That's a startling admission, Marty."

Marty leaned across the table, impetuously.

"John, let me stay here in Paris with you for a year. Oh, I'll cut out all the boozin' and whorin', that was just a spree. I'd like to read all the books you had on your shelves back in Wichita: Dickens, Voltaire, Shakespeare, and then chew over the stories with you to make sure I've got 'em straight. I'd like to buy tickets for the opera, listen to all that music and singing until it sounded like something more than a lot of cats screeching on the back fence. I'd like you to teach me about painting, oh, not to make those daubs myself, but to know why people get so excited about that kid stuff. I'd like to travel all over Europe so I'd know where Switzerland was when people talked about it. John, I want to become educated. It's not too late, is it?"

"You're the only one who knows the answer to that, Marty. What would you do about your bank, and all your other affairs?"

Marty's voice had raised to a high-pitched entreaty. Now all the timbre collapsed, and it sank to a whisper.

"You're right. I can't stop now. I've got to make the bank a success." He looked up, his face animated once again. "But it shouldn't take too long, John, five years maybe, ten at the most. Then I'll be rich . . . secure . . . and I'll have all my time to study . . . get educated. It won't be too late, will it, John?"

9

The day before he was to leave for Wichita, Marty asked if he couldn't throw a farewell party for the painters. John was thoughtful for a moment.

"Since you want to understand art, Marty, I suggest that for your farewell party you sponsor a Marty Buckler Exhibition at the Beehive . . ."

"Say, wouldn't Frances be impressed!"

"And make it a real buying exhibition."

"Fine, but who's going to buy?"

"You are."

"Me? You're plumb loco."

"There isn't a canvas at the Beehive that can't be bought for a few francs."

"Why should I waste my hard-earned money on that useless stuff?"

John asked guilelessly, "Marty, how much does my half of the Buckler enterprises amount to by now?"

"Your . . . what do you mean, John?"

"The hundred dollars I earned from the drawing of the Dalton gang was invested in your laundry. That just about matched your savings, didn't it? Everything you built since then stemmed from the laundry."

The high red color passed out of Marty's face and then returned as a seasick green. Though he never took his eyes from John their gaze became unfocused.

". . . you mean . . . you need money? Anything . . . you want . . ."

"Stop stumbling, Marty, I'm not asking for an accounting. It's just that I invested in you when it looked like I was drawing to a middle straight; I'm asking you to do the same for my friends."

"Why, of course, John. I just didn't realize how keen you were about this whole thing. . . ."

Marty could hardly recognize the men at the Beehive the following evening. "What are they so quiet about?" he asked. "And why are they staring at me bug-eyed?"

"Most of these people have never sold a canvas in their lives. They've been told that you are going to buy fifty paintings, but they find this idea so incredible that they think we are playing some kind of joke on them."

Marty let his eyes wander over the wall slowly, looking at each of the canvases in turn.

"John, they're terrible. I don't like any of them. Couldn't I just give each man a few francs and tell him to keep his canvas?"

"No, no, the few francs is not what's important. It's that you perceive in their pictures something beautiful, true and important. They'll live on that faith, Marty, for months." He turned to Gerald Addams. "Gerald, tell the men that Mr. Buckler is eager to see which fifty canvases Charbert's purchasing committee has selected, so that he can pack them and take them home with him to the United States."

Marty muttered, "John, for heaven's sake, you're carrying this too far. Don't make me take them home, somebody's liable to find out I've got them."

As each winning painter was indicated, the artist rose, took his picture off the wall, carried it to Marty and thanked him in his native tongue.

Riding down to the Crillon in a fiacre, John noticed Marty's crestfallen expression. Suddenly he felt conscience-stricken.

"Look, Marty, I'll admit I took advantage of you. Those paintings aren't worth even the few francs you paid for them, in particular not the John Noble. But if it so happened that you bought a lot of weak shares on the stock market and wanted to recoup your losses, what would you do?"

"Why, I'd buy some strong stocks, obviously."

"Then that's exactly what we're going to do: we are going to buy some strong paintings to offset the ones you acquired tonight."

Marty let out a cry of anguish. "Oh, John, not still more!"

"Tomorrow I'm going to take you around to the important galleries and to the little hole-in-the-wall rooms where the dealers can hardly pay their rent. From these places I can give you a start on one of the finest collections of modern paintings that anybody in America will own."

"But, John, I don't want any pictures," wailed Marty. "I don't want what you call the good ones any more than I want the bad ones."

But John was not listening. "The Martin Buckler Collection!" he said. "Just think of it, Marty, in addition to being a banker you're now becoming a patron of the arts."

They spent the day buying a Pissarro, a Degas and a Renoir at Durand-Ruel's, a Delacroix, an Edouard Manet and a Van Gogh at Goupil's, a Cézanne, a Gauguin and a Matisse at Vollard's, a Seurat and

Toulouse-Lautrec in a furniture store in Montmartre, and an Henri Rousseau in a little teashop in Montparnasse.

"Look, John, do me one small favor, will you?" Marty begged as they were saying good-by at the Gare St. Lazare. "Ship these pictures to my warehouse, instead of to my home . . . they'll be safer that way . . . or at least I will!"

From the station John turned in the direction of the Rue de Fleurus, for the buying expedition had brought him an invitation to visit Gertrude Stein, patron of many of the artists whose canvases he had selected for Marty. At number 27 he found a small pavilion of two stories and behind it a large study. He knocked at the door and after a moment it was opened by the strangest-looking woman he had ever seen: roughhewn, like primitive sculpture, with a powerful jutting nose and chin and overhanging black eyebrows, so that one could not know, except for looking at the long black monkish gown and the string of beads hanging almost to the waist, whether this were a man or a woman.

"So you're John Noble! But where is your cowboy horse and the six-shooters?"

"It is not a role I enjoy playing before Americans."

He walked into the big studio room which was lighted by gas lamps high up near the ceiling. Heavy Italian Renaissance furniture stood against the whitewashed walls, and in the center was a massive Renaissance table looking as solid and hand-hewn as Miss Stein herself. But the most amazing part of the atelier was that the high and spacious walls were covered almost solid with hundreds of paintings and drawings, some framed, some unframed, bearing no relationship to each other in style, age, mood or content.

"Then the wild Westerner is a part you improvise, Mr. Noble? I'm disappointed."

"But why, Miss Stein? Everyone wears a mask in public. Look at yourself, acting as hostess to the poor, unknown artists of Paris. What would you be without it?"

"The greatest writer in the world."

"Perhaps, but who would believe it if you were hidden away somewhere quietly? As the patroness of modern art you have made yourself famous throughout Europe."

"Like all Westerners, you have a streak of brutality in you, Mr. Noble; but you speak honestly."

John smiled, a crooked, tentative smile. "Only sometimes."

He began an inspection tour of the room, walking slowly past Matisse's *La Femme au Chapeau,* a group of Cézanne landscapes, a powerfully etched head of an old woman by Daumier, two riotous Gauguins from Tahiti, several enormous Picasso Harlequins, a tiny Delacroix, many narrowly framed Japanese prints, a Toulouse-Lautrec drawing, pictures by Valloton, Duran and Braque, the pale face and bosom of a delicate French girl by Marie Laurencin.

The room began to fill now. Pablo Picasso came in, a short stumpy man dressed in an incredibly wrinkled suit that looked like burlap, whose eyes were brilliantly alive and all-consuming. With him was his mistress Fernande, with a beautiful face and large dull eyes. Next he was introduced to Alfred Maurer, who arrived with Alice B. Toklas, Miss Stein's companion; then to Mildred Aldrich, an American who had brought a group of German painters who called themselves by a new name, Expressionists; then to Alice Princet with André Derain, whose paintings John had seen and admired.

By now the atelier had become crowded. Looking down toward the end of the room, he saw Gertrude Stein sitting in a high-backed chair, her hands folded monastically in her lap, smiling benignly over her salon as the artists came to her to inquire over the progress of her new work, a long book called *Three Lives.*

Completing his tour of the big atelier, John at last came to a group of adoring young men who surrounded Picasso. A fluffy-haired blond was asking obsequiously:

"When one does not know how or what to draw, should one go to a master or a school?"

"Neither, you should found your own school," replied Picasso.

John's stomach rose, but even as he turned toward the door he saw Picasso's tiny hidden smile and realized that the man was merely entertaining himself at the expense of bores.

Gertrude Stein made her way quickly through the throng.

"Are you leaving so soon, Mr. Noble? Don't we amuse you?"

"I guess I'm just not the salon type, Miss Stein."

"You don't like to run with the herd?" Her voice was faintly mocking.

10

He was walking the streets of Paris in a high wind. It was night. The city was dark. The wind grew stronger and stronger, hurling papers about, sweeping objects up and down the deserted streets. He plunged headstrongly forward though he had no idea of where he was going, feeling only that he must somehow move onward.

The air began to fill with snow, small white flakes drifting lazily downward. He turned his face up toward the sky; the countless white particles now felt round and hard and metallic. They rained on his upturned face and his shoulders and chest, lacerating the skin. He picked up a handful of the flakes. They were dollars, small white dollars, millions of them piling around him, and all of them with Marty's face stamped on both sides, his features etched in silver like the negative plate of one of the photographs he remembered from George Israel's studio in Wichita.

The Marty Buckler dollars beat against him like the big rocks of a hailstorm against a windowpane, bruising every part of his body. He was too tired and hurt and confused to move, but he was not frightened for he knew that he could not be destroyed by these metallic images. He closed his eyes to rest for a few moments. When he opened them the dollars had turned into female dolls, all undressed, all with a fixed smile painted on their faces, and all exactly alike. He rose to his feet; the dolls vanished.

He moved down the dark streets; once again the snow began to fall. This time the flakes were tinted with every color that he had essayed on his canvases; they were of every shape: squares, rectangles, cubes, all the drifting forms to which he had tried to give body. The first one touched the earth. He perceived that it was a painting: line, color, delineated object. Hundreds of canvases began to pile up at his feet, canvases of all sizes, styles, degrees of skill. They covered the streets like the bleached bones of buffalo on the Kansas prairie. He looked upward and saw that the air was thick with paintings, filled so solid there was no oxygen. He tried to move down the street, but he was knee-deep in pictures.

For the first time he felt fear; he started to run, wildly, bringing his legs high into the air. He fell, and when he rose, painfully, he saw that flight was hopeless. He was trapped.

The pictures were falling ever faster; when they beat about his head he saw that these were his own canvases, the tens, the fifties, the hundreds of canvases that he had poured out during the wild months. Had he created a monstrous delusion which was now returning to drown him? Must he perish so ignominiously, buried under his own creations?

No! He would fight his way clear.

Above him he discovered a latticework grill on a stone building. With a mighty effort he pulled himself up, pulled his aching legs free of their encumbrances even as a new gust of wind filled the streets and the buildings, the air and the sky with more and more paintings, thousands of canvases by Charbert, Turnhouse, Leipsche, Giuseppe Donello, Gerald Addams, Tanner, Durchamp, Alexei, all the men of the Beehive.

The slow dying sounds of Paris had whispered into silence. The city about him was lifeless.

Gasping hard, he pulled himself onto the roof of the building. Here too was an endless prairie of paintings over which he had to crawl on his hands and knees. The paint was still fresh; he could smell it in his nostrils, feel its stickiness on his fingers.

Stumblingly he made his way over the roofs of Paris; there were no more streets and no more houses; all crevices and canyons were filled solid with hard-packed pictures and their frames, soldered into one vast leaden indistinguishable lump.

Then he knew what he must do: he must get clear of this city, of this Paris which was buried and dead like Pompeii under the hot sticky lava of Vesuvius. Once out in the country, alone, in the clear free air amidst the wide fields, he would be safe. His body aching, his eyes locked tight, he began to run.

In the distance he saw a great open field. He increased his speed, tearing the skin of his legs and feet, but the more ground he covered the farther away the clearing receded. Panting, exhausted, he sank down on the rough-edged solidity beneath him. This was the end for him.

With a feverish gesture he put his hand inside his shirt and grasped the North Star, took it out on its long string to gaze at it. He saw the face of his mother before him, smiling, loving, infinitely sad. He struggled to his feet, clasping the North Star tightly in his hand.

The air became cool and abundant; his lungs filled with it and his heart began pumping agitatedly. His body began to shake with chills, his teeth chattered so loudly they filled the cavern of his head with the sound of thunder. He rolled from side to side under the buffalo robe, his flesh cold and clammy.

He felt someone leaning over him, brushing the perspiration from his brow with soft finger tips. Painfully, as though he were coming up the path of a steep black cavern, he forced his eyelids open. It was Maud.

"John, what's the matter? Are you ill? I'll go get Gerald; he will call an American doctor."

He reached out, took her hand, crushed her small fingers in his grasp.

"I'm so alone. I'm so lonely."

Maud sat on the edge of the bed, put her cheek on his.

"No, *chère,* you are not alone. I'm here, I'm with you."

"It hurts to be so alone, it hurts up here inside your skull."

"I will get Gerald."

He could hear Maud's high heels tapping down the flights of steps. He stumbled out of the bed, found his way around the balcony to the opposite side of the stairs and made his way to the street. In the next block he bought two bottles of whiskey, drinking one halfway down while the proprietor returned his change. He stood motionless for a moment, gratefully, as the alcohol-laden blood reached his head and began eating away at the edges of the vast pain.

After a time he found his way to the stockyards. He sought out a butcher, shoved a wad of crumbled franc notes into his hand and repeated, "*Cheval, cheval,* horse, horse!"

They brought him an old bay and a discarded bit which he fitted into the horse's mouth. Then he headed for the fields behind the abattoir, alternately taking a long drink, talking to his horse, recounting the earlier years on the plains, the trip up the Rocky Mountains in Colorado and down south to Texas and New Mexico. He was happy to be home in Kansas again, to feel the buffalo grass beneath him. How wrong he had been about Paris and France, for that matter all of Europe! He hated it: the strange people, the strange language, the different customs, the oldness of the houses, the streets . . . why had he ever thought it was beautiful and exciting?

All of this he explained to Wichita Bill, telling the swayback horse that he was smart never to have left Kansas, that he, John, was glad to be back home again. When the second bottle of whiskey was exhausted his speech became mumbled and incoherent; he fell forward, his arms thrown loosely about the horse's neck.

The old bay stood still for a long time, then slowly stumbled its way back to the slaughterhouse.

11

He packed his two bags, gathered up his paints, dismantled his easel and prepared to leave the Ruche, for it had become abundantly clear that he too had fallen victim to the quantitative theory, the slam-bang method of painting first and thinking afterward. He would have to reflect the immensely beautiful but equally private world which he alone knew and he alone could transcribe to canvas.

He glanced about the room with an amused nostalgia, remembering the excitement with which he had entered it the first time; if Wichita had been his infancy, the Beehive had been his irrepressible adolescence. His eye swept the stacks of canvases against the wall. He had made a thousand errors, traversed fields where he did not belong, only to learn that none of the going techniques or theories were for him. He could not copy, join, absorb, fall in line. What he finally put on canvas would be pure John Noble, recognizable across a sea of buffalo grass. His would be a lonely art, not tied up with any age, school or theory; but how could it be otherwise: was he not a lonely man?

With a quick gesture he took his penknife from his pocket and set to work destroying the paintings, even as he had his hundreds of sketches for Cleopatra back in Wichita.

After considerable searching he found a studio which occupied the entire top floor at 7 Rue Belloni. It had had many users before him, but he managed to conceal most of the past with a quick coat of paint. There was a good-sized skylight facing north, but this north light was both dark and cold. He thought, A north light like this can set a man back fifty years in painting.

He had told no one about his studio, not even Gerald Addams or Charbert, his closest friends at the Beehive. He was therefore all the more astonished when the door opened while he was painting the ceiling, and he heard a soft voice say:

"*Tiens, tiens,* what a big empty barn."

He gazed down at Maud from the top rung of the ladder, his broad brush dripping paint onto the floor. She stared back at him boldly, then shrugged her shoulders and laughed.

"If you don't want me to know where you live, you'll have to go back to Wichita."

"See here," he exclaimed, "I want this kept absolutely quiet."

She ignored his spluttering as unworthy of answer, then began looking about the studio and the small adjoining kitchen. He climbed down the ladder and followed her around hostilely.

"Now just get that light out of your eye, Maud. Nobody's going to set up any housekeeping. This is just a workroom. Savvy?"

"You want to sleep on the floor all winter and get pneumonia?"

"Well, no, I've got to have a bed."

"You don't want a stove in that kitchen to make hot coffee for cold mornings?"

"A stove . . . yes . . . I will need coffee."

"You want to eat your food standing up? You don't want a little table and a couple of chairs?"

Defeated, he thrust a roll of bills at her.

"All right. Go buy me a cot and a stove, a kitchen table and a couple of wooden chairs. Nothing else, mind you."

"Not even one comfortable chair, and a little piece of rug for this floor? And what about a pan to fry a beefsteak, and a spoon to stir the sugar?"

"You win, Maud. Go buy what I need, but if you tell one living soul in Paris where I live, I'll move out and leave all your furniture behind."

Aside from keeping his address secret, Maud did none of the things she was instructed. She bought a big double bed with a warm blanket and feather comforter, a good cookstove, a couple of lamps, and two chairs for reading and sitting about in a spare hour. She also bought a wardrobe for his clothes and some secondhand draperies which she hung on pulleys so they could close out the night beyond the skylight. The atelier had rather a cozy air when she had finished, and John could find little to complain about, since she had ransacked Paris and furnished it on half of what it would have cost him for the barest necessities.

"You did a fine job, Maud. Remind me to be grateful to you, sometime."

"*Merci*, no! The minute you Americans begin to feel indebted you find yourselves another girl."

The problem of the darkness or coldness of the north light over his skylight never disturbed him because he now slept during the day and worked all night, rarely bothering to turn on the lamps in the studio but using instead the powerful lights which he felt shining behind his own eyes and his own brow. He mounted a fresh canvas on the easel in the center of the big studio, drew up one of the chairs and sat in the rapidly falling dusk gazing at the blank space; darkness enveloped the studio while he slowly, painfully, still sitting in his chair, shaped in his mind the picture he wanted to paint: thought through to its ultimate conclusion every aspect of the design, the plastic forms, the line and shadow, the juxtaposition of colors to create the mood; then, when the picture had been completely painted inside his head, he rose from the deep chair, lighted a lamp, squeezed the paints out onto the palette, picked up his brushes and transferred it to the canvas with sure swift strokes.

He had no idea how much time elapsed, weeks, months, while he worked this way. He avoided the Beehive and the Café Bullier, went to a remote café on those rare occasions when he left the studio. When he could no longer contain himself within walls, when he felt a need to move his body through space he would set out about two o'clock in the morning and walk the streets alone, almost running, pumping his powerful arms and clenched fists ahead of him like a boxer doing road work.

He started a series of still lifes: the sea at dawn; a crescent moon over a frozen mountain lake; a boat drawn up on a beach with a white horse and a fisherman standing alongside; a single tree on a horizon against a motionless moon. He eschewed action pictures in which something was happening, for he reasoned that whatever was in motion was also in transit, and tried instead to capture scenes in which everything had been resolved, completed, its permanent place taken in an over-all design. On the back of one canvas, a vast buffalo herd against a vaster prairie sky, he wrote, "To see only one part of nature at a time is fractional vision; the universe must be seen and felt whole in order to be understood whole."

For relaxation he pored over the new chemical formulas for making paint and preparing canvas, using German colors and mediums instead of the oil or turpentine which he had been buying at Lefèbre Foinet's ever since Gerald Addams had taken him there. One formula in particular called Feigenmilch called for considerable cooking and so he spent hours over the pots on his kitchen stove, heating, stirring, adding chemicals from little paper bags, looking like a medieval alchemist, his shirt and trousers covered with paint, his skin pale from lack of sunlight, his long, corn-white hair falling over his face and his smoky blue eyes happy, excited, absorbed. Sleep was not in him, and while he waited for the brew to boil he played solitaire on the kitchen table under the kerosene lamp or reread his favorite stories from Poe, "The Murders in the Rue Morgue," "The Gold Bug" and "The Mystery of Marie Rogêt." He would then prepare his canvases with the new mixtures, and during the day put them out in the sun to dry until he had a sparkling background on which to apply his paint; a background which gave the paint an added luminosity.

How bitterly difficult it is to learn what we really are, he thought. How ceaselessly we strive to find our way back to the simple fundamentals of our own nature. Some men never do, they are lost forever in the forest of other people's thoughts. Others struggle long and hard, but never succeed because there is nothing to return to: no core, no base. Some crack the shell of their own nature underfoot, only to find it empty of meat; others peel off subcutaneous layers of orange in a hopeless effort to reach the sweet juice of their own natures and end up with nothing but rind.

12

When after many months of solitary labor he grew tired of himself he enrolled in the famous Acadèmie Julien. His teacher was Jean Paul Laurens, a heavy, bull-jawed fellow. John felt that if anybody could teach someone else how to paint it would be a ruggedly honest man like this. The painters worked all week without criticism or correction, and then early on Saturday morning Laurens started around the room, analyzing each canvas so that everyone in the room could hear and understand. Laurens had a genius for going to the heart of a man's weakness, illuminating it in a fast brutal sentence. It was with a quick smile that John heard him grunt:

"Not so bad, Noble."

Each spring and fall Laurens awarded a prize for the best painting produced by one of his students. John started a night seascape, with a lopsided moon low over the horizon, the waves thick and oily and a small fishing boat making its way through a trough. He called it *Path of the Moon.*

Laurens stood in front of the canvas and barked:

"First prize to Mr. John Noble for *Path of the Moon.*"

That night John wrapped the canvas in heavy brown paper, nailed it into a wooden crate and sent it to his father in Wichita, a gesture of love for the older man's patience and generosity over the years.

By act of winning the Laurens prize, he automatically graduated himself out of the academy. Hearing that Henri Matisse might be willing to take on a few more students, he applied early the next morning at Matisse's *école.*

Matisse wore a neatly trimmed beard and well-fitted spectacles, dressed fastidiously and carried himself with the poise of a banker. He said, "Ah yes, John Noble. Jean Laurens has told me about you."

"Then I may work here in the school, Monsieur Matisse?"

Matisse looked around the big, bare salon of what had been a religious school before the French government took it over and leased it to him for a pittance. About thirty young American and English students were working at their easels. John saw Matisse shake his head in amused despair.

"To each new student as he comes in the front door I say, 'Don't become a little Matisse, don't imitate or copy me. Learn what I can teach you about technique, and absorb it into what you already know,' *mais mon dieu . . .*"

He took John on a tour of the studio. Nearly all of the young students were painting Matisse themes, highly decorative in nature and with the conscious eliminations and distortions which Matisse made in his drawing, the better to achieve his effects: but where Matisse had eliminated details to highlight what he was trying to say, and all elements fitted into an indigenous whole, the imitating students were using Matisse's mechanisms without understanding, accomplishing quite absurd results.

"I see what you mean, monsieur," said John grimly.

At the end of his first week at the art school he was invited to Matisse's flat for the evening. It was his first dinner in a private home in a very long time. Madame Matisse was a scrupulous housekeeper, every inch of her apartment scrubbed and shining the way he remembered his mother's house in Wichita. The Matisses had three small children, and John knew the story of how Matisse, who had been making a fair living by selling conventional, academic canvases, had one day suddenly sickened of the technique and destroyed a canvas which he could surely have sold, the money from which he very much needed. The Matisses had paid heavily for this revolt: they had had to send their two sons to their grandparents in the country; sometimes there had been far too little food in their flat; at one period Madame Matisse had had to open a hat store to support them. But Matisse's judgment had been sound and his craftsmanship the finest to appear in Europe since Paul Cézanne. At this point he was beginning to sell some of his new and radical canvases.

When he sat down to the table with the Matisses, the three youngsters full of high spirits, the family talk commonplace and salutary, John suddenly became homesick for the wonderful hours he had spent at the Noble dinner table in Wichita, homesick for the confidence and love of his parents and brother and sisters, homesick for the solid friendship of Dave Leahy and Victor Murdock, and, above all, homesick for Frances Birchfield Buckler.

In his youth and ignorance he had imagined that artists must be free as the air and wild as the wind, able to come and go, to work or loaf, to paint or talk, to change localities, loves and ideologies as frequently and swiftly as one changed one's shirt; that marriage and a home and children would nail an artist down to the mundane realities, make a conventional being out of him, one whose life would be devoted to putting food into mouths and clothes onto backs. Yet here was a man whom nearly everyone in Paris conceded to have inherited the cloak of Whistler, Manet and Cézanne, living a conventional bourgeois life, happy, working constantly, and creating brilliantly.

All of his years of chaotic drifting suddenly overcame him. Why had he not married Frances and brought her to Paris with him? They could have had a home, had their children, their companionship, their devotion to each other, and he could have lived just as arduous a life with his paints as he could have wanted. Because of these internal churnings he was unable to eat very much of Madame Matisse's delicious dinner; in a stumbling way he poured out the story of his fear of permanence and responsibility . . . and now of his realization that Bohemia was not the only place where authentic art could originate.

"It is no use marrying because you think you should be married," Matisse reassured him; "you must wait until the love and the urge are so powerful that you cannot conceive of living without that marriage."

"Love is not like painting," added Mrs. Matisse quietly. "You don't need years of study and training, of experimentation and failure in order to achieve success. Someday a woman will appear before you, your eyes will rest upon her and your voice will say, 'I love her! This is she.' And your love will be as perfect and complete a work of art as that Cézanne *Bathers* we have on the wall above the buffet."

"If that ever happens to me," mused John, "I will indeed believe in miracles."

Because of his nostalgia for home he found himself going more often to the American Art Association Club. The billiard room had a change of paintings on its walls every twenty-four hours, but John found that the conversation concerned itself more with baseball and women than it did with the newest exploits of *Les Fauves,* or the Wild Animals, a group name now being given to Picasso, Braque, Rouault and Dufy, who were attempting to overthrow Impressionism as a romantic movement and to replace it with a lyrically interpretive realism.

He became better acquainted with Alexander Harrison, who was taking the nude models out of the north-light studios and painting them in the open air with a warm sunlight on their bodies; and with George Luks, the exact opposite of Le Grand Harrison, who was painting deep-bitten subjects, most of them out of proletarian life, people and scenes which had not been considered worthy of the artist's time, yet setting them down with such an intense love and inner force that what had been called sordid and vulgar now shone with a beautiful inner illumination. With George Luks he organized the first American baseball team that ever played in Paris.

He painted often at the Art Students Club where there was no instructor and everyone chipped in to hire the models. Harrison propped his easel beside John's, leaning over from time to time to study John's canvas. One morning he said:

"You're *sui generis,* John, a loose and wandering star in the heavens, with no prescribed route or place. It's futile for anyone to attempt to classify or categorize you. The more I see of you and your work the more I'm convinced that you are a natural-born anarchist, and that you will never concede the existence of hard and fast lines in time, space or reality."

13

He awakened feeling cold inside, not merely exhausted, but actually abandoned, as though everything and everyone had moved out of his head and he had been left alone.

He extricated himself painfully from the bedcovers and doused his face in cold water. Then he looked about him and saw that it was foolish to imagine that he was alone or abandoned: all around him, giving dimension as well as boundary, was the result of his hard and faithful work since he had moved to this studio: dozens of canvases stacked against the walls and lying face down in unused corners.

The ambition of every painter in Paris was to have a one-man exhibition. Very well, he would stage his own one-man show. There would be no eager, nervous, bustling little gallery owner, no officials from the Department of Beaux Arts, no officers from the Academy or Salon, no crowds of people such as he had seen so often at the Vernissage of the Independents or the Salon d'Automne; the room would not quickly be filled with smoke and the sound of excited, disputing voices, and no pictures would be sold. He would have to serve as the gallery owner, critics from the journals, and the crowd of gallery followers who were forever seeking some new and fashionable departure.

But that was as it should be: standing in the middle of his room and his world, he felt that it was time for him to act as spectator, critic and analyst. If these paintings were good he could use their warmth to melt the coldness inside him, the lush richness of their paint to quicken his faint pulse, the excellence of drawing and structure to brighten his eye and refresh his mind.

He propped the pictures against the long walls, framed and unframed canvas standing shoulder to shoulder, and when this space was solid he got out string and tacks and covered the walls all the way up to the ceiling. By making a quick count he judged that he had almost a hundred paintings in varying stages of completion.

He began at his immediate left and studied the canvases, edging slowly along the room, his eyes piercing every stroke of the brush, every concept of organization, every idea behind the drawing. There was no need to hurry; he had not hurried in painting them, he had never added a layer of fresh paint onto still wet paint, had never added the fresh idea on top of half a dozen crusts of error, but had always scraped and cleaned and gone to a fresh new surface both on the canvas and in his own mind.

His disappointment was sudden, unexpected . . . and crushing. Those canvases which were unmistakable imitations he brushed aside quickly: he was not and never could be a skilled pointillist; his café interiors were unrecognizable Toulouse-Lautrec because he had used Pissarro's heavy brush stroke where Toulouse-Lautrec had had the genius to know that such subjects could be captured only with thin flat surfaces; and his efforts to copy Monet by picturing the vague shimmering outlines of a railroad station or a cathedral sacrificed his own ability to draw.

But what about those others which were the fruit of his own creation? What had he painted that extended beyond the borders of the frames, that suggested an infinity behind the simple finite statements? He could not ask less of himself than he demanded of others. Where was the inner glow, the vibrating essence, the divine illumination which he had demanded even of the masters in the Louvre, and without which he had passed a picture by as being amusing or decorative or clever storytelling or photographically accurate, but without a living and permanent importance because it was uninspired?

And where was God in any of these paintings?

If God was not in his work, then for him nothing of genuine beauty or meaning was in it: a painting without God was like a dark room without a light or a prairie wagon without wheels. His draftsmanship was strong and true; his chemical experiments had taught him a great deal about mixing colors; he had rejected petty or meaningless subjects and stuck to heroic themes; he had worked always with force and warmth and love. Then where had he failed? At his wrist, his finger tips, the brush end? For it seemed to him that despite his mightiest efforts none of his feelings had been transferred to the canvas, that he had succeeded only in painting still lifes, empty ships upon an empty sea, a dead sun in empty heavens.

He took the canvases off the walls with slow, exhausted movements, cutting them to pieces with his knives and heaping them in the center of the floor for some convenient annihilation by fire. As the piles grew larger and the walls barer, he began to feel aseptic . . . and more and more dead.

He had deceived himself about the relationship of work to God. He had gone on the assumption that he would find God through his work: through his integrity and rugged dedication to the task on hand. But he was no closer to God now than when he had arrived in Paris. He knew that he had been a fool. No man had any right to search for God: He was not a fact, not a substance, and never a demonstrable reality. Except in the religious sense He was unfindable, or at least unrecognizable; to the individual who insisted upon facing his own particular God, He was uncreatable. God can create man. Man cannot create God.

His hunger and his search had been based on his need: but why did there have to be a God just because he so desperately needed one? The answer was plain to anyone who dared to face it: there was no God. He would no longer search for God in his painting. He would no longer paint.

He felt himself left bare-handed and bare-hearted, the past too painful to look back at, the future too meaningless to contemplate.

SOME time in 1949, after I began work on the biographical novel of Rachel Jackson, I met the woman editor and publisher of *Tomorrow* magazine. She told me of an interesting project she had under way, in which she was asking some twenty to thirty American authors, who had permanently left their home towns, to go back and take a close look, and to write an article about the changes and the memories evoked by such a nostalgic visit. Saroyan had written about his return to Fresno, Carl Carmer to Albion, Mary Ellen Chase to Blue Hill, Vardis Fisher to the Antelope Hills.

I had, of course, been back to San Francisco many times over the years, but this visit was special, because I was looking at the city from a different point of view, with different assaying values. As I walked the streets, a flood of memory swept over me. Voices and sights from as long as thirty years before came back to create a double screen against which I relived the city of my birth and youth. The writing of the story was a journey in nostalgia.

HOMETOWN REVISITED

AT my first literary cocktail party in New York I was introduced to a famous novelist, a big rawboned woman with heavy features, not only plain-faced, I thought, but downright ugly. We went into an adjoining library to sit opposite each other before a wood fire and talk about books and writing. After five minutes I forgot that my companion was ugly; after ten minutes I no longer imagined her to be plain; when we rejoined the party at the end of an hour I believed her one of the most beautiful human beings I had ever known.

San Francisco is rather like that.

At the turn of the century my mother was engaged to a charming young man with whom she was very much in love. One Sunday afternoon she prevailed upon him to take her out to the Cliff House, a cafe at the beach which was considered fast, in the language of the day. They stayed for only the barest moment, but gossip caught the steam train from the Beach to First Avenue, where it transferred posthaste to the car which carried the shocking news downtown to Tehama Street, South-of-the-Slot.

My mother's parents separated the young couple; my mother married my father on the rebound. That fate gave me the wrong father has made little difference to me in the long run, but for my mother, who went through her years without love, it turned San Francisco from a gay romantic exciting city into one of unhappiness, frustration and of early death.

My father, a dull man, found his adventure in playing the ponies. On Saturday noon he would draw his week's pay from the store in which he clerked on Fourth Street, above Howard, and go directly to the Tanforan race track. At dark he would return home without a penny in his pocket to 882 Haight Street, where we rented a dark middle flat in a tall, narrow house from my Aunt Fanny. He would sit at the oilcloth-covered table in the kitchen playing a silent solitaire; there was no fire in the coal stove because there was no scrap of food to be cooked on it. Aunt Fanny would come down the narrow backstairs, sniff the air of the bare kitchen, and march my sister and me up the rear steps to an enormous meal. My mother watched us, big-eyed, but never ate a bite; she was too proud.

This is my mother's story, and mine, rather than the story of San Francisco? True. But every man's tale of his place of birth is the story of how he fared in that city.

On the wall in front of my desk as I sit writing is a colored print called "San Francisco in 1849." There are a few thin masted ships on the green waters of the harbor, and a few wooden houses pasted precariously against the rising hills. There lies the salient of San Francisco: the hills: not because they go up and down so precipitately, but because they are composed of indestructible stone.

San Franciscans, like the amazing hills they have climbed these several generations, are a hard, stony people, astonishingly like New Englanders: stubborn, proud, willful, self-contained, tenacious, fiercely independent, rooted in rocky tradition: not the kind of hardness that is mean or uncharitable, but rather the kind that demands so terribly much of itself. Easterners say, "We can always tell a San Franciscan: there is a touch of accent, of Boston thrown into a crude pioneer settlement; a touch of the arrogance of people who can flourish under difficult circumstances; a submerged grimness of purpose, a shortness of humor, and yet a certain international flavor: cultured (we natives like to boast that we had an opera house and a first-rate literary magazine, the *Golden Era,* before we paved our streets) and yet at the same time curiously insular, almost like an island folk."

All of these things are true about San Franciscans. But a lot more is true, too.

My first actual memory of the city is at the age of three, when I stood on top of Twin Peaks with my mother and grandparents on an April night in 1906, watching San Francisco burn to the ground. My mother said, "We will never live like civilized people again; we'll roam these hills like wild animals, foraging for our food."

On the ashes arose the city in which I grew up, the ugliest city in the world, built of hard wood and harder gray stone, a grim-visaged masculine town with its houses glued together in long, tall, dark, narrow rows, the steps emerging out of the very sidewalks, themselves, mounting the hills like the rungs of a ladder, with no blade of grass, no tree, no flower, no touch of soft feminine earth. The architecture was a haphazard hodgepodge, with every street deciding what it should look like while its houses were in the process of construction. District after district was plain, austere, heavy, unbeautiful.

But you turned a corner unexpectedly, or hurried down Geary Street, cold from the raw inrolling fog, sick at heart over the flinty irresilient nature of the pavement, and suddenly reached the crest of a hill. Below lay the bay, with its bold islands lucidly clear; in the docks along the Embarcadero nestled the dozens of ships being loaded for Oriental ports, and the quaint ferry boats placidly plying the waters; beyond were the lyrical green hills of Oakland and Berkeley. And suddenly the coldness dropped away, the fog vanished, the street and the people grew soft and friendly, and you knew that you lived in a city with mood, with tone, with style, with beauty: probably the most beautiful city in the world.

To a San Franciscan, this happens a dozen times every day. Perhaps that will help you to understand his contradictions.

San Francisco was founded by adventurers from almost every state and every nation. Few came with any great wealth, and whatever social position they may have enjoyed at home they necessarily left behind them. San Francisco created its own wealth, its own society, its own culture. Class lines never had much chance to solidify, for the great lady in the mansion up on Washington Street, was probably as newly arrived as the mining, sugar, railroad, shipping or real estate money with which her husband built the ornate forty-room house. The workingmen lived in Mission district and the white-collar and middle class in the Richmond and Sunset districts, but this distinction was leveled by the fact that the Mission had the most sunshine and the best year-round climate. Rather than class distinctions San Francisco had its ethnic settlements, the Italians in North Beach, the Irish in the Mission, the Norwegians on the Frederick Street side of Twin Peaks, the Japanese on Sutter Street, the Chinese on Grant Avenue, the Jews on MacAllister.

Yet almost anyone who grew up in San Francisco was aware of a double standard of morality: the harsh bourgeois respectability which could tear my mother from the man she loved, and at the same time the biggest, wildest, toughest, most colorful and prosperous red-light district in America, the Barbary Coast. Oddly enough, all of San Francisco approved of this schizoid personality. We heard rumors about the white-slave traffic, but to my young eyes it seemed as though everyone in the Barbary Coast was a volunteer; and having a pretty good time. Then, at about 1914, when San Francisco was preparing for its World's Fair, a small but militant group of reformers managed to close down the red-light district. As a result the former occupants infiltrated every part of town; my Aunt Fanny rented her ground floor, just below us, to two pretty and vivacious girls, who, she declared, were the most popular she had ever seen, what with admirers and taxis arriving all night long! It took her almost a year to catch on, though her older son seemed to have known about it from the very beginning.

Next to the Barbary Coast the most interesting section to us youngsters, and surely the most terrifying, was Chinatown, that large colorful section of which Grant Avenue was the main thoroughfare, where one walked through oriental streets, smelling oriental foods and incense, gazing with breathless fear into bazaars and gambling joints beneath which, our newspapers and police screamed, were vast labyrinths of opium dens. Pretty young white girls who went shopping with their fiances were abducted, to become slaves of underground opium and prostitution. The fact that no one ever met a man or family who had lost such a girl did little to quiet the rumors, rumors which were not lessened by the violent tong-wars which at intervals left half a dozen dead Chinese lying in the streets. As a fifteen-year-old delivery boy for Pauson's clothing store I was so frightened at being obliged to make a Saturday night delivery to the second floor of a dark Chinese rooming house that I rang the bell, flung the package halfway up the steps, and fled down Clay Street.

In 1917, when a young San Franciscan was ready for high school, he encountered another of San Francisco's contradictions: in one of the most democratic cities in America, the young man found it necessary to make a lifetime choice at the age of fourteen: if he hoped to go on to college, he had to enter Lowell; if he intended to become a mechanic, he had to go to Polytechnic; if he was going into business he went to Commerce. These stratifications were occasionally broken by young men of strong resolve, but not very often; the system was too strong.

I wanted to attend the University of California, so I went to Lowell. I worked afternoons and Saturdays selling papers on Market Street, as a delivery boy, stock boy, and later as an usher at the Coliseum Theatre in the Richmond, and at the Republic Theatre downtown where Will King played musical comedy to capacity houses. San Francisco was a good theatre town. Compact structurally and housing about 450,000 people, it thought of itself as a big little city.

We also thought of ourselves as an island folk, since we were surrounded by water on three sides, and what we called "down the Peninsula" was too remote for any large-scale building or commutation. Since we were rarely out of sight of our ocean, strait or bay we maintained that we were seriously limited in land space and hence could never become an enormous city. But this was wishful thinking, because we didn't want any serious influx of strangers; probably half of the land included in the city proper consisted of vast sand dunes, a range of barren hills lying to the west of Twin Peaks where as a boy I hunted Coyotes, and beyond that a forest, clutching in its darkness a forlorn poorhouse, and where I shot birds with my bee-bee gun, roasting them over a twig fire, and starting a forest fire which came close to duplicating the holocaust of 1906.

The center of every San Franciscan's world was Market Street, to which all roads led. There were two sets of streetcar tracks and two competing lines, the Municipal owned by the city, and an older private line. I can remember when I was eight standing on Market Street waiting for a car, and thoroughly annoying my hard-headed cousin by refusing to take the first car to come along, one belonging to the private company, and insisting upon waiting for a Municipal car so I could give my nickel to the city. I can also remember riding the No. 6 car down Masonic Avenue with my Aunt Dora and having a group of angry streetcar strikers throw huge rocks at it, smashing the window immediately behind my head, and showering me with glass.

For therein lies another of San Francisco's contradictions: friendly, hospitable, charming, it was always a tough labor town, just as willing to settle its arguments with stones, clubs or brass knuckles as with conciliatory words. The almost continuous management-labor troubles of the past fifteen years is neither a new development nor an egregious accident, but grows out of our frontier origin, in which men made their own laws, enforcing them at the end of a pistol.

In 1919 my mother and stepfather committed the all-too-common heresy of moving south to Los Angeles, with its lure of warm sunshine and of a new city in the making, where people who had not done so well by middle age imagined they could start afresh and grow with the country. In August of 1920 I returned to the University of California at Berkeley for six years as a student and teacher. Then came a full decade of Europe and New York, before a permanent return with my wife and children to Beverly Hills. Yet no matter where I go, or where I live, I call San Francisco my home port. It's not a city I always like, but certainly it is a city I always love: perhaps the kind of feeling one has for parents, or children, or a husband or wife.

What is the character of San Francisco today? In the midst of a steady, organic change there are the eternalities: the tiny, tart shrimp on Fisherman's Wharf; the open-air cable cars clanging up the perpendicular Powell Street hills; the boys playing baseball on Funston Field, where the DiMaggios got their early training; the garages built under the very center of the houses; the old Spanish tradition of the latchstring being on the outside; the tramp steamers coming through the Golden Gate, their sides discolored from months in the Pacific; the fog racing in from the ocean at a measurable speed of fourteen miles an hour; luncheon in the court of the Palace Hotel; a few stalwarts swimming in the strait off China Beach; the superb panorama of Market Street rolling from the base of Twin Peaks to the very doors of the Ferry Building.

Actually today San Francisco is two cities rather than one. The old stone village still lies embedded in its hills, like a European bastion, its surface changed almost not at all. San Franciscans don't like change; new and swank restaurants decorated with the smartest of modern furnishings close in a matter of months. Even when such fine old hotels as the Fairmont, Mark Hopkins, St. Francis, or Palace are redecorated, or open new entertainment rooms, they must include something of the decor and mood of old San Francisco or people won't come. The White House, City of Paris, and Emporium department stores, though they are kept freshly painted and spotlessly clean, remain essentially the same, generation after generation. Their customers want it that way. All native San Franciscans consider themselves carriage trade.

Yes, the old city remains the same, but a brand new city has encircled the old, even encircled the vast bay, and this new city is changing the old ways and the old customs. It may finally conquer the old city.

During the years between the world wars when Southern California seemed to double its population with every census count, San Francisco stood still; there were no organizations formed to entice outsiders, the natives apparently neither wanted nor needed newcomers, except as visitors, and there was a good deal of inbreeding. Business too, stood still, partly because of an almost continuous series of strikes, still marked with violence, and partly because there was no growth in population, housing or industry. Then, in 1937, the Bay Bridge and the Golden Gate span opened the large stretches of land to the east and north. With the attack on Pearl Harbor in December of 1941 the city became the major base of operations for the war of the Pacific. Hundreds of thousands of people came into the new Bay areas either as servicemen or to produce the materials of war, and so many of them have remained that the city now has almost 800,000 people as against the 450,000 of my youth. Because of the crucial war-role the city played, because of the building of vast factories and shipyards all around the Bay, and the fact that in 1945 it was chosen as the birthplace of the United Nations, San Francisco was pulled out of its lethargy. It became aware that it was a great world city, something everyone had always known . . . except the natives.

Prior to World War II, San Franciscans cared little about automobiles; distances were short, the hills steep. Today the omnipresent automobile has opened up the warm, pleasant peninsula lying to the south, and many of the more prosperous families have moved to wooded estates in Redwood City, Burlingame, Palo Alto, and Atherton, while the great houses they built up on Pacific Heights are now used as a chain of high-class boardinghouses for law students and genteel secretaries. More important, the automobile has made easily available a large area of the city along the Golden Gate Strait and out toward the beach, southward through the sand dunes, which was formerly neglected. When I was a boy the Lake Merced region on the outskirts of the city was considered to be hundreds of miles away, practically in the wilderness; today it is the scene of some of the largest housing projects in America, both in the privately built Stonestown where everything new in modern building and decor has been used to exciting advantage; and in the Metropolitan Insurance Company projects where vast skyscraper apartment houses overlook the Pacific Ocean.

At the beginning of its career, when San Francisco needed more land, it filled in a considerable part of its bayfront to create business property. In 1913, when it needed a big flat space for its World's Fair, it again created space by filling in that part of the strait which lay immediately below the Pacific Heights cliffs. Today the Marina District houses a community of white homes of Spanish architecture. At the same time there is a whole new district at Sea Cliff, an extension of Lake Street, magnificent land which juts out into the Golden Gate Strait, for many years considered too remote and too dangerous for living.

But it was in the beautiful residential section of St. Francis Woods, created out of the forests and hills where I hunted as a boy, that the life of San Francisco began to change most radically. For years the San Franciscans had resented the migration of its people southward to the warmer Los Angeles. Because of their resentment they had also come to ridicule the Southern California way of life: the big lawns, open patios, barbecues, slacks and swim suits: the whole cult of informality, the sunburned and the out-of-doors. Today San Francisco has not only been captured but apparently absorbed by its rival: for the era of small narrow flats, of thin, private dwellings on twenty-five-foot fronts, and almost no backyard, has given way to spacious homes built on what had formerly been the sand dunes, the barren hills and coyote-infested woods, with big lawns, fine trees, excellent gardens—and in the rear, patios with barbecues and protected areas for sunbathing.

These developments have revolutionized San Francisco life, changing it from a city culture to one that is semi-suburban. Though the city still has a first-rate opera company, the commercial theatre is waning and sickly. While I was growing up, San Francisco was a great night-club town, for people did most of their entertaining out of their homes; names like Taits-at-the-Beach, Shorty Roberts, Techeau Tavern were famous all over the country. Today they are gone, and the one big night club remaining, the Bal Tabarin, can operate only two months out of the year, when its attraction is either Ted Lewis or Sophie Tucker, both beloved of San Franciscans. The hotels still get fair crowds when they employ name bands, or play to standing room when they present Hildegarde, but for the rest, San Franciscans are jumping into their cars at five o'clock and rushing home to work in the garden, paint the fence, or put in a fish pond on the two-day week end.

The Barbary Coast is now an innocuous honky-tonk, and only Sally Stanford, the Pine Street Madame, whose girls entertain visiting tycoons for a hundred-dollar fee, can afford to buy survival. Some two thousand automobiles may be found parked on the Marina Green, next to the Yacht Harbor, of a Saturday night; the occupants are probably doing little more than petting, yet there are those San Franciscans who believe that once again it is the automobile which has made a major change in the city's way of life.

The Japanese, who occupied a large section along Post Street, were well liked and respected. Today they are gone, banished during the war, and reluctant to return; while the Chinese who were our allies have now become not only liked, but socially accepted; somewhat like elder citizens for whom San Franciscans have a soft spot because they helped found the city, and helped keep it colorful. The young Chinese are enormously popular in the high schools, and many of them go on to successful careers at the University. North Beach, which for half a century was so solidly Italian that one could walk for a mile without hearing a word of English spoken, has now broken up, the second and third generation having been absorbed into the city's blood stream.

Most of the changes have been, I think, for the best. With the growth of the new home areas, many fine modern high schools have been built, and youngsters attend the school of their neighborhood. In a city where no part of the business or shopping section has changed since its construction after the fire of 1906, it is a joy to see the new, bright, colorful neighborhood shopping centers which cater to the new private-patio homes. People are working a shorter week, forty hours instead of the sixty of my youth, and five days instead of the six and seven. Life in general is pleasanter, more amiable and leisurely . . . and softer.

The old San Franciscans were a determined lot who either crossed the plains in covered wagons, traversed fever-laden Panama, or came around dangerous Cape Horn in sailing vessels. From 1849 to 1939, a ninety-year spread, its people fought earthquake, fire, violence, lived frugally, were satisfied with little short of perfection in art and culture. They were realists who had little use for self-induced illusions, and thought of life as basically a bitter, unending struggle. They grew up, worked, married, bred and died with a profound sense of the tragic in life.

Most of that, today, is gone. Part of it may arise again due to the fears of chemical and atomic warfare. But San Francisco has now extended itself so far southward, metaphorically speaking, and Los Angeles has extended itself so far northward, that soon their two borders will be continuous, and no man will be able to tell them apart. Then the old, cool, flinty, tradition-loving, change-hating San Franciscan will be merged with the new, hot, soft, tradition-hating, change-loving south.

And that, I think, will be too bad: for the San Francisco which rose on the hills above the Bay was a city of legend: colorful, dramatic, exciting, not only the heart and brain but the strong right arm of the entire western migration.

For almost a hundred years the names California and San Francisco were synonymous in every world language. The movies have changed that: Hollywood, and the latter-day migrations to Southern California. But some part of San Francisco will never be changed: the core of the city built, like Rome, on many hills. In fact, or in legend, this core will never be destroyed.

THE biographer always ends up with a great deal of research material that he cannot immediately use, frequently about people who have only momentarily touched his subject at some time in his life. This was true with the work I had to do on Calvin Coolidge for the John W. Davis chapter in *They Also Ran*. I had needed to assemble a considerable folio of notes on President Coolidge in order to draw a proper contrast between his personality and capabilities, and those of John W. Davis.

It was only a few years later that I received a letter from a New York editor, asking if I would participate in a symposium which was to be put out by a major book publisher under the title of *The Aspirin Age*, which would attempt to portray life in America between the two World Wars. The list of writers was a distinguished one, but what caught my interest at once was the assignment the editor was offering. Would I consider doing the chapter on Calvin Coolidge?

CALVIN COOLIDGE

CALVIN COOLIDGE believed that the least government was the best government; he aspired to become the least President the country had ever had; he attained his desire.

By forcing government to lie supine he paved the way for a world depression which led blocks of nations to demand a form of government which would control everything. His lust for nihilism in administration made *laissez faire* seem a plan for dynamic action; he was as responsible as any individual of his age for the socialist revolution now sweeping over Europe and Asia.

In the White House he napped each afternoon through one of the most danger-fraught periods in modern history. By the very act of sleeping with his feet up on the desk he sincerely believed he was making his most valuable contribution to the American way of life: keeping the federal agencies from doing anything which he might have been obliged to permit them to do had he remained awake.

The Washington Monument pierces five hundred and fifty-five feet into the sky to symbolize the greatness of George Washington's contribution to his country; Calvin Coolidge's monument could be a hole dug straight down into the ground to commemorate all the things he failed to do for his country; a railing should be built around this monument to protect the beholder from vertigo.

He was an incorruptible man; all of his sins were sins of omission. He was a living symbol of Yankee frugality, known and trusted in the remotest corner of America. At the height of the pre-1929 stock market hysteria, when the Federal Reserve Board and nearly every economist in Washington implored the President to tighten the money market and avert the imminent crash, Coolidge issued instead a statement that the four billion dollars in brokers' loans was not too much, and that "the increase represented a natural expansion of business in the security market."

Down from his native hills of Vermont, up from the cattle ranges of Texas, out of the green fields of Kansas and the white cotton fields of Alabama, out of the factories of Detroit and the markets of Seattle poured the last of the hard-earned savings of a lifetime, of generations past, to be thrown into the bottomless pit of the stock market, leading the peoples of America directly to the loss of their homes, their farms, their shops, their jobs, their food, their physical and mental health, their confidence in their country and its democratic form of government.

Coolidge represented the residual mind of America, everything it had been and so little of what it was becoming; the fragmentary man who cared nothing for music, poetry, painting or sculpture, the drama, architecture or the ballet, for the amiabilities of social intercourse. Under his influence the ticker tapes exulted at an ever-accelerating pace while the fruits of the intellect withered. To Europe, to South America, and to the Orient we exported not our art but the products of our juvenilia and materialism.

On the afternoon of the day that Treasury Department officials laid on Calvin Coolidge's desk the documented case for immediate and drastic control of the investment market, and he turned them away, defeated by his icy silence, he went down into the basement of the White House to count the number of apples in a barrel sent him by a friend in Vermont.

While Rome burned, Nero at least made music. But President Coolidge counted apples.

In his native Vermont, politics had been an adjunct of business. His forebears had been farmers and shopkeepers at the same time that they held political office. Calvin maintained the family tradition by transferring the seat of power from the White House across Pennsylvania Avenue to the United States Chamber of Commerce. The President's initials and those of the Chamber of Commerce were the same: the two bodies became identical.

After the raucous depredations of the Harding freebooters, Coolidge restored to the people their faith in the personal honesty of their government. Yet Harding's Ohio Gang, operating from the Little Green House on K Street, took in only hundreds of thousands of dollars from "bootleggers, illegal concessions, pardons, paroles, privileges, and general graft." Coolidge's Secretary of the Treasury, Andrew Mellon, realized a profit on the stock market estimated at *three billions!* Coolidge was the most rigorously economical head the Federal Government had known for decades; this thrifty concept of government saved the taxpayers thousands of dollars; his categorical refusal to govern cost them their shirts.

Words with Calvin Coolidge were not a free medium of exchange. They were a rare and precious commodity to be spent only for the world's goods. Very early he cut the umbilical cord between thought and speech. Yet at the end of his life he was lured into loquacity, writing for seventy-five thousand dollars one of the dreariest concoctions of Sunday-school banalities ever put out by a professional publisher. Mr. Coolidge should have protected his life-long investment in silence.

He was the epitome of the joyless soul, with so little need for human warmth or communication that he couldn't envisage this need in others. When reproached for not giving any part of himself to old and trusted friends, he would cry, "But what do they want of me?" When he was five years old he underwent hours of torture before he could force himself to go through the kitchen in which his mother was entertaining friends; fifty-one years later, when he was leaving the White House, he slipped ignominiously out the back way rather than go through the ordeal of saying good-by to the staff that had served him for five years.

He was the easiest President in American history to lampoon, satirize, caricature; yet this external approach missed the inner truth of the man: both for himself and for the nation he was a tragic figure, born with an organic personality dyspepsia. There was a tragedy written across his twisted face, and shortly after he left office there was tragedy written across the twisted, starving face of the nation.

The twentieth century in which he did his work was never quite as astonished at having this atavar in its midst as he was at being there. His earliest biographer comments that whenever Coolidge opened his mouth to speak, a moth flew out. But the real reason that Coolidge spoke so rarely is that he was too astounded for words: the only thing he could have said which would have adequately expressed his feelings was, "What are all you people doing here a couple of hundred years before your time?"

By what twist of fate did Calvin Coolidge, vestigial remnant of the eighteenth century, help plunge the world into a revolution apparently not scheduled in history's notebook until the twenty-first century?

Calvin was born on a Vermont farm which had been cut out of the wilderness by his forebears and worked by five generations of Coolidges. Throughout his life ran his love for the green hills and the stony earth of Vermont. He disliked cities, distrusted cosmopolitan people, and spoke contemptuously of "the affectations of the drawing room," by which he meant even the mildest form of social intercourse.

The Coolidges always had been among the most important men in their community: hard-working, resourceful farmers, mayors, aldermen, and sheriffs. Both Calvin's father and grandfather were fiercely silent and economical by nature, yet Calvin so outdid them that they were moved to oratorical lengths to comment, "He ain't gabby." Nor would Calvin do any of the other things that normal children did: play games, laugh, chat, spend a penny now and then for candy or ice cream. So economical was he that he would go down in history as the only President to save a small fortune while in the White House.

There were two soft but brief influences in Calvin's childhood: his mother and his sister. His mother became bedridden after his birth, and died when he was twelve; his warmhearted and spontaneous sister, whom he adored, died from a burst appendix five years later. He never recovered from the loss of these two gentle women; fear of death lay permanently behind his small, chill eyes. Coolidge said admiringly of his mother, "There was a touch of mysticism and poetry in her nature." Yet all his life he fought a grim battle to put down in himself and discourage in others the slightest suspicion of mysticism or poetry. His grandmother forbade him to dance, and all his life Calvin thought that fun, joy, and sin were three-letter synonyms.

The one great passion of Coolidge's life was politics. During his childhood he drove about the countryside in his father's buggy while the elder Coolidge collected the county's taxes; he attended meetings of the citizenry at which those taxes were set and political officers were elected; he listened to his grandfather and father hear cases as justices of the peace. He was raised in the magnificent tradition of New England's town-hall government, probably the most successful form of democracy ever practiced; thus he grew up with a belief in politics as an honorable and valuable form of service.

Calvin went to the one-room stone schoolhouse in Plymouth, and after school hours and on week ends he did chores around the farm: splitting wood, milking cows, feeding the chickens and pigs, plowing behind a team of oxen. His father was a stern disciplinarian; Calvin was known to get out of his bed on a wintry night to take care of some duty he had neglected, rather than face his father's wrath the next morning. Yet the father's undemonstrative love was even greater than his sense of rigidly Puritan discipline. When Calvin had exhausted the facilities of the Plymouth school, his father sent him to the Academy at Ludlow, where he lived and studied for the next six years. The fact that John Coolidge was willing to spend what must have seemed a formidable sum of money was indicative of his desire that his boy rise in the world; and we have a picture of the father driving the twelve miles down the rough mountainside in a farm wagon to bring his son home for week ends.

In the Academy at Ludlow, Calvin was quiet, mildly studious, enjoyed books on politics, history, and forensics. Occasionally he worked of a Saturday in a toy factory in Plymouth; these few hours constituted the only intimate contact of his lifetime with industrial workers.

The pattern of his following years at Amherst College was prophetic of his next three decades. He entered as a callow, graceless youth and emerged four years later with the respect of his class and the friendship of such discerning students of human nature as Dwight Morrow. From the first class meeting he sat for hours in tombstone silence, sat through its political organization and committee meetings, doing nothing, contributing nothing except the support of his bodily presence; yet at the end of four years he was considered the class political organizer. The feat of young Calvin, who made other New Englanders appear talkative, emerging as the class orator only seemed a contradiction: he did not believe in spending words in idle pleasantries, but he cannily endorsed the use of words in political speeches because those speeches might serve a valuable purpose. In this lies the explanation of the most silent man of his age making the Fourth of July speech in his home town of Plymouth at the age of eighteen, and spending considerable time on a theme which showed the relation between oratory and history.

Calvin left Amherst with a diploma and three segments of pragmatic wisdom: first, that if he sat clear through every last political meeting he would eventually find his place in the organization; second, that he didn't have to mix socially with the men around him for his contemporaries eventually to grow to like him; and third, that if one did not try to interfere with the moral laws of the universe, which were good and enduring, everything would work out extremely well.

He had already decided that he would become a lawyer. When Dwight Morrow asked him where he was going to practice, Coolidge drawled, "Northampton is the nearest courthouse." This was his approach to life; it was not merely his speech which was laconic.

He was twenty-two when he reached Northampton, with the medium height and wiry figure of an Indian—and Calvin was very proud of the touch of Indian blood in the Coolidge family. His hair was a carroty red, his features sharp, his skin pale with big freckles, his mouth thin, and his blue eyes uncommunicative though not unkindly. In all ways he was the essence of the prudent man, walking with "short quick steps, his slightly rigid body giving him a rather prissy gait." His face was expressionless, and no man ever boasted that he knew whether Calvin Coolidge was happy or miserable. His friends of this period said of him that "his expression remained as blithe as a mourning card"; that "he was a sharp-nosed repository of an infinite and chilling silence, but dependable"; and that "he was as expansive as a letter box: anything said to him was received with a click but practically nothing came out." His voice was a high, twangy, unmusical New England drawl.

He secured his opportunity to read law in the Northampton firm of Hammond and Field through a sardonic misapprehension: Judge Field had heard Calvin give his class oration a few months before, and had laughed at Coolidge's satiric quips at his classmates. He agreed to let Coolidge come into his office because, as he said, "I liked to laugh and Calvin Coolidge was very funny." A few months later someone in Field's firm described him as "a cold and errant draft about the office."

His father was still supporting him, and so Calvin lived under the most rigorous regime. Later, when he went up to Boston for the legislature, he occupied a dollar-a-day inner room at a dingy hotel; nor would he take his wife to live with him during the endless months he served as Representative, Senator, Lieutenant Governor, and Governor. When he got to Washington he converted the White House into a hall bedroom: the cook quit because of his parsimony, the staff had the jitters because of his daily inspection of the kitchens and storerooms;

the only time there was the sound of a strange voice or a bit of laughter was when Grace Coolidge insisted that guests be invited to supper. Not since the regime of Franklin Pierce, before the Civil War, had the White House been so dreary.

Calvin read the law for twenty months, watched Hammond and Field practice their profession, and listened to cases at the courthouse. He remembered every decision he read, and where to find it. One day when he was alone in the office, and the town coroner rushed in to ask if he could remove a corpse found in the woods, Calvin chewed his acrid cud for a moment, then put forth the dictum, "Can move body." Shortly afterward he was given an oral examination by a judge and admitted to the Bar.

He knew precisely what the law was; he did not concern himself with what the law ought to be. For him what existed was synonymous with what ought to be: for if it wasn't what it should have been, then how could it have come into existence in the first place? The word "change" never gained admission to his vocabulary.

Calvin Coolidge never intended to practice the law unless he had to; for the next quarter of a century he was actually out of politics only twenty months. He ran for office twenty times and was elected nineteen. He started at the bottom of the ladder as a precinct vote-getter and member of the Northampton City Council, working his way up to City Solicitor, State Legislator, Mayor, State Senator, President of the Senate, Lieutenant Governor, and Governor. He began his political career by going from house to house, saying to strangers: "I am running for office. I need your vote. I would appreciate it," never bothering to mention his qualifications. He ended his Massachusetts tenure by being elected by an enormous majority as Governor.

He was a civil servant of the type more native to the British than the American: his faculties were sharp, and he would do with persistent efficiency and economy every detailed task put before him. He could never be bribed; he would never be slothful; he would not deteriorate in a routine job; he would take pride and pleasure in the performance of his simple duties. Up to the door of the White House itself he served as a faithful executive clerk, dispatching the necessary minimum of governmental business with cold economy. As he had on his father's farm, he transacted the imperative residuum of chores; for the rest he sat in silence. At no time and in no office did he display the qualities of leadership; he was utterly without imagination, without ideas, without the daring of innovation; he would not have permitted himself to be caught dead making policy. Policy was something made by God, by nature, never by the chief executive of a city, a state, a nation.

He was twenty-five when he was admitted to the Massachusetts Bar, but he was not the traditional young man facing with flushed cheeks and palpitant heart a romantic future. He was already an old man, as old as he was at twelve, and as old as he would be at sixty. He had few friends, only one or two nodding acquaintances; and if he had any enthusiasms, he kept them artfully concealed. On those rare occasions when he felt the need for diversion, he would go to a beer garden after office hours, order a seidel of beer, eat two pretzels, and cogitate in lonely grandeur. The beer drunk, he would return to his hall bedroom. During his student days he had read Scott, Shakespeare, Milton, Kipling, Field and Riley; once he had passed the Bar he seems to have put such dilatory pursuits behind him.

The year following his admission to the Bar he campaigned and got himself elected to the City Council. This was in 1898. From this day until his election to the Governorship twenty years later he held public office almost continuously. Coolidge made no promises, no bargains, and no deals; he lived this entire time under an almost fanatical economy, never acquiring a debt in order that he might never betray his office or his own character because of his need for cash. No matter how microscopic his wage, he forced himself to save a dollar or two a year. In an age when politicians were hiding tens of thousands of corporation greenbacks in locked boxes, Coolidge did no man's bidding, maintaining his self-respect so impregnably that he won the admiration of everyone who came in contact with him. His was the valuable contribution of proving that some Americans will serve in political offices with religious honesty.

His mechanism of politics was superb, but the mountain brought forth a mouse: for the content of his twenty years of service is incredibly meager. The only consistent contribution running through his career was a slimming down of the functions of the particular office he held. In his autobiography he states with pride that when he was President of the Massachusetts Senate he cut the number of bills passed by thirty per cent. As City Councilman, as City Solicitor, and later as Mayor of Northampton, the record shows him attempting to get an armory built for the local military company, and increasing teachers' salaries; as a member of the Massachusetts House of Representatives his voting record shows him supporting woman suffrage and direct election of United States Senators, and as the co-drafter of a bill outlawing price cutting, none of which succeeded in getting passed. As a member of the Massachusetts Senate and later as its President, he supported measures for a mothers' aid bill, a bill regulating the work week of women and children, and a bill providing pensions for families of firemen.

As a member of various legislative committees, such as railroads, judiciary, banking, he simplified the mechanism of governmental control. As Governor of Massachusetts he reorganized the governing apparatus, making it more efficient and economical; he also signed the bill for which he had been working many years, establishing a forty-eight-hour week for women and children in industry.

Coolidge said about his legislative years, "I made progress because I studied some subjects sufficiently to know a little more about them than anyone else on the floor. I did not speak often but talked much with Senate personnel and came into contact with many of the businessmen of the state." William Allen White, in his superb biography of Coolidge, *Puritan in Babylon,* comments, "No one can draw so perfect a picture of the mousy, competent little country-man edging his way onward and upward on the path of glory as that he drew of himself. He won his way by diligence in Amherst. He won his way to the top in Massachusetts politics by tempering his diligence with kindly patience and a lively sense of gratitude."

He accumulated sizable debts of favors, which he advanced to everyone providing he could do so in an honest manner; he asked for no small repayments on his debt; he would go down the line for the Republican party and its members. He had a mild touch of Theodore Roosevelt progressivism. However, the higher Calvin rose in the political hierarchy the fainter became his progressivism until at last, when he crossed the threshold of the White House, there was not a symptom left of his youthful infection. In high place he began to feel that the humanitarianism he had backed in his early years was turning to radicalism. He accused liberalism of being "the claim in general that in some way government was to be blamed because everybody was not prosperous, and because it was necessary to work for a living." On being sworn in to the Presidency of the State Senate, Coolidge delivered an address called "Have Faith in Massachusetts." In what is probably his single most delightful remark, he said about this article, "The effect was beyond my expectations. Confusion of thought began to disappear and unsound legislative proposals diminish."

The four existing biographies of Calvin Coolidge do not contain a sum total of four pages of writing about his concrete services or contributions during his twenty-three years of local and state office. Coolidge was what might have been called an efficiency expert in government, except that efficiency experts consider it their job to increase production. He was an efficiency expert to decrease production. If he could have eliminated the very last duty of a councilor or legislator he would have gone with joy to the funeral.

Out of his bathroom window each morning in Northampton, while he shaved, Calvin watched a young lady walking up the hill toward the deaf-and-dumb school, where she was a teacher. To another young man going through his ablutions he drawled, "Likely-looking young woman." When the other man asked if he knew who she was, he replied, "No, but I'm going to marry her."

It was apparent to everyone but Calvin that he could not win the lovely Grace Goodhue, a warmhearted, spontaneous girl, with a fine intuitive intelligence which had been sharpened by extensive reading and four years of study at the University of Vermont. One of the observers of this budding romance said that Calvin's many competitors for the hand of Miss Goodhue laughed at him, for "his conversation upon any subject bloomed like the edelweiss, rarely and in a cold, forbidding atmosphere." Calvin had not the slightest chance—no more chance than he had to become Governor of Massachusetts or President of the United States. He won Grace Goodhue by the same method that he won political office: he outsat everybody else. Grace fell in love with him, understanding his taciturn New England nature, loving him so much that she married him against her mother's bitter protests.

Having married a young lady of outstanding qualities, Calvin Coolidge now proceeded to put her in her place. He rented half of a duplex for twenty-seven dollars and fifty cents a month, and furnished it completely. Only then did he take his wife home so that she might see where she was to live. With the courage of feminine resignation, she settled down in the flat for the next fifteen years, never stirring from it until the Coolidges moved to the Hotel Willard in Washington, following his election as Vice-President of the United States.

Calvin's one defeat in twenty political campaigns came in his marriage year of 1905, when he lost his race for the Northampton School Board because he had devoted part of the campaign period to a honeymoon in Montreal. This defeat further convinced him that it did not pay to waste one's time on frivolity. His marriage too became a grim business: guests were never brought into the home, friends never sat down to the supper table. He revealed to Grace not the slightest shred of what he was doing. "He did not trust my education," wrote Grace

Coolidge in a popular magazine many years later. All she knew of her husband's activities she read in the papers. She bore him two sons, did the family wash, remained alone in her duplex during the countless months that he was in Boston, and walked away from him when, as Heywood Broun reported, he became insufferably ill-natured. Under all her burdens she never ceased loving Calvin Coolidge; women are wondrously strange.

In 1913 Frank W. Stearns, millionaire owner of a large Boston department store, had gone to Senator Coolidge's office to ask him to support a bill for new sewers for their alma mater, Amherst. Coolidge growled, "I'm sorry, it's too late," and dismissed Stearns. A short time later the Amherst Board of Trustees met to discuss the possibilities of promoting an Amherst graduate into the White House. Several of the trustees felt that Calvin Coolidge was a good man to be backed. Stearns said, "Well, if you say it's Coolidge, it's Coolidge. But the only time I ever met him he insulted me."

Without knowing that Stearns was in process of backing him, Coolidge helped pass the Amherst sewer bill the following session, thus proving to Stearns that Calvin was a sound and faithful man if one would only let him work things out in his own peculiar way. Stearns came to admire, then to love, and finally to worship Calvin Coolidge. He covered the state with the pamphlet "Have Faith in Massachusetts," and put not only his vast fortune but the full facilities of his advertising department and his power among Massachusetts corporations at Coolidge's service. Next to Calvin himself, it was Stearns who secured him the Vice-Presidential nomination in 1920 and thus made possible his sitting in the White House with Calvin in utter silence while the two men smoked their cigars. Coolidge was fond of Stearns and grateful for all the older man had done for him; his feeling was similar to that of the old New England farmer sitting in a rocker on the front porch of his house and saying to his wife, "When I think of what you have meant to me all these years, it's almost more than I can bear not to tell you about it."

Stearns had said, "Well if you say it's Coolidge, it's Coolidge." The backing was now solid and the road into the Lieutenant Governorship in 1916 and the Governorship in 1918 was a matter of well-regulated and well-oiled politics.

Governor Coolidge entered the national scene in 1919 during Boston's police strike, making himself a national press hero by refusing to act for the public good and the public safety until a dangerous crisis had been permitted to develop. The Boston police strike need never have broken into violence—in fact, might never have reached the boiling point of conflict—had Governor Coolidge been willing to exercise the normal functions of his office. His refusal to act brought on the ultimate consequence of a city without police, yet thousands of gallons of ink were spilled in his praise when he said, "There is no right to strike against the public safety by anyone, anytime, anywhere." The statement led directly to the Vice-Presidency in 1920 and the Presidency in 1923. It became the single greatest recommendation for the do-nothing political philosophy to be found in our history books.

In the spring of 1919 the Boston police force threatened to strike on the grounds that they were drastically underpaid, and that the living conditions at the station houses were execrable. Few people in Boston denied the justice of the policemen's claims, but Commissioner Curtis refused to admit the policemen's grievances or to negotiate with them. The police then attempted to join the American Federation of Labor so that they might have the right of collective bargaining. Commissioner Curtis promptly suspended the leaders of the union movement. The rest of the force threatened to go out on strike if their leaders were dismissed; Commissioner Curtis refused to reinstate them.

The Mayor's Citizens' Committee heartily recommended arbitration. Commissioner Curtis refused to arbitrate. During the critical week end Governor Coolidge left Boston and kept himself unavailable. When he returned to the city on Monday, Boston's Mayor Peters and the chairman of the Citizens' Committee pleaded with him to come out for arbitration. Coolidge refused to do anything. On Tuesday afternoon the policemen went on strike. Shortly after midnight mobs began raging through the city, looting and destroying. Coolidge refused to see or talk to anyone. It was not until Thursday, after still another night of rioting, that he went to a meeting of his political advisers at the Union Club, and accepted their decision that the time had come for the Governor to act. He then issued his famous fourteen-word statement, "There is no right to strike . . . etc.," called out the state militia, and broke the strike which he could have averted in its entirety six days before.

This philosophy of *laissez faire* got him into the White House in the 1920s; it proved to be the identical philosophy which brought the nation to its economic catastrophe in the 1930s. In Washington President Coolidge refused to act; the hysteria of the stock market spiral was not unlike the upward spiral of violence in Boston which Governor Coolidge condoned by his refusal to do everything in his power to avoid serious dislocation.

Probably the lowest point in American history between the two World Wars was that moment at 1:20 in the morning of June, 1920, when a Senatorial cabal, the most venal since the days of Grant, nominated Warren G. Harding for the Presidency. Harding was Calvin Coolidge's alter ego: a hard-drinking, gambling man who spent many nights in the Little Green House on K Street, or in a third-rate New York hotel room with his inamorata—leaving the government in the hands of as depredatory a gang of swindlers as had been assembled in Washington since the Reconstruction.

Calvin Coolidge was nominated for Vice-President by the Republican convention as a reaction against the type of man that had been forced upon them to head the ticket. After election he served as an astute parliamentarian over the Senate. Invited by Harding to sit in at the Cabinet meetings, he became aware of the corruption and malfeasance inside the government. He said and did absolutely nothing about them.

Since he was determined not only to live within his salary as Vice President but also to continue his savings, he and Mrs. Coolidge, whom he now took with him for the first time, moved into two rooms at the Hotel Willard. Here he was utterly ignored by official Washington, which was roistering in bootleg liquor, poker, and wads of greenbacks. When the Coolidges were invited out to dinner, Calvin accepted the invitations, though he sat through the dinners and the evenings in curdled silence. A sympathetic woman, who saw that he was suffering, asked him why he continued to dine out. He replied churlishly, "Got to eat somewhere." Another pleasant young woman who had the misfortune to be placed next to him said, "Mr. Coolidge, I've made a rather sizable bet with my friends that I can get you to speak three words this evening." Coolidge replied nastily, "You lose." These two anecdotes, which are reported by Coolidge's biographers as being fine examples of his wit, form his complete contribution to Americana from March of 1921 up to the death of Harding in August 1923.

The ceremony of Calvin's father swearing him into the Presidency in the Vermont farmhouse in which he had been born, reading from the Bible by kerosene lamp, was eaten up by the American people not only as colorful and characterful, but as the best possible guarantee that Coolidge would be an antidote to the rapacity of the Harding ring. In point of fact the accession of Coolidge to the Presidency at this time, when respect for our Federal Government had fallen to an estate rarely before known in American history, was good and valuable; Coolidge's demonstrable honesty restored the people's faith in their high-placed servants. What they could not realize was that the Coolidge swearing in ceremony would be symptomatic of his regime: that he would take to Washington with him a political kerosene lamp with which to light his way in an age of vast electrodynamics.

By an actual time count, Calvin Coolidge averaged a shade under four hours of work a day while President of the United States! In his *Forty-Two Years in the White House,* Irwin Hoover, head usher who had known and observed a great many Presidents, commented acidly that Calvin Coolidge worked fewer hours and assumed fewer tasks than had any other President he had known. No man of his day could so completely have turned the Presidency into a civil service sinecure. When Will Rogers asked him how he kept fit in a job that had broken the health of Woodrow Wilson, Coolidge replied in all seriousness, "By avoiding the big problems."

He had done no sleeping in the afternoons when he was State Senator, Lieutenant Governor, or Governor of Massachusetts. Once he became President he waged an unrelenting campaign to keep his desk so clear of papers and business that he could sleep away the afternoons and be in bed again at ten o'clock at night. As President of the Massachusetts Senate he had cut the legislation by thirty per cent; as President of the United States he cut the duties of the Chief Execuive by at least seventy per cent. Wherever possible he mercilessly slashed appropriations for the various federal departments and agencies, forcing them to let out men and reduce their work to a minor fraction. He used every weapon of discouragement, silence, and negation to keep the Congress from passing laws. The brunt of his day's work was pure listening; examination of a daily program shows that he received a large number of people; he listened to what they had to say, and ninety-nine times out of a hundred made no answer whatever.

Whatever self-originated work he did was party politics, quietly bringing Republican officials into line so that his renomination in 1924 was dried and boxed before the party's convention met. In like manner he had called in his debts when he wanted to become Lieutenant Governor.

His election that year was a triumph for the double negative: don't do nothing, don't say nothing. It was also a best-seller success for the newspaper reporters, from whose ranks have risen some of our most prolific fiction writers: through desire to create readable copy out of a dull original, they fabricated the image of a shrewd, droll, colorful, highly efficient and economic executive, zealously guarding the interests of the nation from his vantage point at the brain center of America.

Coolidge co-operated in the gentle fraud: strangulatingly shy by temperament, he posed in outlandish costume for the news cameramen, peering out from the front pages of the papers as an Indian chief in an effort to show the people that he was a reg'lar fellow.

The stratagem worked, as every device in his political tactic had worked: for rarely has there been a public career so uniformly successful in its parts, yet such a tragic failure in its whole. The country was prosperous; relatively few had been hurt in their personal pockets by the Harding gang; people were still surfeited by what they called "Wilsonian idealism" (i.e., the attempt to achieve world peace, and to establish a liberal economy at home which would preserve the best of modern capitalism); but most important, the public scented and scurried after the bitch-in-heat inflation of the fabulous days ahead.

Coolidge won by an overwhelming margin, almost sixteen million votes to something more than eight million, over one of the most likely candidates ever nominated for the Presidency: John W. Davis, Attorney General under Woodrow Wilson, as international-minded as Coolidge was parochial, as creatively progressive as Coolidge was decayingly static, as warmhearted as Coolidge was frigid, as capable of controlling the financial brigands as Coolidge was incapable of subjecting them even to the mildest criticism. In so far as one can second-guess history, John W. Davis would have used every legitimate agency of the Federal Government to control the stock markets and money markets; by every token of his talents, record, and character he would have sharply reduced, if not largely eliminated, the credit zoom of 1925–1929 and its attendant material collapse of 1929–1939.

Coolidge's two lifetime virtues as a public servant manifested themselves as soon as he became President. First, his appointments were honest; he resisted the considerable politico-pressure that had made Garfield cry out under similar circumstances, "What is there in this office that makes anyone think they would want it?" Second, he gave close detailed study to those subjects on which he was going to have to make a decision. But he studied with almost the sole purpose of being able to refute and confound his visitors, and thus resist their demands for some kind of positive action. White says of him, "He was an economic fatalist with a God-given inertia. He knew nothing and refused to learn."

After Calvin Coolidge had been in the White House five months he announced in a speech that "the business of America is business." This perfect flowering of the Philistine mind became the core of his five-year regime. It was his unshakable conviction that "brains are wealth and wealth is the chief end of man."

He loaded the Tariff Commission with men representing special industries and products. These men made their tariff decisions in the best interests of their particular companies, and Coolidge thought it was right that they should do so: if the sugar men protected their own sugar industry, and the oil men protected the oil industry, and the leather men protected the leather industry, then wasn't it obvious that the best interests of the entire nation also would be served? For him it was inexorable logic that the men who ran industry and made the most money should be the exactly right and inevitable people to run the whole economy—from their great and demonstrated talents would flow prosperity for all. Any accusation that in the 1920s the apex of the American industrial world ran the show solely for its own profit, considering not at all the broad base of humanity, he would have called radicalism, of the kind he had so providentially dispelled in 1918.

This was President Coolidge's conviction. It was based on temperament. Neither fact nor condition could alter it.

There was one more step he had to take before he could assume that he was doing his full job as President: he had to give his urgent approval to the bankers and brokers. He believed in speculative credit because speculative credit created business, and from this business came the funds with which to pay the debts accumulated out of speculative credit. He therefore informed his friends in Wall Street that no federal agency would hinder them.

Family savings were being poured into local banks. Local banks poured their funds into Wall Street. Organizations of high-powered salesmen having been set up for the sale of securities, they sold bad securities when there were no good ones; bankers and investment brokers deliberately sold millions of dollars of dubious stock, for they made just as large a commission on the sale of shaky stock as they did on the sound. The savings of the nation having been absorbed by Wall Street, the people were persuaded to borrow money on their farms, factories, homes, machinery, and every other tangible asset, that they might earn high interest rates and take big profits out of the rise in the market. When Wall Street's huge foreign loans and dubious domestic loans were not repaid, America lost not only the cash of its savings but its collateral as well.

In the spring of 1927 the Federal Reserve Board, sensing the danger ahead, attempted to cut the volume of speculative trade; when Coolidge learned about this he slapped his own Board in the face with a public statement that the year would continue to be active and prosperous. When conservative businessmen became alarmed at the orgy of pyramiding stock prices, and tried to warn the country, Secretary of the Treasury Mellon came out with a statement that the saturation point had not yet been reached, or announced a new Treasury plan to approve and buttress the flow of figures and debts. The ill-assorted prosperity twins, Coolidge and Mellon, alternated in boosting the market: when in the summer of 1927 the rise in stock prices began to slow up, Coolidge publicly predicted that the future of business looked to him to be completely sound—whereupon stocks jumped twenty-six points in one day! Coolidge was enormously pleased with himself, thinking that he had increased the wealth of America by the exact ratio of this advance.

Occasionally, with Stearns or some other trusted intimate, Coolidge would become gabby for a half hour, not asking council or seeking information, but merely spilling his thoughts on some decision or other. Then, his little orgasm of human communication spent, he would return for weeks, even months, to his continence. He also became a practical joker. His humor always had had a sadistic turn, consisting mostly of sarcasms like the one thrown at his long-winded associate of the Massachusetts Railroad Commission: "Sand your tracks, you're slipping." Now for amusement he would ring all the bells on his desk at once so that he could watch the large staff come running from distant parts of the grounds; he would ring the bell at the front gate, and then disappear before the sentry, running on the double, could reach the gate; he would walk up the long, white brocaded train of Mrs. Coolidge's new dress while she was trying it on.

How could he indulge in this moronic puerility when the world was in upheaval? How could he find time to supervise the menu of every meal served in the White House, and check his wife's bills to make sure she was not spending too much money, or being cheated? How could he spend a half hour creating a scene because a Secret Service man, to whom he had given a dime to buy a five-cent magazine, had forgotten to return the other nickel?

The answer is simple. He had nothing else to do. To fill in the dragging hours he would carry his rocker out to the White House porch and rock in full view of Pennsylvania Avenue, or wander through the hallways in his nightshirt, his spindly calves showing, or send a servant to tell Justice Hughes of the venerable beard that the barber was ready to give him a haircut and shave.

He never had been a youth. He was now spending his adolescence in the White House. But millions of Americans would grow gray-haired as a consequence of their President's second childhood.

In the summer of 1927 the Coolidges went to the Black Hills of South Dakota for a vacation, while Frank Stearns and the Republican chairmen of every state and county began setting up the machinery for Calvin's re-election the following year. There was no doubt in anyone's mind but that he would triumph as handsomely in 1928 as he had in 1924. However, one day in his office at Rapid City he dictated a ten-word message:

"I do not choose to run for President in 1928."

He then ordered twenty-five copies of the message typed and summoned the newspapermen, to whom he handed the little pieces of paper without facial or vocal expression. The reporters were stunned; one of them managed to gasp, "Mr. President, can't you give us something more on this?" Coolidge silenced them with, "There will be nothing more from this office today!"

He had taken no one into his confidence, asked counsel from neither his wife nor Frank Stearns. Mrs. Coolidge learned the news from Senator Arthur Capper, who had witnessed the scene; Stearns learned it, brutally, from the newspapers. The chairmen succumbed to shock; but Calvin Coolidge achieved the result he had wanted: paralyzing mystification, which made him, not by deed or accomplishment, but by the simple expedient of abstruseness, the center of the world's stage and the hero of millions of spilled words.

He concealed his motives as rigorously as he had concealed his intent. The only sentence he uttered on the subject was said to Senator Capper a few moments after his coup: "Ten years in Washington is longer than any other man has had it—too long!" Rumor, gossip, and scandal washed back and across the nation: he was playing possum; he was fatally ill; his wife had threatened to divorce him if he ran again.

There was evidence to indicate that he hoped the party would overwhelm his wishes, for on the day that the convention nominated Hoover, whom Coolidge sneeringly called "The Wonder Boy," Coolidge threw himself on his bed disconsolately, lying there face down for many hours. However, by this time a number of suspicious cracks were beginning to appear in the American economy, and a sufficient number of persons had warned the President that grave, perhaps calamitous, times lay ahead. It is quite possible that Calvin Coolidge saw the hurricane coming, and that that was why he did not choose to run.

After Hoover's inauguration, the Coolidges returned to Northampton. Calvin bought a big house and grounds called "The Beeches," and wrote his memoirs for *Cosmopolitan* in his now old and shabby law offices. Northampton was wondrously proud of him; everyone wanted to stop him to shake hands and say hello.

Then came the crash of the stock market, and with it, Calvin Coolidge's world: for other men only lost their money, while Coolidge lost his faith and philosophy in life. He became discouraged, then hopeless, then ill, commenting to a friend that in other depressions it had been possible to see something solid on which to base hope, but that he could now see nothing to give ground for hope.

As a crowning symbol, the Northampton Savings Bank failed, along with thousands of others all over the country. The people of Northampton lost their homes, their factories and stores, their jobs. Destitution, illness, misery walked the streets in the eyes of Calvin Coolidge's old friends. Dimly they understood that he had not been their friend, but their mortal enemy. And dimly, Calvin Coolidge saw this understanding in their eyes.

He lived for four years after leaving the White House, lived to see his old associates and advisers discredited, his Wall Street intimates put in the dock of public opinion and branded as malefactors of American life. He lived to see Franklin D. Roosevelt move into the White House and begin to build the plain-board edifice of the common man's life on the ashes of Calvin Coolidge's collapsed and burned-out world.

In the last year or two of his life he began to understand the fullness of the tragedy that had seized the United States. Now, at last, he knew how gravely he had sinned against the little people who had trusted him, how much he had willfully added to their woes. He saw no reprieve for mankind, except in the solace of religion.

Could the ordinary American citizen have known that in voting for Silent Cal he was helping usher in the deluge? Or is such wisdom available only to after-the-fact historians? The answer is as difficult to reach as it is simple to postulate: unless the human race learns wisdom before the fact it will vanish from the earth in the spiraling smoke of the atom bomb, or its twenty-first-century equivalent. The world can no longer afford its do-nothing Calvin Coolidges: the price of error has risen beyond the ability of mankind to pay and survive.

RACHEL DONELSON came with her family into Tennessee from Virginia as a young girl on the *Adventure*. Floating down the Tennessee Valley, their party was fired on by Indians; they shot buffalo and wild swan to live on. They settled in the wilderness in 1779 near Nashville, put up tents, planted corn. In 1785, when she was eighteen, she married good looking Lewis Robards, a Revolutionary War hero, and went to live with him and his mother on their plantation at Harrodsburg, Virginia. Lewis Robards proved to be insanely jealous. After two years of quarreling, he accused Rachel of conspiring with one of their stockade boarders, and sent her home in disgrace. Here at the Widow Donelson's Station she met the young lawyer Andrew Jackson. Robards came for his wife, apologized abjectly; took Rachel back to Harrodsburg. Again there were scenes of jealous rage. Rachel sent word to her mother to have someone come for her. Andrew Jackson came. When Robards threatened to invade the Donelson stockade and retake her by force, Rachel left for Natchez, in Spanish territory, on Colonel Stark's boat. Jackson went along to protect her. They fell in love. She remained at the home of a family friend. Jackson returned to Nashville for the spring court session. Two months later, Jackson was back with the news that Robards had divorced her, through the Virginia legislature, on the grounds of adultery. Rachel and Andrew Jackson were married, and returned to Nashville.

THE PRESIDENT'S LADY

Adultery

IT was a melancholy gray-black day, with the fall sky as heavy as the timbered roof over her head when she heard him coming heavily homeward. Was it possible that she could know from the gait of the horse that something was wrong with the rider? Alarm fragments flashed through her mind: he was ill, he had been wounded, something had gone wrong in court . . . These past two months since he had gone away had been difficult ones: Catherine's nine children had been desperately ill from eating spoiled meat, and Rachel had spent two weeks getting them back on their feet; her sister Mary had gone down with neuralgia, Rachel taking over the management of her brood of twelve; only two days before Jane's station had been attacked by Indians and two of the men defenders killed. And now Andrew . . .

She was slow in getting out of her chair, in opening the door and moving into the yard. One piercing look at her husband's expression and she was almost felled by the instinctive blow that whatever was wrong concerned them: Rachel and Andrew Jackson. He slid off his horse, unsmiling, did not speak or kiss her, but held his cheek against hers so that she could not see his eyes. She bruised her skin on the rough stubble of his cheek in bringing her mouth round to his, felt his reluctant lips hard.

They made their way into the house. The big room was cheerful, logs crackling in the fire, the wall lamps lighted against his return. He slumped into his chair by the fire while she went past the wide stone chimney into the small kitchen, returning in a few moments with hot coffee. When he had gulped down most of it, and spots of color had risen on his cheeks, she sat herself at his feet.

"What has gone wrong, my dear?"

He stared at her almost blankly for a moment, as though the thing that had happened was a nightmare of the road, having no possible reality here in their home with the fire crackling and the lamps spreading a bright glow. He tried several times to form words and get breath behind them before he finally garnered the strength.

". . . it's . . . what you might expect. Robards."

"Lewis? But how?"

"He's . . . done something."

"But what could he do? We're safe, we're married . . ."

She stopped short, her body frozen. Could it be possible . . . had Andrew shaken his head? Or had it been the way he had blinked his eyes and swallowed?

"Andrew, what are you trying to say, that we're not . . . ?"

"No, no!"

He pulled himself out of the chair and sank to his knees in front of her, his long arms clasped passionately about her as she sat immobile on the hard hooked rug.

"We're married. We always have been. We always will be."

In a hoarse voice she said, "Lewis is trying to make trouble. He's challenged our marriage in Natchez . . ."

"No."

". . . everyone said it was legal, the only way we could be married down there."

"It's not that. I only wish it was." He picked himself up, walked blindly about the room for a moment, then returned to her. The words came out in a rush. "He is only now starting suit for a divorce! The report that he got a divorce from the Virginia legislature was not true. They refused his petition. When I rode down the Trace to bring you the news, in July of '91, and we were married . . ."

She pulled back, gazing at him with terror-stricken eyes.

"I was still married to Lewis Robards!"

Her head began to spin. Andrew caught her, his fingers digging into her shoulders.

"I'll kill any man who even dares question . . ."

She did not hear his words, only his tone. She thought, At last Lewis Robards has had his way. He has made me an adulteress.

As she walked into the Donelson dining room and found the family assembled in their ritualistic places around the long table, she saw with stark clarity the character expression on each face; it was like a recapitulation of all the crises in the Donelson family.

At the head of the table sat her mother, with an expression which said, I'm hurt by this, but I still think that no price is too high to have paid for Andrew Jackson. In her father's place at the head of the table sat Johnny, whose expression intimated that at the moment he was more concerned about what was happening to the Donelson name than he was about what had happened to the Jackson marriage. Opposite him sat Alexander, who had no interest in women, love or marriage, and whose expression said, What can you expect if you are foolish enough to marry? At the second seat on the left she saw William the Cautious, sorry that his sister was in trouble, but remembering that he had told her to stay with Lewis Robards. Next to William sat Samuel, his usually creamy skin now mottled with anger, his soft brown eyes deeply hurt: a complete and authentic replica of herself, had she looked in a mirror.

Her regular seat was next to Samuel's. She dropped into it. Andrew sat beside her. She glanced across the table and saw Jane seated next to Alexander, Jane, who was recalling even now, with a gesture of distaste, the scene caused by Lewis at the Hays home. Next to Jane was

Stockly, the former lawyer, too busy trying to figure out the legal complexities of this affair to be concerned over his sister's suffering. Coming back to her own side of the table, she saw Colonel Robert Hays reaching a hand in front of Andrew to clasp hers reassuringly. He was the most dazed one at this table, for he was a genuinely good and tender man, a fighter, second-in-command of the militia under General Robertson, yet a person of such utter decency that he could not conceive of any other human being behaving this way. Next to Robert Hays sat her brother Severn, hollow-cheeked, who rarely gathered at the family conferences any more; and across from him was Leven, without experience or responsibility, whose puzzled look inquired, What are you all so upset about? At the end seats on their side of the table were her two brothers-in-law, John Caffrey and Thomas Hutchings, married to Mary and Catherine. They nodded to her sympathetically, but their expressions said, This is a Donelson affair; we'd be glad to do anything we could to help, but for the time being we'll remain silent. At the end of the table, facing their mother and Johnny, were her two sisters, Mary and Catherine; Mary who had grown plumper and jollier with the arrival of each of her dozen children, and Catherine, who had grown more wiry, and who still sat through these Donelson conclaves in silence.

She felt there was someone missing, yet all of her ten brothers and sisters were here, as well as her four in-laws. Then the door opened and John Overton came in, the water running from his broad-brimmed hat. He took off his sodden boots, slipping into his accustomed place alongside of Leven. Now her family was complete. The council of war could begin.

Stockly was the first one in voice.

"For heaven's sake, Andrew, what has happened? We can't make it out."

Andrew nodded his head down-table to John Overton.

"I guess we'd better let John start. He's the one found out about it."

All eyes traveled down the long table to Overton. When he spoke it was as though he were placing the words one by one in a bowl in the center of the table, for people to help themselves.

"When Andrew and I started for Jonesboro, I learned that the divorce was scheduled to be heard at the Court of Quarter Sessions at Harrodsburg."

Everyone sat waiting quietly. Then Stockly asked:

"What was the matter with the divorce granted by the Virginia legislature?"

John Overton looked steadfastly across at Andrew. He nodded to John to continue.

"We were misinformed. The legislature refused Robards' petition for a divorce. What they actually passed was what we call an enabling act, which merely gave Robards the right to plead his case before a judge and jury."

"But he didn't do it at that time?" inquired Mrs. Donelson sternly.

"No, he waited until April of this year. The court wouldn't hear his case then, and it was put over until this September."

Robert Hays leaned forward across the table, his hands clasped before him. His disciplined mind insisted upon getting at the core of matters. "How could we have believed there was a divorce in the spring of 1791? Who was responsible for spreading that report?"

"I heard it myself from three or four different sources," said Johnny, "men who came from Harrodsburg and Richmond."

"We accepted rumor as truth," replied Andrew bitterly.

"There was more substance than word-of-mouth, Andrew," said Overton. "While you were in Natchez I stopped with the Robards family for several days. It was the assumption of everyone in that family that Lewis and Rachel were divorced. Mrs. Robards told me she was happy that Rachel was free."

These were the first words Rachel had really heard. She looked across at John, blinking her eyes at him as though this might bring further understanding.

"Mrs. Robards said that we were divorced?"

"Yes, and so did her daughter, Jack Jouitt's wife."

"They wouldn't . . . misrepresent," said Rachel tonelessly. "They have always liked me."

"Robards deceived them too," cried Samuel.

"Now, Sam, that may be a little harsh," said Robert Hays. He reached into his coat, took out a letter and unfolded it on the table. "It was only a month or two after the so-called divorce that I got this letter from Robards asking me to sell his land and send him his half of Rachel's inheritance from her father." He placed the letter in the center of the board and pointed out the sentences:

I shall depend on you and Mr. Overton that there is no advantage taken of me in my absence. You will please to write by the first Opportunity if the Estate is divided as I may get my Right. If there is any Opportunity offered of selling my land you will please to let Me know.

Her mind shut out the voices that beat like the rain against the shutters. She lived again through her wedding under the exquisite chandelier at Springfield, through the happy weeks of honeymooning at Bayou Pierre. Should they have stayed in the Spanish territory after all, where this kind of trouble could never have reached them? But that was being disloyal to the happiness she and Andrew had had these past two years. Inside her head an agonized voice was crying: Why? Why has this happened to me? What sins have I committed that this brand should be burned forever into my flesh? I was only a girl when I met Lewis Robards. I never knowingly hurt him. I tried to be a good wife. If I had done something wrong, then I could understand that I should suffer, and do penance. But of what, Almighty God, am I guilty? For what am I being punished?

She heard John Overton speaking quietly, heard each tiny sound in the room, the very breathing and murmuring of the seventeen people around the table, with a terrifying distinctness.

"Robert is right about the letter," commented Overton; "since Lewis asks for his division of the land he owned here and his half of Rachel's legacy from her father, that can only indicate that he believed he was already divorced."

"But how can all this be?"

Rachel had not been watching the table and did not know who had cried out in such naked pain. Suddenly, from the fact that everyone had turned and was looking at her with pity in their eyes, she realized that it had been her own voice and her own pain. She felt Andrew's hand reach over to take hers. Everyone waited for him to speak, but he could not. John Overton assumed the burden.

"Perhaps it's because the whole subject of . . . divorce . . . is so new. Lewis's petition for a divorce was only the second that had come before the Virginia legislature. When the legislature passed the Enabling Act, I think nobody except a few lawyers knew what it really meant; everyone else appears to have assumed that the bill actually granted the divorce, instead of merely the right to go into court to prove the charges."

"And now the case is to be tried. In Harrodsburg!" cried Rachel in anguish.

There was a silence which Andrew broke into, his voice hoarse with self-reproach.

". . . the fault is mine. No one else's. I'm a lawyer. Or supposed to be a lawyer. What right had I to accept the report of the divorce, regardless of how many people repeated it? My first duty to Rachel, to all of you, was to get a copy of the Virginia bill. I should never have gone to Natchez without it."

"Now, Andrew, there's no call for you to castigate yourself," said Stockly. "I used to be a lawyer too, and it never occurred to me that there could be anything wrong. That trip to Richmond would have taken you months . . ."

". . . and we were the first to tell you that the divorce had been granted," broke in Mrs. Donelson; "we had heard it while you were on your way up the Trace after taking Rachel down to Natchez with Colonel Stark."

"Wait a bit," said Alexander in his lazy, loose-jointed way, "I'm just remembering. That spring of '91 I was staying in General Smith's house for a spell; one day he pointed to a Richmond paper and told me he read a notice of the Robards divorce."

But Rachel saw from the way Andrew had his jaw set that no one would ever acquit him to himself.

"I got back here in April and didn't leave until the latter part of July. I could have sent a messenger to Richmond to bring back a copy; I could have gone myself between court sessions if I had taken enough horses and ridden hard . . . I was guilty of the worst kind of stupidity and carelessness. If I served my clients as badly as I served my wife, they would never let me practice law."

Jane Hays had been listening carefully.

"I don't think these post-mortems and soul-searchings are going to help us a bit." Her voice had an astringency which dried up their emotion. "You said, John, that Robards asked for a divorce trial in April of this year. How does it happen that none of us heard about it when there is so much travel back and forth between here and Harrodsburg? And why is Robards trying again now?"

Overton replied, "Early this year Lewis Robards met a woman by the name of Hannah Winn. When he decided he wanted to marry her, he went into court to get a divorce."

"Then he knew all along he was not divorced!" This was Samuel's explosion again. "For two years he let Rachel live . . . implicating herself . . ."

"I don't know about that, Sam. Let's give Robards the benefit of the doubt. Let's assume that when he went for a marriage license he found he couldn't get one . . . because he was not divorced. Or let's assume that his intended father-in-law insisted upon a thorough search of the records. Under the provisions of the Enabling Act, Robards was obliged to advertise eight weeks consecutively in a Kentucky newspaper so that the defendant, in this case Rachel, could learn about the impending suit and enter her defense."

"We get all the papers from Kentucky," said William. "We never saw any such notice. Nobody in the Cumberland ever told us about having seen it."

"No," agreed Overton. "The notice was never published in the papers. I checked on that in Harrodsburg."

"On what grounds will he seek his divorce?" persisted Jane.

"Through fraud!" It was Andrew who had answered tangentially, his face blazing. "His petition to the legislature charged that Rachel had eloped with me from his home in July of 1790, and that we had lived together thereafter. He lied, and he knew he lied, because he followed us to your home and begged Rachel to come back with him."

"That was my fault," cried Samuel. "I had gone for Rachel once, I could have gone a second time."

"Yes," agreed Severn grimly; "there are a lot of us who should have gone. But there seemed such good reasons at the time to stay home."

"If there is any blame to be taken here, I will take it," announced Mrs. Donelson. "Andrew was like one of my sons. We didn't know that Lewis was quarreling over him again. There was no conceivable reason why he shouldn't have gone."

"We can defend . . ." shouted Stockly, but John waved his hand quietly to interrupt.

"There is no need. Robards is no longer bringing that Harrodsburg trip into the case. The divorce papers state that Robards will introduce evidence that Rachel and Andrew lived as a married couple a year later, on the way up the Natchez Trace in September of 1791."

"But that was after we were married!" Rachel was aghast.

"He can't do that!" cried Stockly.

"You are right, Stockly; his original petition to the Virginia legislature charged that Rachel had eloped with Andrew from his home in July of 1790, and it is on that basis that the legislature gave him permission to sue for a divorce. It is that charge he must prove. He has also failed to provide the necessary eight-day notice to the defendant. We can go into that court in Harrodsburg and demonstrate that the divorce will be fraudulently secured; but the more effectively we defend ourselves in Harrodsburg . . . the more surely we throw out Rachel's marriage to Andrew."

There were commingled gasps around the table.

"We've got to stay out of the case," snapped Jane.

Rachel buried her head in her arms, her body shaking convulsively;

for how could one do anything but weep when one was trapped as she was trapped? If she did not defend herself in Harrodsburg, if she did not take this opportunity to go into court and establish her innocence, was that not proof, eternal and indisputable, that she admitted her guilt?

"Do you know who will testify against Rachel at the trial?" It was Johnny, wanting to identify the enemies of the Donelson family. "I think we ought to know."

"Hugh McGary. He testified that he had observed Rachel Robards and Andrew Jackson sleeping under the same blanket on the journey north. The jury will accept that as proof of the charges. It is our misfortune that . . . adultery . . . is the sole grounds on which a divorce can be granted."

Andrew jumped up from the bench and strode out the door into the rain. Rachel raised her head, stared after him, saying, "There is no marriage. It was never legal. It is not legal now; it won't be legal even after Lewis's divorce . . ."

Johnny asked Overton, "Are those records in Harrodsburg permanent?"

"Permanent?"

"Do they stay there forever, or are they thrown out at the end of, say, a court year?"

"Records are never thrown out."

"We could always burn down the courthouse," observed Alexander dryly.

"But it's totally unfair," cried Samuel. He turned to his sister, his eyes blazing. "Rachel, we've got to go into court and defend you. We can prove fraud against Robards, and falsehood as well. The jury will acquit you of the charges. You will be vindicated."

There was a heavy silence, a silence filled with frustration. Mary came in from the kitchen with pots of coffee and milk, followed by two servants with chargers of food. She would take no part in this discussion, but she would keep a supply of food coming in, maintaining, "Even the worst looks better when you have something hot in your stomach."

Mrs. Donelson handed Rachel a cup of coffee. Rachel drank slowly, the hot fluid scorching her throat. John Overton turned to her, his eyes deeply sympathetic.

"We must not defend you against those charges in the Harrodsburg court, Rachel. If Lewis can't get a divorce to marry his Miss Winn . . . neither will you be able to marry Andrew!"

2

It was pitch-black and raining harder than ever when they started for home. Moll, waiting in the little kitchen, gave them hot toddies against the chill, then retired to her own cabin. Overton bade them good night, went to the door, then hesitated.

"Perhaps we ought to look on the more constructive side of this tangle," he suggested blandly. "Suppose Lewis Robards had not wanted to marry Hannah Winn. It might then have been five or ten years before you found out that there never had been an actual divorce. That might really have had serious implications."

"You mean . . . if he should have gone seeking a divorce . . . after children had been born?"

"Yes, Rachel."

He turned his head slightly so that he was focusing on Andrew. "I think Lewis means to keep this trial as quiet as possible. Uncontested, the divorce will be over in a few hours. Robert Hays and I will sign your marriage bond for a new ceremony. That ceremony can also be short and quiet."

"As something we are ashamed of, eh?" Andrew broke in.

"John's trying to help us."

"We're married." Andrew's jaw was set. "We've been married since August 1791."

"Neither of you has ever told me the details of your marriage at Natchez," said Overton a little sternly. "If the Virginia legislature had granted the divorce in 1791 there may never have been any reason to question that Spanish territory ceremony. But now that we're in the middle of a hotchpot . . ."

Rachel stared at him dully. She saw Andrew clenching and unclenching his fists in black anger. He was a fighter: to strike out when he believed himself right was as natural as breathing; but how could he expose her to the battle? No matter how quiet the trial might be, the whole countryside would be twattling again, reviewing her story, embellishing it with these newest, delectable morsels.

Overton put a hand on Andrew's shoulder.

"Andrew, you have no choice; you must get a Nashville license and be married according to the American law."

Rachel stood before him supplicatingly.

"John is right. We must be married again."

Andrew walked away from her, went to the hearth and stood staring wildly into the fire, his hands clasped behind him, pushing roughly against the small of his back, talking into the flames:

"You are wrong, both of you. Terribly wrong. Don't you see what this means . . . we publicly admit that we have not been married these past two years. We plead guilty to the charges thrown against us in that Harrodsburg court, forever exposed to any enemy or scoundrel who wants to plague us with the record." He walked to the door. "Good night, John."

When John was gone he gazed for a moment into the dark night, then turned to Rachel. The anger had drained from his face; in its place came hurt pride.

"In our own eyes we are married, and so are we in the eyes of our family and friends. No one else matters. We've got to stand firm on this one base: that no purpose is served by going through a second ceremony when the first one was legal and adequate."

And now his expression told her why he was so adamant: he was taking upon himself all the blame for allowing her name to be thrown into a public courtroom in Harrodsburg, where her former friends and relatives could hear her character maligned; for everything she was suffering now and everything she would suffer in the future because, together, they had been convicted of adultery. And because she understood this, she knew how to quiet her husband and gain his consent.

She stood with her back to the fire, letting the heat burn in warmth and renewed strength. Andrew remained at the door, avoiding her eyes, sunk deep in his own injured feelings and even deeper in his remorse. She waited patiently until at last he came to her, took her in his arms and now, just as he had tasted the salt of her tears on his lips earlier that day, she felt his tears damp on her cheek. In the whole defeated cast of his body she saw his horror of this trial, the frustration of not being able to contest it, the terrible things they would be forced to admit thereby, and yet the total lack of any other course.

"There's so little we'd need do to stop Robards. Courts don't like to give divorces; the slightest intimation from us of irregularity and it would be all over . . . We have every right and every weapon to defend ourselves; and yet we have to let him appear as the injured party, to paint us black as he pleases; there is not one word we can utter in our own defense. Do you know how hard it is for me to take that?"

"Yes, my dear, as hard as it was for me to take the news you brought to the Villa Gayoso. You quieted me then, and comforted me with your love, by showing me that at last we were free: free to love and free to marry. It was a bitter price to pay for that freedom, Andrew, but you were right. No price is too great if we can spend our lives together. So now it is I who must tell you not to weep, not to storm, and not to defend us. We must not dwell on the injustice, but think only of our two years of wonderful happiness, and all the years of happiness that are to come."

She put her index finger lightly across his lips as he opened them to protest, then took it away and kissed him.

"Do it for me, my darling. Even though you may be right, and I may be wrong, even though you don't want to, and it galls you, do it for my sake, because I want it, because it will help me. Do it because you love me and because . . . when our children come . . . there must be no question, no man must ever be able to hurt them because of something we refused to do before they were born."

"Yes, Rachel, I'll do it for you. I'll do anything you want . . . always."

3

The bleating had turned from the plaintive to the urgent; they quickened their steps, leaning forward against the lateral wind which swept the big flakes downward.

"How did it get out of the barn?" She turned her face full to Andrew in order that the wind would not carry away the words.

"I don't know; George and I locked everything secure last night when this snow began."

A leafless poplar loomed up ahead. At the base in trampled snow they found one of their ewes, licking the moisture off a newly born lamb. Even as Rachel and Andrew reached her side the ewe weakened, began to stiffen in the snow. Andrew went to his knees to examine the animals.

"Is the little one still alive?" She dropped to the ground beside him, pushing the wool hood back off her head so she could see better.

"Just barely."

"Then let's get it up to the house quickly."

Andrew stripped off the long leather coat which he wore over a buckskin shirt and spread it on the snow, lifting the lamb onto its thick warmth. He looked over at the sheep.

"I'm sorry to lose her; she was a stouthearted renegade: broke out of the pasture to mate, and then out of the barn to lamb."

"Isn't that the fate of all renegades?"

Andrew rose with the lamb in his arms. "Only those who don't plan their uprisings for the proper season."

She ran ahead, her black leather boots making holes in the snow, cried out to Moll to bring in warm milk, and spread a plaid wool blanket before the blazing log fire. Moll came quickly with a tumbler of milk.

"Should we put in a drop of whisky?" asked Andrew. He was brushing snow off his hunting shirt, making damp spots on the floor.

"Yes, in you. Moll, please get Mr. Jackson a hot toddy."

They sat in silence, Andrew in his big chair, the soles of his boots exposed to the fire, sipping his drink. She was on the edge of the hearth, her cape tossed aside and her full wool skirt crushed under her as she concentrated on getting the warm milk between the lamb's lips. She caught a curious expression in Andrew's eyes, and said softly, "How precious all life is, even that of a stray lamb we didn't know existed a few moments ago."

Andrew lit his pipe while Rachel stroked the lamb's curly white wool. When his pipe was half ash, he said quietly:

"Rachel, I'm thinking of opening a store."

She looked up at him in astonishment.

"A store? You mean like Lardner Clark's . . . ?"

"Yes, but out here in the country. Even in the raw weather of these past weeks there must have been a full hundred families come over the Cumberland Gap in their Conestoga wagons, and a lot of them are settling out this way. There's a desperate need for goods."

She made no attempt to hide her amazement.

"But Andrew, why? You are attorney general for the territory, the most popular young lawyer . . ."

"Because I want cash money!" His voice sounded doubly loud because he rarely interrupted. "As a lawyer I'm still getting paid in land and livestock, but people will pay cash for what they buy in a store, three times what I can buy the merchandise for in Philadelphia."

The lamb stirred; she moved it gently so that she could nestle its head between her breasts.

"Andrew, how long before we'll know whether it will live?"

"If it's on its feet by nightfall. Now what I'd like to do is gather up all our lands, John will throw in with me, go to Philadelphia, sell them for cash and use that cash to buy stock for the store. Then, when we take our cash profits from the store, we can buy even bigger tracts of land . . ."

". . . to sell in Philadelphia?"

"Yes. The land companies will buy up everything you've got."

"But isn't that going around in a circle?"

"So does the sun. Look at your brother Stockly: he's accumulated hundreds of thousands of acres. Rachel, this is going to become the greatest trading center of the West, the meeting place for goods coming down from Philadelphia and up the Mississippi from New Orleans. The man who opens a trading post here will become the richest man on the frontier."

"It's hard for me to think of you as a shopkeeper, Andrew. Do you have the special kind of shrewdness that has made Lardner Clark so successful?" She noted that the lamb had only its lower teeth at birth, and that its eyes were a light blue behind the nearly shut lids. "Sooner or later you will make just as much money out of your law."

He moved in his chair with a restless gesture, crossing one booted foot over the other.

"It's not that I'm getting tired of the law, but the cases are so alike: conflicting land claims, disputes over the sale of goods, who started a quarrel and who finished it. I've never concealed from you the fact that with me the law is only a means . . ."

Moll bustled in from the kitchen in her gray cotton dress and black apron to see how the lamb was faring. Andrew walked to the window to stare out into the snow. His red hair shone in the brilliant firelight. Though it was not yet four in the afternoon, darkness had fallen.

"I've got it all figured out: together John and I own about fifty thousand acres, and I have thirty thousand in my own name. They've cost us about ten cents an acre; I can get a dollar in Philadelphia. The round trip will take me about two months. There's a cabin on the main road I can buy cheap. Two or three trips to Philadelphia, then we'll be able to open stores up and down the Cumberland Valley, with trading posts in Natchez and New Orleans."

He was pacing the main room of the cabin now, showering off enough sparks to shock the lamb into life.

"But what about your cases, and your attorney general work?"

"John will handle the cases on circuit, Sam can do the paper work in the office. As far as the attorney generalship is concerned, you know the court is delinquent in its pay to me, five years delinquent, ever since we became a territory. So I guess I can be delinquent for one quarter session . . ."

Strange man, she thought: he has this tremendous hunger to accumulate wealth, and yet he can work for five long years without receiving a cent of pay, and never let it be known.

"It'll only be a matter of a few years, Rachel, and then we can have the great plantation I've always dreamed of. I want the finest in the Cumberland for you . . . the finest in all the world. Then we'll be at the top. No one will ever be able to climb up high enough to attack us."

She lowered her head until her chin nestled on the softness of the lamb's head. For a full year now, since they had been remarried, she had known that he was determined to have . . . wealth, power. The higher he rises in the world, she thought, the more untouchable he thinks we will be. For herself, the need for seclusion, for the ability to live her days without being the focus of strange eyes and strange ears and, even worse, strange tongues, now seemed uppermost. It was not that she wanted to shut herself up, but only to live behind an impenetrable privacy. It was a hunger greater than she had ever known for food or drink or sleep, or even laughter.

They had been happy at Poplar Grove until . . . that news from Harrodsburg. During those first two years Andrew had been content: the land was good, they could live comfortably off its yield, it was in no way different or better than twenty others in the neighborhood. Folks still referred to it as the John Donelson station, which meant added anonymity . . . until people had forgotten, until she and Andrew had established themselves. Yet these things which brought her comfort and protection had become increasingly galling and unacceptable to Andrew. It is odd, she thought, that the need for that second ceremony has influenced no one but Andrew and myself. It's going to drive him on relentlessly. If I try to keep him as small and inconspicuous as I want to be, it would kill him.

She raised her head. Her voice was clear.

"I'm sure the store will be a success, Andrew. I'll help all I can."

She felt a slow movement against her bosom. It was the lamb raising its head, the slim legs twitching.

"Look, darling, his eyes are open."

The animal gave a little bleat or two and shook itself.

"You can set him on his own feet now, my dear," said Andrew. "He wants to walk."

She put the lamb down gingerly, holding him just beyond her skirts. He stood there for a moment weakly, looked about the room, backed away in fright from the fire, then suddenly ran straight-legged down to the other end of the cabin and back to Rachel.

4

She rarely left Poplar Grove, even for a brief trip into Nashville. She had developed a sixth sense about people and could tell at the first piercing glance whether her story was so close to the top of their minds that its edges spilled over into their eyes. She feared the probing glances, the guarded talk, the repetitions of the tale: all invasions of her intimate life. She flinched from meeting strangers, even when she encountered them in the homes of her sisters and knew them to be friends of the family. She was no longer always able to keep her gaze steadfast; at the subtlest intimation of prying, querying, her eyes fled in confusion and pain. In her own home, on her own grounds, she had a lulling sense of security. She was happy to have people come to her, for anyone who took the trouble to make the long ride must be a friend, uncritical and accepting; surely only well-wishers broke bread at your board?

She had need of her calm, for the messages from Andrew were disturbing. Owing to a depression that had settled over the East the arrangements he had made by correspondence for the sale of his lands had fallen through by the time he reached Philadelphia. The land he had planned to sell at one dollar an acre he had brought down by slow degrees to twenty cents, and still no takers. At the end of three weeks of vexation he wrote:

Through difficulties such as I never experienced before, they put me in the Dam'st situation ever man was placed in. I would not undertake the same business again for all the lands . . .

Samuel and John Overton frequently came to Poplar Grove to have supper with her; John had recently moved to his own cabin, which he had named Travellers Rest, about five miles south of Nashville. He read the message without his glasses, then put on his specs to see more clearly what he was thinking.

"I told him we ought to keep our land and sell it parcel by parcel to settlers as they came through," said John. "But he was so anxious to go to Philadelphia . . ."

With her husband away she lived in a suspended world in which she filled every hour with endless tasks, making infant gowns for the new baby expected by Johnny and Mary, knitting coarse oversocks for the winter and white hosiery with clocking, sewing a broadcloth riding habit for herself and a fine linen shirt with a double pleated frill of woven linen cambric for Andrew . . . all of her feelings stored against the hour of his return. The Nickajack Expedition of the militia had driven away the hostile Indians and for the first time since coming to the Cumberland she could walk her fields without fear of attack, could plant a rose garden and vegetable patch behind the house. She kept the lamb by her side as a pet. In the first bright April sunshine she directed the field hands in the plowing and planting of the crops, striding across the furrows in her high boots and long skirt of heavy cotton twill, a large straw hat shading her face. By mid-May the rows were showing fresh green lines, and the ewes and cows and horses began dropping their young. There were going to be good crops to harvest, plenty of livestock for food, tallow, wool and leather. She too felt young and vital and fecund; at night her loins ached for her husband, and the child she might carry.

She was prepared to find Andrew disgruntled and upset, but there had been no way to prepare herself for the sight she encountered when she came up from the barn in the heat of a scorching June day to find him sitting slumped in the saddle in front of their cabin. This was hardly the same person who had started out so hopefully three and a half months before; his eyes were sunk in their sockets, his cheeks gray and hollow; the wrinkled brown clothes hung on his body as though he were made of cross-sticks.

She led him into the house, saw to it that he had a bath with plenty of hot water and soap, then got him into a clean white linen sleeping gown and tucked him into bed. He ate lightly, squeezed her hand and fell into a sleep of exhaustion. She let the dark bearskin blind fall over the window to shut out the sunlight, then gently closed behind her the door of Mary Donelson's former prayer room.

When he awakened he wanted to get up at once.

"Right now I'm stronger than you are," she replied resolutely. She stood with her hands on her hips, her apron berry-stained from making preserves, her brown eyes reflecting her happiness at having him home. "You are going to stay in bed for several days."

When they took their first walk across the fields to the river he was delighted with everything he saw.

"You're a wonderful manager, darling, you do a better job than I do."

They slid down the bank to the water's edge. Rachel took off her moccasins and waded at the edge of the shore, her skirts held above her knees. Andrew caught catfish and told her what had happened in Philadelphia. He had been on the verge of leaving the city without a sale of any of the land, and consequently without any merchandise for the store he wanted to open, but rather than admit defeat had sold their holdings to David Allison, a former Nashville lawyer who had gone east and become wealthy buying and selling western lands.

"Only trouble was I had to take Allison's personal notes. We went to Meeker and Cochran where I bought forty-eight hundred dollars' worth of goods, then Allison took me to Evans and Company where they sold me another sixteen hundred dollars' worth on his paper."

His greatest excitement seemed to center about the packet of books he had toted all the way from Philadelphia: Comte Maurice de Saxe's *Memories on the Art of War,* Frederick William von Steuben's *Regulations for the Order and Discipline of the Troops of the United States,* and Vegetius's *De Re Militari,* known as the military bible.

"By the way, my love, I don't think I've ever told you," he said *sotto voce,* "I intend to become major general of our militia."

She threw back her head, laughed heartily, shook loose the long black hair that had been held up by only one small comb. She put her arms about his neck and made him pull her up until their lips were on a level.

"Do I detect a note of disbelief in that laughter?"

"No, General Jackson; it was pure joy. Now I know you are well again."

5

On the Fourth of July, before the heat rose, they walked their horses to the old log cabin Andrew had purchased as his store. The interior was black, with tiny portholes and smoked walls, everything saturated with dust, cobwebs, ashes and the grease that had run down from the wall lamps.

Rachel grimaced. "I'll bring George over this afternoon with a bucket of lye water, also a saw to cut some window holes. By the way, who's going to sell your goods? Surely you're not planning to stand behind the counter?"

"I wouldn't mind. I like the feel of goods and money changing hands. But I've got to ride the circuit again in September, and if Governor Blount's count of our population goes over sixty thousand we'll have a constitutional convention and form ourselves into a state."

She caught the eagerness in his voice. "Apparently you think we are going to have sixty thousand people? And even more apparently, you intend to go to the convention. I thought you weren't interested in politics?"

"Answering your questions, madam, in the backwards order of their presentation: making an independent state of this territory is not politics: we've got to become a state in order to have representatives in Congress. If you saw some of those nabobs in Philadelphia, with their green silk breeches and powdered hair . . . it's hard for me to understand why those aristocrats ever broke away from England when they spend their whole lives aping everything British."

"Now, Andrew . . ."

He smiled. "All right, I won't fight them today. Answering your other question, I certainly do hope to be elected to that convention. Governor Blount told me in Knoxville that he's going to put my name in nomination. I've got a lot of ideas about how this new state should be set up. As far as population is concerned . . ." he chuckled, "there's not a citizen of this territory so mean-spirited that he wouldn't step up and be counted at least three times."

On August 1, Samuel, who had brought Andrew's merchandise by flatboat from Limestone, Kentucky, arrived in Nashville. It took several days to move the goods onto the shelves: nails, axes, cooking utensils, nankeens, striped calicoes, a few bolts of satins and laces, shoes, hats, stationery, pepper, tobacco. Three weeks later they were paying their first visit to John Overton's Travellers Rest, and inspecting the young apple and peach orchard he had just set out, when Samuel arrived with a letter for Andrew which a trader had brought in from Philadelphia. It was marked *Important*.

It was a short message, but from the way the blood drained out of Andrew's face Rachel could see that it was too long at any length.

He looked up, his eyes dazed, his mouth for the moment wide and uncontrolled.

"It's from Meeker and Cochran in Philadelphia. David Allison is in trouble. His notes

". . . now falling due are not generally or regularly paid. We take this early opportunity to make known to you that we have little or no expectation of getting paid from him, and that we shall have to get our money from you, which we shall expect at maturity."

She stood on the garden path listening half to the low hum of conversation among the three men and half to her own insistent voice. Andrew owed Meeker and Cochran forty-eight hundred dollars, half of which he would have to pay on December 1. How were they going to sell enough of the stock to get the cash?

"I'll find a market somewhere," announced Andrew grimly.

"You can't, there isn't that much 'ready' in the entire Cumberland Valley," said John.

"The whole fault is mine, John: I promise you won't lose on it."

Rachel watched John Overton weigh this promise carefully.

"Whatever we manage to collect from Allison we'll divide half and half. Money can squeeze the life out of a friendship quicker than a grizzly bear."

She was saddened not by the loss of the money, which could be earned again, but by Andrew's suffering. It would be a blow to his pride: the fact that he had been defrauded, his judgment proven unsound, his working capital wiped out. He was not the kind of man to indulge in regrets, but to what new ends would he drive himself to reach that state of affluence which appeared to be his primary need?

They rode up the winding path that led to the top of Hunter's Hill, the highest eminence in the countryside, overlooking the Cumberland and Stone rivers. They reached the crest at about noon. Andrew spread a blanket on the lee side of the hill; they could hear the wind above them blowing away the few remaining autumnal leaves.

"We should have brought Lamb with us," said Rachel. "He would have liked to gambol up here."

"You are taking a gambol every time you let him out of the house. You seem to forget that the lamb is now a sheep. One day he'll be jumping the fence to join his kind."

"You could have made a double pun by spelling that last word with an *e* instead of a *d,* and it wouldn't have been any worse than the first one."

After lunch they stretched out side by side in the center of the blanket, her head nestled comfortably on his shoulder. He wrapped the rest of the blanket around them, then began speaking in a light, jocular tone.

"I brought you up here under false pretenses. I really wasn't so anxious for the picnic I dunned you into."

"Oh?"

"It's just that I have a story to tell you and I thought you would like to be sitting on top of the world when you heard it."

"Wherever you are is the top of the world."

"Thank you." He paused. "I've sold the store."

"For enough to meet the Meeker and Cochran note?"

"No, there's no one with cash who'll buy; Elijah Robertson's paying me with thirty-three thousand acres of good land worth a quarter an acre. The Philadelphia people will give me time to sell. We won't come out too badly once I've sold the land. I don't like failure, no man does. But I've learned a lot; I'll not make those mistakes next time . . ."

He lay quietly, looking down at her and stroking the hair back from her forehead, tracing the high arch of her brows with his fingers. Then he said, "Governor Blount sent me word yesterday that the population count is finished. He wants me to help write the new constitution."

She thought, This is what he really came up here to tell me.

"Good. You'll be helping to set up the state that Father dreamed about when he brought us all to the Cumberland. I'd like to see you at the convention speaking to all those men."

"Then it's done! You'll come with me."

She rose from the blanket, walked a little distance and gazed below her at the smoke rising from piles of burning underbrush, at the fences and groves of trees and the creeks and branches shining in the sun.

"Oh, I didn't really mean watch you in the flesh; I meant that I'll read the accounts in the *Intelligencer* and picture you standing there."

She did not hear him come up behind her.

"It's a magnificent view, isn't it?" he asked.

"The finest I've ever seen."

"Could you be happy here?"

"One would live above so much of the . . . struggle . . . that goes on below."

"I'm mighty relieved to hear you say that."

She turned about swiftly.

"Andrew, what do you mean?"

"My dear, you've been picnicking on your own land. I bought Hunter's Hill."

"But how could you? We've been so strapped . . ."

"I'm going to build you the finest home in the whole new state, Rachel. It's going to be the first house of cut lumber in the Cumberland Valley. I brought nails and glass back from Philadelphia and have kept them hidden away. And wait until you see the furniture: beautiful brocade settees, walnut tables, French wallpapers . . ."

"With what, darling? We've just failed in our first business venture. You say the new land is worth twenty-five cents an acre, but you may only get ten cents, or five."

In his excitement he was towering over her like a slender cypress trunk.

"Ah, my dear, that's the time you must dare to pull yourself up to the heights, when you have failed and everyone thinks you are on the road down. Then you yourself, and only yourself, can reverse that trend! You must search out the highest peak in the landscape, climb it and claim it as your own. Then when people see you, as they'll see us at the top of Hunter's Hill in a magnificent home, they'll look up to us. Rachel, the whole world will come to your door . . ."

She slipped her hand into his. "Whatever you want, Andrew, I know you can do."

6

The day before he was to leave for the Constitutional Convention in Knoxville Andrew announced he was posting notice that Poplar Grove was for sale.

"Oh, Andrew, must we sell?"

The words had escaped her. They had lived nearly four years at Poplar Grove: a woman didn't trade a home and happy memories quite as easily as a man did. She added quietly, "Couldn't we just rent, to Samuel, for instance? He's going to propose to Polly Smith any day now."

"We need cash money for the cut lumber from the mill. That's for labor, and they won't take personal notes."

He had instructed her to show the place. The first family or two of prospective buyers were not difficult for her, they were brought by friends and she could pretend it was a social visit. But by the middle of January when complete strangers began drawing up before her door in their wagons, with big-eyed children peering out from under the canvas and the fathers saying from a hunched-over position on the hard wagon seat, "You Miz Jackson, ma'am? We hear tell this place is for sale. We're looking for a likely place, now," she packed her portmanteau and fled across the river to her mother's house.

"You want we should make it look bad, Miz Rachel?" Moll asked. "George and me, we can heap the furniture like a shambles . . ."

"But how we gonna make that sweet earth and the fat animals look bad?" demanded George tartly.

Rachel found herself laughing for the first time in days.

Once she reached the Donelson station she felt brighter, for there was always activity and people here: slow-moving, slow-speaking William the Cautious had fallen in love with young Charity Dickinson and was courting her with all the fast-moving, fast-talking ardor of a seventeen-year-old. There was no regular mail service from Knoxville but the steady flow of travelers brought news each day. Andrew and Judge McNairy had been selected as the two local delegates to help design the government, and Andrew was working fourteen hours a day to create what he called a Jeffersonian constitution: two legislative houses instead of one; the right of all men to vote after six months' residence; only a two-hundred-acre ownership necessary for election to the legislature. Rachel read the newspaper report of Andrew's speech when proposals had been offered to name the new state after George Washington or Benjamin Franklin:

Georgia was named after a King, the Carolinas, Virginia and Maryland after Queens, Pennsylvania after a colonial proprietor, Delaware after a Lord; and New York after a Royal Duke. Since Independence there is no reason for copying anything from England in our new geography. We should adopt for our new state the Indian name of The Great Crooked River, *Tennessee, a word that has as sweet a flavor on the tongue as hot corncakes and honey.*

She returned to Poplar Grove the day before Andrew was due.

"I see you practically worked yourself to the bone trying to sell Poplar Grove before I got back," he commented.

"I hope everybody hates it."

"Vain hope. I've got a buyer, your brother Alexander. Met up with him in Knoxville. He's paying five hundred thirty pounds . . . in cash, enough for me to order my cut lumber and other coin-on-the-barrelhead items to start building Hunter's Hill."

John Overton came to spend the evening. "Do I start calling you congressman now?" he asked Andrew.

"Congressman! I'm not interested in politics."

"Then you can put those military books away, General, because you're evidently not interested in the militia, either. That army is going to evaporate unless Congress repays the thousands of dollars spent for the Nickajack Expedition."

Andrew shook his head in despair.

"Now there's a choice assignment! The War Department forbade us to go out on that expedition against the Indians. General Robertson has had to resign because of his row with Secretary of War Pickering over the battles we fought. The Federal government has declared the whole expedition illegal, null, void . . . and now all you want me to do is to get the Congress to pay for it!"

Rachel found that Andrew's prophecy about Hunter's Hill proved sound: he no sooner started construction of the house, which attracted visitors from all over the Cumberland, than people began to speak of his tremendous success. He acknowledged their accolade by starting on a land-buying spree that surpassed anything he had ever done before: each day he brought home new titles: on March 11, a thousand outlying acres for two hundred and fifty dollars; on April 18, another five thousand acres for four hundred dollars; on April 19, a six-forty for twenty cents an acre; on May 9, three separate purchases: twenty-five hundred acres for two thousand dollars, three thousand acres for three thousand dollars, one thousand acres for one thousand dollars; on May 14, five thousand acres . . .

When she added up the books she found that he had bought some twenty-six thousand acres and spent more than sixteen thousand dollars . . . all on his personal notes. He sometimes sold land too; in her strongbox Rachel held signed papers from at least a dozen men in the Cumberland. Each man's credit was as good as his reputation; but let any one fail, man or reputation, and the whole structure would collapse. Rachel was convinced that this was a pure gambling game, like rattle and snap, played more for excitement and fun than for profit.

Both the excitement and the fun drained out when she learned that Andrew was contemplating buying the six-forty on which she had lived with Lewis Robards. This land, which was part of Clover Bottom, had been sold by Lewis to a Mr. Shannon who was now offering it to Andrew. She was amazed at the ardency with which she did not want to own that land again.

"The fields are innocent . . . and fertile," said John Overton; for at the last moment Andrew, unable to bring Robards' name past his teeth, had asked John to discuss the purchase with Rachel. "It adjoins Hunter's Hill. That particular piece will be indistinguishable from all the rest."

"Then you think I ought to approve?" she asked, swallowing so hard that her audible gulp filled the momentary silence.

"No . . . But is it worth making an issue of?"

"I see." She blinked several times, as though clearing cobwebs from her mind. "Well, I'll get over this feeling. We'll run the furrow straight down from Hunter's Hill to the river."

As soon as word got around that the Jacksons had bought the former Robards six-forty to add to their holdings, a wave of argument swept the valley. It had not occurred to Rachel that it would cause a controversy, with everyone taking sides and resurrecting the Robards-Jackson affair for the many newcomers of the region. She had imagined her reluctance to be something private and personal, and now here she was the center of discussion again, her past revealed and distorted. As far as she could gather, half of the people condemned them for bad judgment: this land could bring nothing but ill luck; the other half accused them of bad taste in wanting to show the world that they had been victorious over Lewis Robards and had thus symbolically absorbed him.

But she did not sense the extent of the argument until she learned that John Overton, who abhorred all forms of physical violence, had actually been involved in a fight in Nashville, and had had his eye blacked for his trouble. When he reached the Jacksons' at Rachel's urgent request, the lid over his right eye was still highly discolored, the bridge of his nose too tender to support his spectacles.

"That's the first time in my life I ever tried to knock a man down," he admitted sheepishly. "Of course I missed by a country mile."

"I don't know whether to be ashamed of you or proud." Then, no longer able to sustain her effort at humor, she cried, "Oh, John, how long will this go on? It's been five years since Andrew and I were first married, and three since that . . . divorce."

"I don't know," he replied grimly; "I thought so much time had elapsed and Andrew had become so important in the state that the whole affair would be forgotten."

"But it's never going to be, is it?"

They moved into Hunter's Hill on a Tuesday toward the end of May; it was the day of the week on which Andrew liked to begin new ventures. The house seemed enormous to Rachel, with its parlor and dining room on either side of the entrance hall, and Moll's kitchen to the left beyond a porte-cochere. The furniture Andrew had selected in Philadelphia was installed in the parlor: a settee and upholstered chairs covered in double damask with flowered figures standing out from the satin background, and on the floor a sixteenth-century Tabriz animal carpet he had purchased at an estate auction.

Behind the two front rooms was a music room, completely empty, and Andrew's study in which he reverentially placed her father's wide walnut desk, then lined the fireplace wall with bookshelves. He took the four big outside drawers of the desk for his papers, and gave Rachel the eight smaller enclosed drawers with the brass knobs, for her household bills and account books. Upstairs there were four bedrooms fitted precisely over the four downstairs rooms, but only their own bedroom had furniture in it, the four-poster which they brought from Poplar Grove. The half-empty rooms doubled her sense of hollowness. Even as the small cabin at Poplar Grove had seemed to hold her close, to protect her, so the vast areas of Hunter's Hill seemed to expose her on all sides. Her husband might find the eminence of Hunter's Hill dominating and powerful; she felt it only made them the more vulnerable.

That summer Andrew worked in the fields to raise the small crop that had been planted in the spring. On July 30 the Tennessee legislature voted him his five years' back pay as attorney general. He used the money to build a road up the hill to the front door, while Rachel supervised the erection of a dairy, smokehouse, storehouse, stable and log cabins for the Negro families.

"We've come to the end of our troubles," he declared with satisfaction. "If I could get back to Philadelphia . . ."

She hated the thought of another separation, but kept all emotion out of her voice.

"You'd really like to be our first congressman, wouldn't you?"

"There's so much I could do," he shot back. "John was right about the money for the Nickajack Expedition. If I could get Congress to appropriate that fund . . . and could collect some of my own money from Allison, enough to buy merchandise for another store . . ."

She gazed at him in awe.

"Andrew, you're going to be the busiest representative in all of Philadelphia!"

7

With what did a childless woman fill the rooms of this big house? she asked herself. It was the first year since their marriage that she and Andrew had been separated at Christmas, for he had been elected to Congress, and left for Philadelphia in November. In an effort to cheer the house with voices and laughter and good memories she planned a Christmas Eve dinner for the family: Mary and John Caffrey and their twelve children, Catherine and Thomas Hutchings and their nine, Jane and Robert Hays and their four, John and Mary and their eight, the latest of which was only a month old; Stockly, Leven, Alexander and Severn, still bachelors; William and Charity, newly married, as were Samuel and Polly Smith; John Overton and her mother.

Because it was really a children's party, Rachel used rock candy for the sauces; two enormous boards were covered with candied and spiced fruits, pickled walnuts, marmalades, honey and jellies, apple-mousse and half a dozen different kinds of pie, along with pear and quince tarts. There was a gift for each of her nieces and nephews: ribbons, bonbons, gloves, rag dolls, embroidery equipment; for the boys: knives, shot pouches, moccasins, hunting shirts. Each child ran to Aunt Rachel to embrace her; the sight of the young ones, the children she so ardently wanted to bring into the world, made her cry out in hunger. When the families had bundled up their youngsters and piled them into the carriages and onto saddles, sometimes as many as four hanging on behind their father, she was alone again.

She lay awake in the high four-poster, the curtains pulled on all sides to afford her an island of warmth and security. But the weather had been raw and the wind had a penetrating quality which invaded the house, the shut door of her bedroom, even the closed-in darkness of the bed. Exhausted and let-down after the big party, she listened to the creaking noises of a new house solidifying itself against winter's attacks, wondering how she would endure the months that lay ahead. All the dictates of logic and expediency had made her agree that Andrew should go east to the Congress; but in the stark shivering clarity of the lonely night she knew that the more past business he settled the freer he would be to set up future business. All of his savings for eight years had been wiped out when David Allison's paper had gone bad; all of his work as well as profit from his store had been nullified when he had been obliged to sell hurriedly; and only that afternoon she had learned that the Blount paper for which he had traded his thirty-three thousand acres had become practically worthless because the Bank of England had suspended its specie payments and thrown the East into a panic. From his letter she could not tell whether Andrew was maddest at having lost his money or at learning that America was still controlled by the Bank of England. She thought of him on this Christmas Eve in some strange inn or boardinghouse, separated from her by a thousand miles and weeks of hard travel . . . for what purpose?

There was no dawn, just an ash-gray light filtering through the windows. She got out of bed, went to the wardrobe and took out the blue silk robe Andrew had bought her in Natchez. The silk was ice to her touch. She went through the center hallway and out the side door, then stood very still: for the light had come up in the east now, and below her the river was frozen solid, the first time it had frozen over since the Donelsons had come west on the *Adventure*. She went into the kitchen building where George had left the fire banked, boiled some water in a pan for coffee, and drank the fluid as hot as she could. Its heat relaxed her; she went back to bed and fell asleep.

She was awakened by a considerable hubbub outside the house, and through the window saw the entire population of Hunter's Hill gathered about a highly polished black carriage with red wheels and a pair of matched iron-gray horses.

She dressed as quickly as she could and descended to the front porch. As she walked toward the carriage she saw that it was empty, then in an unbelieving flash a brilliant red monogram on the door: *R.J.* George opened the door with a flourish and bowed Rachel in. She put her foot on the little iron pedestal. George closed the door behind her. Only then did she realize that Andrew had ordered this carriage for her and had given instructions that it be delivered on Christmas Day. She remembered how hard pressed he had been for cash before leaving for Philadelphia, how he had manipulated and exchanged lands and paper; yet he had thought of her alone on Christmas morning.

Tears sprang to her eyes. She sat as warm and secure as though he were beside her, his arm gripped tightly about her shoulder. How weak she had been: as long as she loved her husband and he loved her they would not be separated. Love was a mighty bridge which crossed frozen rivers and frozen hours: it enabled a man and a woman to walk hand in hand across a sunlit field even when a thousand miles separated them and the field was snow-covered under a leaden sky.

In his next letter Andrew told how the moment he had reached Philadelphia he had ordered a black coat and breeches to be made by a tailor.

They fit me quite well, and I thought I presented a handsome figure. But when I got to the Congress to be sworn in, I found myself the only one with a queue down my back tied with an eelskin. From the expressions of the more elegant nabobs about me, I could see that they thought me an uncouth looking personage with the manners of a rough backwoodsman.

She sensed how this must have galled him, for his manners were courtly; recalling her father's friends from the Virginia House of Burgesses, she knew that Andrew's manners were as gentlemanly as theirs.

In addition his very first act in Congress had antagonized not only a considerable portion of the legislators, but Tennessee as well. This news she learned when she went on a Sunday to her mother's home for dinner; as she came into the big room she perceived several sentences dangling in mid-air like the wool threads of an unfinished coverlet. She said in an impersonal voice:

"Very well, my husband has done something you don't like. Let's get it over with and not spoil Mother's Sunday dinner."

"Let's don't," replied Jane. "You're not responsible for your husband's political ideas."

"My dear Jane, the newspapers will reach me tomorrow."

Samuel lifted his head.

"You remember President Washington's farewell speech to the Congress? The House drew up an elaborate eulogy to make in return. Andrew voted against giving it, said it was a blanket approval and that some of Mr. Washington's acts sorely needed criticizing . . ."

Her eyes swept the room in a quick ring. "Has someone had a letter?"

Robert Hays pulled a paper out of his pocket, then read:

". . . *Every day's paper proves the fact that the British are daily Capturing our vessels, impressing our seamen and Treating them with the utmost severity and brutality, but from the president's speech it would seem that the British were doing us no injury.*"

"I suppose it's all right for him to hate England so intensely while he's here at home," commented William, "but he has no right to make it appear that that's the way everybody in Tennessee feels. If he's not careful he'll get us into a war with the British."

Jane took the letter from her husband's hand and gave it to Rachel, murmuring, "The last paragraph is for you."

Rachel's eyes went quickly to the bottom of the page:

I make one request that you attend to my Dear Little Rachel and soothe her in my absence. If she should want anything get it for her if you can and you shall be amply rewarded.

She returned the paper, a smile on her lips.

During the latter weeks of January the cold intensified until one morning she found ice on the ground and her plants and young shade trees frozen. Moll was missing at breakfast. Rachel knew that she must be very sick indeed if she remained in her cabin. George too was ill. Rachel put her hand to Moll's forehead.

"You've got fever."

Moll leaned up in bed, her teeth chattering. "Sampson and Silvey is bedded too, and Winnie and James and their Orange. Must be the fluenzy."

She made a quick tour of the cabins: the grippe was of epidemic proportions. Among the older folks only one family had escaped, and Moll's niece Mitty. She sent them to bring blankets from the big house and to stack up the logs beside the fireplaces, then dispatched one of the younger boys to Nashville for the doctor. She herself went into the kitchen to brew the bitter tea of herbs and marshmallow root which her own mother used to fight the grippe. She and Mitty carried the steaming pot from cabin to cabin, plying the sick ones with the liquid.

For the next week she nursed her people night and day. She had always respected Andrew for his attitude toward their "black family." She had never seen him deny one of them a pass to visit friends, he never rationed their food or fuel, he refused to separate members of a family, gave them individual kitchens.

"I can't be as easygoing as you are, Andrew," she had once told her husband. "You're not responsible to anyone but yourself, but when you go away and set me tasks to do, I'm responsible to you."

"I think they understand that," Andrew answered; "in any event they accomplish more for you than they do for me."

No sooner had she been able to leave off making night rounds among her sick than she was awakened one midnight by the sound of a horse coming heavily up the road, and by someone pounding on the front door. She opened the window and called:

"Who's there?"

"Mrs. Jackson, ma'am, beggin' ya pardon for wakin' ya this hour at night, it's Tim Bentley, ya neighbor over beyond Willow Spring."

"What can I do for you, Mr. Bentley? What's wrong?"

The man shouted up at the window, the words coming in a frenzied jumble.

"It's the wife, Sarah, and the baby . . . I mean it should be the baby but it just won't get itself borned. I think Sarah's going to die, ma'am, the baby and she both . . ."

"Go around the side to the kitchen house and wake George; tell him to saddle me a horse."

In a matter of minutes she was racing downstairs. In the yellow glow of the porch lamp she saw the face of Tim Bentley. He could not have been more than twenty, but his skin was sallow, he had weak eyes and a chin that vanished at a precipitate angle under his lower lip. She told George to saddle another horse and bring along soap, blankets, sheets, towels, candles and food.

It required little light to indicate the ramshackle nature of the Bentley cabin: the notching was of such an uneven character that one end of the roof had begun to sag; inside, the logs that made up the floor showed gaps of cold damp earth beneath, while the one window had been pasted over with successive layers of brown paper drenched in bear's oil. There were two pots hanging over the fire, a small table stood near the hearth . . . and in the corner a wooden bed with a young girl lying in it, covered by a ragged blanket. The only preparation for the expected baby appeared to be a crude cradle on which rested a linen christening gown they had apparently brought from the East.

Rachel said, "Hello, Mrs. Bentley, I'm your neighbor, Mrs. Jackson, from up on the hill. I'm going to stay right here with you until your baby is born. Why didn't you call someone before?"

"We was hopin' to see it through by ourselves. But it's lasted so long . . . the pains was so hard . . . The minute I heard your horses I felt better." She hesitated. "Are you *the* Mrs. Jackson, ma'am?"

"Who is *the* Mrs. Jackson?"

"The one they talk about so much? But you don't look at all like that kind. That Mrs. Jackson wouldn't come help me."

Rachel stroked the girl's hair soothingly.

"I want very much to help you. I've never had the good fortune to have a baby myself, but my sisters have, dozens of them, and I've helped them. So you see, everything is going to be all right . . ."

While speaking, she had slowly lifted the blanket. Now she glanced down and saw one of the baby's feet protruding. She recognized it as a breech birth; the baby had failed to turn to the proper position so that the head could emerge first. Her sister Mary's first child had been a breech birth; Mary had had the services of the competent French *sage femme* who delivered the youngsters in their county, since women were never attended by male doctors. Rachel remembered the birth vividly, for the midwife had commented that these cases were rare, and that many of the breech babies died in delivery. She spoke to the girl with considerably more calmness than she was feeling herself.

"Your baby is beginning to show itself, Sarah. Before another hour you will be holding it in your arms."

She wiped the girl's face with a cold cloth; every few moments she raised the blanket, watching the baby's second foot emerge, a little later the buttocks, then the two shanks. She recalled the midwife saying that it was best not to try to help the baby at this point. Between times she had the father build up the spindly fire until there was a good blaze. When George arrived with the supplies she washed her hands with hot water and soap, then fixed a basin of water for use at the bedside. She removed the old blanket under Mrs. Bentley and replaced it with a clean sheet; she lined the crib with the quilt George had brought. When she lifted the cover again the baby's hips had fought their way out.

"You're doing fine."

After she was able to take a deep breath, Mrs. Bentley replied, "I can tell I am."

With the next pain the baby's navel appeared. Rachel grew tense. Mrs. Bentley grabbed the sides of the bed, making a strong effort, and with that the baby emerged to the shoulders. Remembering how the midwife had done it, Rachel released the arms and hands, picked up the two feet and held them so that the trunk was perpendicular to the bed and at right angles to the mother; then with her free hand she applied pressure to the lower part of the mother's abdomen.

A minute passed, then two. Nothing was happening. Soon the pressure on the cord would stop the flow of blood to the infant. Rachel doubled her hand into a fist and threw her whole weight on Mrs. Bentley's abdomen. At that instant the mother let out a scream . . . and the baby was born. It was a girl.

Rachel tied the umbilical cord in two places with string, then cut between. Next she spanked its buttocks, hard; and it cried. She sponged the infant, wrapped on a tight bellyband to protect the navel, dressed her in the christening gown and lay her in the cradle before the fire. About twenty minutes had elapsed. She washed Mrs. Bentley with warm water, put her in one of her own white gowns, covered her with the blankets from Hunter's Hill, gave her a cup of coffee and some of Moll's apple cake.

It was some forty hours later before she finally reached home, having installed Mitty in the Bentley cabin. She went into the parlor, sank into a chair in front of the cold hearth. She knew that she should be cold and numb and exhausted; but she wasn't feeling cold at all. Or tired. Or alone. She had not been able to bear a child of her own, but that baby, it would have been dead without her help. This too was a way of creating life. She could feel the infant in her arms, its blood racing against her blood, warming it, warming away the dull ache that had settled in her when she had heard, "Are you *the* Mrs. Jackson?"

8

As long and severe as the winter had been, just so quickly was it gone, with the sun bright overhead and the grass growing green on the hillside. The hickories began to show their fine leaves, the buds opened on the honeysuckle and dogwood; the pelicans came flying in long trains, lighting on the surface of the river below. Andrew had said, "My ambition is to become a gentleman planter." Hunter's Hill had the makings of a rich plantation, the land a fine black mold lying on a bed of limestone; if they farmed it diligently it would not be long before he could build his racecourse and train thoroughbreds. Then he wouldn't have to ride fifty miles, or a hundred, every time he heard there were going to be blooded horses raced somewhere in this county or the next.

At that moment her first real interest in Hunter's Hill was born. The hands worked hard to clear new fields, and their crop this year would be a big one. Even her fear of the former Robards land vanished; it was good earth that could help them create a great plantation here, perhaps the biggest and best in the Cumberland. If that was what was needed to keep Andrew happily at home, then she must go about her plowing and planting with ardor.

She was out in the fields in a short-sleeved cotton dress with a wide skirt, her hair piled in a knot under the wide-brimmed straw hat, when John Overton brought her the news that Andrew had persuaded the Congress to reverse the War Department, legitimatize the Nickajack Expedition and pay back every dollar that Sevier and the rest of the militiamen had invested out of their own pockets.

"At last," she exclaimed, rooting her feet deep into the earth, as though she were a tree that grew there, "something good has happened in Philadelphia!"

On one of her visits to the Bentley cabin, carrying hyson tea, sugar and ginger for Sarah and lightweight cloth for the baby's gowns, she learned that Sarah had served a three-year apprenticeship as a seamstress in Baltimore. Since it was apparent that Tim would have trouble providing for his family, Sarah came to Hunter's Hill one day a week, bringing the baby with her, and sewed draperies of the loose-woven material Rachel had loomed for her spare bedrooms. Rachel passed Sarah along to Jane, who gave her an occasional day's sewing, and also introduced her to a friend in Nashville who was delighted with the way Sarah could fit the fashionable new styles.

Hunter's Hill was fully planted by the time Andrew reached home on April 1. He had not enjoyed his session in the Congress, but as far as Rachel could make out his feeling was more of bafflement than disappointment.

"I just don't feel comfortable in Philadelphia, Rachel. Those Federalist nabobs, I think they've never stopped regretting they admitted us as a state. The House is so crowded, and there were so many spouters. It's for men of a certain temperament, men who like to work with large groups, with plenty of persuasion and debate and compromise. I'm not good at that kind of thing. I like to work alone. Just between you and me and the front hitching post, I'd still like to master one field . . ."

"Say, the state militia?"

He grinned, "Yes, the militia. I assembled a library of military books in Philadelphia. I'll take this plantation off your hands now, darling. From the look of it we're going to be rich come next November."

"Well, not rich," she said smilingly, "but I do think we'll eat good."

He put his arms about her waist, which was as slim as when he had met her, and held her lightly, studying her face. Despite the wide brim of the straw hat she wore in the fields her skin was tanned almost as deep as the brown of her eyes.

"I like you when you make jokes," he said. "And you're going to have your husband home for good. I'm free of all involvements. No more politics, no more circuit riding, no more stores, no more debts. From now on I'm going to be a domesticated animal."

The house that had been so empty these many months was now crowded with visitors from all over the state; not only the foot soldiers who had received their long-due pay, but also the young officers who had been compensated for the money they had laid out for ammunition and supplies came to express their thanks, and remained for serious discussions of what was needed to revitalize the state troops. Rachel had never traveled circuit with Andrew and had not known the relationship between these men and her husband; now she saw that they looked to him for leadership. Many of them brought their wives. They came as friends, enthusiasts, admirers, their loyalty discernible in every word and gesture. She welcomed them all: there was food and drink and entertainment; when the bedrooms were filled in the main house there was always a guest cabin that could be requisitioned, and for the single men an emergency cot in Andrew's study. Strangers who came for an hour, diffidently, knew by the heartiness of their reception that they could stay as long as they liked. What they did not know was that a considerable part of her emotion was gratitude: for here at last was a circle she need not question or doubt, friends who would be her staunch defenders. To them she was Mrs. Jackson, ma'am, and not *the* Mrs. Jackson.

Andrew had carried home Caesar's *Commentaries* in his saddlebag, reading at night before snuffing the candle. Now his boxes of books arrived: military engineering, books on military discipline, on fortifications. But the studies he seemed to take the greatest pleasure in were the ones on the Revolutionary War: David Ramsay's *The History of the American Revolution,* Joseph Galloway's *A Short History of the War in America.* When she saw him reading in these volumes with such intentness and relish, she found herself perplexed. Basically her husband was a gentle soul. How then could he become so intrigued with the art of organized destruction? War meant people killing each other; she hated every aspect of it. Stumblingly, she tried to tell him of her feelings.

"But my dear, you know I'm not bellicose by nature." There was an injured note in his voice. "I wouldn't take a first step to encourage war with England or Spain. But if you could be in the Congress for a little while and see how close we actually are . . ."

He paced the floor and made a wide gesture with his arm to include every new military volume in the room.

"The good general does not lose men in war; his campaigns are so well planned and provisioned that he crushes the opposing army with a few swift blows. But if the commanding officer is untrained, stupid, commits his men needlessly, they butcher not only their own troops but those of the enemy. Only the strong, the equipped, the prepared can keep out of war or, if dragged in, end it quickly and without great loss. The weak are set upon and attacked by every passing bully."

"You make it sound very logical and humane. But do you mind if I just pray for peace . . . among my other prayers . . . ?" She burst into tears. "Oh, husband, how I wish we had a child!"

He took her in his arms.

"Darling, God knows what to give, what to withhold."

"Somewhere in the back of my mind I had given myself until my thirtieth birthday . . ."

". . . and that's tomorrow, June thirtieth!" He released her, strode to the door and began bellowing for George. "You wait here, and don't go out no matter what commotion you hear in the hall."

She sat in Andrew's work chair, her hands folded in her lap, hearing his muffled orders, the movement of feet. After a considerable amount of hammering he came back to the room, his coat off, a smudge across his forehead and his shirt ripped just inside the elbow.

"Andrew, what in heaven's name have you been doing to yourself?"

"Come along, but close your eyes." He led her through the hall, then released her hand. "All right, you can open them now."

In the center of the formerly empty music room was a shiny black pianoforte, smaller and squarer than any she had seen before, standing on four delicately carved legs in front and two at the rear. She went to it, breathlessly ran her fingers over the keys.

"Oh, Andrew, it's beautiful. We couldn't bring ours from Virginia, it would have filled the entire cabin of the *Adventure*."

She played a few chords. From behind her she heard strange sounds. She whirled about in astonishment.

"Why, it's a flute! You never told me you could play a flute."

He lowered his arms, gazing raptly at the ebony instrument.

"I couldn't. There was a man living at Mrs. Hardy's boardinghouse who used to practice in the parlor every night. He offered to teach me. I thought how pleasant it would be if we could play duets."

She jumped off the little bench and flung her arms impetuously about his neck.

"Andrew Jackson, you are the strangest and most improbable creature God ever created! And I am the luckiest of wives."

She had never seen his joy at being home or working in his own fields so great; nor had she ever seen him more effective. Watching him run the big plantation, she decided all over again that he was really a first-rate farmer: she was a conservative farmer, unwilling to try anything new; but time and again she was amazed to find how free and open Andrew's mind was: if he read of a new tool or an improved seed, he would send away for it; if he learned of a breeder who was raising a higher-quality stock, he would experiment in the hope of improving his own breed. He said that most men farmed by intuition, and that that was good if their intuition was good, but farming could become a science if a man would take the trouble to make himself expert at it.

In the early evenings after supper Rachel ran slow scales for him while he practiced the ascending notes on his flute, then they would try the songs they had learned together, *Within a Mile,* and *As Dawn in the Sunless Retreats.* Afterward they would go into his office where he worked on one of his military books, drawing up his own battle maps as he read *The Art of War* by Chevalier de la Valiere. She sat quietly by, reading in the New Testament or one of the volumes of Virgil which Samuel had given her for her last birthday. They retired late, yet frequently when she was awakened by the first rays of the sun she would find Andrew long since risen and reading by candlelight at the little mosaic table under the window.

"Andrew, you shouldn't get up in the middle of the night. You should sleep until dawn."

"Sleep? It's a pure waste, when you're as happy as I am, and interested in as many things." He paced between the window and the bed. "The trouble with that first store was that it was too small to maintain itself; it couldn't have amounted to much even if the Allison paper hadn't gone bad."

His voice became excited as he stood looking down at her.

". . . what I'd really like to do this fall is set up a trading center on the Stone River. I'd build a landing so the boats could bring us everything we wanted; we could run our own ferry. We wouldn't sell just to single customers, we'd make it a real trading center, the biggest between Philadelphia and New Orleans; we'd ship our crops to the highest bidder, North or South, and in return we'd take from them whatever was needed here in the Cumberland. We'd build our own whisky still and lumber mill . . ."

She did not answer. The more he built the busier he would be . . . and the surer to stay home.

9

Out of her bedroom window she saw coming up the road a carriage with two women in it. When they alighted at the front door she recognized them as Mrs. Somerset Phariss, president of the newly formed Nashville Culture Club, and Miss Daisy Deson, secretary of the club. The group was composed solely of Nashville ladies; she had heard about the organization from Jane, who had commented:

"They blackballed Hilda Hinston because she's not from one of the *old* families. Why do they have to start by being snobbish? Why can't they just grow into it gracefully over the years?"

She took a quick look in her dressing mirror, combed into place the loose ends of her hair, straightened the collar of her dress and went down the stairs.

Mrs. Phariss was the cultural leader of Nashville. Married to the wealthy third son of an English peer, and herself a graduate of one of the best girls' academies in Boston, she was still using her impeccably preserved New England accent to express her opinion of everything she found uncouth or provincial on the frontier. She was a big woman, with an enormous bosom, yet modishly dressed. Her companion, Daisy Deson, was a slim attractive young woman of thirty-five who came from one of the best-liked families in the Cumberland. She had charm and talent, but in the midst of being sweet and delightful could suddenly lash out with a single sentence of such penetrating cruelty that everyone in the room would wither under the blow. She had been losing prospective husbands by this method for a full twenty years.

The two women accepted Rachel's offer of a cold drink with hearty thanks. Mrs. Phariss then went about inspecting the house.

"What an interesting pianoforte. It's one of the new Zumpe's isn't it, made in London? This is a double Belfast damask, you can tell by the precise way the flower figures stand out. But perhaps you wondered why we drove out?"

"I think it was most friendly of you." Rachel's voice said only words. Precisely what did these ladies want of her?

"Mrs. Jackson," said Mrs. Phariss, "it's my feeling that town society should join forces with the country society. By working together we can throw off the primitive aspect of our backwoods life, and have our community's social and cultural affairs resemble the finest of the eastern cities. We would like you to join our Culture Club, and attend our meetings every Tuesday. Each week there will be a different attraction: a literary reading, a musicale, an inspirational talk . . . In our membership, which already totals thirty, we have only the *crème de la crème,* I assure you."

Rachel blanched at the thought of walking into a room filled with thirty strange women.

"But I never go out . . . I'm not at all social."

"Come now, Mrs. Jackson, you're being too modest," said Miss Deson, glancing about the large, elaborately furnished parlor. "We've heard about the dinner parties you've given here at Hunter's Hill for the young militia officers, and Mr. Jackson's political friends from Philadelphia . . ."

"No, no," Rachel interrupted; "people just drop in, that's all. And everybody who comes is welcome."

"Well, I know you will want to join the Culture Club," said Mrs. Phariss firmly as she rose from the settee. "The wife of our congressman has a public obligation."

After the women had bid her adieu, telling her they expected her for tea at Mrs. Peter Huygen's house the following Tuesday, Rachel wandered down the hall and into the study. Sitting at the walnut desk covered with Andrew's books and papers, she could see her father sitting before this same desk in the Virginia home, writing letters, drawing his survey maps. She felt the reassuring presence of both men, and a warm glow crept over her. It was kind of Mrs. Phariss and Miss Deson to invite her to join the Culture Club, even though the invitation had sounded more like an order; it was an act of espousal.

Tuesday morning she rose early and set out the new costume she had prepared to wear to the meeting, her town outfit she had called it the evening before when she had modeled the soft brown twill skirt and pelisse for Andrew. The color suited her eyes and sunburned complexion, and the styling gave her added height. The skirt needed a bit of rehemming, but Sarah would do that when she came by. Rachel wondered if all women were as exacting as she, when dressing for a group of other women; she couldn't remember ever having been so finicky.

Sarah arrived while Rachel was at breakfast and went quickly to the sewing room. When Rachel joined her she saw that the girl's eyes were red, the lids damp and swollen. The new skirt lay across her lap but she had given up all pretense of sewing. Rachel stared for an instant, then put a hand on Sarah's shoulder.

"What's wrong, Sarah? Are you ill?"

"No, I'm not sick, Mrs. Jackson, ma'am, unless it's my heart is sick. I can't sew on your skirt for the tea party today, because I can't let you go to that meetin'. They don't want you, really. All day yesterday I sewed at Mrs. Phariss's house; about ten of the ladies was there, and they was fighting over you something awful."

Rachel took the skirt from Sarah and handed the girl her own linen handkerchief.

"Oh, Mrs. Jackson, you're so good, you came to help me when you didn't even know me, and you saved my baby, and found me work. You take care of Mrs. Krudner and her young ones when they be sick, and she's just a poor widow woman. We love you here in the country, you don't belong with them . . . city folk. They say you are a bad woman."

The blood drained from Rachel's face; her fingertips felt like ice.

"Go on, Sarah."

"That Martha Dinsmore, she said she knew you when your husband sent you home to your mother from Kentucky for misbehavin'; Mrs. Quincy said she heard all about you in Harrodsburg, and the trial where they accused you of wrongdoin' . . . and your divorce . . . and she wouldn't belong to any club that let you be a member."

Rachel was too stiff to sink into the chair beside her, much as she ached to relieve the weight on her legs. For a moment Sarah's voice faded out; then she was listening again, intently to every word.

"A couple of ladies said if that was the case they didn't want to associate with you, and that no divorced lady could be considered respectable, and they was surprised at Mrs. Phariss to suggest you come in. Mrs. Phariss said her husband thinks Mr. Jackson is going to be a very important man in Tennessee, maybe even governor someday, and that in the East where she comes from it's considered important for a club to have the wives of men in politics, and that all your furniture come from Philadelphia, and your house would be elegant for big balls . . . When I left Mrs. Phariss's at four o'clock they was still arguin' and fightin' . . . Oh, Mrs. Jackson, ma'am, you can't go to that meetin' with those ladies who think you're sinful."

She looked up at Rachel pleadingly. Rachel would have liked to comfort her; but what good to explain to this child that she was already married to Mr. Jackson when they came up the Natchez Trace with Hugh McGary? What good to explain that she and Mr. Jackson had been married for two full years before they learned that Lewis Robards had never actually divorced her; and that she couldn't go into Harrodsburg court to defend herself?

Out of the bedroom window she saw George bringing her carriage up the drive. He had spent hours shining and polishing it. She lifted Sarah from the chair.

"You go ahead home, Sarah; we won't do any sewing today. And when you get downstairs, tell George I shan't be needing the carriage."

She took the unfinished skirt, folded it and set it in her big cedar chest. Then she went into her own bedroom and pulled the cord to summon Moll. Perhaps some hot coffee would warm her, dissipate the chill.

10

There had always been the chance that when the moment came Andrew might change his mind and decide to go back to Congress; yet the only politics that interested him during the summer were the troubles of his friend and sponsor, Senator Blount, who had been expelled from the Senate for conspiring with the English to drive the

Spaniards out of Louisiana and Florida. He had even rejected the overtures of Blount's friends and political backers who had arrived from Knoxville to inform him that he was the unanimous choice to finish out the unexpired senatorial term.

But most of the crops had been brought in; his yield of seventy-six bushels of corn to the acre was the top figure in the valley; the market was good and the crops sold for high prices. Andrew became restless. She recognized the symptoms. There was a time to cultivate one's fields and raise the crops and harvest them, and this was the time for home and hearth; but there was also a time to be out in a man's world, fighting for the things one believed in. All this was in his character, and had been from the beginning. When the Blount delegation urged him to reconsider the senatorial job, she saw that he was carrying their offer around in his pocket, taking it out every few moments to gaze anew at its contour and complexion.

"Actually it's not so bad an idea as it seemed at first," he offered tentatively. "I think I might like the Senate better than I did the House. I might be able to arrange a new Indian conference, and get back the land we lost under the Holston Treaty. Besides, if we went up to Philadelphia for the Senate, we could buy the merchandise for our new store . . ."

The fear that she would have to remain alone at Hunter's Hill for another long period turned into near-panic as she thought of facing Philadelphia society.

". . . no, I couldn't . . . I have to stay here to manage . . ."

"We can afford an overseer now that we've had such a good season, Rachel. Why shouldn't you want to go out and see the world?" There was a tinge of impatience in his voice. "You're happy when the world comes to you."

Silently she cried, All who seek us here are on our side, they have committed themselves, they believe in me. But when I must go out to meet strangers I become frightened, I withdraw. No, Andrew, I can't go with you.

He left for the Senate on a Friday, in the midst of a torrential downpour, complaining that it was the wrong day to start a journey; but since he was due in Philadelphia on November 13, he could wait no longer.

The rain continued for several more days; even when it ceased the skies remained leaden and the prospect dismal. She thought what bad luck it was always to be left at the most disagreeable time of the year.

Or was it simply the most disagreeable because she was alone? Surely she would not have given up the magnificent spring and summer days with Andrew when they rode over the fields in the bright sunshine, or sat out on the porch during the warm evenings watching the countryside bathed in the light of the full moon.

No, she would not change that; but the Senate term probably would extend into the beginning of next summer; that could be seven or eight months without Andrew. She wished she could somehow fall asleep and not wake up until the following spring, the way grizzly bears did. Then she remembered that her father would disapprove of this thinking: for Colonel Donelson had believed it a sin to wish away the days of the short life God had granted one.

A few days later Jane came to visit and to read Rachel a portion of Andrew's letter to Robert Hays:

"I beg of you to try to amuse Mrs. Jackson and prevent her from fretting. The situation in which I left her—(Bathed in Tears) fills me with woe. Indeed, it has given me more pain than any event in my life, but I trust She will not remain long in her dolefull mood, but will again be cheerfull. Could I learn that was the case I could be satisfied."

"I'm not doleful," protested Rachel. "I'm just plain miserable."

She went to bed as soon as Jane left, slept long and deeply. When she awoke her mouth and lips were dry, and the heat she felt could not be the warmth of the room on this raw autumn day.

"You all right, Miz Rachel?" asked Moll with a troubled face. "I'll bring some coffee."

As always when she was alone, her despair at remaining childless returned to grip her. Women had children after they were thirty, but these were generally added to a long line. Her line seemed to have ended before it began. Why? Her sisters all had children; her brothers' wives all had children. Even Lewis Robards and his wife Hannah now had a son. She alone had never borne a child, to know its love and companionship.

She closed the curtains around her bed. Her mind went back to the first days Andrew had lived in the Donelson stockade. He had said, "I think the greatest thing a man can have is a family." Of how much was she depriving her husband by remaining childless? Last summer he had told her, "Darling, God knows what to give and what to withhold," but she knew that he was not a religious man, resigned to the dictates of God's will. He had said those words to comfort her. The stores he opened, the politics in which he professed not to be interested, the numerous business affairs in Philadelphia, could these be justifications rather than real desires? If there were half a dozen youngsters at Hunter's Hill could he have torn himself away? This was her failure, that she could not perpetuate his name.

Was there another, more serious failure? Was she a different woman from the one with whom Andrew had fallen in love? From that instant she had heard the news of Lewis Robards' Harrodsburg divorce, and learned that she was hopelessly trapped, her gay, warm, demonstrative nature had undergone a change, been replaced by the figure of the woman on horseback, riding across the fields alone at night to visit a cabin where someone was sick. The inescapable engulfment had turned her inward, banked the fires of her open, cheerful spontaneity, and in her self-consciousness made her search people's eyes to see if they thought her innocent or guilty. Would Andrew have loved her if she had been like this when he had first met her?

She grew thin and pale and, after a time, unwilling to distinguish between the gray darkness of night and the gray darkness of day. Only Jane knew that she was ill, and helped her, giving the Donelsons highly plausible reasons why Rachel was not coming to the Sunday dinners. She did not keep track of how long she lay abed torturing herself with self-reproaches, the victim of twisted and poisoned images, but at length the cycle wore itself out. She awakened one morning to find a warm November sun flooding into her bedroom. She groped at the head of the bed for the bellpull, shocked at the white boniness of her hands. When Moll came running she managed a little smile; Moll stopped short in her tracks, clasped her hands between her deep breasts and exclaimed:

"The Lawd be praised, Miz Rachel's come home again!"

"Moll, I'm actually hungry . . . for the first time since I learned that Mr. Jackson was going to the Senate."

Jane came in while she was sitting in her big iron bathing tub, splashing herself with warm water.

"As Moll says, 'The Lawd be praised.' For a while there I thought you had renounced all the pleasures of the flesh."

Rachel gazed down at herself, shaking her head despairingly.

"Doesn't look as though I have much flesh left."

"Moll will put the weight back on your bones; my only worry was that your spirit was getting a little thin."

"Almost to the point of vanishing, my dear. But I think I'm all right now: a great discovery has just come to me."

"Good, I'll leave you alone with it. Get some sunshine on that peaked little face of yours."

"Oh, Jane, I haven't become ugly?"

"No, darling, you could never be ugly; you have a light inside you that shines out warm and bright, and that light will keep you beautiful all your life."

Moll helped her to dress, selecting a warm woolen cape and a bright red knitted coverlet, and Rachel sat on the front porch with her face in the sun, thinking that she had not been joking with Jane when she had told her sister that she had made a discovery. She had thought that her love for Andrew was as great and full as it was possible for a woman to know. Now she realized that she had been cheating him, hoarding, holding back the love and devotion she was reserving for children.

It would be different now. There were no reservations in her mind, no more locked compartments. How much greater her love would be. Nor could she ever be really lonely or unhappy again; the important thing was to know the full extent of one's love and to give oneself to it. She would be able to face the calendars, accept her responsibility and do her work. She would not only survive, but be happy in that survival. Her father had been right: the days vouchsafed to one were so precious and so few.

She had not thought very much about her looks since they had come to Hunter's Hill; she had had to be out in the fields in the strong wind, in the rain, in the hot biting sun. Nights she had been routed from her sleep by neighbors, had gone out in the snow and slush, sat up until dawn in cramped cabins, returning home in time to see the sun rise and to begin the day's work. Andrew had told her she was beautiful, spoke of the velvet quality of her eyes, the softness of her skin, the richness of her long dark hair, the gracefulness of her figure. Had she become an old woman at thirty? Had she thrown away whatever attractiveness she may have possessed?

That afternoon she dressed in her prettiest winter costume over which she wore a heavily lined capote, and had George drive her into Nashville. A good many houses had been erected, both on the main street and along the river, some of them of brick. In the public square she found the Methodist church, the first real church Nashville had known. From the outside the courthouse looked exactly the same as it had when she and her mother and Samuel had gone in to watch Andrew and John try their cases.

She headed directly for Lardner Clark's store and bought some new hairbrushes, a skin cream, some French cologne and a soft scented face powder. Then, a little guiltily, she picked up a small pot of rouge, wondering if she would ever have the daring to use it. She remembered Andrew telling her of the law that had been passed in Pennsylvania decreeing that a marriage might be annulled if it could be proved that during the courtship the wife had "deceived and misled" her prospective husband by the use of cosmetics. But there was nothing in the law that made it illegal for a married woman to hold her husband through a tiny touch of artifice!

She had George carry her purchases out to the carriage, then drove back to Hunter's Hill as fast as she could get there. She sat down before her dressing mirror, and her face shone back at her from the mirror. My hair will need considerable brushing night and morning, she thought, and some of that liquid soap Jane uses. Next she looked for the beginnings of crow's-feet about her eyes. But her skin was firm. Her mouth was full and red-lipped. Her face was thinner, the cheekbones showed slightly, the plumpness was gone from under her chin.

She felt young again, almost like a young girl waiting for her lover to return.

II

Few visitors came to Hunter's Hill that winter of 1797 while Andrew was away. To the people of the neighborhood who had learned that she was available no matter what the nature of the illness or adversity, she became Aunt Jackson. They borrowed a plow horse, an ax, seed for planting, meat and meal. There was not a cabin for miles around where she had not tended the sick, comforted the afflicted, helped bury the dead. She became a familiar sight riding alone through the fields and woods, bringing medications and a rapidly growing knowledge of the illnesses of the Cumberland. She went where she was called, not asking who it was or what the trouble, passing no judgment and wanting no return.

From Andrew's letters, the senators were doing little but sitting in their big red chairs with their binoculars trained on the war between England and France. He had ordered a handsome brown outfit with a velvet collar and vest, and had had his hair cut short. He was staying in a comfortable hostelry where he had attended a dinner party given by former Senator Aaron Burr. Apart from trying to get a raise for John Overton, who had been appointed inspector of revenue, and a job as marshal for Robert Hays, his only important effort was convincing the Senate that an Indian treaty conference should be held in Tennessee.

By the end of January, when both Houses and President Adams had consented to the treaty, the signs of his restlessness began to multiply: he sent home specifications for the store he wanted her to build, and bought six thousand dollars' worth of stock for their new trading center. She was to inquire among her young nephews to see if there was one who would like to come into business with them. Her sister Catherine's boy, John Hutchings, a mild-mannered lad of twenty-two, was delighted at the prospect.

She was sleeping soundly one soft spring night when she awakened to find Andrew standing above her. He had left Philadelphia on April 12 and accompanied his stock of goods to the Ohio Falls, riding the last hundred and eighty miles in three days and nights. He was completely done in.

"I've been drenched by sleet and rain every day for a week; my first horse went lame, the second took sick and died. Some of the cabins I stopped at were the poorest I've ever seen; once the spaces were so wide between the floor logs that I woke up to find a snake in my bed."

"Serves you right. Stay home with your wife."

She was rewarded with a smile, his first. She put on a robe and went to her dressing mirror to comb her hair. After a moment she raised her eyes higher on the mirror and saw Andrew kneeling behind her, gazing at his own countenance.

"You send me away looking clean and fat and sleek and see how I come back to you: I look twice my thirty years. I could hang my rifle on either cheekbone, my eyes are sunk so deep they're coming out the other end. Good thing you didn't marry me for my beauty."

She turned, cupped his rough bearded face in her hands and replied in a gentle voice, "Oh, but I did. And you never looked better to me than you do this very instant."

He put his arms about her and kissed her on the lips.

"Oh, Andrew," she whispered, holding her cheek against his, "to maintain one's love amongst the difficulties of living . . ."

". . . is like maintaining one's life in the midst of a war."

She had been under the impression that Andrew had quit Philadelphia because the Senate had adjourned; a few days later she learned that the Senate was still very much in session. She came upon him in his study, writing his resignation to Governor Sevier.

"I simply had to get out. When our people see the results of the Indian Conference, and all the lands that will be restored to Tennessee, they won't be angry at my resignation. That's what I went up there for, and I came home when my job was done."

He became a whirlwind of activity: the new store proved successful; with the first cash that came in he built a landing and flatboat to serve as a ferry; he worked with the overseer in the fields from dawn until noon, bought a cotton gin he had seen in Philadelphia, and rode over the countryside explaining to the planters how fast the gin worked, offering to process their cotton on a percentage basis. He hadn't bought his first thoroughbred yet, but every time he crossed into Sumner County he managed to find his way to the Hartsville Course for the races. While in Philadelphia he had bought an extensive law library, and was again riding into Nashville to handle a few of the matters that old clients were urging him to take.

"I'm very glad to see you interested in the law again, Andrew," she commented. "I never could understand why you should want to be through with it."

"A lawyer can never be through with the law."

Her hours with him were sweeter than they had ever been: this was what she had; this was what she would always have. Sometimes, watching him carry on the tasks of half a dozen men, she realized that he was not only her child but a whole brood of children; and that to keep him happy and working would require all of her strength and devotion.

One evening late in the fall John Overton rode out from their Nashville office with Andrew. Both men were deep in talk as they entered the house.

"What is it, Andrew?"

"Well, there's a vacancy coming up for the state Superior Court. The legislature has to elect a new man in December. Mr. Blount, General Robertson, Governor Sevier too, they think my name should be put up."

"I agree with them," she exclaimed heartily. "Tell me more about it."

"The appointment is for six years, pays six hundred a year . . . in cash. It's an independent office, outside of political factions and quarrels. I'd have to ride circuit, same as I did when I was attorney general, but I'd still be able to run the plantation and the store . . ."

Rachel pushed back the hair from her brow, and smiled broadly. This is good, she thought. This is secure. Judges are above . . . gossip; no one would ever dare talk against a judge . . . or his wife . . .

12

She did not wait for the legislature to elect Andrew, but spun, dyed and wove some linen cloth. The prospect of six years without change, and a steady routine, kept her making lighthearted jokes as she draped the black material over Andrew's shoulders.

"Judging by the amount of material it takes to cover you," she teased, "you are going to be a very big judge. Pun me no puns."

"But can we afford all this drapery?" he asked as she swathed the material around him, "on a mere six hundred dollars a year?"

"Do you know what I like best about this job? That I will know what to expect tomorrow. Does that seem monotonous to you?"

"I'll draw you a chart for every day in the year. Undrape me now, lady, I've a heap of things to do."

He always had a heap of things to do; he could not abide inactivity: he had built a distillery; he had bought property at Gallatin and Lebanon and was erecting cabins to serve as branch stores. The cotton gin had arrived from Philadelphia and cotton was coming up the river to their landing on flatboats and over the dirt roads in oblong wagons. After the planters had delivered their cotton and bought their supplies Andrew invited them to Hunter's Hill for a visit, a drink and a meal. She found that if she set the noonday table for twenty, the same number her parents had always set for, she would not miss by more than a couple, one way or the other. These men liked Andrew and had confidence in him; in the same sense that his success in the Congress for the Nickajack Expedition had made him the leader of the young militiamen, so his bringing in of the first cotton gin and his successful marketing of the cotton had made him their business leader.

He was formally elected to the Superior Court on December 20, 1798. John Overton came frequently to discuss the impending cases and to theorize about the law.

"Now John, you know I have no gift for abstract thought. Give me a set of facts between two contestants and I'll reach a fair decision."

"But that decision has got to emerge from a universal principle of law."

"And so it will, John, when you are sitting on the Bench; for my own part I'm still going to try to do what is right between two parties. That's what the law means to me."

John paced the study, idly inspecting a group of books stacked on a side table. "What are these military tomes open for?" he asked. "I thought you were reading Blackstone?"

Rachel too had noticed that Andrew was again studying military science. He had a deep-rooted respect for the law and for the position of a judge, but when she saw him consuming the military books with his eyes sparkling, his body poised tensely over the desk, every particle of him vibrantly alive and excited, she could not help but perceive that this was the field in which he had the greatest hunger.

"Andrew, I do believe you would like to become a professional soldier. I mean, a permanent officer of the Federal Army."

"What army?" he snorted. "We have none! Congress, the President, yes, the voters too, they're all deathly scared of a standing army . . . because the armies in Europe were always used against the people."

"That *is* something to be frightened about, Andrew. Even Mr. Jefferson is against . . ."

"Yes, where governments are ruled by monarchs. We could use our army to protect ourselves. England has never really given us up. She'll be back with her troops one day . . . just as sure as you and I are sitting at this desk together."

Looking down at his maps on which he had drawn troops and cannon and horses, it seemed like a game he was playing; yet the ringing conviction in every taut line of his figure portrayed a passion so strong that it at last convinced her too.

Dr. Henning sent a message that her mother had come down with pneumonia. Rachel went immediately to nurse her, and as soon as she was able to travel Andrew brought her to Hunter's Hill. Rachel thought her mother at seventy-six still beautiful; the lines had deepened about her eyes but there was no trace of white in her hair. Andrew fussed about her, saying, "You're going to stay with us permanently now."

"You're very kind, Andrew. But Colonel Donelson and I built our station together, and when it comes time for me to die I want to die at home and be buried there."

Mrs. Donelson watched her daughter's routine with approval.

"You remind me of myself, Rachel . . ."

". . . and Andrew reminds you of Father?"

"Yes. His activities here can no more keep him content than our plantation in Virginia was ever big enough to hold your father. But it was that same will to do things that made me fall in love with him in the first place . . . and kept me in love with him always."

Rachel leaned forward, her elbows on her knees and her face cupped in her hands.

"I used to pray, 'Dear God, make my husband happy here, so that he will want to stay home with me.'"

"And now?"

"Now I pray, 'Dear God, let him find a task and a mission that will be big enough to justify his talents and his energy.'"

Contrary to her expectation that Andrew's elevation to the Bench would put their private lives beyond petty gossip, she found that his becoming a judge had caused the disparagement to be directed against him as well. For the next ten years they would live their lives in the poisoned atmosphere of rumor: every action, every thought would be colored and influenced by it. How easily it spread, how quickly it was absorbed into the blood stream and became a near-truth! Even the brief happy days of respite, when they were free of attack, proved to be in themselves periods for the storing up and creating of material for the next siege. How unerringly rumor fastened onto the vulnerable facts, and sucked its sustenance from them, twisting and perverting until the character lay dead. Despite the fact that Andrew won praise throughout the state for getting rid of weak and crooked sheriffs, for buttressing the authority of the local officers of the court and instilling a rigid respect for the Bench wherever he sat, there were those in Nashville, many of the women of the Culture Club, who set out to prove that Mrs. Jackson was a backwoodswoman who was at home only among the poor and ignorant newcomers to the area, and that Mr. Jackson did not have the dignity or decorum required of a judge. They kept alive his criticism of George Washington, and in particular used him as a whipping boy in the encomiums when Washington died. They accused him of having represented the militia in the House rather than the whole state of Tennessee; and of having left his work unfinished when he walked out on his job as senator. They resurrected stories of his quarrels, one with Judge McNairy, caused by McNairy's brother carrying unfounded tales, which Andrew and his old friend had patched up; another with Senator Cocke, who claimed Andrew had been illegally appointed by Governor Sevier to replace him in the Senate, and which had almost ended in a duel; a third with Governor Sevier three years before, when the first major general of the Tennessee militia was to be elected, and Andrew had defeated the governor's maneuver to delegate the power of military appointments to men of his own choosing. The two men had called each other some unsavory names but in the end had apologized and resumed their friendship.

Rachel thought that John Overton and Samuel looked at her rather strangely when she urged them not to discuss these tales with Andrew; weeks later she learned that her husband was working equally to suppress the whispering campaign against her. Picking up the first of the talk outside his store one day, he had sent a friend to try to locate the source, and to see if the center of the activity was not in the kitchen of Betsey Harbin. The friend had been obliged to write back:

I can't learn that Betsey has said anything injurious of Mrs. Jackson.

Andrew had then inquired if a certain Mrs. Ball was the talebearer. The investigator had replied:

I pledge you that Mrs. Ball did not either directly or indirectly say anything intending to injure the reputation of Mrs. Jackson.

Rachel was shattered at the thought of Andrew devoting his time and energy to combating kitchen gossip. This matter of the unceasing talk about their past had never been discussed by either of them; it was too painful. Each had borne his own burden and pretended he knew nothing of what was going on. Now she sought her husband in his study.

"Andrew, I just can't let you waste your time and energy trying to fight gossip; it's a Hydra-headed monster. Not all the combined armies in the world can stop women from talking."

"But why should they want to hurt us?"

"The fault has been mine. I did not obey Mrs. Phariss's demand that I join her group. I'm going to become a member of the Culture Club, go to their meetings and give parties for them here . . ."

The declaration took all her strength. She sought shelter in his arms. He sat on a corner of his desk and held her close.

"Rachel, make no mistake about it, if they can conquer you with these methods you will not only be their slave but you will be at the mercy of every last person who stoops to slander to gain his ends. We've committed no crime, we've broken none of the commandments, we've hurt no man or woman, and we've helped a good many. We've got to be strong inside ourselves."

She was startled at the grim tone of his voice.

"All I want, Andrew, is for people to stop talking about us."

"We have staunch and loving friends all over Tennessee. In Knoxville and Jonesboro I have been asked again and again, 'Won't you bring Mrs. Jackson with you the next time you come?' By the Eternal, Rachel, you are going with me!"

It was her first trip with Andrew since they had come up the Natchez Trace. For this journey into society she would need traveling dresses, gowns for tea with the ladies of Knoxville and for visits to the courts; cloaks and shawls, slippers and gloves, hats and extra ivory combs. She would make the clothing, the accessories would be bought at Tatum's or Clark's in Nashville. She took inventory of the bolts of cottons and heavier linens stacked on the sewing-room shelves, then estimated how much lace, velvet and sheer linen batiste she would need for the three-month circuit. Sarah Bentley came every morning to sew. Rachel peered over her shoulder at the measurements; no question about it, striding the furrows of newly planted fields had added two inches to her hips!

She filled her hatboxes and Andrew's two aged trunks, then sent to Jane's for another. Her scented handkerchief was clutched into a tiny ball by the time she and Andrew drove down Hunter's Hill in their carriage.

In Knoxville Governor Sevier gave them an official banquet to which everyone in the government was invited. The Blount family held a magnificent ball; William Blount, the former senator, had died a few months before, but Willie, his half brother, was equally devoted to Andrew. At Hartsville they were the guests of honor for the opening of the racing season. She had not realized how many families she had entertained at Hunter's Hill, but every stop on the circuit was the occasion for a gala party. Her trepidation lessened, her natural buoyancy and gaiety rose as she found herself surrounded by old friends from early morning until she and Andrew could escape to their bed late at night. Lying by her husband's side she would close her eyes and think of the most gratifying picture she would take back to Hunter's Hill: Andrew presiding over the Knoxville court, handsome in his black gown, his tall lean figure towering over the courtroom, his face serious, his eyes somber, treated with vast respect by officers, lawyers and clients alike. She knew that he always had his brace of pistols resting on a little table out of sight but within immediate reach, for there was considerable brawling and turmoil in the courts, particularly in those closest to the newly established Indian frontier.

She was constantly amazed at the growth of Tennessee. When Colonel Donelson had ended his *Adventure* journey and the family had put up their tents on Clover Bottom, his group combined with Colonel Robertson's had made up about two hundred people. Now there were more than a hundred thousand people living in the state, with immigrant families pouring in so fast that in some places on the main road their carriages could not move because of the solid stream of wagons coming west. The wilderness through which she and Andrew had made their way on the last leg of the journey up the Natchez Trace was dotted with thriving settlements, the Trace was a tol'able road and on every side she saw cabins, barns, cultivated fields of corn, cotton and tobacco. Where she and Andrew had slept on the ground, cooking their supper over an open fire, there were now comfortable inns, county seats, courthouses, churches.

There was also a mail service to carry news home to her mother and Jane. From Jane she learned that the reports of the many banquets and balls with which she was being honored had had the effect of silencing her detractors.

13

Hunter's Hill and the stores were running at a profit for the time being.

"It's a good thing," groused Andrew. "I've been working for the county, the territory, the state and the nation for some twelve years now and I've yet to make my first dollar over expenses. You sure can't get rich working for the government."

"You're not supposed to, Andrew. Generals don't get rich, either. But they did name that new district Jackson County, after you."

Their serenity was frequently interrupted by outside events: John Overton lost the girl he was courting to a rival; Stockly, who had cleared some two hundred thousand dollars on gigantic speculations, was indicted along with his father-in-law by North Carolina for land fraud, though Governor Sevier refused to honor the request for extradition; in June their stillhouse burned down, consuming upward of three hundred gallons of whisky and rendering the still useless by melting down the caps and worms. At the end of the summer Mrs. Donelson died and was buried on her own plantation as she had requested. Severn, the sickly member of the family, promptly married Elizabeth Rucker, nineteen years younger than himself.

At the turn of the century practically everyone in Tennessee voted the Republican ticket for the election of Thomas Jefferson and Aaron Burr, both of whom were sympathetic to the western states. When by a technicality Burr received the same number of electoral votes as Jefferson, the election was thrown into the House, where the defeated and disgruntled Federalists, who hated Jefferson as a revolutionist, did everything in their power to subvert the election and put Burr into the presidency. Aaron Burr was loved in Tennessee because he had been one of the leaders in the fight to have the state admitted to the Union, but even the Tennesseans wondered why he did not step up to the dais of the House and make the simple declaration that he had run for the vice-presidency, an act of forthright honesty that would have put an immediate end to the paralyzing controversy.

They made a new friend, John Coffee, a captain in the militia and the only man who, in Rachel's estimation, dwarfed her husband physically. Andrew had the determined strength of the man of will and grit, but Coffee wore his easily; powerfully built, he was gentle as the lamb she had raised at Poplar Grove, and so enormous he filled any room he entered. Andrew asked:

"Jax, I try to tell the truth most of the time but it seems to me that I frequently miss by a fraction. How do you manage to drive the center every shot?"

Coffee's face was round and full; his skin sunburned from his outdoor life as a surveyor and from running his own flatboat containing casks of salt to outlying river settlements.

"I'm not clever enough to distinguish between the various kinds of truth," he replied. "They all look alike to me."

Andrew was again plunged into state politics. Governor John Sevier, having served three consecutive terms, was obliged by the constitution to step aside for one session. Up to this time Tennessee politics had been controlled by the Blounts and Sevier on a friendly basis; now the Blount faction, to which Andrew belonged, decided to form its own party and elect its own governor. At a caucus in Blount's home early in the year they selected Andrew's friend and colleague, Judge Archibald Roane. Andrew resisted the considerable pressure put on him to stand for the Congress again.

"I don't want to leave the state," he confided to Rachel. "Major General Conway is ill; within a year I think our militia is going to need a new commanding officer . . ."

Major General Conway died. The election was posted for a new commanding officer. John Sevier immediately announced his candidacy; just as promptly Andrew was nominated by a group of militiamen. Knowing how passionately he wanted this post, Rachel imagined he would resign from the Bench to fling himself into the campaign. Instead he told her:

"I've always believed that the office should seek the man and not the man the office. I'm not saying a chap hasn't the right to be ambitious for a job, to study and prepare himself for it, yes, and even to let people know that he has mastered the field . . ."

"Then you really believe you have a chance?"

"Yes, a good one."

Among the officers of the militia seventeen cast their votes for Sevier, seventeen cast their votes for Andrew Jackson. According to the state constitution the deciding vote had then to be cast by the newly elected Governor Roane. Former Governor Sevier, chagrined at the tie, sent a message to Andrew requesting that he withdraw. Andrew replied that he would not walk out on the men who had supported him, and that he thought the properly constituted authority should make the decision. Bitterly angry, Sevier announced:

"What has this redheaded upstart ever done that entitles him to be military commander in chief of Tennessee? His whole warlike experience and service may be summed up in leading fifteen or twenty men on the trail of about a dozen Indians. He has the reputation of a fighting man, his friends say. Fighting whom?"

Governor Roane cast the deciding vote for Andrew. He was jubilant. Rachel said:

"I thought you were a small boy chasing rainbows."

Andrew laughed. "I'll not let anybody call me general until I win some battles. Nevertheless, the whole discipline of the militia has deteriorated during Conway's illness, and my first task is to rebuild the fighting spirit. The state of Tennessee is going to know they've got a new commanding officer. I'll never rest until it is a first-class fighting force."

She felt his eagerness to begin; yet how could it be possible for a man to sit in the Superior Court and at the same time be a major general of the militia?

For his first general muster in Nashville in May, Andrew had a uniform made, the first he had ever owned. The collar was high, coming up just under his ears, with a long double-breasted coat, a row of buttons down either side, gold-braid epaulets and a broad brightly colored sash.

He tried to persuade Rachel to come with him to the muster, which was the grand event of the year for Nashville. All officers were dressed in their gayest trappings, the soldiers in fringed hunting shirts; the best marksmen in the state would be present for the shooting match. In many aspects the muster was actually a county fair, ringed by peddlers, farmers with horses, cows and pigs to trade, housewives selling their prize preserved fruits, cake men selling ginger cakes, the potters and ironmongers displaying their finest handiwork. It was Andrew's duty to supervise the inspection of the foot soldiers, making sure every commissioned officer had side arms, that every private was provided with either a musket, a cartouche box with nine charges of powder and ball, or a rifle, powder horn, shot pouch, spare flint, one picker and worm. With the horse troop he had to ascertain that every soldier had a good mount at least fourteen hands high, with a serviceable saddle, bridle, pistol, sword and cap, shoe boots, spurs, cartouche box and cartridges. The men received no pay and provided their own horses, uniforms, guns and ammunition, a situation which Andrew was determined to remedy as soon as he could wangle funds out of the state legislature.

He had ridden his fastest horse to the muster, but the bad news reached Hunter's Hill ahead of the returning general. Captain John Coffee brought it, his usually amiable face set in grim lines as he explained:

"The reason I'm here is I'm afraid Mr. Jackson will do something rash. You must calm him. It seems there was a young fellow at the muster, Charles Dickinson, a friend of Sevier's. They say he's the most brilliant young lawyer in Nashville. Trained by John Marshall. Dickinson was standing with a group of friends when the general rode onto the parade ground. Someone asked:

" 'What great military exploit has Mr. Jackson performed that entitles him to such exalted rank and gorgeous trappings?'

"Dickinson had been drinking; he replied in a voice loud enough for everyone to hear:

" 'Why, gentlemen, he has done a most daring exploit. He has captured another man's wife!' "

Rachel placed her weight against the mantel, trembling.

"Dickinson has a reputation as the best shot in the Cumberland Valley, ma'am," continued Coffee. "Andrew's a great commanding officer, but I can outshoot him ten to one. Don't let him challenge Dickinson to a duel; if there's going to be shooting, I want to be at the other end."

She thanked Jax for his offer to fight in her behalf, then ran up to her room and threw herself face down across the bed. She wanted sufficient time to quiet her pounding heart before she had to cope with her husband.

It was unbelievable to her that a gentleman could make such a coarse joke because Andrew had defeated his friend in an election. He had been drinking, Coffee said, and that was some mitigation; but how close to the top of his mind their story must have been if it could spring to his lips so spontaneously.

She thought, Andrew and I have been married a full ten years now. Would they never forget? Charles Dickinson's remark would be repeated all over Tennessee, in every home and shop and tavern . . . her name the loose thread in the idle talk.

Suddenly she sat upright in the center of the bed, for Andrew was winding his way up Hunter's Hill. Her head cleared: bad as Dickinson's remark had been, it had merely intimated that Andrew had won her away from her husband. She would have to make Andrew accept this and allow the affair to pass over. Not that he would forget; but he must not provide the community with further fuel to keep alive their bright fires of scandal.

Reluctantly, Andrew agreed.

14

She sat at the walnut desk with her ledger spread out before her. Andrew came quietly behind her, leaned over and kissed the top of her head.

"A lucky thing your father taught you to figure in that arithmetic book: Hunter's Hill is now supporting all our other activities."

She turned about at the seriousness in his voice, ill concealed under the banter.

"I'm having problems at the store," he confided. "John Hutchings is fine as a clerk, but I've been involved in so many things that the management has fallen on his shoulders . . . and he's just too green."

He also was having considerable trouble with Thomas Watson, whom he had taken in to handle his huge cotton operation, and from whom he had been unable to get any accounting.

The unfortunate incident at the master muster proved to be the start of a series of disturbances. What had appeared to be a friendly break with former Governor Sevier now began to look like a political fight to the finish. After several years in which Andrew's opinions as a judge had been accepted with confidence, two new decisions brought condemnation upon his head. The first was one in which he was sitting with the two other judges of the circuit as a court of appeal involving a case which he himself had tried under Judge McNairy while he was attorney general. Now, as an appeal judge, he reversed himself; and was charged with being inconsistent, changeable, unreliable.

"I can't see that I had much choice," he expostulated to Rachel as they sat over their supper table scanning the criticism in the Knoxville newspapers. "I could have agreed with my reasoning of ten years ago and been called consistent, or decided according to what I thought was legal and proper for today."

The second outburst followed shortly after. Finding that a petitioner was one with whom he had been on unfriendly terms, Andrew summoned the petitioner's lawyer and urged him to ask for a postponement so that the case could be brought before another judge. He was immediately accused of being unable to decide a case on its legal merits. The probability that these attacks were politically inspired was of little comfort to her.

John Sevier, now qualified to run again for the governorship, announced his candidacy. Governor Roane announced his candidacy also. Sevier and his political followers let loose a thunderous blast, accusing Roane, Jackson and their supporters of double-dealing. Andrew maintained that Sevier was no longer fit to be governor.

"I can prove that he was deeply involved in that Glasgow land-fraud case. I'm going to expose him by showing how they changed the sale price on the warrants and falsified the dates. Why, they've stolen almost a sixth of the state of Tennessee."

Rachel was shocked: wasn't this the same affair in which Stockly had been involved several years before?

"Andrew, won't people accuse you of doing it for political purposes, to defeat Sevier in the election? Can't Governor Roane be re-elected without this exposure?"

"No. Sevier is too good an actor. He'll stump the state with that saber rattling at his side and relive the thirty battles he won during the War for Independence."

And he'll win, Rachel thought. His group will come into power again, and Andrew's group will go out. If he wants to stay on the Bench, they'll defeat him.

But she found herself unprepared for the clamor caused by Andrew's accusing letter in the Tennessee *Gazette* of July 27, 1803. Everyone in the state read it or had it read to him; and they discussed with equal avidity Sevier's defense in the *Gazette* of August 8. Andrew left Hunter's Hill to hold court in Jonesboro, took ill on the way and was so racked by diarrhea he was hardly able to remain on his horse. He had no sooner reached the inn than a mob of Sevierites threatened to tar and feather him. Andrew stood with both pistols cocked. The crowd saw "Shoot!" in his eyes; it melted away.

The contest was no longer between two governors; people now asked, "Who are you siding with, Sevier or Jackson?" A few weeks later they elected Sevier by a full one-third majority.

"Who do you suppose had the worst time," Rachel asked Jane, "the Christians who were in the Coliseum being devoured by lions, or their sympathizers in the stands, watching them be devoured?"

"The sympathizers," replied Jane; "they had to wake up the next morning and remember what they had seen the day before."

I'm in an even worse position, thought Rachel; I feel as if I were in the catacombs . . . waiting my turn . . .

On Saturday, October 1, 1803, after the adjournment of his court, Andrew made his way toward the front door of the Knoxville courthouse. In the sunshine he saw John Sevier standing on the top step with a crowd below him. Before he could turn away he heard Sevier say:

"Judge Jackson is an abandoned rascal, a man whom the people have made a judge and thereby promoted to the unmerited status of a gentleman." He shook his cavalry saber in its scabbard, then continued, "I won independence for this state, I drove out the Indians, I formed your first government . . ."

Andrew strode to the top of the steps; he stood face to face with the fifty-eight-year-old Sevier.

"I do not contest your past services to the state of Tennessee, Governor. But by the same token I believe that I have performed public services too, and most of them have met with the approval of my fellow citizens."

"Services?" cried Sevier in a thunderous voice which carried to the other end of the public square. "I know of no great service you have rendered to the country except taking a trip to Natchez with another man's wife!"

Murder sprang into Andrew's eyes.

"Great God! Do you mention *her* sacred name?"

Sevier drew his sword. Andrew swung his heavy walking stick. Shots were fired in the crowd. A bystander was hurt. Friends intervened, carrying Andrew off in one direction and Sevier in another.

Andrew instantly challenged Sevier to a duel.

The remark made by Charles Dickinson had been uttered by an irresponsible young man who had been drinking and who later had denied having made it. But this charge by Governor Sevier in a public square could never be denied or retracted. The passage of the years would not matter now; the length or extent of Andrew's service, or her own years of hard work, simple living, of neighborly kindliness would never wash away the sin of having lived a troubled youth.

For Governor Sevier had accused them before the world of wanton, deliberate adultery . . . John Sevier was the best-known and most influential man in Tennessee; as governor of the state he was its first citizen. If it were acceptable for him to heap calumny upon her character, what reason would there be for anyone, ever, to keep silent on the subject of Rachel and Andrew Jackson? Her personal life had become a political weapon.

When the ache had passed into a pulsating numbness her thoughts returned to Knoxville and to Andrew. The illegality of dueling in Tennessee would not stop him; the two men would meet across the border of the Indian country. The governor of the state, and a member of the Superior Court, dueling on the frontier; what further scandal this would create!

Travelers and friends came in from Knoxville bringing news. Sevier had ignored Andrew's first challenges, confiding to his friend that his advanced years and large family should make it unnecessary for him to satisfy Jackson's demand. When Andrew's friends urged him to drop the challenge out of respect for his judicial robes he offered to resign immediately. When Sevier failed to answer his challenge, he placed an advertisement in the *Gazette*.

To all who shall see these presents Greeting. Know ye that I Andrew Jackson, do pronounce, publish, and declare to the world, that his excellency John Sevier, Captain General, and commander in chief of the land and naval forces of the state of Tennessee, is a base coward and poltroon. He will basely insult but has not courage to repair.

ANDREW JACKSON

Andrew left with his seconds for Southwest Point on the Cherokee boundary. For five days he awaited Sevier's arrival . . . and for five days Rachel plodded through her tasks, dreading the news, yet unable to believe that the two men would seriously injure each other. Surely they had been friends too long to fire for a kill? Many duels were fought but few had serious consequences, at worst a leg wound; adversaries frequently fired into the air, their pent-up anger spent with the bullet.

At last word came: just as Andrew was leaving Southwest Point, Sevier rode up with his party. In the melee Andrew drew his pistols and so did Sevier, advancing on each other with epithets. Members of both parties made overtures, the principals damned each other still once again, but put up their arms.

It was the end of the duel. But not of the strife.

On November 5, Governor Sevier pushed two bills through the legislature, the first of which split the Tennessee militia into two districts; the other provided for a second major general, to have equal status with General Jackson. The next morning Governor Sevier appointed former Senator William Cocke head of the eastern division of the militia, and dispatched him to Natchez with five hundred militiamen to make sure that Spain did not interfere with the transfer of the Louisiana Purchase to the United States. After rigorously training his troops and bringing them to peak form, Major General Jackson had been left twiddling his thumbs at home, his men of the western division deprived of the mission for which they had prepared.

When Rachel walked into his study she found Andrew slumped in his chair, his arms dangling lifelessly to the floor, his face ashen and his usually clear, determined eyes lost in some obscure mist. She had seen him through all manner of complication, adversity and despair, but she had never seen him so completely beaten. What disturbed her most was not that there were no words on his lips, but actually that there were no words being formulated anywhere in his brain. The final victory had been Sevier's; the ultimate defeat Andrew's . . . and hers.

15

On New Year's Day of 1804 they sat alone in their big room before a banked fire. It took no complicated profit-and-loss system or surrounding pile of ledgers for them to know where they stood after their years at Hunter's Hill. They had extended considerable credit at their stores, but a drive to collect the money owed them had been fruitless. The furs and pelts, salt, wheat, tobacco and other merchandise he took in exchange in the stores had been shipped out blind, for he could no longer get prices quoted in advance, and when the merchandise reached the port of New Orleans, or Philadelphia, it was sold for whatever it could bring. Most of the cotton crop in the Cumberland Valley had failed; there were now twenty cotton gins operating in the countryside, and Andrew was getting little outside cotton for processing or sale. In addition he had been obliged to bring suit against his former partner, Thomas Watson. His personal notes were piling up in New

Orleans and Philadelphia, with the interest charges mounting; and he had the immediate obligation of paying back one thousand dollars in cash which had been loaned to him in Pittsburgh.

"There's no help for it, Rachel, I simply must resign the judgeship and devote my full time to getting us straightened out financially. Money, money, money! The deeper we get into business, the larger our stocks and transactions and sales, the worse off we become."

"Ah, the agonies of getting rich," she replied in a light tone; but he was not to be diverted.

Though he still held the title of major general, his command had virtually disappeared. Many of the officers were blaming him for being robbed of their expedition. It also was apparent that he had lost considerable prestige as the result of the personal feuds. The fact that he had quarreled only after his wife had been publicly slandered was lost in the ensuing embroilment.

Because of the investigation his charges against Sevier had started, the title to a considerable portion of their own lands, particularly those in the Indian country, had fallen under a shadow. All of their lands around Nashville were worth more than when he had bought them, and he should have been able to take a sufficient profit to quiet his most demanding creditors; but no one had any cash with which to buy and all he could get were other people's personal notes.

"It looks almost hopeless," he confessed in complete dejection. "We've got to get a fresh start."

She was shocked to learn a few weeks later that his "fresh start" might include shaking the dust of Tennessee from his boots.

"I think we've had enough of the Cumberland Valley, Rachel."

"But where would we go?"

"Now that Louisiana has been turned over to us, President Jefferson has to appoint a governor. Our congressmen in Washington are on my side; they think I have the proper qualifications: the legal training to help write and enforce the laws, the military experience to set up a militia. It's a great opportunity. Spain is angry at the transfer and she'll fight if she can. England is still searching our ships and impressing seamen; if war comes she will bring her troops in through Louisiana just as sure as she will go through the northern lakes . . ."

What an odd solution to our problems, she thought; Thomas Green urged us to stay right there in Natchez in the first place. How much turbulence might have been avoided; how pleasant life might have been.

". . . as governor, everything would be provided: a home, servants, carriages, military staff, and the salary would be clear cash." He came to her and took her in his arms; his voice was low and caressing. ". . . I remember how much you loved those beautiful homes in Natchez. We'd meet new people, make new friends. There'll be plenty of opportunity for a military man down there; we'll make Sevier eat his words about us."

It was not until this moment that she saw clearly why he wanted to go: to leave behind them the incessant talk, the insults to their love and marriage. It was not that he felt defeated, nor that he lacked the stamina to fight back; he had all these requisites and more. He was simply removing his wife from the battlefield.

She took his head between her hands and pressed her lips to his; she felt the tense bony strength of him.

"You'll be the First Lady of the territory," he murmured. "Remember what I told you at Poplar Grove? We've got to get to the top, then no one will be able to climb up high enough to attack us."

There was no word from Washington about the appointment during February. A load of iron which he had ordered from Pittsburgh and which was supposed to constitute half a cargo was sent on alone; when it arrived in Nashville the boatman demanded three hundred and seventy-five dollars for freightage in cash. Andrew tried for days to collect enough to release the cargo, but could not gather anything beyond the little pile of English, Spanish and American coins which John Coffee dumped onto their dining board, obviously his lifetime savings, and the few dollars that John Overton found himself able to contribute.

"Think of it, Rachel: we own a plantation worth ten thousand dollars. We have thousands of dollars' worth of merchandise in the stores, and other thousands already shipped north and south. The total value of all the lands in our name must be a hundred thousand dollars . . . yet after trying desperately for a full week to find three hundred and seventy-five dollars in cash, I cannot raise that insignificant sum."

"Can't you make a quick sale of the iron and use part of the payment for the freight?"

"I've already tried. The only 'ready' available is the two hundred dollars due me in judge's salary."

Toward the end of February, in an effort to recoup their losses by one bold stroke he instructed John Coffee to make the trip north to the Illinoi where a fabulous salt lick had been discovered, and to offer fifteen thousand dollars, if necessary as high as thirty thousand, for it . . . in their personal notes.

Rachel was staggered by the move, even though Jax accepted the instructions without question; how could Andrew be planning to spend another fifteen to thirty thousand dollars when he couldn't raise three hundred and seventy-five dollars to cover a freight charge?

During the next weeks her amazement grew. By that time Andrew had gone to Washington City en route to Philadelphia. The Secretary of War received him in a friendly spirit, confiding to him that the War Department would need two boats built within the next six weeks, to be used in the transportation of troops down the Mississippi. The Secretary also wanted chains for the ferryboats across the Tennessee River; could Andrew provide them?

John Coffee brought Andrew's letter up to Hunter's Hill where Rachel read it a dozen times, shaking her head in disbelief.

"A fabulous man, my husband. The War Department wants boats? He'll build them. They want chains? He'll make them. I'm sure he hasn't ten dollars in his pocket, nor are there more than ten dollars in our strongbox. That's either magnificent folly or magnificent wisdom. Which do you think, Jax?"

"Must be wisdom, Mrs. Jackson," Coffee replied with a slow smile, "because when Mr. Jackson orders me to repair the boat that was damaged at the mouth of the Spring Branch, and have a second one ready in six weeks, he knows I'm going to have them ready. When things got to be done, money's no help, it only gets in your way."

"Surely if Andrew provides these boats, the Secretary of War will let him fill them with his own troops and command the expedition?"

"Couldn't say, Mrs. Jackson; it seems likely."

She did not know when Andrew received the news, but one of the Philadelphia papers brought her the account of President Jefferson's appointment of William C. C. Claiborne as governor of Louisiana. Andrew's scheme of flight, of creating a new life for them, the rebuilding of his pride and prestige, had gone the way of most political appointments. They would have to stay home now and cope with their difficulties as best they could.

I HAD been living in Beverly Hills for some eight years, when I was asked by *Holiday* if I would like to write an article about my distinctive and highly publicized community. Beverly Hills is a town of which one can easily grow fond. It is tranquil, almost pastoral, self-contained, a tree-lined park. For me as a writer it was a particularly good location, because it was the only place I knew in which I could achieve the controlled monotony necessary for the frequent hundred-day stretches of writing that is involved in the setting down of a long and complex book.

We knew our neighbors; when we went to a dinner party, we rarely had to ride more than a half dozen blocks. The Beverly Hills police were no longer asking to see my identification during my evening walks. All of this spelled security for me, in a small village which I found to be amusing and filled with colorful characters.

This was not to be a serious study, for Beverly Hills is not a serious town: except when the entertainment industry goes into a decline, and the storage companies back their empty vans up to two and three houses on each block. The writing was to center around the countless anecdotes and personality yarns that we'd been swapping over the dinner tables for a number of years.

Its repercussions were not all as pleasant. I had unwittingly managed to offend some of my neighbors. Beverly Hills is, to this very day, divided by an ancient and anachronistic set of railroad tracks. The people who live south of the tracks, in the less expensive areas, felt that I had done them an injustice by concentrating my materials north, in the more colorful section of the movie and radio stars. I felt a coolness when I went to PTA meetings at the high school, and for the rest of the school year my five-foot, ninety pound daughter was relentlessly ragged by the six-foot football players whom I had said were too gently reared to win against their rougher neighbors. The football team won only one game that year, but on the night of their victory they came to our house and burned into our front lawn the words "WE WON!" with sulphate ammonia.

About six months after I had written *Beverly Hills,* the editors asked if I would do an article about the Pacific Northwest. I replied that I knew nothing about the Pacific Northwest and added,

"There are three or four first-rate writers up there." I named the names. The editors at *Holiday* were profoundly hurt. It had never occurred to me that editors can be as unhappy about rejections as writers can be.

The Beverly Hills article was selected for a book called *Best Articles of 1953*. As Ernest Hemingway commented to me in Key West in 1935, "What you lose in Boston, you win in Detroit."

BEVERLY HILLS

BEVERLY HILLS is the place where the man with the three-day beard standing next to you at the delicatessen counter buying salami is Robert Taylor; it's the place where the rear half of the horse on the stage of the grammar school during a Cub Scout show is Keenan Wynn; it is also the town where the bylaws of the Cub Scouts stipulate that no food may be served to the boys by butlers; where the daughter of the M-G-M attorney returned from her first day of school crying to her parents, "I'm underprivileged: the other kids in my class have four parents and I only have two;" where the eight-year-old member of a car pool, missing every Thursday morning for a number of months, finally confessed that she had been going to the family psychiatrist; where parents of ambitious boys drive them through the streets in the family cars while the youngsters heave newspapers onto the front lawns; where in my block, the seven-hundreds on Maple Drive, there are by actual count twenty swimming pools out of twenty-four houses; where at the May Day dances at the Hawthorne Grammar School, a billion dollars worth of talent sits on folding chairs in the street watching their young hopefuls with glowing pride: James Stewart, Loretta Young, Ingrid Bergman (when she was here), Gene Kelly, Van Johnson, Robert Young, Dorothy Lamour, Helen Hayes, Joanne Dru and a hundred others. Movie parents are hot parents.

Beverly Hills is the community of thirty thousand people and thirty thousand trees, one for every man, woman and child in the town and, according to the latest pound statistics, ten for every dog: perhaps accounting for the benign fact that no postman has ever been bitten in Beverly Hills.

It is the town where police cars stop all people walking the streets after ten o'clock at night, and with the utmost courtesy ask if they are residents or just going somewhere. If they can't properly identify themselves, the strangers are cordially, without fuss or raised voice, given a lift to the nearest bus. Neckers have a difficult time of it: they have no sooner parked their car in front of the girl's house than a police car draws alongside. Not a word is said, nor do the officers turn their light on the parked car; they simply sit there in discouraging silence. It was truly a peaceful community until some few gangsters fell in love with it and moved in; my next door neighbor, who saved Tony Carnera's life after he was shot in Beverly Hills, and who was summoned too late to save Bugsy Seigel, said to me the morning after:

"Every doctor should be a specialist in those diseases endemic to his community, so I am going back to Johns Hopkins to take a course in gunshot surgery."

It is a town of frequent quick-rich and quicker-poor. People get movie contracts for three thousand dollars a week, buy enormous homes, put in a swimming pool, throw a party for a hundred—and six months later, their options not having been picked up, are gone, the houses and swimming pools of necessity sold for what they will bring.

It is a town of amazing cultural contrasts. In one house you have a newly arrived movie queen who can hardly read the captions under pictures in the newspapers, while immediately next door you will find Eddie Robinson's great art gallery or Jean Negulesco's collection of contemporary French paintings. It is a town literally bisected by railroad tracks: houses on the south side, sometimes as well-built as those on the north, selling for only half as much. A friend who was shopping for a house and was puzzled by this phenomenon asked a passing milkman why this was so.

"Well, lady, I'll tell you, on this side of the tracks live the peasants, on that other side live the pheasants."

Physically, Beverly Hills is one of the most beautiful residential spots in the world. It is a community separate unto itself, a special, privileged island located in the midst of the vast and growing sea of Los Angeles, but having nothing to do with the Los Angeles school system, police or fire departments, culture, mores or government. It is one of the richest per capita communities in the country, families averaging ten thousand dollars per year of fluid spending, yet little of the wealth is industrial money, most of it being earned in the entertainment field and from the attendant professional services such as doctoring, lawyering, and agenting. Its high school has a larger campus than most eastern colleges, and just to indicate how them as has, gets, Beverly Hills High has a producing oil well on its campus which nets the school fifteen hundred dollars a month!

It is a community in which it is impossible to escape the movie-radio-television influence: George Burns and Gracie Allen live across the street from me, and a dozen big Tanner buses draw up each day, disgorging their passengers to take pictures, while hundreds of private cars prowl slowly up and down the street looking for Gracie's house. Not once in the seven years that I have lived here has one tourist turned around to gaze idly at my house. It's not that my feelings are hurt (much) but only that I am afraid this may be an authentic sign of the low estate to which American letters has fallen in this age of micro-airwaves.

Beverly Hills is only twenty-eight years old, still in the flush of its youth. The old-timers who planned and laid out the town are today prosperous and unhappy, dreaming nostalgically of the good old days before the advent of Saks-Fifth Avenue, W. & J. Sloane, I. Magnin. The man who first established the community refused to sell a lot to a merchant who wanted to build a market, saying, "This is going to be a residential district; when the people want to shop let them go somewhere else." Today its shopping district, centering on Wilshire Boulevard, is one of the most sophisticated west of Fifth Avenue. A *fait accompli,* with only a few building lots left in the five-and-a-quarter square mile area, Beverly Hills has turned out to be the most fabulously successful real estate venture in America.

To the early industrialists and merchant princes such as J. W. Robinson, Doheny, Hancock, it was sanctuary, a place remote from the noise and hustle of the work day; to the early movie stars such as Mary Pickford, Douglas Fairbanks, Harold Lloyd, Pauline Frederick, Gloria Swanson, Charles Ray, it was glamour, the set for a Rolls-Royce and a swimming pool; to the butcher and baker it was the ground floor, and to the real estate broker it was gold for the taking. To give an idea of how rich the "take" was: purchased originally as a single Spanish ranch in 1906 for $670,000 by the newly formed Rodeo Land and Water Company, it has brought in over $200,000,000 to its original investors. Today one of the best known and most highly publicized communities in the world, it has accomplished this remarkable feat in less than thirty years, truly a record even for Southern California where, it is reputed, men driving home at night pass twelve-story office buildings which had not even been started that morning when they were on their way to work.

On a sweltering August day in 1769 the Spanish governor of the Californias, Don Gaspar de Portola, made his way with a party of soldiers up a narrow Indian trail past some boiling brea pits and over a fertile plain, camping at dusk at the Spring of the Alders, at the base of a gentle roll of hills. The Indian trail was to become Wilshire Boulevard, the boiling pits with their Pleistocene animal skeletons, the La Brea Tar Pits, and the Spring of the Alders, Beverly Hills. Two years later a group of colonists, priests and soldiers recruited largely in Sonora, Mexico, came north to found the pueblo of Los Angeles. Among them were Louis Quintaro, a tailor, his wife, their fifteen-year-old daughter Sebastiana and their daughter's soldier-husband, Eugenio Valdez. Shortly thereafter a six-year-old boy by the name of Vicente Villa reached the Los Angeles pueblo over the Anza trail of the Colorado desert. These four were the progenitors of Beverly Hills: for young Vicente Villa grew up to marry the daughter of Eugenio and Sebastiana Valdez, Maria Rita Valdez. Sergeant Villa and his Maria were given the *Rancho Rodeo de las Aguas,* which now approximates the community of Beverly Hills, as a pension when he was invalided out of the army.

The Valdezes built two small houses and tried to cultivate a garden, but soon found that their so-called Rancho of the Gathering of the Waters was a euphemism: for Beverly Hills was geographically similar to the Arizona desert, and the problem of water would harass their descendants unto the 1952 generation. The adobe house in which Maria Rita bore and raised eleven children was at what is now Sunset Boulevard and Alpine Drive where, could she have persevered long enough, she would have found herself hemmed in by such charming neighbors as Ginger Rogers, Gloria Swanson, Greto Garbo, Elsie Janis, and Nelson Eddy.

The first census ever taken in Los Angeles, in 1836, revealed a mere twenty-nine people living on the Rancho of the Gathering of the Waters. In 1852 a band of Indians opened fire on Maria Rita's ranch house. A nine-year-old boy slipped out of the house, crawled along the shallow ditch for half a mile, and made his way to the nearest settlement. A group of ranchers was rounded up, came thundering to the *Rancho* on horseback, drove the redskins northward to a walnut grove on which now stands the Beverly Hills Women's Club, and shot and buried the Indians. Half the wealth of the Beverly Hills movie colony has been earned from making this western over and over again in the ring of studios which surround the town.

California was three years old as a state in 1854 when two Americans by the name of Benjamin D. Wilson, one of the original founders of San Gabriel Valley, and Henry Hancock, future oil man, bought the whole of what is now Beverly Hills for five hundred dollars cash and notes for another five hundred dollars. They did so because of the large swamp lands formed by the overflow waters of Coldwater and Benedict Canyons: wild geese flew over the reed grass and lupin and poppies bloomed luxuriantly. Assuming that they had more than enough water, Wilson and Hancock planted two thousand acres in wheat, took out one good crop, and then found they were in the midst of a desert, with parched plains where there had been swamps. They gave up ranching.

In 1865 the Pioneer Oil Company began drilling oil wells, but went broke; in the late sixties Basque sheepherders brought in their flocks, but even the undemanding sheep couldn't find enough to eat in what is now a land of milk and honey. In 1869 a German wool dealer named Preuss bought the entire Rancho for a little over ten thousand dollars, took in a partner and began subdividing the property into seventy-five-acre farm lots, with town lots to be sold for ten dollars. A German colony was founded, the little township was named Santa Maria, but died a quick death, and the land was bought up by Hammel and Denker, who used it as a lima bean ranch.

By the 1880s a steam train began running between Los Angeles and Santa Monica, a small town on the Pacific Ocean, six miles away. A railroad station was now built in the midst of the lima bean fields and the new invisible sub-division was named Morocco. Alas, Morocco didn't last long enough to get its title down to the county recorder, but the choosing of the name was an indication of the kind of thinking which almost ruined Beverly Hills a half century later: the conception that the climate was tropical and that the only way to keep out the fierce and unrelenting sun was to build three-foot-thick cement Spanish and Moroccan houses, so dark inside you couldn't see your hand in front of your face. Today these old Spanish houses are pink white-elephants, sold only to those adventurous newcomers who are willing to knock out the heavy walls and let the semi-tropical California sunshine stream through the rooms.

Present day Beverly, as it is familiarly known, had its accouchement on November 24, 1906, when the Hammel and Denker bean ranch was bought by the Rodeo Land and Water Company, a newly-formed corporation headed by such men as Burton E. Green and Henry E. Huntington. It was named Beverly Hills after Mr. Green's Beverly Farms in Massachusetts. One of the founders of the city, who had been an oil prospector, said, "I've been looking at the rear end of a jackass long enough; I want to look at something pretty, so let's plant thousands of trees."

A landscape architect, Wilbur Cook, from New York, laid out one of the most beautiful cities of modern times, with all the streets between Santa Monica Boulevard and Sunset Boulevard curving in graceful arcs, each street lined with its own special tree: maple, palm, elm, magnolia, acacia, eucalyptus, oak, all houses to face east or west, with a series of alleys between in which garbage and waste was to be collected, packages delivered. The first private home was built in November of 1907, along with the four or five company houses with which to impress tourists who saw the big advertisements in the Los Angeles *Evening Express*. Residential lots in the most exclusive area south of Sunset were priced at one thousand dollars or eight hundred dollars if one paid cash and improved the lot within six months.

The life of the Beverly Hills pioneer was not quite as luxurious as that of his present-day descendant, for if you wanted to have your laundry done you were obliged to carry it to the Beverly Hills Pacific Electric station and give it to Fatty Powell, the obliging motorman of what was known as Westgate Dinky; Powell would take the soiled linen to the check room at Fifth and Hill in Los Angeles where a laundry service would return it to him a few days later, and he would deposit it on the front platform of his car.

The early years were difficult too because the winter winds came over the north canyons with tremendous force, blowing dust and tumbleweed across the expanse of empty lots. Along with the noise of the night winds in the canyons there was the howling of the coyotes in the hills; as late as 1910 the name of Beverly Hills was about to share the fate of Morocco and Santa Maria.

The community was saved by a daring move on the part of its founders: they built a resort hotel on Sunset Boulevard at the foot of the mountains. The Beverly Hills Hotel, under the management of Mrs. Margaret Anderson, was at once successful, attracting many wealthy eastern tourists who found that they liked the hot, dry climate in the shelter of the hotel, and began buying property and building large homes, such as the mansion of King Gillette, the razor man, immediately across from the hotel.

The growth was slow, a 1920 census showing a scanty population of six hundred seventy-two, an increase of only six hundred forty-three people since the census of 1836. It was not until Douglas Fairbanks and Mary Pickford bought a magnificent knoll on Summit Drive in April of 1919 that the future of Beverly Hills was assured: for Miss Pickford and Mr. Fairbanks were the undisputed leaders of the motion picture industry. Doug Fairbanks wanted to build a wall around the entire town and make it a kind of Italian hill village, but he was persuaded to content himself with a wall around his own estate. Very quickly others in the motion picture industry acquired acreage in the neighborhood and built baronial estates: Harold Lloyd, Carl Laemmle (owner of Universal Studios), Thomas Ince, Charles Chaplin, Gloria Swanson and then the dearly beloved Will Rogers. Quickly following this era of bright stars came other rising actors and actresses and such studio executives as Samuel Goldwyn and Louis B. Mayer.

The rush was on, but it took a slam-bang internecine battle to bring Beverly Hills of age. As has been true of three-fourths of the strife in the west, the problem centered around water. The Rodeo Land and Water Company, as its name not only implied but guaranteed, had sold land to prospective residents with the promise that ample water would be made available to them, and had done a good job of sinking wells. However by 1923 the Rodeo people, faced with an expanding population, and wanting to divest itself of its water responsibility, informed Beverly Hills that it would have to sell its water rights and distributing system to Los Angeles . . . which meant being annexed to the city of Los Angeles, and losing its right of self-government.

The town was treated to its first and last dirty political campaign, in which those interests that wanted annexation distributed hand bills reading:

WARNING
Drink sparingly of this water,
as it has laxative qualities.

Bottles of sulphur water were placed on front porches, with a label that read, "This is the water you will drink if you don't annex to Los Angeles." The pioneers were determined not only to preserve their governmental independence, but to keep Beverly Hills a region apart. They won the election five hundred seven votes to three hundred thirty-seven; neither their independence nor the uniqueness of their very special culture has ever again been challenged.

Beverly Hills has made good its resolve to remain independent and well governed. At least once a month a neighbor calls and says, "You've got to attend the Board of Education meeting this afternoon, the issue of the Oregon Sex Education film is coming up." Or, "Don't fail to be at the City Council meeting this Tuesday night, they're going to discuss a new zoning policy." Not only are billboards strictly *defendu*, but even real estate signs on empty lots are rigidly limited in size and number. Another ordinance prohibits the blaring of noise from stores or in the streets from passing trucks. In the early days there was a law prohibiting the shooting of jack rabbits from the rear platform of the red car which ran out to the Beverly Hills Hotel. Today the lapin has been replaced by mink.

It is a New England town meeting government transplanted to the Far West, with every citizen accorded the courtesy and the right to present his petition or point of view from the floor. What is doubly interesting is that no member of the Board of Education, the City Council, the Mayor or the City Treasurer receives compensation. The five city councilmen are selected for four years, and they choose their mayor from among their own number. In the early days Will Rogers was an honorary mayor; he brought the town unending publicity. Will was on tour when the state legislature decreed that all sixth-class cities had to choose their mayor from among the elected councilmen. Informed of the news, he said:

"If I had known Beverly Hills was a sixth-class city I would never have taken the job in the first place; what's more, I maintain that I am the only mayor who was ever legislated out of office."

Within the course of two decades Beverly Hills has increased its population nearly three thousand percent, and so completely filled its five-and-a-quarter square mile area that within a couple of years the Rodeo Land and Water Company will of necessity be out of business. Part of the reason is the warm winter sunshine and the Mediterranean blue skies, while the rest of the nation is freezing; part of the reason is the beauty of the location, with the level plains extending up into the gently rolling foothills. However there are other near-by areas that have been more bountifully blessed: the magnificent mountains of Brentwood, the Pacific Palisades region, where one sits in one's patio and overlooks the Pacific Ocean; the Hollywood hills overlooking the lights of Los Angeles. But the smog stops at Holmby Hills, its western boundary; it's not as windy as the beach areas, not as hot in summer as the San Fernando Valley, nor as cold in winter as the foothills above Pasadena. Adolphe Menjou says the early rush of the movie stars to Beverly Hills took place because, "It was the thing to do, like building a beach house at Malibu and a desert house in Palm Springs; however Beverly Hills had a lasting quality which the others did not, and by now it is our beloved home town."

That "lasting quality," is in part the magnificent quiet, and the beauty of the gardens and trees, cared for by a veritable army of Japanese gardeners. By 10:30 at night, or 11:00 at the latest, there is hardly a light to be seen in a house; the actors and actresses have to be out of their houses by six in the morning in order to be made up and on the sound stages at eight, and what was once thought of as Babylon is now conservative and responsible. Thus you have an almost sylvan retreat in the midst of a noisy and dynamic metropolitan area, enjoying all of the benefits of smallness, with the benefits of bigness, such as a symphony orchestra, opera, a legitimate theatre and a first-rate university, UCLA, all within a few minutes drive.

Part of the attraction to Beverly Hills is its extremely important address. Mention the name in the tiniest hamlet in America, or in any town in Europe and people's faces light up as they exclaim, "Tell me about it." Beverly Hills represents the country's fantasy in terms of its movie royalty, glamour and mythology. A great many people feel that once they have moved to Beverly, they have arrived. Bel-Air and Brentwood carry equal prestige, perhaps even on a higher level, but Beverly is known to contain both the heart and the power of the movie industry. As one of our more successful radio writers said:

"I like Beverly Hills because living there gives one a feeling of status. I do not mean the snob appeal for clerks when you give a Beverly Hills address, nor the snob appeal for the plumbers or electricians who tack an additional twenty percent onto their price because of the Beverly Hills address. What I like about Beverly is that it is a genteel community, but at the same time constantly replenished by colorful people from all over the world. Life is never boring in Beverly Hills."

A great asset of Beverly, oddly enough, is its police system, one of the most intelligent in the world. For example, a short time ago a prowl car saw a moving van drawn up before a house in the block next to mine. The officer courteously asked the men what they were doing there. The men replied that they had rented the house and were going to change some of the furniture. The policeman said, "What do you have to pay for rent on a nice house like this?" The men hesitated for a moment, then one of them replied, "A hundred dollars a month." The policeman knew that such a house would rent for four or five hundred a month, and so they took the two men into the station. They were burglars with long records of moving furniture out of vacant houses.

Outsiders occasionally say that Beverly is over-policed because the prowl cars go by your house every few minutes, but our feelings here are the exact opposite from the big city "Chicky for the cops!" In Beverly the police officers are our friends, and in particular are close to the children who know them and like them. If you are closing your house for a week they will clear papers and packages off your porch, turn on the front light at night, and guard your property. If you are having a big party for your high school daughter with perhaps fifty to a hundred kids coming in, a police car stands by all evening to make sure no strangers crash the party. Patrol cars stand guard outside the high school every afternoon at 3:10, and nothing is sold to the youngsters except Good Humors. When the Cub Scouts gather in buses to see the Rams' football game, there are police cars keeping traffic away from the school block when the buses take off and return.

If a lady of facile virtue should set up shop in the small bachelor apartment region at the southeast tip of the town, the police know about it within a matter of days simply by watching the number of strange men going into the apartment house. They find out that the lady's name is, say, Sadie Thompson. Then an officer rings the bell and asks Miss Thompson politely, "Are you Miss Pearl Paramour? We understand that Miss Paramour is seeing too many strange men at night, and we wanted to warn her to move." By morning, Sadie Thompson is gone.

Chief of Police Clinton Anderson feels that both the Bugsy Seigel and Tony Carnera shootings were unjust blots on the town's escutcheon. Seigel had taken only a four-month lease on the house and had arrived from Las Vegas just a few hours before to spend a quiet weekend with his girl friend, Virginia Hill. Doubtless the gamblers did not want to give their own town a bad name.

Intelligent police work pays off; Beverly Hills is known as the most dangerous place in America for thieves and perverts to operate in. They simply stay away.

But unquestionably the greatest lure of Beverly Hills is its public school system which, along with Bronxville, Oak Park, Scarsdale, and Winnetka, is one of the best public school systems of the western world. Of the four grammar schools, El Rodeo is built on a seven-acre tract and looks like a college campus as you drive past it; the three others, Hawthorne, Vista, and Horace Mann have sun-drenched modern buildings in the midst of large playgrounds. Each elementary school has a full time nurse and a full time physical education teacher. There is also a full time teacher who goes into the homes of children who are sick to keep them up with their work; and one whose job it is to work with problem children, most of whom come from troubled or broken homes. There are also courses in family relations.

When I went to high school we hated our teachers and they loathed us; the students and faculty of Beverly High treat each other not only with respect but actually with love. The salaries start at $3700 to $3900, and go up to $6500. Beverly attracts the best among teachers trained in California and literally thousands of applicants from out of state. The kids can't win football games, they've been too gently reared to compete with the more rugged characters from the surrounding high schools, but they have a championship swimming pool, good courses in tennis and golf, not to mention a course behind the wheel of an automobile!

There is a big sister and big brother system, with seniors taking incoming freshmen out to lunch before school opens, and then guiding them through the first days of classes. There is a minimum of confusion at Beverly Hills High, however, for each student is assigned to his classes during the summer and his program mailed to him weeks before school opens. The student finds his proper books in his classroom the first day and homework is assigned that first day. The school has not only gone to every college in the country to find out what they demand from high school graduates, but actually follows the student through his freshman year of college, learning where he has been inadequately or inexpertly trained, and then shores up those weaknesses. Classes are small, every student has a faculty counselor who watches his grades week by week, and investigates the source of the problem within a matter of days if a student is failing. Little wonder that Beverly High's students are welcomed by institutions of higher learning.

There is criticism that the Beverly Hills schools are reactionary, that they pound the three R's too heavily, and put too much emphasis on Skills and Drills. However, as the grammar school principals say: "We are training leaders, all our children will go on to the universities, and the sooner we give them academic discipline the better off they will be." Their assumption is based on the fact that parents living in Beverly Hills have substantial incomes. Elsewhere in the country this cross-cut of income and social strata would be sending its children to private schools, but the parents of Beverly Hills, predominantly intellectual, artistic, and self-made, are prejudiced against private schools: parents committed to public schools are beholden to live where the best public schooling is available. Though the population of Beverly Hills is generally considered to be unstable, in my son Kenneth's four years at Hawthorne, only three children ever left his class. Basically it is not the parent population that is floating, that moves out when an option is not taken up; despite adversity, parents do their best to hang on until their children are through school.

Land and homes are expensive in Beverly, but as the real estate brokers say, "Our real estate values will never drop as long as we maintain our school system."

Beverly Hills is divided into four separate and distinct parts. Extending from Sunset Boulevard far up into the hills are the large estates such as Pickfair, the enormous Harold Lloyd *dasha,* and the sprawling twenty- to thirty-room mansions occupied for so many years by William Randolph Hearst and Marion Davies, by Louis B. Mayer and such prosperous ten percenters as Sam Jaffee. In a two-mile quadrangle extending from Whittier on the west to Doheny on the east, and only three long curving blocks wide, from Sunset to Santa Monica, lies the residential heart of the city. The bigger houses are Spanish, Mexican, English, Colonial, Hawaiian, and Neo-Contractor. In the early days the mansions were constructed out of oil, lumber and steel fortunes; the two most beautiful homes built within the past year are founded on popcorn, the houses costing between $200,000 and $300,000, and built by men who have the popcorn concessions in the theatre lobbies of America.

In this fine residential quadrangle there are no electric poles, no electric wires and no trucks plying the streets. There are also no native Californians.

From Santa Monica Boulevard south to Wilshire is the business district, and from Wilshire south to Pico is the smaller home or bungalow area, with a few blocks of two-story apartment houses.

Despite the democratic nature of its government, and the friendship existing between all of the many religions represented, the large-home area between Santa Monica Boulevard and the hills, formerly known as the Gold Coast of the film industry, is now composed of three disparate segments which almost never mix! the *haute monde* or old families; the movie, radio and television colony; and the newly-arrived, for the most part prosperous business people from the east and mid-west.

This was not always true, for when Mary Pickford and Doug Fairbanks were the leaders of Beverly Hills society they made a successful synthesis of old California families, wealthy and socially prominent settlers from the east, and the movie colony which they so dearly loved. At Pickfair were entertained the princes and prime ministers of Europe as well as the American economic royalty. Their divorce not only shocked the town but shattered Beverly society.

Today there is no reigning hostess to hold Beverly Hills society together, and so it moves in three distinct circles, each of them shut out from the other. In the first echelon is the exclusive Beverly Hills society, a cultivated group and patron of the arts, but apparently it does not consider the motion picture an art form, for of the thousands of motion picture people living in Beverly Hills only a handful have been accepted: Harold Lloyd, Joe E. Brown, Irene Dunne, George Murphy, Loretta Young.

The movie crowd would probably be astounded to learn that it is being excluded from Beverly Hills society, for only a few have made an attempt to enter it. The movie people are a world unto themselves; they associate with no one except other movie makers, and they talk nothing but shop. They have set up a rigid caste system of their own: top executives, producers, directors, actors and writers associate with no one below them in the motion picture hierarchy, and certainly not with anyone earning less than their own $2500 to $15,000 a week.

The third strata of Beverly Hills society aspires to associate with the other two. For the most part they are the newly wealthy businessmen who have moved to Beverly Hills to hobnob with the stars and enjoy the exclusive parties. They can rub elbows with the stars, for the streets, shops and restaurants are filled with them. Only the other day while shopping for a gift robe for my wife at Saks, and while it was being displayed for me by one of the svelt Saks models, Ava Gardner stood watching my every move, hoping I wouldn't take the robe, so she could have it. The stars are in the enormous, brilliantly lighted super markets every day, pushing their wire baskets, dressed in the simplest clothes, frequently in jeans, and stopping at every different shelf of canned goods to chat with friends.

This much contact with stardom the new Beverly Hills resident will get, but that's all. He will join the golf clubs and participate in civic functions hoping to meet the movie people, but it will do him no good: the gates are firmly closed. As one woman complained to me, "We joined Hillcrest because we knew so many movie stars belonged and we thought we could become friends. Now, after five years, the most I've been able to say to any of them is hello."

The town is jammed with doctors who practice skillful but expensive medicine; but then, the whole town is expensive. A Beverly Hills medical address has become like a Park Avenue address, with the result that there are half a dozen blocks of stunningly designed medical buildings, with only fifteen percent of the practice coming from Beverly itself. When I first moved here seven years ago there were exactly four qualified psychoanalysts; today there are one hundred and twenty!

While the movie industry contributes most of the patients, you almost never find a studio executive, producer or director needing psychiatry or psychoanalysis: their power is too great and the opportunities for self-expression too omnipresent. It is their wives who haunt the psychoanalysts' offices. However the chief source is the actor and writer: the writers because they are made to write what other people want, and develop a guilt complex because they can't bring themselves to quit and create Literature; the actors and actresses because although they are presented to the world as the modern day royalty, and their faces are known in remote Turkey or India, they realize that they have no power whatever, are not only replaceable but almost interchangeable; that the real brains behind them, moving them about like puppets, are the producers, the directors, the cameramen. Perhaps this accounts for some of their socially amoral conduct.

Perhaps the strangest aspect of Beverly is that not one resident in a hundred is a native. At best its residents have but shallow roots here, their main emotional attachments being in the east or south from which they come. The success of the local Communists in raising thousands of dollars in Beverly Hills was due to this fact, and to the further harsh truth that many of the incoming families were without an authentic educational or cultural background. The only ones who offered them anything by way of a cultural base, roots or ties; the only ones who made them feel that they were participating in seemingly liberal causes and taking part in world movements, were the highly organized Hollywood Communists. These Communists gave them a place in the sun, the very best of entertainment at lunches and dinners . . . and drained their purses.

The old-timers don't care for Beverly any more, they hark back to the good old days when they stood around in front of Gunther's Drugstore or went on excursions to Catalina and Del Monte. Back in the twenties Mrs. Marco Hellman, wife of the banker, kept two cows on her estate, while Lucien Hubbard, one of the first motion picture writers to live in Beverly, saddled his horse in the stable at the rear of his home on Hillcrest, rode across the hills to Universal Studios for his day's work, and then rode the horse back home again at dinnertime. All these things are gone, the cows, the horses, the chickens and ducks, even the bridle path on which the movie stars rode for so many years on Sunset Boulevard.

The years have brought interesting changes. In the depression half of the town was for sale. Well built houses south of Wilshire could be had for five thousand dollars and mansions north of Wilshire with magnificent pools and gardens for twenty-five thousand dollars. Starting in 1939 the houses were bought up by a new generation, married couples who had young children they wanted to get into the Beverly Hills school system. The first generation of settlers had died out or moved, their children having grown up and married. Within a few years there will have been almost a complete turnover in population.

Entertaining in the days of Mrs. Basil Rathbone was a matter of white tie and tails; today the black tie suffices and even the mundane tuxedo is thinning out. Dinner for sixty and garden parties for two hundred under specially constructed tents, with orchestras playing, were common before World War II. Today the big casseroles have come out of storage and a good many of the hostesses have gone back into the kitchen. With the movies having suffered a five-year slump, resulting in a quarter to a third of Beverly Hills being unemployed, and with the continued rise in income taxes, the servant who was considered standard equipment for every house in Beverly, is vanishing from the domestic scene. It has become easy and accurate for a housewife to say, "We just can't find the right help;" but it is difficult for a woman involved in the Beverly Hills caste system to explain away last year's suit, hair-do, or automobile.

In the early years, too, big parties were delightful because of the impromptu entertainment: Rubenstein playing "I'm Just Wild About Harry," the only American piece he knew, the town's comedians, George Burns, Jack Benny, George Jessel, Ben Blue falling into comedy routines that left you weak with laughter, the rising musical stars singing their hearts out before a guest list which included half of the important producers and directors in town. Today this is almost entirely gone; serious and troubled conversation about Korea, Iran, the Security Council, and the Bomb have replaced laughter and music. The spirit of gaiety has given way to an overall anxiety, not only about the continuation of the motion picture industry but about the continuation of our human and physical world.

One of the most startling phenomena of Beverly Hills is the rapidity with which houses change hands, several on our block having had five owners within five years. No one who buys a house is content to leave it alone or merely to do a paint job; every new owner rips down walls, adds additional rooms, tears out arches, kitchens and baths. The Beverly Hills building contractors now ask permission to put the new walls on ball bearings and zippers, since they know that they will be moving them again in six months to a year. However, this constant change of ownership has had one salutary effect: most of the old Spanish houses have been converted to moderns.

Having been started as a resort by the Beverly Hills Hotel back in 1912, the town still carries a bit of that feeling even now that it is solidly built. The immaculate cleanliness of Beverly, the newness of practically all its buildings, its unified, low-slung architectural scheme, makes it feel more like a resort than a home community. The town is filled with beautiful girls who come from all over the world to crash the motion picture studios; few of them do, for any length of time, but a surprising number find wealthy husbands, and they can be seen driving the streets of Beverly in their open, light-blue convertibles, dressed in slacks and gay colored blouses, a matching ribbon in their hair. How rich the pickings can be for these girls is seen in the fact that Beverly, really a hamlet in terms of population, has twenty-four stock brokerage houses, and accounts for ten percent of the entire country's transactions on the New York Stock Exchange.

It also seems to be the answer for a number of its inhabitants who want to live in a small community where they can be identified with the PTA, the Cub Scouts, the League of Women Voters, the Delphians, school bazaars and carnivals, and yet to be able to shop in a business district three or four blocks away which has all of the elegance of the Rue Faubourg St. Honoré. None of the adjoining luxury communities has this companionship, comraderie or local self-government. In Beverly Hills a woman can enjoy a social life in its most bouffant aspect while being a good mother, a good housekeeper and a good wife.

It is a community dominated by the automobile. Absolutely no one walks in Beverly Hills. I have spent hours in the early afternoons and evenings walking the residential streets without seeing a soul. Sometimes I feel that I am threading my way through Oliver Goldsmith's deserted village, for Beverly's residents get into their cars in their rear garages and disembark later in the day in the same privacy. The only time I see my neighbors immediately across the street, Mr. and Mrs. Sidney Franklin, is late at night when I take my wirehair for a walk and find them in their pajamas and dressing robes, walking their French poodle.

Today Beverly Hills has an international aspect, with residents from every country in the world enriching its culture. It is more like Carmel than any other town in California, with a great deal of going and coming, to London, Paris, Rome, Berlin. In some aspects Beverly Hills is more of a suburb of New York than of Los Angeles; the air editions of the New York *Times* and *Herald Tribune* are delivered in many homes by special truck at noon of the day of issue, and it takes me less time to get Doubleday, my publishers, on the telephone at Madison Avenue and Fifty-sixth Street than it does to reach my mother-in-law around the corner on Foothill.

Despite the fact that the town is so young, and without deep-rooted tradition, it has a broad cultural base. The Chamber of Commerce underwrites the symphony season, the Forum at the High School attracts everyone from Mrs. Eleanor Roosevelt to the Sitwells. There is a small but first-rate public library, used by many of the writers of the community and by a public well trained in the search for material. The town supports three good bookstores and a charming rare book shop, but by way of contrast, two art galleries recently failed, the public Museum of Modern Art, and the Associated American Artists. Apparently Beverly Hills wants to see its exhibitions in New York and buy its oils in Paris.

Beverly Hills is probably permanent now, with a substantial part of its population outside the entertainment industry. True, it will always be a little temperamental and dominated by option stomach; friends who threw their arms around you when they last saw you in the street will walk by the next time with eyes averted because they are not at the moment working on a picture. But you get used to this kind of aberration, and excuse it on the grounds of the unholy highness of the stakes, not only in money, but in excitement and glamour.

There has to be something wrong with every town; merely having unpaved back alleys isn't enough. Beverly Hills' burden is that it has to hold tranquilly on its trim bosom artists whose excesses and foibles make profitable scare-headlines for the rest of the world. We are hurt when good neighbors whom we love, an Ingrid Bergman or a Franchot Tone, get their lives in a mess, and we grieve for them. But when you are surrounded on all sides by world-famous people, you are bound to get rather too much publicity . . . and some of it is going to be bad.

By the same token, you are also bound to live an exciting life. Over and above its beauty, its climate, its enclosed patios where the families live around their pools, barbecues, tennis, and badminton courts, this is Beverly Hills' greatest asset: it is always intensely and colorfully alive.

MARY TODD was the daughter of a banker in Lexington, Kentucky, known in the 1820s as the Athens of the West. In addition to being well educated, and a man of superb taste, Robert Todd was also a political manager of Henry Clay, and the confidant to Kentucky's rising politicos. The art and science of politics was as natural to Mary as breathing. An attractive young woman, highly cultured, from a leading family, she had ample opportunities to marry among the prosperous horsemen and planters of the Bluegrass, and to live the affluent life of high society. She rejected them all. Her eldest sister, Elizabeth, was living in the new, rude village of Springfield, Illinois, the wife of Ninian Edwards, former governor of the state. Elizabeth had brought the next oldest sister, Frances, to stay with her. When Frances married, she wrote to Mary, "There is now a vacancy in our household." Mary arrived in Springfield in 1839, at the age of nineteen. Here she slowly, somewhat painfully came to know Abraham Lincoln. Here too she apparently rejected Stephen Douglas, in favor of Abraham Lincoln.

LOVE IS ETERNAL

My Heart and My Flesh

SHE awoke from her nap in the steamy midafternoon Missouri heat. Her thoughts came back slowly. Her eyes rested on the stillness of the trees outside her window; it was forbidding weather, hot and still. She hoped that it would not storm; while she had sat waiting to depart in the stagecoach in front of the Globe Tavern in Springfield thunder had knocked the top row of bricks off the still unfinished state house. She had been afraid of thunder since she was three, when Mammy

Sally had told her that it was the voice of the debil booming out in anger at people's misdeeds.

Anne turned over on the other bed, a tiny smile on her heart-shaped face. Mary chuckled as she recalled her uncle Judge David Todd's story the night before of how he had fallen asleep on the bench while one of the attorneys was making a long speech. Waking up suddenly, he had cried out:

"Mr. Clerk, enter up a fine of ten dollars against David Todd for contempt. I'll break up this habit of going to sleep in daylight or I'll break the court."

Anne sat up in bed, awake at once, without any transition.

"What amuses you, Mary?"

She told Anne, then added, "Mr. Lincoln will love this story; he'll add it to his repertoire."

Anne gave her a piercing glance.

"You like Mr. Lincoln, don't you?"

". . . yes."

"More than the others?"

". . . I don't know. Perhaps." Her heart was pounding.

"I remember him. He certainly is . . ." she hesitated, a little perplexed, reaching for the word, ". . . outstanding."

"I'll admit he's not the prettiest man in the world," said Mary, "but he could make a great president."

Anne bounced out of bed. There were furrows between her eyebrows.

"Surely you wouldn't marry a man for just that!"

"Why would you marry your beau?" Mary was angry with herself for having pursued the subject.

Anne flushed. "I'm going to marry him because I love him; what else is marriage?"

"A way of life . . ." She was glad to hear her uncle David's voice calling to them. "We'd better go downstairs."

Her uncle David was the heartiest of all the Todds: a big talkative man who worked hard, ate, drank and slept hard, and had energy left over for a hundred enthusiasms. One of them was the Todd genealogy. After the supper dishes had been cleared and a big lamp set in the center of the table, he spread out his charts and gave Mary a guided tour through her ancestry, the spectacles caught between two humps in his nose, his short chubby fingers tracing their lines of descent back to Scotland in the year 1679, and to the first of the family who had settled in Pennsylvania in 1720.

"You've got some mighty good fighting men in your blood, Mary: your Covenanter ancestors fought the Duke of Monmouth and the established Church of England; your grandfather fought with General Washington, your granduncles fought with George Rogers Clark, not to mention all the young fellows who fought in the Indian Wars and the War of 1812. But fighters isn't all we have: here's one who was first civil governor of Illinois, another was territorial governor of Michigan, another governor of Pennsylvania. We've had lots of other peaceable folk too, but all important in their day: clergymen, educators, senators, judges . . ."

As her uncle rumbled on, her mind recalled the pained silences which had followed her questions to Abraham Lincoln about his background. He had spoken briefly of the Lincolns, though apparently he cared little about them: they had been Quakers originally, who migrated from Pennsylvania to Virginia and then westward to Kentucky. When it came to his mother's family he had sat in a chair with his head down, absorbed in a long chewed-up silence before saying hoarsely:

"They came from undistinguished families in Virginia . . . second families, I should say."

She caught herself up sharply. I'm behaving like a schoolgirl. No matter what happens, I apply it to Mr. Lincoln. By what right has he become my frame of reference? And to what end? Eliza Francis had told her that the few friendships he had had in New Salem had been with safely and serenely married women: Mrs. Bowling Green, who had helped him when he was troubled, Mrs. Jack Armstrong, who made shirts for him and mended his trousers.

"It's time to dress for the ball, Mary."

It was Anne, cutting into her reverie. The girls returned to their bedroom in the rambling two-story wood house. Mary had announced that she would remain for a limited time, but Columbia, a bustling county seat and tobacco center of some seven hundred people, thought differently; there were teas each afternoon, supper parties and now the fourth ball of the week in her honor, for Uncle David had spread the word that she was available for a permanent place in Missouri matrimony. She was being given an exhausting whirl by a half dozen young men, all new to the state and seeking wives.

The two girls dressed in their gowns of sheer white lawn. At eight o'clock they were driven to a brick home at the end of Broadway; the four downstairs rooms and two halls had been thrown open for the reception and dancing. The traditional Virginia reels were played, but much faster than Mary was accustomed to; she felt almost exhausted at the end of each cotillion. Her partner for the evening was a grandson of Patrick Henry, apparently Uncle David's first choice for her husband. David had told her on the afternoon of her arrival:

"Young Henry is an agreeable man and a fine lawyer. Honestly, Mary, I believe he surpasses his noble ancestor in talents. And I do think you should marry a lawyer, you have such a good head for politics."

"Why, Uncle David," she teased, "what happened to that dentist you promised me? I've been counting on him."

"The idiot refused to wait, upped and married just a week ago. But don't you worry, Mary, I've got a dozen fine prospects all strung out for you like nightshirts on a clothesline."

Mr. Henry obviously was smitten. After one of the dances Mary exclaimed, "I can't get over the excitement with which you run your reels. When I get back to Springfield . . ."

"Miss Mary, I simply cannot brook the mention of your return. Don't you like Missouri?"

How could she tell him, this pleasant man with the carrot-red hair and slightly bulging eyes, that she did not like being plunged back into a slave state; that once having lived in freedom the sight of slaves working the tobacco fields, and of their wooden shacks, was like traveling backward in time to another age?

She and Anne left the party at two o'clock, then she waited in the dark of the downstairs hall while her cousin stood outside the front door saying good night to her sweetheart. The girls discarded endless petticoats, brushed their hair, washed their faces with cold water and Boston soap. Anne burst into a romantic ballad.

"It's so glorious to love and be loved, Mary, I can't imagine why anyone should want to live without it."

For all her effervescence, Anne fell asleep the moment her face found its familiar niche in the pillow. Mary lay sleepless. Why indeed should anyone want to live without love? Surely she had never wanted to. She had watched her schoolmates at Mentelle's fall in love with love, and she had set herself resolutely against any such romanticism. She had only one life and one love; she wanted to use them wisely and well. That did not mean she would not one day love as tenderly, yes and as passionately as any of her more sentimental friends; her hand would never be given where her heart was not.

But where was her heart? Not for an instant had it been possible for the music or the gaiety of vivacious Columbia to crowd out Abraham. She was amazed at the tenacity of his hold upon her. Do I love him?

she asked herself. It had not been love at first sight, nor even fifteenth sight; her emotions had grown slowly.

Why? What were Abraham's qualities that she should love him? His honesty? A lot of people were honest, in fact nearly everyone she knew. His simplicity? By itself this would not be important; lots of simple people were dull. His courage? A common commodity on the frontier, possessed in as great quantity by Stephen Douglas as by Abraham Lincoln. Physical strength? Brutes also had physical strength. Spirituality? Not in the accepted sense, for he had not been in a church more than a dozen times. Humor? Some of it was good, though frequently of the barnyard type, but rarely was it subtle or intellectual. Profundity? He had little education or disciplined training. Personality, charm, sparkle, magnetism? There were a dozen men in Springfield and a hundred in Lexington who could outcharm and outscintillate him on ten seconds' notice. Incorruptibility? Perhaps, but as yet with little opportunity to prove itself. Humility? God knew he had enough to be humble about!

Whatever Abraham's qualities, certainly no other young lady in Springfield had caught sight of them. Yet there was something unmistakable there: the Clary's Grove boys had recognized it; the Black Hawk War recruits recognized it; the Illinois Whigs recognized it. Her cousin John Stuart had recognized it. Leadership? What did that mean? That he had learned how to handle, bargain, compromise, control? Many men led who should have been in the rear ranks.

As she lay quietly, watching the leaves of the sycamores and birch with the moon shining upon them, she asked herself the most difficult question of all: Does Abraham love me? If I love, will my love be returned?

He was a man who had been frightened by love. "Love destroys," he had said.

But all that was past. He called her Molly, often with affection. When he was tired or sad or discouraged he had made his way to her sympathetic company. He enjoyed being with her, admired the way she spoke, the manner in which her mind worked. True, he had disappeared for days, and when she left Springfield he had said he would miss her, yet there had been no letter from him, only a scrawled greeting on a copy of *The Old Soldier* he had sent.

Yet she had learned many things about him over the months: he went to no other young lady's house in Springfield, he had danced with no one but her at the cotillion; and when he had confided to her, "I would hate to leave the world without having made it a little better place to live in," he had really bared his innermost thoughts. . . .

She would have to judge carefully . . . both herself and Abraham.

2

She returned to Springfield on a sunny first of September and talked to Elizabeth of her visit while she hung away her clothes. Her uncle David had been disappointed at her leaving; he had believed she would stay. At the good-bye supper Anne had given for her, many of the young people had placed bets that she would return.

When Elizabeth left to attend a meeting of the Episcopal Sewing Society, Mary slipped into a light blue muslin, rolled up the sleeves, got her garden shears and went out to cut the roses that were growing so profusely beneath her bedroom window. She had gathered about two dozen fragrant blooms when she heard a staccato step coming around the banjo drive, and looked up to see the broad-grinning face of Stephen Douglas.

"Mary, I just this instant heard you were back. Springfield has been a dull place without you. Welcome home!"

She was delighted by the heartiness of his greeting. His lips touched her cheek.

"Steve, it's wonderful to see you again. Even if you did give us a trouncing in the legislature election."

"Oh, you heard about that all the way west in the wilds of Missouri, did you?" His chest puffed out with pride. "That's only half the story, Miss Henry-Clay-Whig-from-Kentucky: we're also going to beat you for the presidency."

She refused to be drawn into an argument.

"Will there be something good for a deserving Democrat, Steve?"

He ran his fingers agitatedly through his long bushy hair.

"There'd better be! I've been campaigning for so many months I'm flat busted broke; in fact I'm being sued for debt." He jingled a few coins in his trousers pocket. "Seems like I still got a few cents left; what do you say we walk down to Watson's confectionery?"

She had been interlacing the stems of her roses.

"I'd love to, Steve, but you must let me put a garland of roses on your head."

They laughed together heartily as she rounded the wreath and placed it on his enormous head; then they set off arm in arm. They reached the square, oblivious to the raised eyebrows. She commented on the interesting changes that had taken place during the past two months: Wallace and Diller had hung a huge eagle over the drugstore as an advertisement; there were dozens of buildings under construction; Grimsley and Levering's store had a display of materials in from Philadelphia, Baltimore and New Orleans, as beautiful as anything she had seen in the Lexington shops.

It did not take them long to eat an ice, nor yet to walk back to the Edwards house. When Mary bade Stephen *au revoir* she found Elizabeth and Ninian in the parlor, pleased looks on their faces.

"We've already had three callers," said Elizabeth; "women who saw you downtown, arm in arm, Stephen wearing your garland of roses, having such a wonderful time . . ."

"We're just good friends who enjoy each other."

"Oh." Elizabeth's voice had gone flat. "We thought perhaps you had decided . . . while in Columbia . . ."

When Mary's expression remained unchanged, Elizabeth dropped into a black satin chair. Ninian went to his cigar box, lighted a cigar and puffed noisily on it. Elizabeth tried again.

"But you do like him, Mary? Given time, it could turn into love?"

"No, Liz, it never could. My feelings are no different from what they were three years ago, when I first met him here."

"Why do you say it never could?" Elizabeth rose, stood over her. "Why have you closed your mind against him? He's a fine man and he's going far. You are the right woman to help him. You could have a good life . . ."

"There are some people who are not meant to love each other. Perhaps they're too much alike, as Stephen and I are; perhaps there's no strong current between them . . . as a man and a woman. Besides . . ."

"Yes?" Elizabeth had caught the change in her tone.

"I love someone else."

"You love someone else! Who is it?"

". . . Mr. Lincoln."

There was a silence.

"That's impossible," cried Elizabeth. "He's the last man in the world for you to love."

"Not the last, Liz, the first: first and only."

"But when could this have happened? You were away several months . . . you haven't seen him since you've been back . . ."

She smiled. "I guess it's been happening ever since that first moment he dropped into my life . . . through the trap door in the ceiling of the courtroom."

"Dropped straight from heaven, eh?" Ninian's voice had a cutting edge of sarcasm. "Well, you won't find him an angel."

"I wouldn't want an angel, Ninian. I want a man. You'll not deny that he's a man?"

"I don't need to deny or affirm anything: I simply say that I wouldn't want him in the family."

She saw that Ninian was angry. She went to his side.

"Forgive me, Ninian: you know that I love you and respect your opinion. Then tell me one thing: why is it that you accept Mr. Lincoln for yourself, as a leader of your party, but reject him to lead me . . . to happiness."

"He's a good state-level politician," pronounced Ninian, "but he'll never go beyond that. He has no real ambition; he lives poorly, won't mix with the right people and doesn't know how to set up his business so it will return him the fees he has legitimately earned. He cares nothing for the good things of life, Mary: clothes, a carriage, a home . . ."

"But, Ninian, these limitations belong to his stumbling and difficult youth. He can go as far as any other man, farther than most."

"Why should you be drawn to the man who has the least to offer you?" There was considerable pain in her sister's voice.

"Because that is the one to whom I have the most to give. Oh, Liz, I know it's best in all things to be practical; but shouldn't I have faith in my own judgment? And gifts?"

The late summer flies were buzzing at the windows; there was a heavy smell of honeysuckle in the house. Elizabeth's manner became quiet, patient.

"Mary, it's not that we dislike Mr. Lincoln or have any prejudice against him, but only that we're sure he's the wrong man for you. He might be right as rain for some other girl, but think of the differences in your background. He's a plebeian."

"That may be true, but again I say it's the past you're talking about. I don't intend to live the past. We will make our own future."

"Since when does the future not emerge from the past?"

"These differences you speak of, they are the accidents of circumstance." She was hurt now and she could feel the two red spots flaming on her forehead. Her voice became hoarse. "His parents were poor . . . they lived on frontiers where there were no good schools . . . he had to work from the time he could lift an ax. Cousin John Stuart says he has a natural mind; and look how far he has come already, in spite of his disadvantages! I don't agree with what you say about his being lazy, without taste or ambition. It's simply that he has lacked opportunities for polish, what we Todds call culture. Well then, I've had those opportunities . . ." One corner of her lip turned up slightly. "I'm a highly polished Todd. Why wouldn't I be the best of all possible helpmeets for a man like Abraham Lincoln? You once called him a rough diamond, Liz; but remember the diamond is the most precious of all stones."

"And you will do the polishing?"

"I have the training. I have the love. I can give him the background he needs: a beautiful home . . . ," the Houghan house came into her mind, "filled with books, music . . . the proper entertainment for the proper people. He has his talents, Ninian has admitted them; I have mine. Why shouldn't they be wedded?"

". . . wedded? Then Mr. Lincoln has asked you to marry him?"

". . . No."

From the way the blood drained from her face they saw that she was vulnerable. Elizabeth studied her eyes as a mother would.

"Mary, has he told you that he loves you?"

She turned away, unable to speak.

"Then how can you presume . . . go so far in your mind?"

"Because he does love me; he has told me so in a thousand ways. . . ."

She did not intend to cry, and she had no advance knowledge that she would, but now she felt her strength spent. The tears came. Elizabeth took her in her arms, stroked her hair.

"Darling, you're not to be unhappy. We had to be honest with you. We'll not oppose Mr. Lincoln openly; you are to invite him to the house just as often as you like. . . . The more you see him the less likely you are to remain in love."

3

No one in town had the slightest notion where Abraham Lincoln might be, so she was obliged to go to the *Sangamo Journal* to find out. Eliza Francis had abandoned all hope of living at home and had moved a cookstove, table and cot into the printing office. Simeon was turning out not only the *Journal* but the weekly *Old Soldier* and hundreds of political pamphlets with which the Whigs were attempting to inundate the state. Still smarting from their defeat in the state legislature, Simeon was more than ever determined to bring Illinois in for General Harrison.

"We've got an excellent chance, too," he said, leaning wearily against his press while Eliza stood with her capacious back to them, cooking a broth. "After twelve muddled years under Jackson and Van Buren, the whole country is crying for a change. The committee didn't want Abraham to waste his time canvassing southern Illinois, they've always been pro-slave and pro-Democrat, but he's getting results."

So that's where he is, she thought, down in Little Egypt, talking his heart out to people who don't want to hear him. No wonder he couldn't write letters!

"Simeon, could I help?"

"My girl, you're hired. Suppose you address these boxes of the *Old Soldier,* then you can go through this file of out-of-state papers and shear the good articles for us to reprint."

She took off her gray wool cloak, pushed up the cuffs of her walking dress and pitched in. Abraham's chances of being sent to the Senate, or even of being elected Speaker of the legislature had gone glimmering with the Democratic majority, but if he proved the key figure in carrying Illinois for Harrison surely he would play a role in the new federal government?

Each morning she rose at seven, had coffee and fruit, then went into the north bedroom which had been cleared of furniture and equipped with tables loaded with bolts of flannels, linens, silks; ribbons, laces, thread, tape, cords, needles, patterns. The winter sewing had not yet been started; there were warm wool bonnets, coats and dresses as well as flannel underclothes to be made for the children, new curtains and a bedcover against the impending visit of Cyrus Edwards, Ninian's uncle, and his daughter Matilda. Elizabeth had expressed a desire for a full-skirted merino with a cape, in addition to which Mary wanted to make herself some warm winter dresses with lined skirts. Each day she measured, cut, basted, fitted and stitched until noon, then after dinner she went down to the *Journal* to work with the Franciscs. Every few days they received a clipping from Lincoln, and occasionally a comment on his progress; thus she was able to follow his itinerary.

Despite her tremendous busyness and the sense of expectancy for the future, the passage of the days and weeks involved considerable strain. If only there were some way of knowing what was in Abraham's mind!

At the end of September she stood up at the wedding of her friend Martha Jane Lowry to Sidney Abell. Mary had designed and made Martha Jane's gown of changeable silk that shimmered from gold to blue. The ceremony took place at seven-thirty in the evening because the bridal couple wanted to catch the ten o'clock stage for Chicago.

After the ceremony they sat down to the wedding supper of cold boiled ham, prairie chicken, beaten biscuit and Mr. Watson's bridal cake topped by a miniature bride with a flowing veil and orange blossoms.

Mary returned home as happy as she was exhausted. This was exactly the kind of gay wedding she envisaged for herself and Abraham. But she would prefer a ten o'clock service in church, then a noon bridal dinner. She had no desire to go to Chicago or St. Louis on her honeymoon as most Springfield couples did; she wanted to go east to New York, Philadelphia, Boston, the great cities she had read about since she was a child.

She was having evening supper with Elizabeth and Ninian when she noticed that they were studying her with surreptitious glances. She laid down her fork.

"Is something wrong?"

"Then you don't know that Mr. Lincoln is back?" blurted Elizabeth.

A flame shot through her.

". . . when . . . did he return?"

"Early yesterday."

Despite her effort to conceal her feelings from their unsympathetic gaze, her eyes misted. He had been home two full days and had not let her know! Ninian's voice was speaking to her from across the table; she had not heard the opening phrase.

". . . protect you." Her mind cleared. "We don't want to see you embarrassed, or worse yet to waste your years and opportunities. If the man had any sense of the fitting and proper, if he had the requisite feelings of delicacy about you and your relationship, could he possibly be so . . . indifferent?"

"It's his . . . way. A dozen times before when he has been out of town he has waited several days . . ."

"Mary, how can you expose yourself to being in love with a man who has never indicated that he cares for you?"

"He cares for me." Her eyes were lowered, her voice hard, resolved.

Elizabeth flashed her husband a reproving shake of the head.

"Of course he does, my dear. You would not have given yourself to love had you not seen it in return."

That night and another whole day went by without a word from Mr. Lincoln. She knew that if she went to the *Journal* office and continued her work she would encounter him there; but in her mind she was past accepting an encounter. Mr. Lincoln must come to her.

He did. At seven the next morning, with Elizabeth and Ninian still asleep after their return from Belleville late the night before. She had on a flannel long-sleeved, high-necked robe, old and a little faded, but warm against the early morning chill of the rooms. Her hair was pushed hastily on top of her head with combs. She was in the hall, a half-finished cup of coffee in her hand, about to ascend to the sewing room, when she heard the uncertain knocking of the front clapper. She opened the door.

There he stood, thin, hollow-cheeked, seedy. They gazed at each other across the threshold of silent and separate months. At length she murmured:

"Well, the absent Mr. Lincoln. To what do I owe the honor of this matutinal call?"

"Matutinal? Oh, it is early morning, isn't it?"

"Rather! Have you had your breakfast?"

"No, I didn't come for that . . ."

"I didn't assume you had, but you shall have some anyway. Does this robe and hairdress frighten you? I could change, if you'd like to wait."

"Don't bother; you couldn't look any worse than I do."

"Now that's what I call backing into a compliment," she replied dryly. "Just the kind of thing I've been waiting all summer to hear."

His eyes looked flagellated. She took pity on him.

"Enough of this joy of reunion; come into the dining room and I'll have Bertha bring you breakfast. It looks as though you haven't had anything to eat since I saw you last June."

"I swallowed a lot of things, including political jibes," he replied, "but you couldn't properly call them food: greasy side meat, soggy saleratus biscuits, ill-smelling coffee made from parched corn, breakfast the remains of supper. What we politicians won't do for votes."

Now she was all contrition. She went into the kitchen, asked Bertha if she would please prepare the biggest possible breakfast for Mr. Lincoln, and brought him a cup of hot coffee to tide him over. A little color came into his cheeks as he sipped the excellent Edwards coffee imported from Havana. She sat in silence while the cook brought in hot platters of ham and venison steak, eggs, biscuits and a bowl of honey. She watched him wolf the food.

He was finishing when Elizabeth and Ninian came downstairs. Ninian forgot that he was greeting a potential brother-in-law, demanding news of the Whig progress down around Cairo. Mary seized the opportunity to change into a starched cotton and to comb her hair, tying it back with a wide ribbon. When she returned downstairs she found Mr. Lincoln alone in the sitting room, sprawled comfortably in a big rocker. He said with his first easy smile of the morning:

"I would have come sooner but I was too tired to live. I looked forward to waking to it . . . and this morning I did."

"Then I'm glad you came."

"How did you pass your summer in Missouri, Molly?"

She warmed to the use of the pet name.

"Oh, I took the world easy."

"Quite an accomplishment, in so hard a world." He reached over and took her hand. "Your hands are so soft and beautifully shaped. I did miss you . . . though I never wrote. Simeon told me how hard you worked for the election. I was proud."

She was flustered at the two compliments. She let her hand rest in his bony fingers.

"I always helped Father during the Whig campaigns at home. I'm sorry, Abraham, about the Democrats winning such a large majority in the legislature, but you were re-elected . . ."

"With the smallest number of votes of any Whig. This is probably the last time I'll make it. The country folks are beginning to think I've become big city, but the big city still thinks I'm country."

There was no despondency in his voice, only a matter-of-factness. Nevertheless she rushed to his defense.

"Isn't eight years quite enough in a state legislature, Abraham? It's time you moved up to the national scene. And you will, after Harrison's election."

He described the more amusing aspects of barnstorming: the small-town taverns that were little more than high frame sheds, with three double beds in each room, the snoring so loud that he made no attempt to sleep, reading Burns and Shakespeare all night by the light of a wavering wind-blown candle, his legs sticking out of the short beds from the knees down. Then he asked her to tell him what she had observed of the election in Missouri.

She organized the materials in her mind and gave him an analysis of what she deduced locally and from the national press. He watched her with wide glowing eyes, not knowing that she had been steeped in just such clinical analysis at her father's dinner table.

When she stopped, he leaned across the space between them and gripped her shoulders.

"Molly, you are the most beautiful talker I've ever known. It's like pages read aloud from a book. If only I could talk that way when I'm up before crowds."

"Abraham, you came from a lonely background: the log cabin in the woods with the nearest neighbor miles away, the days spent solitary in the forest with your ax, with no one to talk to but yourself and the trees. I come from a highly convivial background where there were always many people around: twenty in a house, thirty in a classroom, fifty at a cotillion . . ." she chuckled, then added, "all talking at once."

He shook his head soberly.

"Molly, why is it you're the only young lady I feel comfortable with? Only one I ever have, for that matter."

"Perhaps it's because we're friends."

He peered at her for a moment. The room was still, the world locked out.

"It's more than that," he said; "but I know so little of what lies beyond friendship. . . ."

Then again their lips were sealed, as tightly and as mysteriously as they had been on the front porch in June before they had gone their separate ways. She could not think, not while Abraham had his arms crushing her to him, but she knew what she felt: that this was good, and right, and forever.

Slowly, reluctantly he unlocked his lips from hers, eased the crush of his embrace, moved back slightly though without releasing her, and looked at her with glazed, awe-filled eyes.

"Is that . . . what I meant . . . we're in love?"

4

She awakened early, watching the bright rays of the October sunlight lay across the coverlet. She thought how much she would like to give a big party and let the whole world know of their engagement, plan her trousseau, buy their home and furnish it. But as she had explained to her father in Lexington when he had been upset over the news of Frances's sudden marriage, it was not the custom in Springfield to announce engagements or to fix wedding dates.

She jumped out of bed, gaily humming the words of "It Was a Dream, 'Twas a Dream," and sat in her nightgown before the mirror. She thought, I'm prettier now than I've ever been in my life. My eyes seem to be larger, my skin is clear and glowing, my hair is alive, easy to do things with. But I must stop using that scented oil on my brush: it's darkening my hair too much. Abraham may like it lighter. I must ask him.

She slipped into a dressing gown and went down to breakfast and a new world.

Abraham arrived promptly at noon. She smiled as he unnecessarily ducked his head while coming in the front door, a protective habit that had become ingrained during his years of entering log cabins. He was freshly shaved, smelled pleasantly of cologne water, his hair was cut, washed and plastered immaculately back, his suit had been pressed and the white muslin shirt lightened the darkness of his skin.

She put her mouth up to be kissed. He kissed her full on the lips but did not put his arms about her, for they were behind his back. When he had taken his lips from hers he murmured:

"You're beautiful this morning."

"Thank you, Abraham. I might say as much for you."

"Well, Molly, in the matter of looking at one another I have altogether the advantage."

"Not true: love agrees with both of us."

He brought his arms forward, proffering a small package.

"Mr. Diller said you'd like this lavender water; just came off the *Great Western* that docked at New York from England."

"Why, darling, thank you. That was a sweet thought. I have no gift for you. I haven't even been out of the house."

He hunched down almost to her level and whispered against her ear:

"Except the rarest gift of all. . . . Molly, I am not a demonstrative man: when I feel the most deeply I can express the least. But one thing I want you to know; you are the only woman I have ever loved."

After a moment she said:

"I shall wear that golden sentence around my heart."

Dinner was only a little constrained; the men assured each other of Harrison's victory and the value of a Whig administration in Washington. Mary sat quietly.

Afterward she and Abraham took a long walk, heading south into the brilliantly colored autumnal woods, making a wide circle about the town and coming at length to the Houghan estate. She remembered that he had been marking trails while she had gone through the rooms. Dr. Houghan was out, but a servant made them welcome. Mary pointed out the flow of the rooms into each other, the fine detail of the cabinetwork, the wonderful windows bringing in the light and air, how symmetrically the house had been designed. In her enthusiasm she failed to notice that he was growing glum.

"It's mighty big; must have cost a fortune."

"Not necessarily: good taste and design cost no more than bad."

She slipped her hand into his and led him to a front window which overlooked the graceful porch and the forest beyond.

"My dear, might I tell you something? You won't think me forward? My mother, when she died, willed me eighty acres of farm land in Indiana. It comes to me when I . . . marry." She rushed on quickly, not looking directly at him. "Father says the land has increased in value; it should be worth about as much now as this house with its fifteen acres. It will be . . . my dowry."

He was silent, his eyes downcast. She hoped she had not offended him; all girls of good family carried a dowry, and what harm could there be in telling her fiancé about the *dot* she would bring to their marriage? When he raised his head she saw that he was not offended; in fact there was a quizzical humor about his lips.

"Molly, I've never even owned the bed I slept in, let alone the room or house. To jump from half a borrowed bed to a mansion . . ."

"It's not a mansion, just a brilliantly conceived house. As for the jump, I'll agree it's a long one, but only because it's so terribly overdue. After all, you're past thirty, a leader of our party, and one of the best lawyers in the state. You could have afforded a home of your own before this if you had wanted it."

"With the national debt still hanging over me?"

She smiled a bit plaintively.

"I've had good training in the running of a home. I'll manage it just as economically as your income requires."

"What income?" he interrupted. "With John Stuart in Washington and me away politicking the past six months, our practice has vanished. I have fewer cases for the next circuit court session here in Springfield . . ."

"But both you and Cousin John are building for your future. Your political career earns you new friends, and your law practice will benefit accordingly."

"Now, Molly, if I owned a palatial estate like this, the Democrats would really be able to call me an aristocrat." His eyes were laughing at her. "They'd pull up the blinds of my parlor the way I pulled up Colonel Taylor's vest in the public square. Besides, all young married couples go to a hotel to live for a year or two so the bride will have a period of freedom. Cheaper too, we could save money."

"I'll do as you wish, of course, but I so ardently don't want to begin our married life in a hotel. There's no . . . privacy. . . . I'm not frightened at the idea of undertaking the duties of a housewife; I'd most heartily welcome it."

His eyes roamed the woods about them, then settled on the trim wood structure of the Houghan house.

"But why do you want to start at the top, then have nowhere to go?"

"The Houghan house is by no means the top, it's only a temporary residence. In twenty years we'll be living in a much finer house, in fact the finest in the land, and we'll not have to buy or even rent it: people will pay us to live in it!"

Puzzled, he asked, "What house could that be?"

She broke into a radiant smile.

"The White House."

He joined her laughter.

"I assure you, Molly, my ambitions don't reach that high."

"Really? Didn't you aspire to the United States Senate at the age of thirty? Being the debt-ridden, black-futured tyro you have portrayed yourself, why should you not aspire to the presidency as well? The White House over the Senate is a difference of degree rather than kind."

He was amused but also flattered by her logic.

"It's too bad you weren't born a man, Mary Todd, you would have been a great lawyer, and could have aspired to the White House yourself."

It took a little effort, but she matched her tone to his bantering one.

"Since my being a woman is a *fait accompli,* I shall have to enter its portals on your arm. Do you mind?"

5

October was a wonderful month for love. The air was transparent, the sun still carried warmth, the surrounding countryside was a mass of brown and purple foliage.

Each day after dinner she met him at the *Journal* office where they worked side by side on new issues of *The Old Soldier,* or she wrote letters for him. At four o'clock they joined the Pedestrian Club to go nutting or berrypicking. At dusk they gathered at a different person's house for a light supper of prairie hen with corn bread or biscuits and fall garden vegetables; frequently they went on to the Tippecanoe Singing Club which met in the big room above the *Journal.* All the young Whigs in town came to sing the "Song of Tippecanoe, or A Gourd of Hard Cider":

> In the White House, Van Buren may drink his champagne,
> And have himself toasted from Georgia to Maine;
> But we in log cabins, with hearts warm and true,
> Drink a gourd of hard cider t' old Tippecanoe.

Mary played the accompaniment on the piano for the thirty to forty young women who assembled each night, along with the hundred young men. Abraham was in consistently high spirits. Whatever disappointment he had suffered over the Democratic victory in the state legislature was made up by the tremendous ground swell for Harrison. He had few cases and fewer clients; when his politicking was over for the day he made directly for the Edwards house. If their being together so much was noticed at all it was ascribed to the excitement of the political campaign.

One day they rode with Ninian and Elizabeth to Major Elijah Iles's farm for the Fair of the Sangamon County Agricultural Society, where Ninian was proud to win Second Premium for his bull Reformer. Another time they went to the Menagerie and Circus, which was exhibiting the first giraffe and elephant ever seen in Springfield; the poor elephant had to walk all the way from town to town under a heavy blanket because if people saw him on the road they would not pay to come see him in the circus.

In their walks together Abraham made sure they did not pass the Houghan house. She never mentioned it again.

Many evenings they would sit before the fire in the Edwardses' parlor and read aloud from *Tam o'Shanter, Cotter's Saturday Night* and *Epistle to a Young Friend.* He liked books on history, particularly the stories of other elections, and she would read to him from these, though often he seemed more interested in the mind of the author than in the events of history. Once he commented quietly:

"That writer can compress the most words into the smallest ideas of any man I ever heard."

Another time when she had read an involved passage from Greek history and thought he would disapprove, he said: "No, no, you cannot fly a kite high unless you have a long string."

She found herself full of a simple coquetry: she slipped her hand into his, patted his arm, said things she knew would please him, took infinite pains with her clothes so that she would always seem new and lovely, used the graceful feminine gestures she had seen other girls use to attract men, and which she had disdained . . . until now, that she was in love.

He was happy in her company. There were no headaches, no bouts of the "hypo." Even when the weather turned sharply cold he, who had said he never once got warm from autumn to spring, had good color in his cheeks and seemed as comfortable as anyone else.

When she complimented him on his ever present thoughtfulness, he replied:

"'Twasn't always so. Now that other Mary: once a party of us went on horseback to Bowling Green's. We came to a deep stream, and I rode on ahead while the other girls were being helped by their escorts. When she reproved me for my neglect, I told her that I knew she was smart enough to take care of herself. That night she told her sister that I was deficient in those little links which make up the chain of a woman's happiness."

"You just weren't in love, Abraham. You wouldn't let me half drown, would you?"

"Oh, Molly, indeed not! Back in 1830, when my family was emigrating to Illinois in a wagon drawn by two yoke of oxen, and we had foundered across the snow and ice of a prairie stream, I discovered we had left our dog on the opposite bank. It was growing dark and my father said I couldn't return for him. I pulled off my shoes and socks, waded across the icy stream, and returned with the shivering animal under my arm. I loved that bitch."

"Why, Abraham Lincoln, comparing me . . ."

Then she saw the twinkle in his eyes; he had told the story to watch her risibles.

He was a man of contradictions, that she found: the rustic manners against the innate breeding; the melancholy against the insistent humor; the awkward clumsiness against the fabulous strength; the sometime-ugliness against the sometime-attractiveness; the vagabond living against the ambition to rise; the buffoonery against the penetrating logic; the hunger for love against the shyness with women; the Democratic background against the Whig allegiance. He would ever be an extremely difficult man to unravel; no fainthearted woman would survive marriage with him; but then, she thought, no fainthearted woman would have fallen in love with him.

How strange it was that, having planned to go to Washington City with her father if Henry Clay were elected, a Whig success could send her there with a husband instead. She looked forward to the possibility with joy; she would rent a fine home, entertain widely, gather the elite of the capital and of the international society centering there, create an atmosphere and background against which Abraham would stand forth like the tall shining beacon that he was.

When the time came for him to leave Springfield for the last pre-election campaign he bitterly hated to go. She saw how miserable he was and asked:

"Must you? Haven't you done everything you can over the months?"

"It'll only be for two weeks," he grunted. "I'll come back by way of Lawrence County and bring in their votes for recording. The fee is nineteen dollars . . . it will cover the cost of the trip."

Their farewell kiss was light and affectionate. As she watched him walk around the banjo drive and then down Second Street toward the town branch she thought:

When the election is over and he comes home, we will marry.

6

Springfield went politics-mad; all business came to a standstill while both parties made their last frenzied drive to capture votes. The Whigs raised a big log cabin just south of the American House, and here Mary went every evening to hear speeches and exhortations.

By election day, November 2, she and her family and friends were in a state of jubilation, for swift-riding couriers from Pennsylvania and Ohio, where the vote had been cast on October 30, brought the news that these states had gone for Harrison. Within another two days word arrived that Maine and Vermont had gone Whig, as well as such southern Democrat strongholds as Kentucky, Tennessee and Georgia. With Springfield and the surrounding farms giving Harrison a heavy majority, it appeared that Illinois was safe for Harrison too; at last the Whigs would have their great victory.

But down at the *Journal* office a few days later, Simeon Francis was not at all the picture of the triumphant journalist.

"Simeon, what's the trouble? I heard at noon that we took Sangamon County by a two-to-one vote."

"Look at these charts, Mary. We're running a thousand votes behind in Illinois, with many of the pro-Democrat southern counties yet to be counted."

"Abraham spent weeks down there. He must have convinced . . . ?"

"Some, yes, but not enough. We needed a heavy majority in central and northern Illinois to offset the southern counties."

"But will that make a great deal of difference to us, so long as we have a Whig administration in Washington?"

Simeon Francis studied her face for a moment before saying, "I think I'd better let Abraham answer that one."

There was a silence in the printing shop in which the smells of strong black ink and fresh-milled paper dominated.

"Oh, then he has come back?"

"Last night."

She was in no way prepared for the sight that met her eyes when Mr. Lincoln walked into the Edwardses' parlor that evening. His skin was sallow, with a parchmentlike pattern of wrinkles about his eyes; the off-side dimple in his chin seemed to have deepened, giving his face an out-of-focus structure; his Adam's apple stuck out sharply; his thick, coarse black hair lay unkempt over his forehead, while his body sagged at the shoulders, waist and knees. But worst of all were his eyes: opaque, pain-fraught, the left eye high up in its socket in a tortuous imbalance.

She could have wept for him. She wanted to cradle him in her arms as would a protecting mother. Should she say kind and comforting words? Should she kiss the pain away from the dry lips? Was he sunk too low in apathy for humor?

"Well, Abraham, I see the hypo has got you. Where did you annex our charming friend, in Lawrenceville?"

His voice when it finally came was hoarse.

"No, all I picked up in Lawrenceville was ballots."

"With an asp in their midst, no doubt."

"Just Democrats. They carried the state. By less than two thousand votes, but still they carried it. A full year of my life thrown away, my debts piled higher than ever, my law practice gone . . . and Stephen Douglas has beat us again."

"I know. And I know you have a headache. I can tell it from your eyes. But surely that's no excuse for wallowing in self-pity?"

He sank into the sofa and sat with his arms hanging between his legs, clasped hands almost touching the floor.

"I suppose I deserve that."

She smiled sympathetically.

"Never mind about the just deserts. I was only trying to sting you back to life."

His misery so enveloped the room that she could no longer contain herself. She went to him and put an arm about his shoulders.

"Let me get some coffee . . . and food. Abraham, all you need is rest and fun, to get back your perspective. You're the man who in his very first speech in New Salem said to the voters, 'If in your wisdom you see fit to keep me in the background, I have been too familiar with disappointments to be very much chagrined.' "

He seemed to relax a little.

"It's more serious than you think: Stuart and I will have to dissolve our partnership . . . because there is so little law left for us to practice.

In our first year we had sixty-six cases in the July term of the Sangamon County Court. In the session beginning Monday I have eighteen. Most of them to be continued, or dismissed."

"I'm sorry about Cousin Stuart. But both of you have been practicing . . . politics. You'll get a new partner. You'll get new clients. You're a good lawyer, you're the floor leader of the Whigs in the legislature . . ."

His body recoiled in a gesture of refusal.

"Do you know how much I have earned in the past six months? Mighty little, aside from the nineteen dollars paid to me by the state auditor for bringing in the returns from Lawrenceville."

She rose and brought him a cup of coffee from the urn in the kitchen, then stood before him and cried out:

"Abraham, for heaven's sake, where is your sense of humor? *Now* tell stories, now!" She mimicked the high, nasal voice in which he had once said to her, "Ever hear about the first time I was in the legislature? I stood up and tried to deliver a short speech. Three times I cried, 'Mr. Speaker, I conceive . . .' Finally someone in the audience called out, 'Mr. Speaker, the honorable gentleman has conceived three times and brought forth nothing.' "

A wickpoint of light appeared in his eyes, but in an instant the tiny flame went out. She stood for a moment in silence and defeat, then turned, walked out of the room and out of the house.

The following morning she dressed early and went to visit her sister Frances. At noon Dr. Wallace came in from his drugstore at No. 4 Hoffman's Row.

"William, what is the cause of hypochondria?"

The doctor rose, went to his glass-enclosed bookcase and took down one of his medical reference books, *Cyclopedia of Practical Medicine*.

"This book calls *hypochondriasis* a disease, but it's really only a nervous condition. Based largely on fear."

"Fear?" His use of the word had surprised her. "Fear of what?"

"Change it to anxiety: about security, success. An attack can be brought on by overwork, worry, setbacks." He handed her Volume II of the *Cyclopedia*. "Here, read for yourself, it's not too technical."

She settled down to read.

Hypochondriasis . . . a disease remarked by lowness of spirits and an apprehension of extreme danger from the most trifling ailments. Every function of life seems in a state of disorder, and the source of acute and almost perpetual suffering. Patients complain of severe and distressing headache with intolerance of light; pressure on the top of the head threatens to extinguish consciousness; the head is as if squeezed in a vice, the eyes are felt as if starting out of the sockets. The patient suffers an intolerable anxiety, a sense of sinking, fainting, trembling, and apprehends that every minute may be his last. . . .

Dr. Wallace returned as she reached the section titled "Treatment." He glanced over her shoulder, then commented:

"The treatment is simple: it requires no foul-tasting medicines, bleeding, blistering or physicking; instead substitute good food, rest, companionship, laughter, love . . ."

"Love? Evidently that can be bitter medicine too, William. How do you persuade the patient to swallow it when he has his back teeth clamped down?"

She had no word from him for a number of days, then late one evening he appeared. She led him into the family sitting room. His body slumped forward on one leg.

"Mary, I've come to . . . break off . . . our . . . understanding. . . ."

"Break off!"

"Actually, I was a coward. I wrote you a long letter, but when I read it to Speed, he tore it up and threw it in the log fire. Said if I had the courage of manhood I must come tell you myself."

She was too stunned to face the significance of what he had said; she attacked his words tangentially.

"You discussed our relationship with Speed? Abraham, how could you?"

"Well, he is my friend, I needed help . . ."

"And I am not your friend?" Two spots of red were blazoned on her forehead.

". . . it's nothing you've done . . ."

"That's extremely kind," she replied tartly, "considering that all I've done is fall in love with you."

"You're twisting my words . . ."

"A fact which seemed to make you very happy in October, and now appears to be making you equally miserable in November. Which Mr. Lincoln shall I believe, the October Lincoln or the November Lincoln? Or will there be still a third one in December?"

He smiled wanly.

"Anger makes your tongue sharp, Mary."

"And hypochondria makes yours blunt. Because you have suffered a defeat do you want to crawl off somewhere and die?"

"Not die, just sleep through the winter, the way bears do."

"But I am not invited to the cave?" More quietly she asked: "Abraham, do you no longer love me?"

"I never said that. . . . Love's not for me. . . . I can't afford marriage . . ."

"Abraham, do you love me?" she persisted.

". . . yes."

Her eyes closed for a moment, she felt faint.

"I can't afford marriage; my prospects are poor."

"If I'm not frightened, why should you be?"

"Because the responsibility would be mine. I would never want to fail you."

"There are other more important ways not to fail a woman."

He winced, then continued in a high, querulous voice:

"In your world there is so much flourishing about in carriages. You would not have the means of hiding your poverty."

"I should certainly not try to hide it."

"Yes, Mary, you have your pride. But you have not been accustomed to hardship. When I think of that huge Houghan place you want so desperately . . ."

It was her turn to wince.

"I was willful about that. I was wrong to try to force it upon you."

"No, Mary," he cried, "you were right to speak your mind. You deserve just such a house. You have the proper background, culture, tradition . . ."

"Fiddlesticks! Let me decide for myself whether I want to be a snob."

He stretched out his hands, palms open, and raised them up and down slowly, as though trying to balance a heavy weight.

"I can't match you in words, Mary."

"Nor in love . . . ?"

"Mary, let me go. I am unhappy. I have uncertainties. I have nothing to offer you."

"If you love me, and still can say you have nothing for me, then it *is* better that we part."

She walked past him to the front door.

"You are free, my dear."

She opened the door without looking at him.

"Good-bye, Abraham."

"Good-bye, Mary."

He took a step toward the porch, hesitated, half turned to face her. And then they were in each other's arms. She heard him say:

"Forgive me, Molly. I didn't mean it. I have everything to offer you . . . all my love . . ."

The hard, dry tension within her snapped. She had not known the intensity of her own strain. She half collapsed in his arms.

7

Their relationship was never quite the same as it had been during the idyllic weeks of October. Yet in some ways their love had deepened, intensified because they had caused each other pain.

Because she had spent so many evenings dressing for him, then sitting alone through supper and huddled in the big chair in the parlor until the clock struck nine and she knew he was not coming, they had agreed that he would take Sunday dinner with her and that he would come visiting on Wednesday and Saturday evenings. However, the first Wednesday in December he sent a note that he would not be able to come that evening; and an identical note arrived late Saturday afternoon. When he finally appeared on Sunday for dinner, he explained:

"I've been lobbying."

"Lobbying? What might that be?"

"It's an informal club we have, meets in the lobby of the new state house. Members of the Senate and House get together there. We appoint mock committees and have tremendous debates: get all the things off our mind that we're too polite or constrained to say when the House and Senate are actually meeting. I am a member of the Committee on Etiquette, Politeness and Ceremony."

"They couldn't have chosen a better man," she said acidly.

"We've practically put the faro banks, roulettes and coffee rooms out of business," he continued, ignoring her aside. "We satirize all the silly bills presented in both houses. Makes a lot of fellows behave while we're in session."

"I can see what purpose it serves and how much fun it might be," she commented, "but it looks as though I'm going to have to get myself elected to the legislature to see you once in a while."

Prior to their quarrel the feeling of impending marriage had been substantial between them. Now it seemed to have vanished, as though Abraham were reconciled to being in love but had put the idea of marriage out of his mind.

With the legislature open, the town once again was filled with representatives and their families from all over the state, in addition to many attorneys and businessmen who foregathered for the special bills they hoped to promote. The social life of Springfield gathered momentum. There were dinner parties and dances scheduled for nearly every night in the week. To her amazement Abraham refused to accompany her.

"I'll be proud to take you to the cotillion at the American House on December tenth," he said; "that's for the whole legislature; but these other parties, that's too much society for me, I'm not used to it."

"It's easy enough to get used to," she said appealingly. "All these good people want you there. Suppose I pick out half of the affairs that mean the most to me, the others we'll discard. Is that a fair compromise . . . or would I have a better chance if I came down to the lobby tonight and appealed my case?"

He grinned: she could always have her way with him when she fastened him on a point of wit.

Icy winds swept the prairies. Elizabeth came down with a heavy cold. Mary put her to bed. When she took a tray upstairs she found Elizabeth reading a long letter from their cousin Mary Virginia Stuart, who had accompanied her husband John to Washington for his second term of Congress.

"Mary," exclaimed Elizabeth, "did you know that Mr. Lincoln is ill?"

"Ill?" Her eyes began ranging the room. "But with what? I saw him only yesterday."

"It seems that he has begged Cousin Stuart to get Dr. Henry the postmastership here in Springfield on the ground that he needs him desperately."

"Oh, that . . . that's his hypochondria. Dr. Henry talks him out of it every few days."

"And why didn't you tell me about going to Bogotá?"

"Bogotá? Where's that?"

"In Colombia . . . Central America. Cousin Stuart sends word that he'll do everything in his power, as soon as President Harrison is inaugurated, to get Mr. Lincoln appointed *chargé d'affaires* down there."

Mary flushed.

"You mean he never told you he wanted to go?"

When she left Elizabeth's room she sent a note to Abraham asking him to meet her at the earliest possible moment at the picture gallery that had just opened in Caffield's new building on the south side of the square. She dressed hurriedly in a warm wool dress and gaiter boots, put a claret-colored scarf about her neck and waded against the high cold winds as though they were breaking waves. At Caffield's she paid her twenty-five cents admission, walked into the big wood-paneled room and was so delighted with Correggio's *The Holy Family in Egypt*, Albano's *Judgment of Paris*, and Graciano's *Diana and Nymphs* that her uneasiness vanished. She forgot why she had come.

She was standing before a huge canvas called *Coronation of Queen Victoria, June 28, 1838*, at the far end of the hall when she felt him close behind her. Without turning her head, she said:

"Do you like paintings? This is as good a collection as ever we had in Lexington."

He had not even glanced at the pictures. She turned. His eyes were asking why she had sent for him.

"So you are planning to see the world?"

"Oh . . . Bogotá. Then you've heard?"

"By the circuitous route of Washington. *Habla Español?*"

"I didn't mention it because I was convinced Stuart couldn't get the post for me."

"How humble you've become: last summer you were dreaming of the United States Senate; now you're aspiring to some dead-alive hole in the jungle."

"It's a competence."

"Since when have you been unable to make a living?" Indignation flared into her voice. She waited for a moment to gain control over herself. "I've conquered my temper in everything except where you're concerned. When I see you quaking in your mud-splattered boots, all six feet four of you, after I had long since decided that you have the finest talent and future of any man I've met . . . what kind of an idiot does that make me?"

"Pulling my long leg, Molly?"

"Oh, Abraham, how can you think of running? What would you have to come back to four or eight years from now?"

"I'd be coming out the same hole I went in at," he said wanly.

"What about your political career?"

"Gone. I'm mousing around for something to fill the future."

"You haven't said yet whether you intended to take me to Bogotá, but I want you to know that I'd go to purgatory with you if I thought it would serve your purpose. I'd refuse to go to heaven with you if I thought it would hurt your future."

Her figure of speech amused him.

"That's blackmail, Molly; you know I couldn't go to Central America without my most ardent admirer. But I *was* running, wasn't I?" The darkness in his eyes dissipated. "Reminds me of one day during the

Black Hawk War when we had a brisk skirmish. I got into camp late at night and somebody called out, 'Abe, is that you? Thought you were killed.' 'Yes,' I said, 'this is me—ain't killed either.' 'But where have you been all this time? Didn't run away, did you?' 'No,' I said, 'I don't think I ran away; but I reckon if anybody had seen me going, and had been told I was going for a doctor, he would have thought somebody was almighty sick.'"

She heard his story eagerly.

"Well, thank the Lord: our Richard is himself again!"

His eyes swept the exhibition hall, saw that no one was present. He kissed her once, hard, then released her:

"You're entirely right, Molly. Those horrid doubts had put a damp on my spirit. Bogotá is gone . . . back into its jungle."

8

Toward the end of November, Cyrus Edwards, Ninian's uncle, arrived from Alton to take his newly won place in the House: he had come to Springfield determined that the legislature would elect him to the United States Senate. He declined his nephew's offer of hospitality, saying that he would have more freedom to campaign in a hotel room, but he did leave his twenty-year-old daughter Matilda with them to share Mary's room and bed. Matilda was tall and long-legged, in the tradition of her father and Ninian, with corn-blond hair which she wound in a braid around the top of her head.

"She's come to Springfield to find a husband," practical-minded Elizabeth told Mary. "I'm going to give a dinner party for her."

A hundred guests attended, the entire unmarried set of Springfield. The furniture had been removed from the downstairs rooms. After the guests had dined an orchestra took up its position at the rear of the entrance hall. Abraham had come early.

Matilda was the belle of the party, dressed in a tightly laced bouffant black and purple satin, her shoulders bare. Mary remained in the background; she was in high spirits, her face and eyes aglow, her repartee fast and witty. She played Elizabeth's Chinese-red piano when the party wanted to sing, and sang duets with Stephen Douglas.

Without meaning to she garnered a new admirer. His name was Edwin Webb, a short, stocky, prosperous lawyer and legislator from Carmi, descendant of a fine Virginia family, recently widowed and with two small children. His features were blunt, he had a sharp tongue in controversy, but his clothes as well as his manners were elegant. He refused to leave her side, and though he was an old friend of Mr. Lincoln's, made a point of entering into direct competition with him.

Having brought hot rum drinks into the music room for the three of them, and being refused by Lincoln, he asked:

"Wouldn't you like to get drunk just once to see how it seems?"

"Wouldn't that be like sticking your big toe out and letting a rattlesnake bite it just to see how it seems?" retorted Lincoln.

Mr. Webb reached into his vest pocket, pulled out an enormous cigar and handed it to Abraham, saying, "All right then, have a smoke for yourself."

"Thank you, I have no vices."

Mr. Webb took a ruminative pull at his hot rum, his eyes studying the contents of the cup, then decreed:

"It's my experience that men with no vices have plaguey few virtues!"

Lincoln burst into delighted laughter. The orchestra began a waltz. Mr. Webb put down his cup, took Mary by the arm and was whirling her about before she had a chance to open her mouth.

"Miss Mary, I hear you have an understanding with Mr. Lincoln."

Oh, then the town had guessed.

"Don't be hasty. There are other fish in the sea." He shook his head up and down vigorously, his lips pursed in affirmation, as though he were living proof of the point.

"Why, Mr. Webb, I've met you at three or four parties in the past weeks, and you've never noticed me. Besides, that double-width mourning band on your arm: isn't its purpose to tell us girls that we can't make it?"

"Yes, it is . . . or it was, until I got my first clear look at you tonight. I have decided that I shall court you."

"Now then, this party is for Matilda; she's the one you're supposed to court. Even Mr. Lincoln says she has a perfect face."

"Excellent! We'll let Lincoln court Miss Matilda. I assure you, Miss Mary, you're getting the best of this swap. That man's man doesn't know how to appreciate a woman; he ought to marry Joshua Speed and set up housekeeping above the store."

Mary's eyes roamed the room, found Abraham standing in the middle of a group of gesturing, laughing men. She threw back her head and laughed heartily.

The day before Christmas she was shopping in the square when she came across him unexpectedly. The evening before they had been together at the biggest party Springfield had ever seen, a dinner for three hundred and fifty guests given at the Walters'. He had muttered under his breath: "Springfield certainly is becoming a city of dashers. Will you look at the satin and feathers. These ladies must have been kept busy for months making all those dresses."

A smile lighted his face when he saw her; he took her arm, held it to his side and said plaintively:

"Molly, I'd give practically anything I own to spend a quiet evening with you again. It's a long time since we sat before the fire and you read to me from Burns or Shakespeare, and we had a good talk."

"Then we shall have it this very evening."

"Aren't we s'posed to go to supper at the Bakers'?"

"I'll send our regrets; Elizabeth and Ninian are taking Matilda, so we'll have the house to ourselves. What would you like for supper?"

"I don't know one food from another, Molly, even when I'm chewing it. Always loved apples."

She had the cook prepare a roast beef, and had chilled oysters ready to serve in the living room. He arrived with a package in his coat pocket and the warmest embrace she had known in many days. When she told him so, he replied:

"If that's what you like, why don't we stay home more often? We can't go about doing this at dinner parties for three hundred and fifty." He handed her a box. "I know I shouldn't be giving you your Christmas present until tomorrow, but . . ."

She opened the box and found in it a coral necklace with a coral bracelet to match. She admired the depth of the color.

"Put them on me."

First he clasped the bracelet on her wrist, then stood behind her and secured the necklace. His arms were about her and his cheek on hers. She turned easily in his arms and kissed him.

"Abraham, you shouldn't have spent so much money when you don't have any to spend. But I'm happy you did. Is it silly of me to think that it proves you love me?"

After dinner they sat before the fire. He had brought along a copy of Aesop and read several of the fables from it, after which she read a chapter from De Tocqueville's *Democracy in America* which she had bought at Birchall and Johnson's bookstore that afternoon.

He stayed until midnight. The last hour they spent wrapped in each other's arms in the big chair before the fire, quiet and content.

"Molly, I've hurt you sometimes and I haven't meant to. When my spirits flag down and leave me miserable I guess I just make everyone else miserable around me."

"I understand."

"I know how much stock you Bluegrass people take in engagements . . . would you like for us to be engaged?"

"Yes, my darling, I would like that very much."

"When would you want to announce it?"

"Elizabeth and Ninian are having a big family dinner on New Year's Day. When we are toasting each other for the New Year, that would be a wonderful time. . . ."

"We'll announce it then."

Two days later she heard sleigh bells coming up the drive. She put on her heavy cloak with a cape and mitts and he bundled the two of them under the buffalo robe on the little seat. They rode across the white prairies with their black trees wrapped in winter sleep. Abraham had the reins in his left hand, his right arm was about her. The sun was out, clear and cold; when they spoke their breath steamed behind them like frozen white smoke.

After an hour of driving they came to a crossroads inn, little more than a two-room log cabin. Abraham asked for hot food or drink. The innkeeper replied:

"Nobody out, cold day as this. But the old woman got a pot of soup boiling."

"That would be fine," said Mary.

They took off their heavy cloaks, sitting on a split-log bench with their feet stretched to the fire. In a moment two bowls of soup were set down on the table; they took them in their laps, eating as they faced the warmth.

"I should carry you with me on circuit," he said, reaching out his hand for her. "I never fare this well when I'm alone."

"Darling, you've been alone too long. You need someone to take care of you."

"I don't require much caring."

"Then why are you sick so often, a strapping fellow like you? It's because of the bad food you eat, no regular hours . . ."

"Molly, you sound like my mother."

"The Greek dramatists say there is a little incest in all love."

He fell silent, his face darkening. The pain that came into his eyes was unlike any she had seen there before. He tried several times to speak, but could not give breath to the words. What was wrong?

"Abraham, you look as though something is festering . . . deep inside you . . ."

"There *is!*"

The words came like an explosion, startling them by their intensity. But now at least his teeth were unlocked.

"It's . . . my mother. I've said to myself a thousand times it's all so long ago . . ."

He paused, breathing quickly, gathering strength to expose his heart. After a moment he lifted his head heavily.

"It would be an act of kindness not to mention it. Yet if we are to be engaged you have a right to know . . . beforehand . . . from me."

He fell into another groping silence. Her pulse was pounding in her ears. What was this terrible thing he was trying to tell her? At length his eyes went to hers:

"My mother . . . was a natural child. She was born in Virginia. Her mother, Lucy Hanks, brought Nancy to Kentucky when she was two . . . without a father's name. Everybody knew. . . ." He paused for an instant to see what effect his news had had. "I know what my mother endured; I saw the suffering in her eyes. It was something she could never get away from. That's part of my heritage, her suffering: hardly a day goes by but I feel it inside my vitals, eating at me."

The revelation was shocking. She came from high-placed families on both her mother's and father's side, untouched by scandal or irregularities. As she studied the face of the man she loved, watched him sitting on the hard bench, his head low, his hands almost touching the floor, she knew that his suffering was over his mother's unhappiness and his own need to give sound once again to the dreadful words. Surely, she reasoned, no words from her could mean anything unless they contained an avowal as great as his own?

"Abraham, why do we have to wait? Why can't we start our lives together on New Year's? We'll announce the engagement over the champagne, then have the marriage ceremony after dinner."

He raised himself up, love and gratitude in his eyes. Then, as quickly as they had come, they were gone, and another emotion had replaced them. Anxiety? Fear? She could not tell.

". . . more time . . . year or two."

"And what will we have in a year or two that we haven't got now: more youth, hope, courage?"

"Money . . . security."

"Is there security in money? It comes and goes so fast. Isn't our love our only security?"

"That's true, Molly: love is eternal."

"Then, darling, please let us marry now."

He sat in silence, no longer opposing her. She put her cheek on his.

"Thank you, Abraham. You'll never regret it, I promise."

9

Elizabeth was the major-domo in the kitchen, which was warm and steaming with aromatic scents of turkeys being stuffed with walnuts; ducks, geese, sides of venison; pumpkin pies baking in the oven. Since two of the four Edwards servants were busy scrubbing and polishing the house, Mary worked in the kitchen as an aide to Elizabeth, wearing a calico cover-all, her arms deep in the flour for bread and biscuits.

She had not yet said anything to Elizabeth about the engagement or the wedding, but when her sister was ready to mix the batter for the cakes she knew that the moment had come. She walked to where Elizabeth was setting out sugar and spices, put her hand on top of Elizabeth's big capable flour-covered fingers.

"Liz, it was good of you to invite Mr. Lincoln to the family dinner."

"This is your home." Elizabeth spoke without looking up. "Anyone you want is welcome."

"We're . . . we're going to announce our engagement . . . when the champagne is passed and the New Year's greetings are exchanged."

There was a long silence during which Mary could feel Elizabeth reviewing their hopes and dreams, their relationship as sisters. When finally she spoke, all conflicts and concern were gone from her expression.

"Forgive us for opposing you, Mary. But we had to be sure, considering the obstacles, that you were certain in your own mind. We will welcome Abraham into the family. How long will you be engaged?"

Mary broke into a radiant smile.

"The shortest time on record: we'll announce just before dinner, the preacher will arrive just after."

"A wedding dinner? Well, then I'll have to change the plan for these cakes. They'll have to become wedding cakes."

"Liz, be sure not to tell anyone; I want it to be a total surprise."

The day was clear and cold. She came down a little before one, dressed in a new rose-colored painted muslin, her hair parted in the center and pulled back with a gold chain which she looped through the thickness at the nape of her neck. She wore Abraham's coral necklace and bracelet. She inspected the bowls of oranges, English walnuts, candies and winter sweeting apples. Soon the family began to arrive: the Todds, the Wallaces, the Hardins, Edwardses, all with their children. She was tremendously happy and excited and greeted her relatives with extravagant embraces.

She had suggested that Abraham arrive precisely at one-thirty, after the family would be assembled but before the champagne would be served. Elizabeth sought her eye. Mary walked the few steps to the clock in the hall. It was half past one. She nodded to Elizabeth. By the time the champagne was opened and poured, the trays brought into the living room, Abraham would be there. She stood at the edge of the entrance hall so that she would be the first at the door.

But there were no footsteps on the porch, no sound of the front-door knocker. The extra serving girls hired for the day came in with the trays of wine. She refused a glass when it was offered her. What could have happened to detain him?

By now everyone had been served. One of the young Negro women stood before her with a tray. Her cousin Hardin cried out from the other side of the room:

"Mary, you haven't become a teetotaler?"

She gave a quick glance over her shoulder at the clock. It said a quarter to two. Her heart was pounding in her bosom: she accepted a glass, fixed a smile on her face and replied:

"Hadn't you heard, Cousin John J., I've joined the Washingtonians!"

Everyone laughed at this reference to the Temperance Society, then Ninian raised his glass high for silence.

"The best of all possible New Years!"

The family members cried, "Hear! Hear!" drank their champagne. Handshakes and kisses circulated about the big drawing room. To Mary the champagne tasted like vinegar. The clock in the hall struck two. She went to her sister's side.

"Liz, it's all right to start dinner. Abraham must be having trouble getting the license. He'll be here the minute it's issued."

"Oh. Very well, then."

She was grateful for the animated hubbub about the table, and during the serving of the smoked fish and caviar she was able to join in the conversation. But by two-thirty when the roast fowl had been brought in she knew she was lost: the marriage bureau was kept open all day on New Year's and Abraham would not have had trouble securing a license . . . had he gone for one. It was now so late . . . could he be ill . . . but wouldn't he have sent a message . . . ?

She made a show of eating and of talking, holding on by gripping the fingers of her left hand to the bottom of her dining chair. But when Elizabeth rose from her seat at the head of the table to go out to the kitchen to remove the wedding ornaments and decorations from the cakes, she excused herself, went upstairs to her bedroom, locked the door and flung herself face down on the pillow.

The constricting pain around her heart was unbearable. A numbness grew in her arms and legs and chest until her body lay rigid and cold as in death. Each breath was a distinct and painful one. After a while the very process of breathing exhausted her; her body grew limp, her fists unclamped, tears flooded her eyes, first the cold tears of relief from rigidity and then the warm tears of self-pity. She cried hard. Her body shook. Then she lay quietly.

The sun was beginning to go down in its brief winter cycle. The room grew darker and colder. She rose from the bed, poured water into her washbowl, bathed her eyes and her face and the frame of her hair. She took a flannel robe from the wardrobe, slipped it on over her dress, then walked to the fireplace and started a fire going in the grate.

She knew she was in serious trouble. For it was perfectly clear now, as it had not been in the planning or doing, that Abraham never had agreed to their being married today. She had proposed it, argued for it, beat down his objections. Only then, stricken, not knowing what further to say, had he become silent. And she, in her eagerness, in the great surge of her compassionate love, had mistaken his silence for assent.

She had tried to lead him into something which she had thought would be good for him, and had only forced him into an act that was contrary to his whole nature: to fail another human being. She knew how terribly he must be suffering: the remorse, the sense of guilt, the agony of spirit. She felt so sorry for him . . . and for herself. . . . She could have had her engagement, she could have had the knowledge that in the fullness of time, when he was ready, they would be married. Now she had nothing. She had been too strong, too insistent in her plans. She had driven him away, and Abraham would not easily forgive himself for what he had done. It would be a long painful road back . . . if there were a road back.

What was it he had said at their first meeting? "That was the beginning of love for me." It had been the beginning of love for her too: the beginning and the end. And she had no one to blame but herself.

10

The night was sleepless, the sunless dawn a filtering of fine gray ash through the south window. She had lain still, breathing regularly when Matilda came up and prepared for bed, but once the younger girl was asleep Mary opened her eyes and lay staring at the dark lining of the canopy. Was Abraham going to disappear from her life?

If he had failed to appear for their engagement, a relationship he had expressly desired, then she would have had to acknowledge that Mr. Lincoln was hopeless, that he did not love her, and even if he did there was no further room for her to love him: her respect for him would be gone, her own self-respect as well. But in the full cycle of the pain-fraught night she knew that he would have arrived for the announcement . . . had she not compounded his obligation a thousandfold.

She was grateful that no one but herself, Abraham and Elizabeth had known that an engagement announcement was to have been made. Elizabeth never would breathe a word of it, not even to her own husband. As for the minister who was to arrive after dinner for the wedding ceremony: she stifled a groan: should Springfield know about that, her humiliation would be too great to endure.

She slipped into a robe and sat before the mirror studying her face. A ridge of darkness had returned high on the right cheek. She scrubbed her face in icy water, brushed her hair, assumed a small smile. She had had four years of dramatic training at Mentelle's Boarding School; Monsieur and Madame Mentelle had been kind enough to say that she had talent. Very well, she would use it now; it was a basic of the Todd heritage that they could endure any pain or defeat that no one knew about.

Elizabeth's expression was unsolicitous, her voice casual.

"Good morning, dear. Cup of coffee?"

"Thanks, Liz, I could use one."

"Me too. I wonder what it is about family dinners that leaves one so fatigued the next morning?"

It was a rhetorical question with no answer expected. As she felt the warmth of the fluid inside her she thought, Springfield is such a small town: a few streets, a few business blocks. If he doesn't come here, we're sure to meet somewhere before too long: a shop, a friend's home, crossing the square . . . Then we'll slip a hand into each other's . . . words won't be necessary; we'll forgive each other our trespasses.

Though buoyed by hope, the days and nights were interminable; her head seemed to be held in an iron band; her hands and feet were always cold. She stayed in her normal routine, shopping, visiting friends, attending the parties to which she had been invited. Edwin Webb, the widower from Carmi, became her partner, taking her to the dinners and balls, flooding her with gifts: kid gloves, a silver thimble, a lacquered fan. No one commented on the absence of Mr. Lincoln; only among the girls of her own set did she catch an occasional glance of wonderment.

For his part, Mr. Lincoln was apparently following his routine, for the papers reported him spending his days in the legislature voting for an act to incorporate the town of Galesburg in Knox County, in favor of commemorating January 8, the date of the battle of New Orleans, even though Andrew Jackson happened to be a Democrat, opposing investigations of the accounts of the late Board of Public Works. It also was interesting to her that although the circuit and supreme courts were open, Lincoln appeared in only one case, and that, ironically enough, in which he filed a bill for divorce.

It was Ninian who interrupted the interlude, Ninian who was oblivious to the nuances of other people's emotions. He came into the sitting room late one afternoon and said:

"Congratulations, Mary. I knew you'd come to your senses. It's all over town that you've jilted Abraham Lincoln. I've heard that he has had two cat fits and a duck fit since you backed out from your understanding with him."

She sank her teeth into her underlip to stop its quivering. Who had started this story? Had Abraham done so to help her save face? Had people assumed it, since they had not been seen together for this long period? It had been the town's conviction that no one wanted Abraham Lincoln except herself; if they no longer had an understanding, it would be natural to assume that it was she who had abandoned it.

The next afternoon she learned from her cousin John J. that Mr. Lincoln was confined to his bed at Speed's. From a few discreet questions she gathered that it was not the winter fever or ague, but an acute attack of hypochondriasis. She too was suffering, she was sleeping poorly and eating little, but she had nowhere near his capacity for self-torture.

She saw him for the first time a week later, when she was walking to Lindsay and Brother with her sister Frances. She took Frances by the arm and led her into the nearest doorway so that they would not be seen. In a few moments Mr. Lincoln passed, gaunt as a rail, his cheeks and eyes sunk deep, the bones of his body showing skeletonlike through the old black suit. Frances said softly:

"Poor Mr. Lincoln, what has he done to himself?"

She too was stricken by Mr. Lincoln's appearance. To herself she said, My pride has not allowed me to collapse.

The newspaper reported his return to the legislature. Her cousin Stuart wrote from Washington asking what had happened between them, quoting from Lincoln's last letter to him:

I am now the most miserable man living. If what I feel were equally distributed to the whole human family, there would not be one cheerful face on the earth. Whether I shall ever be better, I cannot tell; I awfully forbode I shall not. To remain as I am is impossible; I must die, or be better.

A few nights later James Conkling came to call. He studied her face over the top of his cup of tea and finally exclaimed:

"Poor Lincoln! The fellow can barely speak above a whisper. I've just written to Mercy that his case is truly deplorable." He paused. "Have you decided to accept Edwin Webb, Mary?"

That night as she lay in her bed she was glad Matilda had returned home so that she could have the privacy of her room again. What had James Conkling said about Mr. Webb? Had she decided to accept him? She was grateful for his gallant championing when she so desperately needed someone. But marriage . . . the idea never had entered her head.

"Then your head is the only one it hasn't entered," said Mr. Webb the following evening when he made his formal proposal. "And if I haven't shown it every day for the past month, it has not been for want of trying."

She looked at Edwin Webb head on for the first time since he had been squiring her.

"You've been a good friend . . ."

"I don't want friendship from you," he interrupted. "I'm prepared to offer devotion, marriage, a fine life together; as for my two young ones, they need a mother and they will love you. You need children, not only these two, but many of your own. You will have them."

"Who is caring for your children while you are here?"

"My wife's mother, she lives close by. . . ."

If she had enjoyed any part of Edwin Webb's attentions as a balm to her pride and aching spirit, this reference to the children's grandmother cut it off abruptly. Her lips twitched, her eyes withdrew.

"Why does that upset you?" he asked.

"It's nothing . . . my own grandmother came to my mind. Grandmother Parker, in Lexington . . ."

"Miss Todd, it's my greatest wish that you marry me when the legislature ends, and come back to Carmi as my wife."

She resolved never to seek news of Abraham, but at the beginning of February she heard that he had lost his bachelor home, for Joshua Speed sold his general store and returned to Kentucky to take over his mother's plantation. Lincoln put one saddlebag over each shoulder and walked the four blocks northwest to the Butler home where he was to room now as well as board. He was growing increasingly active in the legislature, guiding his party in the fight to prevent the Democrats from packing the Illinois Supreme Court with five new Democratic justices. When Stephen Douglas called to tell her that he, Douglas, had been appointed a justice she insisted that they open a bottle of wine and toast his success.

"Justice of the Supreme Court! You'll do a fine job, Steve."

"I just about must after what Lincoln said: 'I would not behave as well as *you have to now,* for twice the money.'"

She smiled at Abraham's witticism, for the whole town had followed the political maneuvering necessary to create the new judgeships for deserving Democrats.

Toward the middle of February her cousin Stephen T. Logan invited her to his home at the north end of First Street for Sunday dinner. It was a big house set back on an elevation, with rolling lawns and a split-rail fence. After dinner he asked her into his book-lined study for a drop of sweet brandy; she saw that her thin-lipped, high-voiced cousin was edging slowly toward a delicate subject.

"Edward Baker and I are breaking up our law firm. I need a new partner. I haven't said anything about it yet . . . but it might very well be that Abraham Lincoln is my man. I've been in cases both with him and against him; he's a mighty fine young lawyer, one of the best of his kind."

Cousin Logan had not added in actual words, *What do you think?* but the question was definitely implied. Curious, she thought, how many members of the Todd family want to take Mr. Lincoln into partnership . . . including me!

"What a wonderful opportunity that will be for him," she exclaimed. "Everyone says you're our best student of law."

Stephen Logan nodded vigorously. "I like the man, and I want to have him with me. The legislature adjourns about March first, he could come in with me then."

She rose impulsively from her chair and kissed her cousin's cheek. With the best law partnership in Springfield available to Abraham, surely he would be on the road back to health, confidence . . . and love? She recalled her uncle's phrase about the end of the session: that meant Edwin Webb would be demanding a final answer.

She invited him to tea and told him about the death of her own mother, Grandmother Parker's hatred of Betsy, the tensions and problems it had created within the Todd home.

"Mr. Webb, it will be so much better for you to find someone who has not already gone through such a situation."

"Then you won't consider . . . ?"

"May the Lord forgive me, but I have to start out fresh, a new life with a new man, to make our own new family."

11

The legislature adjourned. President Harrison died in Washington, D.C., throwing Springfield into profound gloom. Lincoln and Logan announced their partnership. Still there was no word from Abraham. When a spontaneous encounter had not occurred within the first weeks of the New Year she resolved that when they came together again it must be of his doing. She avoided the places where she might meet him: political rallies and debates, the Lyceum meetings, the *Journal* office, even the streets he would have to use to get from the Butler house to his office.

The strain within her caused her nerves to grow taut. She stepped up the tempo of her activity, surrounding herself with young men and women, accepting all invitations that came her way. Though she knew she was forcing her excitement and gaiety from the deep well of her reserves, there was every reason to believe that she was playing the role convincingly.

But the nights were bad. When she crawled into her four-poster, lying in wide-eyed sleeplessness, she could make no further pretense. She shivered in the warm room, was chilled under heavy blankets. Every few weeks she would suffer complete exhaustion; during these intervals her brain seemed to be trying to pulsate against the metal vise that was encasing her head in a tight cage.

Spring came early, the prairies were covered with wild flowers, the earth felt soft and fertile underfoot. But she felt hard and sterile within; not even the growing warmth of the April and then the May sun could lessen the coldness around her heart: for it was apparent now that mere physical and economic recovery were not going to bring Abraham back to her. Her cousin Stuart reported that he had written Secretary of State Daniel Webster at Mr. Lincoln's urgent request, in a renewed effort to get him the job of *chargé d'affaires* in Bogotá. Abraham was out riding the circuit now, to Tremont for the Tazewell Circuit Court, then to the McLean Circuit Court, then to Pontiac, Clinton, Urbana, Danville, Charleston.

His being away relieved some of the pain around her heart. If it precluded the familiar long-legged step in the driveway, a pounding of the front clapper, the opening of a door to find him standing, sad-eyed and sad-smiling, but with his arms extended to her, neither did she have to breathe the same air he was breathing, walk the same streets, face the dreaded prayed-for encounter.

In June the Sangamon Circuit Court opened and a retinue of lawyers returned. The firm of Logan and Lincoln had many cases to try, as well as a good number in the Illinois Supreme Court, which would open in July. Abraham was no longer seeking the Bogotá appointment.

Another ghost laid! He had said to her, "Love is eternal." Ah yes, she thought, if only I can live that long!

The June, Titus, Angevine Circus arrived in town and she received a note from the Francises inviting her to go to the opening with them. She sat on a bench under the canvas tent imprisoned between her two bulky friends. They made her sit through the clowns and the animal acts before bringing up the subject they obviously had come to talk about.

"Mary, we cornered Abe the first moment he came back," said Eliza. "He used a peculiar phrase, 'that fatal first of January.' I asked him whether you had caused the fatality or been the fatality. He said the latter."

Simeon Francis picked up the narrative. "So then I asked him, 'Why did you let the fatal first happen? Was it an act of omission or commission?' He replied, 'Both. I couldn't help myself . . . I was sick.' We thought you'd want to know that he accepts full responsibility."

She sat listening to the music of a Negro singing act, thinking, Yes, it is nice to know, but what good does it do me really?

"Did you ever know of the other Mary?" asked Eliza.

Mary nodded. "Abraham told me about her when he asked if he could call me Molly."

"We brought you a letter we would like you to see. We felt it would ease you. It was written by Abe to Mrs. Orville Browning about something that happened in New Salem."

Mary took the sheets of familiar handwriting and while the circus band blared and the gymnasts tumbled in the sawdust, she began to read:

In the autumn of 1836, a married lady of my acquaintance, being about to pay a visit to her father in Kentucky, proposed that on her return she would bring a sister upon condition that I would engage to become her brother-in-law. I had seen the sister some three years before, thought her inteligent and agreeable, and saw no good objection to plodding life through hand in hand with her.

The lady in due time returned, sister in company. I knew she was oversize, but she now appeared a fair match for Falstaff; from her want of teeth, weather-beaten appearance I had a notion that nothing *could have commenced at the size of infancy, and reached her present bulk in less than forty years; in short, I was not at all pleased with her. But I had told her sister I would take her for better or for worse.*

Through life I have been in no bondage, either real or immaginary from the thraldom of which I so much desired to be free.

After all my suffering here I am, wholly unexpectedly, out of the "scrape." After I had delayed as long as I could in honor do, I mustered my resolution, and made the proposal to her direct; but, shocking to relate, she answered, No. I was forced to give it up, at which I verry unexpectedly found myself mortified in a hundred different ways. My vanity was deeply wounded by the reflection, that I had been too stupid to discover that she whom I had taught myself to believe no body else would have, had actually rejected me with all my fancied greatness.

Others have been made fools of by the girls; but I most emphatically made a fool of myself. I have come to the conclusion never again to think of marrying; I can never be satisfied with any one who would be blockhead enough to have me.

Your sincere friend

A. Lincoln

She sat with her head lowered, mute at the callowness and cruelty of the letter, a callowness and cruelty of thinking about himself and others which she had trouble reconciling with his hypersensitivity.

She folded the sheets and handed them back to Mrs. Francis.

"Thank you for showing me the letter, Eliza. It does help . . . in a strange sort of way: I know more surely now that I am not at the core of his problem."

"Mary, would you like me to speak to him?" Eliza asked sympathetically.

"Thank you, no. As Abraham says, 'Every man must skin his own skunk.' "

The June thunderstorms were the worst she had ever known; peal after peal after peal. Terror-stricken, she ran to her room and got under the covers. Elizabeth followed. She sat on the edge of the bed, took Mary's head in her lap.

"Now, Mary, thunder isn't going to hurt you; it's all sound and fury, signifying nothing."

Heavy sweeps of rain beat across the window. Mary wept in Elizabeth's arms. Elizabeth stroked her hair gently, knowing that it was much more than the thunder her sister was weeping about.

Summer clamped down upon them with a heat so intense that there was no air to breathe; the house and the town and the prairies were stifling. Her father wrote from Lexington inviting her to spend the hot months at Buena Vista; her uncle wrote from Missouri urging her to inspect "the whole crop of new eligible bachelors" he had lined up for her. She refused both invitations.

At the end of August, Stephen Logan came to dinner. They talked of Abraham's success before the state Supreme Court on behalf of a young Negro girl who had been sold illegally as a slave. Mr. Lincoln's argument had won the girl her permanent freedom, and all of Springfield was congratulating him at having struck a brilliant blow against slavery. Logan also reported that Abraham had just left for a visit with Joshua Speed's family at their plantation a few miles outside of Louisville.

She slept well that night, though it seemed to be not altogether a natural sleep. The next morning she had a fever and was unable to get out of bed. Elizabeth summoned their uncle, Dr. John Todd, who wrapped Mary in a blanket, then drove her the four blocks north to his own house, one wing of which was set aside as his medical offices. He put her in a big chair in his examining room, rolled up the sleeve of her nightgown to the shoulder, tied a cord tightly around her arm halfway between the elbow and shoulder and, using a spring lance, stabbed her in the blood vessel and took a full quart of blood.

He then gave her an emetic, followed by successive doses of calomel, jalap, then a portion of castor oil. At this point Dr. Todd took out a small cake of tallow, pulverized it with a case knife and sprinkled large yellow Spanish flies over it. One such patch he placed upon her breast, a smaller one on her leg. She was put to bed upstairs and covered with feather quilts. The plasters caused excruciating pain for eight hours. At the end of this time they were removed and the resultant blisters sprinkled with powdered alum.

Frances and Dr. Wallace came to visit the next morning. Dr. Todd was in the country making a call. William Wallace took one look at the blisters, listened to the account of the bleeding, emetic and physicking, then leaned over the bed and kissed his sister-in-law upon the forehead.

"Mary dear, this isn't good professional ethics, but all of the things that have been done were unnecessary. There was nothing wrong with you, except that your . . . difficulties . . . overcame you."

12

Cousin Logan had said that Abraham would return about the middle of September. The date became a new goal for her, the days between a moat across which she must fabricate a bridge. However, it was Joshua Speed who knocked on the front door. She took him into the music room, which was the coolest in the late afternoon, brought in a long drink of bourbon and branch water.

"Have you been busy falling in and out of love, Josh?"

Speed smiled a little wistfully, then replied:

"Lincoln claims that I am in love with Fanny Henning, using as evidence the fact that I dragged him all the way into Lexington so that I could visit with her. He keeps encouraging me into marriage and every time he does I return the compliment."

Winter came early, the darkest, dreariest, rainiest, muddiest winter Springfield had seen. The business district became a sea of black mud with planks and barrels and crates being thrown into it in an effort to provide steppingstones. Many of the nights were so wild with mingled sleet and snow that meetings and parties had to be called off because no one could get through.

She caught a series of colds, her eyes became swollen and red; the worst days she spent in bed. There had been times during her childhood when she had been high-strung, though never during the four years when she was living at Mentelle's, and only occasionally while she was spending the two exciting years of study under Dr. Ward's supervision. Now the feeling of being on edge seemed to be with her always; she had a constant struggle not to be sharp of tongue or bitter of mood. Elizabeth was kind, but running short of patience: why couldn't Mary accept the attentions of James Shields or of Lyman Trumbull, who had been countenancing her quite a lot of late?

With a start she realized that New Year's Day was approaching, and a presentiment grew within her that Abraham would come calling, not in the crowds which began at nine in the morning but just as it had happened two years before; after everyone had gone home and the house was quiet there would be a knock on the door and when she opened it he would be standing there. She would say, "Mr. Lincoln! Last but not least," and he would reply, "This is my first visit today, not my last." She found herself becoming increasingly excited; she planned the new outfit she would wear, made frequent trips into the almost abandoned sewing room.

Dozens of the Edwardses' friends came to pay their respects on New Year's Day. Mr. Lincoln was not one of them.

She paid a high price for her period of near happiness: now she sank into complete lethargy, her headaches returned in a new form, with configurations and black and white designs weaving themselves before her eyes. Only her pride seemed to withstand the torture she was undergoing; it alone generated the strength to go to hear James Shields deliver his oration before the Sangamon Guards in the Methodist meetinghouse, and to try the new railroad to Jacksonville.

Then early in April 1842 she received a letter from Joshua Speed. After many excruciating doubts about his fitness for marriage, he had finally married Fanny Henning and was now confessing that he was "far happier than I had ever expected to be." The important part of his letter, though, was a section he had copied out from one he had just received from Lincoln:

I am not going beyond the truth, when I tell you, that the short space it took me to read your last letter, gave me more pleasure, than the total sum of all I have enjoyed since that fatal first of Jany. '41. Since then it seems to me that there is one *still unhappy whom I have contributed to make so. That still kills my soul.*

I can not but reproach myself, for even wishing to be happy while she is otherwise. She accompanied a large party on the Rail Road cars, to Jacksonville last Monday; and on her return, spoke, so that I heard of it, of having enjoyed the trip exceedingly. God be praised for that.

When she had finished reading these lines of Abraham's she sat gazing at the paper with tear-blinded eyes. She reread the line "there is *one* still unhappy whom I have contributed to make so. That still kills my soul." She recalled the letter he had written about Mary Owens. That had been the letter of a callow boy; this was the letter of a profoundly suffering man, one who had matured under that suffering. Abraham's character had been tempered, strengthened. This she had helped do for him.

As for herself, she felt her heart beating wildly: *No man who spoke this way could very much longer withstand his own suffering over the separation.* Dear God, this was not how she had planned it but she would take him on any terms. . . .

Spring brought with it a surcease of the cold and mud. In an effort to shovel some content into the succession of empty hours she went to the opening of the Jockey Club races late in May, helped Dr. Wallace move the perfumes from his drugstore across the square to his new and modern shop. From the papers she learned that Mr. Lincoln was "off the track" for the legislature. She had no way of finding out whether he had refused to run again, or whether he simply was not being nominated by the Whig convention, sharing the fate that Ninian had suffered two years before.

Summer came again, the heat and tedium with it.

Then early one August morning she received a note from Eliza Francis asking her to come to supper. Eliza led her into the parlor. It was dark, with the blinds drawn against the hot sun. In the center of the room stood Abraham Lincoln.

13

It was almost two years since she had seen him. His eyes were clear, the set of his mouth and chin forceful; he was thin, but he was well and whole.

They said nothing, yet silence was not there: half-formed thoughts darted swiftly within her own mind; behind his luminous eyes she could feel similar thoughts swirling. They stood quietly for a long time and then she found herself held in his arms, his lips were passionately on her own.

"I'm sorry for the trouble I caused you."

When she started to shake her head "no" to the trouble, he tightened his grip on her shoulders.

"More than anything else in the world, Molly, I want us to be together. I wanted it then, that New Year's Day, but I didn't have the strength. . . . You must find some way to forgive me."

"I pressed you, Abraham; we have only to forgive each other. Isn't that what love means?"

They had supper with the Francises around the dining-room table, the light from the green-shaded lamp holding them in the warmth of renewed friendship. After supper Abraham began to write for the *Journal* a letter which he would sign with the name Aunt Rebecca, part of a series attacking the policies of James Shields, Democratic state auditor. The four Whigs got fun out of the discomfort they knew this would cause Shields; but everything was fair in war and politics. He sat before the long sheets of blank galley paper and wrote rapidly. As he passed each page to Mary for her approval their eyes met and held for an instant. She read:

Shields's story was never meant for the truth. . . . With him truth is out of the question, and as for getting a good bright passable lie out of him, you might as well try to strike fire from a cake of tallow.

I seed him when I was down in Springfield last winter at a fair. All the gals about town was there, tied as tight in the middle, and puffed out at both ends like bundles of fodder that hadn't been stacked yet. . . . There was Shields floatin' about just like a lock of cat-fur where cats had been fightin'. He was paying his money to this one and that and sufferin' great loss cause it wasn't silver instead of State paper.

When Simeon approved the letter for publication, Mary rose from the table. Lincoln followed her into the foyer. She put on her bonnet and shawl.

"I'll see you tomorrow, Molly? Shall I come to the house?"

She hesitated.

"No, Abraham. I think it better if we meet here . . . for the time being; there's been so much . . . talk. . . ."

"As you say, Molly. About four o'clock?"

Simeon and Eliza drove her home in their carriage. She ran quietly up the stairs to her room, and once in bed fell into a profound sleep.

Upon awakening she dressed quickly and left the house. Mercy

Conkling was busy being a bride, so she confided in her friend Julia Jayne, a tall, lithe, dark-haired girl with a wonderful sense of humor and complete discretion.

"Julia, you must help me. I don't want Elizabeth and Ninian to know, not until I am more certain . . ."

Julia was delighted to become a party to the tryst.

"Then call for me about midafternoon. We'll walk to the square to do some shopping. After that you can come with me to the Francis home. I'm going to need a chaperone so that the town doesn't put two and two together before Abraham and I have established our own total."

Each afternoon Julia called for her about three o'clock. They walked to the square and then made their way by various routes to the Francis home. A week after Abraham's letter was published, James Shields spoke at a public debate. He was fighting mad and spent two hours tearing apart its accusations. Mary said to Julia:

"I'd like to write the reply to Jimmy Shields. I'd have Aunt Rebecca say, when she learned that Shields was threatening to take personal satisfaction of the writer, 'I was so skart that I thought I would quill-wheel right where I was. If you want personal satisfaction come here and squeeze my hand. But if you insist on fighting, I never fights with anything but broomsticks or hot water or a shovelful of coals. I will give you choice, however, when we fight, whether I shall wear breeches or you petticoats.' "

Abraham was waiting when the two girls reached there. He was amused at Mary's idea for the letter and made her write it down at once. Simeon took it over to the shop, for the *Journal* was to come out the next day.

Shields was so insulted at the new attack that he sent his seconds to Simeon Francis to challenge Mr. Lincoln to a duel. Lincoln had gone to Tremont on business. When Mary learned that Shields and his seconds had set out for Tremont, she persuaded William Butler and the two-fisted Dr. Merryman to overtake them and warn Abraham.

She spent an extremely uneasy forty-eight hours until he returned to Springfield.

"Abraham, I got you into this."

"No, you didn't, Molly. I approved the letter. The responsibility is mine. I'm offering Shields a limited apology for all the letters printed in the *Journal*, but if he won't accept it I'm going to suggest broadswords as the weapon."

"For heaven's sake, Abraham, Jimmy Shields only comes up to your armpits," exclaimed Mary, aghast, "and those broadswords must be three or four feet long. How can he fight a duel against you with those?"

"He can't," laughed Lincoln. "It will surely seem too ludicrous to everyone concerned, and the whole thing will be called off."

Everywhere she went she heard talk about the Lincoln-Shields duel. When Abraham finally returned she could see by the expression on his face that there had been no duel; the seconds had gotten together, he had apologized, and Shields had accepted the apology. At the same time his mouth was set in a most resolute line.

"Molly, I've learned a terrible lesson. I've written anonymous letters to newspapers for years, holding up people to ridicule and satire. I'm through with it, it's no way for a man to proceed. The whole thing is now so painful and distasteful to me I'll never again mention it as long as I live."

She found that he had indeed passed a milestone with the Shields affair. In all things he appeared more consistently resolute. At the beginning of October he announced:

"I have to start traveling circuit in a couple of days, and I'll be gone almost the entire month. I'm not looking forward to the separation. When I return around the first of November, I'm going to ask you to marry me."

She showed no emotion.

"Suppose we let that wait until you get back."

"All right, Molly, but remember that although you haven't accepted me, I've declared for you."

She still made no answer.

She told no one except Julia, who offered to help her assemble her trousseau. Mary shook her head, her own lips resolute.

"Julia, I'm not tempting the fates. I have solid ground under my feet this time, but I don't think I could survive another hurt."

He was back on November 1. He had handled a large number of cases in Clinton, Urbana and Charleston, and while in Coles County had bought his parents a forty-acre tract, deeding it over to them with the provision that it never could be sold. He had spent the early hours of the next day at his Negro friend's barbershop; his hair was neatly cut, washed and combed. He had on a shiny new collar and black silk stock. She stood back from him.

"If you were as beautiful as this throughout the circuit you must have made many conquests."

"I'm monogamous by nature. Will you marry me, Miss Todd, tomorrow or the next day?"

"Is it safe for me to accept?" she asked with a tremulous but mock severity. "You're sure you won't vanish into thin air for the next two years?"

"You name the place and I'll be there. In a brand-new suit with my boots blacked."

She gazed down at his dusty and worn boots, then threw back her head in laughter.

"Well, now I have had a real assurance! If you're willing to go to the extremity of polishing your boots, I know that you've made up your mind."

He grimaced.

"Shall we make it tomorrow afternoon, at the Reverend Dresser's?"

Images of Elizabeth and Ninian floated across her mind.

"I know Springfield is a town of sudden marriages, but I'm going to have a little . . . explaining to do."

"All right, Molly, you set the course, I'll steer the flatboat. Any landing you say."

When she broke the news to her sister the following morning, Elizabeth asked matter-of-factly:

"Mary, must you be married this evening? I would like to plan a formal wedding, one worthy of a Todd, such as we gave Frances."

"That would have been fine some twenty-two months ago, Liz," Mary murmured wistfully. "Isn't it pretty late for that kind of thing now?"

"Then you'll have to be married in front of the Episcopal Sewing Society; they're meeting here tonight and my supper is ordered."

"The Episcopal Sewing Society? Oh, Liz, no!"

"All right, put it off until tomorrow. I'll get up the very best supper I can, but as far as the refreshments are concerned, I'm afraid I'll have to send to Old Dickey's for some of his gingerbread and beer."

Julia Jayne was the maid of honor, the bridesmaids were her uncle John's daughter, Lizzie, and Ann Rodney. Dr. and Mrs. Todd were there, her sister Frances and Dr. Wallace, Helen and Ben Edwards, Dr. Henry, the Butlers with whom Lincoln had lived so long, Mrs. Butler in a yellow satin evening gown.

Mary dressed in a white swiss muslin she had made earlier in the summer but never worn; it was fresh and crisp and the only new white dress she had. She wore the pearl necklace her father had brought her from New Orleans. Poor Father, she thought, he's going to miss still another wedding. For her sister Ann, there would be a vacancy.

Abraham arrived early with his friend James Matheny, who was to be his groomsman, and Justice Browne of the state Supreme Court. At five o'clock the minister arrived in his canonicals. The family and their friends formed a circle in the parlor. The Reverend Dresser began the ring-and-book ceremony:

"'Dearly Beloved, we are gathered here in the sight of God, and in the face of this company, to join together this man and this woman in holy matrimony; which is an honorable estate; and therefore is not by any to be entered into unadvisedly or lightly; but reverently, discreetly, advisedly, soberly, and in the fear of God . . .'"

The rain had started a little earlier. It beat down in powerful onslaughts, wave after wave of it washing against the windows. She knew that rain always depressed Abraham.

"Abraham, wilt thou have this woman to thy wedded wife, to live together after God's ordinance in the holy estate of matrimony?"

"I will."

"Mary, wilt thou have this man to thy wedded husband, to live together after God's ordinance in the holy estate of matrimony?"

"I will."

The Reverend Dresser turned to Lincoln. "Repeat these words, 'With this ring I thee wed, and with all my worldly goods I thee endow.'"

Justice Browne, who had been listening intently, exclaimed:

"God Almighty, Lincoln, the statute fixes all that!"

There was a thin-sliced second of consternation, then everyone burst into laughter, the minister roaring in amazement with the rest. The laughter wiped out the sound of the pounding rain.

The Reverend Dresser handed a gold ring to Lincoln. Abraham placed it on the third finger of Mary's left hand.

"I now pronounce you man and wife."

They had supper, with two beautiful wedding cakes. A small orchestra came, they danced, there was friendship and joyousness, and much of Ninian's excellent champagne.

Shortly before midnight she and Abraham slipped out the front door where there was a carriage waiting for them. They drove to the Globe Tavern.

He remained downstairs to sign the desk register. She went up to the room that had been occupied by John Stuart and his wife, and then by her sister Frances and Dr. Wallace. There was a brand-new spread on the four-poster, bowls of autumn leaves and flowers. She slipped the plain gold band off her finger, walked over to the lamp to gaze at it. It was inscribed:

LOVE IS ETERNAL

A wave of almost unendurable happiness swept over her. Long ago Abraham had said "Love is eternal," and she had thought, If one can live that long. Well, she had endured.

She must always remember that: love ebbed and flowed, now rich and shining, now shabby and disconsolate. One must survive the bad in order to realize the good. Therein lay the miracle of love, that it could eternally re-create itself. She must always be dedicated, no matter what the years held, what the hardships or disappointments, the sorrows or tragedies: she must come through them all, through the most violent and frightening storms; for at the other end, no matter how long it might take or how dark the passage, one could emerge into clear warm sunlight.

She heard his long rangy steps coming down the hallway. His hand was on the door. She turned, her face suffused with love.

ANYONE working in historical or biographical materials, out of which he fashions a novel or a play, has to be reconciled to the iceberg concept: only one-ninth of everything he unearths and sets down either in his notes or his manuscript can ever be published. The other eight-ninths are the portion of the iceberg that remain under the water level. However, no professional in the field has any feeling that this eight-ninths of the material is wasted. It forms the enormously solid base on which the reader walks in confidence across the pages of the book, sensing that what has been printed is buttressed by quantities of knowledge, which give a flavor, an ambiente, and an authentication to the printed word.

This was particularly true of my studies for the biographical novel about Mary Todd Lincoln and Abraham Lincoln. The work of research, in Lexington, Springfield, and Washington, as well as the writing, took between two-and-a-half and three years. I decided that the artistic unity of the novel demanded that I end with Lincoln's death, and not Mary's. But although I was not going to include the remaining, tragic years of Mary Todd Lincoln's life, I needed to know everything that happened in them; consequently, I researched this period as thoroughly as I had any other.

I was always a little uneasy about not having finished Mary Todd's full story; and this feeling was corroborated by a considerable amount of mail, asking, "What happened to Mary Todd Lincoln during the rest of her life?"

Then one day in 1955, a friend and fellow Lincoln buff came to my house with a packet of papers grasped tightly under his arm. He had bought at auction a group of Mary Todd Lincoln's letters which had never before been seen. They not only furnished fresh light on the final years, but also afforded me a motivation for completing the heartbreaking history.

The story was published by *Good Housekeeping*, and was included four years later, in their book, *Good Housekeeping Treasury*.

THE TRIP THAT ABRAHAM LINCOLN PROMISED MARY

THE wife of a great man stands alongside him in the white, hot light of acceptance and acclaim; but on his death that light goes out, leaving the widow in darkness. Sometimes, as with Mary Todd Lincoln, the darkness can be full of demons. With the possible exception of Washington, Abraham Lincoln is the most deeply loved of all American Presidents; without any exception, Mary Lincoln has been the most misunderstood and reviled of Presidents' wives.

The darkness that surrounded Mary has now been pierced. Out of their envelopes, where they have rested, unwanted and unread for almost ninety years, there has emerged a group of intimate, deeply felt letters written by Mary Todd Lincoln to her beloved friend, Eliza Jane Slataper. These letters give us the opportunity to learn from Mary Lincoln's own words much of what she thought and felt about the years following the moment she walked down the steps of the White House for the last time.

Mary Lincoln's reputation had been destroyed during the Civil War, when, since she was Southern born, the South declared her a traitor and the North declared her a spy. But of all the charges levied against her by her enemies, the hardest one for her to bear was that Mr. Lincoln never loved her, that she tricked or forced him into marriage—this about the courageous wife who bore her husband four sons (Eddie, who died of diphtheria at the age of four in Springfield; Tad, who was eight when his father became President; Willie, who died in the White House at eleven; and Robert, who was a student at Harvard University in 1861), fought by his side in adversity, comforted him in defeat, and never failed to keep his ungainly feet in the paths of glory.

"My home for so many years was so rich in love and happiness," she writes to Mrs. Slataper. "Now I am so lonely and isolated."

The discovery of the letters to Mrs. Slataper, the most important single documentary find in Mrs. Lincoln's story, came about through an ironic accident. They were rescued from oblivion *not for their content but for their covers,* by Edward Stern.

Edward Stern, who began collecting stamps when he was a small boy, was a professional philatelist. As a hobby he collected "stampless covers" (more correctly, "prestamped, preadhesive covers")—envelopes with hand-struck postal markings, which preceded the adhesive postage stamp. It was during his search for these "covers" that he stumbled across Mary Lincoln's letters. Though he realized that the Mary Lincoln signature increased the value of the letters, he steadfastly withheld the letters from Lincoln scholars. By the time of his death the letters had disappeared so completely that even Mrs. Stern was unable to locate them.

A friend of Mrs. Stern's remarked, "You know, people sometimes put letters in a book. Let's go through every volume in your library."

A diligent search of the more than a thousand volumes unearthed Mary Lincoln's letters to Mrs. Slataper between the pages of a leather-bound set of *The Lives of the Presidents.* Since all the books in Stern's library were later sold, the Mary Lincoln letters could easily have vanished, never to reappear. Mrs. Stern added them to her husband's collection of autographed checks and franked envelopes and sent them to the Parke-Bernet Galleries of New York City to be auctioned at a public sale.

Now, for the first time, Lincoln scholars learned of their existence. Their importance not only in Mary Lincoln's personal story but for a deeper understanding of the Lincoln marriage was perceived at once. Interested in acquiring the letters were the Illinois State Historical Library of Springfield, Illinois, and the Huntington Library of San Marino, California.

The prize went to Justin Turner, a Lincoln collector who owns three of the five different versions of the Thirteenth Amendment, which freed the slaves; Lincoln's Presidential Seal; and the manuscript of the only lecture Lincoln ever delivered for pay, "Discoveries, Inventions and Improvements." Mr. Turner turned over the Slataper letters to me, suggesting that I write an epilogue to *Love Is Eternal,* my novel about Mary and Abraham Lincoln, which had ended with the forty-six-year-old Mary leaving the White House for the last time.

Mary's letters to Mrs. Slataper are especially revealing because they are written to a new friend with whom she had not already been over every detail of her harrowing life. Her letters to her family are all too frequently constrained, those to her business and legal advisers often technical in nature. But to Eliza Jane Slataper, an intimate whom she could trust, Mary Todd Lincoln revealed the innermost secrets of her heart.

Particularly, the Slataper letters disclose the story of the trip to Europe that Lincoln promised Mary on the very afternoon of his assassination. The story of how, three years later, she walked up the gangplank of the *City of Baltimore* with Tad's hand in hers, even as she had walked down the White House steps three years before, her eyes blinded with tears but her hand securely in her son's, can now be told because of the Letters to Mrs. Slataper.

To grasp the full thrill of her husband's promise, we must go back to Mary Todd's early years in one of the most cultivated cities in America, called the Athens of the West—Lexington, Kentucky. Lexington was a prosperous community; its residents traveled widely; it was visited by people from all over the world. Lexington people bought and read many books; they had a fine college, Transylvania; and everywhere one heard excited talk about the Grand Tour.

Mary could not remember when she did not have a full-blown determination to travel on the Continent. In this ambition she was abetted by her stepmother, Betsy Humphreys Todd, who gave young Mary books about Europe as birthday presents: Dresdin's *The Art of Traveling Comfortably;* Sir Walter Scott's historical novels about Scotland; a packet of richly illustrated books depicting the life of the English and French courts.

By the time Mary was ready for what would be the equivalent of our present-day high school, Monsieur Augustus Waldemare Mentelle and his wife, refugees from the French Revolution, had opened a school for young ladies in Lexington. Monsieur Mentelle not only taught Mary to speak French, but trained her well in French literature, sharpening her interest by discussing the private lives of European nobility.

John Todd could not send his daughter to Europe. In addition to the six children of his second marriage, there were still a number from his first marriage to be reared and educated. If Mary Todd was to tour Europe, she would have to wait until she was married and have her husband take her. That Mary had always known.

But the man Mary Todd chose to marry was not only the homeliest in all Sangamon County and, according to her family, the least promising; he was also one of the poorest. The roseate dreams Mary had of world travel were put aside when she knew she loved Abraham Lincoln and would have none other. Put aside, that is, for the time being.

Pretty, witty, vivacious Mary Todd had among her abiding virtues the virtue of patience. She felt intuitively when she fell in love with Abraham Lincoln that he would one day be important and consequential; but it would take time. She knew that she and her husband would one day make the Grand Tour of Europe; that too would take time.

Then, on the last day of her husband's life, on a drive back from the Navy Yard, with Mary nestling against the warmth and security of his shoulder, the tall, lean, dedicated man who, in his infinite love and wisdom, was planning even to heal all the wounds of the nation, the South's as well as the North's, spoke the words she had been longing to hear since she was a young girl.

"Mary, we have had a hard time of it since we came to Washington. Between the war and the loss of our darling Willie, we have both been very miserable. But I consider that this day the war has come to a close. With God's blessing, we may hope for four years of peace and happiness. We have laid by some money, and we will try to save up some more. When this term is finished, we are going to have the vacation in Europe that you have dreamed about all your life."

That night, in the Presidential box of Ford's Theatre, there was the sudden sound of a shot.

Abraham Lincoln had never broken a promise to his wife. But this last of all promises cruel fate made it impossible for him to fulfill.

But Mary Todd Lincoln had always kept her promises too, particularly those made to Mr. Lincoln. Three years later she boarded the S.S. *City of Baltimore*. She had overcome prostrating grief, illness, and, most importantly, lack of friends to accompany her.

The three years since her husband's assassination had been for Mary Lincoln close to purgatory. An important part of her external difficulties arose from the fact that Lincoln, like so many lawyers before and since, died intestate. This failure to leave a will obliged the court to divide his estate into three parts: one third to his wife, another to his young son Tad, the last to his son Robert. Mary was to have the use of Tad's third to raise and educate the boy; Robert's third was his exclusive possession and consequently was lost to her.

For his time Lincoln had left a good estate. Harry E. Pratt, indefatigable Illinois State Historian, has established that the Lincolns were worth fifteen thousand dollars when they entered the White House, and more than eighty-five thousand dollars at the time of Lincoln's death. The estate was put into the capable hands of one of Lincoln's oldest friends, with whom he had ridden the Eighth Circuit of Illinois: Supreme Court Justice David Davis. Although Judge Davis's astute handling raised the value of the estate to $110,974 by the time it was distributed, three years later, in 1868, in the intervening years Mary received only $3400 a year—$1700 for herself, another $1700 for Tad. This $3400 was not enough to live on, as Mary soon learned.

From the White House, Mary, with sons Robert and Tad, went directly to the Tremont House in Chicago, since she had pleasant memories of her stay there with Lincoln after his election to the Presidency. She was able to remain but a short time, for her first bills proved, in terms of the simplest arithmetic, that she could not afford to live in a first-class hotel.

The Lincolns moved to modest quarters away from the center of town, but twenty-two-year-old Robert so hated their new lodgings that he is reported to have said, "I would almost as soon be dead as be compelled to remain three months in this dreary house."

And so Mary Lincoln was obliged to put all her possessions but the barest necessities into storage and move to a boardinghouse.

In the fall of 1865, she wrote to Mrs. Gideon Welles, wife of the Secretary of Navy under Mr. Lincoln, a devoted friend during White House years, "Everything is so enormously high here. Our means only allow us to board genteelly, and with this just now, I suppose we must be content."

Friends and relatives urged her to return to the home on Eighth Street, in Springfield, Illinois, which the Lincolns had bought in 1844, where she could have lived in modest dignity. But the house held too many poignant memories, and Mary could not bring herself to go back, not ever.

It was at this time that she began her monumental struggle to secure a modest pension from Congress, a five-year contest in which she wrote hundreds of letters seeking support, and rival segments in Congress waged a battle to make it appear to the nation that the rich, extravagant Mrs. Lincoln was singlehandedly trying to bankrupt the United States Treasury.

From her letters to Mrs. Slataper, we learn how much Mary suffered under the merciless attacks of the press of the nation, with the exception of but a few papers that urged her right to the pension. From the personal and vindictive tone of the attacks, one would have thought that Mary Lincoln had either started the Civil War, assassinated her husband, or was a scourge on the American landscape that must be somehow wiped out.

Some time later Mary wrote to her friend, Mrs. Slataper, "I congratulate myself that I am in the south of Europe quite removed from hostile American newspapers."

Then in 1866, Congress made a liberal gesture: The equivalent of a year's presidential salary was paid to Mrs. Lincoln, about $22,000, to enable her to buy a proper home and furnish it.

Mary promptly bought a house at 375 West Washington Street in Chicago, then found that the $3400 a year income from her estate could not keep up the costs of the house, particularly since she wanted to send Tad, who had a speech defect, to the best school. In September of 1867 she wrote, "With the most rigid economy, which I am compelled to practice, I find it absolutely impossible to continue housekeeping on my present means."

Had Congress voted an annuity along with the house, all would have been well. As it was, Mary had to sell the house and go back to boarding.

Mary Lincoln thought she had endured, in the death of her two sons Edward and William, the death of three half-brothers and her beloved brother-in-law in the Confederate Army, and finally the assassination of her husband, all the grief that the human heart could possibly bear. But now the last possible shred of tranquility was stripped from her.

William Herndon, Abraham's former law partner, gave a public lecture in which, giving vent to the long and deep-seated dislike he and Mary had always felt for each other, he claimed that Lincoln, when a young man, had been deeply in love with Ann Rutledge of New Salem, that her death had caused him to lose his mind, that his lifetime melancholy was caused by the loss of Ann, and that, by implication, Abraham Lincoln had never loved Mary Lincoln, his wife for over twenty-three years.

A greater piece of romantic nonsense has never been foisted on the American public. Young Abe had liked Ann very much, and she had liked him (at the time, she was also engaged to John McNamara, who was in the East on a long journey); they had read aloud to each other under the great tree by the main road of New Salem; they had walked hand in hand across the blossoming fields as young couples do in the spring. Had she lived, they might have loved, they might have married; who can say?

But people all over America took up the canard that Abraham Lincoln had never loved Mary Lincoln, that she had harangued him into marrying her, that she was a cross Lincoln had to bear all his days.

This about Mary Todd, whom Abraham Lincoln had told, "You are the only woman I've ever loved"; who had helped him create a life, a career, an indestructible place as one of the world's greatest heroes; who had her weaknesses, her faults, her shortcomings, as which of us has not? but who had never ceased to love Lincoln, to believe in him when he had lost faith in himself, who had never stopped working with him, encouraging him. If Lincoln's life is to be considered heroic, Mary's help as wife, mother of his children, and partner in maintaining a robust marriage must be granted some portion of the credit for that greatness.

How Mary Lincoln, still wearing deep mourning, leading no social life, crying to Mrs. Slataper, "Time brings to me no healing on its wing . . . ," had the strength to endure, how she simply did not turn her face to the wall and die, can only be understood by knowing her tremendous love for Tad, who desperately needed her love, and her determination to go to Europe for the trip she had planned with her husband. All her thoughts were now pointed in this direction.

Mary and Tad Lincoln sailed on October 1, 1868, for Bremen, Germany, on the S.S. *City of Baltimore* shortly after she had attended Robert's marriage to a fine young lady whom she had met in Robert's company during their last months in the White House.

For a full year Mary had been under a doctor's care, suffering from migraine headaches, fainting spells, near blindness from weeping, and obsessive worries about money. During this year of seclusion most of her intimates had fallen away. When it came time to make her preparations for Europe, she was almost alone.

Almost, but not quite; there remained her enduring friendship with Mrs. Eliza Jane Lee Slataper of Pennsylvania, a relationship totally unknown to history until the letters to Mrs. Slataper were found.

There is considerable mystery surrounding Mrs. Slataper. To the best of the knowledge of Lincoln students, thc Lincolns did not know the Slatapers during the White House days, unless President Lincoln met Felician Slataper, born in Trieste, Austria, a division engineer for the Pittsburgh, Fort Wayne and Chicago Railway Company, during a wartime trip. Nor do we know when Mary Lincoln first met Mrs. Slataper, nor how their relationship ripened to the tender devotion that is so manifest in the letters.

It appears that Eliza Jane Slataper was seriously considering responding to Mary's grief-stricken pleas to accompany her to Europe, even if for only a short stay. Mrs. Slataper's son Dannie, about Tad's age, who was in school in Chester, Pennsylvania, wrote to his mother, "I am very glad you did not go over to Europe with Mrs. Lincoln and

Tad. I did think you would because you and Mrs. Lincoln are such friends."

Mary was bitterly disappointed. Nowhere do we see so clearly as in these letters her vast loneliness and terrible need for friendship. Her sense of being abandoned by all the world. She was now afraid she would have to sail without seeing her dearest friend to say goodbye.

On July 12, 1868, Mary wrote to Mrs. Slataper, urging her, "from the depths of an agonized bereaved heart to come to me if only for a day or two. I have been prostrated by illness . . ." And then again, from Chicago on July 27, she wrote, "In my great agony of mind, I write you, I pray you by all that is merciful to come to this place, if but for a few days. I am entirely alone. Come, come to me."

Mrs. Slataper apparently could not leave home; instead she invited Mary, and Tad too, for a stay at the Slataper home in Pennsylvania, a visit that did Mary tremendous good. Mrs. Slataper then agreed to go to Baltimore to see them off, but she fell ill and was unable to keep the appointment. Mary wrote from Baltimore on September 29, "Can I begin to express my disappointment at not seeing your dear face before I leave? Instead of yourself, your telegram came this morning. I am feeling very anxious about your health, and will continue to do so, during the voyage. We sail on Thursday—no more happy hours with you for a long time."

When the S.S. *City of Baltimore* left the dock, and Mary stood at the rail with only her young son's hand in hers and *nobody to wave goodbye to,* she was a tragically unhappy woman, wanting nothing more than, as she wrote in her last letter from Barnum's Hotel in Baltimore, "A change from this gloomy earth . . . to be forever reunited with my idolized husband and my darling Willie would be happiness indeed." She had suffered griefs that ". . . the grave alone can soften."

The moment she set foot on European soil, however, her illness and despondency vanished, her obsession with poverty disappeared. She became once again the vital, keenly interested, and penetrating observer she had been all her life. As her graphic and frequently brilliant letters over the next three years show us, Mary Todd, and then Mary Lincoln, had been right in thinking that, aside from the serious considerations of love and work, foreign travel was the most fun and the most excitement that life had to offer.

Mary felt very much at home in Frankfort, to which she traveled from Bremen, for she had been reading about German cities since childhood. "I came to Frankfort expecting to remain a week," she wrote to Mrs. Slataper in a cheerful and witty letter, "and now Christmas is almost upon us. I expect no place on the habitable globe do they make a greater preparation for it than here. We have quite a little colony at our hotel. . . . My rooms are on the same floor with Consul Murphy and wife, and Mrs. Mason of New York, the wife of Organ Mason, a very superior woman, we are much together. She has acquired that softness of character, without which no woman can be lovely."

Though she was still wearing mourning and would accept no dinner invitations, Mary enjoyed moving about the town, as tourists do, seeing the sights.

"There appears more to tempt me here than elsewhere, the shops are very beautiful, and the prevailing Americans are said to have increased the prices. We are considered in Europe (and very justly) a most prodigal people."

When "two American gentlemen friends" called to pay their respects and asked whether she was homesick, Mary replied, "I pine for a glass of American ice water, the water here is impossible and really dangerous to drink."

An old friend from Philadelphia, Mrs. Orne, happened to come to the hotel to stay. "Before she had taken off her bonnet she was in my room and we sat up all that night talking," Mary wrote. Mary enjoyed the companionable visit, but the poor man in the next room had to rap on the wall and cry, "Ladies, I should like to sleep some."

The basis of her well-being was that she had removed herself from the political arena of the United States, where not only her enemies and her husband's enemies had been sniping at her, but even some of Lincoln's admirers who, in order further to magnify their martyred hero, had been trying to reduce her in stature, never realizing that the wife had been martyred along with her husband.

"I like Frankfort exceedingly, the true secret, I suppose, is that I am enjoying peace which I was not allowed in my native land."

It would be distorting the truth to suggest that Mary Lincoln did not take her weaknesses to Europe with her along with her baggage. Her reverence for royalty, instilled during childhood, was one of her dominating passions. In writing to her friend about her hotel in Frankfort, which she assured Mrs. Slataper was "the aristocratic one," she told of her great pride when "counts, dukes and duchesses frequently laid their cards" on her table, and of her joy when Popp, the famous dressmaker who designed fashions for all the royal families of Prussia, agreed to make her some black silk mourning gowns, trimmed with crepe.

When she went to visit a thousand-year-old castle, she was fascinated by the portraits of fifty German emperors. "The chairs on which these men sat, the stone floors on which they trod," she wrote excitedly, "everything possesses a charm for me."

Though Lincoln's estate had now been distributed and she had received almost $75,000 for her own and Tad's share, she was still concerned about money, a concern she was never to conquer. She engaged the least expensive room in the hotels where she stopped and continued the constant stream of letters to the United States in her fight with Congress to secure her pension. Nevertheless, she sent lovely gifts of amber home to Mrs. Slataper and her family. She also enrolled Tad in the best private school in Frankfort, where the lad was homesick for a long time and struggled mightily with the German language but in a month or so had made friends and was doing well.

She was anticipating with the greatest of joy her visit to Italy. To Mrs. Slataper she wrote, "I wish those dear eyes of yours could become clairvoyant and visit sunny Italy, its churches, paintings, and all objects of interest, with me."

But she could not tear herself away from Frankfort. She stayed on too long in the raw weather, caught cold, and, in February 1869, after a stay of about four months, was sent by her physicians to Nice, on the French Riviera. There she grew stronger, and she quickly threw off the cold.

"Was there ever such a climate, such a sunshine, such air? You cannot tour for flowers, beautiful bouquets, thrust into your very face," she wrote. "I never return from my walks without my hands being filled. My windows are open all day, looking out upon the calm, blue Mediterranean."

By now she was a confirmed sight-seer; on the way down from Frankfort to Nice she had stopped to visit a castle where "The veritable White Lady is said to dwell, and where Napoleon signed his memorable treaty." A lifetime reader and student, Mary knew her history well, not only in terms of each country's literature, but of its wars and politics. Going north to Paris, she visited the romantic courts and palaces that Monsieur and Madame Mentelle had told her about years before.

In July of 1869 she made one of the happiest journeys of her European tour—to the Scotland she had learned to love from Sir Walter Scott's historical novels. It is only fair to let her speak for herself:

"Beautiful glorious Scotland has spoilt me for every other country. It appears to me that we saw every place, yet I presume we might remain five months continually traveling round, without doing so. We visited Abbotsford, Drybourgh Abby, passed six days in charming Edinburgh seeing *oh so much!* Glasgow, journeyed on the Clyde, all through the west of dear old Scotia, Burns' birthplace . . . went to Greenoch, heaved a sigh over poor Highland Mary's grave, visited Balmoral . . . *Glamis Castle,* saw the room and the bed on which poor King Duncan was murdered, stepped on the same step from which Mary Queen of Scots jumped into a canoe from her prison home at Lochleven. We returned via Ostend, Brussels, went out to the battlefield of Waterloo. . . ."

She and her son then returned to Frankfort for another year of school for Tad.

In September of 1870 they made a proper tour of London, then settled down in Leamington, where Mary wrote, "We are three hours and a half by rail from London. This place is the garden spot of England. Kenilworth Castle three miles distant, Warwick Castle nine miles distant. Pleasant drives all of them and spots where I have lingered with so much pleasure."

Tad was doing well. His mother wrote to Mrs. Slataper, "Taddie became quite proficient in the German language, and is now studying very diligently under an English tutor for seven hours each day." Tad was nearly seventeen, growing tall and nice-looking, a lovable boy who was a joy as a son and companion.

After living and traveling in Europe for three years, Mary decided to return home. In Europe she had enjoyed a greater peace and fulfillment than any she had known since her husband's death. But Robert's wife had invited her to visit them in Chicago and see her granddaughter, and at long last she received the news that on July 14, 1870, the United States Senate had confirmed the House bill to grant her a pension of three thousand dollars a year for the rest of her life.

She wrote to Mrs. Slataper, "I have become weary of sight-seeing." And so, in March of 1871, she and Tad sailed back to America—to further tragedy and destruction for them both.

They had been in Chicago only a few weeks when Tad came down with a severe cold. He had been well and had grown like a weed in Europe. In Chicago he could not seem to shake off his illness. On July 15 he died, the third of Mary's four sons to be lost to her.

The blow was as unexpected as Lincoln's death had been, and the loss as heavy. Mary had never managed to make friends with Robert, nor had his father; Robert was reticent and aloof. Tad was really the last child she had left. Mary's letter to Mrs. Slataper, written in October, is heartbreaking:

"I have been so utterly prostrated by my deep, deep grief, that my health has completely given way. Consequently, I am ordered perfect quiet—as much as can be obtained by a person so brokenhearted as my poor self. As anxious as I am to see you, I feel that *it is best* at present that we do not meet. Bleeding wounds would only be opened afresh. In God's own time—I may grow calmer, yet I very much doubt it. As grievious (sic) as other bereavements have been, not one great sorrow ever approached the agony of this. My idolized and devoted son, torn from me, when he had bloomed into such a noble, promising youth. Your deeply afflicted friend."

For the next four years Mary wandered from Wisconsin to Canada to Florida and back to Chicago in an effort to escape her grief. They were among the most painful years of her life. Yet they became as nothing when, in May 1875, her last living son, Robert, had his mother brought into a courtroom in Chicago and publicly tried on charges of insanity.

At the time of Tad's death, Mary Lincoln was fifty-two years old and going through a most difficult transition. Wracked by her ghastly misfortunes, longing only for death, not knowing why she was still alive, she had begun to act irrationally. She spent money extravagantly, foolishly, for things she could not use—sixty pairs of lace curtains, dress goods by the bolt. More seriously, when she was in Florida in March 1875, she was overcome by a hallucination that Robert was ill, telegraphed his physician in Chicago about it, and took the next train north. When she arrived, she was obviously in a disturbed state, claimed that someone had put poison in her coffee at a wayside railroad station. She was also carrying with her thousands of dollars in negotiable securities. It was impossible for Robert to handle her from the hotel room he had rented next to hers; once she tried to go down in the elevator without putting on sufficient clothing.

Robert Lincoln had her tried for insanity before a jury. His mother had been spending too much of her money and, says one biographer, "Robert naturally was fearful she would dissipate her estate; the only way he could get the control of it out of her hands in order to protect her interests was to have her declared legally insane."

Stories of her irrationality, which up to this point had been known only to members of the family and a few outsiders, were spread all over the world in newspapers, so that to this very day Mary Lincoln is thought by segments of the American public to have been insane. Did not the jury say so after her son Robert Lincoln laid the evidence before them?

All Mary Lincoln said was, "Oh, Robert, to think that my son would ever have done this!" Once Robert gained control of her money, nothing could convince Mary that that had not been his motive.

She lived in a room with barred windows. A guard went everywhere with her. She received medical care. She did not believe she was insane, nor did a number of her friends and Mr. Lincoln's friends. They worked for her freedom.

After four months Mary Lincoln was released in the custody of her sister, Elizabeth Edwards, with whom she had stayed when she first came to Springfield and in whose home she had been married to Abraham Lincoln. The control of her money was returned to her.

As she walked out of the asylum, the doctor said, "Mrs. Lincoln, I don't know why you ever came here in the first place."

Mary remained with Elizabeth for nine months, until she could return to Chicago and, in a second trial, be declared sane.

During the next six years that were allotted to her, Mary Lincoln traveled in Europe, mostly staying in her "beloved France and Italy," generally alone, an eccentric woman, immaculately groomed, her mourning dress perhaps a little elaborate, but taking care of herself, responsible to herself and to others. The letters she wrote home showed the original toughness and texture of a good mind.

In March of 1882 Mary returned for the last time to her sister Elizabeth's home in Springfield, occupying the same room she had had when she met and fell in love with a tall, lean, homely, unlikely, yarn-spinning lawyer whom she decided she was going to marry. Here on July 16, 1882, at the age of sixty-three, Mary Todd Lincoln finally found blessed release and, in her own words, "joined her idolized husband, her darling Willie and devoted Tad."

After the assassination of her husband on April 14, 1865, the only true peace and happiness Mary enjoyed was the three years she spent in Great Britain and Europe on the trip that Abraham Lincoln had promised her, the story of which is now available to her sympathizers and admirers in the newly discovered, deeply moving "Letters to Mrs. Slataper."

THIS is the story of the opening of a land and the building of a civilization.

It is told in terms of the people who opened that land and built that civilization, each story an integral part of the mosaic.

The land consists of the present-day states of California, Nevada, Utah, and Colorado, the area designated by geographers as the Far West. This was the vast empire inherited by Mexico when it won its independence from Spain in 1821. Except for a handful of hunters and trappers in the Colorado Rockies, scattered Indian tribes, and a few hundred settlers on the California coast, the region was totally uninhabited.

The land has a common cast of characters. What happens in any one region is of tremendous consequence to the others.

California was settled by such magnificent frauds as "Captain" John Sutter and "Doctor" John Marsh, who first brought the pioneers across the plains and mountains by writing East that "the difficulty of coming here is imaginary." The area became a coveted prize among the nations of Europe, Russia settling north of San Francisco, France sending in spys to map Mexico's defenses, and Britain using its Hudson's Bay Company to reconnoiter for control. The United States Navy seized it twice. By 1846 the California Republic had been established; the discovery of gold in 1848 by John Marshall opened the flood gates to thousands of Americans, and put an end to European dreams of conquest.

It also multiplied the streams of prairie schooners and horsemen making the trek across the lands of the "Great American Desert," known only to such mountain men as Jedediah Smith, Kit Carson, Broken-Hand Fitzpatrick, who became guides to the gold seekers traversing Colorado, then called "a legal fiction"; and followed the pronouncement of Brigham Young to his Saints, "This is the right place," meaning Utah and Nevada, which he named Deseret, with Salt Lake at its center.

MEN TO MATCH MY MOUNTAINS

Color in a Country

THE Forty-Eighter, in pursuit of gold, was a reluctant bridegroom. His portrait bears little relation to his highly publicized cousin, the Forty-Niner, yet in many ways he is the more interesting, or at least purer, personality. Sutter, Marsh, Vallejo, Larkin, Bidwell, Hartnell, Robinson made their hesitant way into the hills, but they did not stay long, and few took out any appreciable sum. The early settlers had not come to California for gold, yet how could a man justify his not stooping to pick up the essence of wealth when all he had to do was scratch it out with his pocket knife?

John Sutter and James Marshall tried to keep their discovery secret, Sutter extracting a promise from the workmen at Coloma to remain for the six weeks necessary to get the sawmill into operation. He also urged his employees at the mill to say nothing of the nuggets. But for a surprising length of time there was no secret to leak: the workmen thought these few gold nuggets to be in the American River by chance. They continued with their tasks. All, that is, except young Henry Bigler, one of the Mormon Battalion working for Sutter; on Sunday young Bigler picked up his gun as though he were going hunting, crossed the stream out of sight of his comrades and searched for gold. He found a few particles. The next day after work he scratched up a little more. The following Sunday he found a full ounce, and on Washington's Birthday he went out in a snowstorm, still ostensibly to hunt game, unearthing a nugget. When he returned to the mill, wet and frozen, his companions demanded an explanation. Bigler untied his shirt tail, scattering $22.50 worth of gold onto their crude table. He also confessed that he had written of his findings to their fellow Mormons at Sutter's flour mill.

Bigler did considerably better than his employer in keeping the secret, for on February 10, only thirteen days after Marshall's arrival at the fort with the packet of gold, the ebullient Sutter wrote to Vallejo: "I have made a discovery of a gold mine which, according to experiments we have made, is extraordinarily rich."

Mariano Vallejo kept the secret without being asked to; like most Californios he knew from the outset that gold was the ultimate gamble.

Sutter, as had the Russians at Fort Ross before him, bought a three-year lease from the Indians around Coloma, the only two such instances on the record books of the Far West. If Sutter gave false reasons for acquiring his lease, it was not because he hoped to keep all the gold for himself, but rather because he needed a few more weeks to complete the work on his flour and saw mills.

By now the dozen employees at Sutter's sawmill, earning about a dollar a day and their keep, saw from Bigler's find that they could mine the American River with their pocket knives for ten to twenty times their wage. Yet not one man ran out on his promise to Sutter to work the six weeks necessary to complete the mill; they simply used their spare hours to go fishing for gold.

Henry Bigler, when he wrote to his Mormon companions at the flour mill, urged them to keep the matter secret but to come up for a short visit. Levi Fifield, Wilford Hudson and Sidney Willis accepted the invitation, came to Coloma and worked over the tailrace where Marshall had seen the first golden glints. Picking through the accumulated sand and gravel they found nuggets weighing in at $6.00. These three members of the Mormon Battalion, by traveling forty-six miles to look for gold, became the first Forty-Eighters.

On their return journey they stopped long enough to prospect on a sand bar about halfway down to Sutter's; here they found gold lying very close to the sand surface. By their stop of perhaps an hour they became the discoverers of Mormon Island, from which a fortune was subsequently taken by other prospectors.

Two things now happened simultaneously to break the news: one of Sutter's haulers, Jacob Wittmer, arriving at Coloma with a wagonful of materials and provisions, was told by one of the young Weimar boys: "We have found gold up here."

When Wittmer ridiculed the idea, Mrs. Weimar gave the teamster a good-sized nugget as a gift to prove her son spoke the truth.

At the same moment John Sutter sent a Mormon in his employ, Charles Bennett, to the governor of California, Colonel R. B. Mason at Monterey, to secure a confirmation of his Indian lease. Bennett was ordered to say nothing about the discovery of gold, but when he met a group of prospectors searching for a coal mine near Dr. Marsh's rancho on Mount Diablo, this was too rare a joke to keep to himself: men grubbing for coal when there was gold lying all along the American River!

Bennett took out his pouch of gold dust and nuggets to convince the unbelieving coal prospectors.

Jacob Wittmer, arriving back at Sutter's Fort, went into a general supply store that had been opened in one of Sutter's outbuildings by Samuel Brannan, ordered a bottle of brandy and put down Mrs. Weimar's gift on the counter to pay for it. Brannan's partner, George Smith, sent for Brannan; they refused to believe this nugget was gold, even as the coal-mining prospectors had refused to believe Bennett's evidence. Jacob Wittmer had no recourse but to send for Captain John Sutter.

Sutter could not lie with the nugget staring back at him from the counter. He confirmed the discovery. The date was February 15, 1848. On the same day Charles Bennett reached San Francisco and showed the gold dust to everyone who would look. With the exception of one man, Isaac Humphrey, a former gold miner from Georgia, nobody believed it was gold. Isaac Humphrey bought a pick, shovel, basin and materials to build a rocker, and left all alone for the hundred-fifty-mile journey to Coloma, the first man of the Exodus.

There was no valid reason for San Francisco to grow excited about a rumor of gold in the distant Sierra Nevada; since that day in 1846 when Frémont had spiked the rusty guns of the presidio the forsaken hamlet of half a dozen mud huts on the cove had grown to a community of two hundred buildings. Two fair-sized hotels had been built, two wharves, warehouses, twelve stores, some of them representing long-established firms in the East and Honolulu. There were billiard and tenpin alleys, an advertisement in the *Star* on March 1, 1848 for a schoolteacher, and on March 5 a public sale of town lots found fifty-two buyers at an average and gratifying price of $22.50. San Francisco might soon become the great city of the Pacific coast, center of trade from the East and Europe and the Orient. The *Californian* reported the discovery of gold on March 15, and the *Star* on the eighteenth, but in a quiet, back-page line.

Now, almost two months after the discovery, Marshall's sawmill was completed; about the twentieth of March the first logs were sawed into planks. Having proved that the sawmill they built could work, the entire crew quit and went prospecting. As John Caughey says in *Gold Is the Cornerstone:*

"The instrument of discovery thus fell victim to the overpowering force that it unloosed."

John Sutter suddenly had the roof over his empire fall in on him: the staff of his just completed $30,000 flour mill also resigned and struck out for the mountains. The tanners in their shop at the fort caught the fever and walked out on two thousand fresh hides which rotted away. His longtime crew of Indians showed admirable restraint in remaining long enough to harvest the forty-thousand-bushel wheat crop, then vanished silently in the night, leaving Sutter's wheat to spoil in the sun because there was no one to thresh, any more than there was anyone to complete the shoes, hats, barrels, blankets or any of the dozen other articles that Sutter had been manufacturing.

Thus Sutter, who had caused the gold to be discovered, also provided the manpower for the official start of the gold rush.

It was Sam Brannan who acted as the catalyst for the outside world. Having milked Mormonism of its last procurable tithe from the Battalion boys in the gold fields, Sam now abandoned the Latter-day Saints, who returned the compliment by excommunicating him for a second time. Clever opportunist, high-powered adventurer, shrewd trader and manipulator, Brannan burst into San Francisco on May 12, riding horseback through the streets, waving his hat over his head and crying at the top of his lungs:

"Gold! Gold! Gold from the American River!"

His histrionics galvanized a city which two months before had gazed indifferently at Bennett's pouch.

Sailors in the harbor deserted their ships, their captains right behind them. Doctors walked out on their patients, judges on their supplicants, the mayor and his city council on their citizens . . . most of whom were already gone. The little school, after its brave start, had to close, the two newspapers shut down for lack of printers, as did the stores because there were neither clerks to sell nor customers to buy. Soldiers walked off their posts and never returned; hotels had neither managers nor guests; farmers made for the hills, leaving their grains and vegetables to die. Property which had been valuable a few days before was hawked for half price with no takers. Within a matter of days the city looked as though a plague had struck it, with only one fourth of its male population left.

In Monterey, when the first gold was shown on the streets, the town emptied out so completely that the Reverend Walter Colton ruefully reported "a general of the United States Army, the commander of a man-of-war and the Alcalde of Monterey, in a smoking kitchen, grinding coffee, toasting a herring and peeling onions!"

Commodore Thomas Ap Catesby Jones, who had inadvertently seized Monterey in 1842, now found that as commander of the Pacific Squadron he did not have enough sailors left to capture Catalina Island.

Sailors who, by jumping ship to get to the mines, sacrificed four years pay, must have felt the way another goldrusher did when he gazed upon the well-filled pouch of a digger:

"A frenzy seized my soul; houses were too small for me to stay in; I was soon in the street in search of necessary outfits; piles of gold rose up before me at every step; castles of marble, dazzling the eye with their rich appliances; thousands of slaves bowing to my beck and call; myriads of fair virgins contending with each other for my love . . . were among the fancies of my fevered imagination. The Rothschilds and Astors appeared to me but poor people; in short I had a very violent attack of the gold fever."

As actual bags of gold began to come down from the mountains, town after town emptied out in dramatic fashion. Sonoma, which had just been laid out as a city and subdivided into lots, "lost two-thirds of its inhabitants. Most of its houses are empty, all work has stopped and here, as every where else, there is not a single carpenter left nor a joiner nor a blacksmith nor any laborer to do the least work."

Thomas O. Larkin wrote from San Jose that "everyone had gold or yellow fever. Nine-tenths of every storekeeper, mechanic and day laborer leave for the Sacramento."

Luis Peralta, an aging Californio gentleman who had been given a vast grant comprising the present cities of Berkeley, Oakland and Alameda, refused to be stampeded. He said:

"My sons, God has given this gold to the Americans. Had he desired us to have it, He would have given it to us ere now. Therefore, go not after it, but let others go. Plant your lands, and reap; these be your best gold fields, for all must eat while they live."

Mariano Vallejo rode up to Coloma, watched other men successfully mining gold, picked up a few flakes as a matter of scientific interest, then rode back to his home in Sonoma, never again bothering to go into the gold fields. Nor did the Californio families from San Luis Obispo south join the rush; they remained on their land and within a year, as Luis Peralta had predicted to his sons, found that their herds of cattle were richer gold fields than Coloma or Mormon Island.

IT'S AS EASY TO FIND GOLD AS STEAL IT

The gold that had been freed from its deposit in the mountains had been carried by the rivers of the Sierra Nevada. The streams naturally found their way down canyons and declivities; the sun circled over the cool, heavily timbered areas for perhaps a couple of hours a day, hardly enough to warm or dry the ravines.

The prospectors were getting their feet wet in some of the coldest melted-snow water to tumble down a mountainside.

Aside from Marshall's settlement in the fairly wide valley at Coloma there were no towns, no houses, no food and no roads on which to get in. The first prospectors from Sutter's went into the mountains on horseback or on foot, carrying a blanket roll inside of which they cached such provisions as were available: flour, bacon, coffee. Dangling from the straps of the blanket roll was the triumvirate of the tenderfoot: a pick, a shovel and a frying pan, all a man allegedly needed to found his fortune.

Reaching the mines from San Francisco was an involved process; prospectors either had to cross the wide bay or make the forty-mile journey down the peninsula almost to San Jose, and then double back northward. Rowboats that had been worth $50 now sold at $500. Wagon trains drawn by oxen or mules made the circling land movement around the bay but the largest number of the prospectors went on foot, rifle in hand. One man crossed alone on Robert Semple's ferry at Martinez late in April 1848; two weeks later he found a hundred wagons waiting for the ferry with a small army of men inside a wide ring of campfires, each name written on a waiting list.

John Bidwell, who had been told immediately by Sutter of Marshall's discovery, made a careful examination of the terrain around Coloma and decided that it was similar to the country on the Feather River where he had bought a large ranch. He returned north, found light particles of gold far down the Feather River and reasoned that the heavier particles would remain near the hills. At Chico he organized his friends and neighbors. Bidwell says that in nearly all the places they prospected they found the color, but his companions felt the gold they were panning was too light, and lit out for the American River.

Bidwell and two friends continued up the Feather River, soon striking a rich deposit which became known as Bidwell's Bar. By discovering the color thirty miles to the north of Coloma, Bidwell opened the entire area as possible gold country.

Pierson B. Reading, who had come in with the Chiles group in 1843 and was ranching at the extreme north of the central California valley, followed Bidwell's example, studied the terrain at Coloma and returned home to find gold on Clear Creek near his own land. Men now fanned out in all directions looking for geographical situations similar to Coloma. By May prospectors were taking out the metal some ten miles west of Coloma toward Sutter's, and ten miles east, deep into the heart of the Sierra Nevada.

Men on foot, searching for new and promising diggings on all the forks and tributaries, laid their blanket rolls under the trees, then built campfires. Those who had come on horseback or with wagons sometimes had tents; a few of the more experienced had brought axes with which to cut timber and build a lean-to. Some anchored their wagons with rocks and slept in them. Thus were the first mining towns born. Few of those who came in on foot could remain more than a week; that was as long as their provisions lasted. There was no way to buy a morsel of food. Most of the prospectors had been skeptical, but what they found or saw others finding sent them back to Sutter's and sometimes all the way back to San Francisco to settle their affairs, buy all the food and tools their money would provide and strike out again, this time to stay.

By July some two thousand Americans were in the mining regions, with another two thousand Californios and Indians working alongside them. With the passing of the months four thousand more Americans, including deserting sailors and soldiers, came to prospect, crawling over the foothills of the Sierra Nevada picking up all the gold in sight.

The first miners to reach the diggings did not bother to stake out claims. They skimmed over the waterways scooping up the surface gold, quickly moving on. As their number increased and knowledge spread as to the gold-bearing potential of each camp or gulch, the men came together at the new general store and held a meeting to decide the size of the claim that each man could call his own, varying from ten feet square in the early camps to ten feet from the center of the stream all the way back to the base of the hills. The setting down of a man's pick or shovel on the spot was enough to make his claim legal.

These first informal meetings were the beginnings of self-government in the mountain mines; Colonel Mason was the military governor of the state, stationed in Monterey, but no other government existed. As Charles H. Shinn says in *Mining Camps:*

"The miners needed no criminal code. It is simply and literally true that there was a short time in California, in 1848, when crime was almost absolutely unknown, when pounds and pints of gold were left unguarded in tents and cabins, or thrown down on the hillside, or handed about through a crowd for inspection. An old pioneer writes me that, 'In 1848 a man could go into a miner's cabin, cut a slice of bacon, cook a meal, roll up in a blanket, and go to sleep, certain to be welcomed kindly when the owner returned.' Men have told me that they have known as much as a washbasinful of gold-dust to be left on the table in an open tent while the owners were at work in their claim a mile distant."

It was as easy to find gold as steal it. Anybody taking his neighbor's gold would be stealing more for fun than profit. One or two tried it toward the end of the year and were hanged without trial or tears.

The mountains were arcadia during 1848; the miners were young, there were no social distinctions, and if one man found a considerable lay of gold today, tomorrow would be his neighbor's turn. Friends or neighbors made a common pot of their food, each man cooking in turn. The result was frequently poor but "no man shall grumble at the cook's failures, under penalty of cooking for twice the usual period." Everyone was openhanded to new arrivals. Shinn reports the story of a ten-year-old boy who arrived in camp alone, starved and without the essential tools for even the simplest mining. The men at the diggings agreed to work one hour for the boy, at the end of that time turning over to him enough gold dust to buy a complete outfit, and the stricture that he would now have to "paddle for himself."

There was no social life in 1848. Few camps had even one woman, though later in the year a few arrived with their husbands to open restaurants or boardinghouses. At night, after work, the men gathered around campfires, spinning yarns, speaking nostalgically of home or their journey to California while they sat in the blackness surrounded by strange giant trees and mountains. Friendship was their greatest pleasure; in this all-male society partnerships were formed that have been described by participants as "indissoluble as marriage." The only family life was that of the Californios, who brought their wives, children and Indian servants, the families dancing in the evenings "on the green, before the tents." The young Americans found it "quite a treat, after a hard day's work, to go at nightfall to one of these fandangoes."

This sylvan aspect lasted almost to the end of 1848, though by late fall the outside influx had begun: Californios up from southern California; the first out-of-state goldrushers from Oregon; four thousand native Mexicans from Sonora; the first gold-rush arrivals by sea, an early contingent from Hawaii and another from Chile.

By October winter descended upon the mountains, with rain, snow and intense cold. A few of the more hardy decided to remain and built rude log cabins. Eight hundred men stayed on at Dry Diggings, later called Hangtown, then Placerville, taking out about five ounces a day. The vast majority, with the waters in the river unendurably icy, made their way out of the hills and into the warmer plains. Some had made their pile, many were disappointed and sick, ragged, grim and bespotted:

"Cursing the country and their hard fate."

By the beginning of September San Francisco had ceased to be a ghost town. Men had begun to return from the mines, some feverish to spend their pouches of gold, others just feverish. By October enough of the City Council had returned to hold a meeting, and one hundred fifty-eight returnees cast their ballots in the alcalde election. At this encouraging sign real estate went up fifty per cent, one courageous soul erecting the first brick house ever built in San Francisco; stores and merchandise that had been hawked for any price they would bring went back to their pre-gold values, and by December land and buildings were selling for double what they had cost.

Enough printers as well as subscribers had returned from the mines for the earliest California papers, the *Star* and the *Californian* to combine and resume publishing; and by December 12 the public school, which had opened for a few weeks in the spring, resumed classes with tuition set at $8.00 a term, probably the best buy in a city where it now took $100 in gold dust to buy a blanket, a pair of boots or a gallon of whiskey.

San Francisco appointed the Reverend T. D. Hunt, a Presbyterian, as town chaplain and the Reverend Mr. Hunt officiated at the first Protestant services, aside from the Mormons', to be held in San Francisco. In San Jose there was a first meeting of Americans looking toward the formation of a government for California, which now had only an alcalde and council in San Francisco, the Reverend Mr. Colton as alcalde in Monterey, alcaldes in Santa Barbara and Los Angeles. Colonel Mason, military governor of the "possession," had so little power that his plan to establish license fees where gold was being dug, in order to collect taxes with which to run the country, was never attempted, most of his army having deserted. However he did assure the people that the United States Congress would soon:

"Confer on them the constitutional rights of citizens of the United States."

Emigration across the plains from Missouri in the spring months of 1848 had been modest. Captain Chiles, who had led a small horseback party through Nevada in 1843, had brought in forty-eight wagons with perhaps one hundred fifty people. Bancroft's *Register* shows only five hundred twenty names of incoming pioneers.

But few phenomena inflame the mind of man so universally as the discovery of gold. For word had to get out: ships leaving San Francisco Harbor plowing the seas to Honolulu, Victoria, Vancouver; members of the Mormon Battalion traveling to Salt Lake; a letter from L. W. Boggs to his brother in Oregon, other letters written by young men wanting to tell their families and friends all over the country about their adventures.

The Baltimore *Sun* had run the first newspaper story about the gold discovery in September, quickly followed by articles in the New York *Herald* and the New York *Journal of Commerce*. But they were too exaggerated to be believed:

"People are running over the country and picking it out of the earth here and there just as 1,000 hogs let loose in a forest would root up ground nuts."

The official reports were more important: Thomas Larkin's report to Secretary of State Buchanan sent east by the flagship *Ohio;* Colonel Mason's report to the Adjutant General, accompanied by either a tea caddy or an oyster can full of gold for visual and tactile proof, sent to Buchanan.

President Polk incorporated Colonel Mason's report in his message to Congress on December 9, 1848, publicly displaying the gold at the War Office, and crying:

"The accounts of the abundance of gold are of such an extraordinary character, as would scarcely command belief were they not corroborated by the authentic reports of officers in the public service."

That would do it.

WHAT GAMBLER EVER REFUSED TO PLAY?

How much did the Forty-Eighters take out of the river beds, sand bars and loose rock? It varied according to a man's strength, ambition and luck. At first nearly everyone could pan from $10 to $15 of gold dust if he worked from dawn to dark. Considering the fact that in San Francisco prior to the discovery a cook received $25 to $30 a month and a clerk $50 to $60, these were considered good findings.

As in all such strikes there were the fortunate ones: John Sullivan, an Irish teamster who had been earning $5.00 a day, took out $26,000 from the diggings named after him on the Stanislaus River. A man named Hudson obtained some $20,000 in six weeks from a canyon between Coloma and the American middle fork. A boy called Davenport found seventy-seven ounces of pure gold one day and ninety ounces the next. At Dry Diggings a Mr. Wilson took $2000 from under his doorstep. Three Frenchmen discovered gold in removing a stump which obstructed the road from Dry Diggings to Coloma and within a week dug up $5000. On the Yuba River middle fork one man picked up nearly thirty pounds of gold from a piece of ground less than four feet square. Amador relates that he saw diggings which yielded $8.00 to every spadeful of earth. He and a companion, with twenty native laborers, took out from seven to nine pounds of gold a day. Robert Birnie, an employee of British Consul Forbes, saw miners at Dry Diggings mining from fifty to a hundred ounces daily.

Soule, who was the closest of the California historians to the gold rush, tells in his *Annals of San Francisco:*

"Well authenticated accounts described many known persons as averaging from one to two hundred a day for a long period. Numerous others were said to be earning from five to eight hundred dollars a day. If, indeed, a man with a pick and pan did not easily gather some thirty or forty dollars worth of dust in a single day, he just moved off to some other place which he supposed might be richer."

A correspondent of the *Californian* wrote from Dry Diggings in the middle of August 1848 that "the earth is taken out of the ravines and is carried in wagons and packed on horses from one to three miles to the water, where it is washed; $400 has been an average for a cart load. Instances have occurred here where men have carried the earth on their backs, and collected from $800 to $1500 in a day."

But there were complications in the golden paradise. Men unaccustomed to hard physical labor found that working knee-deep in the icy water all day, filling a pan or an Indian basket with dirt, lowering it into the water, then shaking the pan vigorously to wash out the sand and clay; sleeping at night in the cold and dampness; eating little more than bacon, sourdough bread and coffee brought them down with colds, fevers, pneumonia, dysentery. With their rudimentary equipment they could mine but shallowly, and the surface gold was quickly exhausted. Though they might earn well for a few weeks they would then have to go scurrying over the mountains looking for fresh deposits.

The supplies which now began to come in over the Indian trails took their prices not merely from the costs of hauling: freighters charged $300 to transport three barrels of flour, one of pork and two hundred pounds of small stores the fifty miles from Sutter's to the diggings; but also from the belief that the men who pick up wealth from the ground should share it with those self-sacrificing enough to deny themselves this great opportunity. Pans worth twenty cents now cost from $8.00 to $16. A fifty-cent box of Seidlitz powders cost $24. Every pill, regardless of its value, cost $1.00. Forty drops of laudanum cost $40. Shirts sold at $16 apiece. The Reverend Mr. Colton, touring the mining area in October, wrote:

"We pay at the rate of $400 a barrel for flour; $4.00 a pound for poor brown sugar, and $4.00 a pound for indifferent coffee. And as for meat, there is none to be got except jerked-beef, which is the flesh of the bullock cut into strings and hung up in the sun to dry."

As entrepreneurs came into the camps to build little hotels and restaurants, prices went even higher. A breakfast at Coloma consisting of a box of sardines, bread, butter, cheese and two bottles of ale cost $43.

By the fall of 1848 those prospectors who were mining an ounce a day, about half of the mining population, were spending their ounce for the basic necessities and consequently were working for their keep. Another quarter, dogged by bad luck or just slower, found that they could not average the ounce a day necessary to live on, and had to go to work for someone who could guarantee their food. The remaining quarter took out a profit ranging from a few hundred dollars to sizable fortunes, the latter accumulated by perhaps five per cent of the prospectors.

What gambler ever refused to play because the odds were heavily against him? No attention was paid to the exhausted, the sick and emaciated who returned, though some of them lay ill for months and many died. The ones who caused the great excitement were those who returned to the towns flashing a pouch full of gold; then another wave of humanity started for the mines.

Even Thomas O. Larkin, who had said, "We cannot imagine the bad results to California if this fever continues," finally could not resist forming a company with the foreman of his Sacramento Valley rancho and a clerk in his office at Monterey to round up all the Indians they could find and go into the mines on shares. He also sent in a supply of goods with which to open a general store.

Dr. John Marsh organized a company among his neighbors. They loaded pack animals with food and mining equipment, donned the red shirts and boots which were becoming standard equipment for prospectors, and made their way north to the Yuba River. Here Dr. Marsh struck a rich bar, taking out $50 of gold an hour from the very beginning.

Larkin was satisfied with a modest three hundred per cent profit on his goods, but Marsh sold beads and sugar to the Indians at the rate of a cup of beads for a cup of gold! When he ran out of supplies he ended by selling the red shirt off his back to an enchanted Indian for $300. But Marsh, now forty-nine, was too old for this rugged existence. He became ill and had to return home, carrying with him $40,000 in gold for something under six months of work; a bonanza, if you don't mind getting sick, and selling the shirt off your back. Nor did John Bidwell stay with mining after his Indians went off to seek gold for themselves; he too opened a store.

Until his discovery of gold James W. Marshall had had little luck or success, partly because he was an irascible wanderer. His tenacity in finding a logical site for a sawmill and getting Sutter to stake him to it should have established him, but no one would work his mill. Throngs of incoming miners squatted on his land surrounding the mill and he could not get them off. His oxen, worth $400 per yoke, "went down into the canyon and thence down hungry men's throats." When he went prospecting he returned to find that migratory miners had taken his mill apart to use for their own purposes. Nor did he have any greater success as a miner; Sutter twice provided him with a prospector's outfit, but the spirits he believed were directing his search were apparently out prospecting on their own:

"Should I get to new localities and commence to open a new mine, numbers flocked in and commenced seeking all around me, and, as numbers tell, someone would find the lead before me, and the ground was claimed. Then I would travel again."

John Sutter, who had no help to run his sawmill, flour mill, tannery, or to thresh his grain, compensated for his losses by opening a store at the fort, which was on the main line to the mines, renting out space to merchants. He also grubstaked several prospectors on a share-and-share basis. He declared optimistically:

"There is no need for me to go into the mountains to make my pile of gold, the gold will flow to me."

The arrival of his twenty-two-year-old son August seemed a more discouraging prospect. It was the imminence of this son in Burgdorf which had obliged Sutter to marry August's mother and endure years of marital unhappiness. Sutter had never intended to see any member of his Swiss family again. When he heard that August was in San Francisco, John Sutter fled to Coloma where he prospected in the bottle, keeping himself drunk to wipe out the gnawing question of, Once the son had arrived, could the mother be far behind?

August Sutter proved to be a loyal and level-headed young man who might have saved his father from the utter ruin that now began to engulf him. August comments:

"Indians, Negroes, Kanakas, and white men of any nation indiscriminately by applying to my father, easily obtained letters of credit from him to any amount for any stores then existing in or about the fort. . . . From the books I received I never could obtain any knowledge of the state of affairs on account of their dreadful confusion."

The widespread rumor that Sutter had been made a millionaire by the discovery of gold brought the rest of his past down upon him. Colonel Steward, new Russian consul in San Francisco arrived at the fort to collect about $31,000 still owed for Fort Ross. James Douglas, head of the Hudson's Bay Company, paid a personal visit to the fort to collect $7000 he claimed Sutter owed them. Antonio Sunol, a Californio neighbor, came to present a bill for $3000 for cattle and supplies. As the unkindest cut of all there arrived a Mr. French who claimed that Sutter owed him $3000 for the loan of the ship on which Sutter had sailed his cargo from Honolulu to Yerba Buena in 1839. Dozens of other creditors presented themselves. Captain John Sutter, who had given away a large part of his patrimony to exhausted emigrants, had only the vaguest notion of what he owed whom.

Half mad with the pressure and confusion, Sutter made his son the legal owner of his holdings and once again fled to the mountains. August faithfully set about the Herculean task of putting his father's accounts in order; the only way he found to do so was to agree to Sam Brannan's proposal that they create a town, to be called Sacramento City, between Sutter's Fort and the Embarcadero on the river, all of which land Sutter owned.

John Sutter had already laid out a town in 1846 which he had proudly named Sutterville. It was three miles down the river and safe from the yearly floods. A few buildings had been put up but the town was off the route to the gold mines and hence got no trade. Sacramento City was a hit from the moment August put the land on the market, enough cash coming in for him to pay off Douglas, Sunol, French and to give Consul Steward $10,000 in cash and $21,000 in lot values in Sacramento. Steward then absconded with the money, the Russians never getting a penny out of Fort Ross.

In a matter of months Sacramento City, a tent and lean-to town, sprang into existence. Sutter's Fort found itself out in the country, abandoned. August sold it for $40,000.

All this money could have paid Sutter's debts many times over, except that Sutter was gone, wandering aimlessly, and the overconscientious son paid all claims presented to him, whether fabricated or real.

Sam Brannan next hatched a conspiracy to cheat the Sutters out of the best of the remaining land of Sacramento City, succeeding so brilliantly that August went down with a fever . . . though not before arranging to have his mother, two sisters and brother brought from Switzerland. In his illness August returned to his father the legal ownership of his estate; but what had been a vast property only two years before was now gone. Nothing remained but the Hock Farm, the first one that Sutter had cultivated outside his fort.

Here Sutter moved with his personal possessions. Onto the Hock Farm came the family from whom he had fled fourteen years before. Here Sutter lived without money, his family doing the house and farm work, but remaining the patriarchal figure of California, visited by hordes of people all of whom he tried to feed and entertain in the grand manner, even as he had at Sutter's Fort.

The discovery of gold had undone him.

By the end of 1848 there were some eight to ten thousand miners in the Sierra Nevada. By the end of the year $10,000,000 worth of gold had been dug out of the golden rectangle, of which $2,000,000 was shipped east to establish credit; $2,000,000 was consumed by the miners in food, clothing and utensils, animals, medications and drink; another $1,000,000 was spent in building the hundred-odd mining communities, a few of which became permanent towns, the majority vanishing when the gold was exhausted. Of the remaining $5,000,000 about half would have been taken by successful miners to their home towns: Sonoma, San Francisco, San Jose, Santa Cruz, Monterey, to be invested in ranches, business and residential property, and to buy or build stores, shops, hotels, homes.

Some of the balance would be saved by thrifty individuals like Dr. John Marsh, but most of it would be spent on luxuries by the comfort-starved miners returning after months of isolation in the mountains, or transferred from excitement-hungry miners to the black pockets of the early gamblers.

The $10,000,000 taken out in gold represented two thirds of the price paid by the United States to Mexico for the Far West, Texas, parts of New Mexico, Arizona and Wyoming, an area of over half a million square miles, between fifteen and twenty per cent of the contemporary United States.

DEDICATED SAINTS

No more startling contrast to the life of the Forty-Eighter can be conceived than the 1848 community being built on the Great Salt Lake. There were about eighteen hundred Saints living on the desert. They had been blessed with a mild winter, so that their rye and wheat were up by February to what Parley P. Pratt described in his *Autobiography* as "a beautiful green that contrasts with the gray, wild wormwood of the countryside." By March three to four thousand acres were under cultivation.

Brigham Young believed that for a people to remain happy they must be kept in constant labor: the symbol of the Mormon community was the beehive. Over the winter the men worked co-operatively to build roads, irrigation ditches, bridges, a twelve-mile stone fence around the jointly owned fields. For private living and capitalistic business enterprise the Saints had also built over four hundred houses, a number of stores, three sawmills, two gristmills, a water-power threshing machine on City Creek. Crude furniture was manufactured, pots made from native clay, shoes, breeches, harnesses by tanners. Expeditions were formed by the Council to send men along the emigrant trail to bring back abandoned metal which the Mormon artisans made into plowshares.

But God was not yet through testing His children. He now sent such visitations that Apostle Rich, preaching out of doors from his open wagon, warned the Saints not to part with their wagons and teams, intimating that they might once again have to go searching for the Promised Land.

Late in March came the rains. The houses which had been plastered with salt desert clay as well as built with clay bricks began to melt. The roofs poured water. Bedbugs came out of the exposed logs and tormented the families. Mice were so mulitudinous that in their burrowings under the houses they weakened the structures; the houses shook at the slightest tremble, and no family would dare to go to bed at night without catching two dozen of them. Wolf packs hunted through the city at night; poisons left on a front porch would kill several.

The rain had been as good for the fields as it had been devastating for the houses. By May the crops were green and thriving. Then came an unexpected frost; all crops were damaged, particularly the corn and wheat. Isaac Haight, inspecting his vegetable garden, saw that the beans, cucumbers, melons, pumpkins and squash had all been killed.

Next came the crickets: big, black, voracious. The Saints had noted them when they first entered the valley the year before but they had not known that they would advance in a solid phalanx, devouring every living thing in their inexorable march for food. They had already eaten a good portion of what had not been destroyed by the frost when, in the words of Priddy Meeks:

"I heard the voice of fowls flying overhead that I was not acquainted with. I looked up and saw a flock of seven gulls. In a few minutes there was another larger flock passed over. They came faster and more of them until the heavens were darkened with them and lit down in the valley till the earth was black with them and they would eat crickets. A little before sundown they left. . . . In the morning they came back again and continued until they had devoured the crickets. . . ."

Without the gulls the crickets would have scorched the earth. With almost two thousand of their fellows due from Winter Quarters and Missouri the Saints considered this deliverance their greatest miracle; ever since, sea gulls have been spared in Salt Lake.

The August harvest of wheat and corn was good enough to send relief parties east with food for the incoming pilgrims. By the end of September five thousand Saints were in the salt desert. Brigham Young and the Council extended the limits of the city so that all new arrivals could share the land equally with the original settlers. They also disbanded the communal fort.

On September 28 the members of the Mormon Battalion who had mined gold at Mormon Island reached Salt Lake, having been separated from their families a total of twenty-six months. A natural gold fever shook the pulse of Salt Lake but it was quickly checked by Brigham Young, who knew the corrosive value of quick and easy wealth, not only on individual character but on a homogeneous church community. He forbade the Saints to mine for gold:

"If we were to go to San Francisco and dig up chunks of gold or find it in the valley it would ruin us."

Should the Saints find any gold in their own front yard in Utah they might not mine that, either.

At a meeting before his congregation on November 26 Brigham Young created a new excitement instead: every Saint when "called," either to preach the gospel in a foreign land or to colonize part of the vast desert between the Rockies and the Sierra Nevada, must sell his possessions and move at once to his assignment.

He laid out the country he thought should belong to and be settled by the Saints: from the Oregon line south to the Mexican border, from the Rockies west to the Sierra Nevada, with a stretch of southern California to give the Saints a seaport. The Mormon state, to be called Deseret, would consist of present-day Utah, Nevada, Arizona, half of Colorado, pieces of Wyoming, Oregon, Idaho, New Mexico and California. This vast empire Brigham Young would settle with skilled dedicated Saints who would make the desert bloom, create cities even as they had Salt Lake where Saints could live in the sweat of work and the sweet of peace, worshiping God according to the dictates of their consciences.

GIVE COLORADO BACK TO THE INDIANS

While California was rocking with the discovery of gold and Brigham Young was solidifying the structure of Deseret, the staggeringly beautiful area of what is modern Colorado, just come into possession of the United States through the treaty with Mexico, had reached its lowest level of settlement in the fifteen years since the Bent brothers built their fort in 1833. The fort itself, after serving as unofficial headquarters for the Santa Fe Trail traders and the United States Army, was about to be sold or abandoned because the fur trade was exhausted. No one lived here now except William Bent and his Indian family, with his partner Ceran St. Vrain, and occasionally old trappers like Broken Hand Fitzpatrick and Old Bill Williams. Pueblo, which had had a start when the sick of the Mormon Battalion and their families stopped there temporarily in 1846, was now falling into ruins, with only a half dozen of the old trappers with their Indian wives and children still remaining in the adobe huts.

The small forts on the North Platte had already been abandoned. Two or three trappers kept a cabin at Hardscrabble, a few miles west of Pueblo, where they planted corn in the spring; four or five families were trying to eke out a subsistence by farming in the San Luis Valley, southwest of Pueblo. In 1847 a man named Hatcher had his horses and mules stolen by the Indians, who then killed all the cattle except three. Hatcher hitched his lone remaining team of oxen to a two-wheeled cart and moved . . . the last white man to attempt a settlement on the Purgatory River for many years. It looked as though Colorado would be given back to the Indians; which was precisely what the Indians intended. Colonel Gilpin and his dragoons had been sent in from St. Louis to wipe out the tribes warring on the white settlers; nothing could have made the Indians more determined that no white man should be allowed to remain in Colorado.

There were only three men to hold out hope that Colorado could ever become a settled part of the United States: Dogged William Bent, who had already buried his two brothers outside the fort, was grimly determined to hang onto the settlement he had created. Old Bill Williams, with William Bent, had found traces of gold, though they paid no attention to their improbable find. Irish-born, well-educated, white-haired, three-fingers-missing Thomas "Broken Hand" Fitzpatrick had begun work as United States Indian agent, attempting to locate a permanent agency in Colorado either at Cherry Creek or at Big Timbers, an Indian wintering place where the Arkansas River left Colorado. Fitzpatrick hoped to hold conclaves between the warring Arapahos, Sioux and Utes, provide them with grants of good agricultural land as well as seed, tools and provisions to get started, and convert them from hunting and warring nomadic tribes to settled peaceable farm families. Broken Hand was known and respected by the tribes; he alone had a chance to end the wars in Colorado and open the region to settlers.

On November 16, 1848, John C. Frémont once again reached Bent's Fort with an expedition, promoted this time by his father-in-law and financed by southern interests seeking the shortest pass through the southern Rockies for the first railroad line to California.

THE MEN DO NOT MATCH THE MOUNTAINS

John Frémont's Fourth Expedition into the Far West was superbly organized. Carrying with him $10,000 worth of equipment and scientific instruments, a portion of which represented his own savings, it included Charles Preuss, the topographer who had been with Frémont since his First Expedition; Antoine Morin and Vincent Tabeau, French voyageurs who had been on the Second Expedition; Charles Taplin, a frontiersman; Thomas E. Breckenridge, an experienced westerner; John

Scott, a hunter; a man named Long; and three California Indians. There were twelve greenhorns along but most of them were scientists, like Frederick Creutzfeldt, a botanist, whose stamina was equal to their dedication.

Frémont reached Bent's Fort in the midst of one of the earliest and severest winters Colorado had known; or so he was told by the Indians. His friend Kit Carson, who had given up his ranch and left his wife for the Third Expedition, could not see his way clear to leaving his family and farm again. Broken Hand Fitzpatrick maintained that as a federal Indian agent he could not leave his post. For a guide Frémont was obliged to settle on Old Bill Williams, wintering in Pueblo to nurse a bullet-shattered arm which he had received fighting against the Utes. Past sixty now, cantankerous Old Bill was an expert mountain man who knew the southern Rockies. To Frémont's question of whether he could get the party through, Old Bill replied:

"Sure, but there'll be trouble."

Now, at Hardscrabble, Frémont's party enjoyed the warmth of adobe cabins for a couple of days while they shucked the corn to be loaded into the packs of their train of more than a hundred first-rate mules. There would be enough food to enable the mules to survive for twenty-five days from Hardscrabble over the three ranges of mountains: the Wet, the Sangre de Cristo and the San Juans, the central bastions of the Rockies, and down into what later came to be known as Gunnison Valley, where there would be grass.

Old Bill Williams rode in the lead, "his body bent over his saddle-horn, across which rested a long heavy rifle, his keen grey eyes peering from under the slouched brim of a flexible felt hat, black and shining with grease."

The Wet Mountains had been accurately named: snows clogged the canyons, which were also choked by thick stands of aspen. The mules fell against the trees and rocks, ripping off their packs and losing corn. At nine thousand feet there was no water. In the Wet Mountain Valley there was no game. Though the journey was in its first few days Dr. Ben Kern wrote in his diary, "After wading through the slush of melting snow . . . all very tired."

Old Bill decreed that they take the Robidoux Pass over the Sangre de Cristo Mountains. They struck heavy snows and a screaming gale. Campfires were impossible to sustain. "The winds were caught in the valley and never got out, and then blew wildly in all directions at once." By December 2 when they started up Robidoux Pass the mules were shaking from cold. The saddlebags of corn were vanishing rapidly.

Frémont, who had always insisted on a full day's march, had to call a halt early in the afternoon for the sake of the shivering animals.

On December 3, in the language of the Colorado trappers, "They took the mountain." They descended the Sangre de Cristo and came onto the floor of the San Luis Valley; it took the party four days to cross the snow-covered dunes and to reach the Rio Grande River, from where they moved to the mouth of Wagon Wheel Gap. Here in an evening conference at the base of the San Juan Mountains, facing straight up into the main assault of the Rockies, a serious dispute arose between Old Bill Williams and Frémont; and a decision was made which proved to be a death warrant not only for eleven men of the Fourth Expedition but subsequently for Old Bill himself.

Frémont was dissatisfied with Old Bill's choice, his instincts telling him that they were headed wrong, that they should turn at this point for Cochetopa Pass, which was less difficult of access. Old Bill swore that "he knew every inch of the country better than the Colonel knew his own garden." Alexis Godey, Frémont's second-in-command, writes:

"Williams was so strenuous in his efforts to carry his point, that I was completely in his favor, and told the Colonel that I myself was perfectly willing to trust Williams and follow him."

Frémont had no choice; what he did not know was that the route Williams proposed taking up to the Continental Divide, the Wagon Wheel Trail, had been his own discovery and was his favorite child.

From the first moment of their assault on the boulder-strewn, snow-packed Alder Canyon the Fourth Expedition's difficulties began: on this day the first mule died, others sinking down in the snow, their packs needing to be reset by men whose fingers were already frostbitten. At night the camping spot was so precipitous that it was impossible for the men to stay on their feet while unpacking the mules. They traveled through three to four feet of snow at the beginning, then snow up to the mules' bellies. Seven or eight miles of pushing upward was a tremendous distance to accomplish from sunrise to sunset, and after a fierce snowstorm struck, two hundred yards an hour was the maximum that could be achieved.

The third day the men and mules were obliged to stumble onward after dark to find any kind of tenable camp. Frémont and his mountain men began to suspect that Old Bill was lost. Already twenty days out of Hardscrabble, most of the corn was gone; the snow was twelve to fourteen feet in height through which the men had to beat a path by flailing ahead with their bodies and clubs. The weather was twenty below zero. The intense cold and high altitude made it painful to breathe. The men were bleeding at the nose.

The suffering of the mules was even greater. They cried all night in the bitter cold. Brandon describes them in *The Men and the Mountain:*

"By now they were skeletal creatures made of heavy flanks and yellow teeth, with mucus frozen at their eyes and nostrils and frozen scabs of sores hanging from their coats."

The men worked all day and much of the night to keep the mules alive. But they were dying slowly, their faces turned away from the storm, their heads sinking lower and lower until they fell.

For the men the passage of time was a continuous nightmare, unable to sleep for the thunder of the snow slides, the roaring gale and above it the pathetic crying of the mules. Yet no man faltered, their loyalty and dedication to Frémont holding firm in the midst of the death-dealing hell. On December 15 as they tried to force a ridge in the teeth of a howling gale and were thrust back, Old Bill lost consciousness while riding his mule.

On December 17 the party camped on the Continental Divide at 12,287 feet, the highest point they would come. They had one more valley to traverse, then up through the narrow Carnero Pass and down the west slope of the Rockies toward warmer climate and grass.

The next morning Frémont broke camp early. They were no sooner started than the worst storm of the journey struck, so fierce that no man could make a yard of progress against it. They were physically blown back into their camp on the crest of Wannamaker Creek.

Here for four days they dug into deep holes in the snow to fend off the howling storm. They spent their time butchering the mules who were dying. Here, on December 20, John Frémont at last admitted defeat, and gave the order for the party to turn back. Had they been able to leave the crest before this ultimate storm struck they could have made their way to Carnero Pass, and the final push would have taken them only a day or two past their twenty-five-day allotted span. Like the Donners, the Fourth Expedition was a matter of hours late.

John Frémont had to turn back, but he would attempt to save all of his equipment and scientific instruments for a future assault.

On December 22 he sent a relief party to make its way down out of the mountains to Taos to bring back supplies and fresh mounts. Three of the most experienced men volunteered, Old Bill, Creutzfeldt and Henry King, who had been with Frémont's former expeditions. Frémont asked Breckenridge to go along. He gave the party sixteen days to make

Taos and to get back, while the rest of the expedition would be working its way down the mountains with the equipment, which they would have to carry on their backs.

A subtle form of disintegration now began to break up what had been a cohesive party. John Frémont had lost or abandoned his gift of leadership; he allowed the men to travel down the mountain in separate messes, spread over the trail by as much as seven to nine miles, with three hundred man-loads of equipment, each man carrying sixty to seventy pounds of weight. Frémont sometimes lost contact with the body of his men trailing behind him, the weakest and oldest bringing up the rear, all still living in the bitter cold with little to eat but frozen mule meat.

The first casualty came on January 9. Raphael Proue, trying to carry a pack across the open flats in what was described as perfectly unbearable cold, collapsed because his legs froze under him. Vincenthaler wrapped a blanket around him, but when he returned from having taken his pack to the river Proue had died. Micajah McGehee said: "We passed and repassed his lifeless body, not daring to stop long enough in the intense cold to perform the useless ritual of burial."

Two days later, since the sixteen days which had been allotted for the relief party to return had passed, Frémont himself set out, not only to find his men, but to reach Taos and send back supplies. He took with him Godey, Preuss, Godey's nephew Theodore and Saunders Jackson, an ex-slave from the Benton household in Washington. He also took some food, a little sugar and tallow candles, leaving the same amount for the remaining twenty-five men.

Two days later he came upon his relief party. They had already eaten their footgear, their belts and knife scabbards, and could no longer travel on their frostbitten feet. Weak and almost unable to see from snow blindness, the experienced Henry King had said, "I can go no further, I am sorry, but I am tired out, will sit here until I am rested. I will follow." When the others stumbled back later to see what had happened to him, he was dead, sitting where they had left him.

With the men left behind, despair set in rapidly. Frémont had appointed as their captain Vincenthaler, a man who was incapable of holding the group together for a last-ditch stand against their common enemy, death.

The men started down the Rio Grande River, their supplies consumed, and no game within sight. Teeth fell out of their mouths, their faces became black from the fires over which they crouched for warmth. Every small scratch became a running sore. They could make only two miles a day, even in the flat country. Henry J. Wise staggered a few feet and fell. Two of the Indian boys dug a shallow grave for him. A third of the Indian boys, Manuel, after having the rotted soles of his frozen feet fall off, laid down and died by the river. Next Rohrer died, insane, then Midshipman Elijah T. Andrews, a young and inexperienced traveler from St. Louis. On the twenty-sixth Benjamin Beadle, one of the veterans, died; then Carver from Illinois, then young George Hubbard from the Iowa border; then John Scott, all perishing of exhaustion and starvation. Every last shred of equipment was left behind on the mountains and the plain.

By the twenty-eighth of January eleven men, more than a third of the Fourth Expedition, were dead. The following day Alexis Godey came in with fresh mounts and Indian guides secured by Frémont in Taos. The remaining men were saved.

John Frémont borrowed money from old friends in Taos and offered to mount and take with him any members of the expedition who still wanted to go on to California, where he had planned to meet his wife Jessie and daughter Lily. While he had been struggling to conquer the icy Rockies they had been making their way to California, the first white woman to cross the tropical jungle of Panama. Two years before, even as Frémont was starting on his return to Washington, riding in disgrace behind General Kearny, he had turned over to Thomas O. Larkin a sum of three thousand dollars with which to buy a fine piece of land called the Santa Cruz ranch, originally cultivated by the mission padres, with vines and orchards already bearing. Frémont had walked over this land with Larkin, and it was to this Santa Cruz ranch that the Frémonts were heading on their separate ways, to build a hearth and a home in California.

Several of the survivors of the expedition decided to accompany Frémont as he set out over the Old Spanish Trail.

Old Bill Williams and Dr. Kern went back into the mountains to retrieve some of the treasure lost there, and were never seen again.

The men had not matched the mountains.

The first of many human sacrifices had been made to the building of a transcontinental railroad to California.

"HOW DO WE GET TO THE GOLD?"

THE Forty-Niner was an out-of-stater who gave up his home, his job and his girl to "see the elephant," that is, experience the ultimate in adventure and hardship. Few knew anything about California. Few cared, for they were going to return home as soon as they had made their pile.

Forty thousand prospectors poured into California by the end of 1849. A handful returned home; the great body remained . . . with or without gold. About two fifths came by sea: the seventeen-thousand-mile journey around Cape Horn, or by sea to Chagres, across Panama on foot or muleback, and then up the Pacific coast, arriving in San Francisco after a seven months journey in good health though bored, in the same outfits that had so startled the people in the streets of New York: red flannel shirts, broad felt hats of a reddish-brown hue, loose coats reaching to their knees, high boots, revolvers and knives at their belts: veteran Californians even as they sailed into the bay.

Their first question as they waded across the shallow waters of the cove was:

"How do we get to the gold?"

Their initial view of San Francisco was disenchanting. The lone brick building had encouraged few followers, tents and shacks still overwhelmed the solid structures, the streets were a funnel of dust in the heat and a swamp of mud in the rain. The city itself was in the throes of a political scandal, Alcalde Leavenworth having been suspended for misappropriation of funds, the sheriff raiding his office to seize the records. Prices were so high that a man could be shorn of his capital before he could get proper directions to the mines. One passenger caustically wrote home:

"Just arrived. San Francisco be damned!"

In 1848 seven hundred ships had sailed into San Francisco Bay, most of them being abandoned by crews that had signed on merely to get a free ride to the gold fields. The bay had become a stick-forest of masts as the ships rotted and sank slowly into the cove mud.

The greater portion of the Forty-Niners came overland, following the California trail blazed by the Bidwell-Bartleson, Chiles-Walker, Kelsey, Bryant, Stevens, Grigsby-Ide, Clyman parties, twenty-five thousand men and over a hundred thousand animals working their way westward. They were equally disenchanted.

By the time the parties reached Utah their supplies were low, their stock lean and tired, with the hardest part of the journey ahead. A portion of the Forty-Niners followed the Mormon Trail into Salt Lake, though many other trains avoided the Mormon city, depriving themselves of important help. Both sides were suspicious and frightened, the Mormons because the emigrant parties originated in Missouri where the Saints had suffered violence; the Forty-Niners because, though they had never laid eyes on a Mormon, they had been taught to believe that the Saints were the incarnation of evil.

Immediately the Mormons found the gentiles (Mormon word for everyone outside their religion) to be friendly, they offered the hospitality of Salt Lake, and there was trading of considerable advantage to both sides. The Saints bought the emigrants' extra solid rations and surplus tools, metals, mechanical equipment; the emigrants received fresh stock and repair services for their wagons. The Mormons asked high prices for their milk, butter and fresh vegetables, but also nursed the emigrant sick, sharing their homes with the trail-weary families and putting up quite a few for the winter, Brigham Young setting the example by offering the hospitality of his own home to incoming strangers.

It was not until the trains started across the desert that real suffering began, not only from thirst but from Asiatic cholera. The trains came into the valley of the Humboldt, which Frémont and Bryant had described as "a valley rich and beautifully clothed in blue grass and clover," and found that the stock of the increasing hordes had consumed all the blue grass and clover. Man and beast alike drank the sparse water. By autumn they were renaming the Humboldt the Humbug and the Hellboldt, one rhymster complaining of:

Scribbling asses
Describing nutritious grasses.

The ordeal of the desert, to be played to a climax a few months later by the Jayhawker and Manly parties on the scorching sands of Death Valley, was marked in the summer of 1849 by a trail of shallow graves, the bleaching skeletons of twelve hundred animals, of abandoned household goods, beds and bureaus, stoves and trunks, and finally of the wagons themselves, their canvas and staves bleaching like the white bones of played-out animals.

"The Humboldt was filled with what the Lord had left over when he made the world, and what the devil wouldn't take to fix up hell."

Water sold for $15 a glass, but only vinegar could cure a man's mouth of scurvy. One thousand wagons were abandoned within a distance of forty-two miles. The weaker folk went insane, one woman setting fire to their camp when her husband refused to turn around and go home. There were heroic marches, men who pushed ahead in the burning heat to find water and bring it back to dying men and animals. Every group except the very early and the very young left part of its family or some of its friends behind forever in the wastes.

When they did reach water and the eastern slope of the mountains, exhausted, rations gone, there was the formidable Sierra Nevada to be crossed, wagons to be hauled up the sides of cliffs, before they could enter the gold mines by following the rivers and canyons down from the seven-thousand-foot height to the mining camps. Little wonder that so few were willing to return home, with such an investment of suffering and fortitude. Their tears and blood had watered the mountains and the plains. California was to be theirs forever. Hulbert says in his *Forty-Niners:*

"The finding of gold is luck; you will not be held blamable if you are unlucky. But making the journey, overcoming obstacles, fighting your way through, that is a matter of grit, not luck. Do that, get there, and you are absolved, you have mastered the part of the game that depended on you."

Most of the Forty-Niners spent most of 1849 in travel; not until August and September did the overlanders begin to reach the mines. By the end of the year there were a hundred thousand people in California, of whom eighty thousand were gold-fever arrivals: eight thousand along the Old Spanish Trail into southern California and then north to the mines; nine thousand Mexicans, mostly from the border province of Sonora; forty-two thousand overland, almost entirely Americans, and thirty-nine thousand by sea, of whom twenty-three thousand were Americans.

The Forty-Niners who had come by ship were largely city men, described as "editors, ministers, traders, the briefless lawyer, starving student, the quack, the idler, the harlot, the gambler, the hen-pecked husband, the disgraced . . ." Then, as a sobering aside, Bancroft adds, "with many enterprising honest men and devoted women."

Those who set out from Missouri for the two-thousand-mile trek across plains, mountains and deserts were by contrast mostly farmers and mechanics who were accustomed to handling wagons and stock and living with the frontier.

Of the eighty thousand arrivals only forty thousand went into the mines, the others staying in the towns and settling the farms; exactly half the gold-fever arrivals making the long hard journey not to mine but to begin a new life in a new country which, they reasoned, must become rich and provide magnificent opportunities for all because of the millions in gold being pumped into the economy.

By fall the Forty-Eighter camp had been converted into the Forty-Niner town, five times as large as its antecedent, with the tents and lean-tos on the hillside giving way to cabins, stores, saloons and hotels on either side of a one-block street. The simple "pan" had given way to the larger and slightly more complex "cradle" or rocker. The Forty-Niner did not find gold paving on top of river streets; he had to use his pick and shovel in order to dig below the sand, raising a bumper crop of blisters. He found gold, over $20,000,000 worth of it in 1849, but with five times as many men digging, the ratio fell off to such an extent that one ounce a day was considered an average take, and many of the emigrants were forced to "mine for beans."

Spectacular finds were less common. The Forty-Eighters believed that the gold was inexhaustible; the Forty-Niners said the gold was there but that it would take hard work and luck to get it.

The atmosphere remained colorful. Vigorous young men in red shirts, pants stuffed in their boots, wearing beards and swathes of hair like sheep dogs constituted an all-male society: hard-working, -drinking, -swearing, -playing; the weaker ones coming down with everything from homesickness through scurvy and dysentery to rheumatism, typhoid, tuberculosis and smallpox. They were buried in their blankets. Doctors tiring of the unaccustomed physical labor of the mines had gone back to their practice, charging one ounce of gold per consultation and one dollar for a drop of medicine. There were still few women: at the dances the men matched to see which should be the ladies. On Sunday the men went down to the river to soap and pound their clothes.

"Have two shirts. Wear one until it is dirty. Hang on a limb exposed to wind, rain and sun. Put on second shirt. Wear until dirty. Then change to clean one."

The first laundresses to reach the mining towns made more money than their prospecting husbands.

Though some of the miners brought their violins or guitars, though they played cards to pass the time, though all holidays were riotously celebrated and elaborate practical jokes played, the Forty-Niners were lonely men isolated from the civilized world. A few had copies of Dickens, Homer or the Bible, but books were scarce and newspapers cost a dollar each. Their being away from home, family, friends and traditions accounted for the rapid success of the saloon and gambling hall, which garnered at least as much of the miner's gold as went into the rapidly developing general stores, grown from packs on mules and supplies sold from open wagons to wooden structures with proper counters where a man, for a price, could now buy anything.

"Preserved oysters, corn and peas at $6.00 a canister; onions and potatoes, whenever such articles made their appearance; Chinese sweetmeats and dried fruits; champagne, ale and brandy, sardines, lobster salad."

Life in the mining region in 1849 changed quickly from the Garden of Eden of 1848. Crime, of which the Forty-Eighter saw little, began to mount. The age of chivalry had lasted only one short season. Though the English, Irish, Australians and Germans were quickly assimilated, and the Californios were liked, the Chileans and Sonorans respected for their mining skills, racial antagonism began to spring up among the thousands of strangers thrown together into a political vacuum. The Indians were run out of their mountains, the Chinese and Mexicans pushed out of the better claims, the French, called Keskydees from their omnipresent question, *"Qu'est-ce que se dit?"* ("What did you say?") remained clannish.

San Francisco became as colorful as any mining camp when the early rains poured down from the skies and the miners poured down from the freezing mountains. The clay streets became quagmires into which the city threw "loads of brush wood and limbs of trees; as a result mules stumbled in the streets and drowned in the liquid mud, and the possibility of being thrown because the horse's legs were entangled in the brush, was a constant dread." Sometimes horse and wagon were swallowed up, the owner barely escaping.

At the corner of Clay and Kearny a sign was posted:

This street is impassable;
Not even jackassable.

A whole cargo of stoves, worthless because so many had arrived at one time, was thrown into the sea of mud and served as excellent stepping-stones . . . unless you happened to land on one of the lids and have it come off!

From San Francisco too the brotherly atmosphere of 1848 had vanished. Among the thousands attracted by gold were men who had been problems back home in settled communities with working governments. This rough element ganged together under the name of The Hounds, and one night descended upon the defenseless colony of Chileans to beat them up, kill a few, and wreck their easily wreckable quarters. The city rose in its wrath to kick The Hounds out of town, reimbursing the Chileans for their losses.

It was a prologue to one of the most violent decades ever experienced by an American city.

NEW STATES FOR THE UNION

THE Americans who came into the Far West had been born into self-government, absorbing its nutritious milk from their mothers' breasts and from the town pump as well. They knew how to set up their own government as surely as they knew how to practice their profession or craft. The twenty-five thousand Americans who came overland to California in 1849 voted their laws and traveled under their elected officials to such an extent that the migration has been called "a marching laboratory of political experiment." To these adepts at democracy the idea of living under a military government was unacceptable, even though amiable Colonel Mason issued few decrees and had even fewer troops with which to enforce them.

As early as December 11, 1848, a meeting had been held in San Jose expressing the need for a constitutional convention representing all of California. This meeting sparked others: in San Francisco, Sacramento, Monterey, Sonoma. On April 15, 1849, Brigadier General Bennett Riley, a sixty-one-year-old Marylander who had fought in the War of 1812, the Black Hawk and the Mexican wars, described by his contemporaries as "a grim old fellow and a fine, free swearer," with no experience whatever in governing, arrived to take over the civil governorship from Colonel Mason. When he learned that Congress, immersed in its near-bloody discussion of whether these new lands acquired from Mexico were to be admitted as slave or free, had adjourned without providing either statutes or government for California, he issued a call for a constitutional convention to take place in Monterey, asking that delegates be elected in August from every district.

California would set itself up as a state, even if Congress did not want it!

In Utah the Mormons were having similar difficulties in being recognized by the federal government. The Great Basin, which they had named Deseret, a *Book of Mormon* word meaning honey bee, had complete civil government. As Franklin D. Richards, one of the Twelve Apostles, said:

"Theoretically state and church are one. If there were no gentiles, and no other government (federal), there would be no civil law."

What the Mormons called their "kingdom" was originally meant in a spiritual sense. Now the Saints spread out geographically and politically: to the south, Fort Utah was built near the present town of Provo, on Utah Lake; to the north, on the road to Ogden, were Bountiful and Farmington. Brigham Young proclaimed that it was not enough to claim a land; his Saints must also occupy it, cultivate it, populate it. Then, when the gentiles came in, the Mormons would predominate and control.

The law of the Church was the total law of the people, a body of law handed down directly from God, through His own selected High Council, and every part of it was for the total good of the Mormons. The High Council, none of whom received a salary (the Mormons have rarely paid a salary to any of its priests or officials), had passed laws controlling prices, divorce, idleness, stealing, profanity and fornication. But the Saints were highly moral and highly obedient, probably the most obedient group in the entire history of the United States, for to have disobeyed would have been to lose their place in the Kingdom of Heaven. The president and Twelve Apostles put paper money into circulation, appointed a clerk, a historian, a meteorologist, a postmaster, a marshal and a military commander over the Nauvoo Legion, in which all Mormons from eighteen to forty-five had to train. The Council disapproved of litigation between Saints, yet there were courts of arbitration. Tithes were set at ten per cent of a man's *gross* earnings; a splinter group which had broken off from Nauvoo after Joseph Smith's murder would fail, among other reasons, because they tithed ten per cent of the *net*.

The Mormons realized they could never get into the Union with a purely ecclesiastical government, and so on March 4, 1849, while Zachary Taylor was being inaugurated President in Washington, D.C., the High Council instructed the marshal to call a public meeting at the Old Fort:

"For the purpose of electing and appointing officers for the government of the people in the Great Salt Lake and vicinity."

When the Saints gathered in the Old Fort it was not to nominate their political officers but to confirm an already named slate headed by Brigham Young for president, Richards for secretary of state, Kimball for chief justice and the bishops or lay leaders of the nineteen wards magistrates for their districts. All political officers except President Young were to serve without pay. Thus the Mormons chose their church government to serve as a political government.

The committee writing the state constitution completed its task so quickly it is logical to assume that Brigham Young had brought to Deseret copies of the New York and Illinois state constitutions it so strongly resembled. There was to be a two-house legislature, a judiciary rising to a supreme court, all free white males over twenty-one were eligible to vote. On April 30, 1849, some two thousand signatures were affixed to a petition asking for a:

"Territorial Government of the most liberal construction authorized by our excellent federal constitution, with the least possible delay."

On July 2 the First Deseret General Assembly met, and Almond W. Babbitt was elected Mormon delegate to Congress. But the petition he was taking to Washington, despite the fact that the Mormons had only one sixth of the population required for statehood, now asked that Deseret be admitted as a state rather than a territory.

The Mormons adopted a firm tone with the United States Congress, reminding it of its sins of omission: failure to provide civil government for any part of the Far West, failure to supersede the rifle, the revolver and the bowie knife by the law of the land. However the Congress need not worry over any lawlessness in Deseret: the Mormons had created a provisional government under which the laws of the land were obeyed. They had also built a legislative hall at their own expense, as fine as any in the East.

But a half century of conflict would pass before Utah and the Saints would take their peaceable place at the Union board.

The California convention opened in Monterey on September 3, 1849, six months after the Mormon meeting, in a solid two-story, native yellow sandstone edifice which the Reverend Mr. Colton had built for a schoolhouse and assembly hall with funds raised from "town lots and gamblers' banks." Forty-eight delegates had been elected, from San Diego on the southern border to the most northerly mining camps on the Trinity River, toward the Oregon line.

Six of the delegates were Californios, representing the finest tradition of the Mexican period: Mariano Vallejo from Sonoma, Andres Pico from San Jose, Jose Carrillo from Los Angeles, Jose Covarrubias from Santa Barbara, Miguel de Pedrorena from San Diego and Pablo de la Guerra of Monterey, whose beautiful and cultured wife made their home a gathering place for the delegates. Mrs. Thomas O. Larkin also extended hospitality, as did Mrs. Jessie Benton Frémont in her charming Spanish house with enclosed patio.

Of the thirty-seven American delegates at the convention, twenty-two came from free states, fifteen from slave; there were four, including John Sutter, who were born out of the country. It was a young man's convention, nine being under thirty, twenty-three under forty. Almost all of the early settlers were there: Thomas O. Larkin representing San Francisco; Joel Walker, Sonoma; Lansford W. Hastings, of the Hastings cut-off, represented Sacramento, rancheros from southern California such as Abel Stearns and Hugo Reid, the Scotsman who had married an Indian girl and planted excellent vineyards. Robert Semple of Benicia, who ran the ferry across the Carquinez Strait, was elected chairman; William Hartnell was named interpreter. There were fourteen lawyers, twelve farmers, seven merchants, a scattering of printers, engineers, bankers, doctors.

The outstanding personality of the convention was William Gwin of Tennessee, newly come to California with the express purpose of being elected one of California's first senators. He was described by a reporter as having "grandeur of exterior, magnificence of person, of herculean figure." He had something of greater importance, copies of the constitutions of New York and Iowa, having gone to the personal expense of having the newest state constitution, that of Iowa, printed in San Francisco so that each delegate might have a copy before him.

The most difficult problem of the convention was where California's eastern boundary should extend. The Gwin-Halleck proposal, which had considerable backing, suggested that California should consist of all the land acquired from Mexico by the Treaty of Guadalupe Hidalgo, that is, the entire Far West. When the actual maps were drawn, the group modestly contented itself with Nevada, the near half of Utah, which included all the Mormon settlements as well as that portion of Arizona embracing present-day Phoenix. The opposition claimed the area was too large to be manageable, and that it included thousands of Mormons who were not represented. The boundaries as sketched on one of Preuss's maps from Frémont's expedition led the delegates to set the eastern border in the Sierra Nevada, which traverses the greater part of the state.

The question of slavery in California never got started, the bill to forbid slavery passing unanimously. There were heated debates on whether dueling should be allowed (it was not); whether women should be allowed to control all property in their possession before marriage (they were). When it was proposed that all persons charged with criminal offenses be tried by a jury of their peers, one delegate shouted:

"What do we want with peers? This ain't no monarchy!"

The convention of near strangers went peaceably through the weeks, evolving a liberal constitution which provided for equitable taxation and a good educational system. Through Gwin's persuasive politicking, as well as the copies he had provided, the constitution of Iowa was largely followed. The Californians, like the Mormons, quickly waved aside the unworthy idea that they should ask for mere territorial status, informing the United States Congress that they were, and would be, a full-blown state.

On October 13, when the last of the delegates had signed the constitution, General Riley fired a thirty-one-gun salute because California expected to the thirty-first state of the Union. John Sutter sprang to his feet and cried with tears streaming down his face:

"Gentlemen, this is the happiest day of my life . . . a great day for California!"

The delegates, aware of the millions in gold coming out of the mines, paid prodigally for all services. Each member received $16 a day plus $16 per mile traveled; $10,000 was appropriated for J. Ross Browne, clerk of the convention, to print the convention's report in English and Spanish; Governor Riley was to be paid at the rate of $10,000 a year as governor, Captain Halleck $6000 as secretary of state until the popular election.

The delegates then assessed themselves $25 each for a gala costume ball, held in the convention hall that evening to celebrate their creation of the new state, the delegates and Monterey society dancing most of the night unrepressed by the chill thought that Congress wanted no part of them.

The canvass for the approval of the constitution and for the election of the state officers was short; there had been so little time for electioneering that one miner exclaimed:

"When I left home I was determined to go it blind. I voted for the constitution, and I've never seen the constitution. I've voted for all the candidates, and I don't know a damned one of them."

All-seeing or blind, the constitution was approved, 12,061 to 811; Peter H. Burnett, one of Sutter's former assistants, was elected governor. General Riley proclaimed that military rule in California was ended.

When the legislature met on December 20, John C. Frémont was elected United States senator on the first ballot, and William M. Gwin on the third.

The character of John C. Frémont was beyond permanent defeat, as it was beyond permanent victory. Having ridden into the Sierra Nevada to inspect his seventy-square-mile totally useless ranch, he discovered gold; not merely "the color" or gold dust, not merely small nuggets that had been eroded by the weather and washed down by the rain and the streams to the valleys below. Here on the Mariposa John

Frémont discovered a mother lode, a body of gold that had been cast up by the vast volcanic action which formed the mountains, veins of gold bedded in the rock of the mountainside.

Within a matter of a year after Frémont had acknowledged defeat on the summit of the Great Divide he became the single largest owner of gold in California, a millionaire, setting forth for Washington as the first elected senator from the fabulously rich and romantic California. He could not be seated until Congress admitted California as a state, but to the Frémonts as to all Californians this was an unimportant detail.

Thus, at the end of 1849, though Nevada was still a totally unoccupied terror-laden desert and Colorado a mountain wilderness occupied by warring Indian tribes, two governments, Deseret and California, had been created, with representatives on their way to Washington to achieve statehood for the folks back home.

By the forced movement of an entire church community of over eleven thousand Mormons to Deseret, and the discovery of gold which cascaded a hundred thousand people into California in a little more than a year, there had been created a totally new phenomenon on the American political scene where territories had been settled slowly and painfully over a long period of years.

DEATH VALLEY EARNS ITS NAME

In October of 1849 there assembled at Provo on Utah Lake, some sixty miles south of Salt Lake, a number of traveling groups, families and young men on horseback, unknown to each other prior to this meeting, which would make up the Death Valley Party. The majority of the party had come south to Provo instead of north around Salt Lake to join the California Trail because they had heard the grisly details of the Donner Party. Judging that it was too late to risk the winter snows of the Sierra Nevada, they decided to take the longer but safer route into southern California, then north to the mines. Word had been spread that there would be a rendezvous at Provo for all wishing to travel the Old Spanish Trail.

In the party when it started for Los Angeles on October 9 there were eighty wagons, two hundred fifty people, and one thousand head of horses and cattle. For their guide they hired Captain Jefferson Hunt, a member of the Mormon Battalion who was being sent to California to buy cattle and seed for the community in Salt Lake. Hunt imposed

Mormon military discipline on the train: it moved like an army, divided into seven divisions, each under its captain. The train named itself the Sand Walking Company.

No crueler nor more accurate title could be divined.

Captain Hunt made an early error: he took a wrong turning. Though he was soon back on the main trail this undermined confidence in him, and when a Captain Smith with a party of nine Mormons heading for the California mines rode up with a map or waybill which claimed that there was a cut-off, what James Reed of the Donner Party had called "a nigher way," over Walker's Pass from which they could descend into the Tulare Valley close to the mines, and save themselves four hundred wearisome miles, the Sand Walking Company went into a Committee of the Whole around a campfire to debate the desirability of taking Smith's cut-off. When Captain Hunt was asked his opinion, he said he doubted if any white man had ever traveled it; that young men alone might make it but families with wagons would have serious trouble:

"If you all wish to go and follow Smith I will go also. But if even one wagon decides to go the original route, I shall feel bound by my promise to go with that lone wagon."

The Reverend John W. Brier, described in the journal of one of the listeners as a "man who always liked to give his opinion on every subject," declared forcibly for the cut-off, despite the fact he was traveling with a delicate wife and three young sons. So did a number of others.

The next morning, as the wagons and men came to the fork in the road, Smith and the Reverend Mr. Brier prevailed, even as Lansford Hastings and James Reed had helped make the decision for the Donners over the advice of experienced mountain men. Only seven wagons continued on the known trail with Captain Hunt. A hundred wagons seceded, including the Briers, Bennetts and Arcanes, the Wade and Dale families, all of whom had children; and the entire Jayhawker party of single men.

For two days Smith's party crossed green valleys with plenty of water. But that was as far as the anonymous map maker had traveled. Caught in an impassable canyon, with evidence of worse terrain ahead, seventy-two wagons turned back to the Old Spanish Trail. Though they never caught up with Hunt, they followed him into southern California, arriving in Los Angeles before the seceders had even reached the heart of their inferno.

Smith had also thought better of his decision; he cut back with his mounted Mormons to the Old Spanish Trail and safety without informing the remaining eighty-five emigrants that he had changed his mind. Meeting about their campfire at Misery Mountain, guideless, they too seemed to have little choice but to turn back, when scouts rode into the camp with the message that they had seen a good pass which would carry them into California.

They decided to plunge ahead, but not as a unified train with a leader; instead they split into three separate groups. The Jayhawkers, young, unencumbered, started out first and fast; the Reverend Mr. Brier's party came next with his three children and two young men who were part of their mess; third, and bringing up the rear, the Bennett, Arcane and Wade families, the two Earhart brothers with two sons, several unattached men, and twenty-one-year-old William Manly, who was to be their guide. It was Manly's first trip west.

Juliet Brier was born in Bennington, Vermont, September 26, 1813, and educated at a seminary. She was a wisp of a woman, nervous by nature, the mother of three sons, aged eight, seven and four. The first white woman to enter Death Valley, the sight that greeted her eyes from the ridge of the eastern range was one to strike terror into the stoutest heart: utter, hopeless, unalleviated desolation: eight to fourteen miles wide, one hundred thirty miles long, with the lower-lying, aptly named Funeral Range in the center. There was nothing living as far as the eye could sweep, only wind-blown and rippled Sahara wastes of sun-baked sand and crusted salt-mud flats, with barren mountains surrounding on all sides and bearing not a tree, bush or blade of grass; what Bancroft calls:

"The region of mirage, accursed to all living things, its atmosphere destructive even to the passing bird."

When the Reverend Mr. Brier went ahead looking for water, says Mrs. Brier, "I was left with our three little boys to help bring up the cattle. Poor little Kirke gave out and I carried him on my back, barely seeing where I was going."

She stumbled on, hour after hour, in the hot choking dust, the cattle bellowing for water. When darkness fell she lost the two men of her group and had to get on her knees to search out the ox tracks in the starlight. Not until three in the morning did she reach camp, where the men had found hot and cold springs.

It was Christmas morning. At the springs, which they named Furnace Creek, one of the men asked, "Don't you think you and the children better remain here?"

"I have never kept the company waiting," replied Mrs. Brier. "Neither have my children. *Every step I take will be towards California."*

The next morning when they reached the Jayhawker camp the Briers found the young men burning their wagons in order to travel faster: for it needed only one surveying look about them to know that they all faced imminent death.

The Briers also abandoned their wagons, packing their rapidly vanishing foodstuffs on the failing oxen. The Reverend Mr. Brier asked the Jayhawkers for permission to travel with them; the Jayhawkers did not want to be encumbered by a woman and small children, and objected. Then they looked at Mrs. Brier, all skin and bones, and relented. William Manly, leading the Bennett Party, also arrived at the springs. He reports:

"She was the one who put the packs on the oxen in the morning. She it was who took them off at night, built the fires, cooked the food, helped the children, and did all sorts of work when the father of the family was too tired, which was almost all of the time."

The combined train struggled through mile after mile of salt marsh, sinking in sand to their shoe tops. One of the Brier boys remembers: "Twenty miles across naked dunes, the wind driving the sand like shot into the faces and eyes."

Their tongues grew swollen, their lips cracked, the oxen laid down in the sand never to rise again. That night the men climbed up the rock-strewn mountain to the snow line, bringing back snow in their shirts, some eating it hard, others melting it for the cattle.

They went for the next forty-eight hours without water, unable to eat the meat of their slaughtered oxen because they could get nothing down their parched throats. A Dr. Carr suggested that they return to Furnace Creek where there was water; he broke down and cried when Mrs. Brier repeated, "Every step we take will be towards California."

By New Year's Day they camped at the head of the Panamint Valley, totally lost. The stronger of the Jayhawkers pushed ahead, leaving in Mrs. Brier's care the older and weaker men.

The first to die of thirst was the fifty-year-old Reverend Mr. Fish, who was traveling to California in hopes of finding the money to pay off his church's debt in Indiana.

On January 6 the two single men who had been in the Brier mess, and who had the only flour in the party, decided they would strike out alone in the hopes of saving themselves. They baked up all their dough except for a small piece they gave to Mrs. Brier, then shook hands good-by. Mrs. Brier baked her dough into twenty-two crackers, all they would have for twenty-two days of nightmare and terror.

Next to die was middle-aged William Isham, who crawled four miles on his hands and knees searching for water, then dropped on his face.

"Give up?" cried Juliet Brier. "Oh! I knew what that meant—a shallow grave in the sand."

Their tongues became black and hung out of their mouths. Ahead there was the cruel mirage of the desert: water, an oasis, trees, greenery. When water came it was a muddy pool at what is now Borax Lake; the few remaining cattle stamped into it first, then the humans scooped up the mud-laden water, forcing it down their parched throats.

The next waterless stretch lasted nearly five days. In camp the men, with burnt faces and skeletal frames, lay down and waited for death. Mrs. Brier went behind a rock, prayed to God for strength, then gave them a combined sermon and tongue-lashing that shocked them back onto their feet. At that moment the Reverend Mr. Richards came running into camp, crying:

"Water! Water! I have found water!"

Four miles away he had come upon a group of Indians, had made friendly signs, then gestures of thirst. The Indians guided him to a brook at the base of the mountains, hidden by shrubs, which ran clear and cold before disappearing into the sands of the desert.

When the party finally struggled to the top of the range and looked back at the valley behind them, they named it Death Valley. But the Mojave Desert into which they descended in the middle of January 1850 was little better; a desert of alkali, with no known trails or springs. Emaciated from dysentery and exhaustion, they faced days of heat, dust, thirst, rocks that cut their feet. One man said, "I will just take a little nap," and never woke up. Another said, "I have a presentiment I shall never reach California," fell off his pony and died. At a spring, another drank too copiously; he was the seventh to perish.

The Reverend Mr. Brier, who had been hobbling along with the aid of crutches, lay down in camp, bade his wife farewell and closed his eyes. Juliet Brier pleaded with her husband to hold on, gathered some acorns, ground and cooked them and fed them to him from a spoon. He survived: to sire three daughters, and campaign for Lincoln.

The Bennett-Manly Party had equally bad luck in trying a southerly trail: they got trapped in the hopeless waste bordered by a black range of mountains through which there could be no conceivable pass. Finding a spring at Tule, near the southern end of the valley, they decided not to dissipate their failing strength, but to remain encamped. Bennett asked young Manly and Rogers, a burly butcher, if they would push on alone, find civilization and bring back relief. There was neither map nor food the men could take with them, nor knowledge of what lay ahead except days of purgatory.

But they went . . . passing the dead bodies of Jayhawkers who had given out. Their trek, as told by Manly in *Death Valley in '49,* is one of the West's great sagas of man's will against the implacable elements:

"Black and desolate ranges and buttes to the south, great dry plains, salt lakes and slippery alkali water to which we walked, only to turn away in disappointment, little sheets of ice that saved our lives, hawk and crow diet, lameness . . ."

They got out in fourteen days, sustaining life by sucking on rocks or single blades of grass, breaking trail over trailless mountains, deserts and valleys until, more dead than alive, they cleared one more range and saw below them the green cattle ranch of San Francisquito.

Settling in for a long wait, the Bennetts took off their wagon covers to make protecting tents for the cattle and themselves against the heat and sandstorms, rationed their food, watched it vanish. Mrs. Arcane, knowing she must abandon her clothing but not wanting it to be too good for the Indians who would inherit it, dressed herself in her finest garments every day. Captain Richard Culverwell, who had gone exploring, died trying to get back to camp. After three weeks the men agreed:

"If those boys ever get out of this hole they are damned fools if they ever come back to help anybody."

Manly and Rogers waited only four days to regain their strength, then borrowed horses to load with oranges and other foodstuffs, and spent the next week retracing their steps, exploring for better passes and water holes. When they got their first view of the camp not a soul was in sight; they concluded they had made the journey for nothing.

Manly fired a shot. From under a wagon a man emerged. He threw his arms high over his head and shouted:

"The boys have come! The boys have come!"

They were saved.

The Brier party also emerged, as images of death, onto the opulent hospitality of the Californios who owned San Francisquito ranch. Mrs. Brier came down out of the San Gabriel Mountains, leading her three sons, in rags, the last of the moccasins she had made of the hides of dead oxen worn through; seventy pounds of bone, grit and indestructibility.

Thirteen men had lost their lives in the Sand Walking Company. The women were tougher; they endured. Juliet Brier's inner strength saved not only her own family but several of the Jayhawkers as well.

NEVADA AND COLORADO SHOW THEIR COLOR

On May 1, 1850, a complete American city government was installed in San Francisco. Through the sale of city-owned lots the Council had $635,000 with which to buy a city hall, build a hospital and extend its wharves, to grade and plank its important business streets. Houses and stores rolled unfalteringly up the hillsides from the beach until the original cove was settled, neighboring valleys were bought and subdivided, with a toll road of planks built out to the Mission Dolores.

This mid-century moment San Francisco ceased to be a mining town. Red flannel shirts were replaced by white linen, slouch hats by beavers, high boots, tuck-in pants and round rough coats by frock coats, trousers and shoes taken from sea chests. Only the gamblers persevered in their colorful costume of diamond-studded shirt, sombrero and scarlet sash.

It was not easy to be a gentleman in San Francisco; laundry was $8.00 a dozen, regardless of whether the article was a handkerchief or long-drawers underwear. The service was so slow that men sent their linen by ship to Honolulu or Canton to be laundered. This unfair competition gave rise to Washerwoman's Lagoon, just over a sand dune, where washermen set up a large-scale industry with boiling kettles, fluted washboards and ironing tents.

"When one of these great, burly long-bearded fellows got a shirt on the board the suds flew and the buttons also."

Early 1850 saw the arrival of three of the Big Four who would build the Central Pacific Railroad and control California for a generation, the dramatis personae who would replace in importance Sutter, Vallejo, Larkin, Frémont. Only Charles Crocker came across the plains in the hope of making his fortune in the gold mines. The other three, Collis P. Huntington, Mark Hopkins and later Leland Stanford, came across Panama and into San Francisco Bay to make their fortunes by trading with the miners.

Charles Crocker was a burly two-hundred-fifty-pounder when at the age of twenty-six he left Indiana with a group of young fellows, including two of his brothers, for the trip over the California Trail to the gold fields. He had been born of poor people in Troy, New York, left school at the age of twelve to help support his family, moved to Indiana with his parents, helped clear the land and farm, then worked in a sawmill and an iron forge. Discovering a small deposit of ore, he built a combination blacksmith shop and forge, which he sold in order to provision himself for the westward journey.

"I grew up as a sort of leader," says Crocker, "I had always been the one to swim a river and carry a rope across."

His quality of leadership was of no help in the California mines where he spent two lean years as an unsuccessful prospector. He then opened a store with his brother in one of the Eldorado mining camps, for which he drove the team and did the hauling, expanded to Sacramento, and here the man who in a few years could boast, "I built the Central Pacific!" made his first success in dry goods.

The most important of his future partners, Collis P. Huntington, worked for one half day as a gold miner, then took the supply of goods he had bought in New York and Panama to Sacramento City. Born in Connecticut, son of a miserly tinker, raised in poverty and painful thrift, he had earned and saved over a hundred dollars by the time he was fourteen. He worked as a hired man on a neighbor's farm, opened a store with his brother in Oneonta, peddled jewelry through Ohio and Indiana, collected bills in the deep South, sold butter in New York City, and while held up on the Isthmus in 1849, rented a little schooner and brought foodstuffs into Panama for $1000 a month profit. By the time he opened his store in Sacramento in 1850 he was one of the shrewdest traders to reach California, so sharp that as financial head of the Central Pacific he would bargain Congress out of $100,000,000 and milk the Far West of billions.

Another partner did not waste even half a day in the mines, for Mark Hopkins was a conservative merchant. The lean man of the Big Four (his partners all weighed over two hundred pounds), he was called "thin as a fence post," was a vegetarian with a bird-like appetite, and refused to smoke, drink, curse, gamble or spend money. A perfect inside man for Huntington, who roamed California buying merchandise cheap and holding it in his warehouses until the supply was scarce, Hopkins was described as too cautious in business ever to become rich. When Charles Crocker said:

"One man works hard all his life and ends up a pauper. Another man, no smarter, makes $20,000,000. Luck has a hell of a lot to do with it," he was describing "Uncle" Mark Hopkins as much as he was himself, the main distinction being that the possession of more than

$20,000,000 was "against Hopkins's better judgment," and he acted "as if he wanted to apologize for his millions."

By the end of 1850 San Francisco had a population of over thirty thousand. "This figure," reports Asbury in *The Barbary Coast*, "included two thousand women, most of whom were harlots from Europe and eastern and southern United States, principally New York and New Orleans."

Salt Lake was growing with equal vigor, with more than eleven thousand Saints in Deseret by the end of 1850. The Mormons had started their first newspaper, the *Deseret News*, chartered a university, the first in the Far West, and organized a Music and Dramatic Society.

And by 1849 Nevada had its first building.

In March of 1849 an expedition was formed in Salt Lake to go to California to mine and trade. The secretary of the expedition was a twenty-four-year-old Mormon by the name of H. S. Beatie, from Virginia, with some college training. Beatie took along a supply of goods to sell, but going through Carson Valley in the spring he fell in love with the country at the eastern base of the Sierra Nevada, a green paradise in the midst of pine and aspen, with clear mountain springs and "oceans of good feed for stock." The spot was about five thousand feet high, with a superb view of Carson Valley and the sagebrush desert extending forty miles east to the Washoe Mountains, while towering behind to the west was the majestic Sierra Nevada.

By building a corral and a double log cabin with rooms connected by a passage but without a roof or floors, Beatie became the father of the first Nevada settlement. His enthusiasm was so great that eight other men of the expedition, including the leader, apparently all Mormons, remained with him. By July, when emigrants started streaming down the Humboldt and Carson valleys on their way to California, and ran out of flour and meat, Beatie found his trade so brisk that he had to make two trips across the Sierra Nevada, the first time driving three yoke of cattle over Carson's Pass to trade for supplies, the next time going over with pack mules to buy goods on the American River.

Beatie had no interest in looking for gold, but Abner Blackburn, who accompanied him on the trading trips, is one of the three men credited by Nevada historians with finding the color. The first was one of the Henry W. Bigler group of Mormon Battalion members who had worked for John Sutter and discovered Mormon Island. Bigler told how his party, coming east across the Sierra Nevada in August of 1848, "discovered gold in western Utah" as Nevada was known.

The following May, 1849, Mormon John Orr stopped his wagon train at noon for a brief respite in the shadow of Sun Mountain. His companion, Prouse, began panning instead of resting, and found sufficient tracings of gold for John Orr to name the canyon in which they had halted "Gold Canyon." The Orr train started over the mountains but when the axle broke in one of the wagons they put back to Mormon Station, and while it was being repaired, Orr and Prouse returned the forty miles to Gold Canyon where Orr found the first piece of gold-bearing quartz.

Abner Blackburn reports in his diary that he went prospecting with his bread pan and butcher knife, scratched up some color in a gulch, and that when he showed it to the other men they "grabbed up pans, knives and kettles and started out. They scratched and paned [sic] until sundown, taking out $9.00 to $10.00 worth of dust." Having neither tools nor provisions, they continued on to California.

By now there was a little community of prospectors in western Utah: Mexicans who had not been kindly treated in the California mines, emigrants to California halting briefly, Mormons coming from California to Gold Canyon to prospect, other Mormons from Salt Lake who had heard that Beatie's trading post had been a success. By late summer there were some twenty lean-to trading posts dotting the Carson Valley, the closest one to Beatie's being fourteen miles away. Spafford Hall, a non-Mormon from Indiana, built a station just a mile and a half from the mouth of Gold Canyon, on Carson River.

Before the snows fell Beatie sold his trading post to a man called Moore and returned to Salt Lake. Most of the other traders collapsed their lean-tos and went east to Salt Lake if they were Mormons, or west to California. In September the last of the twenty-odd prospectors left Gold Canyon, complaining:

"There is no water, no food, only buzzards."

Besides, the gold was mixed in with some unfortunate flaky blue stuff that made mining difficult and unprofitable.

Nevada's flurry proved premature. But soon the young Grosh brothers would come over the Sierra Nevada from Volcano, California, carrying with them books on mineralogy and chemistry, and as full a set of chemicals as they could assemble.

In the mid-century year of 1850 two brothers by the name of Ralston from the Cherokee lands of Georgia, where they had been gold mining, entered Colorado by way of the Arkansas River, leading a party of

Cherokee Indians, to whom they were related by marriage, to the California gold fields. They passed Bent's Fort, the almost deserted village of Pueblo, then turned north along the front range and Pike's Peak. Being experienced miners, they did some experimental panning as they moved north. When they reached the mouth of Cherry Creek they camped for a few days to prospect. Smiley in his *History of Denver* reports:

"They found 'color,' but not enough to hold them from their original obective, California."

The Ralstons and their Cherokee party stayed in California for two years, mining with moderate luck. The memory of the "color" at Cherry Creek never left their minds. They did not return to the Colorado gold fields, but imparted their knowledge to relatives in the Cherokee Territory of Georgia, leading directly to the first real prospecting party and to the incredible Colorado strikes.

In this fashion did the Nevada and Colorado finds result from the original California strike which brought prospectors through the Far West, opening the land and weaving the three greatest American gold fields into an integrated frontier pattern, all parts of a geographical and cultural whole.

GOLD AND MORMONISM SETTLE A LAND

By contrast to vigorous San Francisco and Salt Lake, Los Angeles of 1850 was standing still, a sleepy village of mud huts surrounded by extensive ranchos, without a public school, newspaper or library. With its hot, waterless, dusty near-desert climate, its main activity was fighting Indians who were raiding the ranchos, the Paiutes driving off as many as five hundred head of cattle. Two thirds of the population was illiterate; the one third that could read and write was busy sending petitions to Congress asking that southern California be separated from northern California and called the state of Central California, a separatist movement which was due to the feeling of the southern Californians that they had nothing in common with northern California. At the moment they were right.

San Francisco's first theatrical season began on January 16, 1850, in Washington Hall, with the Eagle Theatre Company playing a farce and a drama. A few weeks later the National was opened, a proper theatre of brick, with a French company. The government was installed in its first City Hall, the former Graham House, a four-story wooden building on the corner of Kearny and Pacific, with four flights of continuous balconies overlooking the busy streets.

In May a fire broke out before dawn in a rickety gambling saloon; for seven hours the wind-driven flames raced up and down the hills, burning three hundred houses, including the City Hall, two sides of Portsmouth Square and the three important business blocks. The loss was over $4,000,000, accounting for nearly half the gold dug out of California in 1849, making Brigham Young sound like a prophet when he told his Saints:

"The true use of gold is for paving streets, covering houses and making culinary dishes."

Within ten days half of the burned city was rebuilt, the first volunteer fire department organized and every home owner warned to keep six buckets of water on hand for future emergencies. It would not be quite enough; not even the five fire companies with pretentious names like the Empire Engine Company, the Protection or the Eureka could keep San Francisco from becoming the most frequently burned-down city in the world. On June 12, forty days later, a fire started in a broken chimney in the Merchants Hotel and the business district from Kearny Street to the waterfront burned down, another $3,000,000 vanishing in smoke; in September one hundred fifty houses burned, in October another $250,000 worth of property, including the City Hospital; in December there was a $1,000,000 loss of wood and corrugated iron wall buildings. . . .

California was having an equally hard time becoming a state. On January 1, 1850, Senator John C. Frémont, his wife Jessie and their daughter Lily had boarded the S.S. *Oregon* in Monterey Harbor en route to Washington to have California admitted. They were rowed out to the ship by Indian boys in a torrential downpour of rain, but no greater than was the torrent of speeches which kept Frémont out of the Senate and California out of the Union through the spring and summer months until the South's unwillingness to admit another free state was compromised. Now on October 18, 1850, the S.S. *Oregon* sailed into San Francisco Harbor flying all its bunting and signaling that California had been admitted.

San Francisco promptly went wild. All business houses and courts were locked, guns began firing from the hills surrounding the city, bands and paraders stomped through the streets, the ships in the harbor broke out their flags, newspapers off the S.S. *Oregon* sold for $5.00 apiece. At night bonfires blazed from the peaks.

"Mounting his box behind six fiery mustangs lashed to the highest speed, the driver of Crandall's stage cried the glad tidings all the way to San Jose, 'California is admitted!', while a ringing cheer was returned by the people as the mail flew by."

On the twenty-ninth of October came the official celebration, with a procession led by marshals in crimson scarves, buglers sounding all the way to Portsmouth Square, the native Californios carrying a banner with thirty-one stars, the Chinese colony in their native costumes attesting their loyalty by carrying a blue silk banner reading *The China Boys.*

By contrast the Saints took their admission as Utah Territory quietly. It was not that the Mormons were against celebrations; on July 24, the anniversary of President Young's arrival in the valley with the first group of Saints, there had been the firing of a cannon, speeches, Captain Pitts's brass band, which had been converted as a unit in England, playing martial music, a feast to which all strangers were invited. It was just that the Mormons were disappointed in not being given their total freedom as a state as California had been. In their status as a territory they would be controlled from Washington, and gentiles would be appointed to be their territorial officers.

Nor was that all in California upon which Brigham Young had cast a covetous eye. He had always wanted the port of San Diego for his state of Deseret, so that newly converted Saints arriving from Europe could come to Salt Lake over a route controlled by Mormons. He also wanted "a settlement in the vicinity of the sea coast, a main route to the Pacific stations between the Iron County [Utah] and California; also to cultivate the olive and manufacture olive oil, grapes, sugar cane, cotton and other desirable fruits and products."

San Diego was now part of the state of California, and so were all the rich farming lands between southern Nevada and the Pacific Ocean. There could be no Mormon route for converts which traversed exclusively Mormon country. Nevertheless two Mormons traveling the San Bernardino Valley, east of Los Angeles, wrote to Brigham Young saying:

"The Williams Ranch contains advantages for a settlement of our people. . . . Here is the soil and climate and water to raise crops of any kind. It is situated within 40 miles of the port of San Pedro and 112 miles of San Diego."

Brigham Young appointed Elders Lyman and Rich to head the expedition, asking for twenty volunteers. Five hundred showed up.

Young's intuition told him that many had been lured by the love of gold.

"I was sick at the sight of so many of the Saints running to California after the gods of this world," said Young, "and I was unable to address them."

The Mormon expedition moved southward toward the spring at Las Vegas. Every stream, field of grass, stand of trees, potential stone quarry was noted for future Mormon stations. From Las Vegas through the Mojave Desert the expedition traveled a barren and destitute stretch, suffering from thirst and exhaustion, pushing across endless uphill wastes, and over a seven-thousand-foot mountain range.

The Los Angeles *Star* announced on May 31, 1851, that one hundred fifty Mormon families were at Cajon Pass, and assumed they were coming to Los Angeles.

"If it be true that the Mormons are coming in such numbers to settle among us we shall, as good and industrious citizens, extend to them a friendly welcome."

The Mormons were doubtless touched by this show of civic rectitude, but they had not the slightest intention of settling among the gentiles; they would carve out their own community. The Elders rejected the Williams rancho and continued their study of the valley. In the meanwhile temporary farming lands were bought and planted; they had brought with them a supply of livestock for milk, butter, cheese. For protection they built a split-log fort of which the west wall consisted of log houses, the other three walls of tightly compacted, twelve-foot willows to keep out raiding Indians. A ditch was dug from a nearby creek into the fort so that the Mormon wives would not have to leave the enclosure to get water. There was no government in the San Bernardino Valley; the Mormons brought their own: a ward and a stake were set up, with its bishop and president, and a high council to serve as a tribunal.

The second Protestant community in southern California was founded in the same valley six weeks later by a group of emigrants from the Oatman Party which had left Independence in 1850, heading for the northern gold fields. They had suffered such severe losses through Indian raids, starvation and thirst that they vowed they would make their home at the first place where there was an abundance of water. This proved to be El Monte, "a wooded spot," about five miles east of Los Angeles.

"Here a little stream trickled through a mass of watercress and rushes while wild grapes matted the willows and alders on the bank."

Here Ira Thompson made camp, persuading others of the exhausted families to settle permanently, "earning the distinction of being the first strictly American settlement in southern California."

Once again, gold and Mormonism were opening and settling a new land.

RISE OF THE VIGILANTES

The years of violence and Vigilance Committees started innocently enough at a special session of the Great Salt Lake County court where on January 3, 1851, the first jury impaneled in Utah tried what the Mormons called "winter Saints" (transients who had decided to spend a comfortable winter in the bosom of the Church) for stealing, a crime unknown to the semi-co-operative Mormon beehives. The miscreants were convicted and sentenced to hard labor, but since no one could be obliged to work harder than the Saints worked voluntarily this could not be considered harsh treatment. Brigham Young released them for deportation to California.

This was no favor to either San Francisco or Los Angeles, which had by now collected their own gallery of rogues. San Francisco's government had not only broken down in the eight months since it was installed but had in large measure been taken over by ruffians and former members of the Australian penal colony. Thousands of strangers were streaming into a town in no way prepared to assimilate them, where businessmen were so busy accumulating profits they refused to serve on juries or to vote. As a consequence the officials voted themselves handsome salaries, began tapping the coffers for cash, spending large sums with no accounting. The police force had become rife with criminals and their allies. Burglaries, holdups, shootings became every-night occurrences.

Then on February 19, 1851, two thieves entered the store of the popular C. J. Jansen, beat him unconscious and robbed his safe of $2000. Two Australians were promptly arrested and identified by Jansen: Robert Windred and James Stuart, the former suspected of a murder at Foster's Bar. An angry crowd tried to take the prisoners from the police, who succeeded in getting them safely into court. Here Stuart claimed he was Thomas Berdue, a respectable British subject.

Saturday when court adjourned, the crowd became convinced that the two culprits would get off, as had others before them. That night five thousand men jammed into Portsmouth Square led by the ubiquitous Sam Brannan.

"We are the mayor, the hangman and the laws!" cried Brannan. "The law and the courts never yet hung a man in California!"

There were a few less bloodthirsty voices, in particular that of William T. Coleman, a twenty-seven-year-old Kentuckian who had come to California in 1849 to open stores in Placerville, Sacramento and now San Francisco. Big, open-faced, tremendous-jawed Coleman stepped forward to address the near mob, managing to cool its blood lust by asking that a committee be formed to name a judge and jury and give the accused a fair trial.

"We're willing to give them a fair trial," cried one man, "so long as we can hang them right after!"

A committee of fourteen, the first Vigilance Committee, was appointed to handle the affair, most of whom were rewarded for their sterling efforts by becoming street names: Jones, Ellis, Howard, Folsom, Green. The next day a jury was appointed, heard the evidence and voted that it was insufficient for a conviction. The two men were then tried in court, and convicted. The hanging was temperately set a month ahead. A good thing, too, for Thomas Berdue was telling the truth: that was his proper name, and his only crime was that he closely resembled James Stuart. He was released.

The committee dissolved itself in a welter of activity, electing an honest mayor, city attorney and marshal.

But there seemed no way to stop what the businessmen were convinced were incendiary fires. On May 4 a fire again devastated the city, after which a volunteer night patrol was established; on June 2, when another fire started, the businessmen had Benjamin Lewis arrested. When the judge quashed the indictment, Sam Brannan called a meeting in his office. Here the real Vigilance Committee was born, Brannan being elected president and spokesman. A constitution was drawn, parliamentary rules set up. Members hastened to enroll, even William T. Coleman, who signed as number 96 on the constitution. Williams in *Vigilance Committee of 1851* describes them as:

"A group of responsible citizens, bound together by a permanent organization, with the declared purpose of protecting lives and property in emergencies where lawful means prove ineffective."

The first official act of the group was to arrest John Jenkins, who had stolen a safe out of Long Wharf and dropped it into a boat. Tried in Brannan's office before a committee jury, Jenkins was declared guilty. When the committee seemed reluctant to execute Jenkins for stealing a safe, even though grand larceny was punishable by death under the 1851 statute, William D. M. Howard threw his cap disgustedly on the table and cried:

"Gentlemen, as I understand it, we came here to hang somebody."

Even the resourceful Coleman could not stop them by pleading a wait until morning. The whole town was in the streets, summoned by a tapping of the California Engine Company bell. Surrounded by a solid phalanx of armed committee members, Jenkins was marched to the old Plaza and hanged.

Within a day or two the coroner's jury publicly listed nine of the men implicated in the hanging, suggesting that they be tried by the courts. The complete list of a hundred eighty men who had signed the constitution was now published by the committee. The courts could not indict so many leading citizens, and did not try to; whereupon the membership rose to over seven hundred, the committee arresting ninety culprits charged with incendiarism, robbery and murder, trying them, hanging three, whipping one, deporting fifteen, turning fifteen over to the regular courts, releasing forty-one.

When Los Angeles heard about San Francisco's Vigilance Committee, the mayor and Council promptly organized one of their own, on July 13, 1851, one day after they had organized southern California's first police force. They needed a Vigilance Committee to protect themselves against San Francisco's committee, whose vigilance drove several thousand desperadoes into the summer vineyards of Los Angeles.

"The backwash of the gold rush, murderers, horse thieves and highwaymen, escaping the nooses of the gold country, made Los Angeles headquarters. The number of individual murders is not known, but according to the records there were forty 'legal' hangings and thirty-seven impromptu lynchings."

Unified by violence, Los Angeles was now incorporated as a city, and welcomed the first child of American parentage on both sides. Doubtless as a direct result, the first public school was opened by the Reverend Henry Weeks, the city helping him with $150 a month. The new city also saw its first freight train, ten wagons loaded with salable goods brought in from Salt Lake by Mormon D. W. Alexander.

The lowest income and education strata of the Californios, feeling unwanted and dispossessed by the transition to American government, became outlaws, preying on life and property. On a still lower social rung there were several thousand Indians living in and around Los Angeles, all that was left of the mission experiment, employed on the ranches during the week. On Saturday nights they assembled in a back street near the Plaza, drank up their week's wage of a dollar, brawled, and at dawn were rounded into a corral for the Lord's Day. On Monday morning they were bailed out by ranch owners who paid their dollar fine as their wage for the coming week's labor.

"Their condition lasted," says Willard succinctly in his *History of Los Angeles*, "until the Indians were all dead."

In Colorado their demise was accomplished more subtly: a treaty was drawn between the United States Government and the Arapaho and Cheyenne Indians as arranged by Broken Hand Fitzpatrick, out of which the Indians got small gifts, pledges, and fifteen days of games, dances and speechmaking.

"Within thirty years," comments Fritz in *Colorado*, "the Indians were treatied out of a state."

THE GLORY OF POLYGAMY

Only in San Bernardino did there remain a vestige of the Terrestrial Paradise.

The Saints had purchased the San Bernardino ranch of thirty-five thousand acres from the three Lugo brothers for a little over $75,000. Though this was a group purchase and the Mormons worked together, sometimes with communal tools, to lay out a town on the same plan as Salt Lake, to build a bowery for their religious meetings, an adobe schoolroom, roads to the timberland and irrigation ditches, yet at the same time it was an individual and capitalist society. Each man secured a city lot and a proportion of the rich agricultural lands; he repaid the Church, which financed the original purchase, from his subsequent earnings. Orchards were laid out, vineyards planted, saw and flour mills built. Neighbors helped each other in planting and building, but beyond that each man kept, aside from his tithe, everything he earned. The community prospered from its inception. With a regularly scheduled wagon line established between San Bernardino and Salt Lake, San Bernardino was on its way to becoming an important city and the second strongest Mormon stronghold.

So it would have been had not the trouble with the "winter Saints" in Salt Lake faded into the larger canvas of a permanent, indigenous problem. That Deseret had needed to become a state was immediately apparent when the first three territorial officers, appointed in Washington, reached that city in July of 1851.

Only a few days after the arrival of Judges Perry E. Brocchus of Alabama, Lemuel G. Brandebury of Pennsylvania, and Secretary of the Territory B. D. Harris of Vermont, President Young spoke at a Founder's Day ceremony. He commented, according to his own recollection:

"I know Zachary Taylor, he is dead and damned and I cannot help it."

Associate Justice Brocchus claimed he said, "Zachary Taylor is dead, and in hell, and I am glad of it."

The difference may have been one of semantics, but Brocchus took umbrage. He asked permission to speak before the general Church conference, appropriately reproved those who had spoken disrespectfully of the federal government, and then addressed himself to the Mormon women, demanding that they return to lives of virtue. The judge, described as a "vain and ambitious man, full of self-importance, fond of intrigues, corrupt . . . ," was also guilty of a nonsequitur: no more virtuous women than the Mormon women ever lived. Those who accepted the tenet that polygamy had been divinely revealed to Prophet Joseph Smith made genuine sacrifices, having not more than one husband, as Judge Brocchus was implying, but considerably less.

The Saints were outraged. President Young cried:

"If I had but crooked my little finger the sisters alone felt indignant enough to have chopped him in pieces."

From that moment there was no peace between the Saints and the territorial officials: Secretary of the Territory Harris claimed that President Young's census taking had been improperly conducted and the legislature illegally elected, therefore it could not meet or pass laws. The Mormons ostracized the three officials, their only intercourse being the exchange of angry letters.

At the end of six weeks the three men departed, taking with them the territorial seal, files and federal funds. Brigham Young knew that their departure could cause serious problems in Washington, perhaps delay statehood; he got out an injunction against their going, but he did not attempt to keep either the men or the materials of office in Utah by force.

Three months later, in Washington, Judge Brocchus made his report, claiming that they:

"Had been compelled to withdraw in consequence of the lawless acts and seditious tendencies of Brigham Young and the majority of the residents; that the Mormon church controlled the opinions, actions, property and lives of its members . . . disposing of the public lands, coining and issuing money at will, openly sanctioning polygamy, exacting tithes from members and onerous taxes from non-members, and requiring implicit obedience to the council of the church as a duty paramount to all obligations of morality, society, allegiance, and law."

Now that the antagonism had begun, the Mormons decided to meet it head on. On Sunday, August 29, 1852, President Young and his Council assembled the Saints in the Salt Lake Tabernacle and announced to the world that plural marriage was an integral part of their religious doctrine, and henceforth would be practiced by faithful Mormons.

Competent observers have said that from the founding of Salt Lake in 1847 until the proclamation that polygamy was an ineradicable part of their Church, only two to three per cent of the Mormons had more than one wife. The process of cultivating the desert would not in five short years have enabled many men to accumulate sufficient resources to support more than one family. In addition the doctrine of plural marriage which the Prophet Joseph Smith had announced as a divine revelation in 1843 had not yet totally convinced the Mormon people. Polygamy had been practiced in privacy in Salt Lake, though Forty-Niners passing through had noted evidence of it.

Brigham Young would have preferred Utah to become a state before announcing the doctrine, so that there would be no federal interference with what the Council considered a purely local religious matter, coming under the heading of the First Amendment to the federal Constitution which declared that the federal government could not legislate on the subject of religion in a state. Now, in August of 1852, Brigham Young apparently felt sufficiently secure in his mountain stronghold to dignify and proclaim officially what the American people were already gossiping about.

At this all-important meeting in the Tabernacle, which was to have nationwide consequences, President Young asked Apostle Orson Pratt to speak first. Pratt began with the basic Mormon premise that since all human souls are immortal, and marriage was a religious sacrament, husbands and wives were united in wedlock:

"Not only for time, but for all eternity."

Since Father Abraham of the Old Testament had assured his descendants that they would be as numerous as sands of the sea, Apostle Pratt informed the congregation that "Multiplication of the species would provide necessary body tabernacles for the countless myriads of pre-existent spirits deserving of earth life, an intermediate stage in the scheme of eternal progression; and plural marriage would facilitate the sacred objectives in this infinity of planning."

He then went on to his most urgent plea:

"I think there is only about one-fifth of the population of the globe that believe in the one-wife system; the other four-fifths believe in the doctrine of a plurality of wives. They have had it handed down from time immemorial, and are not half so narrow and contracted in their minds as some of the nations of Europe and America, who have done away with the promises and deprived themselves of the blessings of Abraham, Isaac, and Jacob. Even those who have only one wife, cannot get rid of their covetousness, and get their little hearts large enough to share their property with a numerous family . . . they do not know what is in the future, nor what blessings they are depriving themselves of, because of the traditions of their fathers; they do not know that a man's posterity, in the eternal worlds, are what constitute his glory, his kingdom, and dominion."

Brigham Young, knowing how greatly his people wanted to avoid conflict, assured his congregation:

"There is not a single constitution of any single state much less the constitution of the federal government, that hinders a man from having two wives; and I defy all the lawyers of the United States to prove the contrary."

When pressed on all sides by almost unendurable pressures to rid Mormonism of plural marriage, Young struck back:

"If you tell them a 'Mormon' has two wives they are shocked . . . if you whisper such a thing into the ears of a gentile who takes a fresh woman every night, he is thunderstruck with the enormity of the crime. They are hired the same as you would hire a horse and chaise at a livery stable; you go out a few days for a ride, return again, put up your horse, pay down your money, and you are freed of all further responsibility.

"I would rather take my valise in my hand today, and never see a wife or a child again, and preach the Gospel until I go into the grave, than to live as I do, unless God commands it. I never entered into the order of plurality of wives to gratify passion. And were I now asked whether I desired and wanted another wife, my reply would be, It should be one by whom the Spirit will bring forth noble children."

When the news reached Washington that the Latter-day Saints had openly acknowledged and were urging all their members to participate in plural marriage, the Mormon delegate to Congress, Dr. John N. Bernhisel, wrote to Brigham Young and his friend Heber Kimball:

"The cat is out of the bag!"

Brigham Young and Apostle Kimball replied:

"The cat has many kittens, which will always be the source of antagonism."

Then Apostle Kimball voiced the most intriguing comment in the whole controversy:

"For a man of God [Latter-day Saint] to be confined to one woman is small business; for it is as much as we can do now to keep up under the burdens we have to carry; I do not know what we should do if we only had one wife apiece."

To understand fully the attitude of the Mormons toward plural marriage after this portentous Tabernacle meeting of August 29, 1852, it is necessary to read the considered comment in the contemporary *Utah: A Guide to the State,* written by the W.P.A.:

"Church doctrine has been that plural marriage was divinely ordained, a high order of marriage, as much advanced over monogamy as monogamy over celibacy. A man's wives and his children added to his glory in heaven, and they shared in that glory. Acceptance of plural marriage was thus, for Church members, an act of faith and belief, an essential expression of religious conviction."

In the indigenous story of the Far West, plural marriage was a fascinating chapter. For the Mormons it invoked bitter strife, conflict that would build and magnify until President Buchanan would declare the Mormons to be in a state of rebellion, and order an army into Utah.

ENTERPRISING AND EXCITABLE YOUNG MEN

In northern California 1852 was a peak year, with one hundred thousand miners digging over a Sierra Nevada rectangle twenty miles wide by sixty miles long, into which the volcanic age had erupted more than $2,000,000,000 worth of obtainable gold. In this year individual entrepreneurs, each his own capitalist by dint of a pick, shovel, rocker and a three-hundred-foot claim, took out $80,000,000. Dr. Fayette Clappe's wife, Dame Shirley, who accompanied her husband to the mines, wrote home to her sister from Rich Bar that they paid a rugged price:

"Imagine a company of enterprising and excitable young men, settled upon a sandy level, about as large as a poor widow's potato patch . . . with no books, churches, lectures, lyceums, theatres and pretty girls, most of them living in damp, gloomy cabins, the most remorseless, persevering rain which ever set itself to drive humanity mad, has been pouring doggedly down, sweeping away bridges, lying in puddles about nearly all the habitations."

Gold fever creates recklessness; with spring, and mining possible again, even those men with good claims from which they were taking more in a month than they had earned in a year at home, went searching for better diggings, tens of thousands of men wandering inside the golden rectangle, passing each other to take each other's claims. Dame Shirley observed:

". . . if a person works his claim himself, is economical and industrious, keeps his health, and is satisfied with small gains he is bound to make money. And yet I cannot help remarking, that almost all with whom we are acquainted seem to have lost."

The isolation of the miner was so complete that there was no way of receiving the tons of mail that came into the tiny San Francisco post office from round Cape Horn, piling up as dead letters while the men languished for news from home. A young miner, Alexander Todd, homesick for mail, started what the miners called the "jackass express," forerunner of the romantic Pony Express.

Determined to go to San Francisco to find the mail he was certain was there, Todd first toured the neighboring camps and registered at a dollar a head those miners who wanted him to bring back their mail. At Stockton the merchants asked Todd if he would also carry their gold to San Francisco; when he agreed they put $150,000 of dust into a butter bag! He charged the merchants five per cent of the gold he carried. Todd was sworn in as a postal clerk, paid the post office twenty-five cents for each letter he collected for a subscriber, then bought a whaleboat and offered passage across the bay for one ounce of gold per passenger, providing the men each pulled one oar. Across the bay, Todd loaded his mail in the saddlebags of his mule and took into the mountains hundreds of letters for which the lonesome miners paid him $4.00 apiece for delivery, and $8.00 for an eastern newspaper.

It was not long before every creek, camp or city had its pony express, carrying mail and gold. "The rider was always a bold, bright young fellow who owned the line, horses and all, and had his 'office' in some responsible store. He would die in the saddle rather than delay ten minutes over the expected time; always a dashing rider, he dressed gayly and blew a small bugle as he went up and down the creek at a plunging rate."

The moving in of supplies was more difficult. Since the mountain trails were narrow and steep, rising to nine thousand feet, all supplying had to be done by slow-moving mule pack, driven by the expert Californios. The trains were a welcome sight, bringing such luxuries as onions, butter and potatoes, which sold for forty cents a pound. The mules were so carefully handled that one miner described them as "sleek and fat as so many kittens."

There were no clergymen in the mines; the Sabbath was consecrated by broken heads. On the Fourth of July there was no Declaration of Independence to read from; the crowd got drunk on whiskey and patriotism and beat up a group of Mexican miners. An outgrowth of San Francisco's Vigilance Committee of the year before was a growing carelessness among the men about taking the law into their own hands. A young Mexican woman, having been intruded upon by a drunken miner, stabbed him and was hanged for her pains, without benefit of jury. At Rich Bar a Mexican who asked an American to return a small sum of money owed him got steel in the chest instead of gold for his pocket; no one paid the slightest attention.

"In the space of twenty-four days, we have had murders, fearful accidents, bloody deaths, whippings, a hanging, an attempt at suicide and a fatal duel."

By the summer of 1852 there were five hundred small mining communities scattered through the mountains, each setting up its own impromptu rules for juries, running from six men to the entire community. There were neither courts nor jails, the facts were heard hurriedly, the punishment inflicted instantly: an Iowan convicted of stealing money was given thirty-nine lashes on the bare back, and run out of town. Two New Englanders found with stolen horses were hanged where they were caught.

Anti-foreign sentiment also reached its peak in 1852; one out of every five miners was a recently arrived Chinese, another one out of five was either Mexican, Chilean or Indian. The Chinese were encouraged in their tong wars because they provided colorful spectacles; whole Indian tribes were massacred over a real or imagined offense by some unidentified Indian.

Retaliation was inevitable; a number of Mexicans who had been badly treated robbed travelers, stores and saloons, organizing into gangs as their success spread through the region. By an odd coincidence, as Joseph Henry Jackson pointed out in *Bad Company*, all the Mexican bandits were called Joaquin, and soon they were thought to be the same man even though Joaquin's crimes, committed on the same day, took place as much as two hundred miles apart.

California newspapers badgered the legislature into appropriating money for a company of mounted rangers, headed by a Texan named Harry Love. In July, Love's rangers came across a band of Mexicans around a fire, killed two of them, and brought back one head in alcohol in order to claim the governor's reward. No one knew what name the head had formerly possessed; they called it Joaquin and the press agreed:

"The famous bandit, Joaquin, whose name is associated with a hundred deeds of blood . . ."

Ranger Love collected his reward, the head traveled California's museum circuit and the matter was about to be interred when a part-Cherokee named "Yellow Bird" published a book in San Francisco called *The Life and Adventures of Joaquin Murieta, Celebrated California Bandit.* It was so completely a work of fiction as to verge on a fairy tale, but the book caught on, was translated into many languages, and is often accepted as a true story about California's Robin Hood.

This chaos in social relations, which had taken only four years to develop from the Elysian atmosphere of the Forty-Eighters, was reflected in the chaotic mining methods which in a few years would drive all of the prospectors out of the mountains and leave the balance of the gold, $1,500,000,000 worth, to big companies with heavy machinery.

"Disorganized enterprise" built ten separate dams within a ten-mile stretch of the Yuba River by ten separate groups. In Iowa Hill ninety different tunnels were dug. Hundreds of miners were each trying to divert a small portion of the Yuba River, spending $3,000,000 in their efforts; but individual capitalism in the winters of 1852 and 1853 began to run out because most of the gold that had been washed down in the streams had been garnered. There were left two major sources, difficult to get at: the solid gold-bearing quartz, buried in the original rock formations, and the layers of rock and sand high upon the hillsides that had been deposited there by rivers long since disappeared.

Hydraulic mining was originated by a man who attached a nozzle to the end of a hose and aimed a stream at a mountainside or cliff to wash down the gravel and gold-bearing sand. It quickly swept the Sierra Nevada clean of its wandering thousands of prospectors. The operation took a combination of men and money, and began the mining of gold as big business. It also began the devastation of the golden rectangle, spewing millions of tons of rock and debris over river and stream banks, and over miles of fields that have never since been cleared.

Nor was the mining of gold the only aspect of organized industry coming to the golden rectangle, to break up the isolation of the miner, the small mining communities and eventually the Far West.

The first stagecoach line for passengers was originated at Sacramento by a twenty-one-year-old Argonaut from Providence, Rhode Island, named James E. Birch, who bought a light emigrant wagon and a team of high-spirited mustangs and carried passengers on a regular schedule to Mormon Island, a distance of thirty miles over what could sometimes pass for a trail road, for a sum ranging from $16 to $30 a person, paid in the fluid form of one to two ounces of gold dust. Birch soon expanded his line so that he had coaches connecting all the towns of central California.

The greatest single need of the Americans in California was the getting of mail in the quickest manner. Letters coming across Panama could now reach California from New York in a month, if all conditions were right; it took additional weeks for the mail first to reach New York from such border areas as Wisconsin or Missouri. Californians tried hard to convince the federal government that mail could go over the Sierra, through the Carson Valley to Salt Lake, then east along the established route. The postal department declared the plan unworkable.

So it might have been if not for the pioneering of Major George Chorpenning, Jr., experienced trail blazer. He set out from San Francisco to determine where by-stations could be established, and how much time would be required for the San Francisco–Salt Lake journey of nine hundred miles over mountains, sand and salt desert. In January of 1851 the federal government asked for bids; Chorpenning was low man among thirty-seven bidders, and was given a four-year contract at $14,000 a year to maintain a monthly service from San Francisco to Salt Lake. Chorpenning contracted to deliver the mail with "certainty, celerity, and security," or thirty days for each leg of the route.

He carried his first consignment to Sacramento on a river steamer, transferred it to muleback and left for Placerville with half a dozen hard-bitten drivers and armed guards. At Placerville, last stop before tackling the crest of the Sierra Nevada, the whole town turned out to scribble hasty notes to their families and cheer the departure of the first overland mail.

Chorpenning made it to Salt Lake in fine fashion; so did his partner, Absalom Woodward. All through the summer and fall they headed the alternate east-west parties. But with winter rose two enemies: marauding Indians, and the relentless mountain snows. The Indians struck first: Woodward left Sacramento with four men in November and was attacked within a hundred miles of Salt Lake City. He and his train were wiped out, the mail lost.

In February, with Woodward gone, Edison Cody and five new recruits left Placerville in the height of the winter storms; the government contract had to be fulfilled every month or it would be canceled. Cody's mules froze to death. The men carried the mail on their backs, living on frozen mule meat. For the last four days before they stumbled into Salt Lake they were totally without food. But they brought in the mail.

After this experience, and the finding of the skeletons of Woodward and his four men, Major Chorpenning could get no one in Salt Lake to accompany him back to San Francisco with the westbound mail. Chorpenning set out alone, making his way over a nine-hundred-mile trail controlled by marauding Diggers and Utes, voracious for plunder. He delivered the mail safely to Sacramento, an exhibition of man's courage and perseverance in a country where courage and perseverance were the coin of the realm.

Late in 1849 Adams and Company had opened an office in San Francisco, advertising in the *Alta California* that it was ready to provide express service to the mines. Owing to a stricture in the California constitution that no corporation could be set up for the purpose of banking, the express companies of necessity became the banking houses, not only in Sacramento and San Francisco but in every mining camp as well; for when the express company took a miner's gold for the purpose of shipment it first had to assay it, then weigh it, give the miner a receipt and guarantee the safety of his deposit. Thus the express company's iron safe became the local bank. Within a short time Adams and Company covered the entire state with its offices, express wagons and riders, earning $500,000 profit in its first year of business.

In Sacramento a group paid scant attention to the state's constitution, opening a bank in a stone house on the river front. The new bank took in one hundred fifty pounds of gold dust in a banking day which extended from six in the morning until ten at night, the three clerks armed with Colt revolving pistols and bowie knives.

Wells Fargo and Company, from which originated some of the most romantic tales of the Far West, was born appropriately enough in the back room of a bookstore in Syracuse, New York, in 1852. Henry Wells had operated an express service between Albany and Buffalo and from Buffalo west to St. Louis. On March 18, 1852, at the Astor House, he launched the Wells Fargo company with $300,000 capital subscribed in $100 shares.

By July two of its experienced men had arrived in California, one to run the express, the other the banking. In its first announcement in the *Alta California*, Wells Fargo explained that it was not only prepared to "forward packages, parcels and freights of all descriptions between the City of New York and City of San Francisco," but also to "purchase and sell Gold Dust, Bullion and Bills of Exchange, the payment and collection of notes, bills and accounts." The most interesting line of the advertisement spoke of "iron chests for the security of treasure and valuable packages," giving birth to the classic line:

"Throw down the box!"

But all this activity was petty cash compared to the $40,000,000 the recently arrived Leland Stanford would take out of transportation across the Far West. Son of a farmer-innkeeper, educated in a Methodist seminary and by three years of apprenticeship in an Albany law firm, Stanford married in 1850 and opened a law office in a small village in Wisconsin Territory, while his five brothers went to California in the gold rush. Two years later, when a fire wiped out his law library, his office and the businesses of most of his clients, Stanford returned his wife to her parents' home in Albany, took a ship for California and was set up in the grocery business by his brother, first in the worked-out mining camp of Cold Springs, then in the thriving camp of Michigan Bluff. When his brothers took over a larger business in San Francisco, Leland Stanford became manager of the Sacramento store. The mushrooming city of Sacramento had become the third largest in California, though its residents insisted that "the valley of the Sacramento was originally and is now during the greater part of the rainy season a part of the Pacific Ocean." When the Sacramento and American rivers overflowed their banks the town, caught between the two rising floods of water, became an American Venice where large quantities of merchandise floated out of the stores, the adobe buildings dissolved, and all traffic moved in whaleboats.

It was here Leland Stanford prospered; here he met three other successful Sacramento merchants: Huntington, Crocker, Hopkins. Here he went into politics with them, and then into the business of building a transcontinental railroad.

Here they became The Big Four.

FOR LOS ANGELES, NEITHER BOOM NOR BUST

San Francisco had transformed itself from a boom site into a world metropolis, developing a water company, horse-drawn omnibuses, a public library with three thousand volumes, twenty foreign consulates, eighteen churches, twelve daily newspapers and ten public schools, all in four frantic years. Where only two years before ships had sailed into the bay to be abandoned and sink into the mud, now more than a thousand ships sailed through the Golden Gate Strait bringing in $35,000,000 worth of goods for sale: a hundred million pounds of beef and pork, of rice, sugar, coffee, tea and particularly liquor, sold in more than five hundred different places, with a bartender for every sixty-eight inhabitants. Even so the lads were overworked.

Times were plush, not only with more than fifty thousand inhabitants but with millions of dollars in gold that was being fed into the construction of six hundred new brick and stone buildings, a hundred sixty hotels and boardinghouses, sixty-six restaurants and twenty bathing houses. The city's waterfront lots, twenty-five feet wide and sixty feet deep, now sold for $10,000 each. Everyone had money, businesses sprang up as fast as there were houses to hold them. The city completed its first telegraph line to the important mining centers of Sacramento, Stockton and Marysville, as well as a southern extension to San Jose. Agriculture was booming, with a hundred ten thousand acres under cultivation.

"There was still the same old energy and vigor among the people, the same rapid making and reckless spending of money, the same extravagance, gambling and vice. But the city had improved immensely in appearance. Its houses resembled palaces; its broad streets bustled with activity; its wharves were crowded; its banks, hotels, theatres, gambling houses, billiard rooms and drinking saloons were filled; its stores and shops contained and displayed the richest articles of taste and luxury; immense amounts of coin circulated; the finest horses and carriages, the most elegant dressing, the costliest delicacies for the table; everybody was young and wide awake. . . ."

So many duels were advertised in the 1853 San Francisco newspapers and drew such large crowds that the year was described as "the most famous slaughter year when everyone who chose killed his man." Though San Franciscans were still importing their ice from Boston, they had a literary magazine, *The Pioneer*, as well as four theatres, the American, Adelphi, Union and Metropolitan, where they could take their choice of the Booths doing Shakespeare, English drama such as *The School for Scandal*, Lola Montez, near naked on a white horse, or little Lotta Crabtree, California's entertainment product from the mines.

The old-timers were becoming conscious of the swath they had cut across history; there was established the Society of California Pioneers with such members as Sutter, Larkin, Vallejo, Marsh, Leese, Hartnell, Semple, Bidwell. Larkin would die enormously wealthy in San Francisco of typhoid fever at the age of fifty-six; Vallejo remained the prosperous patriarch of Sonoma Valley into his eighty-first year; Bidwell became a key figure and large landowner in northern California; Marsh fell in love after a twenty-year hiatus following the death of his Marguerite.

Fifty, wealthy and lonely, John Marsh had written to his brother in New York asking if he could find him a good wife and send her out to California. Instead the good wife found him: Abigail Tuck from Massachusetts, who had come to California to clear up an annoying cough, and became principal of a girls' school just opening near San Jose. Her hosts at the Santa Clara hotel introduced her to many suitors. Abby refused them all. Captain Appleton exclaimed:

"I don't know who will suit you, unless it is John Marsh."

When Appleton had finished telling her about Marsh, Abby said, "He is the very man. I'll set my cap for him and marry him."

She thought Marsh good-looking, was fascinated by his vast fields, vineyards, flocks. She married him quickly, and presented him with a daughter. For Abby, alone in all the world, Marsh opened his purse strings, buying her pearls set as a bunch of grapes, and building her the largest and most expensive stone house in all California.

Their happiness lasted but a short time: Abigail died of tuberculosis, Marsh was stabbed to death by three of his Mexican *vaqueros* with whom he had been ungenerous about pay.

There were new and colorful personalities to take the place of the old-timers. Because of the rapid increase of Chinese in San Francisco, rice was the most ardently sought staple. When ships failed to arrive from China the price soared to ridiculous heights, which caused Joshua Norton, son of British colonists, to build the first rice mill, cleaning and buffing the unhusked rice in from the paddies of China. Norton was already growing rich by buying up shiploads of rice for his mill when he decided to corner the rice market. He did. Then three unexpected ships came in through the strait in a matter of days. The bottom dropped out of the market and Joshua Norton went broke. He also went mad, reappearing some time later as Emperor Norton, wearing a blue military uniform with brass buttons, large gold epaulettes on his shoulders, a high beaver hat with an enormous plume, and in his hand a rough-hewn walking stick, symbol of authority.

Flourishing and graceful San Francisco fully accepted Emperor Norton. He occupied a place of honor in reviewing stands, was welcome in all restaurants and saloons to eat and drink without charge, rode the omnibuses and boats by royal ukase, published his decrees in the local newspapers at no space rates, taxed a citizen or business house for four bits on those rare occasions when he needed cash, and was greeted courteously on the street with:

"Good afternoon, Your Majesty."

Then, in the winter of 1853, came a dry spell: there was insufficient rain to wash out the gold. Production fell sharply. So did the influx of emigrants, warned by their friends and relatives in the mines that the streams of the Sierra Nevada were no longer flowing with gold. There were no buyers for the newly completed homes or business blocks or opened tracts. Real estate operators went broke. Imported goods found no consumers as hundreds of ships glutted San Francisco with more merchandise than could be used in a decade. Businesses that had mushroomed on a shoestring of experience and cash closed their doors.

The crash held off until the beginning of 1855 when a mail steamer brought the news that the banking house of Page Bacon and Company of St. Louis was in financial difficulties. Instantly a run began on the local Page Bacon and Company, forcing it to close. The next day, a Friday, Adams and Company, the oldest and best known express-banking house, failed to open its doors. Thus started the first of the country's Black Fridays, with almost two hundred firms going bankrupt to the red tune of over $8,000,000.

San Francisco had become an inseparable link in the nation's economic chain.

Los Angeles, in contrast to San Francisco, was achieving neither boom nor bust. There were fugitive signs of growth in 1852: the city had started a harbor at San Pedro, sixteen to twenty miles away, the closest body of water resembling a bay; the City Council passed an ordinance which instructed the residents to wash their linen in the little canals instead of the river which provided the town's drinking water; the manufacture of beer and vinegar was begun. The *Star* chronically complained that it took four to six weeks for mail to reach Los Angeles from San Francisco, longer than it took from New York to San Francisco; and an effort was made to collect from the streets, described as pitfalls of filth and mud during a rain, "all the heads and remains of cattle and other dead animals, that they might be set on fire to be thoroughly consumed and the air purified." The city staged a horse race during which the backers of the California horse, wagering $50,000 on their favorite, suffered the equivalent of the closing of Adams and Company in San Francisco, when the Australian horse came in first.

Los Angeles should have been prosperous, for the surrounding ranchers had made fortunes driving their beef to San Francisco and the gold mines, while the vineyardists were sending their wine north; but as late as 1854 the town could boast no more than a chapel facing the Plaza, and fifty buildings, with half a dozen of them two-storied, placed like cardboard boxes on a treeless, flowerless, shadeless, baking semi-desert plain. Apparently the ranchers and wine makers were spending their money elsewhere.

A reign of lawlessness engulfed Los Angeles at the beginning of 1855: David Brown, who had killed a fellow undesirable, and been sentenced to hang, won a stay of execution. The mayor resigned, joined with a group of Vigilantes and lynched Brown. An account of the lynching appeared in the press a number of hours before the actual scene in order that the paper might make a ten o'clock ship leaving for San Francisco.

The lynching did not put an end to the murders; gangs of horse and cattle thieves roamed southern California, killed the sheriff of Los Angeles and three of his posse before being hunted down by United States troops acting with several companies of volunteers.

However Los Angeles was no more lawless than San Francisco. The two cities were part of the wild frontier. In periods of prosperity the government was abandoned by the reputable business community and fell into the hands of those who were determined to use it as a means of getting rich. By 1855 the government of San Francisco, purged by the Vigilantes of 1851, was $1,000,000 in debt, on which it was paying thirty-six per cent interest, and had so far deteriorated that one of its judges had been trained in penology by serving sentences in eastern penitentiaries. If the interlocking pattern of the country's high finance had reached the Pacific Ocean, so had the mechanical genius of the American people made its way west, in the form of a ballot box with false sides and bottom, pre-stuffed with conveniently marked ballots. In one election in San Mateo the political machine achieved the miracle of counting nineteen hundred marked ballots in a community of five hundred citizens.

"DON'T SHOOT, I AM UNARMED!"

It took several cold-blooded public shootings to ring the fire bell of the California Engine Company, summoning the Vigilance Committee of 1856.

The opening shot was fired by handsome Charles Cora of San Francisco's underworld. Of dark melancholy eyes and black mustache, Cora was the lean, supple figure of the professional gambler, dressed in the gambler's uniform of richly decorated vest, a cape thrown carelessly about his shoulders, wearing light kid gloves, carrying himself with the nonchalant air of a gentleman. He had arrived in San Francisco with a pretty young girl, Annabelle Ryan, known as Belle, whom he had taken out of a New Orleans house of prostitution. She was now living with him as his wife. The killing resulted from an outraged sense of the proprieties: Mrs. William H. Richardson, wife of the United States marshal, complained to her husband when Cora brought Belle to a performance at the American Theatre and boldly sat in an open box with his mistress instead of discreetly hiding in a curtained rear stall.

Richardson spoke sharply to Cora, with whom he had been feuding. The next day the two men met in the Blue Wing saloon, apparently settling their quarrel. Once out on the street, Cora seized Richardson by the collar and drew a pistol from his pocket. Richardson cried:

"Don't shoot, I am unarmed!"

Cora shot the marshal through the breast. Richardson died instantly. Sam Brannan made an impassioned speech in an effort to get Cora hanged, but was arrested for inciting to riot. San Francisco believed Cora could be convicted legally.

Before Cora could be brought to trial his employer, one of the town's most notorious gamblers, was made marshal. At the trial Cora was defended by Edward D. Baker of Springfield, Illinois, who received $10,000 from Belle for a spellbinding defense which accomplished what San Francisco considered impossible: a disagreement on the grounds of self-defense.

A second brutal murder crystallized the committee: the shooting of James King of William, editor of the *Evening Bulletin*, by James P. Casey, a former inmate of Sing Sing but now a county supervisor, a reward for having imported the ingeniously false ballot box. King, born in the District of Columbia, was thirty-four; his brother Henry had died on Frémont's relief party to Taos. He had come to California for his health in 1848, served on the Vigilante Committee of 1851, opened a bank, prospered and then lost $250,000 in the depression of 1854. Described as "honest, brave, terribly in earnest, but often rash," King borrowed a few dollars from friends and started the *Evening Bulletin* for the purpose of exposing the underworld control of San Francisco politics. His blistering editorials seared every crook in town.

That is, until he printed the fact that County Supervisor Casey had served a sentence in Sing Sing. As he came out of his printing office and crossed the street, Casey stepped from behind an express wagon and shot him. While King lay wounded, Casey rushed to the police station, which was controlled by his friends. People thronged the streets demanding that Casey be lynched. A brother of King made an impassioned plea that Casey be hanged. The crowds in front of the jail grew dense. Troops arrived to reinforce the jail guard. Mayor Van Ness pleaded:

"Let the law have its course. Justice will be done."

But the people had seen justice perverted in the Cora case. They refused to disperse.

That night William T. Coleman was asked to head a new Vigilance Committee. Coleman declined: he was just back from a two-year stay in the East, he did not approve of extra-legal government. He changed his mind when he was convinced that the mob would riot if the people were not organized and disciplined.

Level-headed, a brilliant organizer, he put a notice in the papers:

The members of the Vigilance Committee in good standing will please meet at No. 105 1/2 Sacramento Street, this day, Thursday, 15 inst. at nine o'clock A.M. By order of the Committee of Thirteen

That morning a crowd gathered in front of the Sacramento Street hall. Before noon fifteen hundred men acceptable to Coleman and the committee had signed. Coleman was elected president; every man took an oath of obedience and secrecy and was assigned a number. By evening two thousand citizens had signed. Coleman had them collect in companies of one hundred, elect their officers, plan for immediate drill. The Executive Committee was extended to thirty-seven members, rotating in groups of twelve, three top officers of each Hundred serving on the Board of Delegates. Members contributed money; muskets and shot were rented from George Law, who had bought them from the government.

By the seventeenth of May, three days after King was shot, the committee had eight thousand members. They leased a three-story building at 41 Scaramento Street and mounted cannon on the roof. Out from the building, extending to the middle of the street, they built an eight-foot-high enclosure of gunnybags filled with sand, placed cannon at the corners and left holes for riflemen inside the enclosure. At the rear there were stables with cavalry and artillery horses. The Vigilance Committee was now an army, organized, disciplined, with $75,000 of contributions available to purchase arms. Its headquarters was named "Fort Gunnybags."

The original 1851 bell which the committee had borrowed from the California Engine Company was sounded to assemble the members, and three quarters of the city's men came running, gun in arm, a piece of white ribbon in the buttonhole.

The committee adopted the same constitution as the Committee of 1851, then set about the business for which they had been formed. On a serene Sunday morning at ten, Coleman's captains gave their companies the command, "Forward, March!" Twenty-five hundred Vigilantes moved on the jail, with fifteen thousand spectators streaming along the route of march. The companies surrounded the jail, a troop of sixty men aimed a piece of field artillery at the jail door. The jail-keeper quickly surrendered Casey, who was taken by Coleman in a carriage to Fort Gunnybags. An hour later the carriage returned for Charles Cora.

On May 20 Casey and Cora were tried before a twelve-man jury selected from the Vigilante Executive Committee and sitting at Fort Gunnybags. Cora asked for a member of the committee to defend him. Witnesses were brought in from the outside to testify. Cora was convicted by a majority vote. He announced himself as satisfied with the trial.

During Cora's trial the grand marshal of the committee had come into the trial room to announce that James King of William had just died.

James Casey was brought in and convicted unanimously. The executions were set for May 22, the date of King's funeral.

Hinged platforms were built outside the second floor of Fort Gunnybags. Three thousand Vigilance troops stood at attention in the streets below. Cora and Casey were led out of tall windows, though not before Belle and Cora were united in marriage. As each man came out on his platform a noose was put around his neck, a white cap slipped over his head.

A church bell tolled. Every bell in San Francisco answered. As the funeral procession of James King of William left the Unitarian Church a block away, the executioner cut the ropes.

During the next weeks the Vigilance Committee called before it dozens of political malefactors, tried and deported them, paying their transportation when necessary. In June, Governor Johnson decided that San Francisco had been out of hand long enough and took steps to put an end to the Vigilantes. He declared a state of insurrection, issued a second call for the state militia, the first call issued by William T.

Sherman having been ignored. When President Pierce refused his request for troops and guns, the governor wrote to U. S. Major General Wool at Benicia and to Navy Captain David Farragut at Mare Island. Both refused.

When arms from the arsenal at Benicia were finally made available to the state guard, the Vigilante Committee raided the boats bringing them to San Francisco, seizing the guns and ammunition.

Having run the rascals out, the Executive Committee decided that it had no further pressing business, and set July Fourth for the official breakup celebration. Then came the gratuitous stabbing of Sterling Hopkins, executioner of Cora and Casey, by Supreme Court Justice David S. Terry.

David Terry, a towering Texan, hot-headed and violent, with an ever ready bowie knife, was born in Kentucky, was a volunteer in the war for Texan independence, and a lieutenant of Texas Rangers in the Mexican War. A lethal fighter in the courts, he had ridden into the state Supreme Court on the tails of weak, Know-Nothing (anti-Catholic) Governor Johnson.

Vigilance President Coleman had issued an arrest order for a James Maloney. Maloney was with Justice Terry when writ-server Hopkins caught up with him. A brawl ensued, during which a revolver went off. Judge Terry drew out his bowie knife and buried it in Hopkins's neck.

The Vigilance Committee was of necessity in business again; but if Hopkins died, could an ex officio committee hang a justice of the state Supreme Court? Terry, a prisoner in Fort Gunnybags, sought help from the captain of the U.S.S. *John Adams,* who demanded that Judge Terry be surrendered or he would be obliged to "use the power at my command," that is, his naval guns.

The Vigilance Committee faced armed conflict with the federal government. However Captain David Farragut quieted the captain of the U.S.S. *John Adams,* Hopkins recovered, and the Vigilance Committee convicted Judge Terry only of assault.

Two more gruesome murders had to be dealt with: one Joseph Hetherington, to whom a Dr. Andrew Randall owed some money, shot the doctor to death in a hotel lobby. Philander Brace, who was serving a term for larceny, killed Captain West of the police force. The Vigilance Committee caught, tried and hanged Hetherington and Brace in the last of its judicial proceedings.

The committee finally disbanded itself on August 18, but retained an informal organization long enough to nominate candidates for all city offices under the heading of the People's Party, and to appoint responsible watchers for the November 4, 1856 election at which Democrat James Buchanan defeated Republican John C. Frémont for the presidency. Having hanged ten murderers, deported political swindlers, (some eight hundred left town of their own volition), the People's Party swept the election. Those policemen who had joined the Vigilantes went back to their jobs, and San Francisco began a decade of clean government.

The Vigilance Committee put on a parade, with a band, the members marching in "long frock coats buttoned up to the neck, with glazed caps and white satin badges shining from their left coat lapels," the officers with "bouquets of flowers on their muskets."

William T. Coleman emerged as a hero and was offered every political nomination up to the presidency of the United States. He rejected them all. Under his stern hand judicial procedure had been followed to the letter; no member, having taken his oath, committed a depredation. Coleman, quoted by James B. Scherer in *Lion of the Vigilantes*, justified the committees of 1851 and 1856 by saying:

"Who made the laws and set agents over them? The people. Who saw these laws neglected, disregarded, abused, trampled on? The people. Who had the right to protect these laws, and administer them when their servants had failed? The people."

A measure of permanent government had come to San Francisco.

"YOU HAVE STRUCK IT, BOYS!"

It is not easy to settle a land, nor to strike a precious vein. Many years are spent, and many lives.

In the spring of 1851 two movements, one consisting of the Reese brothers wagon train out of Salt Lake City traveling west, the other of the Grosh brothers traveling east from Volcano, California, simultaneously began the settling of modern-day Nevada: John Reese, his brother and companions building the first permanent trading post; Allen and Hosea Grosh leading to the mines.

John Reese was a forty-three-year-old New Yorker who migrated to Utah in 1849, setting up a store in Salt Lake. Having heard that the Carson Valley was fertile and unsettled, the Reeses and fourteen companions loaded ten wagons with flour, butter, eggs, beef, tools, made the passage across the salt marshes and sand deserts, and at the western end of Carson Valley either took over Beatie's abandoned post or bought it for two sacks of flour. They built an L-shaped log house, store and fort, two-storied, thirty feet wide, fifty feet deep, with two sides forming a pentagon-shaped fort which became known as Mormon Station.

Sixty thousand gold seekers passed through the Humboldt and Carson valleys on their way to California. Reese said:

"The word came that 1852 was going to be a great immigration year. I mixed things around and plowed up to be ready."

Allen and Hosea Grosh, in their mid-twenties, abandoned the California gold fields where they had done only fairly well. They had heard things about the Nevada gold region which excited their studious young minds. They went farther up Gold Canyon in Nevada than anyone had ever ventured before, bringing down the so-called "blue stuff" which clogged their rocker and essayed some crude tests. They wrote to their father that they were convinced there was plenty of gold in Sun Mountain, and quantities of silver as well.

John Reese too had been confirmed in his particular form of prospecting. His turnips proved to be the "color," bringing one dollar a bunch.

"I never saw such things to make money on," exulted Reese. "I had seventeen men working for me, but not enough could be raised to supply the demand. There were a good many ranches took up. I put up a blacksmith shop."

Nevada, a western county of Utah, four to five hundred grueling miles from Salt Lake, had no government. Though a majority of the settlers were Mormons, and the Utah legislature had squared off Western Utah into three counties by drawing lines due west from the Utah border to California, it sent in no officials or money. Mormon discipline began to erode.

The settlers' first need was to legalize their land claims. On November 12, joined by four others from Eagle Station a few miles away, where a prospector named Frank Hall had shot an eagle and spread its skin before his cabin, Reese and the men of Mormon Station held a meeting and voted to petition Congress for a territorial government, independent of Utah; also to ask Washington for a survey of all their land claims as well as the appointment of one of their members as surveyor. They ended their meeting by appointing a committee of seven to govern. John Reese headed the committee on laws, which appointed a recording secretary and treasurer and decided that each settler, since land in these few fertile valleys was scarce, could claim only one quarter section. In two further meetings, a week later, they set up the framework of an entire government, not the slightest whit deterred by the fact that they had no right to set up such a government. Courts, a justice of the peace, a sheriff and a jury were provided for, all offices being promptly filled; a decree was passed that timbered lands should be held in common; settlers were given the right to sell their claims in order to take up new ones, though the new ones had to be improved $500 worth in six months.

Emigration from the East was so heavy that Reese and Isaac Mott, whose wife was the first woman to settle in Carson Valley, applied to the squatter government to put a toll bridge across the river, receiving permission to do so providing they would also improve the road over the mountain to California. The government set the toll: one dollar for a wagon, twenty-five cents for horses or mules, ten cents per head for horned cattle, two and a half cents per head for sheep. Isaac Mott, who had settled four miles south of Mormon Station, built himself a larger house, then opened his original log cabin as a school.

Thus in Nevada self-government was born almost whole in a small room of a log cabin trading station.

Thomas S. Williams, a merchant-lawyer driving a herd of cattle to California, sent a frantic report to Brigham Young:

"Citizens of Carson Valley declare that they will no longer be governed by nor tried by Mormon laws . . . declare they will pay no taxes what are levied on them from the Territory of Utah."

The Mormons wanted Nevada to remain one of their counties.

It would take ten years before President James Buchanan would sign the bill which made Nevada an independent territory.

Allen and Hosea Grosh went back over the mountains to California, but they were determined to continue their experiments. In the spring of 1853 they returned to Nevada, this time bringing with them a "considerable number of books of scientific works, chemical apparatus and assayers tools."

Though there were some one hundred eighty prospectors in Nevada the Grosh brothers were the only ones to think the country rich in silver; the only ones, that is, except the Mexicans who had gone from Sonora to California in 1850. Experienced silver miners, the Mexicans kept saying, "*Mucho plata*" ("Much silver"), but nobody listened. The prospectors were looking for gold. Neither did they want to be bothered with the Mexicans, to whom they felt superior. The Grosh brothers liked the Mexicans, and gave them friendship, in particular to Old Frank, who surveyed the country with them and showed them the best geological lays for silver veins.

The Groshes built a fieldstone cabin on American Flats, halfway between Six Mile Canyon and what would become Virginia City, with a $370,000,000 metal foundation. They also built two furnaces, one for smelting, the other for assaying, then prospected a vein resembling sheet lead, broken and very fine, a dark gray tarnished mass. They ground the blue stuff to a fine powder, baked it in a rock oven. When it cooled the brothers found a small dark, solid mass. They dropped it into a container of nitric acid, watched the metallic button slowly dissolve. That was all the embryo metallurgists needed to know!

Lyman, in *The Saga of the Comstock Lode,* writes, with a sense of the hyperbole which the Grosh brothers must have felt, sitting all alone on the top of a seemingly solid mountain of silver:

"On the result of that assay hung the fortunes of thousands, national welfare, the future of a race, the outcome of a great war. Out of that assay sprang dozens of millionaires! Blocks of San Francisco's marble buildings! A telegraph cable to girdle the earth! A state, legislation, a great mining school, a mining code! Engineering enterprises that were to make the mountain famous! Out of that assay sprang the pomp of kings, the power of principalities, the glitter of coronets!"

The Groshes decided to keep their find to themselves. They would need more capital, more prospecting, to know how best to proceed.

Non-Mormon emigrants coming over the trail fell in love with Carson Valley, with the land that dipped and rolled toward the mountain range, studded with squat juniper and nut pine, and settled there instead of continuing on. Others failing to find El Dorado in California remembered the sunbursts along the river, the wild peach trees with flame-colored flowers, and came back over the mountain to take up land on the eastern slope of the Sierra Nevada. Brigham Young had been sending in a few families to maintain a Mormon majority, but he hesitated to colonize in strength because of reports that there was gold in Nevada. His hand was forced in February 1853 when, not yet having received territorial status from Washington, a petition was signed by forty-three citizens of Carson Valley asking the legislature of California to annex them.

Edwin D. Woolley, a Mormon from Salt Lake, wrote home:

"I have my doubts whether Mormonism can exist in the country as far as I have seen." He was distressed that the Mormons did not want to meet on Sundays and sing, "The Spirit of God Like a Fire Is Burning," preferring to sing with the gentiles:

The Mormon girls are fat as hogs,
The chief production cats and dogs.

On New Year's Eve the first dance was held at Spafford Hall's station, "nine females attending, including little girls, this number constituting three-fourths of all the fair sex in Western Utah." Unfortunately for Nevada's burgeoning social life the Washoe Indians ran off all the stock while the men were dancing. Marital life in Nevada started out stormily too, the first bride, only fourteen, being taken away from her ardent husband by a returning father, bloodshed being averted by the bride's decision that she would rather continue on and see California.

Shortly after, Elder Orson Hyde arrived at Mormon Station from Salt Lake with a party of thirty-five men and families and quickly called for an election of county officers under the Utah Legislative Act. Since a number of the residents were insistent about being ruled from California, Elder Hyde requested that California run a survey line to determine whether the Carson Valley lay in California or Western Utah. The survey showed it to be in Utah. More and more Mormons poured into Carson Valley, soon numbering two hundred. They were now able to elect their candidates to every office except prosecuting attorney, and organized the area on the Mormon plan: new towns, wide streets, irrigation ditches on either side. They also organized Carson Valley's social life: there was to be no frivolous adornment, everything was for use, with hard work the greatest virtue.

Busy Orson Hyde also changed the name of Mormon Station to Genoa, laid out a second community called Franktown in Washoe Valley, began work on a $10,000 sawmill, prepared to house another sixty to seventy families being sent in by Brigham Young, and dedicated the Carson Valley Mission as a stake of Zion. The rebellious Mormons returned quietly to the fold.

But the Nevada gold fields were petering out. Whatever gold had been washed down the stream beds from the quartz in the mountains seemed to have been gathered up, prospectors rarely earning more than $5.00 a day. Even the frugal Chinese said disgustedly:

"Two pan, one color."

Then the Groshes, in the spring of 1855, "found a perfect monster of a vein." They organized the Utah Enterprise Mining Company, attempting through their father to bring in "kindred and friends from mid-Atlantic states." Throughout 1856 their father remained their sole subscriber. Early in 1857, with a Canadian friend, Richard M. Bucke, they determined to stake out their rich claims and commence mining operations. Only one man in Nevada believed they had anything: George Brown, who owned a trading post and mail station on the Humboldt River. He promised Allen and Hosea his savings of $600 plus all the cash he could raise from the sale of his merchandise and his store.

It would be enough. The monster claim the Groshes staked out as the Frank Mining Company, after their old Mexican friend; other promising stakes they claimed for their Utah Enterprise Company and, as they wrote to their father, "a smaller but richer vein, much more promising because more easily worked," they put in their own name. There still was no government agency with which to file their claims, so they drew accurate maps in their journal.

At this point they gained an admirer: "Pancake" Henry Comstock, mountain man, unsuccessful gold miner, lazy (he got his name because he was too lazy to make bread, just dropping his batter on a hot griddle), shiftless, illiterate. But smart enough to follow the Groshes around.

The Groshes no sooner set to work opening their monster vein than Hosea buried the edge of a pick in his foot. During the last week in August, Laura Ellis, who had come into the valley with her husband in June of 1853, taken up a land claim and built a log house, rode past the Grosh cabin, saw Hosea soaking his foot in a tub in front of their cabin and relayed some additional bad news: George Brown had been killed by the Indians. No money would be available to them.

The Groshes were downcast. Laura Ellis offered them $1500 with which to carry on their operation. Brightening, Hosea picked up a piece of sample ore, pointed at a nearby mountain peak and told Mrs. Ellis that their mine lay at its base. Hosea was pointing at the "monster vein."

On September 2, 1857 Hosea Grosh died of gangrene. His brother Allen was prostrated by grief; he would not continue the mining operation nor, as winter approached, could his friend Bucke get him to start over the mountains for the warmer climate of California. Finally, on November 15, the two men made their start. It was too late. They were caught in a tremendous snowstorm high in the crest of the Sierra Nevada, with all trails obliterated. Forced to kill their mule for meat, they plunged through the trackless snows carrying their supplies on their backs. Their powder and matches got wet, they went for four days without food or fire, their toes froze, then their feet. By the time they stumbled into a Mexican miner's camp their legs were frozen to the knees.

Bucke permitted the amputation of one leg and his second foot. Allen Grosh refused permission to amputate. On December 19 he died of gangrene of the leg, as had his brother Hosea.

The Groshes were not to enjoy any part of their discovery. The harvest of their seven years of study, prospecting, perseverance and faith was to be gathered by other men, strangers to them. Not even their father could collect the few dollars he had scraped together to send to his sons. Yet Allen and Hosea Grosh, like John Sutter and James Marshall in California, go down as the discoverers of the titanic wealth of Nevada.

A few weeks after the death of Allen Grosh, Pancake Comstock, who was now living in the Groshes' abandoned house, went prospecting with John Bishop and a man called "Old Virginia" just below the divide at Devil's Gate where the Groshes had made their strike. Surface-digging with a pick, shovel and rocker they found enough gold to stake out claims. The next morning, Friday, January 29, 1858, some prospectors from Johntown moved up to examine the diggings; others from Chinatown, down the canyon, reluctantly left their homes where they were panning about $5.00 a day.

Those who stayed found about $10 a day in gold dust, built shanties, then log cabins at what became Gold Hill, about a hundred men digging in the barren, rocky, sand and sagebrush desert. They had no idea they were working over vast veins of silver; that secret was buried with Allen and Hosea Grosh.

Then in June 1858 an illiterate prospector by the name of Peter O'Riley, who with his friend Patrick McLaughlin had staked out a claim at the base of Sun Mountain, began digging a ditch up the hillside toward a spring, hoping the extra water would enable them to raise the discouraging wage of $2.00 a day they had been earning. Digging down four feet at the spring in order to make a reservoir, they came upon a strange-looking strata, several feet wide, mixed with blue stuff. They began panning and found they were testing out gold by the pound instead of the ounce.

Pancake Comstock stumbled across the two prospectors, watched them work for a while, then exclaimed:

"You have struck it, boys!"

A fast talker, he also persuaded the two discoverers that he and Old Virginia had already staked out this particular claim. Rather than get involved in a quarrel, O'Riley and McLaughlin wrote the others into their claim, which became the Ophir Mine. Comstock also convinced the prospectors that he owned the spring from which the water was coming, securing another hundred feet for himself below the original three-hundred-foot claim. This became the Spanish or Mexican Mine.

The next morning, June 11, the first miners' meeting was held near Gold Hill, a hundred to a hundred fifty men participating. In protest against Comstock's acquisitions of the day before they voted to adopt the California mining code, which would restrict each man's claim to three hundred feet, with an extra three hundred for the original discoverer.

Within two days the rush was on: the last skeptical ones from Johntown and Chinatown, the farmers from the nearby Carson, Washoe and Eagle valleys, including the future Queen of the Comstock, Eilley Orrum, renegade Mormon. They were still mining for gold, still ignoring the excited cries of the Mexicans who kept saying:

"Mucho plata! Mucho plata!"

Only one man, a spectator, put any credence in the cry, B. A. Harrison, from the Truckee Meadows. He was not tempted to mine, being a confirmed rancher, but when he returned to the Truckee Meadows he tied onto his saddle a bag full of the black rock which everyone was ignoring. Back home, he showed it to a neighbor, J. F. Stone, who ran a trading post. Stone had to cross the mountains to California to buy supplies, and offered to take the stuff along.

Over the crest of the Sierra Nevada and down in Nevada City, California, Stone showed the samples to E. G. Waite, editor of the *Nevada Journal.* Waite split the bag in half, giving each half to an experienced assayer. That same day, even before the assay results could be determined, Judge James Walsh and Joseph Woodworth started over the mountain, reaching Gold Canyon in three days of forced march. They obtained an interest in a rich claim for their gamble.

On July 1, 1858 the *Nevada Journal* published the results of the two assays: the black rock was incredibly rich. It not only proved the Mexican cry of "*Mucho plata*" with its one-third assay of silver, but also contained high proportions of gold, antimony and copper.

Hundreds of miners walked out of the California mines and made their way over the Sierra Nevada on horseback, muleback and foot. The first legal claim office was set up in V. A. Houseworth's saloon. In Gold Canyon the old-timers were lost in a flood of newcomers.

By mid-July all roads and trails over the mountains were jammed with thousands of men pouring into the new fields.

"THERE IS GOLD IN COLORADO. WE SAW IT OURSELVES!"

Colonel William Gilpin was a University of Pennsylvania graduate who, like Nevada's Groshes, had been trained in the natural and geological sciences. After having led troops through the San Luis Valley during the Mexican War and later through the mountain areas pursuing hostile Indians, he reported to Missourians at Independence in January of '49 that he had found evidence of gold in five separate places in Colorado: Cherry Creek, South Park, Pike's Peak, Cache la Poudre, Clear Creek.

No one paid the slightest attention to Colonel Gilpin.

In the next four years a group of hunters from Georgia, being led across the eastern slope of the Rockies, found color at Cache la Poudre. In 1850 the Ralston brothers found traces on the South Platte. In 1852, Parks, a Cherokee dealing in cattle, prospected Ralston Creek and found corroboration of color. Finally in the summer of 1853 a man named Norton, bound for California, went north from Colorado to Fort Laramie and showed a quantity of gold dust. When the men at the fort asked where he had found it, Norton replied:

"Down near Pike's Peak."

That was the end of interest in Colorado's gold for another four years.

Not so the interest in Colorado as a formidable mountain range that had to be crossed in order to push a railroad through to California. Three expeditions came through that year, two of them sent out by Secretary of War Jefferson Davis and financed by the Railroad Survey Act of Congress: the Beale Expedition of twelve, all civilians; the Captain Gunnison Party of twenty-two soldiers and civilian scientists; and John C. Frémont's Fifth Expedition, again financed by Thomas Hart Benton.

The Beale Party, traveling light and in mid-July weather, took the route of Frémont's tragic Fourth Expedition and went across the Pase del Norte for which Frémont had been aiming. Captain Gunnison had with him from Frémont's Fourth Expedition Richard Kern and Creutzfeldt. His twenty wagons went over Cochetopa Pass while he explored unsuccessfully to the north for a lower and easier pass. In July he took his men over the mountains north of Cochetopa Pass, and was killed along with Kern, Creutzfeldt and four soldiers by rampaging

Paiutes. On November 30 of a mild winter John Frémont took his expedition of twenty-two men from Hardscrabble through Williams Pass in the Sangre de Cristo and over the Cochetopa Pass.

But no transcontinental railroad was ever built through Colorado. The Rockies were too formidable.

Then in the spring of 1857 Mexican miners from Sonora panned out a good quantity of gold three miles above Cherry Creek.

It was the first spark in what was to prove a forest fire.

The second came through Major John Sedgwick, campaigning against warpath Indians, who reported he had seen some gold dust found near Cherry Creek by a group of Missouri prospectors. Major Sedgwick's Delaware Indian guide, Fall Leaf, began prospecting, and when he returned to his reservation in eastern Kansas he proudly exhibited the gold he had found.

This was the first Colorado gold actually seen east of the Rockies. Fall Leaf's evidence led to the formation of the fifty-man Lawrence Party, so named because it made up at Lawrence, Kansas, the first party organized for the purpose of discovering gold in Colorado. The leader was John Easter, former town butcher of Independence.

Rumors and tales began to fly through the East. Traders, trappers, army men, Forty-Niners who had passed through Colorado substantiated the rumors:

"It's true. There is gold in Colorado. We saw it ourselves."

The second important party was formed at the instigation of John Beck, a part-Cherokee preacher who had been to California with the Cherokee Party of 1850. He wrote to William Green Russell in Georgia, to whom he was related by marriage, urging Russell to organize a large prospecting party for the spring of 1858, and to be the first to make a strike in Colorado.

Russell and his two brothers, Oliver and Dr. Levi, began work to assemble members. Fifty-seven was a good year in which to recruit, for the panic which San Francisco had disenjoyed two years before had swept the entire country. Businesses were closing down, mortgages being foreclosed on home and farm, savings being wiped out, unemployment was high. To add to rumor and tall tale, the newspapers on the border picked up every yarn and magnified it; expeditions coming through meant business and prosperity. The eastern papers were skeptical, but the unemployed and dispossessed were hungry for an opportunity to repatriate themselves. All one heard was excited talk about "Pike's Peak Gold Region."

The Russell Party of nineteen men from Georgia, plus forty-six Cherokees from their reservation in Indian Territory, reached Bent's Fort on June 12, 1858, with fourteen wagons and thirty-three yoke of cattle, taking the same route used by the Cherokee Party of 1850: past Pueblo and up the front range. With the arrival of the Russell Party, modern Colorado as a mining state can be said to have begun; yet ten days after their arrival John Beck quit in discouragement and took his Cherokees back to their reservation. Some of the Georgians also returned home; the Russells and a small group were left alone in the woods around Cherry Creek.

On July 9 and 10 they found a good site; each man began panning $10 a day. Thus the Russell Party became the first discoverers of gold in Colorado in paying quantities. John Cantrell, a trader on his way from Salt Lake to Missouri, joined the Russells, dug with a hatchet and washed out with a frying pan three ounces of gold, then gathered up a bag of the same silt and continued on his way. The gold he showed to the folks in Kansas, the pouch of gold-bearing earth he took to Kansas City where he had the gold assayed.

The assay ran high. On August 26, 1858 the Kansas City *Journal of Commerce* carried a headline:

THE NEW EL DORADO

The St. Louis *Republican* carried the story on August 29, the Boston *Daily Journal* on August 30. Other eastern newspapers published the story of the gold find. Parties formed on the Missouri border: merchants, mechanics, professional men, adventurers.

In early September the Lawrence Party reached Dry Diggings, laid out a town which they called Montana City and built about twenty cabins. But the pickings were lean. No one came to Montana City. The cabins were abandoned. The party disbanded. Those who were left moved to the head of Cherry Creek and originated the St. Charles Town Company on the east side of the creek, though the only sign of a town was a "four-log improvement," four logs laid in a square on the ground to make their claim legal.

Meanwhile Dr. Levi Russell, because of his medical knowledge, advised his brothers and Georgia friends to move to the head of the creek for the winter. He indicated the west side of the creek for a camp site, and with the Russells' work on a double cabin with a chimney began the characterful and amusing birth of Denver.

The Russells planned for a spring of 1859 attack, Dr. Levi to go south to the San Luis Valley to collect supplies, William and Oliver to return to Georgia to enlist further men and mining equipment.

They were sure the gold was there.

So were the multitudes from the Missouri Valley who arrived from October to the end of 1858 in parties ranging from ten members to seventy. By the end of October a caravan of parties had reached the creek with fifty-six men and the first woman settler. Two merchants arrived with merchandise in four wagons, hauled by oxen, setting up business in a tent until they could complete a double cabin. Jones's squaw wife made some whiskey, with the result that Smith and Jones emptied their Colts at each other.

Culture had caught up with Colorado.

On October 30 one hundred eighty men living on the west side of Cherry Creek held a meeting. The town of Auraria was founded. Because the territory of Kansas extended to the crest of the Rockies, Auraria and St. Charles were in Kansas. St. Charles remained unoccupied until November when a group from Leavenworth and Lecompton headed by William Larimer and including a judge, sheriff and a commissioner appointed by Governor Denver jumped the town site and laid it out as Denver, in honor of the governor of the Kansas Territory.

Rivalry began at once: John Kinna arrived in Auraria with a stock of hardware, sheet iron and tools to make miners' equipment and stoves, but was seduced over the creek by Denver. At its second meeting Auraria voted itself the right to issue scrip at ten per cent interest, and voted a lot to John D. Baker to build a house of entertainment. Then the Reverend G. W. Fisher, a Methodist, preached the first sermon in Denver, making the east bank of the creek the religious center.

Altogether, three hundred people had arrived at the mouth of Cherry Creek by December. The last weeks of 1858 were spent in frantic building on both sides of the creek to provide cabins against the imminent snows.

By New Year's Day 1859, fifty cabins had been completed in Auraria, twenty-five in Denver. "Two forlorn groups of squatty cabins," Smiley describes them in his *History of Denver*, "built of cottonwood logs, roofed with grass and earth, chinked with billets of earth, reinforced outside with plastered clay."

The fact that there still had been only a few gold discoveries did nothing to constrain the lonely miners from writing home glowing reports of the richness of these gold regions: an exaggeration that was to be exceeded only by the reality. The opening of the first saloon in

Auraria, known as the Hote de Dunk until it was corrupted to the Hotel de Drunk, did not help to diminish the stream of golden fiction pouring out of Cherry Creek.

By the end of January the rival towns were prospering, with gun and carpenter shops and an express to Leavenworth which charged a dollar a letter. Yet unless there was a large strike, and soon, both towns would wither; gold had brought people there, there was no other product on which they could exist.

The find was in process in the persons of George A. Jackson, twenty-seven-year-old California miner, originally from Missouri, now broke except for the stock of goods that he wanted to trade with the Indians around Pike's Peak; and John Gregory, described as a "sandy-haired, ill-favored Georgian cracker, whose vocabulary consisted mainly of oaths," en route to the British Columbia gold mines from the Georgia gold mines. Gregory arrived in Fort Laramie as a teamster and heard of gold in the Pike's Peak area.

Jackson struck first. An experienced Indian trader, he had sold all his goods and on December 30, 1858, with two friends, Thomas Golden and James Sanders, moved into the mountains directly west of Denver. On January 1 the trio sighted a herd of elk. Golden and Sanders went hunting; Jackson continued into the mountains to prospect. The three men agreed to meet a week later at their winter quarters some miles away.

Jackson moved resolutely up Mount Vernon Canyon into Clear Creek Valley over several feet of snow. On January 5 he made camp under a fir tree on Chicago Creek, a small tributary of the South Fork of Clear Creek. He had only two days' food left. The next morning, picking the most likely spot, he "built a big fire on the rimrock, or side sand bar to melt the snow and thaw out the gravel." He kept the fire burning all day. The next morning, as he records in his diary, he "removed the fire embers and dug into the rim on the bedrock, farmed out eighty treaty cups of dirt, and found nothing but fine colors. In the 9th cup I got 1 nugget of coarse gold."

On January 9, out of food, he built a new fire over the old one, filled it in with the diggings to conceal it and, marking his find on a pine tree, returned to winter camp. His friend Golden was already there, but Sanders had disappeared. When Jackson shared his news with his friend, they agreed to keep it quiet until the arrival of spring weather and the acquiring of a grubstake.

On March 17 a group of Chicagoans came through with food and mining equipment. Jackson liked the men and wanted to offer them a partnership. Golden disagreed, simply walking out on Jackson and his discovery. Jackson guided the new party to his site, where they staked out claims, formed the first mining district organized in Colorado, and began taking a tremendous amount of gold from the gravel and dirt of Clear Creek.

There was no way to keep the find a secret. At the beginning of May, Jackson had to return to Denver to get supplies. He also had to pay for them with gold dust. Hundreds of gold-starved prospectors followed him back to camp. The gulch was soon solid with miners crawling over the hills and "Chicago Creek."

News of the John Gregory strike reached the two towns within a matter of days. Gregory had worked his way south on the front range, along the Cache la Poudre River, and gone into the Rockies by way of Clear Creek, but a whole mountain away from the Jackson site. On the North Fork he panned the side of a gulch and found good color. Snow and the lack of provisions drove him back to the foothills, to the town of Arapahoe. Here Gregory found his grubstake in a group led by David K. Wall, a former California miner leading a party from Iowa and Missouri.

Wall and his party agreed to grubstake Gregory in return for claims at his find. They moved quickly to Gregory's site and laid out a mining district. In the sides of the gulch they found veins of gold quartz, the mother lode solidified in the Rocky Mountain rectangle, about the same size as the Sierra Nevada rectangle.

The news leaked out through Arapahoe, reaching Auraria and Denver by May 15, 1859. The Gregory rush, more tumultuous than the Jackson scramble, began. By the end of the summer fifteen thousand men were crawling over Gregory Gulch, which was only two hundred yards at its widest point, and two to three miles long! Tent and shack towns sprang up overnight, men breaking their wagons to build shanties.

At this moment Horace Greeley, editor of the New York *Tribune,* A. D. Richardson of the Boston *Journal,* and Henry Villard of the Cincinnati *Commercial* reached Denver and struck out at once for Gregory Gulch. Their vivid dispatches sent east by fast express brought more thousands of panting prospectors.

In color, drama and opulence, Colorado's Fifty-Niners were a match for California's Forty-Niners. "Pike's Peak or Bust" moved fifty thousand men into the region before the year was over, a veritable stampede across the plains in an almost continuous stream of ox teams, wagons, men on horseback and on foot, forcing up the prices of lumber and flour, with tobacco, coffee and sugar exchanged for their equivalent weight in gold dust. There was a percentage who discouraged easily: finding no gold they started east again, and were home in four to six weeks, one of the main differences between the Fifty-Niners and the Forty-Niners.

Fossett in *Colorado* says:

"Gold hunters of this year were the best the states could furnish, men of education, enterprise and energy."

A fourth new land was opened, taking its place alongside California, Utah and Nevada. A fourth rich, dramatic, flamboyant civilization started building.

IN THE early spring of 1955, while I was deeply involved in the Colorado and Utah research for my Far West book, *Men to Match My Mountains*, a telephone call came from an editor friend at *The American Weekly*. We chatted about our families for a moment, then he came to the point. "We've been thinking, here in the office, that we haven't had a story from you for a long time." I agreed, then asked, "What kind of story did you have in mind?" He replied, "Well, frankly, a love story." I laughed. He asked, "Would you have a love story lying around loose in the back of your head?" I answered that I had just been writing any number of heroic love stories, that of Tamsen Donner of the Donner party, Juliet Brier of the Death Valley party, but aside from my Western researches, I didn't have anything either in the front or back of my mind. Finally he came out with it. "Well, we thought that if you didn't have any other love story, you might be willing to do us a love story about Davy Crockett." Davy Crockett was the current rage in America. I asked, "Is there a love story in Davy Crockett's life?" He replied, "We don't happen to know about that, but we thought maybe you could find out." I answered, "The weekend is coming up. I'll go out to the library of UCLA and see what I can locate. I'll call you back on Monday."

I found not one love story, but four in Davy Crockett's life. I also found that, over and beyond the legend, there had existed a discerning and delightful Davy Crockett who had as delicious a strain of pioneer American humor as I had stumbled across in a long while.

The story was pure joy to write.

The Davy Crockett rage passed, but I think often of him with amusement and affection.

FOUR LOVES HAD DAVY CROCKETT

WHEN he was eight years old his father gave him a rifle and turned him loose in the Tennessee woods, but with only enough powder and lead for one shot a day. If Davy missed that one shot he came home empty-handed. By the time he was nine he was returning each dusk after a day of tracking and hunting with a rabbit, possum or a prized wild pig. That one piece of brilliant psychology on the father's part turned the son into what the ballad in Walt Disney's *Davy Crockett* rightly calls, "King of the Wild Frontier."

But the father forgot to teach Davy, and so did his mother, that marksmanship is as important in love as it is in hunting. Twice young Davy rushed out into the wilderness of human emotions with his heart pounding and his hands shaking, took hasty aim and missed his quarry by a country mile.

During his lifetime Davy was best known on the western frontier as an incomparable hunter of bears, bagging forty-seven in one month, one hundred and five in a single year, over a thousand of them during his lifetime.

"I like to hunt bears," said Davy, his dark blue eyes sparkling, his voice soft except when he grew excited. "Bears is witty."

Davy, too, was witty. Once when a fop in a fawn-colored coat said to him, "I understand that you can tell by the scratches on the trees how tall a bear has just gone by, and you know how lean or fat he is by his tracks, and whether it's a he- or a she-bear," Davy replied mildly, "My littlest boy can tell those things."

The gentleman from the big city continued, "And I suppose you people down here in the canebrake eat bear steaks?"

"We salt 'em with a hailstorm," said Davy, "pepper 'em with buckshot, and broil 'em with a flash of lightning. Make good eating."

Davy fell in love for the first time when he was eighteen, and at eighteen Davy was a man. He was over six feet tall, lean and graceful as the "painters" (panthers) he loved to track. Moving through the forest he had a long, loping walk. His friends said that when he ran, it was impossible to tell his effortless stride from that of an Indian's. He had traced his way up the Cumberland Valley and across the Blue Ridge Mountains into Virginia and back across the Appalachian range for five hard, lonely years, ever since the day his father had first hired him out, at the age of twelve, to drive a herd of cattle to Natural Bridge.

Davy's first love was named Miss Kennedy. She was a Quaker from North Carolina, visiting her uncle's farm, which was one hundred and ten miles from the Crocketts' cabin. Like all Quaker women she not only was educated, a rare thing on the frontier, but very much a lady. That did not lessen Davy's ardor.

"My love for her was so hot," he said, "it mighty near burst my boilers."

Davy had just finished working a full year for nothing, had not a pound nor a penny in his buckskin pants. And as he says mournfully, for Davy was the dude of the pioneer hunters, "My clothes was nearly all wore out, and what few I had left was mighty indifferent."

Davy had a sensitive spirit, was something of a freebooting poet, and possessed of an inordinate pride. When he had returned from his second drover's trip, this time to Baltimore, he found his father, who kept a log-cabin tavern on the edge of the forest, badly in debt. Davy was on unfriendly terms with John Crockett. In fact his second long journey had come about because he was running away from a whipping at the hands of his father. Yet his family pride was so strong that he agreed to his father's request that he work out a thirty-six-dollar note held by a neighboring farmer, a task which took young Davy six months. Wanting to earn some money for himself, he then hired out to John Kennedy at two shillings a day, living on the Quaker's farm. After Davy had worked for a week, John Kennedy showed him another long overdue note of his father's for forty dollars.

"You're not responsible for this note, Davy," said Mr. Kennedy, "and I have no right to ask you to work it out. But after watching you for a week, I reasoned that you might want to clear the family debt."

He had reasoned right. Davy gulped, went back to work. At the end of another six months he took the canceled note to his father. John Crockett wept, embraced his son.

This time Davy was free. He returned to live and work at John Kennedy's farm, for he had an abiding affection for the man. We don't know the Kennedy girl's first name. Davy was careful to protect her and, as he grew older, he seldom talked about her for, as he said, "She was a sore spot all my life."

Miss Kennedy was the first grown-up girl Davy had ever known. Living in the same gable-roofed cabin with her, having the opportunity under such intimate conditions to become friends, Davy fell with all the precipitancy of youth into what he called "hard lovin'."

"I thought that if all the hills about there were pure chink," (chink was his word for gold) "and it all belonged to me, I would give them away just to be able to talk to her as I wanted to talk."

Davy had had only four days of proper schooling, and he could neither read nor write.

"When I would think of saying anything to her," he once confessed, "my heart would flutter like a duck in a puddle, and if I tried to outdo it and speak, it would get right smack up in my throat and choke me like a cold potato."

After a time he garnered sufficient words and courage to blurt out his love, asking the girl to marry him. Miss Kennedy was genuinely surprised. Davy apparently had been successful in hiding his tumultuous feelings behind his lean sunburned face and dark blue eyes. The Quaker girl told him, quietly and sympathetically, that she could never marry him because she was betrothed to John Kennedy's younger son.

"I still couldn't help loving her," said Davy, "even though I saw quick enough my cake was dough."

Davy knew that he was a fine figure of a man, broad-shouldered, with high coloring and long black hair. He knew that he was the best shot for miles around. He therefore concluded that the reason Miss Kennedy preferred her young cousin to himself was that Kennedy was educated. That night he went to the farm of Kennedy's older son, who was the schoolteacher on that frontier, and offered to work the farm two days a week if Kennedy would let him attend his school on the other days. The schoolteacher readily assented, even took Davy into his home.

No man ever made a greater sacrifice for love than Davy. Hour after hour he sat in the blab school (so called because the pupils studied aloud and recited in concert) among little children, learning to scratch his name with his quill pen, and to add a column of figures. But Davy was never one to count costs. Besides, as he said, his fire was "fit to burst his boilers." He had "hardly safety pipes enough."

He stayed in school for six long, tortured months, only to learn that his hard-won education could not gain him Miss Kennedy's love, that she had set her wedding date to her cousin.

"I couldn't do any longer without a wife," said Davy, "so I cut out to hunt me one."

What he found was a wildcat. It was Davy's boast that he could "hug a bear too close for comfort," but from this particular fray he emerged badly clawed.

Her name was Margaret Elder and she lived a few miles from the Kennedy place. Davy loved to dance and it was at a dance that he met her. He described her as "the prettiest piece of flesh and blood ever manufactured." She had flashing eyes that could make a man's head spin. They were also inclined to roam.

When the Quaker girl and young Kennedy asked Davy and Margaret Elder to stand up for them at their wedding, Davy decided that he, too, wanted to get married right then. He applied for his license on August 21, 1805, just four days after his nineteenth birthday. His only worldly possessions were his rifle, which he affectionately called Betsy, and a fair suit of clothes. Needing hard cash to buy a piece of land, he set out for a neighboring crossroads where a shooting match was being held.

Davy's rifle was the tool of his trade. He carried it gently. When he used it there was no roughness in his series of movements. He examined the barrel to be sure it was clear. He checked his flint with a touch as light as a feather. He put in the bullet with a supple wrist, raised the rifle swift and easy and, with steady aim, squeezed off the shot well and true.

Since his marriage depended on his aim, he shot brilliantly and walked off with the first prize, a whole beef which he sold for five dollars.

"That was the real grit," exulted Davy. And it was enough for a man to marry on. Returning home, proud and happy, he stopped off to say hello to Margaret's uncle, whose cabin was on the way. Margaret's young sister was there. When she saw Davy she burst into tears.

"Oh Davy," she cried, "Margaret has been fooling you all the time. She's marrying another man tomorrow!"

Davy was stunned. He returned home, moped about the cabin, unable to rid himself of the shame of being jilted.

The family thought he was sick.

"So I was," mourned Davy, "the worst kind: sickness of the heart, and all the tender parts."

His first two attempts at love had been bitter failures. They taught him that in love, as in hunting, he must track sure-footedly, aim straight and squeeze off his shot well and true if it were not to miss the mark.

His youth and high animal spirits reasserted themselves. He picked up his rifle and went hunting, an age-old remedy for broken hearts.

Late one afternoon he came out of the woods to make a call at the home of a Dutch widow who had a daughter "well enough as to smartness," said Davy, "but ugly as a stone fence. Almost gave me a pain in the eyes to look at her."

But the Dutch girl knew instinctively that Davy was not for her.

"Come to the reaping-bee tomorrow," she said, "and I'll show you the prettiest girl you will ever see, ever."

"I guess I was born odd," replied Davy sadly. "No girl for a fellow like me can be found."

"Promise me you'll come to the reaping," urged the girl, "and take just one quick look."

"No," said Davy determinedly, "I won't travel no seventeen miles just to look at another girl, even if she's a sockdologer."

But he did go to the reaping-bee. In fact, he could not keep away.

2

Davy Crockett's opponents accused him of describing himself as half-horse, half-alligator. In a symbolic sense this is true. For even today the figure of Davy is half-fact, half-fiction, which makes him perfect material for an American myth. No matter how outlandish the story one invents for him, it will turn out to be half-true. No matter how solidly documented a description of his character or conduct, it will prove to be half-fiction.

Take the matter of his hunting prowess. The legend of his marksmanship was spread so wide throughout the West that even the animals heard about it, and they would flee the country at the slightest rumor that Davy had shouldered his gun and was headed for the woods. One of his neighbors said of him:

"Why that man Crockett don't even need to shoot game if he don't want to. Out in the woods one day he looked up into the top of a tall sycamore and there was a raccoon. After a moment the 'coon piped up, 'Don't shoot, Davy, I'll come down.'"

Yet here he was, almost twenty, tall, lean, and handsome, with flashing blue eyes. He had been desperately in love twice, but he was still coming home empty-handed. No girl had said, "Don't shoot, Davy, I'll come down."

"I was wary as a possum when I decided to go to the reaping-bee," exclaimed Davy, "because that little varmit, Margaret Elder, treated me bad. But I was as bothered by love as a fly in a tarpot."

When Davy reached the reaping-bee he found that the Dutch girl had told everyone that he was coming acourtin'. The whole countryside knew of his first two fiascoes, and they began joshing him about what a dead shot he was with women.

This was too tender a subject for the usually fun-loving Davy to see any humor in. He was about to trudge back the seventeen miles to his home when the Dutch girl took pity on him, led him to one of the outbuildings and introduced him to sweet Polly Finlay.

Davy was a mixture of Irish and French Huguenot blood. Seventeen-year-old Polly was all Irish. They liked each other immensely and at once.

"I was plaguey well pleased with her from the word go," said Davy. "She had good countenance."

She was every bit as pretty as the Dutch girl had said, with a soft, fair skin and light blue eyes which, Davy noted with pleasure, did not roam.

He asked Polly to join him in a reel. She assented, happily. After the dance he sat alongside her on a bench, and "made as good use of my time as I could."

Polly's mother arrived. Going on the old saying of "salt the cow to catch the calf," Davy was careful to pay attention to her. He and Polly danced and frolicked with the others until daybreak.

"When I got home," said Davy, "I found my mind better reconciled to the whole of things than it had been for some time."

In short, Davy was once again, and for the third time, in love. He determined to marry Polly Finlay, but he knew now that he had to move cautiously through the forest, stalk his game with a sure tread.

He visited the Finlays, made friends with Polly's father and continued to salt the mother, though privately he complained that, "Their tongues go like windmills whether they have grist to grind or not."

He had by now squandered the five dollars he had won in the shooting match, and on which he had intended to marry Margaret Elder. He still owned only his beloved gun, a pair of leather leggings, moccasins, a pair of pants and a butternut jacket. He wanted to marry Polly as quickly as possible, for again as with his first love, Davy cried, "My love is so hot it nearly bursts my boilers."

He arranged with Quaker Kennedy's schoolteacher son to work for him for six months in return for a horse. With a horse and a gun he and Polly could get married.

Two months later he was off on a wolf hunt when, at the end of the day, he wrote, "I saw a little woman streaking it through the woods like all wrath. I cut out after her and found it was Polly. She had been looking for some lost horses for her father."

Somehow, Davy managed to get them both lost, quite an accomplishment for a man who had traveled several thousand miles through strange forests and over unmapped mountain ranges. After dark they came to an abandoned cabin.

"We set up all night courtin'," said Davy, "and by morning I had Polly's promise to marry me . . . just as soon as I paid for the horse."

Once again poor Davy had made a strategical error. When he next went to the Finlays' farm, though Polly's father "treated me very clever, the Old Woman looked at me as savage as a meat ax."

In very plain Irish, Mrs. Finlay told Davy to stay away from her daughter, that if she ever again saw him on the premises she would blast him with her gun.

Two years had passed since Davy had accepted defeat at the hands of Miss Kennedy; nor was this the same Davy Crockett who had been crushed at the news that Margaret Elder was planning to marry another man. This was a fighting Davy Crockett who "hugged bears too close for comfort."

He told Polly he would come after her the next Thursday, informed the neighborhood that there would be a wedding on Thursday, and secured his marriage license on August 1, 1806, seventeen days short of his twentieth birthday. He set out for the Finlay cabin with his brothers, sisters and several young men friends as though he were heading a war party.

"I rode up to the door, asked Polly if she was ready. I told her to light on the horse I was leading, and she did so."

Just as they were about to cut out for the preacher's, Mrs. Finlay relented. She asked them to be married in the house, and even gave the newlyweds "two likely cows and calves," as a wedding present.

Davy rented a small cabin and farm near by, his good friend John Kennedy gave him an order on the store for fifteen dollars, and with this money Polly made their cabin snug.

Davy had imagined that once he was married his world would be complete. "I soon found this was all a mistake, for now having a wife, I wanted everything else, and I had nothing to give for it."

The plain truth was that Davy was not a farmer. He was happiest when he was out hunting, for then Davy Crockett and the world were one.

His neighbors said, "Young Crockett can throw his voice so that it follows the hunting dogs along the ground between the ridges of the hills. His hunting call can travel even around the shoulder of a steep bluff."

He could follow an Indian trace as well as any Indian. The Choctaws and Creeks, the Chickasaws and Cherokees accepted him as one of their own. When he spoke of Old Betsy, his rifle, he said, "She always sends the ball where I tell her. She mighty seldom tells me a lie."

For Davy, hunting was an art, and Davy was one of the great artists of the frontier. But there was little use he could make of his gun in plowing or planting a field.

Davy and Polly were congenial spirits. Two sons were born to them in the next two years. Due to Davy's infallible aim, there was always a variety of fresh meat for the family. But that is about all there was, for Davy could never seem to raise a substantial crop, or cash, either.

After two years on the rented farm he moved his family two hundred miles south, close to the Alabama line. Here he settled in what had always been Indian country, cleared his land and built a cabin. The country was rich in elk, deer, bear, wildcat and cougar. No white man had ever hunted it. It was paradise for Davy. He trained his two sons to be hunters, teaching them to lie quiet and disguise themselves; to give the cry of the female turkey and wait all day until the wild turkey gobbler finally strutted into shooting range; how to make their hearing so sharp that they knew every faint sound of the forest.

The Crocketts lived well. Davy disdained fishing (for that matter he would never shoot small birds), but his sons brought home lines of blue cat, white cat, mud cat, yellow, "some of them weighing a hundred pounds, and smart as a man," said Davy. For cash Davy got twenty-five cents for a pair of 'coonskins, while a dozen pair could be traded at the community store for a supply of flour and sugar.

When the Creek War began, Davy volunteered. Because of his intuitive knowledge of the Indians he was an invaluable scout for Andrew Jackson, and saved his own group from starvation by his hunting skills. But he had no sympathy with the war; he called it a "wicked mischief." He admired the Indians and did not like to kill them. Nor did he like to have the Indians kill his friends, like George Patton.

Davy Crockett enjoyed ten years of love and happy marriage with his "little creature of the fine countenance." Then Polly sickened, soon after giving birth to a daughter. There were no doctors in the wilderness, no medicines. At twenty-seven Polly died.

Davy was heartbroken. Once again he said, "Don't reckon no poor devil was ever cursed with such hard love as mine has always been."

He was thirty years old. He was lonely. He thought that never again would he be "plaguey well pleased with a girl." But not far off, across the creek, lived lonely Elizabeth Patton, widow of his good friend, George Patton.

Soon Davy began crossing the creek nearly every day, in what he called "real good ernest."

3

Elizabeth was vastly different from Davy's other loves. She was the diametric opposite of his beloved Polly, who had been small of stature and bubbled over with an irrepressible sense of fun. Elizabeth was a strong woman with quick, sure movements who could lift a sack of meal as heavy as any man could tote. She worked from dawn to dusk on her farm and in the grist mill. She was also a good businesswoman, a subject about which Davy knew as little as the cougars he hunted.

Davy sensed that he did not love Elizabeth the way he had his first love, Miss Kennedy. Neither could he say of Elizabeth, as he had about Margaret Elder, that "She was the prettiest piece of flesh and blood ever manufactured." Nor could he declare as he had of his wife Polly, "I'm plaguey well pleased with her."

Yet Elizabeth was handsome in her scrubbed cheek, hair-pulled-back-from-the-brow fashion, and though she did not smile much, Davy soon saw that she was unfailingly kind. Perhaps her greatest virtue for Davy was her nearness.

When at thirty-one, Davy Crockett married Elizabeth Patton, and moved with his three children into her "snug little farm," it appears that he looked on this marriage as one of convenience.

"I was as sly about it as a fox when he is going to rob a hen-roost," admitted Davy.

It is entirely possible that if he were asked about his feelings for Elizabeth when he married her, he might have replied, "I like and respect Elizabeth. I don't know that I'll ever love her." He was in for the surprise of his life.

Davy and Elizabeth were married in the spring of 1817. Within a month or two he was referring to the two Patton children as his own. It was a comfortable household and Davy was happy again, his tall, slim figure in its leather-fringed jacket roaming the woods, his dark blue eyes shining out of the sun-tanned face, roughing his long black hair as he crouched by a tree telling hunting tales.

In the fall, after the harvest was in, Davy left with three neighbors to explore the new Alabama Country, just taken over by treaty from the Creek Indians and opened up for settlement. He had been on the southward trail perhaps a month when he fell ill with malaria and he would have died had not his old friends and admirers, the Chickasaws, found him and nursed him back to health.

It was not until early spring, with the wild geese honking overhead on their flight north, that Davy was strong enough to head north himself. When at length he reached the Patton farm, lean to emaciation, Elizabeth cried out, "Davy! You're alive! Men told me they seen you buried!"

The gaunt backwoodsman answered with a wan smile, as he wrapped his arms about Elizabeth, "I knowed that story was a whopper of a lie the minute I heard it."

Then in the summer of 1820 there took place one of those fortuitous accidents which moved Davy Crockett onto the national scene. Up to this time there was little law on the frontier, and less government. The early settlers had needed none and when they did, they made their own law.

"So many bad characters began to flock in on us," said Davy, "we met and made what we called a corporation."

This "corporation," the first government in the area, promptly elected Davy to be a magistrate, reasoning that the "bad characters" would not trifle with the surest shot on the western frontier.

"My warrants had to be in real writing," complained Davy, "and I had to keep a book to write my proceedings in it. This was hard business on me. I could hardly write my own name."

Aside from his six months at the country school, which he had attended when he was eighteen in the hopes of winning Miss Kennedy, Davy had had only four days of schooling. He ran away after whipping a bully who had set upon him, and was afraid the master would whip him in turn. This same fight had been the cause of his running away from his father, and set him to work as a drover on the wilderness roads for three years.

Now, at the age of thirty-four, Davy Crockett sat each evening across from Elizabeth at their rough-hewn table as she patiently helped her husband learn to read and write. Because he was eager, and because of Elizabeth's brightness in teaching, Davy learned rapidly.

"My judgments was never appealed," exclaimed Davy with justifiable pride. "And even if they had been, they would have stuck like wax. I based my judgments on a sense of common justice."

That summer, with the elections falling due for the local militia, a Captain Mathews with whom Davy had fought in the Creek War, came to him with the proposition that Davy support Mathews for Colonel, which was the commanding office, and himself run for First Major.

"We'll be an unbeatable team," Captain Mathews promised the backwoodsman.

Davy was not so sure; he was modest, did not think of himself as a popular character. But when he found that Captain Mathews was double-crossing him by running his own son against Davy, Davy got mad, and a frontier hunter is a dangerous man to make angry. Mathews tried to divert Davy by saying, "Oh, Crockett, you can beat my son easy."

"I'm not running against your son for Major," replied Davy icily, "but against his father for Colonel!"

Davy won, hands down. It gave him the startling idea that there were other offices to which he might be elected. In February of 1821 he offered himself for the state legislature of Tennessee. To Elizabeth, now the confidante of his secrets and aspirations, he said, "When I first got up to speak, my knees felt mighty weak, and it set my heart to fluttering."

Once again, Davy won hands down. He called his win "a breeze of luck."

It was during his first fling at lawmaking that his luck ran out. In the spring freshets his newly constructed grist mill, powder mill and distillery, for the building of which he had borrowed upwards of $3000, more money than he had known in all his life, was "all swept away to smash."

Davy had no way of earning back the $3000. He could have declared himself bankrupt and walked away from his debts. But Elizabeth told him, "Just pay up, Davy, as long as you have a bit's worth in the world. That will make everybody satisfied, and we'll scuffle for more."

"This was what I wanted to hear," said Davy. "A man's wife can hold him devilish uneasy if she begins to scold and fret and perplex him, especially at a time when he has a full load."

But what Davy did not understand was that Elizabeth meant for them to sell her "snug little farm," their comfortable cabin and all their stock, to pay his debts.

When he finally understood, he gazed at his wife in amazement: she would give up everything in the world she possessed, and start out fresh with him in some new wilderness, in order that he might remain a man of honor. As he took her in his arms, he reflected, "I thought I only liked and respected Elizabeth, that I didn't love her. I'm learning that there are as many kinds of love as there are ages of man." He loved Elizabeth, who had by now presented him with two sons, as a mature man loves a fine, mature woman.

In the autumn of 1822 Davy took his wife and their seven collective children two hundred miles northwest to the Shakes country, so named for its tremendous earthquakes, moving what was left of their livestock and personal possessions. They pioneered in the total wilderness, a country hunted only by the Indians. It was a true land of the hunters, with deep buffalo paths, deer ranging the thickets, panthers watching with yellow eyes from the tree tops. The Crocketts made a small clearing, cut down trees, built a log cabin and settled into the life of a hunter's family.

Davy was twice more elected to the Tennessee legislature. In 1826 he decided to try for Congress. He did not speechify. Instead he told his best hunting stories. He had become a wonderful mimic, could reproduce the sounds of any forest full of birds, animals and Indians. His constituents were frontier settlers, they liked the sounds Davy made.

Davy went to Washington City in 1827, where he became known as the "Coonskin Congressman." Elizabeth remained home in the clearing, raising their brood of seven, the family eating well from the supply of fresh meat Davy had laid in before he left for the Capitol.

When he was re-elected his fame spread throughout the nation's twenty-four states as America's greatest hunter, and the most colorful figure in Congress.

So many people wanted to see him that in April of 1834 he was invited on a tour of Baltimore, Philadelphia, New York and Boston. Harvard University offered him an honorary Doctor of Laws degree (shades of his six months in the "blab school" under the Quaker schoolteacher!) and Philadelphia, in a fine public affair, presented him with a long rifle, which he named New Betsy.

The tour was a triumph, but Davy made a fatal political mistake. He tangled with President Andrew Jackson on the subject of the rights of the dispossessed Indian tribes, to whom Jackson was being harsh. Jackson controlled the votes in the State of Tennessee and in his next campaign Davy was defeated.

Always a sensitive man, Davy was hurt. To Elizabeth he cried, "I'm tired of gee-whoa-haw politics!"

To his opponents he said, "You can go to hell. I'm going to Texas."

He promised Elizabeth that he would find good hunting land in this new country of Texas, and when he had made a clearing and built a cabin, he would come back and get them all.

Unfortunately, when Davy reached Texas the Alamo was under siege. Davy had friends in that fort, in particular Jim Bowie. He battled his way through Mexican lines and hostile Indians to join his friends . . . and to die when there was no more powder and shot left for New Betsy.

It is doubtful whether Davy enjoyed the Alamo. He had said, "I don't like war; it's no fun at all, nothing but dog eat dog." The Creek War he had called "a wicked mischief." In killing men, this fabulous hunter took little pleasure, and in getting killed himself, probably less.

On March 6, 1836, the man Davy Crockett died; but an eternal legend was born in his place.

Elizabeth missed him most of all. She never remarried. When her children were grown she went alone to Texas to live in the country which honored his memory.

Davy would have liked that. He would have said, "Elizabeth, I'm plaguey well pleased with you."

MICHELANGELO, born March 6, 1475, was the second of five sons of the Buonarroti, a once wealthy Florentine family which had established its fortune in 1260. He began to draw while still a boy. Desolate because the last of the great school of Tuscan sculptors was gone, he apprenticed himself to the muralist, Ghirlandaio. A year later, Lorenzo de' Medici opened a school for sculptors. Michelangelo spent two years under the master Bertoldo; his native talent attracted the attention of Lorenzo, who invited him to live in the Medici Palace. Here he received a classical education from Lorenzo's Plato Academy, and at sixteen carved his first marbles. Lorenzo died, the Florentines sacked the Palace. Michelangelo fled to Bologna, where he secured his first commission, to complete the Dell'Arca tomb. Returning to Florence, he carved a young Cupid. The Medici cousins suggested that if he would bury the statue in the ground for a time, they could sell it as an antique. The carving was sold for two hundred ducats, but the purchaser, Cardinal Riario, detected the fraud, and sent his envoy to bring Michelangelo to Rome.

THE AGONY AND THE ECSTASY

The City

HE stood on a rise just north of the city. Rome lay below in its bed of hills, destroyed, as though sacked by vandals. Leo Baglioni traced the outlines of the Leonine Wall, the fortress of Sant'Angelo. They got back on their horses and descended to the Porta del Popolo, passing the tomb of Nero's mother to enter the small piazza. It stank from piled garbage. Above them to the left was the Pincio hill covered with vineyards. The streets they followed were narrow lanes with broken cobbles underfoot. The noise of carts passing over the stones was so deafening that Michelangelo could barely hear Baglioni identifying the dilapidated tomb of the Roman emperor Augustus, now a grazing field for cows; the Campo Marzio, a plain near the Tiber inhabited by the poorer artisans whose shops were huddled between ancient palaces that looked as though they would topple at any moment.

More than half of the buildings he passed were gutted. Goats wandered among the fallen stones. Baglioni explained that the previous December the Tiber had flooded and the people had had to flee for three days to the surrounding hills, returning to a dank, decaying city in which the plague struck and one hundred and fifty corpses were buried each morning on the island in the river.

Michelangelo felt sick to his stomach: the Mother City of Christendom was a waste heap and a dunghill. Dead animals lay under the feet of their horses. Wrecking crews were breaking out walls of building stone for use elsewhere, burning marble slabs and columns for their lime content. He guided his horse around a piece of ancient statuary sticking up through the dirt of the road, passed rows of abandoned houses, salt and vines growing in their crumbling mortar. Skirting a Grecian temple, he saw pigs penned between its columns. In a block-square subterranean vault with broken columns half emerging from an ancient forum there was a horrendous odor, rising from hundreds of years of dumped refuse, and generations of men whose descendants even now were squatting over its void, defecating into its depth.

His host led him through a series of dark, winding streets where two horses could barely pass each other, past the theater of Pompey with hundreds of families living in its yawning vault; and then at last into the Campo dei Fiori where he saw his first signs of recognizable life: a vegetable, flower, cheese, fish and meat market, crowded with row upon row of clean colorful stalls, the cooks and housewives of Rome shopping for their dinner. For the first time since they had descended into Rome he was able to look at his host and tender him a wisp of a smile.

"Frightened?" Leo Baglioni asked. "Or revulsed?"

"Both. Several times I almost turned my horse and made a run for Florence."

"Rome is pitiful. You should see the pilgrims who come from all over Europe. They are robbed, beaten, ridden down by our princely processions, bitten half to death by vermin in the inns, then separated from their last denaro in the churches. Bracciolini wrote some sixty years ago, 'The public and private buildings lie prostrate, nude and broken like the limbs of a giant. Rome is a decaying corpse.' Pope Sixtus IV made a real effort to widen the streets and repair some of the buildings; but under the Borgias the city has fallen into a worse condition than that of which Bracciolini wrote. Here's my home."

Standing on a corner overlooking the market was a well-designed house of three floors. Inside, the rooms were small and sparsely furnished with walnut tables and chairs, but richly carpeted, with tapestries and precious cloths on the walls, and decorated with painted wooden cupboards, gold mirrors and red leather ornaments.

Michelangelo's sailcloth bag was carried up to the third floor. He was given a corner room overlooking the market and a staggeringly huge, new stone palace which his host told him was just being completed by Cardinal Riario, who had bought his Bambino.

They had an excellent dinner in a dining room that was protected from the noises of the street. Late in the afternoon they strolled to the cardinal's old villa, through the Piazza Navona, former site of the long stadium of Domitian, where Michelangelo was fascinated by a half-buried, half-excavated marble torso, brilliantly carved, standing before the house of one of the Orsini, a relative of Piero's wife Alfonsina, and which Leo thought might be Menelaus Carrying Patroclus.

They continued on to the Piazza Fiammetta, named after the mistress of Caesar Borgia, son of the Pope, and then to the Riario palace facing the Via Sistina and the city's cleanest inn, the Hostaria dell'Orso, Inn of the Bear. Baglioni filled in his background on Raffaelle Riario di San Giorgio, a grandnephew of Pope Sixtus IV who had been made a cardinal when an eighteen-year-old student at the University of Pisa. The young cardinal had gone for a visit to the Medici palace in Florence, and had been worshiping at the altar in the Duomo when assassins killed Giuliano de' Medici and stabbed Lorenzo. Though Lorenzo and the Florentines had been convinced that it was Pope Sixtus and his nephews who had connived with the Pazzi to murder both Medici, Lorenzo had absolved the cardinal of knowledge of the plot.

Cardinal Riario received Michelangelo amidst piles of boxes and half-packed trunks that were being readied for moving. He read Lorenzo Popolano's letter of introduction, bade Michelangelo welcome to Rome.

"Your Bambino was well sculptured, Buonarroti, even though it was not an antique. I have the impression that you can carve something quite fine for us."

"Thank you, Excellency."

"I should like you to go out this afternoon and see our best marble statues. Start with the arch of Domitian on the Corso, then go to the column of Trajan, after that see the Capitoline collection of bronzes that my granduncle, Sixtus IV, started . . ."

By the time the cardinal finished he had named some twenty pieces of sculpture in a dozen different collections and parts of the city. Leo Baglioni guided him first to see the river god Marforio, a monstrous-sized statue lying in the street between the Roman forum and the forum of Augustus, which was supposed to have been in the temple of Mars. From here they moved on to the column of Trajan, where Michelangelo exclaimed over the carving of the Lion Devouring the Horse. They walked up the winding Quirinal hill where he was stunned by the size and brute force of the eighteen-foot-high marble Horse Tamers and the gods of the Nile and the Tiber, the Nile resting an arm on a sphinx, the Tiber leaning on a tiger, which Leo thought came out of the baths of Constantine. Near them was a nude goddess of breath-taking beauty, "probably a Venus," proffered Leo.

They continued on to the garden of Cardinal Rovere at San Pietro in Vincoli, Leo explaining that this nephew of Sixtus IV was the founder of the first public library and museum of bronzes in Rome, had accumulated the finest collection of antique marbles in Italy, and had been Sixtus's inspiring force in the project to fresco the walls of the Sistine Chapel.

Michelangelo stood breathless when he entered the little iron gate of Cardinal Rovere's garden, for here was an Apollo, just the torso remaining, that was the most staggering piece of human projection he had ever seen. As he had in the Medici palace on his first visit with Bertoldo, he moved half stunned in a forest of sculpture, from a Venus to an Antaeus to a Mercury, his mind captivated, only dimly hearing Leo's voice telling him which pieces had been stolen from Greece, which had been bought by Emperor Hadrian and sent to Rome by the shipload. If Florence were the richest center in the world for the creation of art, surely this miserably dirty, decaying city must hold the greatest collection of antique art? And here was the proof of what he had tried to tell his fellow Ghirlandaio apprentices on the steps of the Duomo: here were marble carvings as alive and beautiful as the day they were carved, two thousand years ago.

"Now we shall go to see the bronze Marcus Aurelius before the Lateran," continued Leo. "Then perhaps . . ."

"Please, no more. I'm quivering inside. I must lock myself in my room and try to digest what I've already seen."

He could eat no supper that night. The next morning, Sunday, Leo took him to mass in the little church of San Lorenzo in Damaso, next to Cardinal Riario's new palace, and attached to it by a break-through in one of its walls. Michelangelo was staggered to find himself surrounded by a hundred marble and granite columns, no two alike, carved by expert stonemasons, each with a differently sculptured capital, "eclectically borrowed from all over Rome," Leo explained, "but mainly from the front of the portico of the theater of Pompey. . . ."

The cardinal wished Michelangelo to come to the new palace. The vast stone edifice, twice the size of the Medici palace, was finished except for the central courtyard. Michelangelo climbed a broad flight of stairs, went through the audience chamber with rich tapestry curtains and mirrors framed in jasper, the drawing room with oriental carpets and carved walnut chairs, the music room with a beautiful harpsichord, until he came upon the cardinal in his red hat and vestments, sitting in his antique sculpture room, with a dozen pieces lying in open boxes filled with sawdust.

"Tell me, Buonarroti, what do you think of the marbles you have seen? Can you do something equally beautiful?"

"I may not carve anything as beautiful. But we will see what I can do."

"I like that answer, Buonarroti, it shows humility."

He did not feel humble, all he had meant was that his pieces would be different from anything he had seen.

"We had best start at once," continued Riario. "My carriage is outside. It can take us to the stoneyard."

As the cardinal's groom drove them across the Sisto bridge and through the Settimiana gate to the Trastevere stoneyards, Michelangelo studied the face of his new patron. It was said that Riario had been so shocked at the Medici stabbings that his face had turned purple; in fact it remained so to this day. He had a long, hooked nose that clamped down on a tight-lipped mouth.

Once in the stoneyard Cardinal Riario seemed impatient. Michelangelo wandered among the blocks wondering how large a piece he dared select. Finally he stopped before a white Carrara column over seven feet tall and four feet thick. His eyes lighted with excitement. He assured the cardinal that there could be a fine statue contained in it. Cardinal Riario quickly paid out thirty-seven ducats from the purse on his belt.

The next morning Michelangelo rose at first light, made his way downstream to the Florentine bridge and crossed the Tiber to Trastevere, densely inhabited section of Rome, home of the potters, tanners, millers, ropemakers, metalworkers, fishermen, boatmen, gardeners, a brawling, sprawling population descended from the original Romans, self-contained within high walls and the Tiber, their crowded quarters unchanged for hundreds of years. He wound through a labyrinth of narrow streets, watched workmen handling raw materials in dark shops, all light cut off by projecting upper stories, the narrow houses jammed together, while above them the roofs pitched angularly, surmounted by bristling square towers. Peddlers were calling their wares, women and children brawling, open fish, cheese and meat marketeers crying out bargains, the whole of the tumultuous noise and smell locked in to overwhelm one's ears and eyes and nose.

He walked along the Via della Lungara to the stoneyard just outside the Vatican wall and Santo Spirito hospital. Not a soul was stirring. He listened through a cacophony of cockcrows before the owner showed up.

"What are you doing here?" he demanded, still half asleep and sullen. "We say we deliver today. What we say, we do."

"I wasn't worried about your failure to deliver. I just thought I'd help load . . ."

"You telling me we don't know how to load?" Now the owner was insulted. "We been carting marble in Rome for five generations, and we need a Florentine statue maker to teach us our business?"

"My family trained me in the Maiano quarries. I'm a pretty good hand with a crowbar."

Mollified, the owner replied, "Quarryman, eh? That's different. We quarry travertine in our family. Guffatti is our name."

Michelangelo made sure there was a sufficient bed of sawdust and that the block was securely lashed before the open-end wagon started on its journey through streets rutted to the hubs of the wheels. He walked behind, patting the end of the column while praying that the rickety farm wagon, in the family for the five generations, would not collapse in a pile of splinters and leave the marble block in the roadbed.

Arriving at the palace, Guffatti asked, "Where do we unload?"

Michelangelo suddenly realized that he had not been told where he would work. He cried, "Wait right here!" ran through the courtyard and up the broad staircase to the reception room . . . to come head on against one of the palace secretaries, who glanced disapprovingly at this bundle of work clothes dashing into the main foyer of the newest palace in Rome.

"I have to see the cardinal immediately. It's urgent."

"Urgent for the cardinal, or you?"

The cool tone slowed Michelangelo down.

"It's the marble block . . . we bought it yesterday . . . it's arrived and I have no place . . ."

He stopped, watching the secretary thumb through an appointment calendar.

"His Excellency has no time available until next week."

Michelangelo stood with his mouth open.

"But . . . we can't wait."

"I'll take the matter up with His Eminence. If you would care to return tomorrow."

He ran back down the central staircase at full speed, out the palace, to the corner and across the street to Leo Baglioni's house. Leo was being barbered, a towel over his shoulders to catch the clipped locks. His eyes danced while he listened to Michelangelo's outburst. He told the barber to wait, removed the towel, rose from the only cushioned chair in the house.

"Come, we'll find a space for you."

Leo located a shed behind the cupola of San Lorenzo in Damaso, in which the workmen who built the palace had left their tools at night. Michelangelo removed the doors from their hinges. Leo returned to his barber. The Guffatti unloaded the marble.

Michelangelo sat on the earthen floor before the block, holding his knees under his chin. "You are a beautiful piece of meat," he said fondly; and fell to musing about the kind of theme a prince of the Church might choose for a life-size figure. Would it not have to be a religious subject? Yet the cardinal had a liking for ancient Greek and Roman carvings.

That afternoon the cardinal sent for him. He was received in an austere room bare of all furniture. There was a small altar at one end, and a doorway beside it. Riario was wearing a severely tailored red cassock and skullcap.

"Now that you are about to undertake a prolonged piece of work, you had better move into the palace. Signor Baglioni's guestroom has a long list of lovely ladies waiting to share it."

"On what terms am I to live in the palace, Excellency?"

"Let us just say that your address is the palace of the Cardinal Riario. And now we must leave you."

No word about what the cardinal wanted sculptured. Or what the price would be. Or whether he was to have regular payments during his year of work. The palace would be his address; he knew nothing more.

But he learned. He was not to live here as a son, as he had in the Medici palace, nor as a close friend as in the Aldovrandi home in Bologna. A chamberlain directed him to a narrow cell at the rear of the ground floor, one of perhaps twenty such rooms, where he unpacked his few possessions. When he went looking for his first meal he found himself relegated to what was known as the "third category" dining room, in which he found his companions to be the cardinal's scriveners, the head bookkeeper, the purchasing agent for the palace, the managers of his far-flung farm lands, timber stands, ships, benefices all over Italy.

The Cardinal Riario had made himself clear; Michelangelo Buonarroti was to live in the palace as one of the crew of skilled workmen. Nothing more, and nothing less.

2

Early the next morning he went to see Baldassare the art dealer, who had just been obliged to return Cardinal Riario's two hundred ducats for the Bambino. Baldassare was a swarthy fat man with three jowls and an enormous stomach which he pushed ahead of him as he came from the back of his open sculpture yard, just off the forum of Julius Caesar. Michelangelo's progress was slow in coming down the yard, for the dealer had a number of antiques mounted on bases.

"I am Michelangelo Buonarroti, sculptor of Florence."

Baldassare made an obscene noise with his lips.

"I want you to return my Bambino. I will repay the thirty florins you sent me."

"Certainly not!" the dealer cried.

"You defrauded me. All you were entitled to was your commission. You sold the marble for two hundred ducats and kept one hundred and seventy."

"On the contrary, it is you and your friend Popolano who are the frauds. You sent me a false antique. I could have lost the cardinal's patronage."

Michelangelo walked fuming out of the yard, half ran down the Via Santa. He crossed the street, stood gazing at Trajan's column until his head cleared. Then he burst into laughter.

"Baldassare is right. It is I who was the cheat. I falsified the Bambino."

He heard someone behind him exclaim:

"Michelangelo Buonarroti! Do you always talk to yourself?"

He turned, recognized a chap of his own age who had been apprenticed to the Money Changers Guild and worked briefly for his uncle Francesco in an early period of prosperity. They might have known each other for a hundred years in Florence and never become friends, but here they fell on each other's necks.

"Balducci. What are you doing in Rome?"

"Working for Jacopo Galli's bank. Head bookkeeper. The dumbest Florentine is smarter than the smartest Roman. That's why I'm moving up so fast. How about having dinner together? I'll take you to a Tuscan restaurant in the Florentine section. I can't stand this Roman food. Wait till you taste the *tortellini* and beefsteak, you'll think you're back in sight of the Duomo."

"There is time before noon. Come with me to the Sistine Chapel, I want to see the Florentine frescoes."

The Sistine Chapel, built between 1473 and 1481, was a mammoth barrel-roofed structure with high windows toward the ceiling and a railed balcony-walk beneath them. The rectangular dome was painted blue with gold stars scattered about. At the far end was the altar, and dividing the sanctuary and the nave, a marble screen by Mino da Fiesole. What would have appeared a clumsily proportioned and graceless building was saved by a magnificent frieze of frescoed panels on both sides of the chapel, running full length to the altar.

Michelangelo went excitedly to the Ghirlandaio frescoes which he remembered from the cartoons in the studio: the Resurrection and the Calling of Peter and Andrew. His admiration for Ghirlandaio's pictorial skill was renewed. Next he went to Rosselli's Last Supper, which he did not find as garish as Ghirlandaio had charged; then turned his gaze raptly to the Botticelli Moses Before the Burning Bush, and to the Umbrian masters, Perugino, Pinturicchio and Signorelli. As he moved about the chapel he sensed that under this awkward, unbalanced roof there had been assembled the greatest combination of masters to be found in Italy. He decided that Perugino's Christ Giving the Keys to St. Peter stood up with the finest of the Florentine tradition, the highest compliment he could pay any artist. He remarked to Balducci how strange it was that this topheavy, cavernous chapel, as inept and arid a piece of architecture as he had yet seen, could have called forth the painters' richest creative efforts.

Balducci had not even glanced at the frescoes.

"Let's get to the *trattoria*. I'm famished."

While eating, Michelangelo learned that Torrigiani was in Rome.

"But you won't see much of him," said Balducci. "He consorts with the Borgias so the Florentines don't receive him. He's doing stuccos for the tower of the Borgia palace, also a bust of the Pope. He has all the sculpture work he wants. He also says he is going to join Caesar Borgia's army to conquer Italy."

That evening Balducci took him to the home of Paolo Rucellai, a cousin of the Rucellai in Florence and hence a distant cousin of his own. Rucellai lived in the district of Ponte, known as "a little Florence, walled within itself." Here, centered around the Florentine consul's house and the Tuscan banks, the Florentines in Rome lived close together, with their own markets, which imported their *pasta,* meats, vegetables, fruits and sweets from Tuscany. They had acquired land on which to build a Florentine church, and had bought the few remaining houses on the Via Canale so that no Romans could move in. The hatred was mutual. The Romans said:

"Better a corpse in the house than a Florentine at the door."

The Florentines reinterpreted the S.P.Q.R. of the Roman's *Senatus Populus Que Romanus* to read, *"Sono Porci, Questi Romani.* They are pigs, these Romans."

The Florentine section of Ponte was the area held within a wide bend of the river, in the center of which was the Florentine bridge leading to Trastevere. In the area were fine palaces, two streets of solidly built houses, with flower and vegetable gardens interspersed. The Florentine banks were on the Via Canale, adjoining the Camera Apostolica, the official bank of the Vatican. At the extreme end of the colony, near the bridge of Sant'Angelo, were the Pazzi and Altoviti palaces. Near the riverbank was an open space filled with flowers and vegetables which became a lake when the Tiber overflowed, as it had the year before.

In the midst of the chaos and filth of Rome the prosperous Florentines swept and washed down their streets every day at dawn, replaced the cobblestones to make a smooth and quiet roadbed, put their houses in a good state of repair, sold or leased only to Florentines. There were prohibitive fines against dumping refuse in the streets or hanging laundry from the front windows instead of the back. Armed guards policed the quarter at night; it was the only section where one was sure not to stumble over a corpse on one's stoop at daybreak.

At the Rucellai house he was presented to the leading families of the community: the Tornabuoni, Strozzi, Pazzi, Altoviti, Bracci, Olivieri, Ranfredini and Cavalcanti, to whom he was carrying a letter of introduction.

Some of the Florentines were bankers, others were silk and wool merchants, jewelers, importers of wheat, gold- and silversmiths, shipowners and shipbuilders who had thriving ports at Ripa Grande and Ripetta, where boats came up the Tiber from the sea carrying luxuries from the Near East, wines and oil from Tuscany, marble from Carrara, timber from across the Adriatic.

A number of the men asked, "Who is your father?" When he replied, "Lodovico Buonarroti-Simoni," they nodded their heads, said, "I know the name," accepting him forthwith.

The Rucellai had converted their Roman house into pure Florentine, with a recessed fireplace surrounded by *pietra serena,* the floor of the dining room tiled in the tradition of Luca della Robbia, and the familiar inlaid furniture so beloved of his countrymen. He did not tell handsome affable Paolo that he too was a Rucellai. The Rucellai had terminated the family relationship with the Buonarroti. His pride would never let him be the first to speak.

He set up his seven-foot block on beams braced from behind so that he could move around it. His disappointment that the cardinal did not immediately present him with a specific subject gave way to the realization that it would be better if he himself knew what he wanted to carve. Then he would not have to ask humbly, "What would Your Excellency like me to make out of this marble?"

"Exercise extreme care," Leo warned him, "not to touch that column until Cardinal Riario gives you permission to do so. He is adamant about his properties."

"I could not hurt the marble, Leo, by rounding the edges and exploring a little. . . ."

He was humiliated at being cautioned like a laborer not to manhandle the property of his *padrone*. Yet he had to promise not to chip a single crystal off the block.

"You can use your time profitably," said Leo placatingly. "There are wonderful things in Rome to study."

"Yes, I know," said Michelangelo. Why try to explain his marble fever? He changed the subject. "Can one secure nude models in Rome? It is not allowed in Florence."

Leo replied mischievously, "That's because we Romans are a clean and moral people. But you Florentines . . . !" He laughed as Michelangelo flushed. "I suppose it's because we have never suffered from the Greek sickness, and Florence has been famous, or should I say infamous?, for it. Here our men have been making business deals, arranging political alignments and marriages while they take their leisure and exercise in the nude."

"Could you arrange for me to have models?"

"Tell me what kind you want."

"All kinds: short, tall, skinny, fat, young and old, dark and light, laborers and idlers, traders."

He set up a low screen to give him a modicum of privacy. The next morning Leo's first nominee arrived, a burly middle-aged cooper who shed his stinking shirt and sandals and moved about unconcernedly as Michelangelo directed him to a variety of poses. Each morning at sunrise he went out to his workshop to prepare his paper, chalk, ink, charcoal, colored crayons, not knowing what new task the day's model would bring: Corsicans who formed the papal bodyguard, German typographers, French perfumers and glovemakers, Teutonic bakers, Spanish booksellers, Lombard carpenters from the Campo Marzio, Dalmatian boatbuilders, Greek copyists, Portuguese trunkmakers from the Via dei Baullari, goldsmiths from beside San Giorgio. Sometimes they were superb figures whom he drew in full frontal or rear positions, posed straining, turning, lifting, pushing, twisting, battling with an array of work tools, clubs, stones. More often the whole figure would not be interesting, only a specially knotted shoulder, the shape of a skull, an iron-corded calf, a barrel chest, and then he would spend the entire day drawing only that one segment, seen from a dozen angles and in differing postures.

His years of training were coming into focus. The months of dissection had given his drawing an authority, an inner truth that had changed the projection of his work. Even the urbane and sophisticated Leo commented on the propulsive force of these figures.

"Each morning you come out to a different model as though you were going on an exciting adventure. Don't you get tired drawing the same thing over and over again: head, arms, torso, legs . . ."

"But, Leo, they are never the same! Every arm and leg and neck and hip in the world is different, with a true character of its own. Listen, my friend, all forms that exist in God's universe can be found in the human figure. A man's body and face can tell everything he represents. So how could I ever exhaust my interest in it?"

Baglioni was entertained by Michelangelo's intensity. He glanced at the batch of sketches under Michelangelo's arm, shook his head unbelievingly.

"What about the inner qualities? In Rome we conceal rather than reveal what we are."

"That is a measure of the sculptor: how deeply can he penetrate the shell? With every subject I say to myself, 'What are you, truly, as you stand naked before the world?' "

Leo pondered on this for a moment. "Then, for you, sculpture is a search."

Michelangelo smiled shyly.

"Isn't it, for all artists? Every man sees truth through his own funnel. I feel about each new figure the way an astronomer does each time he discovers a new star: one more fragment of the universe has been filled in. Perhaps if I could draw every male on earth I could accumulate the whole truth about man."

"Well then," said Leo, "I would recommend that you come with me to the baths. There you can do a hundred in a sitting."

He took Michelangelo on a tour of the staggeringly vast and ornate ruins of the ancient baths of Caracalla, Trajan, Constantine, Diocletian, telling him of how the early Romans had used the baths as clubs, meeting halls, spending every afternoon of their lives in them.

"You have heard the line attributed to Caesar, 'Give the populace bread and circuses.' Several of the emperors felt it equally important to give them water, believing their popularity depended on how beautiful they made their public baths."

Now that the baths were run for profit they were far less lavish, but they had several pools for swimming, steam and massage rooms, courts where the clients entertained each other with the day's gossip while musicians and jugglers made the rounds, food vendors came through hawking their wares, the younger men played a variety of ballgames.

Leo was well known in the bath on the Piazza Scossacavalli which belonged to the Cardinal Riario. After they had had their warm bath and a swim in a cold pool, they sat on a bench at the far end of the area where knots of men were sitting and standing, arguing, laughing, telling anecdotes, while Michelangelo composed scene after scene in a fever of composition, so superb were the modeled planes, curves and masses of the figures against each other.

"I've never seen anything like it. In Florence public baths are for the poor," he exclaimed.

"I will spread the word that you are in Rome on the cardinal's invitation. Then you'll be able to sketch here to your heart's content."

In the weeks that followed he took Michelangelo to the baths connected with the hostels, monasteries, old palaces, to the one in the Via dei Pastini, to Sant'Angelo in the Pescheria. Everywhere Leo introduced Michelangelo so that he could come back alone; and in each new setting of light, wall color, reflection of sun and water on the bodies, he found fresh truths and ways of expressing them in simple bold lines.

But he never quite got used to sketching while he himself was naked. "Once a Florentine . . . !" he muttered to himself.

One afternoon Leo asked, "Wouldn't you like to sketch some women? There are several baths for both sexes within the city walls, run by prostitutes, but with quite respectable clienteles."

"I have no interest in the female form."

"You're summarily dismissing half the figures in the world."

"Roughly, yes." They laughed together. "But I find all beauty and structural power in the male. Take a man in any action, jumping, wrestling, throwing a spear, plowing, bend him into any position and the muscles, the distribution of weight and tension, have their symmetry. For me, a woman to be beautiful or exciting must be absolutely still."

"Perhaps you just haven't put them into the proper positions."

Michelangelo smiled. "Yes, I have. I find it a sight for love, but not for sculpture."

3

He disliked Rome as a city; but then it was not one city but many, the Germans, French, Portuguese, Greeks, Corsicans, Sicilians, Arabs, Levantines, Jews all compacted within their own areas, welcoming outsiders no more than did the Florentines. Balducci had said to him, "These Romans are an ugly race. Or, I should say, a hundred ugly races." He had found it a heterogeneous gathering of peoples who wore different clothes, spoke different languages, ate different foods, cherished different values. Everybody appeared to have come from somewhere else, habitually calling down a pox on the city for its decay, floods, pestilences, lawlessness, filth and corruption. Since there was no government, no laws or police courts or councils for protection, each section governed itself as best it could. The convenient cemetery of crimes was the Tiber, where floating corpses regularly greeted the early morning risers. There was no equitable distribution of wealth, justice, learning, art.

As he walked for hours about Rome he found it a shambles, its widespread walls, which had protected half a million people in the days of the Empire, now enclosing less than seventy thousand. Whole areas that had been populated were neglected ruins. There was hardly a block, even in the heavily populated sections, without black gaping holes between buildings, like missing teeth in an old crone's mouth. Its architecture was a hodgepodge of crude dung-colored brick, black tufa stone, tan travertine, blocks of gray granite, pink and green marble stolen from other eras. The manners of the people were execrable: they ate in the streets, even the well-dressed wives emerging from bakery shops to walk along munching on fresh sugar rolls, chewing pieces of hot tripe and other specialties from the vendors' carts and street cook-stoves, consuming dinner piecemeal in public.

The residents had no pride in their city, no desire to improve it or provide rudimentary care. They told him, "Rome is not a city, it's a church. We have no power to control or change it." When he asked, "Then why do people stay?" he was answered, "Because there is money to be made." Rome had the most unsavory reputation in Europe.

The contrasts with homogeneous Florence, compact within its walls, immaculately clean, a self-governing Republic, inspired of art and architecture, growing rapidly without poverty, proud of its tradition, revered throughout Europe for its learning and justice, were for him sharp and painful. Most personally painful was the atrocious stone-work of the buildings he passed each day. In Florence he had rarely been able to resist running his fingers over the beautifully carved and fitted *pietra serena* of the edifices; here he winced as his practiced eye picked out the crude strokes of the chisel, the gouged and blemished surfaces, the unmatched beveling. Florence would not have paved its streets with these botched building stones!

He stopped in front of a construction in the Piazza del Pantheon, with its wood and iron-pipe scaffolding held together at the joints by leather thongs. Masons putting up a wall of a house were pounding large blocks of travertine, bruising the substance because they did not know how to split it. He picked up a sledge, turned to the foreman and cried:

"Permettete?"

"Permit you what?"

He tapped the end of a block, found its point of stratification, with a swift authoritative blow split it longways. Taking a hammer and chisel from a workman's hands, he shaped and beveled blocks out of the two layers, tooling the surfaces with long rhythmic strokes until the stone changed color as well as form, and glowed beneath his hand.

He looked up to find himself surrounded by resentful eyes. One of the masons growled, "Stonework is for beasts. Do you think we would be here if we didn't have to eat?"

Michelangelo apologized for intruding. He walked down the Via Pellicciaria feeling a fool; yet for a Florentine stonemason the surfacing of a block constituted his self-expression. He was respected by his friends according to his skill and resourcefulness in modeling the stones to bring out their individual character. Working the stone was considered the most venerable of crafts, an inherent part of the elemental faith that man and stone had natural affinities.

When he returned to the palace he found an invitation from Paolo Rucellai to attend a reception for Piero de' Medici, who was in Rome attempting to gather an army, and Cardinal Giovanni de' Medici, who had taken a small house near the Via Florida. Michelangelo was touched to have been included, happy to leave his own dull room and board, to see Medici again.

Saturday morning at eleven, as he finished shaving and combing his hair, forming deep curls on his forehead, he heard the sound of trumpets and ran out to see the spectacle, excited to lay eyes at last on this Borgia Pope whom the Medici had feared and Savonarola had picked as his special target. Preceded by red-robed cardinals and the cross, and followed by purple-cloaked princes, Pope Alexander VI, born Rodrigo Borgia in Spain, dressed all in white, white stole and precious pearls, white robe on a white horse, was leading a procession through the Campo dei Fiori on his way to the Franciscan convent in Trastevere.

Sixty-four-year-old Alexander VI appeared to be a man of enormous virility, built big of bone and flesh, with a widely arced nose, swarthy complexion and fleshy cheeks. Though he was called a theater actor in Rome, he possessed many attributes besides the "brilliant insolence" for which he was known. As Cardinal Rodrigo Borgia he had won the reputation of amassing more beautiful women and vaster sums of wealth than anyone preceding him. As early as 1460 he had been reproved by Pope Pius II for "unseemly gallantry," a euphemism that covered his six known children of varying mothers, of whom his three favorites were Juan, playboy, exhibitionist, prodigious spender of the vast fortunes his father had absorbed from the Roman clergy and barons; Caesar, handsome sensualist, sadist and warrior, accused of clogging the Tiber with corpses; and the beautiful Lucrezia, accused by Rome of having informal love affairs between her growing list of official marriages.

The high walls around the Vatican were guarded by three thousand armed guards, but Rome had developed a communications system that spread news of the happenings therein to the seven hills. If good things occurred, little of it leaked out.

The full panoplied procession having passed, Michelangelo walked up the Via Florida to the Ponte. Because he had arrived too early, Paolo Rucellai received him in his study, a room with dark wood paneling, containing bound manuscripts, marble bas-reliefs, oil paintings on wood, a Florentine carved desk and leather chairs. Paolo's handsome face resembled Bernardo Rucellai's, with its strong regular features, large expressive eyes and light skin, none of which, Michelangelo mourned, had he inherited from his mother's family.

"We Florentines are a tightly knit colony here," Paolo was saying. "As you know by now we have our own government, treasury, laws . . . and means of enforcing them. Otherwise we could not exist in this morass. If you need help, come to us. Never go to a Roman. Their idea of a square deal is one in which they are protected on five sides."

In the drawing room he met the rest of the Florentine colony. He bowed to Piero, who was cool and formal after their quarrel in Bologna. Cardinal Giovanni, despised by the Pope and frozen out of all church activity, seemed genuinely happy to see him, though Giulio was frigid. Michelangelo learned that Contessina had been brought to bed with a son, Luigi, and was again *incinta.* To his eager question about whether Giuliano was also in Rome, Giovanni replied:

"Giuliano is at the court of Elisabetta Gonzaga and Guidobaldo Montefeltro in Urbino. He will complete his education there." The court of Urbino, high in the Apennines, was one of the most cultured in Italy. Giuliano would thrive.

Thirty Florentines sat down to dinner, eating *cannelloni* stuffed with fine chopped beef and mushrooms, veal in milk, tender green beans, drinking Broglio wines and talking animatedly. They never referred to their adversary as the Pope, or Alexander VI, but only as "the Borgia," striving to preserve their reverence for the papacy while expressing their utter contempt for the Spanish adventurer who through a series of calamitous mishaps had seized the Vatican and was ruling on the premise, according to Cavalcanti, that:

"All the wealth of Christendom belongs to the papacy. And we shall have it!"

The Florentines in turn were not popular with the Pope. He knew them to be adversaries, but he needed their banks, world trade, the high import duties they paid on products brought into Rome, their stability. Unlike the Roman barons, they did not wage war against him, they just prayed fervently for his demise. For this reason they favored Savonarola in his struggle against the Pope, and found Piero's mission embarrassing.

Over their port the guests grew nostalgic, spoke of Florence as though they were only a few minutes from the Piazza della Signoria. It was a moment for which Michelangelo had been waiting.

"What about art commissions in Rome?" he asked. "The Popes have always called in painters and sculptors."

"The Borgia summoned Pinturicchio from Perugia to decorate his apartments in the Vatican," said Cavalcanti, "and several rooms in Sant'-Angelo. Pinturicchio finished last year and left Rome. Perugino has frescoed the Borgia's sitting room, as well as the tower in the papal palace. Perugino is gone now too."

"What of marble?"

"My friend Andrea Bregno is the most respected sculptor in Rome; he seems to have a monopoly on tomb carving. Runs a big shop with a number of apprentices."

"I should like to meet him."

"You'll find him an able man, a lightninglike worker who has decorated most of the churches. I'll tell him that you are coming in to see him."

Balducci shared his countrymen's detestation of Rome, yet there was one phase of Roman life that he relished: the seven thousand public women, assembled from all parts of the world. The next Sunday, following their midday dinner at the Trattoria Toscana, Balducci took Michelangelo for a tour. He knew Rome's piazzas, fountains, forums, triumphal arches, temples, not for their historical background but for the nationality of the women who made these areas their headquarters. They walked the streets for hours peering into the faces, adjudging the figures beneath the *gamurre*, while Balducci kept up a running fire of commentary on the virtues, drawbacks, pleasurable qualities of each. The Roman women, carrying parrots or monkeys on their shoulders, covered with jewelry and perfume and followed by their shiny black servants, arrogantly lorded it over the foreigners: the Spanish girls, with their jet-black hair and eyes of great clarity; the tall Greek girls dressed in their native white robes buckled at slender waists; the dark-skinned Egyptian women in cloaks hanging straight down from the shoulders; the blue-eyed blondes from the north of Europe, with flowers twined through their braids; the straight-haired Turkish women, peering from behind veils; the sloe-eyed Orientals swathed in yards of brightly colored silks . . .

"I never take the same one twice," Balducci explained. "I like variety, contrast, different colors, shapes, personalities. That's the interesting part for me, like traveling around the world."

"How can you tell, Balducci, that the first one you pass won't be the most attractive of the day?"

"My innocent friend: it's the hunt that counts. That's why I prolong the search, until late at night sometimes. The externals are different: size, shape, mannerism. But the act? The same, largely the same: routine. It's the hunt that counts. . . ."

Michelangelo was amused. His experience with Clarissa had given him no desire for a simulation of love with some strange hired woman, only a desire for Clarissa.

"I'll wait for something better than routine."

"For love?"

"In a way."

"*Che rigorista!* I'm surprised to find an artist so conventional."

"I save all my unconventionality for my carving."

He could go without carving so long as he was drawing with a sculpture in mind. But the weeks passed and no word came from Cardinal Riario. He applied to the appointment secretaries several times, only to be put off. He understood that the cardinal was busy, for next to the Pope he was said to be the richest man in Europe, running a banking and commercial empire comparable to Lorenzo de' Medici's. Michelangelo never saw the man perform a religious service, but Leo volunteered that he said his offices in the palace chapel early in the morning.

Finally Leo arranged an appointment. Michelangelo carried a folio of sketches. Cardinal Riario appeared pleased to see him, though mildly surprised that he was still in Rome. He was in his office, surrounded by ledgers, the bookkeepers and scriveners with whom Michelangelo had been eating several times a week, but with whom he had not become friends. They stood at tall desks and did not look up from their work. When Michelangelo asked if the cardinal had decided what he might like to see sculptured from the seven-foot block, Riario replied:

"We will think about it. All in good time. In the meanwhile, Rome is a wonderful place for a young man. There are few pleasures of the world that we have not developed here. And now we must be excused."

Michelangelo walked slowly down the broad staircase to the unfinished courtyard, his chin burrowing into his chest. Apparently he was in the same position as he had been with Piero de' Medici: once one was under the roof of these gentlemen they were content; nothing further needed to be done.

Waiting for him in his room was a gaunt figure in black mantle over a white habit, eyes sunken, looking hungry and exhausted.

"Lionardo! What are you doing in Rome? How did you leave our family?"

"I have seen no one," said Lionardo coldly. "I was sent on a mission by Savonarola to Arezzo and Perugia. Now I go back to Viterbo to discipline a monastery there."

"When did you eat last?"

"You may give me a florin to take me to Viterbo."

Michelangelo dug into his money pouch, handed Lionardo a gold coin. He took it without change of expression.

"Don't you say thank you?" Michelangelo asked, nettled.

"For money you give to God? You are helping in His work. In return you will have a chance for salvation."

He had barely recovered from his surprise at seeing Lionardo when a letter arrived from his father, brought in by the weekly mail courier from Florence. Lodovico was writing in a high state of perturbation, for he had fallen into debt over a supply of textiles and the mercer was threatening to take him into court. Michelangelo turned the sheet over several times, searching amidst the news of his stepmother, brothers, aunt and uncle for some clue as to how much the mercer was demanding, and how Lodovico had fallen into debt to him in the first place. There was no clue. Only the entreaty, "Send me some money."

He had been anxious to settle down to a steady project because of his need for a consuming work. Now the time had come to face his money situation. He still did not know how much Cardinal Riario was going to pay him for his sculpture.

"How could His Eminence decide," Leo replied tartly to his question, "when he doesn't know what you are going to carve or how good it will be?"

He had been provided with drawing material and models, and it had cost him nothing to live in the palace; yet the few florins he had saved out from the Popolanos' payment for the St. John were gone. He had been eating with Balducci several times a week at the Florentine restaurant, and had had to buy an occasional shirt or pair of stockings for his visits to the Florentine homes, as well as a warm robe for the coming winter. The thirty florins he had brought to Rome to buy back his Bambino were lightening in his pouch. It appeared that he would have no cash payment from the cardinal until his sculpture was completed; and that would be many months away.

He counted his florins. There were twenty-six. He took thirteen of them to Jacopo Galli's bank, asked Balducci to send a credit draft to Galli's correspondent in Florence. He then returned to his workshop and sat down in deadly earnest to conceive a theme that would compel Cardinal Riario to order. Not knowing whether the man would prefer a religious or antique subject, he planned to prepare one of each.

It took a month to evolve, in rough wax, a full-bodied Apollo, inspired by the magnificent torso in the Cardinal Rovere's garden; and a Pietà which was a projection of his earlier Madonna and Child, at the end of the journey rather than the beginning.

He wrote the cardinal a note, telling him that he had two models ready for His Eminence to choose from. There was no reply. He wrote again, this time asking for an appointment. No answer came. He walked to Leo's house, interrupted his friend at supper with a beautiful woman, and was unceremoniously thrown out.

Leo came by the next morning, urbane as usual, promised to speak to Riario.

The days passed, and the weeks, while Michelangelo sat by, staring at the marble block, aching to get his hands on it.

"What reason does he give?" he stormed at Leo. "I need only one minute to let him choose between the themes."

"Cardinals don't have to give reasons," replied Leo. "Patience."

"The days of my life are going by," groaned Michelangelo, "and all I get to carve out of time is a block of 'Patience.' "

4

He could get no appointment with the cardinal. Leo explained that Riario was worried about a fleet of ships long overdue from the Orient and "had no stomach for art." All he could do, according to Leo, was pray that the cardinal's ships would come up the Tiber. . . .

From the sheer hunger to carve he went to see Andrea Bregno. Bregno was from Como, in northern Italy, a vitalic man of seventy-five. He stood in the middle of a large stable belonging to an ancient palace which he had converted into the most active sculpture studio in Rome by ripping out two of every three stalls, erecting workbenches, and putting a northern Italian apprentice into each of the expanded stalls.

Before going to the studio Michelangelo had stopped to see Bregno's altars and sarcophagi in Santa Maria del Popolo and Santa Maria sopra Minerva. Bregno was prolific, had taste, proficiency in the classical style, and was good at carving decorative reliefs. But he had no more inventiveness than a cat; no idea of creating illusion in carving, perspective, the dimension of depth. He could do anything he thought of with hammer and chisel; but he never carved anything that he had not already seen carved. When he needed new themes he searched for old Roman tombs and copied the patterns.

Bregno welcomed him cordially when Michelangelo told him that he was from Settignano. The old man's speech and manner were staccato, the only evidence of age the maze of wrinkles on his parchmentlike face.

"I did the earliest Riario tomb with Mino da Fiesole. He was an exquisite carver, made the loveliest cherubs. Since you come from his neighborhood, you are as good as Mino?"

"Perhaps."

"I can always use helpers. You see here, I have just finished this tabernacle for Santa Maria della Quercia in Viterbo. Now we are working on this Savelli monument for Santa Maria in Aracoeli. I did my apprenticeship for a silversmith, so we are never rushed and never late because I know within a matter of minutes how long each panel of fruit or spray of leaves will take to carve. I run my *bottega* like a silversmith's shop."

"But suppose you run into something new, Messer Bregno, an idea not carved before?"

Bregno stopped short, wagged his left hand back and forth in front of him.

"Sculpture is not an inventing art, it is reproductive. If I tried to make up designs, this studio would be in chaos. We carve here what others have carved before us."

"You carve it well," said Michelangelo, glancing about at the many projects in work.

"Superbly! I have never had a rejection in half a century. Very early in my career I learned to accept the convention, 'What is, must continue to be.' This wisdom of mine, Buonarroti, has paid me a fortune. If you want to be successful in Rome you must give the people exactly what they have grown up with."

"What would happen to a sculptor who said to himself, 'What is, must be changed'?"

"Changed? For the sake of change?"

"No, because he felt that each new piece he carved had to break through the existing conventions, achieve something fresh and different."

Bregno moved his jaws in a chewing movement, as though trying to pulverize this concept with his teeth. After a moment he spat into the sawdust underfoot, put a paternal hand on Michelangelo's shoulder.

"That is your youth speaking, my boy. A few months under my tutelage and you would lose such foolish notions. I might be willing to apprentice you for two years: five ducats the first, ten the second."

"Messer Bregno, I have already served a three-year apprenticeship under Bertoldo, in the Medici sculpture garden of Florence . . ."

"Bertoldo, who worked for Donatello?"

"The same."

"Too bad. Donatello has ruined sculpture for all you Florentines. However . . . We have quantities of angels to be carved on the tombs. . . ."

The wind-swept rains of November brought with them the departure of Piero de' Medici with troops to reconquer his empire; and Buonarroto's arrival. The rain had driven Michelangelo indoors to his bedroom, where he was drawing by lamplight on an ash-gray afternoon, when his brother appeared, drenched but with a happy smile lighting his small dark features. He embraced Michelangelo.

"I finished my apprenticeship and just couldn't bear Florence without you. I have come to look for work at the Wool Guild here."

Michelangelo was warmed by Buonarroto's affection.

"Come, get into dry clothes. When the rain stops I'll take you over to the Bear Hotel."

"I can't stay here?" asked Buonarroto wistfully.

Michelangelo glanced at the narrow monklike cot, the single chair. "I'm only a . . . guest. The Bear Inn is comfortable. Tell me quickly about Father and the mercer's suit."

"Quiet for the moment, thanks to your thirteen florins. But Consiglio claims that Father owes him much more money. Father ordered the textiles, all right, but what he intended to do with them, not even Lucrezia can find out."

While Buonarroto changed into Michelangelo's dry shirt, drawers and warm wool stockings he related the happenings of the last five months: Uncle Francesco had been ill; Lucrezia too had been bedded, apparently with a miscarriage. With nothing coming in except the rent from the Settignano farm, Lodovico could not meet his bills. He worried about finances night and day. Giovansimone had refused Lodovico's entreaties to contribute to the family coffers.

Buonarroto rented a bed at the Bear Inn; the brothers ate their suppers together at the *trattoria.* By the end of a week it was plain that there was no work for Buonarroto in Rome; the Florentines had no Wool Guild here, and the Romans would not hire a Florentine.

"I think you must return home," said Michelangelo regretfully. "If his four oldest sons are away, contributing nothing, how will Father manage?"

Buonarroto departed amidst a downpour; Piero de' Medici arrived back in Rome equally rain-soaked. The last remnants of his army were scattered, he was without funds, deserted even by the Orsini. He carried on his person a list of the families in Florence he was going to crush once he had regained power. Alfonsina had settled with her children in one of her ancestral homes; from here Piero scandalized Rome by his heavy gambling losses and violent quarrels in public with his brother Giovanni. He spent his mornings at the San Severino palace, then passed the hours until dark with his favorite courtesan of the moment. At night he went into the streets of Rome to take part in every evil the city offered, crawling back at daybreak to Alfonsina's palace. Equally bad, from the viewpoint of the Florentine colony, was his arrogance and tyranny. He announced that he would govern Florence by himself, without the help of any Council, because "I prefer to manage badly on my own account than well by others' help."

Michelangelo was surprised to have delivered to him an invitation written by Piero to attend Christmas dinner at Cardinal Giovanni's. The party was a lavish one. Giovanni's house was beautiful with the objects he had brought from Florence on his first trip: Medici paintings, bronzes, tapestries and silverplate . . . all pledged, at twenty per cent interest, to cover Piero's debts; so that now, as the Florentine bankers commented, "every florin the Medici spend costs them eight lire." Michelangelo was shocked to see the ravages of Piero's life: his left eyelid was almost closed, white patches of scalp showed through where clumps of hair had fallen out. The once handsome face was bloated and red-veined.

"Buonarroti," cried Piero. "I felt in Bologna that you were disloyal to the Medici. But I have learned from my sister Contessina that you saved many valuable gems and works of art at the palace."

"I was fortunate to have the opportunity, Excellency."

Piero imperiously raised his right arm. His voice was loud enough for everyone in the drawing room to hear.

"In return for your loyalty, Buonarroti, I commission you to do me a marble."

"That would make me happy, Excellency," replied Michelangelo quietly.

"A large statue," continued Piero loftily.

"Better make it small," contributed Giovanni, his plump face twisted in a deprecatory smile. "My brother seems to be moving around a lot, and he couldn't carry a life-size Hercules under his arm."

Piero waved his brother's words aside.

"I will send for you shortly. At that time, I shall give you my orders."

"I will await word."

On the way home from the tension-filled evening he caught his first glimpse of Torrigiani. He was with a group of young Romans, richly dressed in camlet with gold braid, his handsome face wreathed in laughter as he walked down the street, arms thrown affectionately about the shoulders of his companions, all of them full of wine and good cheer, roaring with laughter at Torrigiani's performance.

Michelangelo felt ill. He asked himself if what he was feeling was fear. Yet he knew that it was something more, something in his experience akin to the sacking of the Medici palace, the deterioration of Piero, an awareness of the senseless destructiveness that lay inherent in time and space, ready to lash out and destroy.

Cardinal Riario's ships at last reached the Ripetta docks. Leo wangled an invitation for Michelangelo to a New Year's reception.

"I'll get a couple of collapsible black boxes lined with velvet," he explained, "the kind the jewelry people use to display tiaras and crowns. We will put in your two clay models. When the cardinal is surrounded by people he likes to impress, I'll give you the signal."

And so he did. Cardinal Riario was surrounded by the princes of the Church, the Pope, his sons Juan and Caesar, Lucrezia and her husband, cardinals, bishops, the noble families of Rome, the women in gowns of silk and velvet with lavish jewelry.

Leo turned to Riario and said, "Buonarroti has been making sculpture models for you to choose between, Your Grace."

Michelangelo set the black boxes on a table, released the springs and let the sides fall away. He took one of his models in the palm of each hand, extending them for the cardinal to see. There was a murmur of pleasure from the men, while the women clapped their gloved hands discreetly.

"Excellent! Excellent!" cried the cardinal, looking at the models. "Keep working, my dear boy, and soon we'll have the one we want."

Michelangelo asked hoarsely, "Then Your Grace would not have me carve either of these in marble?"

Cardinal Riario turned to Leo. "Bring your friend to me as soon as he has new models. I'm sure they will be exquisite."

Outside the reception room, Michelangelo's anger stormed in torrential words.

"What kind of man is that? He's the one who asked me to carve something, who bought the marble for me. . . . I have a living to make. I could be here for months, for years, and not be allowed to touch that block."

Leo was despondent. "I thought he might like to flatter his guests by letting them choose. . . ."

"That's a fine way to decide what is to be carved out of a seven-foot column of Carrara marble!"

"But better than no decision at all! I'm sorry."

Michelangelo became contrite.

"Forgive my bitterness. I've spoiled your day. Go back to the reception."

Alone, he walked the streets, crowded now with families and children out to celebrate the holiday. From the Pincio hill fireworks of radiating rockets and revolving wheels burst into the air. Soggi was right! Sculpture was on the bottom of everybody's list. He would wander like a peddler singing, "Who wants an Apollo? A Pietà?"

"Time," he muttered to himself. "Everybody wants me to give them time. But time is as empty as space unless I can fill it with figures."

He went into a black funk, unable to speak civilly to anyone. Balducci found a golden-haired Florentine girl to help bring him out of his melancholy. Michelangelo smiled for the first time since he had left Cardinal Riario's reception.

"Ah, Balducci, if life were as simple as you conceive it."

In the Trattoria Toscana they came upon Giuliano da Sangallo, the Florentine architect, friend of Lorenzo, and the first man to instruct Michelangelo in the art of architecture. The luxuriant long golden mustaches still rolled down the sides of his mouth, but he looked lonely. He had had to leave his wife and son behind in Florence while he lived in rented rooms in Rome, waiting for better commissions than his present job of building a wooden ceiling for Santa Maria Maggiore, overlaying it with the first gold brought from America by Columbus. He invited Michelangelo and Balducci to join him, asked Michelangelo how things were going for him here in Rome, listening intently while the younger man spilled out his frustration.

"You are in the service of the wrong cardinal," Sangallo concluded. "It was Cardinal Rovere who came to Florence in 1481 to commission Ghirlandaio, Botticelli and Rosselli to paint murals for his uncle Sixtus IV's chapel. It was he who persuaded Sixtus to start the first public library in Rome, and to assemble the Capitoline Museum of bronzes. When Cardinal Rovere returns to Rome, I shall introduce you."

Heartened, Michelangelo asked, "When does he return?"

"He is in Paris now. He is bitter about the Borgia, and has stayed away for several years. But there is every indication that he will be the next Pope. Tomorrow I will come for you and show you the Rome I like best; not this stinking shambles of today, but the Rome of grandeur, when the world's greatest architects built here; the Rome I shall re-create stone upon stone once Cardinal Rovere becomes Pope. By tomorrow night you'll forget you wanted to sculpture, and give yourself over to architecture."

It was a needed diversion.

Sangallo wanted them to start first with the Pantheon because it was to the top of this magnificent Roman vaulted structure that Brunelleschi had climbed to learn an architectural secret forgotten for fifteen hundred years: that this was not one dome, but two, built one inside the other, the two domes interlaced structurally. With this revelation of Roman genius from 27 B.C., Brunelleschi had been able to return to Florence and apply the idea to closing the dome of the cathedral, which had stood open for more than a hundred years.

Sangallo handed Michelangelo a block of architectural paper, exclaimed, "Very well, now we re-create the Pantheon as the Romans of the time of Augustus saw it."

First they sketched inside, re-establishing the marble-faced interior, with the opening to the sky at the center of the dome. They moved outside, drew the sixteen red and gray granite columns holding up the portico, the giant bronze doors, the dome covered with bronze tiles, the vast brick circular structure as the historians had described it.

Then with paper pads under their arms they made their way to the Via delle Botteghe Oscure, and climbed up the Capitoline hill. Here, overlooking the great Roman forum, they were at the heart of the early Roman capital. Now it was a rubble heap with rough earthen mounds on which goats and swine were grazing, yet here on the two summits had been the temple of Jupiter and the temple of Juno Moneta, from the sixth century B.C.

While Sangallo talked about the roof of the temple of Jupiter, bronze overlaid thickly with gold, as described by Dionysius of Halicarnassus, then about the three rows of columns on the front, the single row on each side, the inside consisting of three parallel shrines to Jupiter, Juno and Minerva, they brought the structure to life on their paper. Plutarch had described the fourth temple of Domitian: slender pillars of Pentelic marble, the buildings of tremendous rustic stone, on the portico enthroned statues before which the emperors and magistrates had made their sacrifices to the gods; all this they sketched.

They scrambled down the side of the hill to the Roman forum, spent the remainder of their hours here, drawing the buildings as they had been in the days of their greatness: the temples of Saturn and Vespasian, the senate house of Julius Caesar, built of severely plain yellow brick; the great columned Castor's temple with its rich Corinthian capitals; then on through the arch of Titus to the colosseum . . . Michelangelo's hands flying faster than they ever had in his life, trying to keep up with Sangallo, who was pouring out a stream of sketches and verbal descriptions.

Night fell. Michelangelo was exhausted, Sangallo triumphant.

"Now you have uncovered the glory that was Rome. Work in it every day. Go up to the Palatine and reconstruct the baths of Severus, Flavian's palace. Go to the Circus Maximus, the basilica of Constantine, the golden house of Nero at the bottom of the Esquiline. The Romans were the greatest architects the world has known."

Michelangelo glanced at Sangallo's mobile, attractive face, the excitement glowing in his eyes.

"Sangallo has old Roman architecture to make his days important, Balducci his girls. And I could use a sculpture commission," he murmured to himself.

5

Deep in his bosom was the growing doubt that he would ever get Cardinal Riario's approval to carve the seven-foot block. In desperation he sought out Piero at the Orsini palace. He would suggest only a small, attractive piece to increase his chance of acceptance. Piero was in the midst of an uproarious quarrel with the servants over the way they had cooked his dinner. Alfonsina sat opposite him at the huge oak table. Her tired eyes gave him a brief flash of recognition.

"Excellency, I have the time now to make you a beautiful sculpture, if you would give me the order to commence."

Piero was half awake.

"Do you not recall? At your Christmas reception you ordered . . ."

"What about it?"

"I have a design for a Cupid, if you think that would please you."

"A Cupid? Well, why not?"

"I only needed your approval."

Piero had started shouting again. Michelangelo knew that he had been dismissed; but he had also been told to go ahead. He walked along the riverbank to the stoneyards by the docks on the Tiber, saw a small block, paid five florins from his dwindling supply, and trudged behind the barrow as a boy wheeled it home for him.

It took him two days to find out that the marble was bad. He had acted stupidly, walked into a yard and bought the first block that looked good to him. He never would have done such a thing in Florence. But here in Rome he had behaved like a novice. His five florins were thrown away.

The next morning at dawn he was in the yard of the Guffatti, from whom Cardinal Riario had bought the seven-foot column. Now he tested the blocks, at length found a white marble that looked translucent in the early rays of the sun, that showed no gullies or fissures when under water. This time he had invested his five florins well; but his purse was reduced to a last three florins.

He sketched for a morning in the workingmen's quarter in Trastevere, children playing in the streets, lying on pallets in front of the clanging metal shops. It was only a matter of days before he had his hammer and chisel raised for the first blows. Balducci asked:

"Hadn't you better get a signed commitment from Piero? He's pouring every florin he can commandeer into mercenaries to mount another attack on Florence."

Piero was not having any contracts.

"My dear Buonarroti, I'll be leaving Rome before you can finish this Cupid. In all likelihood I'll never be back. . . ."

"Are you telling me, Excellency, that you have changed your mind?" His need had put a sharp edge to his tongue.

"A Medici never changes his mind," said Piero coldly. "It's just that I'm preoccupied. Postpone the matter for a year . . ."

Out in the freezing Piazza Sant'Apollinare, Michelangelo cried, "It serves me right!" He had said it out loud, his voice bitter, his face contorted with disgust. Only his eagerness to begin a piece for someone could have considered Piero's flimsy agreement a commitment.

He carved the Cupid anyway, for the joy of working in the white marble and breathing its dust.

Two frustrating months passed before he could get another appointment with Cardinal Riario.

"What have you got for me today?" he asked in good humor. "Something vigorously pagan, to match those fine antiques in the Cardinal Rovere's garden?"

Michelangelo lied quickly. "Yes, Your Grace."

He sat on the bed in his narrow room with the sweat pouring off him as though he had a fever, searching his mind for the most totally joyous, pleasure-giving Greek god he could find. In the Florentine quarter one night, Altoviti had asked:

"Have you ever thought of doing a Bacchus?"

"No, I rarely drink wine."

"Bacchus is also Dionysus, a nature god, symbolizing fruitfulness. He is the god who brought strange and wondrous gifts to man, enabling him to forget his misery, drudgery, the brute tragedy of life. If it is good for man to have pleasure, to laugh, sing, be happy, then we owe much to Bacchus."

Into his memory came a youth he had seen at the baths, with the proportioned body of an athlete: slim legs and waist, powerfully muscled chest and arms, pantherlike.

His work was his only reward: on Good Friday violence broke out in Rome, the cobblestones of the city running with blood. It started with a riot incited by the Pope's Spanish mercenaries, who were so bitterly hated by the Romans that they fought the armed soldiers with clubs and stones; moved on to Lucrezia Borgia's husband, a Sforza, fleeing Rome after announcing that the Borgias were about to murder him because they wanted a Spanish alliance for Lucrezia; moved on to another departure of Piero de' Medici at the head of an army of thirteen hundred mercenaries to storm Florence; moved on to revolt in the Florentine quarter when the Pope excommunicated Savonarola; and ended in the grisly murder of Juan Borgia. Fishermen angling in the Tiber found Juan Borgia's body and brought it ashore, still dressed in velvet coat and mantle, boots and spurs, slashed with nine knife wounds, the hands tied. The Romans did little to conceal their joy.

A reign of terror settled over Rome. The Vatican and the city were paralyzed. The Pope's police forced their way into every house Juan had ever visited, tortured servants in their search for clues, ransacked the homes of the Florentines to prove a conspiracy, accused Lucrezia's rejected husband of the murder, then every noble Roman family that had ever fought the papacy . . . until word got around that the Pope, along with the rest of Rome, was convinced that Caesar had killed his older brother to get him out of the way of his own career.

Cardinal Riario went into mourning with his Pope. The palace was closed to all but the most compelling business. Sculpture was far from compelling business. It was a luxury to be abandoned the moment anything went wrong.

"The cardinal won't talk sculpture for a long time," said Leo Baglioni. "I would advise you to look for another patron."

"In Rome? Won't Cardinal Riario's attitude be reflected all over the city?"

"Unfortunately, yes. But is Florence any better under Savonarola?"

"No. But it's home. Could you arrange one last appointment? So that I can get paid."

"Paid? You haven't made a sculpture."

"I've worked. I've made drawings, models. But you wouldn't let me begin carving. The cardinal's a rich man, and I'm down to my last denari."

He tossed on his bed through the night, was cranky when Balducci insisted that he come with him to hunt ducks in the marshes:

"The air will be good for you. Make a man of you. I spend every spare hour tramping and shooting to keep up my manhood."

Michelangelo knew what Balducci meant by his manhood. He said satirically, "Building up your coin of the realm to spend on the women."

"But of course!" cried Balducci. "Every man builds up his fortune to spend somewhere."

Troubles all come ripe at the same time, like tomatoes. Lionardo showed up again, his habit torn, blood on his face. From his incoherent story, Michelangelo gathered that the monks at Viterbo had turned on him, beaten him and ejected him from the monastery for his championing of the excommunicated Savonarola.

"I want to get home to San Marco," he said hoarsely, licking his cracked lips. "Give me money for the journey."

Michelangelo took his last coins out of the leather pouch.

"I, too, feel badly beaten. My hope is also to get home. But stay here with me for a few days, until you feel better."

"Thank you, no, Michelagnolo. And thank you for the money."

It was the first softness Michelangelo had heard in his brother's voice in years.

The second blow was the news of his stepmother Lucrezia's death, written in a few broken sentences by his father. *"Il Migliore,"* he thought with affection, "The Best." She had bought only the best, and given of her best to all of them, the nine Buonarroti she had undertaken to feed. Had Lodovico loved her? It was hard to say. Had she loved them? This big family into which she had moved as a second wife? Yes, she had. It was not her fault if her only talent or excitement was for cooking. She had given unstintingly of what she had; and her stepson shed a tear for her passing.

A few days later a hotel groom brought a note from the Bear Inn announcing that Buonarroto was back. He hurried over, past the city market in Piazza Navona, the factories and shops between the ruined theater of Pompey and stadium of Domitian, the vegetable gardens leading to Piazza Sant'Apollinare.

"What of Father?" demanded Michelangelo. "How has he taken Lucrezia's death?"

"Badly. Locks himself in his bedroom."

"We must find him another wife."

"He says he would rather live alone than go through another death." He paused, then added, "The mercer is about to have him arrested for the bad debt. Consiglio can prove that Father took the goods, and since we have only a few florins left it could mean prison."

"Prison! *Dio mio!* He must sell the Settignano villa and farm."

"He can't. It's under long-term lease. Besides, he says he would rather go to the Stinche than deprive us of our last inheritance."

Michelangelo was furious.

"Our last inheritance, a house? Our last inheritance is the Buonarroti name. We've got to protect it."

"But what to do? I earn only a few scudi a month . . ."

"And I earn nothing. But I will! I'll make Cardinal Riario see the justice of my position."

The cardinal listened, playing quietly with the long gold chain around his neck.

"I would not expect you to have given this time for nothing."

"Thank you, Excellency; I knew you would be generous."

"Indeed I shall. I relinquish all right and title to the marble block and the thirty-seven ducats it cost me. The marble is yours, in return for patient waiting."

He had only one recourse: the Florentine bankers, Rucellai and Cavalcanti. He would go into debt. He sat down and wrote his father a letter telling him, "I shall send you whatever you ask me, even if I should have to sell myself as a slave," then went to Paolo Rucellai to explain his plight.

"A loan from the bank? No; it is too expensive for you at twenty per cent interest. From me, yes, as a personal loan without interest. Will twenty-five florins help?"

"I will pay it back; you will see."

"You are to forget about it until you have money in your belt."

He ran through the labyrinth of unpaved streets crowded with heavy traffic and clogged with sand from the river, gave Buonarroto the credit slip signed by Rucellai, added to it a note to Consiglio stating that he would take responsibility for the balance of the debt, guaranteeing to pay it within the year.

"That's what Father wanted, of course," Buonarroto said thoughtfully, fingering the two notes. "He's not going to earn anything more; nor is Uncle Francesco. You and me, we are the Buonarroti now. We can expect no help from Lionardo or Giovansimone. And the little one, Sigismondo . . . the Wine Guild has released him. Once Father sees these papers you will have the support of the Buonarroti family on your hands."

Good fortune comes in bunches, as do peaches when the trees turn ripe. Michelangelo finished polishing his Cupid, a lovely child just awakened from sleep and holding up its arms to be taken by its mother. Balducci was enchanted with its lighthearted warmth, the beautiful satiny texture. He asked if they could carry it to the Galli house to show his boss, Jacopo Galli.

There was no Bugiardini to wheel the marble through the streets. Balducci rented a mule with a large saddlebag. Michelangelo wrapped his Cupid in a blanket, led the animal past San Lorenzo in Damaso, through the lane of Lentari in Parione. The Casa Galli had been built by one of Jacopo Galli's ancestors. Galli was grateful to this predecessor because he had begun, at the same time, a collection of ancient sculptures that was second only to the Cardinal Rovere's.

Balducci tied the mule while Michelangelo unwrapped the Cupid. After descending a broad flight of stone stairs, Michelangelo found himself in an atrium, closed on three sides by the house, and on the fourth by the flight of steps, giving the area the illusion of being a sunken garden; or, Michelangelo thought as he glanced hastily about him, a sunken wilderness of statues, marble friezes, crouching animals.

Jacopo Galli, who had been educated at the university in Rome, and had been reading every day of his life since, put down a copy of Aristophanes' *Frogs,* began pulling himself out of a low-lying chaise. He seemed never to stop getting up as he unfolded: six feet, six and a half, surely not seven? the tallest man Michelangelo had ever seen, hunched over at the shoulders from a lifetime of stooping to the short-statured Romans. Michelangelo was as a child before him.

"Ah, you come with a marble in your arms. That is the sight I like best in my garden."

Michelangelo set the Cupid down on the table next to Galli's book, turned to look up into the man's blue eyes.

"I'm afraid I've brought my Cupid into a rough arena."

"I think not," murmured Galli in a voice that he made an effort to keep reasonable-sized. "Balducci, take your friend Buonarroti into the house for a slice of cold watermelon."

When they returned to the garden a few minutes later they found that Galli had removed a torso from a pedestal on the low wall next to the steps and replaced it with the Cupid. He had settled back into the chaise. Standing behind his host, Michelangelo had an opportunity to study the three Greek torsos, Roman sarcophagus, temple frieze, wall slab with huge seated griffin, Egyptian lion with near-human head.

Galli's eyes were twinkling. "I feel as though your Cupid has been sitting there since the day I was born, a lineal descendant of any of these carvings. Would you sell it to me? What price shall we set?"

Humbly, Michelangelo murmured, "That is up to you."

"First, tell me your circumstances."

Michelangelo related the story of his year with Riario.

"So you end up without a scudo of pay, and a seven-foot marble block? Shall we say the Cupid is worth fifty ducats? Because I know you need money I will allow my cupidity to knock the price down to twenty-five ducats. Then, because I detest shrewdness in dealing with the arts, I will take the twenty-five ducats I was going to underpay you, and add them to my original estimate. Do you approve my formula?"

Michelangelo's amber eyes shone.

"Signor Galli, for a year I have been thinking bad things about the Romans. In your name, I apologize to the whole city."

Galli bowed while sitting down. "Now tell me about this seven-foot marble block. What do you think might be carved from that?"

Michelangelo told him about his drawings for an Apollo, for a Pietà, for a Bacchus. Galli was intrigued.

"I've never heard of a Bacchus unearthed hereabouts, though there are one or two that were brought from Greece, figures of old men with beards, rather dull."

"No, no, my Bacchus would be young, as befits a god of joy and fertility."

"Bring me the drawings tomorrow at nine."

Galli brought a purse from the house and handed Michelangelo seventy-five ducats. Michelangelo led the mule through the darkening streets to the stable where he paid for his hire, then walked to Rucellai's to return the twenty-five florins he had borrowed.

The next evening he presented himself in the Galli garden at the appointed time. No one was present. It seemed as though hours passed. He saw himself abandoning his marble, or reselling it to Guffatti for a fraction of its cost and returning to Florence with the next pack train. Then Galli came into the garden, welcomed him, poured them an apéritif, and settled down to study the drawings. Soon Signora Galli, a tall, lithe woman, no longer young but preserving a patrician beauty, joined them for supper over candlelight. A cool breeze stirred the summer heat. When supper was over, Galli asked:

"Would you be willing to move your block here, and carve this Bacchus for me? You could have a room to live in. I would pay you three hundred ducats for the completed statue."

Michelangelo bowed his head so that the candle gleam would not betray him. He had been saved from an ignominious return to Florence, from defeat.

Yet the next morning when he walked alongside the Guffatti wagon carrying his marble column from the Riario palace to Galli's, with his small bag of clothes under his arm, he felt like a mendicant. Was he to spend his years moving from one charitable bedroom to another? He knew that many artists traveled from court to court, from patron to patron, for the most part well housed, fed and entertained; but he also knew he would not be content to do so. He promised himself that one day soon he must become his own man, inside his own walls.

6

He was shown into a bedroom on the wing of the U opposite from the one occupied by the Galli, a pleasant room warm with sunlight. A door on the far side admitted to a fig orchard. At the edge of the orchard was a storage shed with a hard earthen floor. Michelangelo took off the plank roof, letting the fig trees close it over in shade. The building backed onto a rear lane, through which friends could come and visit him and materials be delivered. He could not see the house through the trees, and he was far enough away so that they could not hear his hammering. On the outside he rigged up a barrel so that he could bring water from the well and shower at night before putting on clean clothes and joining the Galli for supper in the garden. Jacopo Galli did not leave his bank at midday; no dinner was served except on Sundays and religious holidays. A servant brought Michelangelo a light meal on a tray, which he ate off his drafting board. He was grateful not to have to change clothes at midday, or be sociable.

He had a letter from his father, acknowledging the twenty-five florins. The mercer had accepted Michelangelo's assurance of payment, but he wanted half of the fifty florins still owed him. Could he possibly send another twenty-five florins by the Saturday post?

Michelangelo sighed, donned a lightweight blouse, took twenty-five ducats to Jacopo Galli's bank in the Piazza San Celso next to the bank of the Chigi family. Balducci was not in, so he went to Jacopo Galli's desk. Galli looked up, gave no sign of recognition. Nor did Michelangelo recognize Jacopo Galli; the face was stern, cold, expressionless. He asked in an impersonal tone what Michelangelo desired.

"A credit . . . for twenty-five florins. To send to Florence."

He put his coins on the desk. Galli spoke to a clerk nearby. The transaction was swiftly made. Galli returned his masked eyes and hard-set mouth to his papers.

Michelangelo was staggered. "What have I done to offend?" he demanded of himself.

It was dark before he could bring himself to return to the house. From his room he saw lights in the garden. He opened the door gingerly.

"Ah, there you are!" cried Galli. "Come have a glass of this fine Madeira."

Jacopo Galli was sprawled relaxedly in his chaise. He asked whether Michelangelo had set up his shop, what more he would need. His change of manner was simply explained. Jacopo Galli apparently could not, or would not, establish a bridge between the halves of his life. At his bank he held himself rigid, brusque. His business associates admired the way in which he dispatched their affairs and brought them the most profitable result, but did not like him as a person. They said he was not human. When he reached home Galli shed his skin as though he were a lizard, was gay, indulgent, humorous. No word of business ever passed his lips. Here in the garden he talked art, literature, history, philosophy. The friends who dropped in each evening loved him, considered him overgenerous with his family and household.

For the first time since he reached Rome, Michelangelo began to meet interesting Romans: Peter Sabinus, professor of Eloquence at the university, who cared little for Galli's sculptures but who had what Galli described as "an incredible number of early Christian inscriptions"; the collector Giovanni Capocci, one of the first Romans to attempt disciplined excavating at the catacombs; Pomponius Laetus, one of Galli's old professors, an illegitimate son of the powerful Sanseverino family, who could have dawdled in idle elegance but lived only for learning, ill clad in buckskins and housed in a shack.

"I used to go to his lecture hall at midnight to get a seat," Galli told Michelangelo. "Then we'd wait for dawn, until we saw him coming down the hill, lantern in one hand, old manuscript in the other. He was tortured by the Inquisition because our Academy, like your Plato Academy in Florence, was suspected of heresy, paganism, republicanism." Galli chuckled. "All perfectly true charges. Pomponius is so steeped in paganism that the sight of an antique monument can move him to tears."

Michelangelo suspected that Galli too was "steeped in paganism," for he never saw a man of the Church at Galli's, with the exception of the blind brothers, Aurelius and Raffaelle Lippus, Augustinians from Santo Spirito in Florence, who improvised Latin songs and poetic hymns on their lyres; and the French Jean Villiers de la Groslaye, Cardinal of San Dionigi, a wisp of a man in an elegantly trimmed white beard and scarlet cassock who had begun his religious life as a Benedictine monk and, beloved by Charles VIII for his devoutness and learning, had been made a cardinal through the king's intervention. He had nothing to do with the corruption of the Borgias, living the same devout life in Rome that he had in the Benedictine monasteries, continuing his studies of the Church Fathers, on whom he was an authority.

Not all the scholars were aged. He made friends with Jacopo Sadoleto from Ferrara, twenty years old, a fine poet and Latinist; Serafino, an idolized poet in the court of Lucrezia Borgia, who never mentioned the Borgias or the Vatican when he visited at Galli's, but read his historical poems while he accompanied himself on the lute; Sannazaro, forty, but seeming thirty, who mingled pagan and Christian images in his verse.

The Galli made the minimum number of gestures of conformity; they went to mass most Sundays and on the important holy days. Jacopo Galli confided that his anti-clericalism was the only gesture he could make against the corruption of the Borgias and their followers.

"From my reading, Michelangelo, I have been able to follow the rise, fulfillment, decay and disappearance of many religions. That is what is happening to our religion today. Christianity has had fifteen hundred years to prove itself, and has ended in . . . what? Borgia murders, greed, incest, perversion of every tenet of our faith. Rome is more evil today than Sodom and Gomorrah when they were destroyed by fire."

"Even as Savonarola has said?"

"As Savonarola has said. A hundred years of Borgias and there will be nothing left here but a historic pile of stones."

"The Borgias can't rule for a hundred years, can they?"

Galli's big, open face was creased by furrows.

"Caesar Borgia has just crowned Federigo as King of Naples, returned to Rome in triumph, and been consigned his brother Juan's estate by the Pope. An archbishop has been caught forging dispensations. A bishop was caught with ten thousand ducats from the sale of offices in the Curia. And so it goes."

Now all the drawings he had made for the Bacchus, the Greek god of joy, seemed superficial and cynical. He had tried to project himself backward into an Elysian age; but he was playing with a myth as a child plays with toys. His present reality was Rome: the Pope, Vatican, cardinals, bishops, the city plunged deep into corruption and decadence because the hierarchy battened off it. He felt a total revulsion for this Rome. But could he sculpture from hate? Could he use his pure white marble, which he loved, to depict the evil and smell of death that were destroying what had once been the capital of the world? Was there not the danger that his marble too would become hateful? He could not bring himself to abandon the Greek ideal of beauty-out-of-marble.

He slept fitfully. Often he went to Galli's library, lit a lamp and took up writing materials, as he had at Aldovrandi's after he had met Clarissa. It had been love that churned him then, made him pour out lines to "cool himself off." Now it was hate, as searing an emotion as love, that caused him to pour out hundreds of lines until, at dawn, he had had his say.

Here helms and swords are made of chalices:
The blood of Christ is sold so much the quart:
His cross and thorns are spears and shields;
and short
Must be the time ere even his patience cease.

Nay, let him come no more to raise the fees
Of this foul sacrilege beyond report!
For Rome still flays and sells him at the court
Where paths are closed to virtue's fair increase. . . .

God welcomes poverty perchance with pleasure:
But of that better life what hope have we,
When the blessed banner leads to nought but ill?

He went searching through the collections in Rome for ancient carvings. The only young Bacchus he could find was about fifteen years old, dead sober. From the way he held a bunch of grapes, negligently, he seemed bored with the fact that he had conceived this strangest of fruits.

His sculpture would have joy in it, try to capture the sense of fertility of Dionysus, the nature god, the power of the intoxicating drink that enabled a man to laugh and sing and forget for a while the sorrow of his earthly miseries. And then, perhaps, at the same time he could portray the decay that came with too much forgetfulness, that he saw all around him, when man surrendered his moral and spiritual values for the pleasures of the flesh. The Bacchus would be the central figure of his theme, a human being rather than a demigod; then there would be a child of about seven, sweetfaced, lovable, nibbling from a bunch of grapes. His composition would have death in it too: the tiger, who liked wine and was loved by Bacchus, with the deadest, dead skin and head conceivable.

He went to the baths to look for models, thinking he might put together a composite Bacchus as he had his Hercules from hundreds of Tuscans: a throat here, a forearm there, a belly in the next place. But when after a few weeks he welded his features together with hard silver pen, his composite portrait was not convincing. He took himself to Leo Baglioni.

"I need a model. Young. Under thirty. Of a high family."

"And a beautiful body?"

"That once was, but is no longer. A figure that has been corrupted."

"By what?"

"Wine. Sensuousness. Self-indulgence."

Leo thought for a moment, flicking over in his mind the figures and features of the Roman youths he knew.

"I may know your man. The Count Ghinazzo. But he's wealthy, of a noble family. What can we offer him by way of inducement?"

"Flattery. That he is to be immortalized as the great Greek god Bacchus. Or Dionysus, if he prefers."

"That might work. He's idle, and can give you his days . . . or what's left of them after he awakens from his bacchanals of the night before."

The count was delighted with his new role. When he had walked through the orchard with Michelangelo, stripped off his clothes and taken the pose Michelangelo requested, he said:

"You know, it's a coincidence my being selected for this. I've always thought of myself as a kind of god."

Michelangelo went to his drawing board, sucked in his breath with pleasure. If he had searched all of Italy he could not have found a more fitting subject than Leo had selected for him: the head a bit too small for the body, the belly soft and fleshy, the buttocks too large for the torso, the upper arm a touch flaccid, the legs as straight and firmly molded as a Greek wrestler's. It was a figure desexed, the eyes unfocused from too much wine at dinner, the mouth dazedly half open; yet the arm that held the wine cup aloft flexed with muscular power, and over all a flawless satin-smooth skin glistened in the strong frontal sunlight that made him appear illumined from within.

"You're perfect!" Michelangelo cried impulsively. "Bacchus to the very life."

"Delighted you think so," said Count Ghinazzo without turning his head. "When Leo first proposed serving as a model I told him not to be a bore. But this may prove to be interesting."

"What time can I expect you tomorrow? And don't hesitate to bring your wine with you."

"That makes everything splendid. I can remain the entire afternoon. Without wine, the day is so dull."

"You will never appear dull to me, *messere*. I will see you in a new light every minute."

He cast the man in a hundred poses, his right leg bent sharply at the knee, toes barely touching the rough wooden base; the body slumped over on one leg, striving to stand up, the torso leaning backward; the small head thrust forward, turned one way and another, moving slightly, satiated with pleasure. And in the late afternoons, when Ghinazzo had drunk much wine, Michelangelo wound bunches of grapes through his hair, sketching him as though the grapes were growing there . . . which amused the Roman inordinately. Until one afternoon he drank too much of the wine, began to sway dizzily, fell off the wood block and hit his chin on the hard earth, knocking himself out. Michelangelo revived him by throwing a bucket of water over him. Count Ghinazzo shivered into his clothes, disappeared through the orchard and from Michelangelo's life.

Jacopo Galli found him a lively boy of seven, with curling golden hair and large tender eyes, a delightful lad with whom Michelangelo made friends as he sketched. His only problem was to get the boy to maintain the difficult pose of holding his left arm in a *contrapposto* position against his chest, so that he could crush the bunch of grapes in his mouth. Next he went into the countryside, spending a whole day drawing the legs, hoofs and curling fur of the goats cropping the hillsides.

That was how his pen finally designed his sculpture: in the center the weak, confused, arrogant, soon to be destroyed young man holding cup aloft, behind him the idyllic child, clear-eyed, munching his grapes, symbol of joy; between them the tiger skin. The Bacchus, hollow within himself, flabby, reeling, already old; the Satyr, eternally young and gay, symbol of man's childhood and naughty innocence.

Sunday morning he invited Galli to the workshop to show him his drawing: the bowl held high in Bacchus's hand, the intertwined grapes and leaves that made up his hair, the long, curving bunch of grapes that formed a structural bond between the Bacchus and the Satyr, the tree trunk on which the Bacchus leaned and the Satyr would be sitting, and lastly the tiger skin held in the Bacchus's falling hand, winding down through the Satyr's arm, its head hanging between the Satyr's open-stanced goat's hoofs, the hollow tiger head a picturization of what would happen to the Bacchus's head, ere long.

Galli asked countless questions. Michelangelo explained that he would do some wax or clay modeling, some carving on scrap marble to test the component parts, "the way the Satyr's head rests against the Bacchus's arm, for instance."

"And the way the boy's thigh melts into the furry leg of the Satyr."

"Exactly."

Galli was fascinated. "I don't know how to thank you."

Michelangelo laughed a little embarrassedly.

"There is one way. Could you send some florins to Florence?"

Galli hunched his huge shoulders over Michelangelo protectively. "Would you like our correspondent in Florence to deliver a few florins each month to your father, I mean regularly? Then you won't be distressed each time a packet of mail arrives. It will cost you no more that way; and we'll keep a record for you against the commission price."

". . . it isn't his fault, really," Michelangelo proffered, his pride hurt. "My uncle is ill, there are some debts . . ."

7

He lowered his column to a horizontal position on the ground, secured it on tightly wedged beams, then, using a point, bit into the corner where the wine cup would emerge. He concentrated on the frontal view, then started to join up the two sides to establish the visual flow. After heading for the high points of the fingers of the hand holding the cup, and the extended right kneecap, he struck in between to find the stomach, to establish the relationship between the highest projections and the deepest penetration. The intermediary forms would follow in natural sequence, as the forms of the side and back would take their cue from the front. He massed about the upper torso to indicate the reeling position of the upright figure, then turned the block over clockwise so that he could work on the width-plane, roughing out the cup-arm which was in the key position.

He summoned one of the Guffatti to help him set the column vertical again. Now the marble presented its personality: its size, proportion, weight. He sat in front of the block, studied it concentratedly, allowed it to speak, to establish its own demands. Now he felt fear, as though he were meeting an unknown person. To sculpture is to remove marble; it is also to probe, dig, sweat, think, feel and live with it until it is completed. Half the original weight of this block would remain in the finished statue; the rest would lie out in the orchard in chips and dust. His one regret was that he would sometimes have to eat and sleep, painful breaks when his work must stop.

The weeks and months of uninterrupted carving flowed by in a continuous stream. The winter was mild, he did not have to put back the roof of the shed; when the weather was sharp he wore his wool hat with its earmuffs, and a warm tunic. Thoughts, feelings, perceptions often came in a flash as the Bacchus and Satyr began to emerge, but to express these ideas in marble took days and weeks. Inside himself he had to grow as his sculpture grew and matured. The unfinished block haunted him at every hour of the night and day. It would be dangerous to release the bowl and the flexed knee in space; he would have to keep a webbing of marble between the outstretched bowl and forearm, between the knee and elbow, between the base and knee to give them support while he dug deeper. Now he was chiseling the side plane, the face and head, part of the neck and curls of grapes, now the depth of the left shoulder, thigh and calf. At the rear he evolved the Satyr, the stump he was sitting on, the grapes he was eating, the tiger cloth tying the two figures together. It was the most complicated piece he had yet attempted. He turned the Satyr's head, arms and grapes adroitly to the Bacchus's arm, yet ran out of marble.

His real battle began the moment a muscle became defined or a structural element began to emerge. Standing out from the rough blocking, he felt a thumping in his heart to shed away quickly the rest of the marble skin to reveal the human form below. The marble was tenacious; he was equally tenacious to achieve the delicate play of muscle under the fleshy stomach, the soft, claylike trunk of the tree, the spiral torsion of the Satyr, the grapes on the Bacchus's head which seemed to be part of the vine of his hair. Each completed detail brought peacefulness to all of the faculties he had used in its creation; not only to his eyes and mind and bosom, but to his shoulders, hips and groin.

When unable to formulate a detail he dropped his tools, walked outside and gazed up through the trees to the skies. When he returned he approached the marble from a distance, saw its contours and masses, felt its continuity. The detail became part of the whole. He grabbed his tools again and worked furiously: one two three four five six seven strokes; then one two three four of rest, every few cycles stepping back to see what he had accomplished. His feelings were always ahead of his physical capacity to carve. If only he could work the four sides of the block at once!

When he was releasing a rounded kneecap, the hairy leg and hoof of the Satyr, the tiger skin, he strove to pull out as much wholeness as possible in one "Go." Each day had to be fruitful, he had to find a handful of form for each session of carving before he could put aside his hammer and chisel. Upon awakening he was heavily charged with nervous energy and his hours were one long drive. He could not leave one finger of a hand in a more advanced state than the others, for he worked in units. Each day's work was a full unit. It was these small bundles of intense entities throughout his sculpture that characterized his potency as a sculptor.

Just before retiring he looked over his work, spotted what had to be done the next day. During the evening, when he wrote to his family, he proudly signed the letters:

Michelangelo, Sculptor in Rome.

Because he would take no time off for friends or rest or social life, Balducci accused him of trying to escape the world by fleeing into marble. He admitted to his friend that he was half right: the sculptor carries into the marble the vision of a more luminous world than the one that surrounds him. But the artist was not in flight; he was in pursuit. He was trying with all his might to overtake a vision. Did God really rest on the seventh day? In the cool of that long afternoon, when He was refreshed, might He not have asked Himself, "Whom have I on earth to speak for Me? I had best create another species, one apart. I will call him 'artist.' His will be the task to bring meaning and beauty to the world."

Nevertheless Balducci arrived faithfully every Sunday afternoon in the hope of seducing him out of the shed. He found for Michelangelo a girl so like Clarissa that Michelangelo was tempted. But the marble was exhausting. Between the two there could be no choice.

"When I have completed the Bacchus, I'll go out with you," he promised Balducci.

Balducci shook his head in despair.

"Just think of putting off the good things of life for so long. It's throwing time into the Tiber!"

Keyed up with his own fulfillment, Michelangelo threw back his head and laughed heartily with his friend.

His deepest emotional reaction came when breaking through a supporting web, noting the translucent quality of the marble where the breakthrough was to take place, aware that space would shortly be pouring through, the space that gave the limbs their freedom of movement, their independence, that permitted his forms to breathe air the moment his point felt no resistance.

His most delicate task was carving away the marble between the arm that held the lovely, ornamented wine cup and the side of the tilted head. He worked with infinite gentleness until he reached the sloping shoulder line. He did not yet feel secure enough to hammer away the web supporting the upheld arm and outstretched knee.

Balducci ragged him mercilessly.

"This is sheer prejudice. How come you didn't keep a column to hold up the poor fellow's privates? Suppose they fell off? That would be worse than his dropping that bowl you're so frightened of losing."

Michelangelo reached for a handful of marble dust and threw it at him.

"Have you never had a thought that didn't originate in the erogenous zone?"

"Does anyone?"

He finally acceded to Balducci's importuning that he watch some of the Roman spectacles, and went with him to Mount Testaccio to see Rome celebrate carnival before Lent. They stood on a hillside while four young pigs, combed and tied with ribbons by special barbers, were bound into beflagged carts. At a signal from the trumpeters the carts were rolled down the hill toward the Aventine, with the populace rushing after them, armed with knives, yelling, *"Al porco! Al porco!"* At the bottom of the hill the carts smashed, the people fell upon the animals, fighting each other to see who could slice off the best pieces of meat.

When Michelangelo returned to the house he found the French Cardinal Groslaye of San Dionigi there. Galli broke a self-imposed rule by asking if they might take the cardinal out to the workshop to see the Bacchus. Michelangelo could not refuse.

In the lamplighted shed Michelangelo explained that he was working all around the figure simultaneously, to keep the forms advancing in the same stage of development. He showed how, in order to open the space between the two legs, and between the left arm and torso, he worked the front and then the back of the block, continuously making the marble web thinner and thinner. As the Cardinal of San Dionigi watched, he picked up a point and demonstrated the extremely light tapping required for the breakthrough, then used an *ugnetto* to remove the rest of the web, freeing the limbs.

"But how do you achieve in a half-finished figure this sense of throbbing vitality? I can feel the blood and muscle under your marble skin. It is good to see new marble masters arising."

A few days later a servant brought a note to the workshed from Galli. *"Won't you join Groslaye and myself for supper tonight?"*

Michelangelo quit work at sundown, went to the baths close by, steamed the marble dust out of his pores, put on a fresh shirt and hose, brushed his hair forward over his brow. Signora Galli served a light supper, for the cardinal still followed the disciplines of his early years, ate no meat, and touched all foods sparingly. His fading eyes gleamed in the candlelight as he turned to Michelangelo.

"You know, my son, I am growing old. I must leave something behind me, something of singular beauty to add to the beauties of Rome. A tribute from France, from Charles VIII and my humble self. I have secured permission from the Pope to dedicate a sculpture in the Chapel of the Kings of France in St. Peter's. There is a niche that will take a life-size sculpture."

Michelangelo had not touched any of Galli's excellent Trebbiano wine, but he felt as though he had drunk more than Count Ghinazzo on a warm afternoon. A sculpture for St. Peter's, the oldest and most sacred basilica in Christendom, built over the tomb of St. Peter! Could it be possible that the French cardinal would choose him? But from what? The little Cupid? The still nascent Bacchus in his workshed?

By the time he brought his senses back to the table, the conversation had changed. The cardinal was telling Jacopo Galli of the writings of two unorthodox post-Nicene Fathers. Then the cardinal's carriage came for him. He bade Michelangelo a pleasant good night.

That Sunday Michelangelo went to mass in St. Peter's to see the Chapel of the Kings of France and the niche about which the Cardinal of San Dionigi had talked. He climbed the thirty-five stairs of marble and porphyry leading up to the basilica, crossed the atrium, passed the center fountain surrounded by porphyry columns and stood at the base of the Carlovingian bell tower, aghast at the dilapidated condition of St. Peter's, which was leaning sharply to the left. Inside he found the Chapel of the Kings of France to be of modest size, dark, the main light coming from small windows up near the roof, the only ornamentation some sarcophagi borrowed from pagan and early Christian tombs, and a wooden crucifix in a niche on the side. He measured with his eye the vacant niche on the opposite wall, disappointed to find it so deep that a statue would be seen only from the front.

It was seven days before Galli brought up the subject again.

"You know, Michelangelo, this commission of the Cardinal of San Dionigi's could be the most important since Pollaiuolo was assigned to do a tomb for Sixtus IV."

Michelangelo's heart began to pound. "What are my chances?"

Galli counted on his long supple fingers as on an abacus that reckoned artistic probability.

"First, I must convince the cardinal that you are the best sculptor in Rome. Second, you must conceive a theme that will inspire him. Third, we must secure a signed contract."

"It would have to be a spiritual theme?"

"Not because Groslaye is a member of the Church, but because he is a deeply spiritual man. He has lived in Rome for three years in such a state of grace that he literally has not seen and does not know that Rome is rotten at its core."

"Is it innocence? Or blindness?"

"Could we say that it is faith? If a man is as pure in heart as the Cardinal of San Dionigi, he walks with God's hand on his shoulder; he sees beyond present evil to the Church Eternal."

"Can I create a marble that would have the hand of God on it?"

Galli shook his leonine head.

"That is a problem you must wrestle with yourself."

To carve decay all day, and at the same time conceive a devout theme, seemed an impossible undertaking. Yet he knew very soon that his theme would be a Pietà: Pity, Sorrow. He had wanted to do a Pietà ever since he had completed his Madonna and Child: for just as the Madonna and Child was the beginning, the Pietà was the end, the preordained conclusion of everything that Mary had decided in that fateful hour God had allotted to her. Now, thirty-three years later, her son was again on her lap, having completed his journey.

Galli was intrigued with his thinking, took him to the Cardinal of San Dionigi's palace, where they waited for the cardinal to complete the five daily hours of prayer and offices required of every Benedictine. The three men sat in the open loggia, facing the Via Recta, with a painted Annunciation behind them. The cardinal was ashen after his long devotions. Michelangelo's practiced eye could perceive almost no body lines beneath his robe. But when the cardinal heard about the Pietà his eyes sparkled.

"What about the marble, Michelangelo? Could you find such a perfect piece as you speak of, here in Rome?"

"I think not, Your Grace. A column, yes; but an oblong block that is wider than it is tall, and cut deep, that I have not seen."

"Then we must turn to Carrara. I shall write to the brothers in Lucca, asking for aid. If they cannot find what we need you must go yourself to the quarries and find our marble."

Michelangelo bounded out of his chair.

"Did you know, Father, that the higher one quarries the purer white the marble becomes? No earth stains, no pressure to make holes or hollows. If we could quarry at the peak of Monte Sagro, there we would find the supreme block."

On the way home Galli said, "You must go to Carrara at once. I will advance the expenses for your trip."

"I can't."

"Why not?"

"I must finish the Bacchus," he replied.

"The Bacchus can wait. The cardinal can't. One day soon God will rest His hand just a trifle more heavily on his shoulder, and Groslaye will go to heaven. From heaven he cannot commission a Pietà."

"That is true. But I cannot stop work now," Michelangelo insisted stubbornly.

"I release you from our agreement. When you have finished the Pietà you will come back to the Bacchus."

"For me there is no coming back. The sculpture is growing complete in my mind. I must finish it now to get it perfect."

"I'm always amazed to find a romantic in affairs of practical business." Galli sighed. "I shan't burden the cardinal with the details of your orthodoxy."

"Until the Bacchus is completed the Pietà cannot begin. I behave virtuously because I must."

8

He removed the short column between the base and the heel of the Bacchus, and the right foot which was half suspended in the air, poised on its toes. Then he raised his drill to release the web between the elbow and the cup, drilling a series of holes close to the arm, delicately filing away the remaining marble. Finally he cut away the right-hand corner under the cup, to free the hand and cup now extending high into space. The Satyr in the lower left-hand corner and the cup at the upper right completed each other. His whole figure in the round was balanced superbly. He walked about it, satisfaction in his face and shoulders as his eye reviewed the line from the thrust of the right knee to the tip of the opposite shoulder; the tension from the edge of the bowl through the crotch to the corner of the Satyr's hoof.

The emphasis of his figure was in its weight masses. In the head projecting forward, the hard torso projecting outward, then flowing into the stomach, which pulled the whole body downward toward the loins. In the rear the too heavy buttocks served as a steadying weight, the balance held by the beautiful legs, though not too securely because the body was reeling; the left foot planted solidly, the right on tiptoe increased the sense of vertigo.

"You're like an engineer," said Galli when he saw it, his expression rapt as he traced Michelangelo's design.

"That's what I told Bertoldo a sculptor had to be."

"In the days of the emperors you would have been designing colosseums, baths and reservoirs. Instead, you've created a soul."

Michelangelo's eyes glowed yellow at the compliment.

"No soul, no sculpture."

"Many of my ancient pieces were found broken in several places, yet when we put them together their spirit persisted."

"That was the sculptor still alive in the marble."

The following Sunday he went to dine with the Rucellai, eager to hear news of Florence. Savonarola was at the heart of most of the happenings. The Florentine colony had been delighted with him for defying the Pope, for advising the Borgia that unjust excommunications were invalid, and for celebrating three forbidden masses in San Marco at Christmas. Savonarola had then written to kings, statesmen and churchmen all over Europe urging that a council be called to purge the Borgia, and to institute sweeping reforms that would rid the Church of simony, the purchase not only of cardinalates but of the papacy itself. On February 11, 1498, he had again preached in the Duomo against the Pope, and two weeks later had walked outside the cathedral with the host in his hand, before thousands of Florentines packed into the piazza, and beseeched God to strike him dead if he deserved excommunication. When God refrained, Savonarola celebrated his vindication by ordering another Burning of the Vanities. Florence was once again looted by the Army of Boys.

Savonarola's letters calling for a reformation were circulated secretly by the Florentines in Rome, to whom he had become an idol. When Michelangelo described to them the Burning of the Vanities that he had witnessed, the hundreds of irreplaceable manuscripts, books, paintings, sculptures that had been destroyed, they were not distressed.

"Any price is cheap in a famine," cried Cavalcanti. "We must destroy the Borgia at any cost."

Michelangelo was thoughtful.

"What will you think of this price in a few years when the Pope and Botticelli are both dead? There will be another Pope, but there can never be another Botticelli. All the works he threw on that fire are gone forever. It seems to me you are approving lawlessness in Florence to rid yourselves of lawlessness here in Rome."

If he could not touch them with his reasoning, the Pope touched them where it hurt: he promised to confiscate all business properties of the Florentines and to turn them out of the city penniless unless the Signoria of Florence sent Savonarola to Rome to stand trial. From what Michelangelo could gather, the colony made a complete capitulation: Savonarola had to be silenced; he had to honor his excommunication, to seek absolution from the Pope. They petitioned the Signoria to act in their behalf and to send Savonarola under guard to Rome. All the Pope asked, they explained, was that Savonarola come to Rome and receive absolution. Then he could return to Florence to save souls.

Before the end of March a rumor spread through Rome that sent Michelangelo racing to the Ponte: Savonarola's second in command, Fra Domenico, had committed himself to an ordeal by fire. The colony assembled at the home of the patriarch, Cavalcanti. When Michelangelo entered the house he was plunged into a hubbub that tumbled down the stairs from the drawing room.

"What does it mean, ordeal by fire?" he asked. "Is it what Savonarola tried before carnival, asking to be struck dead if his words were not inspired by God?"

"Similar. Except that fire burns."

This last development had been originated either by Fra Domenico himself or by the Dominicans' enemy in the struggle for power, the Franciscans, led by Francesco di Puglia. In a fiery sermon in defense of their leader, Fra Domenico had declared that he would enter fire to prove that everything Savonarola taught was inspired by God; and he challenged a Franciscan to enter with him. The next day Fra Francesco di Puglia accepted the challenge, but insisted that Savonarola himself must enter the fire, saying that only if Savonarola came through the fire alive could Florence believe him to be a true prophet. Meeting for supper at the Pitti palace, a young group of *Arrabbiati* assured Fra Francesco and the Franciscans that Savonarola would never accept; that by his refusal he would prove to Florence that he had no true faith in God's saving him.

At this point the voters of Florence turned against Savonarola politically. They had already endured seven years of wrangling, the Pope's threat to put an interdict on the entire population, which amounted to an excommunication that could paralyze trade and cause bitter turmoil. The city needed a three per cent tax on church property which the Pope now agreed to allow, once Savonarola was quieted. They defeated the Signoria pledged to Savonarola and elected a new Council which was against him. Florence was threatened with another Guelph and Ghibelline-like civil war.

On April 7 a platform was erected in the Piazza della Signoria, the logs smeared with pitch. A vast crowd assembled to watch the show. The Franciscans refused to enter the piazza until Fra Domenico agreed not to take the host into the fire. After a number of hours of waiting, a fierce winter rainstorm drenched the platform, scattering the crowd and putting an end to any burning.

The following night the *Arrabbiati* mobbed the monastery of San Marco, killing a number of Savonarola's followers. The Signoria moved in, arrested Savonarola, Fra Domenico and Fra Silvestro, the third in command, and jailed them in the bell tower of the Palazzo della Signoria. The Pope sent a courier to Florence demanding that Savonarola be deliverd to him in Rome. The Signoria refused, but appointed a Commission of Seventeen to examine Savonarola and secure a confession that his words were not divinely inspired.

Savonarola refused to recant. The commission tortured him; first using the rack and the screw, then roping him to a pulley, raising him in the air, dropping him with a sudden jerk of the rope. Savonarola became delirious, agreed to write a confession. He was released to his cell. What he wrote was not satisfactory to the Signoria. He was tortured again. Weak from fasting and all-night prayers, Savonarola again succumbed, signed a confession written by a notary; but not before he rejected the paper and had to be tortured a third time.

The commission declared Savonarola guilty of heresy. The special advisory council called by the Signoria sentenced him to death. At the same time the Pope granted the city its long-desired three per cent tax on all church property in Tuscany.

Three platforms were built from the steps of the Palazzo della Signoria into the square. The throng began filling the piazza during the night, pushing up against the gibbet. By dawn the square and all the streets leading into it were a seething mass.

Savonarola, Fra Domenico and Fra Silvestro were led out onto the Signoria steps, stripped of their vestments, their tonsures scraped. They mounted the scaffold, praying silently. They climbed a steep ladder to the top of the gibbet. Ropes and chains were put about their necks. Within an instant, all three were dangling, their necks broken.

The pyre under the gibbet was lighted. The flames rose. The three bodies were held aloft by the chains after the ropes had burned. The *Arrabbiati* stoned the half-consumed corpses. The ashes were collected, carried in carts to the Old Bridge, and dumped into the Arno.

The martyrdom of Savonarola shook Michelangelo profoundly. He had sat as a boy and listened to Pico della Mirandola recommend to Lorenzo that the friar be invited to Florence. Savonarola had contributed to the deaths of Lorenzo, Pico, Poliziano, and now he too was dead. He hardly knew what to think or feel: except pity.

He turned to his work. Marble was dependable in a chaotic world. It had its own will and intelligence and stability. With marble in his hands, the world was good.

He became impatient to be finished with the Bacchus. He had only indicated the position of the forehead, nose, mouth, wanting to let the rest of the figure suggest the expression on the face. Now he completed the features, the expression dazed as the Bacchus stared at the cup of wine; the eyes bulging, the mouth opened greedily. For the grapes he used a drill, making each one round and juice-laden. To achieve the hair on the Satyr's goat legs he sliced the rough-edged marble with a fully rounded chisel which brought out the rhythmic play of curls, each tuft designed separately.

There was left two months of polishing to get the glowing flesh effects he wanted. Though this work involved infinite care and precision, it was technical in nature and used only that part of him which was the craftsman. It left his mind free during the warm spring hours to reflect on the Pietà and its meaning. In the cool of the evenings he began searching for this last moment that mother and son would spend together.

He asked Jacopo Galli if he could now complete a contract with the Cardinal of San Dionigi. Galli explained that the cardinal's monastery in Lucca had already ordered a block to Michelangelo's dimensions. The block had been cut, but the quarry at Carrara had refused to ship it to Rome before being paid. The monastery at Lucca had in turn refused to pay until the cardinal approved the block. The quarry had grown tired of holding it and had sold it to a buying agent.

That night Michelangelo wrote an agreement which he thought would be fair to himself and to the Cardinal of San Dionigi. Galli read it without expression, said he would take it to his bank and put it in a safe place.

By the end of summer the Bacchus was finished. Galli was overjoyed with his statue.

"I feel as though Bacchus is fully alive, and will drop his cup at any moment. The Satyr is innocent and naughty at the same time. You have made for me the finest sculpture in all Italy. We must place it in the garden and give it a party."

The blind Augustinians, Aurelius and Raffaelle Lippus, studied the Bacchus with their sensitive fingers, running them over every detail and saying they had never "seen" a male figure so powerful in projecting its inner life force. Professor Pomponius Laetus, who had been tortured by the Inquisition for paganism, was moved to tears, avowing that the statue was pure Greek in its structure and its gleaming white satiny finish. Serafino, the poet from Lucrezia Borgia's court, hated it on sight, declaring it "ugly, wanton, without any sense of loveliness." Sannazaro, the poet who mixed Christian and pagan images in his verses, declared it "a complete synthesis, Greek in carving, Christian in emotion, combining the best of both," even as the Plato Four had commented on his Madonna and Child. Peter Sabinus, professor of Eloquence at the university, collector of Christian inscriptions, and his friend Giovanni Capocci, who was excavating the catacombs, came back three times to debate the statue's virtues between themselves, finally concluding that, although they did not care for antique themes, this Bacchus was something new in the art of sculpture.

It was Giuliano da Sangallo's opinion Michelangelo valued most. Sangallo gleefully traced the intricate structural design. "You've built this Bacchus the way we build a temple or a palace. It was a dangerous, and courageous, experiment in construction. You could easily have suffered a collapse of material. This fellow will stand erect as long as there is space for him to displace."

The following night Galli brought home a contract he himself had written between Michelangelo and the Cardinal of San Dionigi, and which the cardinal had signed. In it Michelangelo found himself called *maestro* for the first time; but he was also described as *statuario*, statue maker, which was deflating. For the sum of four hundred and fifty ducats in papal gold he agreed to make a Pietà of marble, one hundred and fifty ducats to be paid as he began, and a hundred ducats every fourth month. By the end of a year the statue was to be completed. In addition to guaranteeing the cardinal's payments to Michelangelo, Galli had written:

I, Jacopo Galli, do promise that the work will be more beautiful than any work in marble to be seen in Rome today, and such that no master of our time will be able to produce a better.

Michelangelo gazed at Galli with affection.

"You must have written this contract at home, rather than the bank."

"Why?"

"Because you have taken quite a gamble. Suppose when I finish the cardinal says, 'I have seen better marbles in Rome.' What happens then?"

"I give His Grace back his papal ducats."

"And you are stuck with the carving!"

Galli's eyes twinkled. "I could endure it."

He went searching the stoneyards of Trastevere and the ports for the kind of block he needed; but a seven-foot-wide, six-foot-tall, three-foot-deep cut of marble was rarely quarried on the chance of sale. It took him only two days to complete the rounds; there was nothing even faintly resembling the massive block he needed. The next day, when he had decided that he would have to go to Carrara at his own expense, Guffatti came running up the rear alley to his workshed, crying out:

". . . just unloaded a barge . . . the very size you're looking for. It was cut for some order in Lucca. The quarry never got paid, so they sold it."

He dog-trotted down to the Ripetta dock. There it stood, gleaming pure and white in the summer sun, beautifully cut by the quarrymen high in the mountains of Carrara. It tested out perfect against the hammer, against water, its crystals soft and compacted with fine graining. He came back before dawn the next morning, watched the rays of the rising sun strike the block and make it as transparent as pink alabaster, with not a hole or hollow or crack or knot to be seen in all its massive white weight.

His Pietà block had come home.

9

He removed the last reminders of the Bacchus, settled down to the Pietà. But the Bacchus had become a controversial figure. Many people came to see it. Galli brought the visitors to the workshop or sent a servant to the shed to ask if Michelangelo would mind coming to the garden. He found himself plunged into explanations and defenses, particularly from the Bregno enthusiasts, who attacked it as "a perversion of the Dionysus legend." When there were admirers he found himself involved in describing his concept and technique. Galli wanted him for supper every night now, and Sundays, so that he could make as many friends as possible, open the way to more commissions.

The Rucellai, Cavalcanti, Altoviti were proud of him. They gave parties in his honor, from which he awoke the next morning feeling tired. He yearned to put the Bacchus behind him, to wipe the slate of his mind clean of the pagan carving and make the transition to the spirituality he needed to think about the Pietà. After a month of festivities it became clear that he was not going to be able to conceive or carve a Pietà under these diverting conditions; that with his emergence as a professional sculptor had come the time to establish his own quarters and workshop where he could live quietly, secluded, work night and day if he wished, dedicate himself to abstemiousness. He had grown up, he was on his own. He could see no other way.

Perceptive Jacopo Galli asked, "Something is troubling you, Michelangelo?"

"Yes."

"It sounds serious."

"Just ungrateful."

"You owe me nothing."

"The men to whom I owe the most have all said that: Lorenzo de' Medici, Bertoldo, Aldovrandi, and now you."

"Tell me what you want to do."

"To move out!" he blurted. "Life with the Galli family is too pleasant. . . ." He paused. "I feel the need to work in my own household. As a man, rather than a boy, and perennial guest. Does this sound foolish?"

Galli gazed at him wistfully. "I want only that you be happy, and that you carve the most beautiful marbles in Italy."

"For me they are one and the same."

He was directed to several houses in which the ground floor was available, one recommended by Altoviti in the Florentine quarter, another near the Piazza del Quirinale, with a fine view of Rome. They were too elaborate and expensive. On the third day, on the Via Sistina, across from the Bear Inn and on the edge of the Campo Marzio lying below the embankment of the Tiber, he found a big corner room with two windows, one facing north for steady light, the other east for the sharp sunlight he sometimes needed. At the rear was a smaller room with a fireplace. He paid a few scudi for two months' rent, drew up the oiled linen on wooden frames that served as window covering, and studied the shabby space: the wooden floor, thin in spots, broken in others, cement crumbling between the stones of the walls, the ceiling plaster falling in patches, exposing variegated colors of decay where the rain had leaked through. He put the key in his pocket and returned to the Galli's.

He found Buonarroto waiting for him. His brother was jubilant. He had come as a guard on a mule train, and so the trip had cost him nothing. He was going back the same way. Michelangelo gazed with pleasure at the stubby features, the hair combed over Buonarroto's brow in imitation of his own. It had been a year since they had seen each other.

"You couldn't have come at a better time," he cried. "I need help in setting up my new home."

"You have taken a place? Good, then I can stay with you."

"Wait till you see my palatial quarters before you settle in," said Michelangelo, smiling. "Come with me to Trastevere, I need a supply of plaster, whitewash and lye. But first I will show you my Bacchus."

Buonarroto stood gazing at the statue a long time. Then he asked: "Did people like it?"

"Most did."

"I'm glad."

That was all. Michelangelo observed to himself, "He doesn't have the faintest notion of what sculpture is about. His only interest is that people approve what I've done, so that I can be happy, and get more work . . . none of which he will ever understand. He's a true Buonarroti, blind to the meaning of art. But he loves me."

They bought the supplies, had dinner at the Trattoria Toscana, then Michelangelo took his brother to the Via Sistina. When Buonarroto entered the room he whistled sharply.

"Michelangelo, surely you're not thinking of living in this . . . this hole? The place is falling apart."

"You and I are going to put it back together," replied Michelangelo grimly. "It is adequate work space."

"Father would be distressed."

Michelangelo smiled. "Don't tell him." He set a tall ladder in the center of the room. "Let's scrape this ceiling."

When they had scraped and given the ceiling a coat of plaster, they began on the walls, then set to work patching the broken floor with odd-sized pieces of wood. Next they turned their attention to the private courtyard. The only door to it was from the side of his room, but the other tenants had access from their windows, as a result of which it was covered with a thick compost of garbage and debris. The odor was as thick as the enclosing walls. It took two days to shovel the refuse into sacks and carry it through his own room to a vacant lot below the Tiber.

Balducci, who held all physical labor in abhorrence, showed up after Michelangelo and Buonarroto had finished their repairs. He knew a second-hand furniture dealer in Trastevere, where he bargained shrilly for the best prices on a bed, rope mattress, kitchen table, two cane chairs, chest of drawers, a few pots, dishes and knives. When the donkey cart arrived a few hours later, the brothers set up the bed under the window to the east, where Michelangelo would be waked at first light. The chest of drawers went on the back wall, next to the opening to the kitchen. Under the front north window he placed a table of four planks on horses, for his drawing, wax and clay modeling. The center of the big room he kept clear for his marble. In the rear cubicle they installed the kitchen table, two chairs, pots and dishes.

Balducci returned, having explored the neighborhood.

"There's a plump little partridge lives just behind your rooms: blond, about fifteen, beautifully made, French, I think. I could persuade her to become your servant. Think how pleasant it would be to finish work at noon and find her in your kitchen over a pot of hot soup." Balducci did a little dance. ". . . and at night, to find her in your bed. It's part of their job; and you're going to need a little natural warmth in this cave."

Michelangelo and Buonarroto chuckled at Balducci's ebullience. In another minute he would be out the front door and down the street after the girl.

"Look, Balducci," cried Michelangelo. "I want no entanglements, and have no money for a servant. If I need anyone, I'll stick to the artist's custom of taking in a young apprentice and training him in return for services."

Buonarroto agreed. "I'll keep my eyes open in Florence for a bright young lad."

Buonarroto settled Michelangelo in, shopped and cooked the food, cleaned the rooms. The housekeeping went downhill the moment he left. Immersed in his work, Michelangelo took no time off to cook, to go out to a restaurant or eat in the streets. He lost weight, even as his rooms lost their tidy appearance. He saw nothing about him but his workbench and the huge white block sitting on beams in the center of the floor. He never bothered to make his bed or to wash the dishes he left on the kitchen table. The rooms became covered with dust from the street, ashes from the kitchen fire where he boiled water for an occasional hot drink. He knew by the end of a month that this system was not going to work. He even began to eye Balducci's little French girl, who passed his door more frequently than he thought strictly necessary.

Buonarroto solved his problem. Michelangelo answered to a knock late one afternoon to see standing in the street a plain-faced, olive-complected lad of about thirteen, travel-stained, holding out a letter on which Michelangelo recognized his brother's handwriting. The note introduced Piero Argiento, who had come to Florence looking for a sculptor to whom he could be apprenticed. He had been sent by someone to the Buonarroti house, then made the long trip on foot to Rome.

Michelangelo invited him in, studied the boy while he told of his family and their farm near Ferrara. His manner was quiet, his voice plain.

"Can you read and write, Argiento?"

"The Ingesuati fathers in Ferrara taught me to write. Now I need to learn a trade."

"And you think sculpture might be a good one?"

"I want a three-year apprenticeship. With a Guild contract."

Michelangelo was impressed by the forthrightness. He gazed into the muddy brown eyes of the stringy lad before him, at the soiled shirt, wornout sandals, the thin, hungry cheeks.

"You have no friends in Rome? No place to go?"

"I came to see you." Stubbornly.

"I live simply, Argiento. You can expect no luxury."

"I am of *contadini*. What is to eat, we eat."

"Since you need a home, and I need a helper, suppose we try it for a few days? If it doesn't work out, we part as friends. I'll pay your way back to Florence."

"Agreed. *Grazie*."

"Take this coin, and go to the baths near Santa Maria dell'Anima. On the way back, stop at the market for food to cook."

"I make a good soup-of-the-country. My mother taught me before she died."

The fathers had taught Argiento not only to count but also to be doggedly honest. He left the house before dawn for the markets, carrying with him a scrap of crayon and paper. Michelangelo was touched by the way he painfully kept his accounts written down: so many denari for vegetables, so many for meat, for fruit, for bread and *pasta*, with every coin accounted for. Michelangelo put a modest amount in a cooking pot as their weekly allowance. Argiento was a relentless pursuer of bargains. Within a week he knew every stall selling produce. His shopping took him the better part of the morning, which suited Michelangelo because it gave him the solitariness he sought.

They established a simple routine. After their one-dish midday dinner, Argiento cleaned the rooms while Michelangelo took an hour's walk along the Tiber to the docks to listen to the Sicilians sing as they unloaded the boats. By the time he returned home Argiento was taking his *riposo* on the truckle bed in the kitchen under the wooden sink. Michelangelo had two more hours of quiet at his workbench before Argiento woke, washed his face noisily in the basin, and came to the worktable for his daily instruction. These few hours in the afternoon appeared to be all the teaching Argiento wanted. At dusk he was back in the kitchen, boiling water. By the time dark settled in he was asleep on his truckle bed, a blanket drawn securely over his head. Michelangelo then lit his oil lamps and returned to his workbench. He was grateful to Buonarroto for sending Argiento to him; the arrangement looked as though it would be satisfactory, despite the fact that Argiento showed not a shred of talent for drawing. Later, when he began working the marble, he would teach the boy how to use a hammer and chisel.

In the Bible he read from John 19:38–40:

After this Joseph of Arimathea, who was a disciple of Jesus . . . asked Pilate to let him take away the body of Jesus . . . so he came and took Jesus's body away; and with him was Nicodemus . . . he brought with him a mixture of myrrh and aloes, of about a hundred pounds' weight. They took Jesus's body, then, and wrapped it in winding-clothes with the spices; that is how the Jews prepare a body for burial.

Listed as present at the Descent were Mary, Mary's sister, Mary Magdalene, John, Joseph of Arimathea, Nicodemus. Search as he might, he could find no place where the Bible spoke of a moment when Mary could have been alone with Jesus. Mostly the scene was crowded with mourners, such as the dramatic Dell'Arca Lamentation in Bologna, where the grief-stricken spectators had usurped Mary's last poignant moment.

In his concept there could be no one else present.

His first desire was to create a mother and son alone in the universe. When might Mary have had that moment to hold her child on her lap? Perhaps after the soldiers had laid him on the ground, while Joseph of Arimathea was at Pontius Pilate's asking for Christ's body, Nicodemus was gathering his mixture of myrrh and aloes, and the others had gone home to mourn. Those who saw his finished Pietà would take the place of the biblical witnesses. They would feel what Mary was undergoing. There would be no halos, no angels. There would be two human beings, whom God had chosen.

He felt close to Mary, having spent so long concentrating on the beginning of her journey. Now she was intensely alive, anguished; her son was dead. Even though he would later be resurrected, he was at this moment dead indeed, the expression on his face reflecting what he had gone through on the cross. In his sculpture therefore it would not be possible for him to project anything of what Jesus felt for his mother; only what Mary felt for her son. Jesus's inert body would be passive, his eyes closed. Mary would have to carry the human communication. This seemed right to him.

It was a relief to shift in his mind to technical problems. Since his Christ was to be life size, how was Mary to hold him on her lap without the relationship seeming ungainly? His Mary would be slender of limb and delicate of proportion, yet she must hold this full-grown man as securely and convincingly as she would a child.

There was only one way to accomplish this: by design, by drawing diagrams and sketches in which he probed the remotest corner of his mind for creative ideas to carry his concept.

He started by making free sketches to loosen up his thinking so that images would appear on paper. Visually, these approximated what he was feeling within himself. At the same time he started walking the streets, peering at the people passing or shopping at the stalls, storing up fresh impressions of what they looked like, how they moved. In particular he sought the gentle, sweet-faced nuns, with head coverings and veils coming to the middle of their foreheads, remembering their expressions until he reached home and set them down on paper.

Discovering that draperies could be designed to serve structural purposes, he began a study of the anatomy of folds. He improvised as he went along, completing a life-size clay figure, then bought yards of an inexpensive material from a draper, wet the lightweight cloth in a basin and covered it over with clay that Argiento brought from the bank of the Tiber, to the consistency of thick mud. No fold could be accidental, each turn of the drapery had to serve organically, to cover the Madonna's slender legs and feet so that they would give substantive support to Christ's body, to intensify her inner turmoil. When the cloth dried and stiffened, he saw what adjustments had to be made.

"So that's sculpture," commented Argiento wryly, when he had sluiced down the floor for a week, "making mud pies."

Michelangelo grinned. "See, Argiento, if you control the way these folds are bunched, like this, or made to flow, you can enrich the body attitudes. They can have as much tactile appeal as flesh and bone."

He went into the Jewish quarter, wanting to draw Hebraic faces so that he could reach a visual understanding of how Christ might have looked. The Jewish section was in Trastevere, near the Tiber at the church of San Francesco a Ripa. The colony had been small until the Spanish Inquisition of 1492 drove many Jews into Rome. Here, for the most part, they were well treated, as a "reminder of the Old Testament heritage of Christianity"; many of their gifted members were prominent in the Vatican as physicians, musicians, bankers.

The men did not object to his sketching them while they went about their work, but no one could be persuaded to come to his studio to pose. He was told to ask for Rabbi Melzi at the synagogue on Saturday afternoon. Michelangelo found the rabbi in the room of study, a gentle old man with a white beard and luminous gray eyes, robed in black gabardine with a skullcap on his head. He was reading from the Talmud with a group of men from his congregation. When Michelangelo explained why he had come, Rabbi Melzi replied gravely:

"The Bible forbids us to bow down to or to make graven images. That is why our creative people give their time to literature, not to painting or sculpture."

"But, Rabbi Melzi, you don't object to others creating works of art?"

"Not at all. Each religion has its own tenets."

"I am carving a Pietà from white Carrara marble. I wish to make Jesus an authentic Jew. I cannot accomplish this if you will not help me."

The rabbi said thoughtfully, "I would not want my people to get in trouble with the Church."

"I am working for the Cardinal of San Dionigi. I'm sure he would approve."

"What kind of models would you prefer?"

"Workmen. In their mid-thirties. Not bulky laborers, but sinewy men. With intelligence. And sensitivity."

Rabbi Melzi smiled at him with infinitely old but merry eyes.

"Leave me your address. I will sent you the best the quarter has to offer."

Michelangelo hurried to Sangallo's solitary bachelor room with his sketches, asked the architect to design a stand which would simulate the seated Madonna. Sangallo studied the drawings and improvised a trestle couch. Michelangelo bought some scrap lumber. Together he and Argiento built the stand, covering it with blankets.

His first model arrived at dusk. He hesitated for a moment when Michelangelo asked him to disrobe, so Michelangelo gave him a piece of toweling to wrap around his loins, led him to the kitchen to take off his clothes. He then draped him over the rough stand, explained that he was supposed to be recently dead, and was being held on his mother's lap. The model quite plainly thought Michelangelo crazy; only the instructions from his rabbi kept him from bolting. But at the end of the sitting, when Michelangelo showed him the quick, free drawings, with the mother roughed in, holding her son, the model grasped what Michelangelo was after, and promised to speak to his friends. . . . He worked for two hours a day with each model sent by the rabbi.

Mary presented quite a different problem. Though this sculpture must take place thirty-three years after her moment of decision, he could not conceive of her as a woman in her mid-fifties, old, wrinkled, broken in body and face by labor or worry. His image of the Virgin had always been that of a young woman, even as had his memory of his mother.

Jacopo Galli introduced him into several Roman homes. Here he sketched, sitting in their flowing gowns of linen and silk, young girls not yet twenty, some about to be married, some married a year or two. Since the Santo Spirito hospital had taken only men, he had had no experience in the study of female anatomy; but he had sketched the women of Tuscany in their fields and homes. He was able to discern the body lines of the Roman women under their robes.

He spent concentrated weeks putting his two figures together: a Mary who would be young and sensitive, yet strong enough to hold her son on her lap; and a Jesus who, though lean, was strong even in death . . . a look he remembered well from his experience in the dead room of Santo Spirito. He drew toward the composite design from his meticulously accurate memory, without need to consult his sketches.

Soon he was ready to go into a three-dimensional figure in clay. Here he would have free expression because the material could be moved to distort forms. When he wanted to emphasize, or get greater intensity, he added or subtracted clay. Next he turned to wax because there was a similarity of wax to marble in tactile quality and translucence. He respected each of these approach techniques, and kept them in character: his quill drawings had a scratchiness, suggesting skin texture; the clay he used plastically to suggest soft moving flesh, as in an abdomen, in a reclining torso; the wax he smoothed over to give the body surface an elastic pull. Yet he never allowed these models to become fixed in his mind; they remained rough starting points. When carving he was charged with spontaneous energy; too careful or detailed studies in clay and wax would have glued him down to a mere enlarging of his model.

The true surge had to be inside the marble itself. Drawing and models were his thinking. Carving was action.

10

The arrangement with Argiento was working well, except that sometimes Michelangelo could not figure who was master and who apprentice. Argiento had been trained so rigorously by the Ingesuati that Michelangelo was unable to change his habits: up before dawn to scrub the floors, whether they were dirty or not; water boiling on the fire for washing laundry every day, the pots scoured with river sand after each meal.

"Argiento, this is senseless," he complained, not liking to work on the wet floors, particularly in cold weather. "You're too clean. Scrub the studio once a week. That's enough."

"No," said Argiento stolidly. "Every day. Before dawn. I was taught."

"And God help anyone who tries to unteach you!" grumbled Michelangelo; yet he knew that he had nothing to grumble about, for Argiento made few demands on him. The boy was becoming acquainted with the *contadini* families that brought produce into Rome. On Sundays he would walk miles into the *campagna* to visit with them, and in particular to see their horses. The one thing he missed from his farm in the Po Valley was the animals; frequently he would take his leave of Michelangelo by announcing:

"Today I go see the horses."

It took a piece of bad luck to show Michelangelo that the boy was devoted to him. He was crouched over his anvil in the courtyard getting his chisels into trim, when a splinter of steel flew into his eye and imbedded itself in his pupil. He stumbled into the house, eyes burning like fire. Argiento made him lie down on the bed, brought a pan of hot water, dipped some clean white linen cloth and applied it to extract the splinter. Though the pain was considerable Michelangelo was not too concerned. He assumed he could blink the splinter out. But it would not come. Argiento never left his side, keeping the water boiled, applying hot compresses throughout the night.

By the second day Michelangelo began to worry; and by the second night he was in a state of panic: he could see nothing out of the afflicted eye. At dawn Argiento went to Jacopo Galli. Galli arrived with his family surgeon, Maestro Lippi. The surgeon carried a cage of live pigeons. He told Argiento to take a bird out of the cage, cut a large vein under its wing, let the blood gush into Michelangelo's injured eye.

The surgeon came back at dusk, cut the vein of a second pigeon, again washed out the eye. All the next day Michelangelo could feel the splinter moving, pushing. By nightfall it was out.

Argiento had not slept for some seventy hours.

"You're tired," said Michelangelo. "Why don't you take a few days off?"

Argiento's stubborn features lit up with pleasure. "I go visit the horses."

At first Michelangelo had been bothered by the people going in and out of the Bear Hotel across the street, the noise of their horses and carts on the cobbles, the cries of the grooms and babble of a dozen dialects. By now he had grown to enjoy the interesting characters who came from all over Europe for their pilgrimage, some wearing long gowns, others short tunics of brilliant greens and purples, others stiff hats. They served as an unending source of models for him to sketch at his worktable as he saw them through the open window. Soon he came to know the clients; as a guest reappeared he quickly pulled out his drawing, made corrections or additions, caught the bodies in a variety of movements: unloading carriages, carrying valises, unshouldering packs, getting on and off mules.

The noise in the street, the voices, the welcomes, the departures gave him company without intruding upon his privacy. Living in isolation as he was, this sense of other people in the world was companionable. It was all he needed, for with marble in his hands he would never stand on the periphery looking in; he would stand at the focal core looking out.

In his pen and ink sketches for the Pietà he had crosshatched the negative spaces, those parts of the block that had to be thrown away, indicating the tool strokes that should be used. Now, with hammer and chisel in hand, he found this roughing out unpleasing, impatient for that first moment when a flicker of a buried image shone through, when the block became a source of life that communicated with him. Then, from the space outside the block, he entered into his composition. After he had completed the sculpture, life would vibrate outward from the figures. But at this beginning moment the action was in reverse: the point of entry must be a force that sucked in space, pulling inward his gaze and attention. He had envisaged so big a block because he wanted to sculpture with an abundance of marble. He did not want to have to compress any portion of his forms, as he had had to compact the Satyr close to the Bacchus.

He broke into his marble block at the left side of the Madonna's head, worked to the left of the block, the north light behind him. By getting Argiento to help him turn the block on its beams he was able to have the shadows fall exactly where the cavities were to be carved, a play of light and shadow to show him where he must cast out stone; for the marble he took away was also sculpture, creating its own effects.

Now he had to plunge in boldly to find his principal features. The weight of the material of the Madonna's head covering, forcing her head downward to the inner hand of Christ that crossed her heart, compelled attention to the body stretched across her lap. The tight band which ran between the Virgin's breasts was like a tight hand constricting and crushing a palpitating heart. The lines of the drapery led to the Madonna's hand, with which she held her son, securely, under his arm, then to the human aspects of Christ's body, to his face, the eyes closed serenely in deep sleep, the nose straight but full, the skin clear and firm, the soft mustache and delicate curling chin whiskers, the mouth filled with anguish.

Because the Madonna was gazing down on her son, all who looked must turn to her face, to see the sadness, the compassion for all men's sons, asking with tender despair: "What could I have done to save him?" And from the depth of her love, "What purpose has all this served, if man cannot be saved?"

All who saw would feel how insupportably heavy was her son's dead body on her lap, how much heavier was the burden in her heart.

It was unusual to combine two life-size figures in the same sculpture, revolutionary to put a full-grown man onto the lap of a woman. From this point of departure he left behind all conventional concepts of the Pietà. Once again, even as Ficino had believed that Plato could have been Christ's most loving disciple, it was Michelangelo's desire to blend the classical Greek concept of the beauty of the human body with the Christian ideal of the immortality of the human soul. He banished the lugubrious death throes of the earlier Pietàs, bathed his two figures in tranquility. Human beauty could reveal sacredness as clearly as could pain. At the same time, it could exalt.

All of this, and much more, the marble must be persuaded to say. If the end result were tragic, then doubly must they walk in beauty; beauty that his own love and dedication could match in this flawless white block. He would make mistakes, but the mistakes would be made with loving hands.

Winter came down like a clap of thunder: cold, wet, raw. As Buonarroto had predicted, there were leaks. Michelangelo and Argiento moved his workbench and bed to dry sections of the room, brought the forge in from the courtyard. He wore his Bologna cap over his head and ears. His nostrils swelled, giving him constant pain, making breathing difficult.

He bought a black iron brazier to put under his work stool, which warmed him posteriorly; but the moment he moved to another section of the room his blood froze. He had to send Argiento out for two more braziers, and baskets of coal, which they could hardly afford. When his fingers were blue he tried to carve while wearing woolen mittens. Within the hour he had an accident, some marble fell away and he felt his heart go down to his feet as the chunk hit the floor.

One Sunday Argiento returned from an outing feeling hot and strange. By midnight he had a high fever. Michelangelo picked him up off his truckle bed and put him into his own. By morning Argiento was in a delirium, sweating profusely, crying out names of relatives, fragments of stories, of beatings, accidents. Michelangelo wiped him dry, and a number of times had to restrain him from jumping out of bed.

At dawn he summoned a passer-by and sent him for a doctor. The doctor stood in the doorway, cried, "It's the plague! Burn everything he has touched since he came in here!" and fled.

Michelangelo sent a message to Galli. Maestro Lippi took one look, said scoffingly:

"Nonsense, it is not the plague. Quartan fever. Has he been around the Vatican lately?"

"He walked there on Sunday."

"And probably drank some stagnant water in the ditch beneath the walls. Go to the French monks on the Esquiline, they make a glutinous pill of sagepen, salt, coloquint . . ."

Michelangelo begged a neighbor to sit with Argiento. It took him almost an hour in the pelting rain to cross the city, go down the long street from Trajan's forum, past Augustus's forum and the basilica of Constantine, the colosseum, then up the Esquiline hill to the monastery. The pills lessened Argiento's headache, and Michelangelo thought he was making good progress during two quiet days; then the delirium returned.

At the end of the week Michelangelo was exhausted. He had brought Argiento's bed into the big room, and was catching a few moments of sleep while Argiento dozed, but worse than the lack of sleep was the problem of food, for he was unwilling to leave the boy alone.

Balducci knocked on the door.

"I told you to take that French girl at the rear. Then when she got sick, her family would have nursed her."

"Let's not go backward," said Michelangelo wearily. "Forward is hard enough."

"You can't keep him here. You look like a skeleton. Take him to the Santo Spirito hospital."

"And let him die?"

"Why should he die any faster at a hospital?"

"Because they don't get any care."

"What kind of care are you giving him, Dr. Buonarroti?"

"I keep him clean, watch over him. . . . He took care of me when I hurt my eye. How can I abandon him to a ward? That's not Christian."

"If you insist on committing suicide, I'll bring you food each morning before I go to the bank."

Michelangelo's eyes filled with gratitude. "Balducci, you just play at being cynical. Here's some money, buy me towels, and a sheet or two."

Michelangelo turned to find Argiento watching him.

"I'm going to die."

"No, you're not, Argiento. Nothing kills a country man but a falling cliff."

The illness took three weeks to pass. What hurt most was the loss of almost a month of work; he began to worry that he could not finish his statue within the stipulated year's time.

Winter was mercifully short in Rome. By March the *campagna* was flooded with a bright, brittle sunlight. The stones of the workshop began to thaw. And with the warmer weather came the Cardinal of San Dionigi to see how his Pietà was faring. Each time Michelangelo saw him there appeared to be more material and less body in his robes. He asked Michelangelo if he had been receiving his payments regularly. Michelangelo assured him that he had. They stood in front of the massive white block in the middle of the room. The figures were still rough, with much webbing left for support; but he had done considerable carving on the two faces, and that was what interested the cardinal most.

"Tell me, my son," he said softly, "how does the Madonna's face remain so young, younger than her son's?"

"Your Grace, it seemed to me that the Virgin Mary would not age. She was pure; and so she would have kept her freshness of youth."

The answer was satisfactory to the cardinal.

"I hope you will finish in August. It is my dearest wish to hold services in St. Peter's for the installation."

11

He carved in a fury from first light to dark, then threw himself across his bed, without supper and fully clothed, like a dead man. He awoke around midnight, refreshed, his mind seething with sculptural ideas, craving to get at the marble. He got up, nibbled at a heel of bread, lit the brass lamp in which he burned the dregs of the olive oil, and tried to set it at an angle that would throw light on the area he was carving. The light was too diffused. It was not safe to use a chisel.

He bought some heavy paper, made a hat with a peak, tied a wire around the outside and in the center fashioned a loop big enough to hold a candle. The light, as he held his face a few inches from the marble, was bright and steady. Nor did his pounding waken Argiento under the kitchen sink, blanket over his head. The candles burned quickly, the soft wax running over the peak of his paper cap and onto his forehead, but he was delighted with his invention.

Late one night there was a sharp rap at the door. He opened it to find Leo Baglioni, dressed in an indigo velvet cloak, surrounded by a group of his young friends who were holding horn lanterns or wax torches on long poles.

"I saw the light and came to see what you were doing at this ungodly hour. You're working! What's that stuff all over your eyebrows?"

Michelangelo proudly showed them his cap and candle. Leo and his friends burst into a paroxysm of laughter.

"Why don't you use goat's tallow, it's harder, you won't be eating it all night," exclaimed Leo, when he caught his breath.

Argiento disappeared the next day after supper, came back at the second hour of evening weighed down with four heavy bundles which he dumped on the bed.

"Signor Baglioni sent for me. These are a present."

Michelangelo extracted a hard yellow taper.

"I don't need his assistance!" he cried. "Take them back."

"They have broken my arm from the Campo dei Fiori. I won't carry them back. I'll set them in front of the door and burn them all at once."

"Very well, let me see if they are better than wax. But first I'll have to widen this wire loop."

Leo had known what he was talking about: the goat's tallow melted more slowly and remained in a pool where it fell.

He divided the night into two halves, one for sleep, the other for work, and made rapid progress carving the voluminous outer folds of Mary's robe, Christ's lower torso, his legs, the inner one raised so that it would be visible from the front, leaving a webbing connecting it with Mary's outstretched hand to protect it.

He refused all invitations, saw few of his friends though Balducci kept bringing the news: Cardinal Giovanni, unwanted and unnoticed by the Borgia, had left to travel in Europe; Piero, trying to raise an army for a third attack on Florence, had been ostracized by the colony; Florence's intermittent war with Pisa had flared again; Torrigiani had joined Caesar Borgia's troops as an officer to help conquer the Romagna for the Vatican. The Borgia was excommunicating lords and churchmen, appropriating their lands; no Florentine knew when his turn would be next.

It was on a glorious summer morning with the air so translucent that the Alban hills seemed only a piazza away, that Paolo Rucellai sent for him to come as soon as possible. Michelangelo wondered what news it could be that Paolo considered urgent.

"Michelangelo, you look so thin."

"The sculpture grows fat, I grow thin. That is the natural order of things."

Rucellai regarded him in wonderment. "I had to tell you that on yesterday's post I received a letter from my cousin Bernardo. Florence is planning a sculpture competition."

Michelangelo's right hand began to tremble; he put his left hand over it to quiet it.

"To compete for what . . . ?"

"Bernardo's letter says: *'To bring to perfection the marble column already blocked out by Agostino di Duccio, and now stored in the workshop of the cathedral.'* "

"The Duccio block!"

"You know it?"

"I tried to buy it from the Signoria for my Hercules."

"That could be an advantage, if you remember it well."

"I can see it before my eyes as though it were lying at our feet in this room."

"Can you make something good of it?"

Michelangelo's eyes shone. *"Dio mio."*

"My letter says the Council described the marble as 'badly blocked.' "

"No, no, it is a noble block. The original massing in the quarry was badly done, and Duccio dug in too deeply at the center . . ."

"Then you want to try for the competition?"

"More than anything in my whole life! Tell me, what must the theme be: political, religious? Is it for Florentine sculptors only? Must I be there to compete? Will they . . ."

"Whoa, whoa," cried Rucellai, "I have no further information. But I will ask Bernardo to send me full particulars."

"I'll come next Sunday to hear the news."

Rucellai laughed. "There won't be time for a reply, but come to dinner and we'll fatten you up for the competition."

"May I wait until you receive an answer?"

It took three weeks for Rucellai to summon him. Michelangelo sprinted up the steps to the library.

"Some news, not much. The date of the competition has not been set. It won't be until next year at the earliest. Themes can be submitted only by sculptors in Florence. . . ."

"I shall have to be back there."

"But the nature of the work has not yet been determined by the Council of the Wool Guild and the overseers of the cathedral."

"The cathedral? Then it will have to be a religious marble. After the Pietà, I was hoping to carve something different."

"The Wool Guild is paying, so I imagine the choice will be theirs. If I know these gentry, it will be a Florentine sculpture."

"Florentine? Like Marzocco?"

Rucellai chuckled at Michelangelo's dismay.

"No, not another lion. A symbol representing the new Republic, perhaps. . . ."

Michelangelo scratched his scalp in perplexity, using his fingers like a toothed chisel.

"What kind of statue would represent the Republic?"

"Perhaps that will be part of the competition? For the artist to tell them."

Paolo kept feeding him the news as it arrived over the Sabatini mountains from Florence: the competition would take place in 1500, to celebrate the hundredth anniversary of the competition for the Baptistery doors. The Wool Guild hoped that, like the Ghiberti, Brunelleschi and Della Quercia competition a century before, the Duccio block would attract sculptors from all over Italy.

"But this is already summer of '99. I have so much work left on the Pietà." His face was anguished. "I cannot rush, it is too important, too dear to me. Suppose I don't finish in time . . ."

Paolo put an arm about his trembling shoulders.

"I will bring you information steadily. The Wool Guild will debate through many meetings and many months before they set the terms."

It was the Cardinal of San Dionigi who lost the race with time. His Grace never did get to see his sculpture completed, though he sent the last hundred ducats to Galli's bank at the beginning of August, when the sculpture was to have been installed. The cardinal died quietly in the midst of his offices. Jacopo Galli attended the funeral with Michelangelo, standing below the catafalque sixteen feet long between the columns of the church, and nine feet wide, with singers behind the main altar. Returning to the Galli home, Michelangelo asked:

"Who decides whether or not the Pietà is 'more beautiful than any work in marble to be seen in Rome today'?"

"The cardinal already decided that. After his visit with you in May. He said you were fulfilling the contract. That's good enough for me. When do you think it will be finished?"

"I have still six to eight months of work."

"In time for the Centennial Year, then. That will give you an audience from all over Europe."

Michelangelo shifted uneasily in his seat.

"Would you send that last hundred ducats to my family? They are in some kind of trouble again."

Galli looked at him sharply. "That was your last payment. You say you have six to eight months of work left, and I have sent almost all of the cardinal's ducats to Florence. It begins to look like a bottomless well."

"This money I want to invest in buying a shop for my brothers, Buonarroto and Giovansimone. Buonarroto cannot seem to find a place for himself. Giovansimone, since Savonarola's death, takes jobs, then disappears for days. If they could find a good shop, and I shared in the profits . . ."

"Michelangelo, if neither of them is a good businessman, how are they going to make a profit?" Galli was exasperated; but when he spoke again his voice was solicitous. "I can't let you pour your last money down a hole. You must be practical and protect yourself against the future. Eighty per cent of your money from the Bacchus and the Pietà has gone to your family. I ought to know, I'm your banker."

Michelangelo hung his head, whispered, "Buonarroto won't work for anyone else, so I must set him up in business. And if I don't get Giovansimone in a straight path now, I may never have another chance."

The money was transferred to Florence, Michelangelo keeping a few ducats for himself. At once, he began to need things: equipment for his carving, utensils for the house, clothes for himself and Argiento. He went on short rations, gave Argiento money for nothing but the simplest foods. Their clothing became ragged. It took a letter from Lodovico to bring him to his senses.

Dearest Son:

Buonarroto tells me that you live there in great misery. Misery is bad, since it is a vice displeasing to God and to one's fellowman, and also will hurt the soul and the body. . . . Live moderately and mind not to be in need, and abstain from discomfort. . . . Above all, take care of your head, keep it moderately warm and never wash yourself. Allow yourself to be rubbed, but do not wash yourself.

He went to Paolo Rucellai, borrowed the twenty-five florins he had returned two years before, took Argiento to the Trattoria Toscana for *bistecca alla fiorentina.* On the way home he bought himself and Argiento each a new shirt, a pair of long hose and sandals.

The next morning Sangallo arrived at the studio in a state of agitation, his golden mustaches bristling.

"Your favorite church, San Lorenzo in Damaso, is being destroyed. The hundred carved pillars are being pulled out."

Michelangelo was unable to follow his friend.

"Here, sit down. Now start over. What is happening to San Lorenzo?"

"Bramante, the new architect from Urbino. He has ingratiated himself with Cardinal Riario . . . sold him the idea of removing the pillars from the church and using them to complete his palace courtyard." Sangallo wrung his hands, as though wailing manually. "Do you think you could stop Bramante?"

"Me? But how? I have no influence with the cardinal, I have not seen him for almost two years . . ."

"Leo Baglioni. He has the cardinal's ear."

"I will go at once."

As he made his way to the Campo dei Fiori he tried to recall what he had been told about Bramante: fifty-five years old, from Urbino, he had worked as an architect for the Duke of Milan, and had come to Rome early in the year, intent upon living on his Lombard savings until he had studied and mastered the architectural genius of the ancient Romans; somewhat, thought Michelangelo, as Sangallo had.

He had to wait several hours for Baglioni. Leo listened with his features still, as he always did to other people's outbursts, then said quietly:

"Come, we'll go to see Bramante. It's his first commission in Rome. Since he's ambitious, I doubt if you'll be able to get him to relinquish it."

On the short walk to the palace courtyard Leo described Bramante as "a quite amiable man, really, delightful to be with, always gay and cheerful, and a magnificent teller of jokes and riddles. I've never seen him lose his good nature. Bramante is making a lot of friends in Rome." He glanced sidewise at Michelangelo. "I can't say as much for you!"

They approached the palace. Leo said, "There he is now, measuring off the bases for the columns."

Michelangelo stood at the opening to the court, gazing at Bramante, disliking intensely at first sight the big-skulled head, bald, a few remaining curls at the nape, the big-boned forehead and eyebrows, the pale green eyes; a snubbed nose and rosebud-like mouth lost in the hugeness of the head. As Michelangelo watched, Bramante moved some stones aside, his bull-neck and muscled shoulders showing the power of an athlete.

Leo introduced them. Bramante greeted Michelangelo jovially, told them a humorous anecdote. Leo laughed heartily. Michelangelo was not amused.

"You do not like to laugh, Buonarroti?" asked Bramante.

"Reducing San Lorenzo to a shambles doesn't strike me as funny."

Bramante hunched his shoulders up around his jowl, as though he were a boxer protecting himself. Both men looked to Leo. Baglioni was remaining neutral.

"What business of yours are those columns?" asked Bramante, still courteous. "Are you Cardinal Riario's architect?"

"No, I'm not even his sculptor. But I happen to think this church one of the most beautiful in Italy. To destroy it is pure vandalism."

"On the contrary, those columns are coin of the realm. You know they were taken from the theater of Pompey in 384 to put in the church? All of Rome is quarry for those who know how to use its stone. There is nothing I would not tear down if I had the opportunity to build something more beautiful in its place."

"Stone belongs in the place for which it was designed and carved."

"That's an old-fashioned idea, Buonarroti; stone belongs wherever an architect has need for it. What is old, dies."

"And a lot of new things are born dead!"

Bramante's good temper was exhausted.

"You do not know me. You cannot have come here of your own accord. Someone has put you up to it. Tell me, who is my adversary?"

"Your critic is the finest architect in all Italy, builder of Lorenzo de' Medici's Poggio a Caiano villa, designer of the palace of the Duke of Milan: Giuliano da Sangallo."

Bramante burst into sneering laughter.

"Giuliano da Sangallo! What has he been doing in Rome? Restoring the ceiling of a church! That's what the old fossil is good for. Within a year I shall chase him out of Rome forever. Now if you will take yourself out of my way, I'll continue with the work of creating the most beautiful courtyard in all the world. Come back sometime and see how Bramante builds."

Walking to Baglioni's house, Leo said, "If I know Rome, he will make his way to the top. A bad man to have as an enemy."

"Something tells me I've got him," said Michelangelo grimly.

12

It was his task to impregnate the marble with manifest spirit; yet even in a religious theme he felt deeply for the whole man, alive to every nerve, muscle, vein, bone, to the skin and hair, fingers, eyes and mouth. All must come alive if he were to create power and monumentality by incorporating into the marble the strength of man. He carved upward, using his knowledge of the forms already released below, and an intuition as old and deep as the long-buried marble, to achieve the expression for Mary that emerged not only from her emotion but from the feeling of the whole sculpture. He stood with his head lower than Mary's, his hands opposite his forehead, the tools angled upward, carving as close as he could get to the drama of the Pietà. The block saw him face to face, the sculptor and the sculptured involved in the tender restrained sadness. He left far behind him the dark, unforgiving Pietàs, their message of love blotted out by blood. He would not sculpture agony. The nail holes in Christ's hands and feet were tiny dots. There was no sign of violence. Jesus slept peacefully in his mother's arms. Over the two figures there was a suffusion, a luminosity. His Christ awakened the deepest sympathy, not abhorrence for those who stood outside the sculpture and had been responsible.

His religious faith he projected in terms of the sublimity of the figures; the harmony between them was his way of portraying the harmony of God's universe. He did not attempt to make Christ divine, since he would not have known how, but exquisitely human. The Virgin's head emerged delicate, the features Florentine, the face of a maiden with silent pale composure. In her expression he made a distinction between divine and sublime; sublime, for him, meant supreme and perfect. He reflected, "The meaing of the figures lies in their human qualities; the beauty of face and form portrays the grandeur of their spirit."

He found that he was achieving a tactile richness, with the forms mirroring the loving days he had devoted to them.

Balducci brought him the news that Sansovino, his fellow apprentice in the Medici garden, had returned to Florence after working for a number of years in Portugal, and been commissioned to do a marble group of St. John Baptizing Christ for the Baptistery. He was looked upon as the logical choice to win the Duccio block commission.

"Sansovino is a good sculptor," said Michelangelo loyally.

"Better than you?"

He swallowed hard before he replied. "He finishes well everything he starts."

"Do you think he can win over you?"

Again Michelangelo struggled with his answer. "We both will do our best."

"I've never seen you modest before."

Michelangelo blushed. He was grimly determined to outdesign Sansovino and win the contest; but he would not talk Sansovino down.

"Leo Baglioni tells me I have few friends. Sansovino is a friend. I intend to keep him."

"Torrigiani is also entering the competition, and is telling everyone that he will get the Duccio marble because he was an anti-Medici man; and that, since you backed Piero, you won't be allowed to compete. Paolo Rucellai says you must return to Florence in time to make your peace with the Signoria."

This intelligence cost him several nights of sleep. He had occasion to bless Baglioni for his generous supply of goat tallow candles.

In mid-January snow began to fall, and fell heavily for two days, accompanied by wind from the north. The piercing cold lasted for several weeks. Michelangelo's enclosed courtyard was piled high with snow. Inside the rooms were frigid. There was no way to keep the icy boreal wind from coming in through the wood and linen shutters. The three braziers made no impression. Michelangelo worked with his hat and earmuffs on, and a blanket pinned around his shoulders. Again in February the snow and ice came. The city was still, the markets abandoned, the shops closed because the ice, sleet and frozen mud made the streets impassable.

Michelangelo and Argiento suffered. Michelangelo took the boy into bed with him to combine their warmth. Damp oozed through the whitewash on the walls. The leaks were slower under the compacted snow, but lasted longer. Coal was in short supply, the price went up so heavily that Michelangelo could buy only a minimum amount. Argiento spent hours scratching in the snow of the surrounding fields looking for wood for his fire.

Michelangelo caught cold, went down with fever. Argiento found two bricks at an interrupted building job, heated them in his fire, wrapped them in towels and alternated them on Michelangelo's feet to keep down the chill. He fed him hot beef broth. No work was done; for how many days Michelangelo lost count. Fortunately there remained only the polishing. He did not have the strength for the heavy manual labor involved in the cutting.

For his Pietà he hoped to achieve the highest polish of which marble was capable, a faultless velvety loftiness. On the first warm day he walked to Trastevere and bought several large lumps of pumice, divided them with a blow of the hammer, searching for flatter surfaces. Now he could grip the pieces in the palm of his hand, using the long, silky parallel strands to polish the broad planes of the Madonna's robe, of Christ's chest and legs: slowly, with infinite patience, over long days and weeks.

Now he needed sharper edges, split the pumice with his chisel, cut the appropriate shapes to reach into the recessions, cavities and undulations of hair, cloth, fingernails. Finally, he made sharp-edged slivers that looked like primitive arrowheads to polish the curves around Christ's nostrils. He did not finish the back of Mary since the statue was to sit in a niche, but left the marble lined and blocked, as were the rough rocks on which she was sitting. The white marble, polished and gleaming, lighted up the dingy room as though it were a stained-glass chapel. The homely artist had indeed created a work of beauty.

Sangallo was the first to see the finished sculpture. He made no comment on the religious aspect of the marble, but congratulated Michelangelo on the architecture of the triangular composition, the balance of lines and masses.

Jacopo Galli came to the studio and studied the Pietà in silence. After a time he said softly, "I have fulfilled my contract with the Cardinal of San Dionigi: this is the most beautiful work in marble to be seen in Rome today."

"I'm nervous about the installation," said Michelangelo. "Our contract doesn't say that we have the right to put the Pietà in St. Peter's. With the cardinal dead . . ."

"We won't ask any questions. We'll install it without a sound. What no one knows, no one can object to."

Michelangelo was aghast. "You mean, sneak my sculpture in?"

"Nothing furtive. Just discreet. Once the Pietà is sitting in its niche, no one will bother to have it removed."

"But the Pope was fond of the cardinal. He gave him a three-day funeral. He granted him permission to put a sculpture in the Chapel of the Kings. Why should anyone want to have it removed?"

"I'm sure they won't," said Galli reassuringly. "Suppose you hire those stoneyard friends of yours to help you. Tomorrow, after dinner, while the city is resting."

There were so many obtruding parts: hands, feet, folds, that he did not dare to entrust the moving of the marble to beams or crowbars, no matter how securely he wrapped it. He asked Guffatti to come to the workshop, showed him the Pietà and discussed the problem with him. Guffatti stood in front of the sculpture in silence, then said:

"I bring the family."

The family turned out to include not merely three husky sons but a variety of cousins. They would not allow Michelangelo to touch the piece, wrapping it in a half dozen mangy blankets and then, accompanied by a medley of cries, arguments and commands, lifting it on its base. They carried the Pietà, eight strong, to the ancient wagon with its bed of straw, and roped it in. With Michelangelo guarding the tailgate, they made their way cautiously along the cobbled Via Posterula, across the Sant'Angelo bridge, then down the newly opened, smooth Via Alessandrina, which the Pope had rebuilt to celebrate the Centennial Year. For the first time since he had come to Rome, Michelangelo had occasion to bless the Borgia.

The Guffatti stopped their wagon at the foot of the thirty-five steps. Only the fact that they were under a sacred burden kept them from cursing as they carried the heavy marble up the first three sections of seven steps, set it down to rest and wipe the perspiration from their brows, then picked it up again to carry to the atrium, past the splashing fountain and to the church door.

Here, while the Guffatti stopped once more to rest, Michelangelo had a chance to observe that the basilica was leaning even more sharply than when he had begun work. It was now so dilapidated it seemed beyond repair. He swallowed hard at the thought of putting his lovely Pietà in a basilica which had not long to remain upright. Surely the first wind to roar down off the Alban hills would flatten it? He had an image of himself crawling over the rubble to find the fragments of his shattered statue, was reassured only when he remembered Sangallo's architectural drawings which showed how St. Peter's could be counterpropped.

The Guffatti once again picked up the load. Michelangelo led them into the basilica, with its five corresponding naves and hundreds of columns assembled from all over Rome; then into the Chapel of the Kings of France, to the left of a huge figure of Christ enthroned. The Guffatti lowered their bundle carefully before the empty niche, unwrapped the blankets, wiped their hands clean of sweat, raised the Pietà reverentially to its place. Michelangelo straightened it to the position he wanted. The Guffatti family bought candles from an old woman in black, lit them before the statue.

They refused to take one scudo for their hours of backbreaking labor. "We take our pay in heaven," said the father.

It was the best tribute Michelangelo could receive. It was also the only tribute he received.

Jacopo Galli came into the chapel, accompanied by Balducci. His head bobbed with pleasure. Guffatti, standing amidst his relatives, asked: "Is this all? No services? No blessing by the priest?"

Galli answered, "It was blessed in the carving."

The Guffatti and Argiento knelt before the Virgin, crossed themselves, murmured a prayer. Michelangelo gazed up at the Pietà, feeling sad and depleted. As he reached the door of the chapel and turned back for a last look, he saw that the Virgin too was sad and lonely; the most alone human being God ever put on earth.

He returned to St. Peter's day after day. Few of the city's pilgrims bothered to visit the Chapel of the Kings of France. Those who did hastily genuflected before the Pietà, crossed themselves and moved on.

Because Galli had advised discretion, few in Rome knew the statue had been installed. Michelangelo could get no reaction, even of the mixed kind he had received in Galli's garden from the poets and academicians. Paolo Rucellai, Sangallo, Cavalcanti visited St. Peter's; the rest of the Florentine colony, grieved over the execution of Savonarola, refused to go inside the Vatican walls.

After nearly two years of dedicated work, Michelangelo sat in his cheerless room, now empty, despondent. No one came to speak of sculpture. He was so exhausted that he could not even think of the Duccio block. Nor did Galli believe this the appropriate time to cry up a new job for him.

One afternoon he wandered into St. Peter's, saw a family with several grown children, from Lombardy, he guessed by their clothes and dialect, standing in front of his Pietà, making elaborate gestures of the hands. He went to their side to eavesdrop.

"I tell you I recognize the work," cried the mother of the family. "It is by that fellow from Osteno, who makes all the tombstones."

Her husband waved the fingers of both his hands loosely, shaking off this idea as a dog shakes off water.

"No, no, it is one of our countrymen, Cristoforo Solari, called 'The Hunchback,' from Milan. He has done many of them."

That night Michelangelo made his way through the streets, green sailcloth bag in hand. He entered St. Peter's, took a candle from the bag, put it in the wire loop of his hat, reached into the bag again for hammer and chisel. He raised his tools, leaned forward across the Christ so that the candle cast a steady glow on the Virgin's bosom. Onto the band going tightly between the breasts he cut in swift, decorative letters:

MICHAEL·ANGELVS·BONAROTVS·FLORENT·FACIEBAT

Michelangelo Buonarroti of Florence made this.

He returned to his rooms, packed his things. The hundreds of drawings he had done for the Bacchus and Pietà he burned in Argiento's fire, while Argiento summoned Balducci. Balducci arrived, his shirt askew and hair tousled, promised to resell the furniture to the dealer in Trastevere.

Just before dawn, each carrying a sailcloth bag, Michelangelo and Argiento made their way to the Porta del Popolo. Michelangelo rented two mules, joined the pack train, and at first light set out for Florence.

THE SPRING of 1958, I was living in Rome and researching my biographical novel about Michelangelo. I saw a handsome prospectus for a new art magazine being projected in New York, for a popular audience, albeit on a fairly high level. The news was gratifying, because a decade before I had suggested to a group of my associates the need for just such a magazine. Our plans had never gone past the talking stage, since we each had a full-time job of our own.

My pleasure was considerably increased, a few weeks later, when I was invited to contribute a story to the opening issue of *Horizon*. We agreed that I would write about Simonetta, the shining beauty who makes immortal so many of Botticelli's great canvases.

Since I was already completing my second year of research in the artists of the Italian Renaissance, and knew Botticelli quite well, I thought that this would be a simple task. It proved to be one of my more foolish errors, for I soon learned that it was impossible to understand the Simonetta story, or the truth about her marriage and her character, as well as her relationship with the young Giuliano de' Medici, without knowing a great deal about the Vespucci family into which she had married, its background, personality and position in Tuscan society. Very little had been written about the inter-relations of the Vespucci family. I had to return to the Florentine archives, to the family documents, diaries, and letters of the times.

The digging paid off. In order to make sure of my conclusions, I made the journey to I Tatti, to show the article to the late, great Bernard Berenson. He agreed with my deductions.

What I had thought would be a week of pleasant work, since I had long idolized Simonetta, and Botticelli as well, turned out to be six weeks of very arduous labor. When I added up the actual outlay to my researcher and other expenses involved, I found that I had spent several dollars more than the promised check from *Horizon*. But then, I suppose one should not get paid for a labor of love.

THE PERFECT BEAUTY

SHE was born at Porto Venere, near Genoa, precisely where the Italians believe Venus to have emerged from the blue waters after her birth in the Mediterranean. At her death at the age of twenty-two the city of Florence went into mourning, following her funeral train from the Palazzo Vespucci to the Church of the Ognissanti. She lay in state while men and women alike walked past her bier with the tears streaming unashamedly down their cheeks as they gazed for the last time at her long, silken textured honey-copper hair, the gold over fresh cream skin, remembering the wide-set, radiant and yet tender eyes, the features sculptured with the flawless symmetry of Donatello's living marble.

Lorenzo the Magnificent said, "Her manners were so sweet and attractive that she gave everybody who was familiar with her the absolute certainty that she loved him. It seemed impossible that she was loved by so many men without any jealousy and praised by so many women without envy."

Who was Simonetta Vespucci, who could arouse such adoration among the beauty-drenched Florentines, and today, almost five hundred years later, still cause men to fall in love with her at first breathtaking sight?

The facts of her life are few, simple and obscured in the mists of romantic literature. She was born Simonetta Cattaneo in 1453, of an old and noble Genoese family. Though their wealth was on the decline there was still enough money for her mother, Cattocchia di Marco Spinola, to travel frequently throughout Italy where she was connected by ties of blood and friendship with many of the great houses of Tuscany, including that of the ruling Medici.

It was on one such trip, when Simonetta had just turned sixteen, that her mother betrothed her to Marco Vespucci. The Vespucci had been leaders of Florentine political life and trade since the fourteenth century, in the same social strata as the Pitti, Strozzi, Pazzi, Tornabuoni families. Their relationship with the Medici went back to the founder of that dynasty; they were still not only intimate friends but business partners in world commerce and banking.

Because of the decline in the Cattaneo fortunes, Cattocchia had to be content with a member of one of the lesser branches of the Vespucci: sixteen-year-old Marco, son of a seafaring father who at one time was in command of the Florentine galleys voyaging from Pisa to Barbary and Syria. A relative, Jacopo III d'Appiano, ruler of Piombino, provided Simonetta's dowry, "a certain quantity of iron from the mines" at Piombino.

Simonetta and Marco had never met. Around August of 1469 Marco and his family arrived in Genoa, where the wedding ceremony was performed. It was a good marriage for Simonetta, in Florentine terms, where the family into which one married was more important than the appearance or the character of the bridegroom. The young newlyweds then started south for Florence, home of the greatest painters, sculptors, poets and humanists amid the rebirth of Greek culture and the birth of the modern world.

Each branch of the Vespucci family had a palace in the Borgo d'Ognissanti, close to the Porta Prato through which they brought in the wine from their estates. Simonetta moved into one of the lesser Vespucci palaces, with the family coat of arms above the door, living with Marco's parents and his sister Bice, next-palace to her new cousin Amerigo Vespucci, two years older than she and Marco, who would continue the explorations of the New World begun by Cristoforo Colombo, Simonetta's fellow-Genoese.

Simonetta could have been expected to settle down to the anonymous life of the aristocratic Florentine wife, bearing numerous children, plying her needles on the open loggia penthouse in warm weather, amusing herself at the colorful processions, tournaments and receptions with which Lorenzo the Magnificent kept the pleasure-mad Florentines entertained. And so she might have, had not two men fallen in love with her. The first was her own age, Giuliano de' Medici, handsome and dashing younger brother of Lorenzo, co-inheritor of the incredible wealth, power, talent, and wisdom of the Medici dynasty. The second was a penniless and friendless artist, Sandro Botticelli, son of a tanner and nine years her senior. Without Simonetta's face to glow in his pictures, Botticelli might well have remained little more than a magnificent technician like his contemporary Ghirlandaio. Without Botticelli to paint her, Simonetta might have emerged as an interesting footnote in the turbulent history of the Medici.

Together Botticelli and Simonetta immortalized each other. Today it is to lonely and unloved Botticelli that she belongs, rather than to her husband, Marco Vespucci, or her prince-gallant, Giuliano de' Medici. Art conquers all.

On January 28, 1475, twenty-one-year-old Giuliano de' Medici staged a spectacular tournament in the Piazza Santa Croce. It is reputed to have eclipsed in splendor even that of Lorenzo of 1469. The nobility of all Europe was invited. The youths of the noblest families entered the jousts dressed in brilliant silks adorned with pearls and rubies. Giuliano's silver armor and velvet mantle cost eight thousand gold florins. Each contestant was backed by twenty young men in jeweled armor made by Florence's world-famous goldsmiths, and followed by a full troop of soldiers. Each cavalier carried a banner on which had been painted, by such artists as Verrocchio, the lady of his love.

Giuliano called in Botticelli to paint the exquisite Simonetta on his banner. It was the only time that she was ever painted from life. Botticelli conceived her as Pallas, the fully-armed goddess of wisdom; she wore "a dress of fine gold down to her knees, and under that a white gown shaded with golden powder, a pair of azure half boots, standing with her feet upon two flames of fire, in a meadow full of flowers . . ."

The twin climax of the pageantry came when Giuliano, not unexpectedly, was acclaimed champion of his own tournament, and Simonetta was crowned Queen of Beauty to the roared approval of the entire population of Florence.

In a box of honor on the side of the piazza, surrounded by collateral Vespucci, sat Marco, watching his wife being honored by a Medici who was obviously in love with her. We have no portrait of Marco, for the alleged picture of him in the Vespucci chapel of the Ognissanti, painted by Ghirlandaio, has been proven to be another, more important Vespucci. He was a quiet young man, blessed with no particular talent or ambition, working undistinguishedly in the Vespucci wine and silk business. But he had a temper, he could grow embittered; he fought back when he thought his rights were being violated.

Was Giuliano Simonetta's lover? The original charge was made in a long poem by Poliziano, most brilliant of the humanists in Lorenzo's Platonic Academy, "*La Giostra di Giuliano de' Medici*," written after Simonetta's death, and telling the story of the tournament. Here Poliziano calls Simonetta Giuliano's mistress. Vasari, bad painter but excellent biographer of the Renaissance artists, who was born thirty-five years later, took up Poliziano's charge, labeling Simonetta Giuliano's "innamorata," and generations of art historians have repeated it.

Was Simonetta chaste? The women of Florence, with whom she

spent her days, and who might well have hated her for her matchless beauty, thought so. The old men warming themselves in the early morning sun on the benches before the palazzi knew everything that had transpired during the night; by sundown their transmission would have covered the whole valley of the Arno.

The documents of the period are voluminous, for the Florentines were inveterate letter and journal writers. From the hundreds still existing we know precisely to whom everyone was making love, there being no tidbit the Florentine more enjoyed setting down. But no syllable about Simonetta is to be found, in letter or journal, during her lifetime or after her death, that suggests infidelity.

The Vespucci loved and respected her; her father-in-law expressed the deepest affection for her; she was buried in the Vespucci vault with full honors. It was not in the character of the Vespucci family to take in silence a public cuckolding, to allow Florence to call one of them the ugliest word in the Italian language, "Cornuto!" with the first and little fingers extended upward to symbolize horns.

Lorenzo, who ruled his family, and also ruled Florence without laws granting him the power to do so, without an army, without even an armed guard to accompany him on the streets, well knew the danger of outraging such a wealthy and powerful clan. The Florentines could drive him out any time they pleased, as was demonstrated just three years after Giuliano's tournament when the Pazzi family prompted by Pope Sixtus IV, rose in conspiracy and stabbed Giuliano to death during a High Mass in the Duomo, almost killing Lorenzo as well. Two and a half years after Lorenzo's death the Florentines, disliking the arrogance of Lorenzo's son Piero, sacked the Medici Palace and drove the family into exile.

That Giuliano was in love with Simonetta there can be no doubt, nor does his fathering of an illegitimate son, the later Pope Clement VII, permit any denial of his carnal Florentine nature. But this was also the heyday of extolling Dante's idyllic love for Beatrice, Petrarch's for Laura. The lusty Florentines were not averse to a poetic passion.

Even Vasari contradicts himself when he writes, "Simonetta was virtuous and chaste. Giuliano was madly in love with her. She returned his love, but their love was pure, Platonic love at that time being the nature of the intercourse between many young Florentine lovers."

Is it important to establish Simonetta's character? Much as we may admire the linear beauty of Botticelli's paintings, it is difficult to love reverentially the image of an adulteress. The purity of Simonetta is implicit in her beauty. Take away that goodness and what remains is an exquisite mask, or, changing the figure of speech, the shell on which the Venus emerges. One can long for Simonetta, but never lust for her. Was Sandro Botticelli, who was never known to love any woman of the world, nor to be loved, perhaps projecting in paint every man's mother image, even as Michelangelo carved her in the marble of the Pietà?

The historians tell us the poets of the time wrote long stanzas about Simonetta, that the painters painted her. Nothing could be farther from the truth. The poetry came after her lifetime, as did the portraits. Except for the portrait painted on Giuliano's banner, which was apparently destroyed shortly after Vasari had seen it, all of the alleged portraits by Botticelli, by Leonardo da Vinci, Piero di Cosimo, Ghirlandaio and Pollaiuolo were done from memory, if indeed they are of Simonetta at all. No authentic portrait of Simonetta exists anywhere in the world. Not in the Uffizi, in the Pitti, in the Ognissanti, in Chantilly; not in Frankfurt or in Berlin. All have been championed by experts over the centuries; for art history is a delightful field of conflict where opposing forces do continuous battle, in which fortune changes sides with each issue of an art journal.

The likeness in the Gemälde-Galerie in Berlin appears authentic to the extent that whoever painted it might have seen Botticelli's banner painting of 1474–75; there are numerous similarities to the description by Vasari. The Piero di Cosimo portrait in the Musée Condé at Chantilly, with the ripe, naked breasts and the serpent around the throat (a symbolism curiously combining Simonetta's tuberculosis and the death legend of Cleopatra) was painted a number of years after Simonetta's death, and her name added below the portrait later still. The portrait of a drab in the Pitti, called "Bella Simonetta," attributed to Botticelli, must make both Simonetta and Botticelli turn over in their neighborly crypts in the Ognissanti. The profile drawing by Leonardo in the Uffizi looks astonishingly like a self-portrait; the odds against Leonardo ever having seen Simonetta are long, and the drawing was done after Simonetta's death. The portrait by Ghirlandaio in the Vespucci chapel of the Ognissanti, credited with having been done from life, has been proven to be a young woman of the Vespucci blood line. The portrait by Pollaiuolo in the Poldi Pezzoli Museum in Milano has been renamed "Portrait of an Unknown Woman."

Of Botticelli's many portraits, done after she died, which is the real

Simonetta? All of them, yet none of them. The Simonetta he created represents his dream of beauty. He was a sad and lonely man. All of his Simonettas are sad and lonely—two emotional ingredients needed for transcendental beauty. There are prettier girls in Renaissance painting, brighter, gayer, with more surface charm, with whom one can become infatuated . . . Botticelli's Simonetta appeals to the very deepest strata of man's tragic soul, to his inescapable knowledge that death is implicit in life.

She remains the embodiment of the Renaissance ideal, "a perfect woman nobly planned." But which particular Simonetta? In *La Primavera* she is not only Spring, but also the Venus and each of the Three Graces. In the *Birth of Venus* she is Venus, (to this observer the most beautiful woman ever painted) the nymph and the zephyr as well. In *Calumny* she is the naked Truth, in *Pallas and the Centaur* she is Pallas, as she is the near-divine Madonna in both the *Madonna of the Pomegranate* and the *Madonna of the Magnificat*. All of them are authentic projections, if not of Simonetta as she saw herself in the mirror, then of Botticelli who saw her mirrored in the eyes of his own longing. Who is to say that an intuitive painter does not see a woman more clearly and penetratingly than she sees herself?

There is no true historical Simonetta. She is the eternal feminine, Venus arising from the blue waters of the Mediterranean, the woman a man loves. This is why she is immortal.

[illegible] Palladio [illegible]

[illegible] The [illegible] to [illegible] [illegible] [illegible] was [illegible] [illegible] of the [illegible] and [illegible] [illegible] [illegible] are [illegible] There are [illegible] [illegible] painting [illegible] [illegible] of [illegible] [illegible]

[illegible] [illegible] [illegible] the [illegible] [illegible] in the [illegible] [illegible] [illegible] the [illegible] [illegible] of [illegible] [illegible] are [illegible] [illegible] in the [illegible] [illegible] of his [illegible] [illegible] [illegible] was [illegible]

[illegible] [illegible] is [illegible]